Editors
The Best from Five Decades

Also by Keith Botsford:

Out of Nowhere
The Master Race
The Eighth-Best-Dressed Man in the World
Benvenuto
The March-Man

As I. I. Magdalen:

The Search for Anderson
Ana P.

Also by Saul Bellow:

Ravelstein
The Actual
It All Adds Up
Something to Remember Me By
The Bellarosa Connection
A Theft
More Die of Heartbreak
Him with His Foot in His Mouth and Other Stories
The Dean's December
To Jerusalem and Back: A Personal Account
Humboldt's Gift
Mr. Sammler's Planet
Mosby's Memoirs and Other Stories
Herzog
Henderson the Rain King
Seize the Day
The Adventures of Augie March
The Victim
Dangling Man

Saul Bellow & Keith Botsford

Editors
The Best From Five Decades

COMPILED BY
Keith Botsford

ASSISTED BY
Sassan Tabatabai

The Toby Press, *London & Connecticut*

EDITORS: The Best From Five Decades
prepared by Keith Botsford with the assistance of Sassan Tabatabai

First published in 2001 by
The Toby Press *Ltd, London & Connecticut*
www.tobypress.com

Copyright © 2001

ISBN 1-902881-35-4 (HC)
ISBN 1-902881-36-2 (PB)

A CIP catalogue record for this title is available from the British Library

Designed by Fresh Produce, London

Typeset by
Rowland Phototypesetting Ltd., Bury St Edmunds

Printed and bound in Great Britain by
St Edmundsbury Press Ltd., Bury St Edmunds

Contents

Contents

Contents

Contents

Contents

xiii

Contents

Each of us has his private necrology.
This anthology is for all those who have left us
but left their traces in these pages.

Editors

Keith Botsford

On the Facts

This aspect of friendship—the common endeavor—has had an unusually long life. Nearly a half-century. The magazines we have published together have been intermittent: a burst in the sixties and seventies, with *The Noble Savage* and *ANON*; another from 1989 to the present with *Bostonia*, which I edited and to which Saul was a Contributing Editor, and *News from the Republic of Letters*, or TRoL as we call it.

Obviously we had a common need, or a shared dissatisfaction, and I at least must have magazines in my blood, since my first appeared in 1944. Why we've had magazines together is explored in the several introductory texts that follow. My view is that, given the disparate nature of our backgrounds, their appearance smacks of the miraculous.

We think magazines are ephemera. Ours have had varying histories: *The Noble Savage* was published by Meridien Books, with Aaron Asher and a clutch of sometimes helpful and often skeptical contributing editors. The occasion of its founding was the presence, together, at Bard College, in 1953, of its first three editors Saul, myself and Jack Ludwig. Bard was a small college with a strong commitment to the arts (among others, Mary McCarthy and Paul de Man, had taught there, as had Irma Brandeis, the Dora of Montale's poems); we met there, the trio busted up there, and we'd all gone our separate professional ways when the magazine came out. Its organizing meeting was at the old Algonquin in New York, where most of the writers we had convoked to launch the project—Arthur Miller, Ralph Ellison, Sid Perelman, Herbert Gold et al.—thought we were mad even to dream of such a thing. *The Noble Savage* lasted five solid bi-annual issues before disintegrating in a publishing debacle when the times they started a'changing.

ANON was concocted in Texas and set on an IBM Varityper by a secretary who hit herself over the head with (another) typewriter to cover embezzlement; it had originated as a project called *Locations*, in conjunction with Tom Hess and Harold Rosenberg. It lasted a single issue for two reasons: writers didn't really like anonymity and I left Texas. *ANON* had one peculiarity which makes me regret its passing. That was our attempt to revive serial publication, by which means we hoped that contemporary writers, like their predecessors in the 19th century would both be compelled to finish their books (for which readers would be waiting) and improve them by the comments of our readers. I still think it's a good idea.

And though other projects surfaced from time to time (Saul captured one, *The Ark*, in *Humboldt's Gift*), it wasn't until 1989, and in Boston, that I had another magazine. *Bostonia* figures here in a minor role, and Saul, who became a contributing editor—one who contributed with his usual generosity, cannot be held responsible for its hybrid nature at the margins of the Academy. It had been Boston University's alumni magazine; I edited it for five years as a general magazine; it then reverted to what it had been. Nonetheless, a good deal of what we published there was of great quality—not least his piece on Mozart (included) and the two-part interview we did together (since reprinted).

News from the Republic of Letters came into being from our continued dissatisfaction with other magazines, from the absence of things we wanted to read and the way serious readers were being exiled to the waste-lands of Mammon and the Academy. We decided to put our money where our mouth was and the steady growth of the magazine, which has no real likes, continues to astonish us. There are Readers and there are Writers out there and it seems a long time since they had anywhere to go. TRoL is the first opportunity we've had to create ideal conditions for a magazine. As it depends on no one, it is entirely free, and as it comes out irregularly—when the rabbi's cup of water is filled and not before—it need publish only the best.

From the beginning we have stuck to the principle that as editors we should also write in our magazines. If this were simply a matter of self-gratification, that would be one thing; as we regularly read and (we hope) help each other, it is another matter. When we write in our magazines it is to expose ourselves to the scrutiny of our readers: this is what we do, and that is what others do. Good writing should jostle other good writing, and what we think of as good writing should be visible.

Readers curious about how we edit together may be surprised to know how simple the process can be when the editors know who they are, know what they like, and have catholic tastes. Manuscripts arrive in the mail (or are, very rarely, solicited—rarely because a writer you ask for a text is likely to be offended if you turn it down) and are read by one of us or by our deputies, who have always been discerning. Some pieces just go right in: they are *obviously* good. Others go right back: they are just as clearly not what we want. Some require work, with which we try to help.

It happens that our tastes coincide, though not altogether our natures. It is of the nature of friendship to forgive defects in the other. Our only rule—for those occasions when we disagree, so rare that I can count them on the fingers of one hand—is that each has one absolute right of inclusion and one of exclusion.

We've edited in Chicago, Texas, Boston, Puerto Rico, along the Hudson, or wherever we were. We don't meet, editorially, all that often; nor do we need to. Nor do we have staffs to clutter up the place, nor offices, nor advertisers, lawyers, distributors (thieves to a man), nor specialists in grant applications, tax-men, expense accounts or little cenacles. We don't think some people belong in the Republic and others don't; we read words and judge by the way those words are put together. We look for voices, for people who have something to say and a way to say it that is entirely their own.

The reader of these pages, which recapture only a part of what we've published, will want to know why we have chosen this and not that. Apart from the fact that it would be foolish to republish pieces that are readily available (for instance, the twelve *Dream Songs* of John Berryman we published in 1960, or Ralph Ellison's "And Hickman Arrives," which has since found its way into *Juneteenth*), the only standard for selection has been that the pieces have to stand up: that is, they read as sharply as they did all those years ago. It is amazing how many do. Only some of the Arias, or shorter pieces, are reprinted primarily because they represent the spirit of the times and are therefore of historical interest.

5

The order is more orderly (we perhaps delude ourselves) if time rules. Thus the pieces printed here follow in order of publication under the rubrics we've steadily stuck by: Arias, Lives, Archives, Texts and so on. It is a form of order, which both distinguishes the magazines from each other and reflects the times.

—*K. B., August, 2000*

6

For scholars and literary historians, and because we have never been indexed— nor for that matter have we had a vast audience—, the reader will find a complete list of the contents of our three joint magazines at the back of this book. News from the Republic of Letters (its full name) is still going strong and may be obtained (at $25 per four issues, $32.50 for Canada and Mexico and $37.50 for the rest of the world) by writing to 120 Cushing Avenue, Boston, Massachusetts 02125; by fax at (617) 265 7186, via e-mail at rangoni @ bu.edu or on our website at www.bu.edu/trl.

Saul Bellow

Great and Not So Great Expectations

We will now discuss in a little more detail the struggle for existence.

Darwin, *The Origin of Species, 3*

The wise money was not on *The Noble Savage (TNS)*. We were told by our friends, and indeed it should have been obvious to everyone, that it was ridiculous in this day and age to bring out a new magazine. And the editors themselves felt ridiculous, a bit under the ridiculous shadow of the Edgar A. Guest poem:

> Somebody said that it couldn't be done
> But he with a smile replied
> That maybe it couldn't, but he would be one
> Who wouldn't say no till he'd tried.
> So he buckled right in, with a bit of a grin

And tackled the thing that couldn't be done
And he *did* it!

(quoted from wincing memory)

The horror of some necessary enterprises is that they are recommended by idiocy even more strongly than by wisdom.

But there is something horrible too about the attitudes of knowledgeable people. "Oh, God! You can't be serious. There's nothing doing anywhere. You'll just stir up a lot of dust. If *you* have anything, there are plenty of magazines already. They'll print it. It tires me out even to think what you'll be up against."

Such attitudes are perversely challenging—or challenging to people of a certain perverse stubbornness. It takes a certain amount of blunt stubborn blindness to launch a magazine like this. What our knowledgeable friends say is true: there are plenty of magazines already. The trouble is that they do not refresh you. In the respectable quarterlies you read endless cottony essays on "The Legend of Sleepy Hollow" which come apart in your hands and fill your hair with lint, and in the more radical journals you find young men with fringe beards and triple goggles looking for something to subvert which hasn't already been overturned by the restless and discontented middle class of this country. They try very hard.

From an interview given by one of the newest writers to a lady intellectual comes dialogue like the following:

"Do you masturbate?"—It is the writer who asks the interviewer.

"I prefer other people," says the interviewer, very properly.

And the writer, "When did you have sex last?"

"About two months ago."

"With a man?"

"A Frenchman, in fact . . . very serious, very intelligent. Don't you think a serious person can have sex?"

"Perhaps," says the writer. "Is his sex big?"

"Yes."

"I would not have thought so. Hm. Mine is very small."

"I would have thought so," says Miss Interviewer. "You have small fingers." (Ann Morrisett: "Dialogue with Arrabal," *Evergreen Review*, No. 15.)

Now, this sort of exchange is not only absolutely delightful, it is socially useful as well. A clever lady in Central Park was recently heard to

8

tell her friend that *Lolita* had done her a great deal of good; that she herself had been a nymphet in her early years and had always lived under a shadow from which, thanks to the book, she was now freed. The value of such hygiene is beyond estimate and no one can object if people, in speech or print, are franker than they used to be.

But now and then one feels the need of something more substantial in a magazine. One gets tired of the Tweedledee and Tweedledum battles of the Cleans and the Dirties, of the literary Nixons scolding the literary Trumans for saying Damn! and of the Peck's Bad Boys scrawling Shit! defiantly on every fence. And one has had just about enough of pedantry, lunacy, low seriousness, owlishness, social climbing, log-rolling, density, phony rebellion, and echoes of surrealism and bohemianism from a world long dead.

Can something be done about this? Not necessarily. But how can we be blamed for wishing to try?

So we have been trying. We took no space in the first number for a declaration of purpose. It's no use starting with declarations. You may or may not have goods to deliver. Moreover, by defining your aims you make it easier for your enemies to dismiss you. They don't even need to read what you print; it's enough for them that you propose to do something impossible, ridiculous, something that defies the *Zeitgeist*.

Now, the editors of *TNS* are a very mixed group. In a more healthy situation some of us would be rivals and enemies. But we have come to be tired of shrugging at one another ironically when we meet in one or another of the false situations that constitute the life of letters on the eastern seaboard. And so we have buried a few hatchets, and we have told one another that we would publish a magazine and that this magazine would be open to anyone who had anything to say, some breath left in his body, a little style, a little vigor. The *Zeitgeist* was precisely the brute we wanted to avoid.

It might, however, have been predicted that a program or rather a variety of programs would be ascribed to us anyway, and we have been called all sorts of things—a middlebrow conspiracy of middle-aged writers to set up a literary Establishment; a political bunch with underground connections to C. P. Snow and his British bunch; the new spokesmen of the Death Wish; a band of criminally desperate optimists and Affirmers; the enemies of the New; the pretorian guard of the senile publishing interests; undso-weiter. To the young radicals, we represent a *power group*, and when the first number appeared, they cried out, "Power group—power group!" They did not need to see more than the first table of contents. It is terribly curious that they should think in terms of faction, publicity, program, power and organization. But it seems to come natural to them.

As for the older generation, the statesmen of the one time avant garde, they wonder why we, their juniors, are not tired, too. A recent conversation with the editor of what was once a Little Magazine revealed that he had read in *TNS* only one article, the one on The Common Reader. Did we call *that* literary criticism? No, not as Tate and Trilling etcetera practiced that art; but what of the poems and stories in our magazine? He said without apology that he hadn't read 'em. Why should he? The names of the writers were unknown to him, and he assumed that these unknowns were sending in the kind of junk he'd become familiar with in his twenty years as an editor. And there was no reason why a busy man at the height of the New York season, drinking, chasing, gossiping, and improving his social and financial position, should bother to read yet another magazine. Poems and stories were junk, junk, and more junk! All a sensible editor could hope for now was a neat little piece on "Sleepy Hollow," a re-reading of "The Turn of the Screw;" or a good scandal, an offbeat, downbeat, meaningful, diagnostic, *Zeitgeist* sort of scandal. For everything else, the time was over. "Everything?" *"Everything!"* he said with mountainous solemnity.

Such was the attitude, and a representative attitude, too, of a nice man, one of our commissars of culture—a plain, foursquare, grumbling, honest character who loves to drink good Scotch and eat lobster and shish-kebab, and is in many ways an estimable and amiable character who knows how to make his very neuroses contribute to his well-being. He will never need psychoanalysis.

And since he is estimable, he is not altogether wrong. People do write a lot of junk. It arrives in every mail—a dreadful, endless, well-nigh paralyzing tide of junk in gray envelopes, in brown envelopes, in stationery boxes, in wrapping paper, and in fancy parcels from Park Avenue and Central Park South.

First there is the poetry, a lot of poetry, most of it sterile. A lot of exercises in style; exercises in other people's styles. Few of the poets that submit to us seem to have understood that a world exists; a poor thing, but our own, and thus far our only one. And a WORLD! No, they write of their own dissatisfaction, and their disappointments and of their victimization. Poetry is becoming a distant satellite, Parnassus has turned into a kind of Cape Canaveral, and soon we shall need elaborate radar equipment to tune in on the strange beeps the poets are emitting.

Then there are the stories, most of them machine-made. It moves awe in the soul to see so many machine-made stories. We read these mechanical productions. When one gets the hang of them, they seem easy to do. 'It is day. The sun wobbles up. Minnie is brooding over her cocoa. Should she tell John about the package? He defied her about the lawn mower. Yesterday he had a bruise on his arm. Who hit him? Who had the courage to strike John?' For the question is always the same one: "WHO STRUCK JOHN?"

Yet sometimes we hear a faint voice down in the works, and we try to extricate a writer from the mechanical horror. It isn't that we see no good, original, genuine, and even beautiful stories. We believed that we would turn up more than a few, and we were right. We have printed Mr. Hoagland and Mr. Yurick and Mr. Harris and Mrs. Paley and Mrs. Ribnikar and many others. But what comes in the tide of envelopes is mainly the dull and insistent questioning of the wronged, "WHO STRUCK JOHN?" So dull, so lacking in any human emotion or desire are most of the stories that arrive that we feel no anger in reading them, only unutterable boredom and, cumulatively, a sort of desperate concern. And finally it occurs to us that these are the people who are doing us in. "*Le mauvais goût mène aux crimes,*" said a profound thinker. No doubt of it, bad taste and crime are brothers, like Sleep and Death.

But we did not want to have a *literary* magazine. We wanted also to print memoirs, documents, personal essays, the views of originals and eccentrics. We hoped to have a magazine for writers, edited by writers—that is, people who think and feel and express themselves in that way. We wished, by giving writers more freedom—of form, of length, of subject, even of anonymity, if they wished it—to grant them what had once been their privilege and power, the right and duty to look at the world clearly and comment on it. We hoped to break down specialization, let novelists write on politics and politicians on art (if they were literate): in short, to enlarge the scope of all the writers we knew and free them from the suffocating choice between the literary quarterly and the slick. To put an end to their absurd isolation.

What has been the result? Meager. Our own contributing editors are slow to join in. We would not be willing to state under oath that they all read the magazine.

11

Are we not writing, as Herzen once challenged the intellectuals of his day, because we have nothing to say? Among the people we've solicited things from, one wouldn't contribute poetry because John Berryman, who is an editor, wouldn't like his stuff; another thinks that A or B or C is a bum and wouldn't appear with him. Another says, "You tell me you're free, but I know you're not." A third says, "Why should I write about such and such? No one would be interested." This is factionalism, ugliness, fearfulness, jealousy, false humility. Sometimes the real truth of the matter seems to be that few writers in this country wish to write. They no longer appear to understand what it is to write *about* something *for* someone. They often complain that no one reads any more; it is possible that not enough of them are writing what anyone would care to read. But even with the little *TNS* has done in the way of what it wanted to do, it has sold remarkably well. We must be on the right track.

What are words made of that writers should feel them to be such precious coin, to be struck one at a time and hoarded for years on end? Words are to be spent. They are the currency of the mind. And what is the matter with writers? Are they lazy? Tired? Sick? Distracted? Despairing? Well, of course, in the trade, one knows what they are. They are in a strange state now. Some think it best to intensify that state. That is their artificial derangement of the senses. Some will not disturb themselves by reading anything new. Some suffer from pernicious megalomania and save their strength to utter the single word which will lay everyone low—the last and most perfect word.

And *TNS?* It is doing what it can.

The time is out of joint. O cursed spite
That ever I was born to set it right!

Lucky Hamlet. He had only *one* uncle to kill.

Saul Bellow

Hidden Within Technology's Empire, a Republic of Letters

When I was a boy "discovering literature," I used to think how wonderful it would be if every other person on the street were familiar with Proust and Joyce or T. E. Lawrence or Pasternak and Kafka. Later I learned how refractory to high culture the democratic masses were. Lincoln as a young frontiersman read Plutarch, Shakespeare and the Bible. But then he was Lincoln.

Later when I was traveling in the Midwest by car, bus and train, I regularly visited small-town libraries and found that readers in Keokuk, Iowa, or Benton Harbor, Mich., were checking out Proust and Joyce and even Svevo and Andrei Biely. D. H. Lawrence was also a favorite. And sometimes I remembered that God was willing to spare Sodom for the sake of 10 of the righteous. Not that Keokuk was anything like wicked Sodom, or that Proust's Charlus would have been tempted to settle in Benton Harbor, Mich. I seem to have had a persistent democratic desire to find evidence of high culture in the most unlikely places.

For many decades now I have been a fiction writer, and from the first I was aware that mine was a questionable occupation. In the 1930's an elderly neighbor in Chicago told me that he wrote fiction for the pulps. "The people on the block wonder why I don't go to a job, and I'm seen puttering around, trimming the bushes or painting a fence instead of working in a factory. But I'm a writer. I sell to Argosy and Doc Savage," he said with a certain gloom. "They wouldn't call that a trade." Probably he noticed that I was a bookish boy, likely to sympathize with him, and perhaps he was trying to warn me to avoid being unlike others. But it was too late for that.

From the first, too, I had been warned that the novel was at the point of death, that like the walled city or the crossbow, it was a thing of the past. And no one likes to be at odds with history. Oswald Spengler, one of the most widely read authors of the early 30's, taught that our tired old civilization was very nearly finished. His advice to the young was to avoid literature and the arts and to embrace mechanization and become engineers.

In refusing to be obsolete, you challenged and defied the evolutionist historians. I had great respect for Spengler in my youth, but even then I couldn't accept his conclusions, and (with respect and admiration) I mentally told him to get lost.

Sixty years later, in a recent issue of *The Wall Street Journal,* I come upon the old Spenglerian argument in a contemporary form. Terry Teachout, unlike Spengler, does not dump paralyzing mountains of historical theory upon us, but there are signs that he has weighed, sifted and pondered the evidence.

He speaks of our "atomized culture," and his is a responsible, up-to-date and carefully considered opinion. He speaks of "art forms as technologies." He tells us that movies will soon be "downloadable"—that is, transferable from one computer to the memory of another device—and predicts that films will soon be marketed like books. He predicts that the near-magical powers of technology are bringing us to the threshold of a new age and concludes, "Once this happens, my guess is that the independent movie will replace the novel as the principal vehicle for serious storytelling in the 21st century."

In support of this argument, Mr. Teachout cites the ominous drop in the volume of book sales and the great increase in movie attendance: "For Americans under the age of 30, film has replaced the novel as the dominant mode of artistic expression." To this Mr. Teachout adds that popular novelists like Tom Clancy and Stephen King "top out at around a million copies per book," and notes, "The final episode of NBC's 'Cheers,' by contrast, was seen by 42 million people."

On majoritarian grounds, the movies win. "The power of novels to shape the national conversation has declined," says Mr. Teachout. But I am not at all certain that in their day "Moby Dick" or "The Scarlet Letter" had any considerable influence on "the national conversation." In the mid-19th century it was "Uncle Tom's Cabin" that impressed the great public. "Moby Dick" was a small-public novel.

The literary masterpieces of the 20th century were for the most part the work of novelists who had no large public in mind. The novels of Proust and Joyce were written in a cultural twilight and were not intended to be read under the blaze and dazzle of popularity.

Mr. Teachout's article in *The Journal* follows the path generally taken by observers whose aim is to discover a trend. "According to one recent study, 55 percent of Americans spend less than 30 minutes reading anything at all . . . . It may even be that movies have superseded novels not because Americans have grown dumber but because the novel is an obsolete artistic technology."

"We are not accustomed to thinking of art forms as technologies," he says, "but that is what they are, which means they have been rendered moribund by new technical developments."

Together with this emphasis on technics that attracts the scientific-minded young, there are other preferences discernible: It is better to do as a majority of your contemporaries are doing, better to be one of millions viewing a film than one of mere thousands reading a book. Moreover, the reader reads in solitude, whereas the viewer belongs to a great majority; he has powers of numerosity as well as the powers of mechanization. Add to this the importance of avoiding technological obsolescence and the attraction of feeling that technics will decide questions for us more dependably than the thinking of an individual, no matter how distinctive he may be.

John Cheever told me long ago that it was his readers who kept him going, people from every part of the country who had written to him. When he was at work, he was aware of these readers and correspondents in the woods beyond the lawn. "If I couldn't picture them, I'd be sunk," he said. And the novelist Wright Morris, urging me to get an electric typewriter, said that he seldom turned his machine off. "When I'm not writing, I listen to the electricity," he said. "It keeps me company. We have conversations."

I wonder how Mr. Teachout might square such idiosyncrasies with his "art forms as technologies." Perhaps he would argue that these two writers had somehow isolated themselves from "broad-based cultural influence."

15

Mr. Teachout has at least one laudable purpose: He thinks that he sees a way to bring together the Great Public of the movies with the Small Public of the highbrows. He is, however, interested in millions: millions of dollars, millions of readers, millions of viewers.

The one thing "everybody" does is go to the movies, Mr. Teachout says. How right he is.

Back in the 1920's children between the ages of 8 and 12 lined up on Saturdays to buy their nickel tickets to see the crisis of last Saturday resolved. The heroine was untied in a matter of seconds just before the locomotive would have crushed her. Then came a new episode; and after that the newsreel and "Our Gang." Finally there was a Western with Tom Mix, or a Janet Gaynor picture about a young bride and her husband blissful in the attic, or Gloria Swanson and Theda Bara, or Wallace Beery or Adolphe Menjou or Marie Dressler. And of course there was Charlie Chaplin in "The Gold Rush," and from "The Gold Rush" it was only one step to the stories of Jack London.

There was no rivalry then between the viewer and the reader. Nobody supervised our reading. We were on our own. We civilized ourselves. We found or made a mental and imaginative life. Because we could read, we learned also to write. It did not confuse me to see "Treasure Island" in the movies and then read the book. There was no competition for our attention.

One of the more attractive oddities of the United States is that our minorities are so numerous, so huge. A minority of millions is not at all unusual. But there are in fact millions of literate Americans in a state of separation from others of their kind. They are, if you like, the readers of Cheever, a crowd of them too large to be hidden in the woods. Departments of literature across the country have not succeeded in alienating them from books, works old and new. My friend Keith Botsford and I felt strongly that if the woods were filled with readers gone astray, among those readers there were probably writers as well.

To learn in detail of their existence you have only to publish a magazine like *The Republic of Letters*. Given encouragement, unknown writers, formerly without hope, materialize. One early reader wrote that our paper, "with its contents so fresh, person-to-person," was "real, non-synthetic, undistracting." Noting that there were no ads, she asked, "Is it possible, can it last?" and called it "an antidote to the shrinking of the human being in every one of us." And toward the end of her letter our correspondent added,

"It behooves the elder generation to come up with reminders of who we used to be and need to be."

This is what Keith Botsford and I had hoped that our "tabloid for literates" would be. And for two years it has been just that. We are a pair of utopian codgers who feel we have a duty to literature. I hope we are not like those humane do-gooders who, when the horse was vanishing, still donated troughs in City Hall Square for thirsty nags.

We have no way of guessing how many independent, self-initiated connoisseurs and lovers of literature have survived in remote corners of the country. The little evidence we have suggests that they are glad to find us, they are grateful. They want more than they are getting. Ingenious technology has failed to give them what they so badly need.

Saul Bellow & Keith Botsford

Dialogue: As Seen from the Ground

I hear that you're starting another magazine. Clearly you are out of your head. What could possibly make you want to do such a thing?

19

A to B

You heard correctly. You are referring to motives? Obviously the man who starts a magazine believes the world needs to be ordered in a certain way—as far as words and ideas can help order the world, a doubtful proposition, these days!—and that means he isn't satisfied with the actual state of affairs.

In two ways. First, no one is doing the job right: the job of editing a magazine. He has a vision of an audience that isn't getting what it wants, because he is not getting what he wants.

Second, he has larger dissatisfactions. He feels like Carlo Porta's Donna Fabia Fabron de Fabrian:

I have to agree with you
in toto,
This world's coming
to an end;
I see us all set
to go to
ruin, signs of a kind
of kingdom come
when our world's
about to be undone:

Plots, muggings, rape,
gent against gent,
felony, riot, death
to every Rex;
violence, filth and
subversion spent
against all power and
morality, wrecks
made of old beliefs, each
man a marauder
set at the heart of
the social order.

Change the last line to its being a matter of *intellectual* order and you have a motive. One part of an editor is his finger in the dike, the other is his dream of conducting a full orchestra—orchestrating the world of Art and Ideas to his own taste.

B to A

Maybe there are other motives? You're not famous. People only vaguely know your name. You've written books, but who's read them? Are you starting a magazine to put your name on the map? You want the power. Don't kid yourself. A magazine's made for a man who wants to cut a figure. Look at Podhoretz, Solotaroff, Mel Lasky. Who ever paid Jason Epstein much heed before *The New York Review of Books*?

A to B

I'll wait. Andy Warhol has announced that "In the future, everyone will be world-famous for fifteen minutes." Already we have reached the point where fame only lasts a few months. I am still young. Relatively. I should make it.

Anyway, this magazine is going to be anonymous. And there are just two ways to think about anonymity: either you accept it because you have to, or you go looking for it deliberately. The way things are today, the latter seems to me a moral necessity.

Fame is one thing; immortality is another. I suspect, however, that behind every anonymous act there is a fearful arrogance.

I wouldn't mind being immortal: in the flesh—as long as my friends were immortal too, for I'd hate to *outlive* a world that matters to me—and I feel my words are going to have to shift for themselves anyway.

I'm very lofty. On good days. I'd like to be able to take the very long view consistently. Like de Gaulle, when he was asked "What has been the most significant event in 20th century history?" People thought he would say the first man on the moon, the Russian Revolution or the splitting of the atom; but he answered "The Vatican Council". I would love to look at my times from that millenial elevation. But as an editor you have to feel that the everyday world is sliding out from under your feet.

A to B

I have something to add to yesterday's letter.

Last night I was getting into bed with my lovely mate and I was full of bile. It had been a terrible evening. The Dallas Cowboys had been wiped out. Then my secretary returned from a convention of computer-men in Houston (her husband is a man who keeps statistical track of crime.) She was flushed with sake and she wanted us to turn on Flip Wilson. Marcel Marceau was on, doing his mime with the masks, trying despairingly at the end to get that grinning, idiot mask off. The audience tittered: Marceau made them uneasy; they didn't know quite how to take him. But then Wilson mimed Marceau in his natural blackface and the audience (canned?) laughed and laughed. There was no art to make them edgy; only vulgarity. Then we ate and watched Montgomery Clift struggle for facial expressions while poor Shelly

Winters was drowned and *A Place in the Sun* tipped over Dreiser's canoe.

I was, I said, in a foul mood. I poured out my bile on her. What right have these dacron-suited businessmen to lollygag around on Houston's silken cushions? My secretary said she saw a lot of beards: Christ! I thought, they're even adopting our disguises now! And why did Marceau lend himself to the odious middlebrowness of Flip Wilson? For money! Goddam you, Marceau! As for Dreiser, no one *cared* any more for what was true, real, important or art. They preferred abominations.

I decided the times are so bad they are times for Silence, Exile and Cunning. And yet you don't want to leave the world to fools. So you give the option of anonymity to them as wants it. Give eminent writers, scholars and thinkers an opportunity to put off the burden of eminence. Let them fly free again, as they did in the obscene beginning. For many the name they have made is now a prison. Remove a few bars with the hacksaws of anonymity. A second chance at original liberty! Anonymity makes you completely independent. You lean on no one, owe no one.

22

B to A

Fine! What are you going to use for money? A magazine costs something.

A to B

I'm going to use my own. That was always a problem. Where can you go for *honest* money for a magazine? Foundations won't hear of anything so fugitive and trouble-making as periodicals. This isn't Europe and publishers here have never understood how the *best* magazine brings the best writers. And in their defense, let it be said that our writers here have little loyalty: a few more bucks can always get them to move. So you can go to an institution. A university. Do we want that?

B to A

Go to the universities? Those elephant graveyards of magazines. The odor of their decay and that of the English Department blends. Join the weighty quarterlies way down upon the Sewanee Review? The professors are already the commissars of what to read, who to read and even how to read. They're the real enemies of any serious work being done today: they're where their bread-and-butter is, with Joyce, Yeats, Eliot—one shudders for the unfastidious but industrious hands these good men have fallen into, these Warlords of the Recent Past.

Besides, they have a dirty amicable relationship to the mass-media, all these academic pros. It's a farm-system. They feed and lodge their writers, train up the graduate-students. In return the mass-media send back to the academy batches of smart opinion and fashionable ideas.

We forget that all that Playboy-Evergreen tripe is just a rehash of modernism, the dying gasp of a worn-out avant-garde; and that the avant-garde itself is an academic invention, a professional label.

No, I'm against going to the universities. That's where all your high-level culture has washed up today. In today's America, where else should they go? But why should they have the magazines? Ask yourself why they want them? Well, it enables them to keep assorted members of the avant-garde as living effigies. We know the avant-garde has to be kept alive. It's a necessity for intellectual consumers, who are many. Then I suppose it makes the universities feel good; it gives them a certain cachet, as patrons of the arts. But dig a little deeper and I think you'll be able to see their true aim. They want to have a monopoly on High Culture. I'm only grateful for this insofar as it isn't the government with the monopoly. But it's a rotten system.

23

I know I sound more like Edmund Burke every day, but I enjoy it less and less.

A to B

As a famous writer, you're being tooled up right now. I thought you'd just had your third Ph.D. *Hon.*, of course.

Even worse are the youngest, with-it academics. Can you imagine a generation of readers brought up on Herman Hesse, Joe Heller, Barth, Zen and Herbert Marcuse? It's enough to give a man clap with one hand. The universities are full of bright young men giving light-shows and taped lectures, a bunch of bell-bottomed prophets to the boondocks. In the provinces (and that's where our universities *live*) ideas don't even have to be new; they just have to be novel to the natives. The model to be followed in the USA is the business model: everyone is looking for something to sell and ideas are no sooner born than they're marketed.

Maybe that's why the young repudiate the whole notion of culture: because no one's around for whom it's new, clear, pure, true.

B to A

Your letter made me reflect on the magazines I *used* to respect. Partisan! There used to be a gang; but then the gang succeeded, took power, made money and they wind up a small mafia, the toothless old praetorians pensioned off after they lost their daggers. A velvet drawer for a rusty old spoon, that's Rutgers with P.R.

As for the mass-magazines, they are garbage. A serious writer's in there as a deodorant. *Playboy, Esquire*, stink up mind and soul. They know how to pry off the lid and get inside.

A to B

Obviously if you start a magazine you have to say what you're *not* going to be. It would be nice if there were a wider choice of things not to be. But if you step down from the academic quarterlies to the mass mags, you still haven't stooped low enough. There's the Underground waiting for you. The unhappy fact is that the first victim of any revolution is style. Underground mags exist to give kids a confirmation in print that they are loved: if by no one else, then by themselves.

The fault's with the *editors*. They could do otherwise; they don't.

In all this, what chance has Art got? I suspect few of them have the patience to recognize, or try and recognize, the signs of art that pass through their hands. When you feed the multitudes, you can't bandy words with them. The Sermon on the Mount wasn't a dialogue.

A news-stand today is an ambush: all those guerrilla-editors are in there waiting to get to you. The public no longer likes getting fired at by something unfamiliar, and thereby maybe stimulating: as it walks into the ambush, it waves its hands and climbs up the rocks to join the commando of its choice.

24

B to A

All magazines. No magazines. You devour them. I'm more selective, as befits a more orderly mind. I think I know by now what I want: you love to be surprised by a new desire. You always hope; I am usually disappointed.

There are serious magazines that I don't or can't read. I don't expect to write in *Speculum*, or *Domus*. I haven't been asked to contribute to the *NAR*, *NYR*, or *Commentary*. A man can't have everything.

So, thanks to the CIA originally, we have *Encounter*. That's the only one I read consistently, no staunch supporters of the arts, rare fiction and not much good, tone-deaf to music, blind to the visual arts, over-estimating, in *echt* Germanic fashion, the importance of reportage and controversy *per se*. *Encounter* appeases in me a certain unrest and anxiety. It knocks down certain questions. Then I don't have to deal with them any more. A good magazine disposes of false questions with dispatch and deals with true questions just as rapidly.

A to B

I'll be accused of timidity if I don't say a word about the *NYR* and its 90,000 readers. It's fashionable to hate it now, but most of the time I have no strong feelings about it one way or the other. It's a puisné *TLS*. It mistakes, on occasion, and when chic demands it, a broken garter-belt for a genuine blue-stocking. Those New York women get under my skin. An opinionated lot. They want to drive the bus *and* be helped to a seat. Some of them can't cope with a grocery list.

I suppose people read the *NYR* to know what's going on in the intellectual haut-monde. I think it's dangerous to read the *NYR* for that because the editors themselves are on a fashion-treadmill.

But it's literate. One is enormously grateful for that. Almost no one else is. (I just saw this morning a magazine that announces that it will "Cater neither to the New Left or the Old." And, "while avoiding doctrinaire attitudes, it simultaneously endeavors to formulate a political position that gives a measure of credibility to the perspective of significant revolutionary change." I instantly decided I would not be A Charter Subscriber to *Modern Occasions*. However, I keep an open mind. "The Vigor of the literary process can only be maintained" the Editors say—you can see old P.R. hands fallen

on hard times—"By resisting the claims of crass political virtue and piety."
(I don't even *think* I know what that means.)

True, the *NYR* owes a lot of this "tone of literacy to the wholesale
importation of lesser British minds, who are taught that sort of Middle Style
in school, to pass exams." It's as though the apex of their career would be,
as writers, to write obituaries in the *Times*. However, they do a very good
job of cutting their enemies down to size: that's the supreme High Table
art. And of course the main enemy is always at home. You do not really
mean to overthrow it—only to induce nausea by incessant rocking of the
Establishment boat. Authority is now seasick.

On the other hand, who can take so much perfervidness? Self-
righteousness. It's a magazine, on politics, without a smidgeon of skepticism.
It is as though it never entertained an honest doubt. Consequently, it reduces
our world to black-and-white.

Finally, I have against it what I have against the *TLS*, too. And the
quarterlies And the *New York Times Magazine*, etc. They're all *about* things.
Its writers write *on* art, music, literature; they don't create those things in
the magazine. So I consider them basically parasites. The body they feast on
is my own. As much as the worst Ph.D. candidate. It's as though *Creation*
were of negligible importance.

So maybe there is room for another . . .

B to A

The social struggle is replacing art. People want to think about social
issues: they think they *are* thinking about them.

Anyone can finger-paint at social concerns.

The function of Art used to be to *absorb*. They don't want to make
Art, these people. On the other hand, they'd love to be *artists*. They think
that Art is a matter of casting a magic spell over the horror around them.
Besides it's an awfully easy way to join the artist caste.

Artists are the legitimate heirs of the aristocracy. Business didn't inherit;
none of the dictatorships inherited. The 19th century saw this and raised
the artist to his place as the real Aristocrat in society: Now it's the turn of
the kids to be the *noblesse*. They don't understand the work involved; they
won't do their assignments. The 19th century had a beautiful concern with
Questions; people today are infatuated with the art of Wrapping it up. It is

said of Gertrude Stein on her death bed that she was muttering "What is the answer—what is the answer?" But just before she died she asked "What is the question?" This last act of intelligence perhaps saved her soul.

High-minded individuals preach that literature is dead, art is dead, fiction is dead. I mutter back: lack of accepted models—it's authority that's perishing. Literature needs commanding voices—and where are they? That's a task you could set a magazine, to speak for a standard. Of course the public thinks there *are* commanding voices, but most of the prominent writers are prominent for the wrong reasons: because they stabbed their wives or ran for mayor, because they picket the Pentagon, paint their hair blue or became voyeurs of the electric chair. Art is supplanted by its by-products.

People say that fiction is boring, and so much of it is. Tolstoy acknowledged that the oft-told tale becomes tedious when the original sustaining interest dies out. For him that sustaining interest was the progress of spirit among human beings. Spiritual stasis causes boredom. So the Greek myths bore, Christ on his cross bores; Marx bores; Lenin is getting to be boring; Mao will be boring. Readers want *subjects* and so a man's life gets to be a *luxury*, for which no one has time.

But the real fictions are never discredited. They just pass *inaperçus*. Today facts have the primacy, and social facts more than internal facts. What people mean by "facts" is a look in the mirror. That's democratic society looking at itself. So now people truly believe, alas! that there's nothing more interesting than themselves; their own consciousness is now the most important single *fact*. They don't really mean "facts".

The whole thing has a profoundly romantic root. Art, said the Romantics, does not deal with Truth; but Truth is what counts. Beyond Art there is a greater reality than Art is able to touch. Marx—that Prince of Romantics—said that the proletariat would create a revolution which would redeem mankind from unreality. Like so many today, he was living a populist fantasy.

How are you going to get writers to go against this flood? They are making the old, familiar mistake today, choosing the wrong role at the wrong time. Wanting social prominence. Rebellion. To be swingers. *And* sages. They have no sense of community. None of them care what others are up against. When they make it, they make it rich. They belong to the Jet Set; they have tax problems; they become television actors. Their ideas are really very old-fashioned. A man of taste would have to say there's too much riffraff in the republic of letters.

A to B

How can I answer your question about writers without saying, "You and I are willing, why shouldn't they be?"

I think it's a question of making the magazine really different: in some way specifically satisfying to writers and readers alike. From the writers' standpoint, what do we feel a magazine ought to be like? Well, we know what it ought *not* to do. Writers hate: to waste ideas; to have no place to print those ideas; hate being told what they should be writing rather than welcomed to write what they want; receiving pretexts from editors instead of explanations; being abused instead of used; having editors' words substituted for their own; being held up for months, going unanswered, being arbitrarily cut. We could start by not doing any of those things.

For the whole business is upside down in America. Writers are made to feel that editors and publishers are doing them a bloody favor by publishing their work, when in fact editors, agents, publishers, critics, publicists—the whole lot—are usually parasites: nothing without the writer. I think a magazine that remains *open* to good writers, and consistently open, will make its way. I would like to think of the new magazine as the kind of magazine that writers would want to read: where they are, in part, their own audience.

Then a magazine can do things other magazines don't do; and it can do what other magazines do in a different *manner*.

Of the things other magazines don't do, the most important is: to let writers *write*, to know that they have a place which is theirs: to which they do not have to "sell", but where they are taken on faith, on the evidence of their skill in the old craft of writing. For I think that once a man can write he is almost equivalently interesting on *anything*. He can—he will—make mistakes; but even his mistakes will be more interesting than the pedestrian successes of the writer working to order. In short, if he must, he ought to be allowed to talk through a cocked hat. And then take what is coming to him, when someone points this out.

Next is the troublesome question of genre, length, style. Most magazines have a readily visible formula. I myself have written pieces which—remaining unpublishable by magazine X because Editor Y got promoted to another review—could not be moved to another journal: because they had been written for X, in the style of X. Similarly, most magazines have preconceived notions as to whether or not they will publish poetry, plays, non-fiction, long stories, novels, criticism, etc. If you happen to write in form X at length Y, don't bother to send it to the Z Journal; they don't go in for that. What bothers me about this situation is that there is always, to every subject, a form apt for it. And here I'd like to be as near perfect flexibility as possible. If a piece is too long, carry it across several issues; and what form have you and I not, in skillful hands, read with pleasure? So writers might collaborate in— and readers enjoy—a magazine in which just about anything goes.

Next there is the question of subject. Again, I'm a thousand-flowers man. It's a fault, perhaps, that I lean equally to Law, Philosophy, Sports, History, Science, Art—you name it! I believe anything can be written on well and I deplore the decline of that 19th century cultural giant, the truly *general* magazine, that patronized neither writers nor readers by assuming that there were subjects in which neither could be genuinely interested. I don't expect all writers or all readers to be equally interested in everything we do, but I'll sure as hell cast the nets wide.

Then there are specific forms which I should like to see revived by a first-class magazine. What I'm calling ARIAS, in honor of the old *Noble Savage*, for instance; the free essay, of any length of comment; or the LIVES, to which I hope to give particular attention. No other magazine does this consistently. I find lives interesting. And instructive. Biography is a fine way to comment on or make a point about the world we live in; our readers have their own lives and can make connexions. Lives embody ideas and feelings and reality; they are a less abstract form of fiction. SERIALS of works-in-progress are a good way for a writer to get a look at what he's in the process of doing; it helps him make his text objective; he can get something back from his readers, if they read. It was a good idea a century ago, common and healthy.

Finally, there's a little something buried in the name ANON. It's an old idea. I dream of a journal where texts produce their effects because they produce those effects, where readers read because they read: not because X's name appears on a text and to hell with Y, we've never heard of him. Also maybe this way X and Y can both feel a little freer. Of course no good writer is ever anonymous, but you could say I'm striking a little blow against the current immodesty of my profession, against the Cult of Personality in Art.

And then perhaps X is Secretary of Defense, Science Advisor to the White House, President of a large corporation, head of an advertising agency or giant brokerage firm. Who knows who might not be moved to speak up if we can provide an appropriate and encouraging atmosphere for the Xs and the Ys? Very good writers will welcome the opportunity to write anonymously to escape from success or from the hardening of their own manner.

And suppose a poet were to begin again—now—unknown: how would his poems be received? It is worth finding out how much flexibility remains in some of these established men of mature years.

B to A

All very good. You are living in a dream world. All that and you want to get your magazine out often? How can you maintain the quality? People are tired of magazines which are little more than anthologies of one man's peculiar tastes.

I disagree violently. I'd like a weekly. Or maybe a daily. Which would have to be brief. How much good stuff is there going around? Well, if you take in the whole world and all sorts of interests, there's probably enough. But get it out often. That makes it deliciously expendable. Man, having read, moves on. Besides it's good to have a fire lit under the magazine: every so often *we* have to move on, too. It also means a closer community between the magazine and its readers. A quarterly arrives on my doorstep and it's too fat to read; I've forgotten what it was all about; I can't follow an argument or a writer I like. A magazine tells a story. You have to keep it in mind. If you come out often enough, you have some hope of having *some* bearing on matters. Things die quickly enough, you have to run to keep your eye on them.

A journal shouldn't consider *perfection*. The best magazines to me are those which in retrospect seem to me good *statements* in periodical form, of what the *current status* of Art and Thought was. In final, fixed form, these statements became books. And a book, we know, is a dead thing. Unchanging. But nonetheless the relationship between ephemeral publication in a magazine and final publication in book form is rich and complex. Magazines make for the general movement of ideas, for good talk between artists and their publics, for the clarifying and redefining, the testing of ideas, subjecting them to criticism and reaction, the forging of groups with common interests, the education of a public towards what that group stands for . . .

I don't favor the less good over the good, but I'm less sure than you seem to be about what is good. In fact I'd hate to think I had the *answers* to Art and Culture, wouldn't you? That would take the fun out of it. Anyway, unlike a lot of intellectuals I really feel no Moral Imperatives on these or any other subjects. So that I tend to think the writer is usually right about his own work. As much as he sees, as conscious as he is.

For the same reasons I'm for being not just frequent, but cheap: cheap to produce. Cheap to buy. America has bred a Versailles complex in editors: some of their magazines are *all* appearance. My print may be small, but it's the text that counts. We'll be naked that way: take a look at its pages and there's no doubt what it's up to. Things—disparate, different subjects, styles, cultures, periods—jostle each other.

And look, I know the audience for the first-class is diminishing steadily: from want of getting it and want of knowing what it is. It's like the diminishing number of people who'd know good bread if they had it and who've got teeth enough left to chew a real crust. But probably a good magazine can do something to bring those scattered souls together. I'm not going to leave them to the mercies of the various corrupters that abound, unchallenged.

Arias

Saul Bellow

Pains and Gains

I n this number of *The Noble Savage* (*NS: 1*) Harold Rosenberg speaks of the middlebrow principle: every loss a profit. On the philosophical side we may be able to trace this back to Nothing Is Lost in Nature, on the commercial, Nothing Goes to Waste in the Stock Yards. It's the psychological aspect of the matter that concerns me now. We say in the words of the old joke, the tag of which is so much better than the story, "So it shouldn't be a total loss." Not only for the middlebrow, but for everyone, the personality seems to perform some secret operations to prevent total loss, taking great pride in its alertness, in its power to recapture the initiative in a crisis, and sometimes simply in its vigilance against possible waste.

People who are about to cross a room will sometimes chart their course so as to perform a few useful actions as they pass. Very few of us neglect these small economies. Sleepers in the first moments of waking begin to think what they may accomplish on the way to the bathroom or the kitchen, and contrive to close a drawer as they stumble by, rinse a dish, put a sock in the hamper, tear a leaf from the calendar. This is not necessarily compulsive behavior. It's better explained by the law of combined operations and may have something to do with the brevity of life. (Another middlebrow idea?)

But as soon as something goes wrong, the mind turns to thoughts of salvage. The curve of disaster doesn't rise very high before it is intersected by the arc of insurance. I think sometimes the idea of compensation arrives even faster than the awareness of pain.

As I walked uphill on 112th Street one day, a heavy middle-aged woman sat crying on the stone ramp beside an apartment building, rubbing her leg. She had evidently had a fall.

"Was it bad?" I said.

As soon as she heard my voice, she took up her purse and clutched it under her arm, overcome by tears and pain as she was. Now that I think of it, this may have been a sound thing to do. There are plenty of people whose pitch is to approach you with solicitude in order to rob you blind. And then, too, there are quite a few people even in New York who are *bien elevé*, who have nice, kind middle-class hearts, such hearts as need a little of the free zwieback of casual charity now and then. So my kind heart took the first bite of this windfall of zwieback and I watched the tears drop, big, brilliant, and swift from her round face and soak into the buff cloth of her coat. Finally she was able to speak, and she said, "Go find me the super, the sidewalk is broken. I tripped." I looked at the cement and saw nothing, not even a small crack.

"You want me to help you home?" I said.

"No, I want the super, right away."

I understood then that she was going to sue for damages. "Yoy," I said to myself. But having offered my help I couldn't abandon her. I had eaten of the zwieback, so I went to look for the super. He had a booth in the lobby and was sitting in it bawling out a young woman who wouldn't keep her carriage in the carriage room but left it in the lobby where the tenants complained about it. They were speaking in furious tones. I said to the super, "A woman has fallen in front of your building. She wants to see you."

"Tell her wait," he said.

I went back to the weeping woman and said, "The super is coming." Her shin was swelling, and I asked her again whether she wanted me to help her home or to get a cab.

"No, all I want from you is your name and address," she said.

"Lady, I'd be glad to help you"—Oh, Boy Scouts of America, I learned more from you than tying knots and building fires! "But I didn't actually see you fall. What sort of witness would I be? You don't want me to come to court and give false evidence, do you?"

"Well, go away then. Be on your way. Don't hang around," she cried at me. The tears were still falling, and the running mascara distorted her eyes. "Go, go!" she said.

Marvelous presence of mind! Probably at the instant of her fall, before she came to the ground, even as she felt the little crevice in the concrete under her toe, she was already thinking that she could collect damages. We must be prepared always to turn defeat into victory—always! Perhaps it's one of the greatest glories of our humanity. As we lose our teeth, and the face wrinkles and the hair thins and turns gray, we still strive to exchange our losses for gains and haggle with chance and with death.

A pregnant woman, seven months gone, falls in the street and lies on her swollen belly. People run up exclaiming "Are you hurt? Do you want an ambulance?" She holds her husband's ankle grimly and shrieks, "Don't move me till a cop comes. I want him to see." The husband in his leather jacket, black haired, says nothing. His hands are in his pockets. They are going to sue the city. "The pavement is cold," says a motherly sort of lady, "and it may be bad for the child. You'd better get up." Meddlesome old zwieback eater. She doesn't understand what a stroke of luck the parents have had. The infant now, very now, before his birth, may have found through a lucky crack in the pavement his scholarship to Harvard. "Don't nobody bother me" screams the mother from her swollen belly as the cold wind blows. She waits to be seen by the legal and qualified eyes of the cop. She knows the gods have sent her good fortune through an accident, and while she moans she also reckons. Our fate is to suffer. But we are able also to wrest compensation from the universe.

37

Anonymous

The Seeing Eye

Some time ago an ad appeared in *The New York Times*, large enough to make the visual shock impressive, of a bus and several burning cars at the scene of an appalling accident. The caption under this photograph read:

READ ABOUT IT BEFORE THEY TOW THE CARS AWAY!

The ad went on to say that in the vital fast-moving world in which we now live (and die) the reader couldn't afford to wait till tomorrow to learn about the events that happened today. The event pictured—one of the worst of its kind—derived both its importance and news value from the fact that it was captured before the cars had been towed away.

What appetite, perhaps we should say what lust, is being gratified in this manner? Do we have, today, a pornography of violence? Are these *hot* snapshots of meaningless horror the equivalent of the breasts and thighs, the human poultry display that ornaments our news racks? Does the look somehow gratify what the sensation itself seems to withhold? There is no end of sex in America, but the hunger for the look of sex appears to increase, rather than decrease, with the decline of the taboos. There is no end of violence in America, both before and after the cars are towed away, but the lust for violence remains ungratified by the event itself. We seem to feel, with the criminal, a compulsion to return to the scene of the crime.

Has the camera eye, with its command to LOOK, and the LOOK that increasingly commands our attention, made it possible for us to look without seeing anything? Do we have at our disposal, today, a nonseeing eye? Strange as it seems, the scene of the disaster and the anonymous nude perform the same function—seen through the nonseeing eye they supply the thrill without the risks. The reassurance we seem to need that we are alive, and that life can be seen going on around us, we get in the form of visual shock capsules. The viewer himself supplies the shock-absorbers. There is nothing like death—nothing like somebody else's—to remind the man who doubts that he is really *living*, that he is, in most respects, still very much alive.

The magazine writer, with the photographer in tow, goes from room to room in John Doe's new house, looks over the gadgets and peers under the beds, and coyly probes into the teenager's sex life. The magazine consultant, like the visiting nurse, probes the inhabitants for cavities that need treatment—but a cavity worth probing is a private thing. The pleasure-pain is reserved for a private tongue. Cavities, like diaries, are hard to breed in a doorless home. At what point does the private world of Picasso assume more importance than his painting—at what point, that is, does the public feel entitled to it? The question itself defines a new conception of privacy. It is the last commodity that a man has to sell. It parallels a now old-fashioned notion of virginity. Revelation illuminates privacy and explains why it is that life is empty without it—exposure merely reduces such privacy as we have. It leaves us, naturally, with a lust for what we have relinquished. We turn to anyone who claims to have it, with appetite.

In this fashion, the pathology of the Peeping Tom becomes the license of a new profession—if the *Life* photographer knocks on the door, someone opens it. What is an inside story without somebody's insides? It is the camera that takes the picture, and it is the data that assures the voyeur he is not being cheated—for that is how he feels.

These men are under orders, *our* orders, to get the shot. Our appetite being what it is, we require these shots in ever stronger doses—our visual diet is nonvegetarian, we like our meat rare. To supply this carnivore with his supply of raw meat the news hound acts as a species of vulture, swooping down to *cover* the scene of the accident. We want the bloom of it, and what

40

we want we get. When we ask ourselves by what potion we have come to such a pass, it is by appetite, first, and second, by degrees. If each day you increase the dosage, each day you reduce the effect. Not too long ago, the words *horrible accident* would have been more than enough. A picture, any picture, would have been considered barbarous. Now we lust to be there before the bodies are carted away. With the accumulation of these pointless exposures the mind becomes a portable waste basket—a news file where the shockers are stored for future reference. Such a clogged mind naturally cries out for a periodic housecleaning, a burning of useless debris to make room for more of it. This burning we get, in a vicarious form, from the eyewitness reports of senseless conflagrations, the wide-scale ruin of hurricanes and floods, or those atomic explosions that actually change the face of the earth. Such awesome sights seem to purge the exhausted mind of its waste material, and restore, for a brief moment, the power of sensation.

The disappearance of a private life of our own generates in us a lust for the private lives of others. By sympathetic magic we hope to absorb it through our eyes. Picture magazines, movies, documentary studies, and the mindless eye of the newsreel camera, all feed this craving for the private life of somebody *else*. Anybody. It matters less now than it once did that this carrion we feed on is famous or unknown. We hardly care so long as we are fed on the private parts. Our appetite for these details is insatiable. Eating habits, sleeping habits, active and inactive leisure habits, reading, talking, fighting, and loving habits, all are tossed into the maw of our lust for life. For that, in substance, is what it is.

We say the camera never lies, but it were truer to say that it cannot tell the truth. The truth is a concept, and the camera cannot conceive. If and when it does it will no longer be a camera. It will be a human, like the rest of us, suffer from delusions, migraine, and fallout, expiring before its time from the abuses of a world it is obliged to face. But for the time being *that* model is not available. The camera buyer must still supply the seeing-eye himself.

It is this eye, faced with the meaningless event, that transforms it into meaning. Out of the scene's incoherence a sense of coherence can be seen to emerge. It may well bring a message to chill the heart, or feed a lust that is better unmentioned, but it will not stand idle while the cars are being towed away.

41

Stephen Spender

Doctor of Science,
Patient of Poetry

Ever since C. P. Snow opened the famous debate on the Two
Cultures, there has been much discussion on whether writers should learn
science, and scientists read more literature. The idea that science can be
considered as an alternative culture has been challenged, but nowhere have
I seen any discussion of writers, outside the new worlds of science fiction,
who really have been influenced by science.

Despite the considerable display of scientific knowledge in *Ulysses,* and
of political economy in the *Cantos,* Joyce and Pound are cited as examples
of "literary experimenters" who had no science and no one has disputed
this. It also seems to be taken for granted that if writers knew more science,
their writings would become more "progressive," because their imaginations
would be fired by the potentialities of science to feed people in the under-
developed areas of the world.

I hope that someone is making a study of those writers in whom the
gap between literature and science has been bridged. One of them is Gottfried
Benn, a selection of whose prose and poetry, translated by various hands,
has just been published [by the Bodley Head in London and New Directions
in New York] under the general title of *Primal Vision.*

In Benn's work, the gulf between the two cultures is bridged and the results are terrifying. Gottfried Benn was a doctor of medicine (skin and venereal diseases). He was also the German poet who, in his old age, shortly after the war, in 1947, was hailed by many German critics as—to cite one of them—"German poetry's last internationally presentable figure." As a doctor who worked in Berlin during the worst postwar years, he appears to have been conscientious, disinterested, and humane. As a scientist (and he never lets us forget for a moment in his writings that he is one) he cultivates a detachment which is inhuman.

As a poet, he is not so much doctor or man of science as patient, victim of a twentieth-century literary disease which will one day perhaps be isolated, and connected with the names of such writers as Ezra Pound, Wyndham Lewis, and Stefan George: the disease of a kind of creative anti-humanity. It is connected undoubtedly with the political disease of Fascism.

To really understand these writers, a study of Fascism is necessary, and so, to really understand Fascism, is a study of these writers. The root causes of the disease are: (1) a vivid nostalgia for a European past of Greece, Rome, the Renaissance; (2) an unqualified hatred of modern life, which is viewed exclusively in terms of chaos and dissolution; and (3) the writer's own personal arrogance, based on his feeling that he belongs to a race apart, a race of lonely giant survivors of Renaissance genius.

The symptoms are: (a) symbolism or imagism (the preference for non-human, mineral, hard, or mythological imagery, to the personal and human); (b) when writing of the modern world, the most violent metaphors of expressionism; (c) the proud and self-dramatizing isolation of the ego of the writer compulsively projected throughout his work; (d) intellectual arrogance accompanied by pretensions toward omniscience and universality; (e) contempt; (f) Fascism.

Obviously not every writer who has some of the symptoms suffers from the disease: indeed the symptoms are rather widespread. The passionate nostalgia for the past, and total condemnation of the present which are strikingly present in Yeats, for example, might have included the other attitudes. Gottfried Benn is the most complete and remarkable case I know of: the doctor is the absolute patient.

The most disquieting thing is that it is the scientific view which, so far from cutting a way out of his entrenched nostalgia, completed the circle, providing him with a modern reason for feeling superior to his contemporaries. This rationalism complemented his romantic (or equally, one might say, his classicist) love of the past. From his historically nostalgic eminence he regarded people as ghosts and shadows; from his scientific eminence, as mere lumps of meat, carcasses.

The result, as it affected his writing, was, as nearly as seems possible, a life work of total solipsism. This is disguised as a high-flown, rather coy, nihilism. Although he defended his nihilism in many of his writings, Dr. Benn didn't like to be called a nihilist by mere reviewers, critics, professors, colleagues, and scum of that kind. To interviewers who pestered him, he had lofty words of dismissal when, inevitably, they mentioned the word "nihilism": it was not a matter of nihilism, but of what you put into it, he told them.

His prose works, written in extremely opaque brittle images woven into expressionist subject matter, are entirely concerned with trying to relate the enormously superior, isolated consciousness of a doctor called Roenne to the world of material bestiality and spiritual inferiority surrounding him. The basic problem was that if Roenne were real, and of material substance, how could other phenomena, so different in quality, so outside the world bound up in his past vision, be real also? Roenne can never decide which is real: he, Roenne, or what is called reality:

45

> A man decamped. A man hurled himself into his harvest, to be bound by reapers offering wreaths and verse. A man drifted out of his fields, aglow under crown and plumage, immeasurable: he, Roenne.

The Nazis provided an answer to his problem of reality. As with Pound and Lewis, something appallingly vulgar underlying an anti-human attitude, based perhaps on an awareness of genuine intellectual superiority, was exposed in him by Fascism. For Benn-Roenne, the Leader Principle—the Nazi Movement—objectified attitudes which, until then, had seemed insulated in his ego. They were the historic movement fusing nostalgia for past history with scientific method and poetic myth, interpreted by Benn as a program for producing a world superior to reality itself, above all human considerations. It was the total unrealism of the Nazis that appealed to him during a period when he wrote pages upon pages of this kind of thing:

> Again and again I have shown the central significance of form to Europe, and especially to Germany. But it can also be defined as the very opposite: a hard-earned knowledge of a possible new ritualism.

It is an all but religious attempt to shift art from aestheticism to anthropology. . . . In terms of sociology, this would mean the anthropological principle of form—pure form, formal compulsion—into the center of cults and rites. One might even call it the immaterialization of matter.

The "immaterialization of matter" in the name of rites was taken to its logical conclusion in the gas chambers of Auschwitz and Buchenwald. But, of course, Benn was no supporter of these, and by this time he was truly disillusioned with the Nazis. His disillusionment was partly the result of the contempt which turned him against Hitler and Goebbels, as against other all-too-human beings.

The case of Gottfried Benn seems to indicate that the bridging of the gulf between literature and science in the minds of the leaders of a fused two cultures, need not necessarily lead to the broadening of science with imagination, the liberalizing of the literary tradition by progressive ideas. It might lead simply to the creation of an elite with a two-headed superiority complex made double by its members, combining the most nostalgic with the most advanced, ideas. If the elite consisted of writers who also had a great admiration for powerful administrators and political leaders, the temptations of using literature to create myths of science and history supporting anti-human politics, are obvious.

Saul Bellow

The 11:59 News

Agentleman near Chicago reports that he will mount a machine gun at the door of his bomb shelter, to keep out strangers in flight from blast, heat, and radiation. Citizens in New Jersey are talking of barricades and armed men to halt fleeing motorists from New York City just before or just after the Bomb drops. Similar news comes from suburbs in California. Pessimists have too easy a time of it with such information. There *is* a hopeful view, and we must take it.

47

Everyone agrees that there are two alternatives: it drops or it doesn't. If it does, think of those gun battles in Skokie, Secaucus, and Santa Monica. (The motorists, having read the papers, will have brought their own weapons.) What a day for neo-Malthusians: while the slothful stay-at-homes switch off their radios and lie down on their wall-to-wall carpets to sicken or disappear, the suburban vigilantes and hotrodding seekers of *Lebensraum* will shoot it out under the poplars. Thus this method of population control now has an extra refinement. An area meant for renewal should be cleaned thoroughly, even if it takes old-fashioned bullets for the mopping up.

And if it doesn't drop, though continuing to hang more and more heavily, these first signs of new enmities portend a deep change in the unnatural order. The class struggle will become truly obsolete. What are the wars of landlord and tenant, employer and employee, white and Negro, but paltry tussles compared with the struggles for position in civil-defense geopolitics? The super in the basement will lord it over the vulnerable occupants of the penthouse. A tenement by the river will beat Fifth Avenue. In Congress it has already been said that "at three o'clock in the morning in every major city in America, if the best shelters are large downtown buildings, the people that you will save will be skid row drunks, prostitutes, a few people in hospitals, and maybe the night shift on newspapers."

What this means for society is obvious. Fragmented and alienated modern man will begin to coalesce, to rejoin. Anomie, the sociologists will note, will shrivel. The novel of manners will again become possible, as the new classes develop their own languages, their own habits, their own cuisines. Crowds will be less lonely and selves will blossom. And those of our ancestors who spoke well of the future of science will have been right after all.

Keith Botsford

Obit on a Witness

The recent death of Whittaker Chambers in Maryland brought statements from a good many eminent people. *TNS* would like to join Richard M. Nixon and others in a short tribute. Whittaker Chambers was certainly a devout anti-Communist. The case that he made against Alger Hiss was unassailable. Mr. Hiss, shod in the white shoe which commands so much loyalty—the right schools, the right social background, the right friends and connections—is a peculiarly disagreeable figure. In his rigid denials of guilt he made matters all too easy for Mr. Chambers, who was all over him, saving and denouncing him simultaneously. For Mr. Chambers, filled with Dostoevsky, Victor Hugo, and Quakerism, his thought richly dyed by the journalistic techniques of *Time*, felt himself to be the agent of a dramatic Destiny. In this view of himself he was strongly and ably supported by officialdom, by the papers, and by an influential group of ex-Communists who performed a sort of service in exposing the Communist conspiracy but who, I think it can be argued, kept at it much too long.

Despite this support, Whittaker Chambers considered his life a martyrdom. He seems to have had a rich and occasionally somewhat sophomoric cloak-and-dagger, movie-thriller view of himself. Alas, there is nothing to keep people from painting themselves in remarkable colors—nothing, that is, except reality. Mr. Chambers was a hunted man, a betrayed man, a martyr and—one of the chief editors of *Time*. Today his autobiography, *Witness*, makes curious reading—touching. Sidney Hook, reviewing it in the *Times Book Review*, thought it would eventually be regarded like the *Confessions of St Augustine*—as a religious work. It turns out to be a rather posturing book, but Professor Hook, not terribly famous as a friend to religions, was perhaps venturing too far on unfamiliar ground in his political enthusiasm.

Mr. Chambers was a courier for the GPU. His sin was dark and terrible, his atonement was rich, full, and lengthy. I'm sincerely sorry for him—though no one is any longer so innocent as to believe that this sin and suffering could not carry with it a perverse pleasure. In his expiation, Chambers seems to have tasted some pleasure, too. Some people can have it both ways. Mr. Chambers hid himself, but he did come out again. His sin was enormous, but he redeemed himself gloriously, publicly at that, in the sight of millions of readers. Marvelous! I am tempted to say, What a perfect script! Why didn't Hollywood buy it? Really, the movies deserve to remain tenth-rate!

But now what of the secrets that Mr. Chambers carried to the Russians—were they really so damaging? Was there anything in them that Soviet Intelligence could not have discovered from official publications and from newspapers? What sort of information did he—and allegedly Mr. Hiss—transmit? Somehow I can't bring myself to believe that what they did was nearly so damaging as what the government itself did or failed to do in its relations with the Soviet Union. Was any of it as serious as letting Russia so cheaply into the war against Japan, or failing to secure the approaches to Berlin? My opinion is that Mr. Chambers did more harm to the country as an editor than as a Russian agent. He was for years in charge of "the back of the book" at *Time*, filling minds with all sorts of harmful nonsense about literature, education, the theater, religion, painting, etc.

The conservatives will canonize Chambers. He was an interesting man, albeit inordinately self-dramatized and confused. We leave this note of dissent to the hagiographers of the future.

Saul Bellow

Mr. Wollix gets
an Honorary Degree

Swayed like sea lettuce in the great tides of American life, Mr. Wollix
received an honorary degree from a great American university. Mr. Wollix,
an acquaintance of one of the editors, when he was offered this distinction
did not feel able to turn it down. Out of sheer decency, and because universities have taken such punishment for the sins of society as a whole (all must
take their sad turn on one symbolic Calvary or another), he accepted. Mr.
Wollix is really a retiring sort who loves to work mathematical puzzles in
the privacy of his own apartment in St Louis, Mo. He shuns ceremonies,
public exposure, but (mathematicians' superstition) his number was up.
Elderly, a bachelor, he thought to sleep with an old girl friend in New York,
but she was spoken for that way and he had to take her to dinner instead—
a minor disappointment at his time of life.

A high functionary of the University phoned him at the hotel to say
that a trustee, Mrs. Moxton Wiles, would call for him in her limousine in
the morning to bring him to Madison Square Garden, and would he be on
the sidewalk outside the Westbury at half past eight. Moxton Wiles! Mr.
Wollix was impressed. One of the historic names in Society. Fur trading,
the Revolutionary War, Manhattan real-estate, the great house in Newport.
The charming lady came punctually in her sombre elegant air-conditioned

51

car. A woman of sixty, she seemed all that a person of her position should be. She carried her billions with admirable lightness. She was intelligent, she was attractive, her small-talk did not appear to be small. Wollix was happy to be with her. New York was already sweating. Laborers were pushing their wagons through the garment district and the sallow crowds came up from the subway ready for the day's suffering in Midtown.

At the Garden, Mr. Wollix and Mrs. Moxton Wiles were escorted by assistants in academic gowns to non-public elevators and rose to upper floors, to private chambers. There, they were robed and received by the Chancellor and more dignitaries. The commencement speaker was introduced: Professor Maltz, a Nobel Prize Laureate in Biology.

Since his return from Sweden, Professor Maltz has used his new prestige to attack the government. He is against the war in Vietnam, against pollution, against the military-industrial complex, for civil rights. Mr. Wollix also is for civil rights, against the military-industrial complex as he understands this entity, against pollution and against the war in Vietnam. He says he is for all the good things and against all the bad things. In private conversation with Prof Maltz, he could not determine whether the Professor was pro-Arab or pro-Israel. Here his position was unclear. The Professor was however unreservedly on the side of radical students in all universities and in every case without exception. He expressed the greatest loathing for colleagues who would not give passing marks to student strikers who had walked out of courses in protest over Kent State. Mr. Wollix said that the shootings at Kent State were criminal, a disaster. He failed to see however that it improved matters to attack the universities. Where but in the universities was free discussion possible?

At this, Professor Maltz no longer glanced at Mr. Wollix. Professor Maltz has a free expression, a face full of simple natural goodness under a druidic profusion of gray hair. On his feet, under the elegant academic robe, were farm boots. Mr. Wollix inferred that Prof Maltz, when not in the laboratory was with his cattle. But he was not able to ask the Professor whether he had a farm in Connecticut since the Professor's attitude towards him had entirely changed, and Professor Maltz now looked far beyond; his eyes, those spiritual fluids, on horizons Mr. Wollix would never see. Mr. Wollix felt himself judged for his backwardness; forgiven, only just. The Professor turned from this limited intellectual technician, Mr. Wollix. Mr. Wollix was glad to be released from his charismatic eyes with their intimation of higher connections. He spoke next to Mrs. Nattash, a black lady from the UN, immense and timidly coughing. These small gusts of coughing jingled the many medals pinned to her bosom. If ever a woman was built for decorations, it was Mrs. Nattash. It was her country that was under-developed, according to Mr. Wollix, not herself. From the palm of her hand, her lips sucked up little cough drops. Still her body meekly shook with suppressed coughs. She was a dear woman, thought Mr. Wollix: in unsuitable company. And he thought of inviting her to lunch, but she was taken away from him by the Marshall. The procession began. In drag. Through robed hosts of dental surgeons and electronic engineers and bearded BAs, accountants, architects and a dozen more learned professions. The orchestra played something suitably distinguished. Everyone sat. The meeting was blessed by ministers and a rabbi, commended to God's attention, as usual; the usual wheedling. Mr. Wollix thought that he, if he were God, would rather be dead than listen to these guys; but then God had reservoirs of judgment and comprehension which would never be fathomed by the likes of Mr. Wollix.

Next came a Black lady in cap and gown. She carried her three hundred pounds with wonderful lightness of foot. She sang, "He's Got the Whole World in His Hand", adlibbing a few verses on civil rights and the war in Vietnam. These were matters on which all could agree (more or less) and the great crowd signified its pleasure. No doubt the Administration had consulted its Psychology Department, and the Department had recommended starting out with symbols of solidarity. In fact, as Mr. Wollix judged, the thing had been planned with unearthly ingenuity. When the song ended, the valedictorian, a black young lady—delicious looking, Mr. Wollix reports—gave an intelligent speech, suitably militant. Next the honorary degrees were given and Dr. Maltz went to the lectern and began to attack the government, the Pentagon, the courts, the universities, the cities, the states, capitalism, the press, pollution. There was no great originality in these attacks and they gave Mr. Wollix a curious sensation. There was so much to agree with, and so much to disagree with. Of course the Federal judiciary had not exactly distinguished itself in Chicago. But Mr. Wollix, burying his ears (as Nietzsche said he buried his in the music of Bizet) in Dr. Maltz's rhetoric, heard at once the brasses and woodwinds of demagogy. It was artistic, Wagnerian demagogy, because Dr. Maltz was after all not seeking political power. His motives were entirely emotional, collective, orgiastic. He

53

wooed, he loved, he courted, he won love from the crowd. Mr. Wollix better understood now the drops of visionary schmaltz in the eyes of the Nobel Laureate. Professor Maltz was the bearer of strong emotions. But it was not peace that was primary, nor social justice; the primary thing was this lust to embrace and be embraced by a host. To Mr. Wollix, this rabble rousing was both fascinating and distressing. A reader of Plutarch, he began to appreciate the fact that Scipio Africanus had retired into solitude. The difference here was that Dr. Maltz's raptures were those of a man who had at last burst from the solitude of his laboratory. He would never go back.

The event was not peaceful, for Dr. Maltz began to accuse the US of war crimes, of being in fact the only modern nation guilty of war crimes. At this, part of the crowd began to howl. The parents and relatives, from Flatbush, Astoria, Jamaica, Hoboken and Elizabeth, could not bear any more of this and began to denounce Dr. Maltz and cry him down. Behind the honored guests, the seated faculty representatives, in their caps and gowns, began to scream back. Among the graduating students several Asiatics rose to reply to Dr. Wald. They shouted about Red Imperialism. Then the Marshalls, also gowned, entered the scene. They bulged with muscle. Mr. Wollix realized that the gowns were disguises, and that these were actually the police! Yes! Well, it stood to reason. What sort of Administration would not be prepared for a riot? The place was full of bouncers.

At this point, as Mr. Wollix tells it, Mrs. Moxton Wiles put her hand on his knee. "There's going to be a riot. This is a riot. Isn't it exciting! This is simply marvelous!"

But there was no riot. The President of the University took hold. Most impressively he moved in, a clever smooth fellow and courageous, he rescued Dr. Maltz and pacified the screaming proletariat with a few words. He raised his hand. He said, "We may not agree with Dr. Maltz, but he is our honored guest and besides he is entitled to the constitutional right of Free Speech."

Free Speech did it. The President radiated a symbolic light. Before his eyes, Mr. Wollix (and this in itself was worth the trip) had one of those miracles of social psychology heretofore contemplated only in books. The warring factions were checked. For half a minute there was a sort of animal growling in the vast hall: lowerclass patriotic fury. Then the hall was still. Dr. Maltz resumed. "Some of you, a minority," he said, "shouted: Go back to Russia. Russia? If I were not a patriotic American I should not express these sentiments . . . I shall lead you all in The Pledge of Allegiance."

He then began to recite the Pledge.

Mrs. Moxton Wiles whispered, "What the hell is the man doing! Is he crazy?"

"Only basically," (Mr. Wollix, quoting himself, had a certain small gleam in the eye.) "Don't worry. Superficially he's perfectly sane."

But Dr. Maltz was shouting: "With Liberty and Justice for All. Do you hear?—For all! For every race!" Etcetera.

And there was wild applause. No disorders. The bouncers relaxed and faded back into the aisles.

"What a moment!" said Mrs. Moxton Wiles. "I wouldn't have missed it." She added, "I don't dare tell my chauffeur what happened. He's very conservative. I think he's a John Bircher. I'd never hear the end of it."

Mark Harris

Nixon and Hayakawa

Suddenly fellows I formerly knew have become President of one thing or another. Dick Nixon has become President of the United States, and Don Hayakawa has become President of San Francisco State College.

Has the world changed? Has it suddenly happened that mediocrities enter high places? Or is it only the past repeated, men of the forefront unfit for foremost places this year as always? This was the triumph of democracy Tocqueville saw, come to think of it, and Thoreau afterward, and Henry Adams after Thoreau, who looked upon the election of Grant to the Presidency as the refutation of all theories of evolution. The common man is king, and kings together these days unite to elect a President to do their bidding, their work, the will of the commonplace everyday king who is presumed to run things.

For indeed, Dick Nixon wants to do nothing more and be nothing more than the servant of the people, and Don Hayakawa, too, each with the same need to be not only liked, not only well-liked, but very well-liked by hordes, by tons of people, countable, shown numerically, their love proveable; effects plauditable, leaders mountable upon platforms for speeches; attending dinners in their own honor at so-many dollars per plate.

It is their way of serving, however much it may at first appear like a way of being served. The President honors not subjects beneath him but kings above him. Not every man a king, as Huey Long said, but every man a Presidentmaker. (The President is made to feel that he is in the stream of policy, directing the flow.) The President goes over Niagara in a barrel, calling behind, "Waters, follow me."

Under attack, Nixon wants to be sure his attackers are seen as a minority. After his speech last November 3, when he outlined his plans for withdrawing from Vietnam, he was photographed with piles of telegrams supporting him. Arriving on tour in Indianapolis, he cites the numbers of people who have come to greet him, appearing to be surprised, as if he had not realized until this moment how really very well-liked he is, as if he had expected no crowd at all at the airport.

Don Hayakawa, at Northeastern in Boston, tells protesting students that the more they attack him the higher go his lecture fees. (Somewhere, greater audiences appreciate him.) As a teacher at San Francisco State College in the "fifties" he reckoned the success of his course by the size of his enrollment. Longing to be liked by WISHING students, he made the work easy for them. At San Quentin prison he wooed the approbation of prisoners, telling them that their problem was not that they had committed crimes but a failure of communication had occurred. Poor fellows, they heard that not they were at fault; it was something called "semantics." Building in their minds the case for their own innocence and exoneration, and hearing such things from a reputable and even famous speaker, you can bet they were in raptures. A decade later, at San Francisco State College, he truly achieved fame by calling the cops. "Calling the cops" makes it look like a one-sided piece of mischief on its part. There were two sides, certainly, at San Francisco State. I don't like the bold statement of blame. Now everyone knew him at last. Throughout California was talk of his running for the Senate. He was invited to the White House by Dick Nixon.

Every corner grocer will agree that whatever sells is good. The quantification of souls has always been basic to the points of view of both men. LBJ, too, pulling poll-figures out of his pocket. Of different parties nominally, their truest party is the party of pragmatism. Whatever sells or works is good. Was Dick Nixon guilty of petty dishonesty years ago—some sort of scandal of money—of no interest except as a measure of his ethical perception? We shall never know. His reply was, "let the public decide," speaking that night in 1952 from a stage-set made to look like a private home. Many thousands of people watching him became persuaded of his honesty (or had already been persuaded), and sent him telegrams. Dwight Eisenhower, now persuaded of Nixon's honesty, declared he would retain him as his running-mate. Here was trial by public, sale by television.

There was always some dislocated pride in Don Hayakawa. If he failed of a promise he did so proudly in his own way, as if it were a signal of his toughness, his firm sense of reality. He was no fool of an idealist. He told me once how, as a struggling young man in Vancouver, he drove a taxicab. Sometimes he carried men to brothels. Then, said I, quite amiable (for we were friends then): You were an accessory to prostitution. This he denied. He simply drove the men where they wanted to go, he said.

If the great public cared, Dick or Don would do things another way, and maybe this situation is ideally suited to good action: if the best thought in America can rally itself, and be or appear to be numerous, Dick Nixon will listen closely. He may pretend to be watching pro football or he may say that he cannot be persuaded a different way, but he will defer to the clearest wish, for nobody has ever wanted the love of the many more dearly than President Nixon. Notice, for example, the speedy action in revising the military draft: first making a lottery of it, and then—that not silencing the vocal classes—suggesting a volunteer army. These steps do not really cure the headaches of militarism, but they show deference to major segments of the electorate. Whatever we ask him to do he will do, for no convictions impede his action; no personal rage (like Johnson's) stands in his way.

Luckily, it may be that he now believes himself loved at last. When his assistant, Ron Ziegler, recently complained of his (Ziegler's) bad treatment by the press, the President replied (it is said),

"That's nothing. You should have heard what they used to say about me."

Outer deference had changed his sense of himself. Don Hayakawa, after the commotions at San Francisco State College, told of receiving hundreds of greetings by mail, telephone, and what-not, all of them favorable, he said. He appeared to be holding that public endorsement proved his judgment right. His wife, in the same little interview in the newspaper, said that her husband was "a man without any hangups." Yet this capacity to judge oneself only by outer criteria must have some name, some designation in classical psychology. (In sociology, the principle is approbativeness.)

Mark Harris

Possibly it suggests a lack of self-respect. The man who will surrender private judgment to public response, who will speak in public tediously, saying nothing new, tends to make us skeptical when he speaks of caring for the quality of life. Quality! The polls show it to be a good word.

60

Saul Bellow

White House and Artists

One of the editors of *The Noble Savage*, because the magazine has made so important a contribution to American culture, was invited to attend a White House dinner in honor of M. André Malraux, the French Minister of Culture, and to mingle with two hundred writers, painters, actors, musicians, and administrators and patrons of the arts. In this crowd, *TNS*'s representative saw several novelists and poets at one time strongly alienated, ex-intransigents, former enemies of society, old grumblers and life-long manger-dogs, all having a hell of a good time, their faces beaming, their wives in evening gowns (could they afford them?) Readers who remember H. G. Wells' *The Island of Dr. Moreau*, with its apes, dogs, and horses changed by the mad surgeon into approximately human forms, have only to think of these same creatures in formal dress (black tie) to get a bit of the flavor.

Casting back in history for a parallel, one wit spoke of the Jacksonian horde trampling the White House furniture (a proto Beat occasion). A few old-time Washington matrons might have been ready to agree. But this was not in the least a Beat evening. It was Square. Even the drunks were well behaved, though at the end of the evening the Schubert trio seemed to be getting to them and some were tapping the time on their neighbors' knees.

There was nothing Jacksonian about the planning and the protocol, the Marines in braid, the butlers, the dance orchestra which played a sort of Catskill-intercourse music. Only Mr. Stevenson preserved a shade of intellectual irony. Everybody else seemed absurdly and deeply tickled. A certain painter whispered privately to me that of course all this was a lot of crap, and meant nothing to him. "But my *sister!*" he said.

"Where is she?"

"Home with the kids. But absolutely beside herself with excitement. It's a great day for my sister."

What he really meant was, "If Mama could only see me now."

Several old lions, accustomed to first honors always, spoke to no one, but swept through the crowd with an extraordinary brazen fixity of expression, demanding recognition. At the other extreme were some humble souls who confessed a little brokenly that they were not worthy. A few writers, among them veterans of the Popular Front and believers in the upgrading of the masses, declared that a new era was beginning. The American Presidency, for so many years sewed up in longjohns, a rube Presidency, was at last becoming modern. Henceforth the country would begin to respect culture. Others, however, said that Mr. Kennedy was getting ready to exploit the eggheads. He could get them cheaply; they were falling all over themselves. The government could then show the world that it was an enlightened government, that it knew how to encourage the arts, that American philistinism was a thing of the dead past. But the real truth, said the grumblers, was that Congress and the Administration, though willing to fork over millions of dollars to oil companies in the form of depletion allowances, or to cranberry growers to keep up their bogs, would not put up a cent to build a cultural center in Washington. All that dough for Billie Sol and not a penny for singers and playwrights. But Congress has always taken a low view of the arts. It would have filled the White House with hogcallers, or with stag shows. Now, grudgingly, it had given the land for a new cultural center but left the raising of funds to the benevolent rich. Finally, these critics declared, the Congress *is* representative—it *does* represent the mind, the spirit, and feelings of the people. Why should painters and writers lend themselves to schemes designed to conceal the true state of things?

My own feeling was that if the government really did intend to seduce and exploit American artists it might do these artists little harm. The hand of the seducer obviously made their hearts beat a little faster and put a fine glow into their cheeks.

Mr. Kennedy's after-dinner speech was very witty, and a witty President is worth more to artists than a congressional porkbarrel. M. Malraux, an impressive-looking man, spoke in greater earnest, saying that America had not sought imperial power and dominion. In private, Mr. Edmund Wilson exclaimed irascibly, in the tones of Mr. Magoo, "Hooey!" There *was* an American empire! I felt it would be a pity to waste Mr. Wilson's fine old rumblings on a lousy republic and that his eccentricities deserved at least an imperial setting. But putting it all together again—the Philippines, Latin America, the fierce Cuban invasion, the sins of Aramco, the haste with which Germany was reconstructed, the fascinating history of Chiang Kai-shek—I couldn't believe that we were ready to claim the elevation to the rank of empire.

But this is the sort of quibble it takes a left-wing sectarian to appreciate. When Russia invaded Finland the Trotskyites and Ohlerites suffered nearly as much as the Finns, but from another cause. They could not agree about the character of the Soviet state. Was this an imperialist invasion? Could a degenerated workers' state wage an imperialistic war? Can such questions of definition really matter much? Did Augustus Caesar have a stock-pile of atomic bombs? Can an American name be fitted into the list of imperial personalities—Augustus, Charles the Fifth, Napoleon, Gladstone even? Do we dare to add the name of Eisenhower? Kennedy?

Is it to be Emperor Kennedy, then? Well, that is a title to interest poets and artists and philosophers in a different fashion. Poor Descartes died because Queen Christina of Sweden, a spartan bluestocking, had him up at dawn to give her lessons in mathematics. He was accustomed to lie abed until noon. There he had always done his best work. Pushkin complained about the Tsar, but then the Tsar took him seriously enough to oppress him, which is more than the American government cares to do for its writers. Voltaire quarreled with Frederick the Great, but it was perhaps to his credit that he could not make out with that militaristic Kraut. Ezra Pound suffered terrible miseries until he had found himself a Caesar. If Mr. Wilson is right about the American empire we must think the whole thing through clearly. What is to be done? How shall we behave?

Boswell and Johnson throw some light on this matter. Johnson was honored by the King, who engaged him in private conversation in the library at the Queen's House. "His Majesty approached him, and at once was courteously easy," says Boswell. When the King complimented him handsomely, Johnson made no reply, explaining later, "It was not for me to bandy civilities with my sovereign." To the King's questions about one Dr. Hill, Johnson answered "that he was an ingenious man, but had no veracity." Urged to say more, he declined to louse up Dr. Hill. "I now began to consider that I was depreciating this man in the estimation of his Sovereign, and thought it was time for me to say something that might be more favorable."

Boswell relates that Oliver Goldsmith was lying on the sofa during all the time in which Johnson was telling of his meeting with the King, "fretting with chagrin and envy at the singular honor Dr. Johnson had lately enjoyed. At length the frankness and simplicity of his natural character prevailed. He sprung from the sofa, advanced to Johnson, and in a kind of flutter from imagining himself in the situation which he had just been hearing described, exclaimed, 'Well, you acquitted yourself in this conversation better than I should have done; for I should have bowed and stammered through the whole of it.'"

This is the sort of thing that may happen in a fairly easygoing monarchy tending toward the constitutional form. But what happens in a large bureaucratic society? In the Han Dynasty men of letters became functionaries and the state passed into the long torpor of orthodoxy and dogmatism. A better understanding between writers and the imperial state has its dangers. I can foresee a bureaucratic situation, partly created by men of letters, in which the very call girls (who owe so many of their privileges to the Federal tax-structure) may be required to pass Civil Service examinations administered by poets!

One final outcome of this White House dinner should be noted. One of the guests was Mr. David Rockefeller of the Chase Manhattan Bank. With him President Kennedy had a long conversation about the economy which resulted in an exchange of letters between the two. These letters were published by *Life*. So far as I know there have been no letters about the state of American culture. We can wait until the other crises are over.

Felix Pollak

The Poor Man's Civil Defense Manual

1. In case of an H-bomb attack, drive to your nearest curb and roll up your window. Don't remain in the car, as it presents an easy target for H-bombs. Go—*walk, don't run!*— to your nearest air-raid shelter.

2. If you don't know where your nearest air-raid shelter is located, ask your nearest policeman or air-raid warden. They will be happy to direct you.

3. Should your nearest policeman or air-raid warden be dead or otherwise occupied, don't panic! That is what the enemy wants you to do. Panic leads to the disregard of traffic regulations and you might get yourself run over by a car on its way to the nearest curb. Or you may be hit by falling houses or trees, depending upon whether you are in a city or in the country. Remain calm and go—*walk, don't run!*—to your nearest air-raid shelter.

4. If you don't know where your nearest air-raid shelter is located, and any officials or persons you might meet are dead, panicky, or equally uninformed, telephone the police or your nearest air-raid warden.

5. Should the telephone be out of order, or you out of dimes and there is

no one with the proper change available, send a telegram to the White House, Washington, DC, and ask for directions to your nearest air-raid shelter. Give your nearest air-raid shelter as return address and wait for a reply. Due to circumstances beyond control, the reply may be subject to unavoidable delays. However, do not allow yourself to become panicky or impatient. Take an aspirin or a tranquilizer.

6. Should you be out of aspirin or tranquilizers and your nearest drugstore be bombed out, burning, unattended, or closed for remodeling, go to your nearest air-raid shelter. *Walk, don't run!* You will find a supply of aspirin or tranquilizers next to the snack bar.

7. On your way to your nearest air-raid shelter, avoid being hit by flying objects, like fallout, debris, propaganda leaflets, or H-bombs and parts thereof. A direct hit may be fatal, and even an indirect hit can cause grave bodily harm and psychological shock.

8. Should you be hit despite your caution, go—*walk, don't run!*—to your nearest air-raid shelter and ask the air-raid warden on duty to direct (transport) you to your nearest hospital. The proper guide will be happy to direct (transport) you.

9. A good means of avoiding dangerous fallout is the opening of an umbrella or a parachute. This is, however, only a temporary measure, as fallout particles are liable to bounce up from the pavement and hit you in the face from below. (On dirt roads, substitute "dirt road" for "pavement.")

10. On your way to your nearest air-raid shelter, avoid conversations with strangers. They may be enemy agents trying to lead you into traps or cause you to mistake craters or other holes in the ground for your nearest air-raid shelter. Also avoid breathing, as the fumes emanating from burning buildings or trees are often poisonous and bad for your lungs.

11. Should you be in doubt whether the stranger you are conversing with is a spy or an enemy agent, or whether the hole in the ground you are looking at is your nearest air-raid shelter, ask your nearest air-raid warden for information or send a telegram, collect, to the White House. You will

find an auxiliary Western Union station at your nearest air-raid shelter, in the vicinity of the snack bar.

12. Due to circumstances beyond control, you may learn that the White House has been moved from Washington, DC, to a safe, top-secret destination. In that case, call Information and ask for the new telephone number and address. Give your nearest air-raid shelter as your home address and proceed there—*walk, don't run!*

13. When you, by all these means, arrive safely at your nearest air-raid shelter, don't panic! Get immediately in touch with your nearest air-raid warden and identify yourself. Your driver's license or any other suitable identification will be your identification. Should your nearest air-raid warden be absent, ask your nearest air-raid warden as to his whereabouts. He may be in another air-raid shelter nearby. If so, proceed there without delay—*walk, don't run!*—in order to identify yourself.

14. However, should your nearest air-raid warden be present but dead, wounded, panicky, drunk, or otherwise incapacitated, occupied, or disgruntled, proceed without delay to elect another air-raid warden. Let yourself be guided by the unmistakable signs of leadership among your fellow-air-raidees, as, for example, the readiness to give advice, the gift of knowing all the answers, the ability of organizing square dances and other creative leisure-time activities, etc. An excellent morale-builder is TV watching, especially the avoidance of news broadcasts. This will keep the inhabitants of air-raid shelters from becoming panicky, sick, restive, bored, hungry, or otherwise dissatisfied. Should disagreements arise as to which programs to watch, and should *Robert's Rules of Order* prove ineffective in settling such disputes, or should the situation get completely out of hand due to temporary reception disturbances or the unavoidable absence of programs, take an aspirin or tranquilizer and go to your nearest air-raid shelter. *Walk, don't run!*

67

15. In case the situation remains unsatisfactory for any length of time, ask your nearest White House to commence immediate negotiations with the enemy. During these negotiations, it is of the utmost importance not to display any pacifistic tendencies or to resort to cowardly policies of appeasement. Offer yourself as adviser to your nearest White House, and be firm

and unyielding. Try to gain time to cover your rear, in case your rear has been unavoidably uncovered, damaged, or denuded during your preceding precarious position. Should the enemy intimate that he has hopes of surviving your retaliatory attack owing to his well-organized system of Civilian Defense, laugh in his face. Tell him to go jump in his car—*walk, don't run!*—and roll up his window. Tell him to go to his nearest air-raid shelter. Tell him to take an aspirin or a tranquilizer. But be careful not to die laughing.

16. Should your negotiations with the enemy for some reason break down, wait for the air-raid sirens, then immediately drive to your nearest curb and roll up your window. Don't remain in the car, as it presents an easy target for H-bombs. Go—*walk, don't run!*—to your nearest air-raid shelter and proceed according to the instructions given in point 1. above.

Philip O'Connor

A Few Notes on the Changing World

1. There are many indications of a changing conception of the individual, and an ethical revaluation of individual action. "Obviously." But coherent accounts are few, and a general prospectus of the new world, as far as I know, nonexistent in the West.

2. What is obviously dying with rhetorical protests and a misinterpretation of the word "freedom": the association of individuality with competitive potential, and especially with competitive economic power.

3. What is being born: the fruitful association of noncompetitive individualism with a socialist community; leading to a *noncynical* realization that what is economically good is psychologically good: leading to the revolutionary premise that a high standard of living is ethically beneficial: leading to the end of Puritanism.

4. Wanting: a persuasive indictment, without a provocative use of Marxist terminology, of the barbarism of associating self-expression with destructive potential (which is the romanticism of worse-than-babes); of limiting Christian ethics to their uses as inhibitors of barbaric instincts carefully fostered,

to provide that mental fog conducive to a fairly obedient population—obedient to those who lack such inhibitions. Hence, a falsely "revolutionary movement, now almost senile but still strutting, associating 'truth' and 'honesty' with open aggression and lawlessness. If an American can disentangle freedom from the ability to destroy, he will become legally un-American. In England he would be merely eccentric.

5. Ninety percent of our fictional, theatrical, and personal drama employs the useless frustrations created by the coexistence of two systems of ethics, Christian and competitive-economical. Drama is become frustration; liberation of the individual is hopeless in present contexts; the hero died long ago, though he is often resurrected in imbecilic forms, from Hemingway onward. All stems from the primary and archaic attachment of individuality with aggressive potential, the conditioned creature of our competitive economic system.

6. Hence, a hugely disproportionate amount of reality is become psychological. Within the dreadful confines of the domestic nest, ritual gestures exacerbate individuals to the delusions of living in the world; each nuance in the shadow play is emphasized in order that the total lack of developmental action shall be unnoticed.

7. Psychology is becoming the chief agent of reaction, a repair shop foregroggy vessels from a stormy sea. It can be no more than this while it continues to regard the present social reality as rigid and unchangeable; nevertheless it may adapt too far for its own purposes.

8. Peace is consistently kept at sentimental levels; love is employed to discount planning; the inhibitory Christian ethic is exploited to justify what it inhibits; positive values are thrown out by negative ones.

9. Liberty truly is liberty to give and not to take; but to give fearlessly there must be no fear of not surviving. Socialistic economics would ensure against this. Safety is man's most propitious social atmosphere; little boys are taught the insane opposite.

10. Again, man's true lust is contributory, which terror inverts to acquisitory.

Acquisitiveness is the opposite of enjoyment; such misery is inimical to thought and life. To give is, and has always been, release and joy, which is life; man's civilization begins when he can be assured of enough to enable him to give even more. This is now technologically possible.

11. Christian ethics were prophetic of socialist communities; the Kingdom of Heaven was a blueprint. The ideal was exploited to prevent its material application. Having built up a whole system of inhibitory ethics, the Christian ideal would if applied make the lot useless, unemploy rosy preachers and their industrial masters in thousands. As Shaw pointed out, deism was the real enemy of the Christian message.

12. Waste: the proportion of talent—of genius—wasted on competitive marketing of the products; vitiation of the purity of the artistic concept by the same necessity; vulgarization of the person into the Personality, the cornily branded mark of 'uniqueness' which makes monsters out of harmless beginnings. Great art demands anonymity, almost: can only allow the existence of the artist when conditions are such that he doesn't get another fee for being that. Art is a woman being steadily raped into the persona of the Artist, a kind of retarded gangster. Communication has become shameful, and a serious economic liability to a *serious* artist. Vulgarity is enthroned. It was Picasso's conscience, not his consciousness, that made him a Communist.

71

13. The futile refusal to analyze the meaning, ethical and social and psychological, of Marxian economics has done much to bog us down in our atavistic economic warfare; we throw out baby with bathwater, and are condemned, I fear, to authoritarianism. No man in his senses can refuse to acknowledge the civilizedness of socialist economics who hasn't a vested interest in the opposite. History has made socialism *natural*; capitalism proliferates unnatural objections, including the bogus booby of the economically free individual. This sacred cow yearns for the slaughterhouse, and lives on religious drugs.

14. Social schizophrenia—private money-making, gregarious living—is the basis of neurosis: not the wish to sleep with Mummy. The wear and tear of nerves is created by this anomaly, this necessity to keep economically apart, which becomes the easier necessity to despise and/or to hate all others; so that identity depends upon the absence of recognition of other identities

(enter the witch-doctor psycho), superiority is composed of the inferiorities of others. Lunacy at an apex of establishment.

15. Decline of God, pathology of belief in Leaders, the crawling conceit of human worship.

16. Sweat-bath in "Christian love"; blood-bath in ideological war.

17. Christianity provides hurdles; socialism provides roads.

18. And sex! The fluid amenable to every canalization, especially against itself. The ideas of Wilhelm Reich—whatever extravagances (and are they?) one might discount, opened up the road to the understanding of this servant of life. That authority paralyzes the individual for the competitively prosperous perversity of poor sexual lives I do not at all doubt. In a word, the engine of competition derives from frustrations of all kinds; it is organized waste.

Saul Bellow

View from Intensive Care

I had visited friends and relatives in the intensive care units of various hospitals and with the natural stupidity of a sound, healthy man had refused to consider that *I* might one day be the person strapped down, plugged into the life-supporting machines.

But my lungs had failed. I was now the dying man. A machine did my breathing for me. Unconcious, I had no more idea of death than the dead have. But my head (I assume that it was the head) was full of visions, delusions, hallucinations. These were not dreams or nightmares. Nightmares have an escape-hatch ... I was on a drug called Verset, which is said to deaden the memory. But my memory has always been tenacious. I can remember being turned often. Someone was pounding my back and ordering me to breathe.

But mostly I recall that I thought I was wandering about, having a heavy time of it. In one of my visions I am on a city street looking for the place where I am supposed to pass the night. At last I find it. I enter what was long ago, in the Twenties, a movie palace. The ticket booth is boarded up. But just behind it, on a tile floor that slopes upwards are folding army cots. There is no film being shown. The hundreds of seats are empty. But I understand that the air in here is specially treated and that it will be good for your lungs to breathe it in. You get medical points toward your recovery for spending the night here. So I join half a dozen others and lie down. My wife is supposed to pick me up in the morning. The car is in a parking lot nearby. Nobody here is sleepy. Nor are the men talkative. They get up. They mooch about the lobby or sit on the edge of a cot. The floor hasn't been mopped in fifty years or more. But you sleep fully dressed and lie in your overcoat wearing your shoes. Hats or caps are not removed.

Even before my release from the intensive care unit, I climbed out of bed thinking that I was in Vermont and that one of my granddaughters was skiing around the house. I was annoyed with her parents for not having brought her in to see her grandfather. It was a winter morning, or so I thought. Actually, it must have been the middle of the night, but the sun seemed to be shining on the snow. I climbed over the bedrail without noticing that I was attached by tubes and needles to hanging flasks containing all kinds of intravenous mixtures. I saw as if they were someone else's, my bare feet on the sunny floor. They seemed unwilling to bear my weight but I forced them to obey my will. Then I fell, landing on my back. At first I felt no pain. I was vexed by the cancellation of my faculties. As I lay helpless, an orderly ran up and said, "I heard you were a troublemaker."

One of the doctors said that my back was so inflamed that it looked like a forest fire seen from the air. The doctors put me through a CAT scan. It seemed to me that I was on a crowded trolley car and that I was being stifled and pushed from behind. I begged to be let out. But nobody was willing to oblige me.

I was then on heavy doses of blood thinner and my fall was dangerous. I was bleeding internally. The nurses put me into a restraining vest. I asked my grown sons to call a taxi. I said I'd be better off at home, soaking in the bath. "In five minutes I could be there," I said. "It's just around the corner."

Often it seemed to me that I was just underneath Kenmore Square in Boston. The oddity of these hallucinatory surroundings was in a way liberating. I wonder sometimes whether at the threshold of death I may not have been entertaining myself lightheartedly, positively enjoying these preposterous delusions—fictions which did not have to be invented.

I find myself in a vast cellar. Its brick walls had been painted ages ago. In places they were still as white as cottage cheese. But the cheese had grown soiled. Overhead were fluorescent tubes. Under these lights, table after table of thrift-shop items—women's clothing, mainly, donated for resale; underwear, stockings, sweaters, skirts. The place made me think of Filene's Basement, where customers would soon be pushing and quarreling. In the far distance were young women who seemed to be volunteers doing charity work. I was sitting, trapped, among hundreds of leather lounge chairs. Escape from this grimy cheese-corner was out of the question. Behind me, huge pipes came through the ceiling and sank into the ground.

I was painfully preoccupied with the restraining vest or pullover I was forced to wear. This hot khaki vest was constricting—it was killing me, binding me to death. I tried, and failed, to unravel it. I thought: if only I could get one of those Social Register charity volunteers to bring a knife or a pair of shears! But they were several city blocks away and they'd never hear me. I was in a far, far corner surrounded by hundreds of Barca-loungers.

Another memorable experience was this:

A male hospital attendant on a step-ladder was hanging Christmas tinsel, mistletoe and evergreen clippings on the wall fixtures. This attendant didn't much care for me. He was the one who had called me a troublemaker. But that didn't stop me from taking note of him. Taking note is part of my job-description. Existence is—or was—the job. So I watched him on the three-step ladder—his sloping shoulders and wide backside. Then he came down and carried his ladder to the next pillar. More tinsel and prickly evergreen.

75

Off to the side there was another old fellow, small, nervous and fretful, going back and forth in carpet slippers. He was my neighbor. His living quarters opened at the end of my room, but he wouldn't acknowledge me. He had a thinnish beard, his nose was like a plastic pot-scraper and he wore a beret. He would *have* to be an artist. But it seemed to me that his features were lacking in interest.

After a time, I recalled having seen him on television. He *was* an artist, much respected. He lectured while drawing. His themes were fashionable—environmentalism, holistic remedies, cures, and so on. His sketches were vague, suggesting love of and responsibility for our natural surroundings. On a blackboard he had first produced a hazy sea surface, and then with the side of his chalk he evoked a lurking face. You saw the wavy hair of a woman. These were glimpses or hints of a human aspect or presence of nature. Maybe an Undine or a Rhine maiden. You couldn't actually accuse this fellow of mystification. All you could nail him for was self-importance and petty vanity—*suffisance*, in French. In my disheveled way, never mastering the language, I have studied French for eighty odd years (my mother was something of a Francophile). I like *suffisance* better than smugness, just as I prefer the English suffocating to the French *suffoquant—Tout suffoquant et blême* (Verlaine?). If you're choking, why worry about being pale?

This Ananias, or false artist, was settled here—he had an apartment along the side of the building. His quarters were around the corner, so I couldn't see them from my bed. I had only a glimpse of his bookcases and a green wall-to-wall carpet. The Christmas tinsel and evergreen attendant was very deferential to the artist, who, for his part, took no notice of me. Nil! By which I mean only that I didn't fit into any of his concepts. And as a tabloid publisher, for I am a tabloid journalist, I can't feel superior to anybody. I am the easiest man in the world to cut.

This TV *artiste*, anyway had the air of being long settled here, but today he was leaving. Cardboard boxes were being carried out of his flat—or wing. The movers were stacking crates and trunks. They worked at top speed. The books were disappearing from the shelves, the shelves themselves were dismantled in a tremendous hurry. A van was backed in and swiftly loaded, and then in a green-gold long gown the artist's old wife came out, stooped, and was helped into the cab of the truck. She wore a silk cap. The TV artist stuck his carpet slippers into the pockets of his topcoat, he put on loafers and crawled in beside her.

The male attendant was there to see him off, and then he said to me, "You're next. We need the space. My orders are to get you out this minute." Immediately a crew dismantled the shelves and took everything to pieces. The surroundings were knocked down like theater flats. Nothing was left. A moving-van meanwhile backed in and my street-clothes, my Borsalino, electric razor, toilet articles, tabloids, CDs, pills, etc. were stuffed into supermarket shopping bags. I was helped into a wheelchair and lifted into a trailer truck. There I found a nurse's station, small but complete. The tail gate came up; the upper doors however were left open, and the van roared directly underground, into a tunnel. It continued for a time at top speed. Then we stopped. The giant engine idled. It went on idling.

There was only one nurse in attendance. She saw that I was agitated and offered to shave me. I admitted that I could use a shave. She therefore lathered me and did the job with a disposable Schick or Gillette. Few nurses understand how to shave a man. When you haven't been soaped and soaked the scraping blade pulls the stubble and your face stings.

I said to the nurse that I was expecting my wife at four o'clock, and it was already well past four on the big circular clock. "Where do you think we are?" The nurse couldn't say. My guess was that we were under Kenmore Square, and if they had stopped the idling van we would have been able to hear the Green Line subway trains. It was now suddenly six o'clock, whether AM or PM who could say? We began docking slowly beside a pedestrian passageway where people—not too many—went up into the street or came down from it.

"You look a little like an Indian brave," the nurse said. "Also, because of weight loss you're more wrinkled, and the beard grows inside the furrows. There, it's hard to get at. Were you stout once?"

"No, but my build has changed many times. I always looked better sitting than standing," I said, and despite my sad heart I laughed.

She wasn't able to make anything of these remarks.

And there had been no van. I had had to vacate my room, it was urgently needed and I was moved in the night to another part of the hospital. "Where have you been?" I said to my wife when she arrived. I was annoyed with her. But she explained that she had suddenly sat up in her bed wide awake and uneasy about me. She telephoned the intensive care unit, learned that I had been transferred, jumped into a dress and rushed over.

"It's evening," I said.

"No it's dawn."

"And where am I?"

The attending nurse was remarkably quick and sympathetic. She pulled the curtain around my bed and said to my wife, "Take off your shoes and get in with him. A few hours of sleep are what you need. Both of you."

One more brief vision, for purposes of orientation. Vela figures in this one. Vela had been my wife for one decade—I married her at 65 and she took off on my 75th birthday. Perhaps the most beautiful of all my wives, if you go by photographic standards or by feminine measurements or statistics. Her advantages made her a very confident woman. She had an unusual degree of self-appreciation and declared and also silently asserted that she was a real beauty. And something else, which may be rendered, translated or explicated as: "Judge for yourselves what sort of match I made in marrying this deficient person—nothing but a tabloid publisher."

So here are the two of us on exhibit for all the world to judge. Her open elegant hand directs attention to my uneasy posture and the scar tissue over my cheekbones, caused by skin infections a very long time ago.

She and I find ourselves in this curious scenario, confronting the polished stone wall of a bank interior—an investment bank. Vela and I had several times been separated, and on this occasion we were again on the outs. But I had come to the bank meeting at her request. She was escorted by a Spanish-looking and very elegant male person in his mid-to-late twenties. A third man was present as well, a banker in a frock coat who spoke French. Before us, set into the glamorous marble wall, were two coins: One a US dime, the other a silver dollar with a diameter of ten or twelve feet.

Vela introduced me to the Spanish companion. It wasn't much of an introduction, since he did not acknowledge me. She then said, explaining simply, "Until now I never had any experience of glamorous sex and I figured, in what you always call the sexual revolution, I should have a sample of it—to find out once and for all what I was deprived of with you."

"By golly," I said. "It's like a huge rabbit hutch, thousands of rabbits, with each doe sampling all the buck-rabbits."

But this first phase of the meeting was quickly behind us. Its purpose, evidently, was to fill me with guilt and inject me with a mental solvent or softener.

"Can you tell me where we are?" I said. "And why we are meeting here in front of these coins? They signify—what?"

Then the banker came forward and said that over a period of years the dime on the right would turn into the dollar with the ten foot diameter.

"How long a period?"

"A century or a little more."

"Well, I don't doubt the arithmetic is right—but for whom would this be done?"

"For yourself," said Vela.

"Me? And how do you figure it?"

"Through cryonics," she said. "A person lets himself be frozen and stored. A century later they thaw him or her back to life. Don't you remember that *Brillig's*, your own rag, reported how Howard Hughes had himself frozen and would be thawed and revived when they found a cure for the disease which was killing him? This is called cryonics."

"Let's hear what you want me to do. Guesswork is no use. What have you got in mind—when would you like to have me frozen?"

"You'd do it now. I'd go later. Then we'd wake up together in the 22nd century."

The gray glow and the high polish of the marble slabs were calculated to persuade the deepest skeptic of eternal dollar stability. But it was also the facade of a cold-storage plant—or crypt. This was foolish, perhaps. This was not your resting place. Your body would be stacked with the bodies of other investors elswhere. You would lie in a lab far from the marble facade. Technician-priests would tend you generation after generation, regulating the temperature, the moisture, and keeping tabs on your condition.

"You'd live again." Vela said. "Figure the compound interest per million. We both would live."

"Companions in old age? . . ."

The bank man, actually wearing a cutaway coat, said in a practiced voice, "By then the life span will be upwards of 200 years."

"It's the only chance for our marriage," Vela told me.

There was a certain Serbian grace-note (B-flat A, B-flat C) at the great word "marriage."

"Oh, for Christ's sake, Vela! This is no way to approach the subject of death. To postpone it for a century solves nothing!"

I must remind you that I had already died and risen again and there was curious distance in my mind between the old way of seeing (false) and the new way (strange but liberating).

English was not Vela's first language and she couldn't reformulate anything because so much effort had gone into composing the formulations she put forward. All she could do was repeat what had been said. She again stated the facts as she understood them, which didn't advance the discussion.

I told her, "I can't do this."

"Why can't you do this?"

"You're asking me to commit suicide. Suicide is forbidden."

"By who is suicide forbidden?"

"It's against my religion. Jews don't commit suicide unless they lose the siege as they did at Masada, or are about to be hacked to pieces, as in the Crusades. Then the martyrs put their children to death before they kill themselves."

"You never fall back on religion except to win an argument," said Vela.

"Suppose you were to turn around and sue the bank, as soon as I'm frozen," I said. "Trying to claim my estate because I'm dead. They can't prove that I might be thawed out and restored to life without thawing me out. Or do you think they'd bring me back just to win the lawsuit? The whole thing argued before some judge who couldn't find his ass with both hands?"

When lawsuits were mentioned the bank's representative went pale and in a way I sympathized with him, although I wasn't well, myself; my heart having sunk so low.

"You *owe* me this," said Vela.

What did she mean? But it is a principle with me not to argue with irrational people. I simply shook my head and repeated "It can't be done, it can't be, and I won't do it."

"No?"

"You don't understand what you're asking," I said.

"No?"

"You mean by the way you say it that *I* don't know what *I'm* doing. Fair enough. I was never more out of line than when we stood together in the judge's chambers to be married. If ever my granddaughter wanted evidence that I was *non compos mentis* she would have to do no more than show the film made by Treshansky, who turned up with his camcorder that day as if to put it on record that his boss was off his rocker."

Treshansky—one of the editors of my tabloid mag, *Brillig's*—was greatly taken with Vela. He whispered in my ear, as the judge was looking for the marriage service in his book, "Even if this doesn't last six months— even if it's only a month, it's still worth it—with that bosom and those hips, and a face like hers."

Resuming the dialogue in the bank with Vela, I could hear myself saying, with the conviction of ultimate seriousness, "I adjusted myself long ago to dying a natural death, like everybody else. I've seen plenty of dying, in my time, and I'm prepared for it. Maybe I've been a little *too* imaginative about the grave—the dampness and the cold. I've pictured it in too much detail and feel it a little too much. I feel abnormally for the dead. There's not a chance in the world of convincing me to put myself in the hands of experimental science. I feel insulted by your proposition. But if you could once induce me to marry you perhaps you feel that I can also be talked into being frozen for a century."

"Yes, I do think you owe me something," said Vela, on top of what I was saying.

One of our difficulties, and a source of much misunderstanding, was that my outlook was incomprehensible to her. Dogs can understand a joke. Cats never, but never, have occasion to laugh. Vela, when others were laughing, would join in. But if cues were lacking ("This is funny") she didn't smile. And I, when I amused a dinner table, was suspected by her of making her the butt of my jokes.

I may not have been aware, when I believed myself to be in a bank, with a small dime and huge dollar set side by side in polished marble, that in the real world my life was being saved. Doctors by drugs, nurses by tending me, technicians with their skills, were all working to assist me. When or if I was saved, I would go on with my life.

And if I hadn't been associated with a tabloid, Vela would never have suggested my being frozen for a century. Meanwhile she would do lewd things with the Spanish boyfriend (by the way, he never said so much as good morning to me) while I lay frozen—a block of ice, awaiting resuscitation or resurrection. *She* attributed a tabloid outlook to *me!*

And I did not doubt the reality of this bank, these coins, those companions—Vela, her Spanish stud, the investment counselor and Vela's remarks about the sexual revolution.

"That meeting in the bank you believe in," my wife, the real wife, later said, after I had described this moment to her. "Why should it be always the *worst* things that appear to you so real? I'll never be able to talk you out of being sadistic to yourself."

"Yes," I agreed. "It has a specific kind of satisfaction, the bad of it guarantees it as real experience. This is what we go through, and it's what existence is like. The brain is a mirror and reflects the world. Of course we see pictures, not the real things, but the pictures are dear to us, we come to love them even though we are aware how distorting an organ the mirror-brain is. But this is not the moment to turn metaphysical."

I, too, was being misleading. On this subject I couldn't be entirely straight even with Trudi, my incomparable wife.

Saul Bellow

Graven Images

arry S. Truman liked to say that as president of this country he was its most powerful citizen—but sometimes he added, smiling, the photographers were even more powerful. They could tell the commander-in-chief where to go, make him move his chair, cross his legs, they might instruct him to hold up a letter, order him to smile or to look stern. He acknowledged their power and, as a political matter, deferred to their judgment. What the people thought of their chief executive would to some extent be decided by the photographers and the picture editors. Photographers may claim to be a priesthood interpreting the laws of light, and light is a universal mystery which the picture-takers measure with their light meters. "In nature's book of infinite mystery, a little I can read," says the Egyptian soothsayer in *Antony and Cleopatra*. Pictures taken in the light must be developed in the shallow mystery of darkrooms. But photographers have nothing in common with soothsayers. Their interests, apart from the technical one, are social and political. To some extent, it is they who decide how you are to be publicly seen. Your "visual record" is in their hands.

Broadly speaking, your *amour propre* is the territory invaded by the picture-takers. You may wish or not wish to be in public life. Some people have not the slightest desire to be in the papers or on TV. Others feel that papers and TV screens confer immortality. TV crews on a city street immediately attract big crowds. The arrival of television cameras offers people the opportunity each and every one of them has dreamt of—a shot at eternity. Not by deeds, not by prayers, but solely by their faces, grinning and mugging.

But this aspect of modern image-making or idolatry is not, for me, the most interesting one. What I discover when I search my soul is that I have formed a picture of myself as I wish to be seen, and that while photographers are setting up their lights and cameras I am summoning up and fortifying that picture. My intent is to triumph over the photographers' vision of me—their judgment as to what my place in photographic reality is to be. They have *technics*—Science—on their side. On my side there is vanity and deceit—there is, as I have already said, *amour propre*; there is, moreover, a nagging sense that my powers of candor are weakening and sagging, and that my face betrays how heavily it is mortgaged to death. *Amour propre*, with all its hypocritical tricks, is the product of your bourgeois outlook. Your aim is to gain general acceptance for your false self, to make propaganda, concealing your real motives—motives of personal advantage. You persuade people to view you as you need to be viewed if you are to put it over on them. We all are, insofar as we live for our *amour propre*, loyal to nothing except our secret, crippled objectives—the objectives of every "civilized" man.

Etcetera.

Yes, we're all too familiar with *amour propre*, thanks to the great romantic writers of the nineteenth-century. But give clever people something to understand and you can count on them to understand it. So in racing the photographers it's not the exposure of my *amour propre* that concerns me. What I feel in making innumerable last-minute ego arrangements is that the real me will decide to withhold itself. I know that the best picture-instruments of Germany or "state-of-the-art" Japan are constructed for ends very different from mine. What need is there to bring these powerful lenses up to the very tip of my nose? They will meaninglessly enlarge the pores of my skin. You will supply them with shots that remind viewers of the leg of a mosquito photographed through a microscope. The truth about you is that you have lost more hair than you thought and that your scalp is shining through—the truth is that you have huge paisley shaped bruises under your eyes and that your bridge work when you smile is far from "photogenic." You are not simply shown—you are exposed. This exposure can not be prevented. One can only submit to the merciless cruelty of "pure objectivity" which is so hard on your illusions.

Then, too, from a contemporary point of view, the daily and weekly papers—to say nothing of television—do not feel that they are honoring the truth if they do not tear away the tatters of vanity that cover our imperfections. No one is safe from exposure except the owners, the main stockholders and the leading advertisers of the great national papers. Things weren't always like this. The "gentlemen" described by Aristotle are immune to shame—they are made that way; nothing shameful can touch these aristocrats. But Adam and Eve, when they had eaten the apple of self-consciousness, sewed fig-leaves together to cover their nakedness.

It is the (not always conscious) premise of the photographer that his is the art of penetrating your private defenses. We, his subjects, can learn not to care. But we are not by any means an Aristotelian class, trained in the virtues. We are democrats and lead our petty lives in the shadow of shame. And for this as for all our weaknesses and vices there arise, in all civilized countries, entire classes of people, categories of specialists who specialize in *discovery* and exposure.

Their slogan is: Let the Record Show. And what the record shows is, of course, change and decay, instability, weakness and infirmity, darkness as endless and winding as the Malabar Caves as E. M. Forster years ago described them in *A Passage to India*.

A photograph that made me look worse than the Ruins of Athens was published by *Time* together with a line from William Blake—"The lineaments of gratified desire." Nowhere in the novel *Time* was reviewing had I so much as hinted that my face, with its lineaments, was anything like the faces Blake had in mind (faces of prostitutes, as his text explicitly tells us). But there was my dreary, sullen, tired and aging mug. I was brought low by Blake's blazing words. But it is the prerogative of the mass media to bring you down when they think that you have gotten ahead of yourself—when they suspect you of flying too high. It doesn't damage us to be exposed, to appear in distorted shapes on film or slick paper or newsprint. I often remember how, at the age of ninety-nine, Freud's grandmother complained that in the paper "they made me look a hundred years old."

But picture editors and journalists often seem to feel that they are the public representatives of the truth, and even that they are conferring some sort of immortality on you by singling you out. But you had better be prepared for rough treatment. Often your "privacy" is to them a cover for the lies and manipulations of *amour propre*.

Who would have thought that minor vanities might lead to such vexations. Your secrets will die in the glare of publicity. When the police strip Dmitri Karamazov to his foul underpants, he says to them, "Gentlemen, you have sullied my soul."

But the world has undergone a revolutionary transformation. Such simple, romantic standards of personal dignity and of the respect due to privacy are to be found today only in remote corners of backward countries. Maybe in the Pyrenees or in the forgotten backlands of Corsica—places where I shouldn't care to live. Everywhere else, the forces of insight are on the lookout. The function of their insights is to make your secrets public, for the public has a right to know and it is the duty of journalists to deliver the secrets of people "in the news" to their readers. For every story has a story behind it—which is to say that your face, in its own way a story, the story that you present—has another, sometimes very different story underlying it, and it is through the skill of the photographer that these layers of story are revealed.

Painters and sculptors, whose publics are smaller, also approach our heads and faces with insight. They class themselves as artists and are more intellectually sophisticated—better educated than photographers. They have generally absorbed a certain amount of twentieth-century psychology and their portraits may be filled or formed by their ideas and they may have a diagnostic intent. Do you want to know whether X, our subject, is a violent narcissist? Or whether his is a real, a human face, not a false ideological mask or disguise.

The photograph—to narrow it down—reduces us to two dimensions and it makes us small enough to be represented on a piece of paper or a frame of film. We have been trained by the camera to see the external world. We look *at* and not *into*, as one philosopher has put it. We do not allow ourselves to be *drawn* into what we see. We have been trained to go by the externals. The camera shows us only those, and it is we who do the rest. What we do this *with* is the imagination. What photographs have to show us is the external appearance of objects or beings in the real world, and this is only a portion of their reality. It is after all a convention.

I have known—and still know—many excellent photographers whose work I respect. There are demonic, sadistic camera technicians, too. All trades are like that. But neither the kindly nor the wicked ones can show us the realities we so hope—or long—to see.

Finally, there is the ancient Jewish rule forbidding graven images. My maternal grandfather refused to have his picture taken. But when he was dying, my mother brought in a photographer and hid him behind the bushes.

This faded picture is one of my Old World legacies. I also inherited the brass family samovar and my mother's silver change-purse. In this purse I now carry Betapace, Hytrin, and Coumadin tablets.

My grandfather's picture was taken in the late 1890s. He is sitting, dying in an apple orchard, his beard is spread over his upper body. His elbow rests on the top of his walking stick and his hand supports his head. His big eyes tell you that he is absorbed in *olam ha'ba*—the world to come, the next life. My mother used to say, "He would have been very angry with me. To make pictures was sinful (an *averah*) but I took the *averah* on myself."

When we were very young my parents told us that until we came of age they would be responsible for our transgressions. But that is an altogether different matter. What I am saying here is that nowadays not even the nobs have their portraits painted, and the masses preserve the faces of ancestors in daguerrotypes and Kodaks. The critical mind sees an insignificant photographer hidden in the bushes inserting a plate and pulling the cloth over his head. Perhaps the old man knew perfectly well that his picture was being taken. My mother was then old enough to bear the burden of this sin. She committed it because she loved him and was afraid of forgetting what he had looked like.

In any case, I have been not only photographed but cast in bronze and also painted. Since I am too impatient to sit still, painters and sculptors have worked from photographs. The Chicago Public Library exhibits the busts of bookish local boys. The artist who did my head was obliged to measure it while I was watching the Chicago Bulls on television. It was an important game and I didn't intend to miss it.

Considering the bronze head on display in the Harold Washington Library, I think that Pablo Picasso would have done it better. He might perhaps have given me a third eye and two noses. I'd have loved two noses.

But for a one-nose job, the bust in the Chicago Library isn't at all bad.

Philip O'Connor

Last Journal—or, Philippics?

I magine my posthumous amusement: the stars look down at a possible
reader of these last farewells. WHO DOES HE THINK HE IS? Laughter.
He doesn't. Infuriating equals or idiots has long made the grave a merry place.
There are constant upheavals which cause cracked tombs, wrongly ascribed to
"vandals." No, only the dead can laugh without a care in the world.

I repeat with joy what Quentin Crisp must often have been asked:
the above. I think he thought he was no one: a boastful person. I am even
more boastful; I think I am someone. Would you believe it! Please don't,
or I'll have to resign from even this last farewell. I so love these rehearsals.

WHO DO I THINK I AM? Look at me, Equals. And blare your
trompette. I misjudged Orwell. The picture of sad humility. Am I more
equal than others? Ask that literary trailer, Lady Annan. What a fool!

O, I am so equal, nearly invisible among more competitive Equals.

A strange joy when one thinks of leaving the world forever. I begin
to imagine the thrills after the gymnastics of life! And as one recedes from
life, one becomes astonished at the enthusiasm, the passion, with which
mortals kill each other. Are they not certain of death? Recession makes for
wonderful perspectives: those avenues down which the humming-birds flew.

But imagine if one in my condition (into mind and matter) were to recover? Into senility? Or intelligent peace? Where? How? I cannot imagine.

Amusing piece by Bellow in that *Republic of Letters*. Like me, he jumped from his bed dragging those horrible intravenous tubes; got mixed up about his wives (I didn't do that) and was called a "trouble-maker." The last of my generation. Spender gone. All in their eighties. God, if I recover, may I write the golden book we all dream of writing? Who ever did write it? No, it's the dream book. Now I'm almost satisfied with writing in my head. Typing becomes banal. Why bother? I am approaching the wise silence.

Broke my drinking mug. Which naturally I take as a dreadful symbol— the end? I've been drinking out of the same mug for donkeys' years. Now, just a glass. Not the same. My darling old mug's game!

To see what you think is awful. Am I a camera? I think "dead rat" and see one: it's a grey handkerchief. I think "villain" and see him. The myopic dreamer in the wasteland? God forbid. I think, don't I? Nothing else to do! I now think what everyone has thought about. I think (don't I?) of the connection or relationship between what a person "is" and what happens to the person. The Hindus call that "karma"; idiot westerners call it "fate," and the enlightened call it "destiny."

I cannot see the connection. Does Kasparov, beaten by a computer, have an idea of it? Idiots pose the pop question: Can computers think? The answer is, yes. The question is, Can human beings think? That remains a question.

A woman puts up with love; a man tries to make it.

Fell (always falling—like Bohumil Hrabal, out of the hospital window) into strange hands. Recall, re-shape. Fall into the strange hands of Keith Botsford, against whom some straight but conventional writer friends had warned me, and Saul Bellow and their *News from the Republic of Letters* where, it seems, my stories shall be published. I had expected nothing.

Bellow's experiences in the intensive-care unit comically echo mine in the re-animation section of the Bagnols hospital. I raved, they said, from alcoholism. Later, they strapped me down. Regarding the magazine: an attempt to restore the art of literature to what it was before the recent lot nearly strangled it, to produce purple-red, choking, turkey-cock "passion" and "violence," the contemporary, vulgar cocktail, slurped after birth into the TB box. It reminds me, as I began to write, to ponder more on the individuality of individualists, to lighten the weight of my bloc definitions. In a word, more "souls." I shall.

It has been necessary for me to wear, after long construction, a typecast garment, to wear it until I retire from the scene, an ancient winer, nearly 81, declaring himself *un très pauvre écrivain*. That will damp down the family Anglophobia.

I insist on distinguishing Communism from dictatorial Stalinism. Strange (that overused word) that a later development of Communism should be called "bourgeois revisionism"—the harsh moral and cultural categories of Stalinism were certainly bourgeois. I wouldn't be surprised to hear Blair support "working-class realism" (naturalism), which is also bourgeois. Romantics have always been anti-bourgeois; the bourgeoisie skimmed the milk of America in Hollywood "romances," now turned into iron bars of soap. For me, it [communism] was a leap into the void, a jungle story of my day. Not knowing has become religious. But I set about knowing by a lifetime's observation and reading. The local neo-Nazi movements have read neither Marx nor *Mein Kampf*, or anything else relevant. This bliss of ignorance is in for a short life. They don't want to know, don't want to hear: on the road to disaster.

Yes, the wine and the music still make me play the typewriter. But rather too early in the morning. About to cook luncheon, I'm already primed at 10:15. Still, only three days before re-entry into hospital. My refuge! And after that, if there is an after? Afterword. *Vive le mot!* I wonder, I suppose then that I live.

91

> *Let the lake (Lausanne) linger longer*
> *oh yes, dear, on the forked tongue*
> *of, let's say, indigent man.*
> *Lakes are for memory, lakes are the mind*
> *where all dips*
> *to provide a certitude*
> *never surfacing, hiding well below*
> *the thrones of man, mankind.*

Words will no longer carry poetry. As Charon said: My boat is full of the dead. An idiot wrote to me: Those who say poetry is dead are they who cannot write it. And I say: They who cannot write it know it cannot be written.

Words have lost the music. Shakespeare was the last, and Eliot was the least. No, even the nearest (the best) is but the humming of lost melodies. (Apart from Lawrence's "Humming Birds," but that was a requiem to poetry.) We pruriently continue, but it's a rectal rhetoric. The ideal never existed: that is its beauty. But is that why it never will exist? Do we make images of our future selves? Michelangelo's *Christ* isn't someone round the corner. Isn't he therefore anyone? And isn't anyone the embryonic someone we see in babes? What is a foetus but a crumpled god? And she said of his "Christ," "I wouldn't go near him." I didn't say, "He wouldn't go near you!" The ideal is the inexpugnable part of the human psyche: we wouldn't go near it, so we go to church. But what if he (it) were realized?

"Woman, what hast thou to do with me?" I began this research into the ideal, the Royal Mail. I shall cease to scoff. The ideal is male, but the meat is . . . ? Not male, but merely his mortal excrescence; and after that, what's left of him? Blair. There's nothing on either side to argue about. She made him renounce his meat, but he met his mate. And because neither knew the difference between body and soul, the race continued, engineered by this exciting ignorance.

Solitude is Christianity by the scruff of its neck. Orwell couldn't wear the old Etonian tie.

I know/see souls. I don't know bodies other than as representations of the "picture" soul.

Is shared solitude better that solitude alone? I don't know. But can solitude be shared? By the millions, but not by two persons? The millions rub along, the mass of bodies exhaling a feeling of community—a false feeling kept alive by irritation.

Recovery is unimaginable, so maybe is still desirable? The territory of love is terribly restricted to the psychic. I wish I'd been religious, because in religion this is an organized, an enduring spectacle. I am religious: but without a church, except an "ideal" communism. And Spender? He had no faith, but made beautiful protests against having no faith. Perhaps his true poetry died young, so that he came to represent it.

If I could be born again, I'd be my ideal—common. Haven't arrived there, but can smell it as a distant, as the only flower of this fatuously ferocious species. Faith! A sumptuous idea, the trappings of a mule sauntering on the paradisiacal roads and leering at his stolen treasure. (Better than the self-made man's!). To resemble those we hate, to love those who seem unlike us. Playing naughty games of self-deprecation to assume superiority! O the rats of life! The boring stupidity of the bourgeois! Their end and my end are nigh. God be blessed. Yes, the river is dry and the bed shows its death. Narcissus.

Stare as they will, no stars return. Thus is reflection perverted into thought. Reflect reality? No, it doesn't; it reflects a donkey minus trappings. But the repose! I can imagine the repose after ambition, after greed, jealousy, vanity, competition, after all that I hate and therefore see in others. But the river-bed is dry and . . .

Another abortive project for the last book. This new abortion is to be a "Chanson" and addressed to her, my beloved. The whine begins early today (11.5.97). Hospital tomorrow.

Do women loathe their divinity? Have they the ambition to become human? If so, let them not take men as models.

Why do I, from the age of eleven, constantly look at myself in the mirror? (Lady Annan) Answer: For that which the lady hath not the brains to imagine. To show me that which, from the age of three, I have doubted! That I exist. That I am real, a person. That bloody fool.

I know fewer and fewer differences: all's becoming a cloud of unknowing.

Shop-keepers, gnash your gums! You can no longer bite!

Blanchisserie de la mort. Laundered money.

The mad fear of being, or "going" (how come?) mad. As though I had a sanity from which to proceed. No, I have rehearsed to myself and others the conformist walk, smile, behavior. As [John] Berger said, I am an actor. The idiot doesn't know we're all actors. This unstoppable rehearsal—laughter. In Search of a Search of an Identity sing the clowns of deportment (sales department: "Bladies blunderwear next whore, Sir!") My abysmal apologies and my filthiest curses both to Her. My dismal gratitude for the slightest "recognition," as I like to call it. The turning of this worm would be insanity.

My photos today: [*O'Connor's wall contained a number of these—* Ed.] On the right, Einstein looks on doomingly. Spender, as often, totally ambiguous. For a poet, he certainly "got on" in the world. But this last photo (a few months before he died) shows that the world "got on" to him. He looks ruined; yet there's a beam of light, kindness, like a candle in a forest. My mother: smiling it through. Monkey face, Burmese. One eye retired, the other glaring. Einstein's face the truest.

93

And what would be Phil's last words—he thinking of Beckett's good title for (as usual) an unreadable work of woe? On the back of *L'Hygiene de l'assassin* by Amélie Nothomb, which I'm taking into hospital this afternoon: "*La littérature, la vraie, est faite de larmes et de sang.*" That is a lie. True literature is made with words; and lovers of them are temporarily dying out. Blood and tears are the mere raw materials; we all have them. What we don't all have is that *vraie cuisine dans la bouche: le Mot.*

Long live the Word. First was the Word, and it was God.

Are vaginas the wells of loneliness? Is the penis a gun escaping from the Welfare State? Laughter ringing down the corridors. Laughter, my merry men, will outlast woe. Joyce was genial; Beckett was his chamberpot Muzak.

There is no last word.

This text was sent us on May 11, 1997, the day before Philip O'Connor was to be admitted to hospital, at the age of 82, for yet another cancer operation. He died the following year, in 1998. In his introduction to a recent re-issue of O'Connor's Memoirs of a Public Baby, *Mr. Bellow pointed to O'Connor's tendency "to let things all hang out." A lot of writers do that; the difference lies in having something worthwhile to let hang out. —K. B.*

James Wood

Real Life

Going to the theater is generally unrewarding; even Ibsen in New
York, this summer, was tedious. I watched a new production of *A Doll's House* with mounting dismay, and was reminded of mild, slippery Chekhov telling Stanislavsky in a quiet voice as if it were something too obvious to say: "But listen, Ibsen is no playwright! . . . Ibsen just doesn't know life. In life it simply isn't like that."

No, in life it simply isn't like that. Outside the Broadway theater the traffic sounds like an army that is always getting closer but which never arrives, and the fantastic heat is sensual, and the air conditioners drip their sap, their backsides thrust out of the window like Alisoun who does the same in Chaucer, and everything is the usual chaotic obscurity. Nothing is clear. But inside, here is Ibsen didactically ordering life into three trim acts, and a cooled audience obediently laughing at the right moments and thinking about drinks at the interval—the one moment of Chekhovian life is that, in the lobby, the barman can be heard making too much noise putting out glasses. The clinking is disturbing Ibsen's simpler tune.

A Doll's House, of course, tells the story of a woman's subjection to and eventual escape from her husband. Ibsen is not entirely clumsy; he does not make Nora's husband, Torvald, monstrous so much as he makes him uncomprehending. And yet he cannot help neatly underlining how uncomprehending Torvald is, just in case we miss it. Nora deceives her husband in order to protect him. He discovers the deception and is furious. Toward the end of the play, Nora tells him that she is leaving him because she sees that she has never been more than his toy. She cries because he does not understand her complaint, and Ibsen hammers this home: "Why are you crying?" Torvald asks her. "Is it because I have forgiven you for your deception?" At this moment the audience snickered, knowingly. Poor, foolish Torvald! Someone behind me, caught up in the play's melodramatic slipstream, whispered: "He is dreadful!"

Ibsen is like a man who laughs at his own jokes: he relishes too obviously the dramatic ironies of the situation. Ibsen's people are too comprehensible—we comprehend them not as we comprehend real people but as we comprehend fictional entities. He is always tying the moral shoelaces of his characters, making everything neat, presentable, knowable. Their secrets are of the formal, bourgeois, novelistic kind: a former lover, a broken contract, a debt, an unwanted relative, a blackmailer on the prowl. Ibsen's task is to drag these secrets to light and make them the engine of the drama. It is because Nora's "secret"—the fraudulent contract she signs to borrow money—is revealed that the play is set in motion.

But these are merely knowable secrets. Chekhov deals in true privacies. I sat in the theater and considered Chekhov's idea of art, a bashful, milky complication, not a solving of things. How does Chekhov make us feel, in *Uncle Vanya*, or in the great stories, that his art is not hustling life into comprehensibility? One way is through a pioneering use of what is called stream-of-consciousness. He allows his characters to speak as if they are turning a mental stream-of-consiousness outward. The particular loveliness of Chekhov is that what people say to each other and think to themselves feels arbitrary, like life or like memory. And this is also why it so often strikes us as comic, for watching a Chekhov character is like watching a lover wake up in bed, half awake and half dreaming, saying something odd and private which means nothing to us because it refers to the receding dream. In life, at such moments, we often laugh, and say: "You're not making any sense, you know." Chekhov's characters have a similar dreaminess.

The key to the great freedom of Chekhov's characters lies in his use of how thought works, and how we put this into words. You can see this very beautifully in "The Steppe," Chekhov's first major story, which he wrote when he was 28. A small boy, Yegorushka, goes on a journey across the steppe. He is going to a new boarding school, accompanied by two men—a trader and a priest. As he watches a cemetery go by, the boy thinks to himself:

> From behind the wall cheerful white crosses and tombstones peeped out, nestling in the foliage of cherry trees and seen as white patches from a distance. At blossom time, Yegorushka remembered, the white patches mingled with the cherry blooms in a sea of white, and when the cherries had ripened the white tombs and crosses were crimson-spotted, as if with blood. Under the cherries behind the wall the boy's father and his grandmother Zinaida slept day and night. When Grandmother had died she had been put in a long, narrow coffin, and five-copeck pieces had been placed on her eyes, which would not stay shut. Before dying she had been alive, and she had brought him soft poppy-seed bun rings from the market, but now she just slept and slept.

One sees here why Joyce admired Chekhov (and watching *A Doll's House*, alas, one sees why Shaw admired Ibsen). "Before dying she had been alive . . . but now she just slept and slept." This is not only how a small boy thinks, but how all of us think about the dead, privately: *Before dying, she had been alive.* It is one of those obviously pointless banalities of thought, an accidental banality which, being an accident, is not banal. Chekhov's genius was to see how often we speak like this, too. When the little boy cries (he misses his mother), Father Christopher, the priest, comforts him. But his solace has no dramatic "point," in the Ibsen sense. It furthers no ideological argument. Indeed, in Chekhovian fashion, it is not really solace at all. The priest is simply thinking aloud, selfishly:

> Never mind, son . . . Call on God. Lomonosov once travelled just like this with the fishermen, and he became famous throughout Europe. Learning conjoined with faith yields fruit pleasing to God. What does the prayer say? "For the glory of the Creator, for our parents' comfort, for the benefit of church and country." That's the way of it.

Father Christopher is speaking in the same way that, a minute before, the little boy was thinking: aimlessly.

The great innovation of the stream-of-consciousness is that it allows absent-mindedness into fiction. Buried deep in their subjectivity, people forget themselves while thinking, and go on safaris of detail. Or rather, they don't exactly forget themselves. They forget how to act as purposeful fictional characters. They forget what they are supposed to do. They mislay their scripts. They stop being actors, and become people. Remember the virginal soldier in Chekhov's "The Kiss," who kisses a woman at a party, and longs to tell his fellow-soldiers about it. When he finally gets the chance, he is amazed that his anecdote takes only a few seconds. Because he has been hoarding his story, he "had imagined it would take until morning." The soldier forgets that he is in Chekhov's story, because he is so involved in his own. Think of how often Chekhov brings his characters out of their fantasies and into real life. How often in his fiction we encounter the formulation: "And suddenly he realized that . . ." or "It was not until that moment that he knew . . ."

Some of this became clear as I sat watching *A Doll's House*. This, partly, is what Chekhov means by real life: he means real mental life, with its wrong turnings and cul-de-sacs and random, intimately treasured banali-

ties. He lets his characters speak their minds. Isn't this what Henry James meant when he spoke of wanting to let his characters exist in the irresponsible, plastic way?" Ibsen's characters are always stage actors. Chekhov's characters forget to be Chekhov's characters, and nothing could be more irresponsible than that.

Martin Amis

Of Cars and the Man

Road Rage is nothing new in America. It began, no doubt, with 99
Dirt-Road Rage, or Horse Rage, followed by Pony-and-Trap Rage, Stage-
coach Rage, etc., until the era of the automobile dawned. Nowadays Americans gun each other down on the thruways as a matter of routine. What
we're waiting for, over there, is Sidewalk Rage, Moving-Walkway Rage, and
Escalator Rage—or the rage of any other arena in which adult males exercise
their right to mobility and gun ownership.

Over here, where civic tradition celebrates the conciliatory and the
ovine (and where men generally go unarmed), we greet Road Rage as a fresh
phenomenon. But we're getting used to it. To take a recent example: in
September, 1997, a young couple had their engagement cut short when their
car was rammed and shoved over the dividing line and into the oncoming
stream. Evidently the car behind did this to the car in front because the car
in front was going "too slowly." The case seems clear-cut. Means: a car with
a man in it. Opportunity: the car was in motion, among other cars. Motive:
the car in front was going too slowly.

About eighteen months ago there was a Road Rage epidemic. The
incidence of layby stabbings and emergency-lane bludgeonings climbed high
enough to induce an episode of mass paranoia. For a while we steered our

way around London wearing expressions of exaggerated innocence, orderly, diffident, effaced (not a headlight flashed, not a horn sounded). "After you," we pouted at each other—"No, after you"—"No, sir, please: after you." It reminded me of a similar attack of national neurosis: 1993, and the aftermath of the murder of the infant James Bulger by two ten-year-old Liverpool schoolboys. Suddenly, in the general misery and nausea, the sight of a school uniform would make you sweat with disgust; the cap and blazer looked as frankly incriminating as the trooped overalls of a cartoon convict. Just so, during the Road Rage pestilence, every motorist in England seemed to be sporting the mark of Cain.

Road Rage is, of course, the sewage trench—the *Cloaca Maxima*—of car culture. The Road Rager kills in the name of his Range Rover, or his twin-cam turbocharged Nissan 200 SX, or his Mini; he strikes out at anything that impedes or retards his heroic progress along highway or byway; he is car culture's hitman. The Road Rager is a special kind of moron—unaware, for instance, that the culture he kills for is itself already dead. The car continues to serve its purpose, an A-to-B device, it ferries its passengers from A to B, and then on to C, or back to A again. But time has purged it of all content and expressiveness—all culture. So to add to his charm, the Road Rager (thrashing and spluttering in his septic tank) is also a ghoul and a zombie: Nosferatu behind a wheel.

Needless to say, the penny hasn't yet dropped, and car culture thinks it's still flourishing. In the TV ad, the big-chinned hunk still speeds towards the catwalk brunette in aerodynamic splendor, along deserted roads (or deserted beaches, or deserted deserts). The billboard for the Motor Show still digs your ribs with the promise of "sexy models" unveiling themselves. The oily magazines are still there on the shelves. The newspapers still carry whole sections called "Motoring." Motoring: a dead word. The motorist, a dead notion. As dead as the moustachioed enthusiast in his curvy Bugatti, with the lap rug, the thermos, the waggling ear-flaps.

It is a question of evolution.

Here, at any rate, is my autobiography.

I hit the road in 1966 at the age of seventeen, perched on the saddle of a scooter. The very choice of vehicle was a statement of pack aggression, for this was the age of Mods and Rockers. Mods rode—and crashed—scooters; Rockers rode—and crashed—motorbikes. Whenever we encountered one another, we would rev and veer and dice, race, chase, flee, yaw, skid, crash. But I needed no Rockers to help unseat me—to send me skittering like a hockey puck over the bitumen. I did it all by myself, at least once a day. Invariably traveling much too fast, I had great difficulty slowing down when things appeared in my path: cars, trucks, pedestrians, brick walls. One winter night, enjoying my usual speed trial through the side streets of Chelsea, I noticed an obstacle up ahead. It was a main road. My attempt to slow down met with the usual snag: I was traveling much too fast. Rammed side-on by a tomato-red Jaguar Mk II, I spent that Christmas in hospital. My Vespa Sportique was a cuboid ruin. I had owned it for four months.

With my apprenticeship served, I graduated to four wheels. I no longer crashed scooters. Now I crashed cars. I crashed my car all the time. My friends crashed their cars all the time. We crashed each other's cars all the time. Occasionally, while practicing handbrake-skid U-turns or hot-rubber starts, we crashed our cars into each other's cars. We drove everywhere as fast as we could, with busted indicators, faulty brakes, and flat tyres. We drove drunk and we drove stoned and we drove on LSD. One night I careened across fifteen miles of black ice with my head out of the window and one eye open; my flared jeans were hanging from my waist entirely unseamed, like cowboy's chaps (I had attempted to kick in a wall-mounted cigarette machine on Sloane Street). Where was the law? In those days, driving did bear some resemblance to its PR. The roads were empty (you could park where you liked) and amazingly underpoliced. Cars meant freedom, mobility, and power assisted self-expression (however suicidal). Even the sexuality of the auto was at that time no fiction: access to any old rattletrap seemed to increase one's erotic pull by several thousand percent.

The existence of the motor car lends strong support to the view that all men should be locked up from the ages of fifteen to thirty-five inclusive. Throughout my twenties I continued to be a tail-gating, blind-siding, march-stealing, flanker-pulling, fist-shaking, oath-spitting swine and cur, a source of exasperation, anxiety and mortal danger to anyone who shared my road. Men's lives are all about rivalry, competition, preferment; put a man in a car and he thinks he is being tested, against other men, in a race or a game of Chicken. I know the feeling. And it is only now, as I near fifty, that I have siphoned off the grosser hormones and formulated some kind of highway code. I passed my test at the age of eighteen but I've been a Learner for thirty years.

It was an embarrassingly slow education in the obvious. Thinning testosterone, combined with parenthood, did most of the work; but there were also two minor refinements in road etiquette that had a disproportionate effect on me. Once upon a time, when a motorist felt himself affronted, he would present his antagonist with a frown. Somewhere along the line; the frown became the sneer. Concern for safety had evolved into contempt for ineptitude; and there we all were, sitting behind windscreens with scrolled upper lips. I didn't enjoy finding myself doing this. The second development involved the use of the horn. Nowadays, if someone cuts a corner (for example), and you parp at them, they parp back! After a while I knew I could no longer involve myself in this cretinous exchange, or any other in which the horn serves merely as an amplified obscenity. You can honk to avert an accident and you can honk to say hi to a friend. All other applications are the preserve of the yahoo.

How miserably revealing it is that there's no standard topic-sentence beginning with the words "Men drivers." There are plenty of (male) arias about female frailty on the road, but none of them points out that women drivers, by most estimates, are responsible for fewer than 5 percent of all accidents. Women may cause delays interposing an extra few seconds between the hot swain and his next red traffic light. And it always surprises me that women use their horns at all, but they do (simply, one senses, because it's there, and has a function). Yet a woman will prod you with just a toot or a beep: nothing like the majestic bellow of the roused male. And here's another thing that women drivers seldom go in for—they don't reach for their machetes as they force you off the road.

It takes time for a certain equation to dawn on the male. This equation has to do with velocity, mechanical mass, and human bodies. He knows the equation; but it takes time for the male to grasp it. A while ago I saw a documentary about an accident involving a big car and a small boy. The incident was reconstructed at three different road speeds: 30, 60, and 70 mph. At 30, everything felt containable. At 60, everything felt contingent. At 70, it was all headlong and breakneck, with the guaranteed inadvertency of nightmare. The motorist had struck the boy at 70 mph. His mother confessed to absolute consternation at what such an impact could do to a child; she had been incapable of accompanying the body in the ambulance, and had since felt torment for what she saw as a final dereliction. It is, of course, infinitely otiose to speculate on the sex of the driver. More recently there has been a TV campaign on road speed and pedestrian safety in built-up areas. A 30-mph impact is usually survivable; a 40-mph is usually fatal. Well, that settled it for me. Formerly, though, like every other male on wheels, I respected velocity for its own sake. And I would confess to a speeding offence with the standard male mixture of weary indignation and uncompromising pride. But things have changed. Now I understand that *E* equals *mc* squared.

Last summer I gained a privileged insight into the personality of the Road Rager. It happened when the large but decrepit Chevrolet I was driving suddenly transformed itself into a Ragemobile. Quite unbidden, its lights started flashing and its horn started honking (in abrupt, irregular blasts). With my younger son snickering and squirming in the passenger seat, I blazed and blared my way along the sedate back roads of Long Island. What would I be, I wondered, if this car were under my full control? What kind of personality would I be expressing? That drive felt altogether farcical. My inner being underwent massive travesty.

Road Rage isn't funny, but it is roundly ridiculous. The modern automobile begins life on a conveyor belt—and never leaves it, not these days. The roads themselves are conveyor belts. From their users they call for anonymity: for the utter suppression of the self. When you climb into a car, your job is to sit and steer through the great reeking swirl—to stay in the damned thing until it gets you where you want to go. Nothing that happens to you out there should be worth a milliliter of adrenaline. Nothing can humble you because you are already humbled.

Our Rager can't accept this—indeed, he is enraged by it. And there's another element in his makeup. When a certain kind of man gets behind a wheel, he suddenly thinks he weighs a ton and a half. He thinks his stare can dazzle at a hundred yards. He thinks his voice—his shout, his curse—can waken the dead. Look at the shoulders on the guy, the great grooved haunches, the chronic beergut, the winking carbuncles on his broad backside. Most of us come to nurse this modest ambition: to get through life without killing anyone. When we drive, we are most at risk of failing. It isn't that way for the Rager. He'll climb out of his car and, still rippling with its powers, he'll get the thing done at the side of the road.

103

Julia Copeland

Objective Correlative

If I say you have a great body, will you hold it against me?

(T-shirt worn by a bass player with herpes)

Orchestras were among the first and most successful gender-blind employers, with their union-enforced meritocracy, with their behind-the-screen auditions where one was cautioned not to speak, lest one's voice give away something personal. Those of us who entered orchestras in the golden, feminist years of the seventies and eighties were barely conscious of this as something new.

It was our due, and we took it as such. I myself just assumed I was exactly like the guys. One of the guys. Complaining with the guys about the boredom of orchestra life, the relentlessness of the work.

We believed we never transcended. We said we believed that. We said we were jaded and disillusioned. That music was just a business, something we did for the money, that we were artistic whores. This was a kind of boast, meant to conceal the years of awkward precocity, the years of molelike existence in tiny windowless practice rooms, the inability to play any kind of ball (save those fingers!), the sense of having, in our concentration on music, missed the generational—maybe even the universal—train of life experience.

We believed we were stuck forever in the sort of artistic compromise represented in our experience by Ravel's *Bolero*. Beloved by audiences, who fell for the unabashed sexuality of its sustained crescendo, *Bolero* was pure tedium to us, pure been-there-done-that monotony. We knew how it ended.

We faked the required frenzy, yawning behind our arms.

But whatever we said, and we said a lot of things—said, for instance, that we were just blue-collar workers (unionized, too), just cogs in a wheel, or, more inventively, that our relation to actual art was tenuous: if the art in question was a novel, say, then we were not even individual words but merely the keys of the typewriter, mechanical entities moving according to someone else's whim and producing, or reproducing, someone else's master-piece—whatever we said, we still experienced, perhaps more often than we realized, that undeniable ecstasy of performance. What it was to scrape, bang, swell our way through the soupy chords of a Brahms symphony, that arousal of hormones—adrenaline certainly, and who knows what others?—that would send us out into the post-concert night overheated and overjazzed and full of unexpended energy. . . No wonder we would, in an unknown city, tend to surge here or there in large, numbers-emboldened groups, in search of something to match our charged longings for more. No wonder that, expelled into the foreign night full of misplaced inebriation, like dizzy tourists leaving a brewery at midday, we wandered into redlight districts as if by instinct.

So it was that we found our way, in Hamburg, into the Reeperbahn—the redlight district, we were told, to beat all redlight districts. Not for the faint of heart, the squeamish, the girlish. In the Reeperbahn we sat at small round tables, drinks before us, awaiting the big moment: *live sex on stage!* But what a strange performance it turned out to be. Live, maybe, but far from alive. As perhaps we should have guessed from the outset, knowing what we knew about simulated frenzy. But this was the weird thing, the unexpected difference between representation and reality: while even the simulated sex of a porn movie required some pretense of passion, *real* live sex, it turned out, did not. How heavy was the apathy, his and hers, how dutiful her mechanical, clearly crucial (the show must go on! One must placate its necessary star!) massaging of his organ to some degree of tumescence. The difference between art and life—the clear superiority of the former to the latter, for thrills—that revelation, and not the advertised act itself, seemed to constitute the most memorable part of the show.

That, and the cellist who stuck his unwelcome tongue deep in my ear. Unwelcome because I'd assumed we were all men together, that I had won the audition, been admitted to the club. Here I was, experiencing a revelation about reality versus art, about simulation versus performance, about how we, too, had to perform every night, had to make *Bolero* as throbbingly believable as it had really been to us the first time we played it, had to create nightly the tension and passion just like real tension, real passion, and here was this tongue in my ear. I never could remember whether the personal was political or the political was personal, and frankly I had no desire to think about such things, because, you know, I was one of the guys. I thought I was exempt.

Q: Why are women so bad at gauging distance?
A: Because all their lives they've been told that this (hold thumb and forefinger 107
very close together) is six inches.

Sex and music. Someone asked me about that half in jest, but it's a great connection, a central connection, like love and death, like death and taxes, like apple pie and cheese. Music and sex, that was the question. Dirty jokes it was, specifically. And that got me thinking. Not just about randy goaty musicians I have known (before I even got to my first rehearsal as part of the big-city orchestra I was soon to be touring with, I had been told which letches to watch out for, and who had herpes), but about life as a girl violinist.

Because those randy goaty musicians, overly friendly at all times, tolerated in those days because Boys would be Boys back then and a balding guy running his fingers down your back, checking for a bra as you walked onstage, was something to be laughed with, not at—those randy musicians were part of the fabric of orchestral life, standing in the wings, hoping to get lucky, but in their leering hopefulness not so much threatening as (this was a long time ago, remember) flattering.

And who were those old jokers, before they learned to leer? Boys in awkward kneepants, stuck in the house practicing while the other boys were out on the street playing stickball. Or locked in a practice cabin somewhere in upstate New York by an overzealous mother, then sneaking out, pudgily sweating, to pump gas at a nearby filling station. The exhilaration of the ordinary, when one has been strapped to dreams of the extraordinary. There's some of that, a lot of that, I think, in the raunchy humor musicians favor. Imagine the orchestra as a damp, disappointing, awakening. The soggy left-overs of a dreaming life. Because every musician, especially every string player, dreamed of solo glory, rode as a youth the Big Kahuna of career aspiration, only to be dropped, panting and defeated, on the anonymous floorboards of some symphony hall.

But notice the terms I'm using: kneepants; wet dreams. Wasn't I going to talk about life as a girl violinist? Of course that's my point—life as a girl violinist was in every way colored and shaped by life as a boy violinist, by life as a boy violinist in a culture in which the violin case was a sign of effeminacy. I was, for example, forgiving of the cellist with his tongue in my ear. Oh, why not? A certain generosity seemed necessary.

A modern woman, a nineties woman, would probably have slapped him silly. So I am led to believe. But I was something else. Part of some awkward transitional stage, at a period when the rope stretching between virgin and whore seemed easily negotiable. All you had to do was be a man, but with a woman's body. Simple. Then you could be both simultaneously.

We younger players were modern women too, but of the eighties. Like that first female sportswriter allowed into a team locker room, we were inductees into a previously off-limits world of men. Unlike the older women in the orchestra, who kept pretty carefully to their prescribed roles as wives and mothers, we wanted to hang out with the guys, to be guys ourselves.

What we achieved was something messy, something that did not exactly break new ground. We were all Rosalind Russell, in *His Girl Friday*, or Eve Arden, in just about any movie, wisecracking our way through the poker games or martini lunches, women around whom it was unnecessary to watch one's language.

Which was no doubt why several of us younger women, giddy with a power derived (unfairly?) from separating ourselves from the standard-issue feminine model of our recent pasts, seeking perhaps to curry favor with the men at the expense of less liberated others of our kind, were anxious to attend the Ames Film Festival.

Iowa, where the men are men and the sheep are scared.

That was in Ames, Iowa. Not exactly Hamburg, but much improved, in our anticipation, by the knowledge that one of the brass players had gone to a great deal of trouble and expense to bring to us, in a conventioneers' theater within the motel, a smorgasbord of pornographic films the like of which, he assured us, we would not find elsewhere, not even in Hamburg.

Yes, the Ames Film Festival, where all the men in the orchestra, and most of the younger women, gathered in one of those motel conference spaces with patterned carpet that gave off a slight odor of vomit—in fact sat on that carpet, in the dark. The Ames Film Festival, where men were men but women, it turned out, were marked by how much or how little pornography they were willing to tolerate. An interesting and peculiarly modern dilemma.

There was implicit the understanding that these women, while expected to show solidarity with their sex-crazed, unrepressed generation by attending the festival, were also expected to fade at a certain point, or to fold—to back out decorously but firmly, claiming a surfeit of this good thing, this completely unobjectionable good thing.

One by one, the women, the young women (the older ones had simply not shown up), crept away. And as each one left, the position of the remaining women changed subtly. We were, for one thing, outnumbered. We were, for another, forced to see our colleagues' departures as statements of some kind, as objections. So that, while we had begun the evening as equals of our male colleagues, as buddies, as joking comrades, we were moment by moment turning into something else. Not the jokers, but the jokees.

Martha and I were the last to leave. The onscreen writhings were not noticeably worse than they had been, but the desertion of the other women had changed our perceptions of what we were seeing and doing. We were clear on the difference between representation and reality, but we could not count on everyone else to be as sure. Something like that. In a certain light—the light that came in from the hall each time another woman deserted—the activity onscreen looked less like good fun than like the degradation and objectification of comely young women. In that case, then, who were we?

And who were these men all around us, not one of whom had seen the need to leave the room? We slipped out too.

Being a girl

These anecdotes were supposed to come together in a grim nineties reassessment of the past, in which men are unregenerate pigs and women are eternal victims and music is merely a front for all the old sexual inequities. But what I overlooked in that view (as we overlooked the ecstasy in our simulated onstage passion night after night), was pleasure.

The songwriter Johnny Green used to conduct our orchestra occasionally, and he would totter to the podium and there sing out, with seemingly genuine gusto, "I a-dore being a girl." A strange reversal, perhaps, those words in the mouth of a man, but no stranger than the one we were trying to achieve. Because we did adore being girls, and we also adored, for the little time that was allowed to us, being boys. It was just a brief crack in the wall separating the sexes, as it turned out, but it was a moment that looked as if it would last forever, and we were almost its beneficiaries.

Back in my room, after creeping out of the Ames Film Festival, I picked up the ringing phone and found Martha on the other end. She was irked about missing the rest of the films, and I realized I felt the same way. We'd been having fun. We liked our freedom. Somehow in passing the test of genteel femininity (leaving the room early) we had failed the test of— oh, let's call it sexual parity. Walking the tightrope of female definition, we had looked down, had seen the crowd calling us back to the old ways, calling us back from some wildness we had barely even caught sight or scent of. Girl violinists, talking on the phone, circa 1983: "I didn't want to leave, did you?" said Martha. And I had to admit I'd wanted to stay too. She laughed and added, "I think I left a wet spot on the rug."

Archives

Samuel Butler

Ramblings in Cheapside

Walking the other day in Cheapside, I saw some turtles in Mr. Sweeting's window, and was tempted to stay and look at them. As I did so, I was struck not more by the defences with which they were hedged about, than by the fatuousness of trying to hedge that in at all which, if hedged thoroughly, must die of its own defencefulness. The holes for the head and feet through which the turtle leaks out, as it were, on to the exterior world, and through which it again absorbs the exterior world into itself— "catching on" through them to things that are thus both turtle and not turtle at one and the same time—these holes stultify the armour and show it to have been designed by a creature with more of faithfulness to a fixed idea, and hence onesidedness, than of that quick sense of relative importances and their changes, which is the main factor of good living.

The turtle obviously had no sense of proportion; it differed so widely from myself that I could not comprehend it; and as this word occurred to me, it occurred also that until my body comprehended its body in a physical material sense, neither would my mind be able to comprehend its mind with any thoroughness. For unity of mind can only be consummated by unity of body; everything, therefore, must be in some respects both knave and fool to all that which has not eaten it, or by which it has not been eaten. As long as the turtle was in the window and I in the street outside, there was no chance of our comprehending one another.

Nevertheless, I knew that I could get it to agree with me if I could so effectually buttonhole and fasten on to it as to eat it. Most men have an easy method with turtle soup, and I had no misgiving but that if I could bring my first premise to bear I should prove the better reasoner. My difficulty lay in this initial process, for I had not with me the argument that would alone compel Mr. Sweeting to think that I ought to be allowed to convert the turtles—I mean I had no money in my pocket. No missionary enterprise can be carried on without any money at all, but even so small a sum as half a crown would, I suppose, have enabled me to bring the turtle partly round, and with many half-crowns I could in time no doubt convert the lot, for the turtle needs must go where the money drives. If, as is alleged, the world stands on a turtle, the turtle stands on money. No money, no turtle. As for money, that stands on opinion, credit, trust, faith—things that, though highly material in connection with money, are still of immaterial essence.

The steps are perfectly plain. The men who caught the turtles brought a fairly strong and definite opinion to bear upon them, that passed into action, and later on into money. They thought the turtles would come that way, and verified their opinion; on this, will and action were generated, with the result that the men turned the turtles on their backs and carried them off. Mr. Sweeting touched these men with money, which is the outward and visible sign of verified opinion. The customer touches Mr. Sweeting with money, Mr. Sweeting touches the waiter and the cook with money. They touch the turtle with skill and verified opinion. Finally, the customer applies the clinching argument that brushes all sophisms aside, and bids the turtle stand protoplasm to protoplasm with himself, to know even as it is known.

But it must be all touch, touch, touch; skill, opinion, power, and money, passing in and out with one another in any order we like, but still link to link and touch to touch. If there is failure anywhere in respect of opinion, skill, power, or money either as regards quantity or quality, the chain can be no stronger than its weakest link, and the turtle and the clinching argument will fly asunder. Of course, if there is an initial failure in connection, through defect in any member of the chain, or of connection between the links, it will no more be attempted to bring the turtle and the clinching argument together, than it will to chain up a dog with two pieces of broken chain that are disconnected. The contact throughout must be conceived as absolute; and yet perfect contact is inconceivable by us, for on becoming perfect it ceases to be contact, and becomes essential, once for all inseverable, identity. The most absolute contact short of this is still contact by courtesy only. So here, as everywhere else, Eurydice glides off as we are about to grasp her. We can see nothing face to face; our utmost seeing is but a fumbling of blind finger-ends in an over-crowded pocket.

Presently my own blind finger-ends fished up the conclusion, that as I had neither time nor money to spend on perfecting the chain that would put me in full spiritual contact with Mr. Sweeting's turtles, I had better leave them to complete their education at someone else's expense rather than mine, so I walked on towards the Bank. As I did so, it struck me how continually we are met by this melting of one existence into another. The limits of the body seem well defined enough as definitions go, but definitions seldom go far. What, for example, can seem more distinct from a man than his banker or his solicitor? Yet these are commonly so much parts of him that he can no more cut them off and grow new ones, than he can grow new legs or arms; neither must he wound his solicitor; a wound in the solicitor is a very serious thing. As for his bank—failure of his bank's action may be as fatal to a man as failure of his heart. I have said nothing about the medical or spiritual adviser, but most men grow into the society that surrounds them by the help of these four main tap-roots, and not only into the world of humanity, but into the universe at large. We can, indeed, grow butchers, bakers, and greengrocers, almost *ad libitum*, but these are low developments, and correspond to skin, hair, or finger-nails. Those of us again who are not highly enough organized to have grown a solicitor or banker can generally repair the loss of whatever social organization they may possess as freely as lizards are said to grow new tails; but this with the higher social, as well as organic, developments is only possible to a very limited extent.

The doctrine of metempsychosis, or transmigration of souls—a doctrine to which the foregoing considerations are for the most part easy corollaries—crops up no matter in what direction we allow our thoughts to wander. And we meet instances of the transmigration of body as well as of soul. I do not mean that both body and soul have transmigrated together, far from it; but that, as we can often recognize a transmigrated mind in an alien body, so we not less often see a body that is clearly only a transmigration, linked on to someone else's new and alien soul. We meet people every day whose bodies are evidently those of men and women long dead, but whose

115

appearance we know through their portraits. We see them going about in omnibuses, railway carriages, and in all public places. The cards have been shuffled, and they have drawn fresh lots in life and nationalities, but anyone fairly well up in medieval and last-century portraiture knows them at a glance.

Going down once towards Italy I saw a young man in the train whom I recognized, only he seemed to have got younger. He was with a friend, and his face was in continual play, but for some little time I puzzled in vain to recollect where it was that I had seen him before. All of a sudden I remembered he was King Francis I of France. I had hitherto thought the face of this king impossible, but when I saw it in play I understood it. His great contemporary Henry VIII keeps a restaurant in Oxford Street. Falstaff drove one of the St Gothard diligences for many years, and only retired when the railway was opened. Titian once made me a pair of boots at Vicenza, and not very good ones. At Modena I had my hair cut by a young man whom I perceived to be Raffaelle. The model who sat to him for his celebrated Madonnas is first lady in a confectionery establishment at Montreal. She has a little motherly pimple on the left side of her nose that is misleading at first, but on examination she is readily recognized; probably Raffaelle's model had the pimple too, but Raffaelle left it out—as he would.

Handel, of course, is Madame Patey. Give Madame Patey Handel's wig and clothes, and there would be no telling her from Handel. It is not only that the features and the shape of the head are the same, but there is a certain imperiousness of expression and attitude about Handel which he hardly attempts to conceal in Madame Patey. It is a curious coincidence that he should continue to be such an incomparable renderer of his own music. Pope Julius II was the late Mr. Darwin. Rameses II is a blind woman now, and stands in Holborn, holding a tin mug. I never could understand why I always found myself humming "They oppressed them with burthens" when I passed her, till one day I was looking in Mr. Spooner's window in the Strand, and saw a photograph of Rameses II. Mary Queen of Scots wears surgical boots and is subject to fits, near the Horse Shoe in Tottenham Court Road.

Michael Angelo is a commissionaire; I saw him on board the *Glen Rosa*, which used to run every day from London to Clacton-on-Sea and back. It gave me quite a turn when I saw him coming down the stairs from the upper deck, with his bronzed face, flattened nose, and with the familiar bar upon his forehead. I never liked Michael Angelo, and never shall, but I am afraid of him, and was near trying to hide when I saw him coming towards me. He had not got his commissionaire's uniform on, and I did not know he was one till I met him a month or so later in the Strand. When we got to Blackwall the music struck up and people began to dance. I never saw a man dance so much in my life. He did not miss a dance all the way to Clacton, nor all the way back again, and when not dancing he was flirting and cracking jokes. I could hardly believe my eyes when I reflected that this man had painted the famous "Last Judgment" and had made all those statues.

Dante is, or was a year or two ago, a waiter at Brissago on the Lago Maggiore, only he is better-tempered-looking, and has a more intellectual expression. He gave me his ideas upon beauty: "Tutto ch' è vero è bello," he exclaimed, with all his old self-confidence. I am not afraid of Dante. I know people by their friends, and he went about with Virgil, so I said with some severity, "No, Dante, il naso della Signora Robinson è vero, ma non è bello"; and he admitted I was right. Beatrice's name is Towler; she is a waitress at a small inn in German Switzerland. I used to sit at my window and hear people call "Towler, Towler, Towler," fifty times in a forenoon. She was the exact antithesis to Abra; Abra, if I remember, used to come before they called her name, but no matter how often they called Towler, everyone came before she did. I suppose they spelt her name Taula, but to me it sounded Towler; I never, however, met anyone else with this name. She was a sweet, artless little hussy, who made me play the piano to her, and she said it was lovely. Of course I only played my own compositions; so I believed her, and it all went off very nicely. I thought it might save trouble if I did not tell her who she really was, so I said nothing about it.

I met Socrates once. He was my muleteer on an excursion which I will not name, for fear it should identify the man. The moment I saw my guide I knew he was somebody, but for the life of me I could not remember who. All of a sudden it flashed across me that he was Socrates. He talked enough for six, but it was all in *dialetto*, so I could not understand him, nor, when I had discovered who he was, did I much try to do so. He was a good creature, a trifle given to stealing fruit and vegetables, but an amiable man enough. He had had a long day with his mule and me, and he only asked me five francs. I gave him ten, for I pitied his poor old patched boots, and there was a meekness about him that touched me. "And now, Socrates," said I at parting, "we go on our several ways, you to steal tomatoes, I to filch ideas from other people; for the rest—which of these two roads will be the better going, our father which is in heaven knows, but we know not."

I have never seen Mendelssohn, but there is a fresco of him on the terrace, or open-air dining-room, of an inn at Chiavenna. He is not called Mendelssohn, but I knew him by his legs. He is in the costume of a dandy of some five-and-forty years ago, is smoking a cigar, and appears to be making an offer of marriage to his cook. Beethoven both my friend Mr. H. Festing Jones and I have had the good fortune to meet; he is an engineer now, and does not know one note from another; he has quite lost his deafness, is married, and is, of course, a little squat man with the same refractory hair that he always had. It was very interesting to watch him, and Jones remarked that before the end of dinner he had become positively posthumous. One morning I was told the Beethovens were going away, and before long I met their two heavy boxes being carried down the stairs. The boxes were so squab and like their owners that I half thought for a moment that they were inside, and should hardly have been surprised to see them spring up like a couple of Jacks-in-the-box. "Sono indentro?" said I, with a frown of wonder, pointing to the boxes. The porters knew what I meant, and laughed. But there is no end to the list of people whom I have been able to recognize, and before I had got through it myself, I found I had walked some distance, and had involuntarily paused in front of a second-hand bookstall.

I do not like books. I believe I have the smallest library of any literary man in London, and I have no wish to increase it. I keep my books at the British Museum and at Mudie's, and it makes me very angry if anyone gives me one for my private library. I once heard two ladies disputing in a railway carriage as to whether one of them had or had not been wasting money. "I spent it in books," said the accused, "and it's not wasting money to buy books." "Indeed, my dear, I think it is," was the rejoinder, and in practice I agree with it. Webster's Dictionary, Whitaker's Almanack, and Bradshaw's Railway guide should be sufficient for any ordinary library; it will be time enough to go beyond these when the mass of useful and entertaining matter which they provide has been mastered. Nevertheless, I admit that sometimes, if not particularly busy, I stop at a second-hand bookstall and turn over a book or two from mere force of habit.

I know not what made me pick up a copy of Aeschylus—of course in an English version—or rather I know not what made Aeschylus take up with me, for he took me rather than I him; but no sooner had he got me than he began puzzling me, as he has done any time this forty years, to know wherein his transcendent merit can be supposed to lie. To me he is, like the greater number of classics in all ages and countries, a literary Struld-brug, rather than a true ambrosia-fed immortal. There are true immortals, but they are few and far between; most classics are as great impostors dead as they were when living, and while posing as gods are, five-sevenths of them, only Struldbrugs. It comforts me to remember that Aristophanes liked Aeschylus no better than I do. True, he praises him by comparison with Sophocles and Euripides, but he only does so that he may run down these last more effectively, Aristophanes is a safe man to follow, nor do I see why it should not be as correct to laugh with him as to pull a long face with the Greek professors; but this is neither here nor there, for no one really cares about Aeschylus; the more interesting question is how he contrived to make so many people for so many years pretend to care about him.

Perhaps he married somebody's daughter. If a man would get hold of the public ear, he must pay, marry, or fight. I have never understood that Aeschylus was a man of means, and the fighters do not write poetry, so I suppose he must have married a theatrical manager's daughter, and got his plays brought out that way. The ear of any age or country is like its land, air, and water; it seems limitless, but is really limited, and is already in the keeping of those who naturally enough will have no squatting on such valuable property. It is written and talked up to as closely as the means of subsistence are bred up to by a teeming population. There is not a square inch of it but is in private hands, and he who would freehold any part of it must do so by purchase, marriage, or fighting, in the usual way—and fighting gives the longest, safest tenure. The public itself has hardly more voice in the question who shall have its ear, than the land has in choosing its owners. It is farmed as those who own it think most profitable to themselves, and small blame to them; nevertheless, it has a residuum of mulishness which the land has not, and does sometimes dispossess its tenants. It is in this residuum that those who fight place their hope and trust.

Or perhaps Aeschylus squared the leading critics of his time. When one comes to think of it, he must have done so, for how is it conceivable that such plays should have had such runs if he had not? I met a lady one year in Switzerland who had some parrots that always travelled with her and were the idols of her life. These parrots would not let anyone read aloud in their presence, unless they heard their own names introduced from time to time. If these were freely interpolated into the text they would remain as still as stones, for they thought the reading was about themselves. If it was not about them it could not be allowed. The leaders of literature are like these parrots; they do not look at what a man writes, nor if they did would they understand it much better than the parrots do; but they like the sound of their own names, and if these are freely interpolated in a tone they take as friendly, they may even give ear to an outsider. Otherwise they will scream him off if they can.

I should not advise anyone with ordinary independence of mind to attempt the public ear unless he is confident that he can out-lung and out-last his own generation; for if he has any force, people will and ought to be on their guard against him, inasmuch as there is no knowing where he may not take them. Besides, they have staked their money on the wrong men so often without suspecting it, that when there comes one whom they do suspect it would be madness not to bet against him. True, he may die before he has out-screamed his opponents, but that has nothing to do with it. If his scream was well pitched, it will sound clearer when he is dead. We do not know what death is. If we know so little about life which we have experienced, how shall we know about death which we have not—and in the nature of things never can? Everyone, as I said years ago in *Alps and Sanctuaries,* is an immortal to himself, for he cannot know that he is dead until he is dead, and when dead how can he know anything about anything? All we know is, that even the humblest dead may live long after all trace of the body has disappeared; we see them doing it in the bodies and memories of those that come after them; and not a few live so much longer and more effectually than is desirable, that it has been necessary to get rid of them by Act of Parliament. It is love that alone gives life, and the truest life is that which we live not in ourselves but vicariously in others, and with which we have no concern. Our concern is so to order ourselves that we may be of the number of them that enter into life—although we know it not.

Aeschylus did so order himself; but his life is not of that inspiriting kind that can be won through fighting the good fight only—or being believed to have fought it. His voice is the echo of a drone, drone-begotten and drone-sustained. It is not a tone that a man must utter or die—nay, even though he die; and likely enough half the allusions and hard passages in Aeschylus of which we can make neither head nor tail are in reality only puffs of some of the literary leaders of his time.

The lady above referred to told me more about her parrots. She was like a Nasmyth hammer going slow—very gentle, but irresistible. She always read the newspaper to them. What was the use of having a newspaper if one did not read it to one's parrots?

"And have you divined," I asked, "to which side they incline in politics?"

"They do not like Mr. Gladstone," was the somewhat freezing answer; "this is the only point on which we disagree, for I adore him. Don't ask more about this, it is a great grief to me. I tell them everything," she continued, "and hide no secret from them."

"But can any parrot be trusted to keep a secret?"

"Mine can."

"And on Sundays do you give them the same course of reading as on a week-day, or do you make a difference?"

"On Sundays I always read them a genealogical chapter from the Old or New Testament, for I can thus introduce their names without profanity. I always keep tea by me in case they should ask for it in the night, and I have an Etna to warm it for them; they take milk and sugar. The old white-headed clergyman came to see them last night; it was very painful, for Jocko reminded him so strongly of his late . . ."

I thought she was going to say "wife," but it proved to have been only of a parrot that he had once known and loved.

One evening she was in difficulties about the quarantine, which was enforced that year on the Italian frontier. The local doctor had gone down that morning to see the Italian doctor and arrange some details. "Then perhaps, my dear," she said to her husband, "he is the quarantine." "No, my love," replied her husband. "The quarantine is not a person, it is a place where they put people"; but she would not be comforted, and suspected the quarantine as an enemy that might at any moment pounce out upon her and her parrots. So a lady told me once that she had been in like trouble about the anthem. She read in her Prayer Book that in choirs and places where they sing "here followeth the anthem," yet the person with this most mysteriously sounding name never did follow. They had a choir, and no one could say the church was not a place where they sang, for they did sing—both chants and hymns. Why, then, this persistent slackness on the part of the anthem, who at this juncture should follow his papa, the rector, into the reading-desk? No doubt he would come some day, and then what would he be like? Fair or dark? Tall or short? Would he be bald and wear spectacles like papa, would he be young and goodlooking? Anyhow, there was something wrong, for it was announced that he would follow, and he never did follow; therefore there was no knowing what he might not do next.

I heard of the parrots a year or two later as giving lessons in Italian to an English maid. I do not know what their terms were. Alas! since then both they and their mistress have joined the majority. When the poor lady felt her end was near she desired (and the responsibility for this must rest with her, not me) that the birds might be destroyed, as fearing that they might come to be neglected, and knowing that they could never be loved again as she had loved them. On being told that all was over, she said "Thank you," and immediately expired.

Reflecting in such random fashion, and strolling with no greater method, I worked my way back through Cheapside and found myself once more in front of Sweeting's window. Again the turtles attracted me. They were alive, and so far at any rate they agreed with me. Nay, they had eyes, mouths, legs, if not arms, and feet, so there was much in which we were both of a mind, but surely they must be mistaken in arming themselves so very heavily. Any creature on getting what the turtle aimed at would overreach itself and be landed not in safety but annihilation. It should have no communion with the outside world at all, for death could creep in wherever the creature could creep out; and it must creep out somewhere if it was to hook on to outside things. What death can be more absolute than such absolute isolation? Perfect death, indeed, if it were attainable (which it is not), is as near perfect security as we can reach, but it is not the kind of security aimed at by any animal that is at the pains of defending itself. For such want to have things both ways, desiring the livingness of life without its perils, and the safety of death without its deadness, and some of us do actually get this for a considerable time, but we do not get it by plating ourselves with armour as the turtle does. We tried this in the Middle Ages, and no longer mock ourselves with the weight of armour that our forefathers carried in battle. Indeed the more deadly the weapons of attack become the more we go into the fight slug-wise.

Slugs have ridden their contempt for defensive armour as much to death as the turtles their pursuit of it. They have hardly more than skin enough to hold themselves together; they court death every time they cross the road. Yet death comes not to them more than to the turtle, whose defences are so great that there is little left inside to be defended. Moreover, the slugs fare best in the long run, for turtles are dying out, while slugs are not, and there must be millions of slugs all the world over for every single turtle. Of the two vanities, therefore, that of the slug seems most substantial.

In either case the creature thinks itself safe, but is sure to be found out sooner or later; nor is it easy to explain this mockery save by reflecting that everything must have its meat in due season, and that meat can only be found for such a multitude of mouths by giving everything as meat in due season to something else. This is like the Kilkenny cats, or robbing Peter to pay Paul; but it is the way of the world, and as every animal must contribute in kind to the picnic of the universe, one does not see what better arrangement could be made than the providing each race with a hereditary fallacy, which shall in the end get it into a scrape, but which shall generally stand the wear and tear of life for some time. *"Do ut des"* is the writing on all flesh to him that eats it; and no creature is dearer to itself than it is to some other that would devour it.

Nor is there any statement or proposition more invulnerable than living forms are. Propositions prey upon and are grounded upon one another just like living forms. They support one another as plants and animals do; they are based ultimately on credit, or faith, rather than the cash of irrefragable conviction. The whole universe is borne along on the credit system, and if the mutual confidence on which it is based were to collapse, it must itself collapse immediately. Just or unjust, it lives by faith; it is based on vague and impalpable opinion that by some inscrutable process passes into will and action, and is made manifest in matter and in flesh: it is meteoric— suspended in mid-air; it is the baseless fabric of a vision so vast, so vivid, and so gorgeous that no base can seem more broad than such stupendous baselessness, and yet any man can bring it about his ears by being over-curious; when faith fails, a system based on faith fails also.

Whether the universe is really a paying concern, or whether it is an inflated bubble that must burst sooner or later, this is another matter. If people were to demand cash payment in irrefragable certainty for everything that they have taken hitherto as paper money on the credit of the bank of public opinion, is there money enough behind it all to stand so great a drain even on so great a reserve? Probably there is not, but happily there can be no such panic, for even though the cultured classes may do so, the uncultured

123

are too dull to have brains enough to commit such stupendous folly. It takes a long course of academic training to educate a man up to the standard which he must reach before he can entertain such questions seriously, and by a merciful dispensation of Providence university training is almost as costly as it is unprofitable. The majority will thus be always unable to afford it, and will base their opinions on mother wit and current opinion rather than on demonstration.

So I turned my steps homewards; I saw a good many more things on my way home, but I was told that I was not to see more this time than I could get into twelve pages of the *Universal Review;* I must therefore reserve any remark which I think might perhaps entertain the reader for another occasion.

D. H. Lawrence

The Portrait
of Maurice Magnus

This little known text was first published as the preface to *Memoirs of the*
Foreign Legion, by "M. M." The author was one Maurice Magnus, and only
the following facts need to be added to the biographical information given
by Lawrence. In 1915 Magnus joined the French Foreign Legion. He deserted
before seeing combat and crossed the frontier into Italy. In 1917 Magnus
wrote of his adventures in the Legion, and it was this manuscript, originally
entitled *Dregs*, that was published seven years later, with Lawrence's preface.
According to Norman Douglas—the "N. D." of "The Portrait" and the
author of *South Wind—Memoirs of the Foreign Legion* was considerably expur-
gated in its references to what he called "certain ultra-masculine peculiarities
of legionary life." When the book was published, Douglas attacked Lawrence's preface, claiming that "in exposing the frailties of Maurice Magnus
[Lawrence] has contrived, like a true Boswell, to expose his own." Such
disputes can no longer move us: Magnus and his book now live only in
Lawrence's first-class epitaph, whose balance of truth and falsehood is lost
in the overall verity of its character.

On a dark, wet, wintry evening in November 1919, I arrived in Florence, having just got back to Italy for the first time since 1914. My wife was in Germany, gone to see her mother, also for the first time since that fatal year 1914. We were poor; who was going to bother to publish me and to pay for my writings, in 1918 and 1919? I landed in Italy with nine pounds in my pocket and about twelve pounds lying in the bank in London. Nothing more. My wife, I hoped, would arrive in Florence with two or three pounds remaining. We should have to go very softly, if we were to house ourselves in Italy for the winter. But after the desperate weariness of the war, one could not bother.

So I had written to N. D. to get me a cheap room somewhere in Florence, and to leave a note at Cook's. I deposited my bit of luggage at the station, and walked to Cook's in the Via Tornabuoni. Florence was strange to me: seemed grim and dark and rather awful on the cold November evening. There was a note from D., who has never left me in the lurch. I went down the Lung' Arno to the address he gave.

I had just passed the end of the Ponte Vecchio, and was watching the first lights of evening and the last light of day on the swollen river as I walked, when I heard D.'s voice:

"Isn't that Lawrence? Why, of course it is, of course it is, beard and all! Well, how are you, eh? You got my note? Well, now, my dear boy, you just go on to the Cavelotti—straight ahead, straight ahead—you've got the number. There's a room for you there. We shall be there in half an hour. Oh, let me introduce you to M."

I had unconsciously seen the two men approaching, D. tall and portly, the other man rather short and strutting. They were both buttoned up in their overcoats, and both had rather curly little hats. But D. was decidedly shabby and a gentleman, with his wicked red face and tufted eyebrows. The other man was almost smart, all in grey, and he looked at first sight like an actor-manager, common. There was a touch of down-on-his-luck about him too. He looked at me, buttoned up in my old thick overcoat, and with my beard bushy and raggy because of my horror of entering a strange barber's shop, and he greeted me in a rather fastidious voice, and a little patronizingly. I forgot to say I was carrying a small handbag. But I realized at once that I ought, in this little grey-sparrow man's eyes—he stuck his front out tubbily, like a bird, and his legs seemed to perch behind him, as a bird's do—I ought to be in a cab. But I wasn't. He eyed me in that shrewd and rather impertinent way of the world of actor-managers: cosmopolitan, knocking shabbily round the world.

He looked a man of about forty, spruce and youngish in his deport-ment, very pink-faced, and very clean, very natty, very alert, like a sparrow painted to resemble a tom-tit. He was just the kind of man I had never met: little smart man of the shabby world, very much on the spot, don't you know.

"How much does it cost?" I asked D., meaning the room.

"Oh, my dear fellow, a trifle. Ten francs a day. Third rate, tenth rate, but not bad at the price. Pension terms of course—everything included—except wine."

"Oh, no, not at all bad for the money," said M. "Well, now, shall we be moving? You want the post-office, D.?" His voice was precise and a little mincing, and it had an odd high squeak.

"I do," said D.

"Well, then, come down here—" M. turned to a dark little alley.

"Not at all," said D. "We turn down by the bridge."

"This is quicker," said M. He had a twang rather than an accent in his speech—not definitely American.

He knew all the short cuts of Florence. Afterwards I found that he knew all the short cuts in all the big towns of Europe.

I went on to the Cavelotti and waited in an awful plush and gilt drawing-room, and was given at last a cup of weird muddy brown slush called tea, and a bit of weird brown mush called jam on some bits of bread. Then I was taken to my room. It was far off, on the third floor of the big, ancient, deserted Florentine house. There I had a big and lonely, stone-comfortless room looking on to the river. Fortunately it was not very cold inside, and I didn't care. The adventure of being back in Florence again after the years of war made one indifferent.

After an hour or so someone tapped. It was D. coming in with his grandiose air—now a bit shabby, but still very courtly.

"Why, here you are—miles and miles from human habitation! I *told* her to put you on the second floor, where we are. What does she mean by it? Ring the bell. Ring it."

"No," said I, "I'm all right here."

"What!" cried D. "In this Spitzbergen! Where's that bell?"

"Don't ring it," said I, who have a horror of chambermaids and explanations.

"Not ring it! Well, you're a man, you are! Come on then. Come on down to my room. Come on. Have you had some tea—filthy muck they call tea here? I never drink it."

I went down to D.'s room on the lower floor. It was a littered mass of books and typewriter and papers: D. was just finishing his novel. M. was resting on the bed, in his shirt sleeves: a tubby, fresh-faced little man in a suit of grey, faced cloth bound at the edges with grey silk braid. He had light blue eyes, tired underneath, and crisp, curly, dark brown hair just grey at the temples. But everything was neat and even finicking about his person.

"Sit down! Sit down!" said D., wheeling up a chair. "Have a whisky?"

"Whisky!" said I.

"Twenty-four francs a bottle—and a find at that," moaned D. I must tell that the exchange was then about forty-five lire to the pound.

"Oh, N.," said M., "I didn't tell you. I was offered a bottle of 1913 Black and White for twenty-eight lire."

"Did you buy it?"

"No. It's your turn to buy a bottle."

"Twenty-eight francs—my dear fellow!" said D., cocking up his eyebrows. "I shall have to starve myself to do it."

"Oh, no you won't, you'll eat here just the same," said M.

"Yes, and I'm starved to death. Starved to death by the muck—the absolute muck they call food here. I can't face twenty-eight francs, my dear chap—can't be done, on my honour."

"Well, look here, N. We'll both buy a bottle. And you can get the one at twenty-two, and I'll buy the one at twenty-eight."

So it always was, M. indulged D., and spoilt him in every way. And of course D. wasn't grateful. *Au contraire!* And M.'s pale blue smallish round eyes, in his cockatoo-pink face, would harden to indignation occasionally.

The room was dreadful. D. never opened the windows: didn't believe in opening windows. He believed that a certain amount of nitrogen—I should say a great amount—is beneficial. The queer smell of a bedroom which is slept in, worked in, lived in, smoked in, and in which men drink their whiskies, was something new to me. But I didn't care. One had got away from the war.

We drank our whiskies before dinner. M. was rather yellow under the eyes, and irritable; even his pink fattish face went yellowish.

"Look here," said D. "Didn't you say there was a turkey for dinner? What? Have you been to the kitchen to see what they're doing to it?"

"Yes," said M. testily. "I forced them to prepare it to roast."

"With chestnuts—stuffed with chestnuts?" said D.

"They *said* so," said M.

"Oh, but go down and see that they're doing it. Yes, you've got to keep your eye on them, got to. The most awful howlers if you don't. You go now and see what they're up to." D. used his most irresistible grand manner.

"It's too late," persisted M., testy.

"It's *never* too late. You just run down and absolutely prevent them from boiling that bird in the old soup-water," said D. "If you need force, fetch me."

M. went. He was a great epicure, and knew how things should be cooked. But of course his irruptions into the kitchen roused considerable resentment, and he was getting quaky. However, he went. He came back to say the turkey was being roasted, but without chestnuts.

"What did I tell you! What did I tell you!" cried D. "They are absolute—! If you don't hold them by the neck while they peel the chestnuts, they'll stuff the bird with old boots, to save themselves trouble. Of course, you should have gone down sooner, M."

Dinner was always late, so the whisky was usually two whiskies. Then we went down, and were merry in spite of all things. That is, D. always grumbled about the food. There was one unfortunate youth who was boots and porter and waiter and all. He brought the big dish to D., and D. always poked and pushed among the portions, and grumbled frantically, sotto voce, in Italian to the youth Beppo, getting into a nervous frenzy. Then M. called the waiter to himself, picked the nicest bits off the dish and gave them to D., then helped himself.

The food was not good, but with D. it was an obsession. With the waiter he was terrible. "*Cos' è? Zuppa? Grazie. No, niente per me. No! No! Quest' acqua sporca non bevo io.* I don't drink this dirty water. What—What's that in it—a piece of dish clout? Oh, holy Dio, I can't eat another thing this evening—"

And he yelled for more bread—bread being war rations and very limited in supply—so M. in nervous distress gave him his piece, and D. threw the crumb part on the floor, anywhere, and called for another litre. We always drank heavy dark red wine at three francs a litre. D. drank two-thirds, M. drank least. He loved his liquors, and did not care for wine. We were noisy and unabashed at table. The old Danish ladies at the other end of the room, and the rather impecunious young Duca and family not far off were not supposed to understand English. The Italians rather liked the noise, and the young signorina with the high-up yellow hair eyed us with profound interest. On we sailed, gay and noisy, D. telling witty anecdotes and grumbling wildly and only half whimsically about the food. We sat on till most people had finished, then went up to more whisky—one more perhaps—in M.'s room.

When I came down in the morning I was called into M.'s room. He was like a little pontiff in a blue kimono-shaped dressing-gown with a broad border of reddish purple: the blue was a soft mid-blue, the material a dull silk. So he minced about, in *demi-toilette*. His room was very clean and neat, and slightly perfumed with essences. On his dressing-table stood many cut-glass bottles and silver-topped bottles with essences and pomades and powders, and heaven knows what. A very elegant little prayer book lay by his bed—and a life of St Benedict. For M. was a Roman Catholic convert. All he had was expensive and finicking: thick leather silver-studded suit-cases standing near the wall, trouser-stretcher all nice, hair-brushes and clothes-brush with old ivory backs. I wondered over him and his niceties and little pomposities. He was a new bird to me.

For he wasn't at all just the common person he looked. He was queer and sensitive as a woman with D., and patient and fastidious. And yet he *was* common, his very accent was common, and D. despised him.

And M. rather despised me because I did not spend money. I paid for a third of the wine we drank at dinner, and bought the third bottle of whisky we had during M.'s stay. After all, he only stayed three days. But I would not spend for myself. I had no money to spend, since I knew I must live and my wife must live.

"Oh," said M. "Why, that's the very time to spend money, when you've got none. If you've got none, why try to save it? That's been my philosophy all my life; when you've got no money, you may just as well spend it. If you've got a good deal, that's the time to look after it." Then he laughed his queer little laugh, rather squeaky. These were his exact words.

"Precisely," said D. "Spend when you've nothing to spend, my boy. Spent *hard* then."

"No," said I. "If I can help it, I will never let myself be penniless while I live. I mistrust the world too much."

"But if you're going to live in fear of the world," said M., "what's the good of living at all? Might as well die."

I think I give his words almost verbatim. He had a certain impatience of me and of my presence. Yet we had some jolly times—mostly in one or other of their bedrooms, drinking a whisky and talking. We drank a bottle a day—I had very little, preferring the wine at lunch and dinner, which seemed delicious after the war famine. D. would bring up the remains of the second litre in the evening, to go on with before the coffee came.

I arrived in Florence on the Wednesday or Thursday evening; I think Thursday. M. was due to leave for Rome on the Saturday. I asked D. who M. was. "Oh, you never know what he's at. He was manager for Isadora Duncan for a long time—knows all the capitals of Europe: St Petersburg, Moscow, Tiflis, Constantinople, Berlin, Paris—knows them as you and I know Florence. He's been mostly in that line—theatrical. Then a journalist. He edited the *Roman Review* till the war killed it. Oh, a many-sided sort of fellow."

"But how do you know him?" said I.

"I met him in Capri years and years ago—oh, sixteen years ago—and clean forgot all about him till somebody came to me one day in Rome and said: 'You're N. D.' *I* didn't know who he was. But he'd never forgotten me. Seems to be smitten by me, somehow or other. All the better for me—ha-ha!—if he *likes* to run round for me. My dear fellow, I wouldn't prevent him, if it amuses him. Not for worlds."

And that was how it was. M. ran D.'s errands, forced the other man to go to the tailor, to the dentist, and was almost a guardian angel to him.

"Look here!" cried D. "I *can't* go to that damned tailor. Let the thing wait, I can't go."

"Oh, yes. Now look here, N., if you don't get it done now while I'm here, you'll never get it done. I made the appointment for three o'clock—"

"To hell with you! Details! Details! I can't stand it, I tell you."

D. chafed and kicked, but went.

"A little fussy fellow," he said. "Oh, yes, fussing about like a woman. Fussy, you know, fussy. I *can't stand* these fussy—" And D. went off into improprieties.

Well, M. ran round and arranged D.'s affairs and settled his little bills, and was so benevolent, and so impatient and nettled at the ungrateful way in which the benevolence was accepted. And D. despised him all the time as a little busybody and an inferior. And I there between them just wondered. It seemed to me M. would get very irritable and nervous at midday and before dinner, yellow around the eyes and played out. He wanted his whisky. He was tired after running round on a thousand errands and quests which I never understood. He always took his morning coffee at dawn, and was out to early Mass and pushing his affairs before eight o'clock in the morning. But what his affairs were I still do not know. Mass is all I am certain of.

However, it was his birthday on the Sunday, and D. would not let him go. He had once said he would give a dinner for his birthday, and this he was not allowed to forget. It seemed to me M. rather wanted to get out of it. But D. was determined to have that dinner.

"You aren't going before you've given us that hare, don't you imagine it, my boy. I've got the smell of that hare in my imagination, and I've damned well got to set my teeth in it. Don't you imagine you're going without having produced that hare."

So poor M., rather a victim, had to consent. We discussed what we should eat. It was decided the hare should have truffles, and a dish of champignons, and cauliflower, and zabaioni—and I forget what else. It was to be on Saturday evening. And M. would leave on Sunday for Rome.

Early on the Saturday morning he went out, with the first daylight, to the old market, to get the hare and the mushrooms. He went himself because he was a connoisseur.

On the Saturday afternoon D. took me wandering round to buy a birthday present.

"I shall have to buy him something—have to—have to—" he said fretfully. He only wanted to spend about five francs. We trailed over the Ponte Vecchio, looking at the jewellers' booths there. It was before the foreigners had come back, and things were still rather dusty and almost at pre-war prices. But we could see nothing for five francs except the little saint-medals. D. wanted to buy one of those. It seemed to me infra dig. So at last coming down to the Mercato Nuovo we saw little bowls of Volterra marble, a natural amber colour, for four francs.

"Look, buy one of those," I said to D., "and he can put his pins or studs or any trifle in, as he needs."

So we went in and bought one of the little bowls of Volterra marble. M. seemed so touched and pleased with the gift.

"Thank you a thousand times, N.," he said. "That's charming! That's exactly what I want."

The dinner was quite a success, and, poorly fed as we were at the pension, we stuffed ourselves tight on the mushrooms and the hare and the zabaioni, and drank ourselves tight with the good red wine which swung in its straw flask in the silver swing on the table. A flask has two and a quarter litres. We were four persons, and we drank almost two flasks. D. made the waiter measure the remaining half-litre and take it off the bill. But good, good food, and cost about twelve francs a head the whole dinner.

Well, next day was nothing but bags and suitcases in M.'s room, and the misery of departure with luggage. He went on the midnight train to Rome—first class.

"I always travel first class," he said, "and I always shall, while I can buy the ticket. Why should I go second? It's beastly enough to travel at all."

"My dear fellow, I came up third the last time I came from Rome," said D. "Oh, not bad, not bad. Damned fatiguing journey anyhow."

So the little outsider was gone, and I was rather glad. I don't think he liked me. Yet one day he said to me at table:

133

"How lovely your hair is—such a lovely colour! What do you dye it with?"

I laughed, thinking he was laughing too. But no, he meant it.

"It's got no particular colour at all," I said, "so I couldn't dye it that!"

"It's a lovely colour," he said. And I think he didn't believe me, that I didn't dye it. It puzzled me, and it puzzles me still.

But he was gone. D. moved into M.'s room, and asked me to come down to the room he himself was vacating. But I preferred to stay upstairs.

M. was a fervent Catholic, taking the religion, alas, rather unctuously. He had entered the Church only a few years before. But he had a bishop for a god-father, and seemed to be very intimate with the upper clergy. He was very pleased and proud because he was a constant guest at the famous old monastery south of Rome. He talked of becoming a monk, a monk in that aristocratic and well-bred order. But he had not even begun his theological studies: or any studies of any sort. And D. said he only chose the Benedictines because they lived better than any of the others.

But I had said to M., that when my wife came and we moved south,

I would like to visit the monastery some time, if I might. "Certainly," he said. "Come when I am there. I shall be there in about a month's time. Do come! Do be sure and come. It's a wonderful place—oh, wonderful. It will make a great impression on you. Do come. Do come. And I will tell Don Bernardo, who is my *greatest* friend, and who is guest-master, about you. So that if you wish to go when I am not there, write to Don Bernardo. But do come when I am there."

My wife and I were due to go into the mountains south of Rome, and stay there some months. Then I was to visit the big, noble monastery that stands on a bluff hill like a fortress crowning a great precipice, above the little town and the plain between the mountains. But it was so icy cold and snowy among the mountains, it was unbearable. We fled south again, to Naples, and to Capri. Passing, I saw the monastery crouching there above, world-famous, but it was impossible to call then.

I wrote and told M. of my move. In Capri I had an answer from him. It had a wistful tone—and I don't know what made me think that he was in trouble, in monetary difficulty. But felt it acutely—a kind of appeal. Yet he said nothing direct. And he wrote from an expensive hotel in Anzio, on the sea near Rome.

At the moment I had just received twenty pounds, unexpected and joyful, from America—a gift too. I hesitated for some time, because I felt unsure. Yet the curious appeal came out of the letter, though nothing was said. And I felt also I owed M. that dinner, and I didn't want to owe him anything, since he despised me a little for being careful. So partly out of revenge, perhaps, and partly because I felt the strange wistfulness of him appealing to me, I sent him five pounds, saying perhaps I was mistaken in imagining him very hard up, but if so, he wasn't to be offended.

It is strange to me even now, how I knew he was appealing to me. Because it was all as vague as I say. Yet I felt it so strongly. He replied: "Your cheque has saved my life. Since I last saw you I have fallen down an abyss. But I will tell you when I see you. I shall be at the monastery in three days. Do come—and come alone." I have forgotten to say that he was a rabid woman-hater.

This was just after Christmas. I thought his "saved my life" and "fallen down an abyss" was just the American touch of "very, very—" I wondered what on earth the abyss could be, and I decided it must be that he had lost his money or his hopes. It seemed to me that some of his old buoyant assurance came out again in this letter. But he was now very friendly, urging me to come to the monastery, and treating me with a curious little tenderness and protectiveness. He had a queer delicacy of his own, varying with a bounce and a commonness. He was a common little bounder. And then he had this curious delicacy and tenderness and wistfulness.

I put off going north. I had another letter urging me—and it seemed to me that, rather assuredly, he was expecting more money. Rather cockily, as if he had a right to it. And that made me not want to give him any. Besides, as my wife said, what right had I to give away the little money we had, and we there stranded in the south of Italy with no resources if once we were spent up? And I have always been determined *never* to come to my last shilling—if I have to reduce my spending almost to nothingness. I have always been determined to keep a few pounds between me and the world.

I did not send any money. But I wanted to go to the monastery, so wrote and said I would come for two days. I always remember getting up in the black dark of the January morning, and making a little coffee on the spirit-lamp, and watching the clock, the big-faced, blue old clock on the campanile in the piazza in Capri, to see I wasn't late. The electric light in the piazza lit up the face of the campanile. And we were then, a stone's throw away, high in the Palazzo Ferraro, opposite the bubbly roof of the little *duomo*. Strange dark winter morning, with the open sea beyond the roofs, seen through the side window, and the thin line of the lights of Naples twinkling far, far off.

At ten minutes to six I went down the smelly dark stone stairs of the old palazzo, out into the street. A few people were already hastening up the street to the terrace that looks over the sea to the bay of Naples. It was dark and cold. We slid down in the funicular to the shore, then in little boats were rowed out over the dark sea to the steamer that lay there showing her lights and hooting.

It was three long hours across the sea to Naples, with dawn coming slowly in the East, beyond Ischia, and flushing into lovely colours as our steamer pottered along the peninsula, calling at Massa and Sorrento and Piano. I always loved hanging over the side and watching the people come out in boats from the little places of the shore, that rose steep and beautiful. I love the movement of these watery, Neapolitan people, and the naïve trustful way they clamber in and out the boats, and their softness, and their dark eyes. But when the steamer leaves the peninsula and begins to make

135

away round Vesuvius to Naples, one is already tired, and cold, cold, cold in the wind that comes piercing from the snow-crests away there along Italy. Cold, and reduced to a kind of stony apathy by the time we come to the mole in Naples, at ten o'clock—or twenty past ten.

We were rather late, and I missed the train. I had to wait till two o'clock. And Naples is a hopeless town to spend three hours in. However, time passes. I remember I was calculating in my mind whether they had given me the right change at the ticket window. They hadn't—and I hadn't counted in time. Thinking of this, I got in the Rome train. I had been there ten minutes when I heard a trumpet blow.

"Is this the Rome train?" I asked my fellow traveller.

"*Si.*"

"The express?"

"No, it is the slow train."

"It leaves?"

"At ten past two."

I almost jumped through the window. I flew down the platform.

"The *diretto!*" I cried to a porter.

"*Parte! Eccolo la!*" he said, pointing to a big train moving inevitably away.

I flew with wild feet across the various railway lines and seized the end of the train as it travelled. I had caught it. Perhaps if I had missed it fate would have been different. So I sat still for about three hours. Then I had arrived.

There is a long drive up the hill from the station to the monastery. The driver talked to me. It was evident he bore the monks no good will.

"Formerly," he said, "if you went up to the monastery you got a glass of wine and a plate of macaroni. But now they kick you out of the door."

"Do they?" I said. "It is hard to believe."

"They kick you out of the gate," he vociferated.

We twisted up and up the wild hillside, past the old castle of the town, past the last villa, between trees and rocks. We saw no one. The whole hill belongs to the monastery. At last at twilight we turned the corner of the oak wood and saw the monastery like a huge square fortress-palace of the sixteenth century crowning the near distance. Yes, and there was M. just stepping through the huge old gateway and hastening down the slope to where the carriage must stop. He was bareheaded, and walking with his perky, busy little stride, seemed very much at home in the place. He looked up to me with a tender, intimate look as I got down from the carriage. Then he took my hand.

"So *very* glad to see you," he said. "I'm so *pleased* you've come."

And he looked into my eyes with that wistful, watchful tenderness rather like a woman who isn't quite sure of her lover. He had a certain charm in his manner; and an odd pompous touch with it at this moment, welcoming his guest at the gate of the vast monastery which reared above us from its buttresses in the rock, was rather becoming. His face was still pink, his eyes pale blue and sharp, but he looked greyer at the temples.

"Give me your bag," he said. "Yes, do—and come along. Don Bernardo is just at Evensong, but he'll be here in a little while. Well, now, tell me all the news."

"Wait," I said. "Lend me five francs to finish paying the driver—he has no change."

"Certainly, certainly," he said, giving the five francs.

I had no news, so asked him his.

"Oh, I have none either," he said. "Very short of money, that of course is *no* news." And he laughed his little laugh. "I'm so glad to be here," he continued. "The peace, and the rhythm of the life is so *beautiful!* I'm sure you'll love it."

137

We went up the slope under the big, tunnel-like entrance and were in the grassy courtyard, with the arched walk on the far sides, and one or two trees. It was like a grassy cloister, but still busy. Black monks were standing chatting, an old peasant was just driving two sheep from the cloister grass, and an old monk was darting into the little post-office which one recognized by the shield with the national arms over the doorway. From under the far arches came an old peasant carrying a two-handed saw.

And there was Don Bernardo, a tall monk in a black, well-shaped gown, young, good-looking, gentle, hastening forward with a quick smile. He was about my age, and his manner seemed fresh and subdued, as if he were still a student. One felt one was at college with one's college mates.

We went up the narrow stair and into the long, old, naked white corridor, high and arched. Don Bernardo had got the key of my room: two keys, one for the dark antechamber, one for the bedroom. A charming and elegant bedroom, with an engraving of English landscape, and outside the net curtain a balcony looking down on the garden, a narrow strip beneath the walls, and beyond, the clustered buildings of the farm, and the oak woods and arable fields of the hill summit; and beyond again, the gulf where the world's valley was, and all the mountains that stand in Italy on the plains as if God had just put them down ready made. The sun had already sunk, the snow on the mountains was full of a rosy glow, the valleys were full of shadow. One heard, far below, the trains shunting, the world clinking in the cold air.

"Isn't it wonderful! Ah, the most wonderful place on earth!" said M. "What now could you wish better than to end your days here? The peace, the beauty, the eternity of it." He paused and sighed. Then he put his hand on Don Bernardo's arm and smiled at him with that odd, rather wistful smirking tenderness that made him such a quaint creature in my eyes.

"But I'm going to enter the order. You're going to let me be a monk and be one of you, aren't you, Don Bernardo?"

"We will see," smiled Don Bernardo. "When you have begun your studies."

"It will take me two years," said M. "I shall have to go to college in Rome. When I have got the money for the fees—" He talked away, like a boy planning a new role.

"But I'm sure Lawrence would like to drink a cup of tea," said Don Bernardo. He spoke English as if it were his native language. "Shall I tell them to make it in the kitchen, or shall we go to your room?"

"Oh, we'll go to my room. How thoughtless of me! Do forgive me, won't you?" said M., laying his hand gently on my arm. "I'm so awfully sorry, you know. But we get so excited and enchanted when we talk of the monastery. But come along, come along, it will be ready in a moment on the spirit-lamp."

We went down to the end of the high, white, naked corridor. M. had a quite sumptuous room, with a curtained bed in one part, and under the window his writing-desk with papers and photographs, and near by a sofa and an easy table, making a little sitting-room, while the bed and toilet things, pomades and bottles, were all in the distance, in the shadow. Night was fallen. From the window one saw the world far below, like a pool the flat plain, a deep pool of darkness with little twinkling lights, and rows and bunches of light that were the railway station.

I drank my tea, M. drank a little liqueur, Don Bernardo in his black winter robe sat and talked with us. At least he did very little talking. But he listened and smiled and put in a word or two as we talked, seated round the table on which stood the green-shaded electric lamp.

The monastery was cold as the tomb. Couched there on the top of its hill, it is not much below the winter snow-line. Now by the end of January all the summer heat is soaked out of the vast, ponderous stone walls, and they become masses of coldness cloaking around. There is no heating apparatus whatsoever—none. Save the fire in the kitchen, for cooking, nothing. Dead, silent, stone cold everywhere.

At seven we went down to dinner. Capri in the daytime was hot, so I had brought only a thin old dust-coat. M. therefore made me wear a big coat of his own, a coat made of thick, smooth black cloth, and lined with black sealskin, and having a collar of silky black sealskin. I can still remember the feel of the silky fur. It was queer to have him helping me solicitously into this coat, and buttoning it at the throat for me.

"Yes, it's a beautiful coat. Of course!" he said. "I hope you find it warm."

"Wonderful," said I. "I feel as warm as a millionaire."

"I'm so glad you do," he laughed.

"You don't mind my wearing your grand coat?" I said.

"Of course not! Of course not! It's a pleasure to me if it will keep you warm. We don't want to die of cold in the monastery, do we? That's one of the mortifications we will do our best to avoid. What? Don't you think? Yes, I think this coldness is going almost too far. I had that coat made in New York fifteen years ago. Of course in Italy" he said It'ly—"I've never worn it, so it is as good as new. And it's a beautiful coat, fur and cloth of the very best. *And* the tailor." He laughed a little, self-approving laugh. He liked to give the impression that he dealt with the *best* shops, don't you know, and stayed in the *best* hotels, etc. I grinned inside the coat, detesting best hotels, best shops, and best overcoats. So off we went, he in his grey overcoat and I in my sealskin millionaire monster, down the dim corridor to the guests' refectory. It was a bare room with a long white table. M. and I sat at the near end. Further down was another man, perhaps the father of one of the boy students. There is a college attached to the monastery.

We sat in the icy room, muffled up in our overcoats. A lay brother with a bulging forehead and queer, fixed eyes waited on us. He might easily have come from an old Italian picture. One of the adoring peasants. The food was abundant—but, alas, it had got cold in the long cold transit from the kitchen. And it was roughly cooked, even if it was quite wholesome. Poor M. did not eat much, but nervously nibbled his bread. I could tell the

139

meals were a trial to him. He could not bear the cold food in that icy, empty refectory. And his stickiness offended the lay brothers. I could see that his little pomposities and his "superior" behaviour and his long stay made them have that old monastic grudge against him, silent but very obstinate and effectual—the same now as six hundred years ago. We had a decanter of good red wine—but he did not care for much wine. He was glad to be peeling the cold orange which was dessert.

After dinner he took me down to see the church, creeping like two thieves down the dimness of the great, prison-cold white corridors, on the cold flag floors. Stone-cold: the monks must have invented the term. These monks were at *compline*. So we went by our two secret little selves into the tall dense nearly-darkness of the church. M., knowing his way about here as in the cities, led me, poor wondering worldling, by the arm through the gulfs of the tomb-like place. He found the electric light switches inside the church, and stealthily made me a light as we went. We looked at the lily marble of the great floor, at the pillars, at the Benvenuto Cellini casket, at the really lovely pillars and slabs of different coloured marbles, yellow and grey and rose and green and lily-white, veined and mottled and splashed: lovely, lovely stones—And Benvenuto had used pieces of lapis lazuli, blue as cornflowers. Yes, yes, all very rich and wonderful.

We tiptoed about the dark church stealthily, from altar to altar, and M. whispered ecstasies in my ear. Each time we passed before an altar, whether the high altar or the side chapels, he did a wonderful reverence, which he must have practised for hours, bowing waxily down and sinking till his one knee touched the pavement, then rising like a flower that rises and unfolds again, till he had skipped to my side and was playing cicerone once more. Always in his grey overcoat, and in whispers; me in the black overcoat, millionarish. Se we crept into the chancel and examined all the queer fat babies of the choir stalls, carved in wood and rolling on their little backs between monk's place and monk's place—queer things for the chanting monks to have between them, these shiny, polished, dark brown fat babies, all different, and all jolly and lusty. We looked at everything in the church— and then at everything in the ancient room at the side where surplices hang and monks can wash their hands.

Then we went down to the crypt, where the modern mosaics glow in wonderful colours, and sometimes in fascinating little fantastic trees and birds. But it was rather like a scene in a theatre, with M. for the wizard and myself a sort of Parsifal in the New York coat. He switched on the lights, the gold mosaic of the vaulting glittered and bowed, the blue mosaic glowed out, the holy of holies gleamed theatrically, the stiff mosaic figures posed around us. To tell the truth, I was glad to get back to the normal human room and sit on a sofa huddled in my overcoat, and look at photographs which M. showed me: photographs of everywhere in Europe. Then he showed me a wonderful photograph of a picture of a lovely lady, asked me what I thought of it, and seemed to expect me to be struck to bits by the beauty. His almost sanctimonious expectation made me tell the truth, that I thought it just a bit cheap, trivial. And then he said, dramatic:

"That's my mother."

It looked so unlike anybody's mother, much less M.'s, that I was startled. I realized that she was his great stunt, and that I had put my foot in it. So I just held my tongue. Then I said, for I felt he was going to be silent forever:

"There are so few portraits, unless by the really great artists, that aren't a bit cheap. She must have been a beautiful woman."

"Yes, she *was*" he said curtly. And we dropped the subject.

He locked all his drawers *very* carefully, and kept the keys on a chain. *141* He seemed to give the impression that he had a great many secrets, perhaps dangerous ones, locked up in the drawers of his writing-table there. And I always wonder what the secrets can be, that are able to be kept so tight under lock and key.

Don Bernardo tapped and entered. We all sat round and sipped a funny liqueur which I didn't like. M. lamented that the bottle was finished. I asked him to order another and let me pay for it. So he said he would tell the postman to bring it up next day from the town. Don Bernardo sipped his tiny glass with the rest of us, and he told me, briefly, his story—and we talked politics till nearly midnight. Then I came out of the black overcoat and we went to bed.

In the morning a fat, smiling, nice old lay brother brought me my water. It was a sunny day. I looked down on the farm cluster and the brown fields and the sere oak woods of the hill-crown, and the rocks and bushes savagely bordering it round. Beyond, the mountains with their snow were blue-glistery with sunshine, and seemed quite near, but across a sort of gulf. All was still and sunny. And the poignant grip of the past, the grandiose, violent past of the Middle Ages, when blood was strong and unquenched and life was flamboyant with splendours and horrible miseries, took hold of me till I could hardly bear it. It was really agony to me to be in the monastery and to see the old farm and the bullocks slowly working in the fields below, and the black pigs rooting among weeds, and to see a monk sitting on a parapet in the sun, and an old, old man in skin sandals and white bunched, swathed legs come driving an ass slowly to the monastery gate, slowly, with all that lingering nonchalance and wildness of the Middle Ages, and yet to know that I was myself, child of the present. It was so strange from M.'s window to look down on the plain and see the white road going straight past a mountain that stood like a loaf of sugar, the river meandering in loops, and the railway with glistening lines making a long black swoop across the flat and into the hills. To see trains come steaming, with white smoke flying. To see the station like a little harbour where trucks like shipping stood anchored in rows in the black bay of railway. To see trains stop in the station and tiny people swarming like flies! To see all this from the monastery, where the Middle Ages live on in a sort of agony, like Tithonus, and cannot die, this was almost a violation to my soul, made almost a wound.

Immediately after coffee we went down to Mass. It was celebrated in a small crypt chapel underground, because that was warmer. The twenty or so monks sat in their stalls, one monk officiating at the altar. It was quiet and simple, the monks sang sweetly and well, there was no organ. It seemed soon to pass by. M. and I sat near the door. He was very devoted and scrupulous in his going up and down. I was an outsider. But it was pleasant— not too sacred. One felt the monks were very human in their likes and their jealousies. It was rather like a group of dons in the dons' room at Cambridge, a cluster of professors in any college. But during Mass they, of course, just sang their responses. Only I could tell some watched the officiating monk rather with ridicule—he was one of the ultra-punctilious sort, just like a don. And some boomed their responses with a grain of defiance against some brother monk who had earned dislike. It was human, and more like a university than anything. We went to Mass every morning, but I did not go to Evensong.

After Mass, M. took me round and showed me everything of the vast monastery. We went into the Bramante Courtyard, all stone, with its great well in the centre, and the colonnades of arches going round, full of sunshine, gay and Renaissance, a little bit ornate but still so jolly and gay, sunny pale stone waiting for the lively people, with the great flight of pale steps sweeping up to the doors of the church, waiting for gentlemen in scarlet trunk-hose, slender red legs, and ladies in brocade gowns, and page-boys with fluffed golden hair. Splendid, sunny, gay Bramante Courtyard of lively stone. But empty. Empty of life. The gay red-legged gentry dead for ever. And when pilgrimages do come and throng in, it is horrible artisan excursions from the great town, and the sordidness of industrialism.

We climbed the little watchtower that is now an observatory, and saw the vague and unshaven Don Giovanni among all his dust and instruments. M. was very familiar and friendly, chattering in his quaint Italian, which was more wrong than any Italian I have ever heard spoken; very familiar and friendly, and a tiny bit deferential to the monks, and yet, and yet— rather patronizing. His little pomposity and patronizing tone coloured even his deferential yearning to be admitted to the monastery. The monks were rather brief with him. They no doubt have their likes and dislikes greatly intensified by the monastic life.

We stood on the summit of the tower and looked at the world below: the town, the castle, the white roads coming straight as judgment out of the mountains north, from Rome, and piercing into the mountains south, toward Naples, traversing the flat, flat plain. Roads, railway, river, streams, a world in accurate and lively detail, with mountains sticking up abruptly and rockily, as the old painters painted it. I think there is no way of painting Italian landscape except that way—that started with Lorenzetti and ended with the sixteenth century.

We looked at the ancient cell away under the monastery, where all the sanctity started. We looked at the big library that belongs to the State, and at the smaller library that belongs still to the abbot. I was tired, cold, and sick among the books and illuminations. I could not bear it any more. I felt I must be outside, in the sun, and see the world below, and the way out.

That evening I said to M.:

"And what was the abyss, then?"

"Oh, well, you know," he said, "it was a cheque which I made out at Anzio. There should have been money to meet it, in my bank in New York. But it appears the money had never been paid in by the people that owed it me. So there was I in a very nasty hole, an unmet cheque, and no money at all in Italy. I really had to escape here. It is an *absolute* secret that I am here, and it must be, till I can get this business settled. Of course I've

143

written to America about it. But as you see, I'm in a very nasty hole. That five francs I gave you for the driver was the last penny I had in the world: absolutely the last penny. I haven't even anything to buy a cigarette or a stamp." And he laughed chirpily, as if it were a joke. But he didn't really think it a joke. Nor was it a joke.

I had come with only two hundred lire in my pocket, as I was waiting to change some money at the bank. Of this two hundred I had one hundred left or one hundred and twenty-five. I should need a hundred to get home. I could only give M. the twenty-five, for the bottle of drink. He was rather crestfallen. But I didn't want to give him money this time—because he expected it.

However, we talked about his plans: how he was to earn something. He told me what he had written. And I cast over in my mind where he might get something published in London, wrote a couple of letters on his account, told him where I thought he had best send his material. There wasn't a great deal of hope, for his smaller journalistic articles seemed to me very self-conscious and poor. He had one about the monastery, which I thought he might sell because of the photographs.

144

That evening he first showed me the Legion manuscript. He had got it rather raggedly typed out. He had a typewriter, but he felt he ought to have somebody to do his typing for him, as he hated it and did unwillingly. That evening and when I went to bed and when I woke in the morning I read this manuscript. It did not seem very good—vague and diffuse where it shouldn't have been—lacking in sharp detail and definite event. And yet there was something in it that made me want it done properly. So we talked about it, and discussed it carefully, and he unwillingly promised to tackle it again. He was curious, always talking about his work, even always working, but never *properly* doing anything.

We walked out in the afternoon through the woods and across the rocky bit of moorland which covers most of the hill-top. We were going to the ruined convent which lies on the other brow of the monastery hill, abandoned and sad among the rocks and heath and thorny bushes. It was sunny and warm. A barefoot little boy was tending a cow and three goats and a pony, a barefoot little girl had five geese in charge. We came to the convent and looked in. The further part of the courtyard was still entire, the place was a sort of farm, two rooms occupied by a peasant-farmer. We climbed about the ruins. Some creature was crying—crying, crying, crying with a strange, inhuman persistence, leaving off and crying again. We listened and listened—the sharp, poignant crying. Almost it might have been a sharp voiced baby. We scrambled about, looking. And at last outside a little cave-like place found a blind black puppy crawling miserably on the floor, unable to walk, and crying incessantly. We put it back in the little cave-like shed, and went away. The place was deserted save for the crying puppy.

On the road outside, however, was a man, a peasant, just drawing up to the arched convent gateway with an ass under a load of brushwood. He was thin and black and dirty. He took off his hat, and we told him of the puppy. He said the bitch-mother had gone off with his son with the sheep. Yes, she had been gone all day. Yes, she would be back at sunset. No, the puppy had not drunk all day. Yes, the little beast cried, but the mother would come back to him.

They were the Old World peasants still about the monastery, with the hard, small bony heads and deep-lined faces and utterly blank minds, crying their speech as crows cry, and living their lives as lizards among the rocks, blindly going on with the little job in hand, the present moment cut off from all past and future, and having no idea and no sustained emotion, only that eternal will-to-live which makes a tortoise wake up once more in spring, and makes a grasshopper whistle on in the moonlight nights even of November. Only these peasants don't whistle much. The whistlers go to America. It is the hard, static, unhoping souls that persist in the old life. And still they stand back, as one passes them in the corridors of the great monastery, they press themselves back against the whitewashed walls of the still place, and drop their heads, as if some mystery were passing by, some God-mystery, the higher beings, which they must not look closely upon. So also this old peasant—he was not old, but deep-lined like a gnarled bough. He stood with his hat down in his hands as we spoke to him and answered short, hard, insentient answers, as a tree might speak.

"The monks keep their peasants humble," I said to M.

"Of course!" he said. "Don't you think they are quite right? Don't you think they should be humble?" And he bridled like a little turkey-cock on his hind legs.

"Well," I said, "if there's any occasion for humility, I do."

"Don't you think there is occasion?" he cried. "If there's one thing worse than another, it's this *equality* that has come into the world. Do you believe in it yourself?"

"No," I said. "I don't believe in equality. But the problem is, wherein does superiority lie?"

"Oh," chirped M. complacently. "It lies in many things. It lies in birth and upbringing and so on, but it is chiefly in *mind*. Don't you think? Of course I don't mean that the physical qualities aren't *charming*. They are, and nobody appreciates them more than I do. Some of the peasants are *beautiful* creatures, perfectly beautiful. But that passes. And the mind endures."

I did not answer. M. was not a man one talked far with. But I thought to myself, I *could* not accept M.'s superiority to the peasant. If I had really to live always under the same roof with either one of them, I would have chosen the peasant. Not because the peasant was wonderful and stored with mystic qualities. No, I don't give much for the wonderful mystic qualities in peasants. Money is their mystery of mysteries, absolutely. No, if I chose the peasant it would be for what he *lacked* rather than for what he had. He lacked that complacent mentality that M. was so proud of, he lacked all the trivial trash of glib talk and more glib thought, all the conceit of our shallow consciousness. For his mindlessness I would have chosen the peasant, and for his strong blood-presence. M. wearied me with his facility and his readiness to rush into speech, and for the exhaustive nature of his presence. As if he had no strong blood in him to sustain him, only this modern parasitic lymph which cries for sympathy all the time.

"Don't you think yourself that you are superior to that peasant?" he asked me, rather ironically. He half expected me to say no.

"Yes, I do," I replied. "But I think most middleclass, most so-called educated people are inferior to the peasant. I do that."

"Of course," said M. readily. "In their *hypocrisy*—" He was great against hypocrisy—especially the English sort.

"And if I think myself superior to the peasant, it is only that I feel myself like the growing tip, or one of the growing tips of the tree, and him like a piece of the hard, fixed tissue of the branch or trunk. We're part of the same tree: and it's the same sap," said I.

"Why, exactly! Exactly!" cried M. "Of course! The Church would teach the same doctrine. We are all one in Christ—but between our souls and our duties there are great differences."

It is terrible to be agreed with, especially by a man like M. All that one says, and means, turns to nothing.

"Yes," I persisted. "But it seems to me the so-called culture, education, the so-called leaders and leading-classes today, are only parasites—like a great flourishing bush of parasitic consciousness flourishing on top of the tree of life, and sapping it. The consciousness of today doesn't rise from the roots. It is just parasitic in the veins of life. And the middle and upper classes are just parasitic upon the body of life which still remains in the lower classes."

"What!" said M. acidly. "Do you believe in the democratic lower classes?"

"Not a bit," said I.

"I should think not, indeed!" he cried complacently.

"No, I don't believe the lower classes can ever make life whole again, till they *do* become humble, like the old peasants, and yield themselves to real leaders. But not to great negators like Lloyd George or Lenin or Briand."

"Of course! Of course!" he cried. "What you need is the Church in power again. The Church has a place for everybody."

"You don't think the Church belongs to the past?" I asked.

"Indeed I don't, or I shouldn't be here. No," he said sententiously, "the Church is eternal. It puts people in their proper place. It puts women down into *their* proper place, which is the first thing to be done—"

He had a great dislike of women, and was very acid about them. Not because of their sins, but because of their virtues: their economies, their philanthropies, their spiritualities. Oh, how he loathed women! He had been married, but the marriage had not been a success. He smarted still. Perhaps his wife had despised him, and he had not *quite* been able to defeat her contempt.

So he loathed women, and wished for a world of men. "They talk about love between men and women," he said. "Why, it's all a *fraud*. The woman is just taking all and giving nothing, and feeling sanctified about it. All she tries to do is thwart a man in whatever he is doing. No, I have found my life in my *friendships*. Physical relationships are very attractive, of course, and one tries to keep them as decent and all that as one can. But one knows they will pass and be finished. But one's *mental* friendships last forever."

"With me, on the contrary," said I. "If there is no profound blood-sympathy, I know the mental friendship is trash. If there is real, deep blood-response, I will stick to that if I have to betray all the mental sympathies I ever made, or all the lasting spiritual loves I ever felt."

He looked at me, and his face seemed to fall. Round the eyes he was yellow and tired and nervous. He watched me for some time.

"Oh!" he said, in a queer tone, rather cold. "Well, my experience has been the opposite."

We were silent for some time.

"And you," I said, "even if you do manage to do all your studies and enter the monastery, do you think you will be satisfied?"

"If I can be so fortunate, I do really," he said. "Do you doubt it?"

"Yes," I said. "Your nature is worldly, more worldly than mine. Yet I should die if I had to stay up here."

"Why?" he asked, curiously.

"Oh, I don't know. The past, the past. The beautiful, the wonderful past, it seems to prey on my heart, I can't bear it."

He watched me closely.

"Really!" he said stoutly. "Do you feel like that? But don't you think it is a far preferable life up here than down there? Don't you think the past is far preferable to the future, with all this *socialismo* and these *communisti* and so on?"

148

We were seated, in the sunny afternoon, on the wild hill-top high above the world. Across the stretch of pale, dry, standing thistles that peopled the waste ground, and beyond the rocks was the ruined convent. Rocks rose behind us, the summit. Away on the left were the woods which hid us from the great monastery. This was the mountain top, the last foothold of the old world. Below we could see the plain, the straight white road, straight as a thought, and the more flexible black railway with the railway station. There swarmed the *ferrovieri* like ants. There was democracy, industrialism, socialism, the red flag of the communists and the red, white, and green tricolour of the fascisti. That was another world. And how bitter, how barren a world! Barren, like the black cinder-track of the railway, with its two steel lines.

And here above, sitting with the little stretch of pale, dry thistles around us, our back to a warm rock, we were in the Middle Ages. Both worlds were agony to me. But here, on the mountain top, was worst: the past, the poignancy of the not-quite-dead past.

"I think one's got to go through with the life down there—get somewhere beyond it. One can't go back," I said to him.

"But do you call the monastery going back?" he said. "I don't. The peace, the eternity, the concern with things that matter. I consider it the happiest fate that could happen to me. Of course it means putting physical things aside. But when you've done that—why, it seems to me perfect."

"No," I said. "You're too worldly."

"But the monastery is worldly too. We're not Trappists. Why, the monastery is one of the centres of the world—one of the most active centres."

"Maybe. But that impersonal activity, with the blood suppressed and going sour—no, it's too late. It is too abstract—political maybe—"

"I'm sorry you think so," he said, rising. "I don't."

"Well," I said. "You'll never be a monk here, M. You see if you are."

"You don't think I shall?" he replied, turning to me. And there was a catch of relief in his voice. Really, the monastic state must have been like going to prison for him.

"You haven't a vocation," I said.

"I may not *seem* to have, but I hope I actually have."

"You haven't."

"Of course, if you're so sure," he laughed, putting his hand on my arm.

He seemed to understand so much, round about the questions that   *149*
trouble one deepest. But the quick of the question he never felt. He had no real middle, no real centre bit to him. Yet, round and round about all the questions, he was so intelligent and sensitive.

We went slowly back. The peaks of those Italian mountains in the sunset, the extinguishing twinkle of the plain away below, as the sun declined and grew yellow; the intensely powerful medieval spirit lingering on this wild hill summit, all the wonder of the medieval past; and then the huge mossy stones in the wintry wood that was once a sacred grove; the ancient path through the wood that led from temple to temple on the hill summit, before Christ was born; and then the great Cyclopean wall one passes at the bend of the road, built even before the pagan temples; all this overcame me so powerfully this afternoon, that I was almost speechless. That hill-top must have been one of man's intensely sacred places for three thousand years. And men die generation after generation, races die, but the new cult finds root in the old sacred place, and the quick spot of earth dies very slowly. Yet at last it too dies. But this quick spot is still not quite dead. The great monastery couchant there, half empty, but also not quite dead. And M. and I walking across as the sun set yellow and the cold of the snow came into the air, back home to the monastery! And I feeling as if my heart had once more broken— I don't know why. And he feeling his fear of life, that haunted him, and his fear of his own self and its consequences, that never left him for long. And he seemed to walk close to me, very close. And we had neither of us anything more to say.

Don Bernardo was looking for us as we came up under the archway, he hatless in the cold evening, his black dress swinging voluminous. There were letters for M. There was a small cheque for him from America—about fifty dollars—from some newspaper in the Middle West that had printed one of his articles. He had to talk with Don Bernardo about this.

I decided to go back the next day. I could not stay any longer. M. was very disappointed, and begged me to remain. "I thought you would stay a week at least," he said. "Do stay over Sunday. Oh, do!" But I couldn't, I didn't want to. I could see that his days were a torture to him—the long, cold days in that vast quiet building, with the strange and exhausting silence in the air, and the sense of the past preying on one, and the sense of the silent, suppressed scheming struggle of life going on still in the sacred place.

It was a cloudy morning. In the green courtyard the big Don Anselmo had just caught the little Don Lorenzo round the waist and was swinging him over a bush, like lads before school. The prior was just hurrying somewhere, following his long fine nose. He bade me good-bye; pleasant, warm, jolly, with a touch of wistfulness in his deafness. I parted with real regret from Don Bernardo.

M. was coming with me down the hill—not down the carriage road, but down the wide old paved path that swoops so wonderfully from the top of the hill to the bottom. It feels thousands of years old. M. was quiet and friendly. We met Don Vincenzo, he who has the care of the land and crops, coming slowly, slowly uphill in his black cassock, treading slowly in his great thick boots. He was reading a little book. He saluted us as we passed. Lower down a strapping girl was watching three merino sheep among the bushes. One sheep came on its exquisite slender legs to smell of me, with that insatiable curiosity of a *pecora*. Her nose was silken and elegant as she reached it to sniff at me, and the yearning, wondering, inquisitive look in her eyes made me realize that the Lamb of God must have been such a sheep as this.

M. was miserable at my going. Not so much at my going, as at being left alone up there. We came to the foot of the hill, on to the town highroad. So we went into a little cave of a wine-kitchen to drink a glass of wine. M.

chatted a little with the young woman. He chatted with everybody. She eyed us closely, and asked if we were from the monastery. We said we were. She seemed to have a little lurking antagonism round her nose, at the mention of the monastery. M. paid for the wine—a franc. So we went out on the highroad, to part.

"Look," I said. "I can only give you twenty lire, because I shall need the rest for the journey—"

But he wouldn't take them. He looked at me wistfully. Then I went on down to the station, he turned away uphill. It was market in the town, and there were clusters of bullocks, and women cooking a little meal at a brazier under the trees, and goods spread out on the floor to sell, and sacks of beans and corn standing open, clustered round the trunks of the mulberry trees, and wagons with their shafts on the ground. The old peasants in their brown home-spun frieze and skin sandals were watching for the world. And there again was the Middle Ages.

It began to rain, however. Suddenly it began to pour with rain, and my coat was wet through, and my trouser-legs. The train from Rome was late—I hoped not very late, or I should miss the boat. She came at last, and was full. I had to stand in the corridor. Then the man came to say dinner was served, so I luckily got a place and had my meal too. Sitting there in the dining-car, among the fat Neapolitans eating their macaroni, with the big glass windows steamed opaque and the rain beating outside, I let myself be carried away, away from the monastery, away from M., away from everything.

At Naples there was a bit of sunshine again, and I had time to go on foot to the Immacolatella, where the little steamer lay. There on the steamer I sat in a bit of sunshine, and felt that again the world had come to an end for me, and again my heart was broken. The steamer seemed to be making its way away from the old world, that had come to another end in me.

It was after this I decided to go to Sicily. In February, only a few days after my return from the monastery, I was on the steamer for Palermo, and at dawn looking out on the wonderful coast of Sicily. Sicily, tall, forever rising to her gem-like summits, all golden in dawn, and always glamorous, always hovering as if inaccessible, and yet so near, so distinct. Sicily, unknown to me, and amethystine-glamorous in the Mediterranean dawn: like the dawn of our day, the wonder-morning of our epoch.

I had various letters from M. He had told me to go to Girgenti. But I arrived in Girgenti when there was a strike of sulphur-miners, and they threw stones. So I did not want to live in Girgenti. M. hated Taormina—he had been everywhere, tried everywhere, and was not, I found, in any good odour in most places. He wrote, however, saying he hoped I would like it. And later he sent the Legion manuscript. I thought it was good, and told him so. It was offered to publishers in London, but rejected.

In early April I went with my wife to Syracuse for a few days: lovely, lovely days, with the purple anemones blowing in the Sicilian fields, and Adonisblood red on the little ledges, and the corn rising strong and green in the magical, malarial places, and Etna flowing now to the northward, still with her crown of snow. The lovely, lovely journey from Catania to Syracuse, in spring, winding round the blueness of that sea, where the tall pink asphodel was dying, and the yellow asphodel like a lily showing her silk. Lovely, lovely Sicily, the dawnplace, Europe's dawn, with Odysseus pushing his ship out of the shadows into the blue. Whatever had died for me, Sicily had then not died; dawn-lovely Sicily, and the Ionian Sea.

We came back, and the world was lovely: our own house above the almond trees, and the sea in the cove below. Calabria glimmering like a changing opal away to the left, across the blue, bright straits, and all the great blueness of the lovely dawn-sea in front, where the sun rose with a splendour like trumpets every morning, and me rejoicing like a madness in this dawn, day-dawn, life-dawn, the dawn which is Greece, which is me.

Well, into this lyricism suddenly crept the serpent. It was a lovely morning, still early. I heard a noise on the stairs from the lower terrace, and went to look. M. on the stairs, looking up at me with a frightened face.

"Why!" I said. "Is it you?"

"Yes," he replied. "A terrible thing has happened."

He waited on the stairs, and I went down. Rather unwillingly, because I detest terrible things, and the people to whom they happen. So we leaned on the creeper-covered rail of the terrace, under festoons of creamy bignonia flowers, and looked at the pale blue, ethereal sea.

"What terrible thing!" said I.

"When did you get back?" said he.

"Last evening."

"Oh! I came before. The *contadini* said they thought you would come yesterday evening. I've been here several days."

"Where are you staying?"

"At the San Domenico."

The San Domenico being then the most expensive hotel here, I thought he must have money. But I knew he wanted something of me.

"And are you staying some time?"

He paused a moment, and looked round cautiously.

"Is your wife there?" he asked, sotto voce.

"Yes, she's upstairs."

"Is there anyone who can hear?"

"No—only old Grazia down below, and she can't understand anyhow."

"Well," he said, stammering. "Let me tell you what's happened. I had to escape from the monastery. Don Bernardo had a telephone message from the town below, that the carabinieri were looking for an Americano—my name—Of course you can guess how I felt, up there! Awful! Well—! I had to fly at a moment's notice. I just put two shirts in a handbag and went. I slipped down a path—or rather, it isn't a path—down the back of the hill. Ten minutes after Don Bernardo had the message I was running down the hill."

"But what did they want you for?" I asked dismayed.

"Well," he faltered. "I told you about the cheque at Anzio, didn't I? Well, it seems the hotel people applied to the police. Anyhow," he added hastily, "I couldn't let myself be arrested up there, could I? So awful for the monastery!"

"Did they know then that you were in trouble?" I asked.

"Don Bernardo knew I had no money," he said. "Of course he had to know. Yes—he knew I was in *difficulty*. But, of course, he didn't know—well—*everything*." He laughed a little, comical laugh over the *everything*, as if he was just a little bit naughtily proud of it: most ruefully also.

"No," he continued, "that's what I'm most afraid of—that they'll find out everything at the monastery. Of course it's *dreadful*—the Americano, been staying there for months, and everything so nice and—well, you know how they are, they imagine every American is a millionaire, if not a multi-millionaire. And suddenly to be wanted by the police! Of course it's *dreadful!* Anything rather than a scandal at the monastery—anything. Oh, how awful it was! I can tell you, in that quarter of an hour, I sweated blood. Don Bernardo lent me two hundred lire of the monastery money—which he'd no business to do. And I escaped down the back of the hill, I walked to the next station up the line, and took the next train—the slow train—a few stations up towards Rome. And there I changed and caught the *diretto* for

Sicily. I came straight to you—Of course I was in *agony:* imagine it! I spent most of the time as far as Naples in the lavatory." He laughed his little jerky laugh.

"What class did you travel?"

"Second. All through the night. I arrived more dead than alive, not having had a meal for two days—only some sandwich stuff I bought on the platform."

"When did you come then?"

"I arrived on Saturday evening. I came out here on Sunday morning, and they told me you were away. Of course, imagine what it's like! I'm in torture every minute, in torture, of course. Why, just imagine!" And he laughed his little laugh.

"But how much money have you got?"

"Oh—I've just got twenty-five francs and five soldi." He laughed as if it was rather a naughty joke.

"But," I said, "If you've got no money, why do you go to the San Domenico? How much do you pay there?"

"Fifty lire a day. Of course it's *ruinous*—"

"But at the Bristol you only pay twenty-five—and at Fichera's only twenty."

"Yes, I know you do," he said. "But I stayed at the Bristol once, and I loathed the place. Such an offensive manager. And I couldn't touch the food at Fichera's."

"But who's going to pay for the San Domenico, then?" I asked.

"Well, I thought," he said, "you know all those manuscripts of mine? Well, you think they're some good, don't you? Well, I thought if I made them over to you, and you did what you could with them and just kept me going till I can get a new start—or till I can get away—"

I looked across the sea: the lovely morning-blue sea towards Greece.

"Where do you want to get away to?" I said.

"To Egypt. I know a man in Alexandria who owns newspapers there. I'm sure if I could get over there he'd give me an editorship or something. And of course money will come. I've written to—, who was my *greatest friend*, in London. He will send me something—"

"And what else do you expect?"

"Oh, my article on the monastery was accepted by *Land and Water*—thanks to you and your kindness, of course. I thought if I might stay very quietly with you, for a time, and write some things I'm wanting to do, and collect a little money—and then get away to Egypt—"

He looked up into my face, as if he were trying all he could on me. First thing I knew was that I could not have him in the house with me; and even if I could have done it, my wife never could.

"You've got a lovely place here, perfectly beautiful," he said. "Of course, if it had to be Taormina, you've chosen far the best place here. I like this side so much better than the Etna side. Etna always there and people raving about it gets on my nerves. And a *charming* house, *charming*."

He looked round the loggia and along the other terrace.

"Is it all yours?" he said.

"We don't use the ground floor. Come in here."

So we went into the *salotta*.

"Oh, what a beautiful room," he cried. "But perfectly palatial. Charming! Charming! *Much* the nicest house in Taormina."

"No," I said, "as a house it isn't very grand, though I like it for myself. It's just what I want. And I love the situation. But I'll go and tell my wife you are here."

"Will you?" he said, bridling nervously. "Of course I've never met your wife." And he laughed the nervous, naughty, joky little laugh.

I left him, and ran upstairs to the kitchen. There was my wife, with wide eyes. She had been listening to catch the conversation. But M.'s voice was too hushed.

"M.!" said I softly. "The carabinieri wanted to arrest him at the monastery, so he has escaped here, and wants me to be responsible for him."

"Arrest him, what for?"

"Debts, I suppose. Will you come down and speak to him?"

M. of course was very charming with my wife. He kissed her hand humbly, in the correct German fashion, and spoke with an air of reverence that infallibly gets a woman.

"Such a beautiful place you have here," he said, glancing through the open doors of the room, at the sea beyond. "So clever of you to find it."

"Lawrence found it," said she. "Well, and you are in all kinds of difficulty!"

"Yes, isn't it terrible!" he said, laughing as if it were a joke—rather a wry joke. "I felt dreadful at the monastery. So dreadful for them, if there was any sort of scandal. And after I'd been so well received there—and so much the Signor Americano—Dreadful, don't you think?" He laughed again, like a naughty boy.

We had an engagement to lunch that morning. My wife was dressed, so I went to get ready. Then we told M. we must go out, and he accompanied us to the village. I gave him just the hundred francs I had in my pocket, and he said, could he come and see me that evening? I asked him to come next morning.

"You're so awfully kind," he said, simpering a little.

But by this time I wasn't feeling kind.

"He's quite nice," said my wife. "But he's rather an impossible little person. And you'll see, he'll be a nuisance. Whatever do you pick up such dreadful people for?"

"Nay," I said. "You can't accuse me of picking up dreadful people. He's the first. And even he isn't dreadful."

The next morning came a letter from Don Bernardo addressed to me, but only enclosing a letter to M. So he was using my address. At ten o'clock he punctually appeared, slipping in as if to avoid notice. My wife would not see him, so I took him out on the terrace again.

"Isn't it beautiful here!" he said. "Oh, so beautiful! If only I had my peace of mind. Of course I sweat blood every time anybody comes through the door. You are splendidly private out here."

"Yes," I said. "But, M., there isn't a room for you in the house. There isn't a spare room anyway. You'd better think of getting something cheaper in the village."

"But what can I get?" he snapped.

That rather took my breath away. Myself, I had never been near the San Domenico Hotel. I knew I simply could not afford it.

"What made you go to the San Domenico in the first place?" I said. "The most expensive hotel in the place!"

"Oh, I'd stayed there for two months, and they knew me, and I knew they'd ask no questions. I knew they wouldn't ask for a deposit or anything."

"But nobody dreams of asking for a deposit," I said.

"Anyhow, I shan't take my meals there. I shall just take coffee in the morning. I've had to eat there so far, because I was starved to death, and had no money to go out. But I had two meals in that little restaurant yesterday; disgusting food."

"And how much did that cost?"

"Oh, fourteen francs and fifteen francs, with a quarter of wine—and such a poor meal!"

Now I was annoyed, knowing that I myself should have bought bread and cheese for one franc, and eaten it in my room. But also I realized that the modern creed says, if you sponge, sponge thoroughly; and also that every man has a "right to live," and that if he can manage to live well, no matter at whose expense, all credit to him. This is the kind of talk one accepts in one's slipshod moments; now it was actually tried on me, I didn't like it at all.

"But who's going to pay your bill at the San Domenico?" I said.

"I thought you'd advance me the money on those manuscripts."

"It's no good talking about the money on the manuscripts," I said. "I should have to give it to you. And as a matter of fact, I've got just sixty pounds in the bank in England, and about fifteen hundred lire here. My wife and I have got to live on that. We don't spend as much in a week as you spend in three days at the San Domenico. It's no good your thinking I can advance money on the manuscripts. I can't. If I was rich, I'd give you money. But I've got no money, and never have had any. Have you nobody you can go to?"

"I'm waiting to hear from—. When I go back into the village, I'll telegraph to him," replied M., a little crestfallen. "Of course I'm in torture night and day, or I wouldn't appeal to you like this. I know it's unpleasant for you "—he put his hand on my arm and looked up beseechingly—"but what am I to do?"

"You must get out of the San Domenico," I said. "That's the first thing."

"Yes," he said, a little piqued now. "I know it is. I'm going to ask Pancrazio Melenga to let me have a room in his house. He knows me quite well—he's an awfully nice fellow. He'll do *anything* for me—*anything*. I was just going there yesterday afternoon when you were coming from Timeo. He was out, so I left word with his wife, who is a charming little person. If he has a room to spare, I know he will let me have it. And he's a *splendid* cook—splendid. By far the nicest food in Taormina."

"Well," I said. "If you settle with Melenga, I will pay your bill at the San Domenico, but I can't do any more. I simply can't."

"But what am I to *do?*" he snapped.

"I don't know," I said. "You must think."

"I came here," he said, "thinking you would help me. What am I to do, if you won't? I shouldn't have come to Taormina at all, save for you. Don't be unkind to me—don't speak so coldly to me." He put his hand on my arm, and looked up at me with tears swimming in his eyes. Then he turned aside his face, overcome with tears. I looked away at the Ionian Sea, feeling my blood turn to ice and the sea go black. I loathe scenes such as this.

"Did you telegraph to—?" I said.

"Yes. I have no answer yet. I hope you don't mind—I gave your address for a reply."

"Oh," I said. "There's a letter for you from Don Bernardo."

He went pale. I was angry at his having used my address in this manner.

"Nothing further has happened at the monastery," he said. "They rang up from the *questura*, from the police station, and Don Bernardo answered that the Americano had left for Rome. Of course I did take the train for Rome. And Don Bernardo wanted me to go to Rome. He advised me to do so. I didn't tell him I was here till I had got here. He thought I should have had more resources in Rome, and of course I should. I should certainly have gone there, if it hadn't been for *you here*—"

Well, I was getting tired and angry. I would not give him any more money at the moment. I promised if he would leave the hotel I would pay his bill, but he must leave it at once. He went off to settle with Melenga. He asked again if he could come in the afternoon. I said I was going out.

He came, nevertheless, while I was out. This time my wife found him on the stairs. She was for hating him, of course. So she stood immovable on the top stair, and he stood two stairs lower, and he kissed her hand in utter humility. And he pleaded with her, and as he looked up to her on the stairs the tears ran down his face and he trembled with distress. And her spine crept up and down with distaste and discomfort. But he broke into a few phrases of touching German, and I know he broke down her reserve and she promised him all he wanted. This part she would never confess, though. Only she was shivering with revulsion and excitement and even a sense of power, when I came home.

That was why M. appeared more impertinent than ever, next morning. He had arranged to go to Melenga's house the following day, and to pay ten francs a day for his room, his meals extra. So that was something. He made a long tale about not eating any of his meals in the hotel now, but pretending he was invited out, and eating in the little restaurants where the food was so bad. And he had now only fifteen lire left in his pocket. But I was cold, and wouldn't give him any more. I said I would give him money next day, for his bill.

He had now another request, and a new tone.

"Won't you do *one more* thing for me?" he said. "Oh, do! Do do this one thing for me. I want you to go to the monastery and bring away my important papers and some clothes and my important trinkets. I have made a list of the things here—and where you'll find them in my writing-table and in the chest of drawers. I don't think you'll have any trouble. Don Bernardo has the keys. He will open everything for you. And I beg you, *in the name of God*, don't let anybody else see the things. Not even Don Bernardo. Don't, whatever you do, let him see the papers and manuscripts you are bringing. If he sees them, there's an end to me at the monastery. I can *never* go back there. I am ruined in their eyes for ever. As it is, although Don Bernardo is the best person in the world and my dearest friend, still— you know what people are, especially monks. A little curious, don't you know, a little inquisitive. Well, let us hope for the best as far as that goes. But you will do this for me, won't you? I shall be so eternally grateful."

159

Now a journey to the monastery meant a terrible twenty hours in the train each way—all that awful journey through Calabria to Naples and northwards. It meant mixing myself up in this man's affairs. It meant appearing as his accomplice at the monastery. It meant travelling with all his "compromising" papers and his valuables. And all this time, I never knew what mischiefs he had really been up to, and I didn't trust him, not for one single second. He would tell me nothing save that Anzio hotel cheque. I knew that wasn't all, by any means. So I mistrusted him. And with a feeling of utter mistrust goes a feeling of contempt and dislike—And finally, it would have cost me at least ten pounds sterling, which I simply did not want to spend in waste.

"I don't want to do that," I said.

"Why not?" he asked, sharp, looking green. He had planned it all out.

"No, I don't want to."

"Oh, but I *can't* remain here as I am. I've got no *clothes*—I've got nothing to *wear*. I *must* have my things from the monastery. What can I do? What can I do? I came to you, if it hadn't been for you I should have gone to Rome. I came to you—Oh, yes, you *will* go. You *will* go, won't you? You *will* go to the monastery for my things?" And again he put his hand on my arm, and the tears began to fall from his upturned eyes. I turned my head aside. Never had the Ionian Sea looked so sickening to me.

"I don't *want* to," said I.

"But you *will!* You will! You *will* go to the monastery for me, won't you? Everything else is no good if you won't. I've got nothing to wear. I haven't got my manuscripts to work on, I can't do the things I am doing. Here I live in a sweat of anxiety. I try to work, and I can't settle. I can't do anything. It's dreadful. I shan't have a minute's peace till I have got those things from the monastery, till I know they can't get at my private papers. You will do this for me! You will, won't you? Please do! Oh, please do!" And again tears.

And I with my bowels full of bitterness, loathing the thought of that journey there and back, on such an errand. Yet not quite sure that I ought to refuse. And he pleaded and struggled, and tried to bully me with tears and entreaty and reproach, to do his will. And I couldn't quite refuse. But neither could I agree.

At last I said:

"I don't want to go, and I tell you. I won't promise to go. And I won't say that I will not go. I won't say until tomorrow. Tomorrow I will tell you. Don't come to the house. I will be in the Corso at ten o'clock."

"I didn't doubt for a minute you would do this for me," he said. "Otherwise I should never have come to Taormina." As if he had done me an honour in coming to Taormina; and as if I had betrayed *him*.

"Well," I said. "If you make these messes you'll have to get out of them yourself. I don't know why you are *in* such a mess."

"Any man may make a mistake," he said sharply, as if correcting me.

"Yes, a *mistake!*" said I. "If it's a question of a mistake."

So once more he went, humbly, beseechingly, and yet, one could not help but feel, with all that terrible insolence of the humble. It is the humble, the wistful, the would-be loving souls today who bully us with their charity-demanding insolence. They just make up their minds, these needful sympathetic souls, that one is there to do their will. Very good.

I decided in the day I would *not* go. Without reasoning it out, I knew I *really* didn't want to go. I plainly didn't want it. So I wouldn't go.

The morning came again hot and lovely. I set off to the village. But there was M. watching for me on the path beyond the valley. He came forward and took my hand warmly, clingingly. I turned back, to remain in the country. We talked for a minute of his leaving the hotel—he was going that afternoon, he had asked for his bill. But he was waiting for the other answer.

"And I have decided," I said, "I won't go to the monastery."

"You won't." He looked at me. I saw how yellow he was round the eyes, and yellow under his reddish skin.

"No," I said.

And it was final. He knew it. We went some way in silence. I turned in at the garden gate. It was a lovely, lovely morning of hot sun. Butterflies were flapping over the rosemary hedges and over a few little red poppies, the young vines smelt sweet in flower, very sweet, the corn was tall and green, and there were still some wild, rose-red gladiolus flowers among the watery green of the wheat. M. had accepted my refusal. I expected him to be angry. But no, he seemed quieter, wistfuller, and he seemed almost to love me for having refused him. I stood at a bend in the path. The sea was heavenly blue, rising up beyond the vines and olive leaves, lustrous pale lacquer blue as only the Ionian Sea can be. Away at the brook below the women were washing, and one could hear the chock-chock-chock of linen beating against the stones. I felt M. then an intolerable weight and like a clot of dirt over everything.

"May I come in?" he said to me.

"No," I said. "Don't come to the house. My wife doesn't want it."

Even that he accepted without any offence, and seemed only to like me better for it. That was a puzzle to me. I told him I would leave a letter and a cheque for him at the bank in the Corso that afternoon.

I did so, writing a cheque for a few pounds, enough to cover his bill and leave a hundred lire or so over, and a letter to say I could *not* do any more, and I didn't want to see him any more.

So, there was an end of it for a moment. Yet I felt him looming in the village, waiting. I had rashly said I would go to tea with him to the villa of one of the Englishmen resident here, whose acquaintance I had not made. Alas, M. kept me to the promise. As I came home he appealed to me again. He was rather insolent. What good to him, he said, were the few pounds I had given him? He had a hundred and fifty lire left. What good was that?

161

I realized it really was not a solution, and said nothing. Then he spoke of his plans for getting to Egypt. The fare, he had found out, was thirty-five pounds. And where were thirty-five pounds coming from? Not from me.

I spent a week avoiding him, wondering what on earth the poor devil was doing, and yet *determined* he should not be a parasite on me. If I could have given him fifty pounds and sent him to Egypt to be a parasite on somebody else, I would have done so. Which is what we call charity. However, I couldn't.

My wife chafed, crying: "What have you done! We shall have him on our hands all our life. We can't let him starve. It is degrading, degrading, to have him hanging on to us."

"Yes," I said. "He must starve or work or something. I am not God who is responsible for him."

M. was determined not to lose his status as a gentleman. In a way I sympathized with him. He would never be out at elbows. That is your modern rogue. He will not degenerate outwardly. Certain standards of a gentleman he *would* keep up: he would be well-dressed, he would be lavish with borrowed money, he would be as far as possible honourable in his small transactions of daily life. Well, very good. I sympathized with him to a certain degree. If he could find his own way out, well and good. Myself, I was not his way out.

Ten days passed. It was hot and I was going about the terrace in pyjamas and a big old straw hat, when, suddenly, a Sicilian, handsome, in the prime of life, and in his best black suit, smiling at me and taking off his hat!

And could he speak to me? I threw away my straw hat, and we went into the *salotta*. He handed me a note.

"Il Signor M. mi ha data questa lettera per Lei!" he began, and I knew what was coming. Melenga had been a waiter in good hotels, had saved money, built himself a fine house which he let to foreigners. He was a pleasant fellow, and at his best now, because he was in a rage. I must repeat M.'s letter from memory: "Dear Lawrence, would you do me another kindness? *Land and Water* sent a cheque for seven guineas for the article on the monastery, and Don Bernardo forwarded this to me under Melenga's name. But unfortunately he made a mistake, and put Orazio instead of Pancrazio, so the postoffice would not deliver the letter, and have returned it to the monastery. This morning Melenga insulted me, and I cannot stay

in his house another minute. Will you be so kind as to advance me these seven guineas? I shall leave Taormina at once, for Malta."

I asked Melenga what had happened, and read him the letter. He was handsome in his rage, lifting his brows and suddenly smiling.

"*Ma senta, signore!* Signor M. has been in my house for ten days, and lived well, and eaten well, and drunk well, and I have not seen a single penny of his money. I go out in the morning and buy all the things, all he wants, and my wife cooks it, and he is very pleased, very pleased, has never eaten such good food in his life, and everything is splendid, splendid. And he never pays a penny. Not a penny. Says he is waiting for money from England, from America, from India. But the money never comes. And I am a poor man, signore, I have a wife and child to keep. I have already spent three hundred lira for this Signor M., and I never see a penny of it back. And he says the money is coming, it is coming. But when? He never says he has got no money. He says he is expecting. Tomorrow—always tomorrow. It will come tonight, it will come tomorrow. This makes me in a rage. Till at last this morning I said to him I would bring nothing in, and he shouldn't have not so much as a drop of coffee in my house until he paid for it. It displeases me, signore, to say such a thing. I have known Signor M. for many years, and he has always had money, and always been pleasant, *molto bravo,* and also generous with his money. *Si, lo so!* And my wife, *poverina,* she cries and says if the man has no money he must eat. But he doesn't say he has no money. He says always it is coming, it is coming, today, tomorrow, today, tomorrow. *E non viene mai niente.* And this enrages me, signore. So I said that to him this morning. And he said he wouldn't stay in my house, and that I had insulted him, and he sends me this letter to you, signore, and says you will send him the money. *Ecco come!*"

163

Between his rage he smiled at me. One thing, however, I could see: he was not going to lose his money, M. or no M.

"Is it true that a letter came which the post would not deliver?" I asked him.

"*Si, signore, è vero.* It came yesterday, addressed to me. And why, signore, why do his letters come addressed in my name? Why? Unless he has done something—?"

He looked at me inquiringly. I felt already mixed up in shady affairs.

"Yes," I said, "there is something. But I don't know exactly what. I don't ask, because I don't want to know in these affairs. It is better not to know."

"*Già! Già! Molto meglio, signore.* There will be something. There will be something happened that he had to escape from that monastery. And it will be some affair of the police."

"Yes, I think so," said I. "Money and the police. Probably debts. I don't ask. He is only an acquaintance of mine, not a friend."

"Sure it will be an affair of the police," he said with a grimace. "If not, why does he use my name! Why don't his letters come in his own name? Do you believe, signore, that he has any money? Do you think this money will come?"

"I'm sure he's *got* no money," I said. "Whether anybody will send him any, I don't know."

The man watched me attentively.

"He's got nothing?" he said.

"No. At present he's got nothing."

Then Pancrazio exploded on the sofa.

"*Allora!* Well, then! Well, then, why does he come to my house, why does he come and take a room in my house, and ask me to buy food, good food as for a gentleman who can pay, and a flask of wine, and everything, if he has no money? If he has no money, why does he come to Taormina? It is many years that he has been in Italy—ten years, fifteen years. And he has no money. Where has he had his money from before? Where?"

"From his writing, I suppose."

"Well, then why doesn't he get money for his writing now? He writes. He writes, he works, he says it is for the big newspapers."

"It is difficult to sell things."

"Heh! Then why doesn't he live on what he made before? He hasn't a soldo. He hasn't a penny—But how! How did he pay his bill at the San Domenico?"

"I had to lend him money for that. He really hadn't a penny."

"You! You! Well, then, he has been in Italy all these years. How is it he has nobody that he can ask for a hundred lire or two? Why does he come to you? Why? Why has he nobody in Rome, in Florence, anywhere?"

"I wonder that myself."

"*Sicuro!* He's been all these years here. And why doesn't he speak proper Italian? After all these years, and speaks all upside-down, it isn't Italian, an ugly confusion. Why? Why? He passes for a signore, for a man of education. And he comes to take the bread out of my mouth. And I have a wife and child, I am a poor man, I have nothing to eat myself if everything goes to a mezzo-signore like him. Nothing! He owes me now three hundred lire. But he will not leave my house, he will not leave Taormina till he has paid. I will go to the *prefettura*, I will go to the *questura*, to the police. I will not be swindled by such a mezzo-signore. What does he want to do? If he has no money, what does he want to do?"

"To go to Egypt, where he says he can earn some," I replied briefly. But I was feeling bitter in the mouth. When the man called M. a mezzo-signore, a half-gentleman, it was so true. And at the same time it was so cruel, and so rude. And Melenga—there I sat in my pyjamas and sandals—probably he would be calling me also a mezzo-signore, or a quarto signore even. He was a Sicilian who feels he is being done out of his money—and that is saying everything.

"To Egypt! And who will pay for him to go? Who will give him money? But he must pay me first. He must pay me first."

"He says," I said, "that in the letter which went back to the monastery there was a cheque for seven pounds—some six hundred lire—and he asks me to send him this money, and when the letter is returned again I shall have the cheque that is in it."

Melenga watched me.

"Six hundred lire—" he said.

"Yes."

"Oh, well, then. If he pays me, he can stay—" he said; he almost added: "till the six hundred is finished." But he left it unspoken.

"But am I going to send the money? Am I sure that what he says is true?"

"I think it is true. I think it is true," said he. "The letter *did* come."

I thought for a while.

"First," I said, "I will write and ask him if it is quite true, and to give me a guarantee."

"Very well," said Melenga.

I wrote to M., saying that if he could assure me that what he said about the seven guineas was quite correct, and if he would give me a note to the editor of *Land and Water*, saying that the cheque was to be paid to me, I would send the seven guineas.

Melenga was back in another half-hour. He brought a note which began: "Dear Lawrence, I seem to be living in an atmosphere of suspicion.

First Melenga this morning, and now you—" Those are the exact opening words. He went on to say that of course his word was true, and he enclosed a note to the editor, saying the seven guineas were to be transferred to me. He asked me please to send the money, as he could not stay another night at Melenga's house, but would leave for Catania, where, by the sale of some trinkets, he hoped to make some money and to see once more about a passage to Egypt. He had been to Catania once already—travelling *third class!*—but had failed to find any cargo boat that would take him to Alexandria. He would get away now to Malta. His things were being sent down to Syracuse from the monastery.

I wrote and said I hoped he would get safely away, and enclosed the cheque.

"This will be for six hundred lire," said Melenga.

"Yes," said I.

"*Eh, va bene!* If he pays the three hundred lire, he can stop in my house for thirty lire a day."

"He says he won't sleep in your house again."

"*Ma!* Let us see. If he likes to stay. He has always been a *bravo signore.* I have always liked him quite well. If he wishes to stay and pay me thirty lire a day—"

The man smiled at me rather greenly.

"I'm afraid he is offended," said I.

"*Eh, va bene! Ma senta, signore.* When he was here before—you know I have this house of mine to let. And you know the English signorina goes away in the summer. Oh, very well. Says M., he writes for a newspaper, he owns a newspaper, I don't know what, in Rome. He will put in an advertisement advertising my villa. And so I shall get somebody to take it. Very well. And he put in the advertisement. He sent me the paper and I saw it there. But no one came to take my villa. *Va bene!* But after a year, in the January, that is, came a bill for me for twenty-two lire to pay for it. Yes, I had to pay the twenty-two lire, for nothing—for the advertisement which Signor M. put in the paper."

"Bah!" said I.

He shook hands with me and left. The next day he came after me in the street, and said that M. had departed the previous evening for Catania. As a matter of fact the post brought me a note of thanks from Catania. M. was never indecent, and one could never dismiss him just as a scoundrel.

He was not. He was one of these modern parasites who just assume their right to live and live well, leaving the payment to anybody who can, will, or must pay. The end is inevitably swindling.

There came also a letter from Rome, addressed to me. I opened it unthinking. It was for M., from an Italian lawyer, stating that inquiry had been made about the writ against M., and that it was for *qualche affare di truffa*, some affair of swindling: that the lawyer had seen this, that, and the other person, but nothing could be done. He regretted, etc., etc. I forwarded this letter to M. at Syracuse, and hoped to God it was ended. Ah, I breathed free now he had gone.

But, no. A friend who was with us dearly wanted to go to Malta. It is only about eighteen hours' journey from Taormina—easier than going to Naples. So our friend invited us to take the trip with her, as her guests. This was rather jolly. I calculated that M., who had been gone a week or so, would easily have got to Malta. I had had a friendly letter from him from Syracuse, thanking me for the one I had forwarded, and enclosing an IOU for the various sums of money he had had.

So, on a hot, hot Thursday, we were sitting in the train again running south, the four and a half hours' journey to Syracuse. And M. dwindled now into the past. If we should see him! But no, it was impossible. After all the wretchedness of that affair we were in holiday spirits.

The train ran into Syracuse station. We sat on, to go the few yards further into the port. A tout climbed on the foot-board: Were we going to Malta? Well, we couldn't. There was a strike of the steamers, we couldn't go. When would the steamer go? Who knows? Perhaps tomorrow.

We got down crestfallen. What should we do? There stood the express train about to start off back northwards. We could be home again that evening. But, no, it would be too much of a fiasco. We let the train go, and trailed off into the town, to the Grand Hotel, which is an old Italian place just opposite the port. It is rather a dreary hotel—and many bloodstains of squashed mosquitoes on the bedroom walls. Ah, vile mosquitoes!

However, nothing to be done. Syracuse port is fascinating too, a tiny port with the little Sicilian ships having the slanting eyes painted on the prow, to see the way, and a coal boat from Cardiff, and one American and two Scandinavian steamers—no more. But there were two torpedo boats in the harbour, and it was like a *festa*, a strange, lousy *festa*.

Beautiful the round harbour where the Athenian ships came. And wonderful, beyond, the long sinuous sky-line of the long flat-topped table-land hills which run along the southern coast, so different from the peaky, pointed, bunched effect of many-tipped Sicily in the north. The sun went down behind that lovely, sinuous sky-line, the harbour water was gold and red, the people promenaded in thick streams under the pomegranate trees and hibiscus trees. Arabs in white burnouses and fat Turks in red fezzes and black alpaca long coats strolled also—waiting for the steamer.

Next day it was very hot. We went to the consul and the steamer agency. There was real hope that the brute of a steamer might actually sail that night. So we stayed on, and wandered round the town on the island, the old solid town, and sat in the church looking at the grand Greek columns embedded there in the walls.

When I came in to lunch, the porter said there was a letter for me. Impossible! said I. But he brought me a note. Yes. M.! He was staying at the other hotel along the front. 'Dear Lawrence, I saw you this morning, all three of you walking down the Via Nazionale, but you would not look at me. I have got my visés and everything ready. The strike of the steamboats has delayed me here. I am sweating blood. I have a last request to make of you. Can you let me have ninety lire, to make up what I need for my hotel bill? If I cannot have this I am lost. I hoped to find you at the hotel but the porter said you were out. I am at the Casa Politi, passing every half-hour in agony. If you can be so kind as to stretch your generosity to this last loan, of course I shall be eternally grateful. I can pay you back once I get to Malta—"

Well, here was a blow! The worst was that he thought I had cut him—a thing I wouldn't have done. So after luncheon behold me going through the terrific sun of that harbour front of Syracuse, an enormous and powerful sun, to the Casa Politi. The porter recognized me and looked inquiringly. M. was out, and I said I would call again at four o'clock.

It happened we were in the town eating ices at four, so I didn't get to his hotel till half-past. He was out—gone to look for me. So I left a note saying I had not seen him in the Via Nazionale, that I had called twice, and that I should be in the Grand Hotel in the evening.

When we came in at seven, M. in the hall, sitting, the picture of misery and endurance. He took my hand in both his, and bowed to the women, who nodded and went upstairs. He and I went and sat in the empty lounge. Then he told me the trials he had had—how his luggage had come,

and the station had charged him eighteen lire a day for deposit; how he had
had to wait on at the hotel because of the ship; how he had tried to sell his
trinkets, and had today parted with his opal sleevelinks—so that now he
only wanted seventy, not ninety lire. I gave him a hundred note, and he
looked into my eyes, his own eyes swimming with tears, and he said he was
sweating blood.

Well, the steamer went that night. She was due to leave at ten. We
went on board after dinner. We were going second class. And so, for once,
was M. It was only an eight hours' crossing, yet, in spite of all the blood he
had sweated, he would not go third class. In a way I admired him for sticking
to his principles. I should have gone third myself, out of shame of spending
somebody else's money. He would not give way to such weakness. He knew
that as far as the world goes, you're a first-class gentleman if you have a
first-class ticket; if you have a third, no gentleman at all. It behoved him to
be a gentleman. I understood his point, but the women were indignant. And
I was just rather tired of him and his gentlemanliness.

It amused me very much to lean on the rail of the upper deck and
watch the people coming on board—first going into the little customs house
with their baggage, then scuffling up the gangway on board. The tall Arabs
in their ghostly white woollen robes came carrying their sacks: they were
going on to Tripoli. The fat Turk in his fez and long black alpaca coat with
white drawers underneath came beaming up to the second class. There was
a great row in the customs house; and then, simply running like a beetle
with rage, there came on board a little Maltese or Greek fellow, followed
by a tall lantern-jawed fellow, both seedy-looking scoundrels suckled in
scoundrelism. They raved and nearly threw their arms away into the sea,
talking wildly in some weird language with the fat Turk, who listened
solemnly, away below on the deck. They then rushed to somebody else. Of
course, we were dying with curiosity. Thank heaven I heard men talking in
Italian. It appears the two seedy fellows were trying to smuggle silver coin
in small sacks and rolls out of the country. They were detected. But they
declared they had a right to take it away, as it was foreign specie, English
florins and half-crowns, and South American dollars and Spanish money.
The customs officer, however, detained the lot. The little enraged beetle of
a fellow ran back and forth from the ship to the customs, from the customs
to the ship, afraid to go without his money, afraid the ship would go without
him.

At five minutes to ten, there came M., very smart in his little grey overcoat and grey curly hat, walking very smart and erect and genteel, and followed by a porter with a barrow of luggage. They went into the customs, M. in his grey suède gloves passing rapidly and smartly in, like the grandest gentleman on earth, and with his grey suède hands throwing open his luggage for inspection. From on board we could see the interior of the little customs shed.

Yes, he was through. Brisk, smart, superb, like the grandest little gentleman on earth, strutting because he was late, he crossed the bit of flagged pavement and came up the gangway, haughty as you can wish. The carabinieri were lounging by the foot of the gangway, fooling with one another. The little gentleman passed them with his nose in the air, came quickly on board, followed by his porter, and in a moment disappeared. After about five minutes the porter reappeared—a red-haired fellow, I knew him—he even saluted me from below, the brute. But M. lay in hiding.

I trembled for him at every unusual stir. There on the quay stood the English consul with his bull-dog, and various elegant young officers with yellow on their uniforms, talking to elegant young Italian ladies in black hats with stiff ospreys and bunchy furs, and gangs of porters and hotel people and on-lookers. Then came a tramp-tramp-tramp of a squad of soldiers in red fezzes and baggy grey trousers. Instead of coming on board they camped on the quay. I wondered if all these had come for poor M. But apparently not.

So the time passed, till nearly midnight, when one of the elegant young lieutenants began to call the names of the soldiers, and the soldiers answered, and one after another filed on board with his kit. So, they were on board, on their way to Africa.

Now somebody called out, and the visitors began to leave the boat. Barefooted sailors and a boy ran to raise the gangway. The last visitor or official with a bunch of papers stepped off the gangway. People on shore began to wave handkerchiefs. The red-fezzed soldiers leaned like so many flower-pots over the lower rail. There was a calling of farewells. The ship was fading into the harbour, the people on shore seemed smaller, under the lamp, in the deep night—without one's knowing why.

So, we passed out of the harbour, passed the glittering lights of Ortygia, past the two lighthouses, into the open Mediterranean. The noise of a ship in the open sea! It was a still night, with stars, only a bit chill. And the ship churned through the water.

Suddenly, like a revenant, appeared M. near us, leaning on the rail and looking back at the lights of Syracuse sinking already forlorn and little on the low darkness. I went to him.

"Well," he said, with his little smirk of a laugh. "Good-bye, Italy!"

"Not a sad farewell either," said I.

"No, my word, not this time," he said. "But what an awful long time we were starting! A *brutta mezz'ora* for me, indeed. Oh, my word, I begin to breathe free for the first time since I left the monastery! How awful it's been! But of course, in Malta, I shall be all right. Don Bernardo has written to his friends there. They'll have everything ready for me that I want, and I can pay you back the money you so kindly lent me."

We talked for some time, leaning on the inner rail of the upper deck.

"Oh," he said, "there's Commander So-and-so, of the British fleet. He's stationed in Malta. I made his acquaintance in the hotel. I hope we're going to be great friends in Malta. I hope I shall have an opportunity to introduce you to him. Well, I suppose you will want to be joining your ladies. So long, then. Oh, for tomorrow morning! I never longed so hard to be in the British Empire—" He laughed, and strutted away.

In a few minutes we three, leaning on the rail of the second-class upper deck, saw our little friend large as life on the first-class deck, smoking a cigar and chatting in an absolutely first-class-ticket manner with the above mentioned Commander. He pointed us out to the Commander, and we felt the first-class passengers were looking across at us second-class passengers with pleasant interest. The women went behind a canvas heap to laugh, I hid my face under my hat-brim to grin and watch. Larger than any first-class ticketer leaned our little friend on the first-class rail, and whiffed at his cigar. So *dégagé* and so genteel he could be. Only I noticed he wilted a little when the officers of the ship came near.

He was still on the first-class deck when we went down to sleep. In the morning I came up soon after dawn. It was a lovely summer Mediterranean morning, with the sun rising up in a gorgeous golden rage, and the sea so blue, so fairy blue, as the Mediterranean is in summer. We were approaching quite near to a rocky, pale yellow island with some vineyards, rising magical out of the swift blue sea into the morning radiance. The rocks were almost as pale as butter, the islands were like golden shadows loitering in the midst of the Mediterranean, lonely among all the blue.

M. came up to my side.

"Isn't it lovely! Isn't it beautiful!" he said. "I love approaching these islands in the early morning." He had almost recovered his assurance, and the slight pomposity and patronizing tone I had first known in him. "In two hours I shall be free! Imagine it! Oh, what a beautiful feeling!" I looked at him in the morning light. His face was a good deal broken by his last month's experience, older looking, and dragged. Now that the excitement was nearing its end, the tiredness began to tell on him. He was yellowish round the eyes, and the whites of his round, rather impudent blue eyes were discoloured.

Malta was drawing near. We saw the white fringe of the sea upon the yellow rocks, and a white road looping on the yellow rocky hillside. I thought of St Paul, who must have been blown this way, must have struck the island from this side. Then we saw the heaped glitter of the square facets of houses, Valletta, splendid above the Mediterranean, and a tangle of shipping and dreadnoughts and watchtowers in the beautiful, locked-in harbour.

We had to go down to have passports examined. The officials sat in the long saloon. It was a horrible squash and squeeze of the first- and second-class passengers. M. was a little ahead of me. I saw the American eagle on his passport. Yes, he passed all right. Once more he was free. As he passed away he turned and gave a condescending affable nod to me and to the Commander, who was just behind me.

The ship was lying in Valletta harbour. I saw M., quite superb and brisk now, ordering a porter with his luggage into a boat. The great rocks rose above us, yellow and carved, cut straight by man. On top were all the houses. We got at last into a boat and were rowed ashore. Strange to be on British soil and to hear English. We got a carriage and drove up the steep highroad through the cutting in the rock, up to the town. There in the big square we had coffee, sitting out of doors. A military band went by, playing splendidly in the bright, hot morning. The Maltese lounged about, and watched. Splendid the band, and the soldiers! One felt the splendour of the British Empire, let the world say what it likes. But, alas, as one stayed on even in Malta, one felt the old lion had gone foolish and amiable. Foolish and amiable, with the weak amiability of old age.

We stayed in the Great Britain Hotel. Of course one could not be in Valletta for twenty-four hours without meeting M. There he was, in the Strada Reale, strutting in a smart white duck suit, with a white piqué cravat.

But, alas, he had no white shoes: they had got lost or stolen. He had to wear black boots with his summer finery.

He was staying in an hotel a little further down our street, and he begged me to call and see him, he begged me to come to lunch. I promised and went. We went into his bedroom, and he rang for more sodas.

"How wonderful it is to be here!" he said brightly. "Don't you like it immensely? And, oh, how wonderful to have a whisky and soda. Well, now, say when."

He finished one bottle of Black and White, and opened another. The waiter, a good-looking Maltese fellow, appeared with two siphons. M. was very much the signore with him, and at the same time very familiar: as I should imagine a rich Roman of the merchant class might have been with a pet slave. We had quite a nice lunch, and whisky and soda and a bottle of French wine. And M. was the charming and attentive host.

After lunch we talked again of manuscripts and publishers and how he might make money. I wrote one or two letters for him. He was anxious to get something under way. And yet the trouble of these arrangements was almost too much for his nerves. His face looked broken and old, but not like an old man's, like an old boy's, and he was really very irritable.

173

For my own part I was soon tired of Malta, and would gladly have left after three days. But there was the strike of steamers still, we had to wait on. M. professed to be enjoying himself hugely, making excursions every day, to St Paul's Bay and to the other islands. He had also made various friends or acquaintances. Particularly two young men, Maltese, who were friends of Don Bernardo. He introduced me to these two young men: one Gabriel Mazzaiba and the other Salonia. They had small businesses down on the wharf. Salonia asked M. to go for a drive in a motor-car round the island, and M. pressed me to go too. Which I did. And swiftly, on a Saturday afternoon, we dodged about in the car upon that dreadful island, first to some fearful and stony bay, arid, treeless, desert, a bit of stony desert by the sea, with unhappy villas and a sordid, scrap-iron front; then away inland up long and dusty roads, across a bone-dry, bone-bare, hideous landscape. True, there was ripening corn, but this was all of a colour with the dust-yellow, bone-bare island. Malta is all a pale, softish, yellowish rock, just like Bath brick: this goes into fathomless dust. And the island is stark as a corpse, no trees, no bushes even: a fearful landscape, cultivated, and weary with ages of weariness, and old weary houses here and there.

We went to the old capital in the centre of the island, and this is interesting. The town stands on a bluff of hill in the middle of the dreariness, looking at Valletta in the distance, and the sea. The houses are all pale yellow, and tall, and silent, as if forsaken. There is a cathedral, too, and a fortress outlook over the sun-blazed, sun-dried, disheartening island. Then we dashed off to another village and climbed a church-dome that rises like a tall blister on the plain, with houses round and corn beyond and dust that has no glamour, stale, weary, like bone-dust, and thorn hedges sometimes, and some tin-like prickly pears. In the dusk we came round by St Paul's Bay, back to Valletta.

The young men were very pleasant, very patriotic for Malta, very Catholic. We talked politics and a thousand things. M. was gently patronizing, and seemed, no doubt, to the two Maltese a very elegant and travelled and wonderful gentleman. They, who had never seen even a wood, thought how wonderful a forest must be, and M. talked to them of Russia and of Germany.

But I was glad to leave that bone-dry, hideous island. M. begged me to stay longer: but not for worlds! He was establishing himself securely: was learning the Maltese language, and cultivating a thorough acquaintance with the island. And he was going to establish himself. Mazzaiba was exceedingly kind to him, helping him in every way. In Rabato, the suburb of the old town—a quiet, forlorn little yellow street—he found a tiny house of two rooms and a tiny garden. This would cost five pounds a year. Mazzaiba lent the furniture—and when I left, M. was busily skipping back and forth from Rabato to Valletta, arranging his little home, and very pleased with it. He was also being very Maltese, and rather anti-British, as is essential, apparently, when one is not a Britisher and finds oneself in any part of the British Empire. M. was very much the American gentleman.

Well, I was thankful to be home again and to know that he was safely shut up in that beastly island. He wrote me letters, saying how he loved it all, how he would go down to the sea—five or six miles' walk—at dawn, and stay there all day, studying Maltese and writing for the newspapers. The life was fascinating, the summer was blisteringly hot, and the Maltese were *most* attractive, especially when they knew you were not British. Such good-looking fellows, too, and do anything you want. Wouldn't I come and spend a month? I did not answer—felt I had had enough. Came a postcard from M.: "I haven't had a letter from you, nor any news at all. I am afraid you are ill, and feel so anxious. Do write—" But, no, I didn't want to write.

During August and September and half October we were away in the north. I forgot my little friend; hoped he was gone out of my life. But I had that fatal sinking feeling that he *hadn't* really gone out of it yet.

In the beginning of November a little letter from Don Bernardo— did I know that M. had committed suicide in Malta? Following that, a scrubby Maltese newspaper, posted by Salonia, with a marked notice "The suicide of an American gentleman at Rabato. Yesterday the American M. M., a well-built man in the prime of life, was found dead in his bed in his house at Rabato. By the bedside was a bottle containing poison. The deceased had evidently taken his life by swallowing prussic acid. Mr. M. had been staying for some months on the island, studying the language and the conditions, with a view to writing a book. It is understood that financial difficulties were the cause of this lamentable event."

Then Mazzaiba wrote asking me what I knew of M., and saying the latter had borrowed money which he, Mazzaiba, would like to recover. I replied at once, and then received the following letter from Salonia:

Valletta, 20 November 1920.

My dear Mr. Lawrence,

Some time back I mailed you our Daily Malta Chronicle *which gave an account of the death of M. I hope you have received same. As the statements therein given were very vague and not quite correct, please accept the latter part of this letter as a more correct version.*

The day before yesterday Mazzaiba received your letter, which he gave me to read. As you may suppose, we were very much astonished by its general purport. Mazzaiba will be writing to you in a few days; in the meantime I volunteered to give you the details you asked for.

Mazzaiba and I have done all in our power to render M.'s stay here as easy and pleasant as possible from the time we first met him in your company at the Great Britain Hotel. [This is not correct. They were already quite friendly with M. before that motor-drive, when I saw these two Maltese for the first time.] He lived in an embarrassed mood since then, and though we helped him as best we could both morally and financially, he never confided to us his troubles. To this very day we cannot but look on his coming here and his stay amongst us, to say the least of the way he left us, as a huge farce wrapped up in mystery, a painful experience unsolicited by either of us, and a cause of grief unrequited except by our own personal sense of duty toward a stranger.

Mazzaiba out of mere respect did not tell me of his commitments toward M. until about a month ago, and this he did in a most confidential and private manner merely to put me on my guard, thinking, and rightly, too, that M. would be falling on me next time for funds; Mazzaiba having already given about £55 and would not possibly commit himself any further. Of course, we found him all along a perfect gentleman. Naturally, he hated the very idea that we or anybody else in Malta should look upon him in any other light. He never asked directly, though Mazzaiba (later myself) was always quick enough to interpret rightly what he meant and obliged him forthwith.

At this stage, to save the situation, he made up a scheme that the three of us should exploit the commercial possibilities in Morocco. It very nearly materialized, everything was ready, I was to go with him to Morocco, Mazzaiba to take charge of affairs here and to dispose of transactions we initiated there. Fortunately, for lack of the necessary funds the idea had to be dropped, and there it ended, thank God, after a great deal of trouble I had in trying to set it well on foot.

Last July, the police, according to our law, advised him that he was either to find a surety or to deposit a sum of money with them, as otherwise at the expiration of his three months' stay he would be compelled to leave the place. Money he had none, so he asked Mazzaiba to stand as surety. Mazzaiba could not, as he was already guarantor for his alien cousins who were here at the time. Mazzaiba (not M.) asked me and I complied, thinking that the responsibility was just moral and only exacted as a matter of form.

When, as stated before, Mazzaiba told me that M. owed him £55 and that he owed his grocer and others at Notabile (the old town, of which Rabato is the suburb) over £10, I thought I might as well look up my guarantee and see if I was directly responsible for any debts he incurred here. The words of his declaration which I endorsed stated that "I hereby solemnly promise that I will not be a burden to the inhabitants of these islands, etc.," and deeming unpaid debts to be more or less a burden, I decided to withdraw my guarantee, which I did on the 23rd ult. The reason I gave to the police was that he was outliving his income and that I did not intend to shoulder any financial responsibility in the matter. On the same day I wrote to him up at Notabile, saying that for family reasons I was compelled to withdraw his surety. He took my letter in the sense implied and no way offended at my procedure.

M., in his resourceful way, knowing that he would with great difficulty find another guarantor, wrote at once to the police saying that he understood from Mr. Salonia that he (S) had withdrawn his guarantee, but as he (M) would be leaving the island in about three weeks' time (still intending to exploit Morocco) he begged the Commissioner to allow him this period of grace, without demanding a new surety. In fact he asked me to find him a cheap passage to Gib. in an ingoing tramp steamer. The police did not reply to his letter at all; no doubt they had everything ready and well thought out. He was alarmed in not receiving an acknowledgment, and, knowing full well what he imminently expected at the hands of the Italian police, he decided to prepare for the last act of his drama.

We had not seen him for three or four days when he came to Mazzaiba's office on Wednesday, 3rd inst., in the forenoon. He stayed there for some time talking on general subjects and looking somewhat more excited than usual. He went up to town alone at noon as Mazzaiba went to Singlea. I was not with them in the morning, but in the afternoon about 4:30, whilst I was talking to Mazzaiba in his office, M. again came in looking very excited, and, being closing time, we went up, the three of us, to town, and there left him in the company of a friend.

On Thursday morning, 4th inst., at about 10 a.m., two detectives in plain clothes met him in a street at Notabile. One of them quite casually went up to him and said very civilly that the inspector of police wished to see him re a guarantee or something, and that he was to go with him to the police station. This was an excuse, as the detective had about him a warrant for his arrest for frauding an hotel in Rome, and that he was to be extradited at the request of the authorities in Italy. M. replied that as he was in his sandals he would dress up and go with them immediately, and, accompanying him to his house at No. 1 Strada S. Pietro, they allowed him to enter. He locked the door behind him, leaving them outside.

A few minutes later he opened his bedroom window and dropped a letter addressed to Don Bernardo which he asked a boy in the street to post for him, and immediately closed the window again. One of the detectives picked up the letter and we do not know to this day if same was posted at all. Some time elapsed and he did not come out. The detectives were by this time very uneasy and as another police official came up they decided to burst open the door. As the door did not give way they got a ladder and climbed over the roof, and there they found M. in his bedroom dying from poisoning, outstretched on his bed and a glass of water close by. A priest was immediately called in who had just time to administer extreme unction before he died at 11:45 a.m.

At 8:00 a.m. the next day his body was admitted for examination at the Floriana Civil Hospital and death was certified to be from poisoning with hydrocyanic acid. His age was given as 44, being buried on his birthday (7th Novr.), with R. Catholic rites at the expense of his friends in Malta.

Addenda: Contents of Don Bernardo's letter:

"I leave it to you and to Gabriel Mazzaiba to arrange my affairs. I cannot live any longer. Pray for me."

Document found on his writing-table:

"In case of my unexpected death inform American consul.

"I want to buried first class, my wife will pay.

"My little personal belongings to be delivered to my wife. (Address.)

"My best friend here, Gabriel Mazzaiba, inform him. (Address.)

"My literary executor N. D. (Address.)

"All manuscripts and books for N. D. I leave my literary property to N. D. to whom half the results are to accrue. The other half my debts are to be paid with:

"Furniture etc. belong to Coleiro, Floriana.

"Silver spoons etc. belong to Gabriel Mazzaiba. (Address.)"

178 *The American Consul is in charge of all his personal belongings. I am sure he will be pleased to give you any further details you may require. By the way, his wife refused to pay his burial expenses, but five of his friends in Malta undertook to give him a decent funeral. His mourners were: the consul, the vice-consul, Mr. A., an American citizen, Gabriel Mazzaiba, and myself.*

Please convey to Mrs. Lawrence an expression of our sincere esteem and high regard and you will kindly accept equally our warmest respects, whilst soliciting any information you would care to pass on to us regarding the late M.

Believe me, my dear Mr. Lawrence, etc.

[Mrs. M. refunded the burial expenses through the American consul about two months after her husband's death.]

When I had read this letter the world seemed to stand still for me. I knew that in my own soul I had said: "Yes, he must die if he cannot find his own way." But for all that, now I *realized* what it must have meant to be the hunted, desperate man: everything seemed to stand still. I could, by giving half my money, have saved his life. I had chosen not to save his life.

Now, after a year has gone by, I keep to my choice. I still would not save his life. I respect him for dying when he was cornered. And for this reason I feel still connected with him: still have this to discharge, to get his book published, and to give him his place, to present him just as he was as far as I knew him myself.

The worst thing I have against him is that he abused the confidence, the kindness, and the generosity of unsuspecting people like Mazzaiba. He did not *want* to, perhaps. But he did it. And he leaves Mazzaiba swindled, distressed, confused, and feeling sold in the best part of himself. What next? What is one to feel towards one's strangers, after having known M.? It is this Judas treachery to *ask* for sympathy and for generosity, to take it when given—and then: "Sorry, but anybody may make a mistake!" It is this betraying with a kiss which makes me still say: "He should have died sooner." No, I would not help to keep him alive, not if I had to choose again. I would let him go over into death. He shall and should die, and so should all his sort: and so they will. There are so many kiss-giving Judases. He was not a criminal: he was obviously well intentioned: but a Judas every time, selling the good feeling he had tried to arouse, and had aroused, for any handful of silver he could get. A little loving vampire!

179

Yesterday arrived the manuscript of the Legion, from Malta. It is exactly two years since I read it first in the monastery. Then I was moved and rather horrified. Now I am chiefly amused; because in my mind's eye is the figure of M. in the red trousers and the blue coat with lappets turned up, swinging like a little indignant pigeon across the drill yards and into the canteen of Bel-Abbes. He *is* so indignant, so righteously and morally indignant, and so funny. All the horrors of the actuality fade before the indignation, his little, tuppenny indignation.

Oh, M. is a prime hypocrite. *How* loudly he rails against the Boches! *How* great his enthusiasm for the pure, the spiritual Allied cause. Just so long as he is in Africa, and it suits his purpose! His scorn for the German tendencies of the German legionaries: even Count de R. secretly leans towards Germany. "Blood is thicker than water," says our hero glibly. Some blood, thank God. Apparently not his own. For according to all showing he was, by blood, pure German: father and mother: even Hohenzollern blood!!! Pure German! Even his speech, his *mother-tongue*, was German and not English! And then the little mongrel—!

But perhaps something happens to blood when once it has been taken to America.

And then, once he is in Valbonne, lo, a change! Where now is sacred France and the holy Allied Cause! Where is our hero's fervour? It is *worse than* Bel-Abbes! Yes, indeed, far less human, more hideously cold. One is driven by very rage to wonder if he was really a spy, a German spy whom Germany cast off because he was no good.

The little *gentleman!* God damn his white-blooded gentility. The legionaries must have been gentlemen, that they didn't kick him every day to the lavatory and back.

"You are a journalist?" said the colonel.

"No, a *littérateur*," said M. perkily.

"That is something more?" said the Colonel.

Oh, I would have given a lot to have seen it and heard it. The *littérateur!* Well, I hope this book will establish his fame as such. I hope the editor, if it gets one, won't alter any more of the marvellously staggering sentences and the joyful French mistakes. The *littérateur!*—the impossible little pigeon!

But the Bel-Abbes part is alive and interesting. It should be read only by those who have the stomach. Ugly, foul—alas, it is no uglier and no fouler than the reality. M. himself was near enough to being a scoundrel, thief, forger, etc., etc.—what lovely strings of names he hurls at them!—to be able to appreciate their company. He himself was such a liar, that he was not taken in. But his conceit as a gentleman *keeping up appearances* gave him a real standpoint from which to see the rest. The book is in its way a real creation. But I would hate it to be published and taken at its face value, with M. as a spiritual dove among vultures of lust. Let us first put a pinch of salt on the tail of this dove. What he did do in the way of vice, even in Bel-Abbes, I never chose to ask him.

Yes, yes, he sings another note when he is planted right among the sacred Allies, with never a German near. Then the gorgeousness goes out of his indignation. He takes it off with the red trousers. Now he is just a sordid little figure in filthy corduroys. There is no vice to purple his indignation, the little holy liar. There is only sordidness and automatic, passionless, colourless awful mud. When all is said and done, mud, cold, hideous, foul, engulfing mud, up to the waist, this is the final symbol of the Great War. Hear some of the horrified young soldiers. They dare hardly speak of it yet.

The Valbonne part is worse, really, than the Bel-Abbes part. Passionless, barren, utterly, coldly foul and hopeless. The ghastly emptiness, and the slow mud-vortex, the brink of it.

Well, now M. has gone himself. Yes, and he would be gone in the common mud and dust himself, if it were not that the blood still beats warm and hurt and kind in some few hearts. M. "hinted" to Mazzaiba for money, in Malta, and Mazzaiba gave it to him, thinking him a man in distress. He thought him a gentleman, and lovable, and in trouble! And Mazzaiba—it isn't his real name, but there he is, real enough—still has this feeling of grief for M. So much so that now he has had the remains taken from the public grave in Malta, and buried in his own, the Mazzaiba grave, so that they shall not be lost. For my part, I would have said that the sooner they mingled with the universal dust, the better. But one is glad to see a little genuine kindness and gentleness, even if it is wasted on the bones of that selfish little scamp of a M. He despised his "physical friendships," though he didn't forgo them. So why should anyone rescue his physique from the public grave?

But there you are—there was his power: to arouse affection and a certain tenderness in the hearts of others, for himself. And on this he traded. One sees the trick working all the way through the Legion book. God knows how much warm kindness, generosity, was showered on him during the course of his forty-odd years. And selfish little scamp, he took it as a greedy boy takes cakes off a dish, quickly, to make the most of his opportunity while it lasted. And the cake once eaten: *buona sera!* He patted his own little paunch and felt virtuous. Merely physical feeling, you see! He had a way of saying "physical"—a sort of American way, as if it were spelt "fisacal"— that made me want to kick him.

Not that he was mean, while he was about it. No, he would give very freely: even a little ostentatiously, always feeling that he was being a *liberal gentleman*. Ach, the liberality and the gentility he prided himself on! *Ecco!* And he gave a large tip, with a little winsome smile. But in his heart of hearts it was always himself he was thinking of, while he did it. Playing his role of the gentleman who was awfully nice to everybody—so long as they were nice to him, or so long as it served his advantage. Just private charity!

Well, poor devil, he is dead: which is all the better. He had his points, the courage of his own terrors, quick-wittedness, sensitiveness to certain things in his surroundings. I prefer him, scamp as he is, to the ordinary

181

respectable person. He ran his risks: he *had* to be running risks with the police, apparently. And he poisoned himself rather than fall into their clutches. I like him for that. And I like him for the sharp and quick way he made use of every one of his opportunities to get out of that beastly army. There I admire him: a courageous, isolated little devil, facing his risks, and like a good rat, *determined* not to be trapped. I won't forgive him for trading on the generosity of others, and so dropping poison into the heart of all warm-blooded faith. But I am glad after all that Mazzaiba has rescued his bones from the public grave. I wouldn't have done it myself, because I don't forgive him his "fisacal" impudence and parasitism. But I am glad Mazzaiba has done it. And, for my part, I will put his Legion book before the world if I can. Let him have his place in the world's consciousness.

Let him have his place, let his word be heard. He went through vile experiences: he looked them in the face, braved them through, and kept his manhood in spite of them. For manhood is a strange quality, to be found in human rats as well as in hot-blooded men. M. carried the human consciousness through circumstances which would have been too much for me. I would have died rather than be so humiliated, I could never have borne it. Other men, I know, went through worse things in the war. But then, horrors, like pain, are their own anaesthetic. Men lose their normal consciousness, and go through in a sort of delirium. The bit of Stendhal which Dos Passos quotes in front of *Three Soldiers* is frighteningly true. There are certain things which are *so* bitter, *so* horrible, that the contemporaries just cannot know them, cannot contemplate them. So it is with a great deal of the late war. It was so foul, and humanity in Europe fell suddenly into such ignominy and inhuman ghastliness, that we shall *never* fully realize what it was. We just cannot bear it. We haven't the soul-strength to contemplate it.

And yet, humanity can only finally conquer by realizing. It is human destiny, since Man fell into consciousness and self-consciousness, that we can only go forward step by step through realization, full, bitter, conscious realization. This is true of all the great terrors and agonies and anguishes of life: sex, and war, and even crime. When Flaubert in his story—it is so long since I read it—makes his saint have to kiss the leper, and naked clasp the leprous awful body against his own, that is what we must at last do. It is the great command, *Know Thyself.* We've got to *know* what sex is, let the sentimentalists wiggle as they like. We've got to know the greatest and most shattering human passions, let the puritans squeal as they like for screens.

182

And we've got to know humanity's criminal tendency, look straight at humanity's great deeds of crime against the soul. We have to fold this horrible leper against our naked warmth, because life and the throbbing blood and the believing soul are greater even than leprosy. Knowledge, true knowledge, is like vaccination. It prevents the continuing of ghastly moral disease.

And so it is with the war. Humanity in Europe fell horribly into a hatred of the living soul, in the war. There is no gainsaying it. We all fell. Let us not try to wriggle out of it. We fell into hideous depravity of hating the human soul; a purulent smallpox of the spirit we had. It was shameful, shameful, shameful, in every country and in all of us. Some tried to resist, and some didn't. But we were all drowned in shame. A purulent smallpox of the vicious spirit, vicious against the deep soul that pulses in the blood.

We haven't got over it. The smallpox sores are running yet in the spirit of mankind. And we have got to take this putrid spirit to our bosom. There's nothing else for it. Take the foul rotten spirit of mankind, full of the running sores of the war, to our bosom, and cleanse it there. Cleanse it not with blind love; ah, no, that won't help. But with bitter and wincing realization. We have to take the disease into our consciousness and let it go through our soul, like some virus. We have got to realize. And then we can surpass.

M. went where I could never go. He carried the human consciousness unbroken through circumstances I could not have borne. It is not heroism to rush on death. It is cowardice to accept a martyrdom today. That is the feeling one has at the end of Dos Passos's book. To let oneself be absolutely trapped? Never! I prefer M. He drew himself out of the thing he loathed, despised, and feared. He fought it, for his own spirit and liberty. He fought it open-eyed. He went through. They were more publicly heroic, they won war medals. But the lonely terrified courage of the isolated spirit which grits its teeth and stares the horrors in the face and *will* not succumb to them, but fights its way through them, *knowing* that it must surpass them: this is the rarest courage. And this courage M. had: and the man in the Dos Passos book didn't *quite* have it. And so, though M. poisoned himself, and I would not wish him *not* to have poisoned himself; though as far as warm life goes, I don't forgive him; yet, as far as the eternal and unconquerable spirit of man goes, I am with him through eternity. I am grateful to him; he beat out for me boundaries of human experience which I could not have beaten out for myself. The *human* traitor he was. But he was not traitor to the

183

spirit. In the great spirit of human consciousness he was a hero, little, quaking and heroic: a strange, quaking little star.

Even the dead ask only for *justice:* not for praise or exoneration. Who dares humiliate the dead with excuses for their living? I hope I may do M. justice; and I hope his restless spirit may be appeased. I do not try to forgive. The living blood knows no forgiving. Only the overweening spirit takes on itself to dole out forgiveness. But justice is a sacred human right. The overweening spirit pretends to perch above justice. But I am a man, not a spirit, and men with blood that throbs and throbs and throbs can only live at length by being just, can only die in peace if they have justice. Forgiveness gives the whimpering dead no rest. Only deep, true justice.

There is M.'s manuscript then, like a map of the lower places of mankind's activities. There is the war: foul, foul, unutterably foul. As foul as M. says. Let us make up our minds about it.

It is the only help: to realize, *fully,* and then make up our minds. The war was *foul.* As long as I am a man, I say it and assert it, and further I say, as long as I am a man such a war shall never occur again. It shall not, and it shall not. All modern militarism is foul. It shall go. A man I am, and above machines, and it shall go, forever, because I have found it vile, vile, too vile ever to experience again. Cannons shall go. Never again shall trenches be dug. They *shall* not, for I am a man, and such things are within the power of man, to break and make. I have said it, and as long as blood beats in my veins, I mean it. Blood beats in the veins of many men who mean it as well as I.

Man perhaps *must* fight. Mars, the great god of war, will be a god for ever. Very well. Then if fight you must, fight you shall, and without engines, without machines. Fight if you like, as the Roman fought, with swords and spears, or like the Red Indian, with bows and arrows and knives and war paint. But never again shall you fight with the foul, base, fearful, monstrous machines of war which man invented for the last war. You shall not. The diabolic mechanisms are man's, and I am a man. Therefore they are mine. And I smash them into oblivion. With every means in my power, *except* the means of these machines, I smash them into oblivion. I am at war! I, a man, am at war!—with these foul machines and contrivances that men have conjured up. Men have conjured them up. I, a man, will conjure them down again. Won't I? But I will! I am not one man, I am many, I am most.

So much for the war! So much for M.'s manuscript. Let it be read.

184

It is not this that will do harm, but sloppy sentiment and cant. Take the bitterness and cleanse the blood.

Now would you believe it, that little scamp M. spent over a hundred pounds of borrowed money during his four months in Malta, when his expenses, he boasted to me, need not have been more than a pound a week, once he got into the little house in Notabile? That is, he spent at least seventy pounds too much. Heaven knows what he did with it, apart from "guzzling." And this hundred pounds must be paid back in Malta. Which it never will be, unless this manuscript pays it back. Pay the gentleman's last debts, if no others.

He had to be a gentleman. I didn't realize till after his death. I never suspected him of royal blood. But there you are, you never know where it will crop out. He was the grandson of an emperor. His mother was the illegitimate daughter of the German Kaiser; D. says, of the old Kaiser Wilhelm I, Don Bernardo says, of Kaiser Friedrich Wilhelm, father of the present ex-Kaiser. She was born in Berlin on October 31, 1845; and her portrait, by Paul, now hangs in a gallery in Rome. Apparently there had been some injustice against her in Berlin, for she seems once to have been in the highest society there, and to have attended at court. Perhaps she was discreetly banished by Wilhelm II, hence M.'s hatred of that monarch. She lies buried in the Protestant Cemetery in Rome, where she died in 1912, with the words *Filia Regis* on her tomb. M. adored her, and she him. Part of his failings one can *certainly* ascribe to the fact that he was an only son, an adored son, in whose veins the mother imagined only royal blood. And she must have thought him so beautiful, poor thing! Ah, well, they are both dead. Let us be just and wish them Lethe.

M. himself was born in New York, November 7, 1876; so at least it says on his passport. He entered the Catholic Church in England in 1902. His father was a Mr. L. M., married to the mother in 1867.

So poor M. had Hohenzollern blood in his veins: close kin to the ex-Kaiser Wilhelm. Well, that itself excuses him a great deal: because of the cruel illusion of importance *manqué*, which it must have given him. He never breathed a word of this to me. Yet apparently it is accepted at the monastery, the great monastery which knows most European secrets of any political significance. And for myself, I believe it is true. And if he was a scamp and a treacherous little devil, he had also qualities of nerve and breeding undeniable. He faced his way through that Legion experience: royal nerves dragging themselves through the sewers, without giving way. But, alas for royal blood! Like most other blood, it has gradually gone white, during our spiritual era. Bunches of nerves! And whitish, slightly acid blood. And no bowels of deep compassion and kindliness. Only charity—a little more than kin, and less than kind.

Also, M.! Ich grüsse dich, in der Ewigkeit. Aber hier, im Herzblut, hast du Gift und Leid nachgelassen—to use your own romantic language.

Joseph de Maistre

The Executioner

COUNT: There are questions, you might say, so close to each other that it is   *187*
easy to slip imperceptibly from one to the other. For instance, from asking: *Why should the best men suffer?* one hardly notices being led to ask,
Why does man suffer? Which is completely different and poses a question
concerning the origins of evil. So, let us begin by setting aside all possible
equivocation. *Evil there is on this earth.* Alas! No proof is needed. But
there is more to it: *it is just that evil should exist on earth,* and *God cannot
be the author of this evil.* This truth, I hope, you and I do not doubt, so
I need not prove it. After all, I know who I am talking to.

SENATOR: I do believe, with all my heart, and without cavil; but such a
profession of faith, being so broad, must be explained. Your St Thomas
said, with that species of laconic logic which is all his own: *God is the
author of the evil which punishes, but not of the evil which defiles. (Summ.
Theol. I, qu, 49, Art, iii)* In one sense he is assuredly correct; but we
must be clear: God is the author of that evil *which punishes,* that is,
of physical evil or pain, just as the sovereign is the author of those
penalties which are exacted under the law. Remotely and indirectly,
it is indeed God who hangs and who breaks on the wheel, for all
authority and any legitimate execution derives from him. More directly

and immediately, it is the thief, the forger and the murderer who are the real authors of that evil which punishes them; they build the prison, erect the gibbets and scaffolds. Like Homer's Juno, the sovereign acts, in that respect, entirely *of his own free will, but with the greatest reluctance.* So it is with God. God cannot in any way be the author of moral evil or *sin*; it is just as difficult to see him as the original author of physical evil, for physical evil would not exist if intelligent creatures had not made it necessary by an abuse of *their freedom*. Plato said it, and nothing is more self-evident: *He who is good can cause no harm.* When a father punishes his son justly, we do not think he ceases to be a good man; no more so when he kills an enemy in battle or when he sends a criminal to his deserts. As you said a while back, my dear Count, we should beware of being less just toward God than towards men. Any right-thinking man intuitively knows that evil cannot derive from an all-powerful Being. So in former times, inspired by this infallible sentiment, Roman good sense joined together, as if the two were bound by a necessary link, the two august titles of MOST GOOD and MOST POWERFUL. This splendid expression was born of Paganism; nonetheless, it seemed so fitting that it has passed into your own religious vocabulary, which is so delicately nuanced and so exclusive. And in passing I don't mind telling you that more than once I've thought that the classical inscription IOVI OPTIMO MAXIMO could readily be incised on the pediments of the great Latin churches: IOV-I is surely IOV-AH?

COUNT: Well, I see you understand that I have no wish to argue with what you say. I myself have no doubt whatever that *physical evil only came into the world through the fault of free creatures; it can only exist as a remedy or an expiation and therefore cannot have God as its direct author*. This, for us, must be unassailable dogma. Now to return to you, Sir. A while back you agreed that we were wrong to quibble with Providence about the *parcelling* out of good and evil: the real scandal lay in the apparent impunity of male-factors. But can you abandon the first objection without doing likewise for the second? If there is no injustice in the way in which evil is distributed, on that basis does virtue make its complaint? The world is governed by general laws only; I scarcely believe you would argue that if suddenly the foundations of this terrace on which we stand and talk were to be tossed up in the air by some upheaval underground, God should of necessity suspend the law of gravity in our favor, just because here stand three men who have neither robbed nor killed. I fear we should certainly tumble and be crushed. The same would occur were we three Bavarian Illuminati or the Committee of Public Safety. A heavy hail falls: should the just man's field be spared? That would be a miracle. But supposing that after the harvest this just man happens to commit a crime? His harvest should then rot in his barns? That would be another miracle. So every moment calls for a miracle: and miracles become the usual state of the world. Which would mean that there could be no more miracles: the exception has become the rule; disorder: order. I need only mention such notions to dispose of them.

On this point, our mistake is often the following: that we find it impossible to keep from ascribing to God, quite unbeknownst to ourselves, those notions we have concerning the dignity and importance of individuals. We are all subject to the established order of society, therefore insofar as they concern us, these notions are exceedingly well-founded; when, however, we apply these notions to the general order of the universe, we are like that queen who said: *You may be sure God thinks twice before damning the likes of us.* Elizabeth of France mounts the scaffold; Robespierre in the next breath. When they came into the world, Angel and Monster both submitted themselves equally to the general laws which obtain here. No words are strong enough to describe the awful crime of those who shed the purest and most august blood in the world; but as far as the general order of things is concerned, there is no injustice: it is a misfortune implicit in the human condition and that's that. *As a man, each man is subject to the misfortunes of all humanity:* the rule is universal, and hence not unjust. To hold that the dignity or worth of an individual should exempt him from some iniquitous or erroneous action by a court of law would be to hold that for the same reasons he is exempt from apoplexy, or for that matter, from death itself.

I beg you to notice, however, that despite these universal and necessary laws, the supposed equality, on which I have so far placed such stress, in practice hardly exists at all. As I told you, I made that assumption *to give myself the better argument:* but as you will see, nothing could be further from the truth.

189

First you must forget all about the individual: the general, visible and obviously just law is that *the greatest part of happiness, even here below, belongs to virtue itself, not to the virtuous man*. Were it otherwise, there would be neither vice nor virtue, neither merit nor fault; thus, no moral order. If every virtuous act were *paid for*, by some worldly advantage for instance, the act would have ceased to be a supernatural act, and so could no longer merit a supernatural reward. To argue the other side, suppose that by divine ordinance, the hand of a thief were necessarily to drop off in the act of robbery: then men would desist from thieving in much the same way as they desist from putting their hands under the butcher's knife. Once again, no moral order. No, to make this moral order (which, experience demonstrates, is the only order fit for intelligent creatures) concord with the laws of justice, it was necessary that virtue be rewarded and vice be punished: and punished even here below, though not always, nor always immediately. It was likewise necessary that the far greater part of good fortune be awarded to virtue and ill fortune be returned to vice in due proportion. In neither case, however, could the individual be sure of the result.

This, in fact, is how things are arranged. Any other hypothesis, and you will be led straight to the destruction of the moral order or the creation of another world.

But to get down to detail, why don't we start, if you don't mind, by human justice. As God wished men to govern other men, at least in external appearance, he gave sovereigns the right to punish crimes: it is in that rôle especially that they are His representatives. There is an admirable passage on the subject in the Laws of Manu: with your permission, I should like to read you a brief extract from the third volume of the works of Sir William Jones; it happens to be over there, on my table.

KNIGHT: Read, by all means. But pray tell me, before you begin, who is this King Manu? I don't believe I ever had the honor of being presented to him.

COUNT: Manu, Sir, is the Great Legislator of India. He is, so some say, the Sun-Child; according to others, the son of Brahma, the first person of the Indian trinity. Both these opinions are probably equally true; but I confess I find myself caught between them, unable to decide. What's more, I would unfortunately find it just as difficult to inform you at what period either one of these putative fathers is supposed to have engendered Manu. Sir William, he of learned memory, holds that the Great Legislator's code precedes the Pentateuch; and is *certainly* more ancient than that of all the Greek legislators. We have, however, a certain Mr. Pinkerton, who also has a right to our confidence; he, however, has taken it into his head to make fun of the Brahmins, and he moreover believes himself capable of demonstrating to them that their Manu was no more than an honest law-giver from the 12th century. Well, it is not my custom to argue over trifling differences; so I beg you gentlemen, we will leave the date blank and I will read you the excerpt. Listen well:

In the beginning, Brahma created the Spirit of Punishment for the use of kings. To this spirit, he gave a body of purest light. He is Brahma's own son: justice incarnate and protector of all living things. For fear of this spirit all sentient beings, fixed or locomotive, are kept to the confines of their natural enjoyments and do not stray from their duties. Let the king then, having only weighed place and occasion, his own powers and divine law, inflict just punishment on all who act unjustly: punishment is an active governor, the true administrator of all public affairs, the dispenser of all laws, and wise men call him the guarantor of the four orders of the state, each for the exact accomplishment of its duties. Punishment governs all humanity; punishment preserves it; punishment watches while human guardians are asleep. The wise man considers punishment as the perfection of justice. Let an indolent monarch cease to punish and the strong will prey on the weak. The entire human race is held in order by punishment which enables the universe to enjoy the good fortune allotted to it. If all barriers were let down, every class would become corrupt. If punishment were no longer inflicted or were unjustly meted out, there would be nothing but confusion among men. But if the judge is just, then when Punishment, dark-visaged, fiery-eyed, steps forth to punish crime, the people are saved.

191

SENATOR: Admirable! Wonderful! What a splendid man you are to have dug up that little treasure of Indian philosophy. I think you are quite right: the date makes no difference at all!

COUNT: I must say, it made the same impression on me. I find it splendidly combines European rationality with just enough of that oriental emphasis which is so pleasing when it is not overdone. In fact, I'll go so far as to say I do not believe it possible to state more nobly or more energetically that terrible prerogative of kings: *The punishment of the guilty.*

But I note your downcast expressions, gentlemen. Allow me to draw your attention, briefly I assure you, to a subject which I know offends the sensibilities, but which is, however, very much worthy of your attention.

I have just mentioned an awesome prerogative; accompanying it, there must also exist one whose fate it is to inflict on the unrighteous those punishments decreed by human justice. Though it seems to be impossible to explain how he comes into being. You might say such a man exists nearly everywhere. Certainly, it would not seem that there is in the nature of man any rational motive for a man to take up this particular profession. Gentlemen, I do you credit. I presume you are too much accustomed to thought for this to be the first time you meditate on the person of the Executioner.

Who *is* this inexplicable creature who has, in preference to the myriad agreeable, lucrative, honest and even honorable crafts which are within the power and dexterity of men, chosen that of tormenting or putting to death his fellow-men? Is there not something about such a man that is peculiar and alien to our nature? I myself have no doubt on this score. The Executioner is like us in appearance; he is born as we are born. But he is no ordinary being, and some special provision or decree, some *fiat* of the Creator is needed for him to make his appearance as a member of the family of man. He is created as a world is created. Think on what he is in the opinion of his fellow-creatures; and try to understand, if you can, how he finds it possible to ignore or defy this opinion! Authority no sooner designates his dwelling-place, he no sooner moves in, than every other inhabitant flees until the Executioner's house is well over the horizon. With his female and his young he lives alone in the middle of the solitude and emptiness that has formed all around him; through them he knows what a human voice sounds like, and without them he would know only of cries of pain . . . A dismal, dark signal is given; some abject functionary of the administration of justice comes to knock on his door and tell him he is needed; he quits his house; he steps out into a public square, every inch of which is pullulating, quivering with people. Then a victim is tossed his way: a poisoner, a parricide, a blasphemer. He lays his hands on him; he stretches him out; he binds him down to a cross laid flat on the scaffold; he lifts his hand. At that moment a horrible silence seizes the mass: in which nothing is heard but the howls of the victim and the cry of bones cracked on the bar. He unfastens his victim; he binds him to a wheel and his fractured arms and legs dangle, woven among the spokes; his head hangs down, hair standing on end; his mouth is as wide-open as the mouth of a furnace, but all that comes out are a few blood-soaked sounds begging death to hurry. There, the Executioner has done his job. His heart beats fast, but gladly; he is well pleased with himself and in secret he says to himself, *No man breaks on a wheel better than I!* He comes down off the scaffold, his bloody hand held out before him: and into that hand justice, from a goodly distance, throws a smattering of gold, which the Executioner then carries away through a double row of men who shudder away from him in horror. At home, he sits down and eats. Then he goes to bed. Then he sleeps. And when he wakes up the next morning he thinks of other things, not of what took place yesterday. This is a man? Yes: God receives him in his temples and allows him to pray. He is no criminal; but no known language calls him *virtuous, an honest man, an upright man*, etc. No moral praise attaches to him or would be appropriate; for all moral praise supposes relations with mankind, and he has none.

193

Yet all greatness, all power, all subordination rest on the Executioner: he is the horror and the bond of human association. Remove from this world this incomprehensible agent and instantly order yields to chaos, thrones crumble and society goes under. God is the author of sovereignty; he is also the author of punishment. He has set both these poles down on our earth: *for Jehovah is the master of the two poles, and on these he makes the world turn.*

Victor Hugo

The Interment of Napoleon

There is no film, no newsreel, no television in 1840. The individual eye matters.   *195*
Hugo was a young man; his watching serves his own purpose. The experience is
not generalized. "I was there on that day," he says; and gives us his account, in
detail.—K. B.

1840, December 15

I'd been hearing the call to arms since six-thirty. At eleven, I leave the
house. The streets are empty, the shops shut. Here and there an old woman
walks about. You can feel all of Paris tilt to one side, like water in a basin.
It's very cold. A fine sun and some wisps of cloud in the sky—The gutters
are iced over. As I reach the Louis Philippe Bridge, the north wind lowers
a cloud on us and a few flakes of hard snow rap my face.—Passing Notre
Dame, I note the great bell's given up.

Rue Saint-André-des-Arcs, you begin to sense the festivities.—Yes,
festivity: a corpse-in-exile is coming back in triumph. Up ahead of me, three
young workmen, the kind going about in tatters cold and hungry all winter,

stride along joyfully. One leaps up in the air, does a little jig, and shouts, "Hurrah for the Emperor!" Some pretty little shopgirls, all dressed up out of their usual grey, are pulled along by their student friends. Cabs clatter towards the Invalides. The snow thickens as I reach the Rue du Four. The sky goes black, with the flakes on it like white tears. God's out too, hanging his funeral cloth.

But it doesn't last long. A pale shaft of white light strikes the corner of the rue de Grenelle and the rue du Bac: that's where the the guardsmen stop all vehicles. I step through. Two great empty carts pushed by soldiers rumble behind me and turn into their quarters at the end of the rue de Grenelle at the very moment when I emerge into the vastness of the Invalides. For a moment, I think it must be all over, Napoleon's already passed by: a solid mass of people is heading my way, as though returning from the event. But no, it's just a row of guardsmen on foot, pushing them back. I show them my ticket for the first stand on the left and step through.

The stands are enormous scaffoldings that run from the river all the way to the railings of the dome itself: there are three of them on either side, and they cover all the grass.

As I arrive, the stands on my right still hide the plaza. The air is filled with a huge, lugubrious noise: like the cadence of endless hammers on boards. These are the hundred thousand spectators; jammed in the stands, frozen by the wind, they stamp their feet until the cortege arrives. I climb the scaffolding. The oddity of the scene persists: women, nearly all of them veiled and wearing thick bootees, sink into masses of fur; the men wear extravagant nose-guards.

The decorations? Some good, some bad. Cheap laid on grandiose. On both sides of the main avenue, heroic, giant-sized statues, pale in this wintry sun; they carry it off. But their marble is plaster. In the distance, opposite the dome, a bronze statue of the Emperor. Only the bronze is also plaster. Between each statue, a tasteless gilt-painted pillar on which is mounted a stock-pot: for the time being, it contains only snow. Behind the statues, the stands and the crowd; between them, a scattering of guardsmen; rising over the stands, sixty splendid pointed masts on which float, magnificently, red-white-and-blue pennants.

It seems there hasn't been time to complete the decoration of the main entrance to the palace. Over the main gate is a sketchy triumphal arch put together out of canvas and crepe; the wind toys with it as with laundry hung out the attic window of some hovel. A row of bare masts, undressed and dry, rises over the cannons—from a distance they look like matchsticks children might prop up in sand. Rags and tatters, pretentiously decked out in black with silver stars.

Furthest away, the dome, blurred by the high mists in the luminous sky, together with its flag and mourning bunting, its icy shards of reflected metal, looks both somber and splendid.

It's noon.

Every quarter-hour, the cannons boom. The crowd mills about and stamps its collective foot. Policemen in civilian clothes—betrayed by spurs and high-collared uniforms—stroll about. Across from me, a vivid shaft of light falls on a sorry statue of Joan of Arc: she holds a palm in her hand as though shielding her eyes from a painful sun.

Nearby, a fire built in a pile of sand, at which guardsmen warm their feet.

Now and then a batch of uniformed bandsmen break into the orchestra between two stands opposite me. A mournful fanfare ensues, then they tumble back down and vanish back into the crowd: only to reappear, but with dance-tunes instead of fanfares. A peddler turns up offering lamentations and a program for a penny each. I buy one of each.

All eyes are fixed on the corner of the Quai d'Orsay, from which the funeral cortege is due to appear. The cold makes the crowd all the more impatient. Sullen detonations, puffs of smoke, black and white, pop up from the misty distances of the Champs Elysées.

Suddenly, the guardsmen fall in. An artillery officer on horseback gallops across the avenue. A double rank is drawn up. Workmen prop ladders up on the lamp-stands and light their fires. The heavy artillery in the eastern corner of the plaza fires a noisy salvo; a thick yellow smoke, broken up by flashes of lightning, blankets the whole area. From where I'm standing, I can see the guns being tended—two fine old field-pieces from the seventeenth century, whose very smoke smells of bronze.

It's now twelve-thirty.

At the river end of the esplanade, the grave arrival of a double row of mounted grenadiers, caparisoned in yellow: the Seine Gendarmerie, the vanguard of the cortege. At that very moment, the sun does its duty and shines with its full splendor. This is Austerlitz time.

After the fur busbies of the Seine Gendarmerie, the brass helmets of the Paris Municipal Police; then the Lancers, their tri-colored pennants fluttering charmingly in the wind. Drums and fanfares.

On the stand opposite me, a man in a blue smock climbs up the scaffolding at risk of life and limb. No one helps him. A man in white gloves stares at him, but doesn't lend a hand. Nonetheless, the man makes it to the top.

The procession, with generals and marshals mixed in, is a splendid sight. The sun beats down on the Carabineers' breast-plates; each chest becomes a flaming star. Proud and grave, the three great military academies march past. Then the artillery, the infantry, with full packs, as if off to war, each gun-carriage with a spare wheel lashed behind.

In the middle distance, an oversized statue of Louis XIV, heavily draped, elegant, and gilt by the sun, stares at all this pomp with amazement.

Now the Mounted National Guard appears on horseback. The crowd murmurs. In good order, perhaps; but they lack real glory; they make a dead spot in the procession. People laugh. I hear the following: "Look at that fat colonel! That's a funny way to grip a sword!" "Who's that?" "Montalivet."

Interminable legions of National Guardsmen now parade by, on foot, their rifles as bedraggled as their ranks. A mounted guardsman drops his chapska and gallops about bare-headed to the joy of the crowd, a hundred thousand strong.

From time to time the procession halts, then sets off again. The brasiers between the statues are now all lit and smoke like huge punch-bowls. All crane their necks. Here's the Almoner's coach from the Belle-Poule: and black, with silver trim. In its dark depths, the priest himself, in deep mourning. Then the great black, mirror-paneled carriage belong to the Saint Helena Commission. Four horses for each.

Suddenly, cannons roar at three points of the compass. This triple peal wraps the ear in a magnificent triangle of noise. Drums roll on the parade-grounds.

The Emperor's carriage comes into sight. The sun, intermittent, makes a magnificent reappearance.

In that mix of sun and mist, against the grey-and-rust backdrop of the trees of the Champs-Elysées, and perceived through the great white statues, like so many specters, a slow-motion, mountainous mass of gold progresses. So far, all one can see is a sort of luminous sparkle: here, on the carriage, stars; there, flashes of lightning. The whole wrapped in an immense blanket of sound. It seems that, as torches trail smoke, so this carriage train is made of the acclamation of a whole city.

As it veers into the esplanade, the carriage, almost haphazardly, stops by a statue on the corner of the avenue and the quay. Later, I established that the statue was of Marshal Ney.

When the carriage-catafalque appears, it is one-thirty.

The procession starts up again. The carriage advances slowly; one begins to discern its shape.

Here come the imperial pall-bearers', the marshals' and generals' saddle-horses. Here are the eighty-six legionary under-officers carrying the banners of the eighty-six departments. Nothing could be finer than this solid block of men with their forest of flags on high. One might as well be tramping through a field of giant dahlias.

Here is a white horse, covered from head to tail in violet, led by a chamberlain in sky-blue embroidered in silver, and two footmen in green braided with gold, the imperial livery. The crowd quivers: "It's Napoleon's own war-horse!" Most are convinced. Supposing the horse had mounted Napoleon, he'd be thirty years old. A fine age for a horse! But the truth is this palfrey is a walk-on horse. For ten years he's played the war-horse part in every military funeral arranged by the authorities.

This straw charger bears on his back a proper saddle: the one which Napoleon used at Marengo, a saddle of crimson velvet—somewhat the worse for wear.

Behind the horse, in strict and compact ranks, the five-hundred sailors of the Belle-Poule. They are mostly young. They're in combat dress: full jackets, round tarred hats, pistols in their belts, boarding-grapples in hand, sword—short sword with a large pommel of polished steel—by their side.

The salvoes continue. The crowd trades stories: that this morning, the cannon's muzzle not having been unstopped, the first shot had cut a Municipal Guardsman in two; that on the Place Louis XVI, a man had slipped under the carriage and had been crushed by its wheels.

The carriage is now close by, immediately preceded by the officers of the Belle Poule, commanded by the Prince de Joinville on horseback. The Prince features a beard (blond), which I believe to be against Navy regulations.

He is wearing, for the first time, his sash as a Commander of the Legion of Honor: up to now, he was no more than a simple Chevalier.

As the carriage arrives before me, some unforeseen obstacle stops it. For several minutes it stands still between the statues of Joan of Arc and Charles V. I can study it at my leisure. I must say, the whole has a certain grandeur. By its size, for it has great mass, all gilt. Four great gilded wheels bear a pyramid of different levels. There are fine details to be noted under the great, bee-strewn, violet cloth that covers the whole from top to bottom: there are great, startled eagles on the base; the fourteen victories of his coronation bear, on a tablet of gold, the effigy of a coffin. The real coffin is invisible. It is contained in a coffer at the base.

That is the great defect. The carriage hides what we want to see, what all of France has called for, what the people expect—Napoleon's coffin.

On the simulacrum sarcophagus lie the Emperor's insignia: his crown, his sword, his sceptre, his cloak. In the golden gorge between the victories on the roofing and the eagles at the base, one can clearly see, despite the already-flaking gilt, the seams where the pine-boards meet. Another defect: all this glister is but show. Pine and marbled paper-board is the reality, and for the Emperor's carriage I could have wished a splendor more genuine.

The rest of this sculptured mass is not without pride and art, though its general design and ornamentation lie uneasily between Renaissance and Rococo.

Two huge sheaves of flags from all the nations of Europe flutter splendidly fore and aft of the carriage. Fully loaded, the carriage weighs twenty-six thousand pounds; the coffin alone, two-and-a-half tons. Nothing could have been more magnificent than the caparison of the sixteen horses that pulled the great carriage. Enormous, terrifying beasts, white-plumed to the hindquarters, covered from head to hoof in cloth-of-gold, so that all one sees is their eyes, and they look like ghost-horses.

Footmen in imperial livery lead this formidable cavalcade.

By contrast, the worthy and venerable generals who hold the pall-bearers' ropes look anything but fantastic. They are led by two marshals— the Duke of Reggio, short and with his eye shut down by a stroke, on the right, and on the left, Count Molitor. Behind them follow: on the right, an admiral, Baron Duperré, a fat, jovial sailor, and on the left, a lieutenant general, Count Bertrand, a broken, old, worn-out man, a noble, illustrious personage. All four wear red sashes.

The carriage, be it said in passing, should have had only eight horses. Eight is a symbolic number with a special meaning in this ceremony. Seven horses is a carter; sixteen, a show-off; eight is an emperor.

The spectators let up stamping their feet only as the catafalque passes them by. For that, the feet fall silent. One can feel great thoughts run through the crowd.

Once again the carriage starts up. The drums roll. Cannons fire. Napoleon is at the portals of the Invalides. It is ten minutes before two.

Follow the hearse: all surviving imperial servants; all surviving soldiers of his guard, still kitted out in those old uniforms that have become unfamiliar to us; and then, behind them, the rest of the great procession, the various regiments of the Army and the National Guard, filling, it is said, the whole of the Quai d'Orsay, the Louis XVI bridge, the Place de la Concorde as far as the arch at the Etoile.

The carriage does not penetrate the courtyard of the Invalides: Louis XIV's portals are too low to admit it. It wheels right, and one sees the sailors enter its coffer, emerge with the coffin, and then enter through the portico to the courtyard.

For the spectators outside, that's the end of it. Noisily and hastily they tumble down from the stands. At intervals, they regroup before boards which announce: "LEROY, LEMONADES, rue de la Serpe, near the Invalides— Fine Wines and Hot Pies."

I can at last study the decorations along the central avenue. Nearly all these plaster statues are poor stuff; some of them are absurd. Seen from a distance, Louis XVI had some stature; from close up, he is grotesque. Macdonald and Mortier are decent likenesses; and Ney too, had they not made his brow too high. The sculptor sought to show us melancholy; he merely exaggerated and makes us laugh. The head is far too big. It is said that in their hurry, the authorities gave out the wrong measurements; on the great day, Marshal Ney was a foot too tall. So what did Fine Arts do? It sawed a foot-long slice out of his torso and joined the two remaining parts any which way.

The Emperor's plaster, painted in bronze, in cloudy with stains; the imperial robes look like much-mended, old, green serge.

This brings to mind—how ideas spring to mind is a mystery!—that in the summer, when I visited M. Thiers, I heard Napoleon's valet, Marchand, tell the company that Napoleon felt most comfortable in old clothes, a liking I understand and share. For a working brain, a new hat is torture.

"The Emperor," Marchand said, "took with him from France three suits of clothes, two frock coats and two hats; he made them do for the six years he spent in Saint Helena. He did not wear his uniform."

He offered some other curious details. When in residence at the Tuileries, Napoleon seemed to make sudden, quick costume changes. There was nothing to it, Marchand explained. Customarily, he wore civilian clothes: white, cashmere breeches, white silk stockings and buckled shoes. But in a little ante-room he kept a pair of knee-high riding boots lined with white silk. When circumstances required him to mount of a horse, he took off his shoes, put on his boots, got into his uniform coat, and there he was, in uniform. When he came back, he removed his boots, put his shoes back on, and returned to civilian status. His breeches, stockings and shoes were good for the day only. On the morrow, this imperial detritus became the property of his valet.

202 It's three o'clock. A salvo of artillery announces that the ceremony at the Invalides is over. I meet B., who has just come from the ceremony. The sight of the bier provoked great emotion; the language simple yet grand. M. de Joinville addressed the King thus: "Sire, I present you with the body of the Emperor Napoleon." The King replied, "I receive it for France." Then he said to Bertrand, "General, lay the Emperor's glorious sword on his bier." And to Gourgaud, "Lay the Emperor's hat on his bier."

Mozart's *Requiem* caused no great stir. Fine music, but showing its age. Alas! Music grows wrinkles, too!

The catafalque was finished barely an hour before the coffin arrived. B. got into the church at eight: the draperies were only half-hung, and workmen with their tools and ladders stood all about. The crowd was already gathering.

M. de Joinville, who hadn't seen his family in six months, kissed the Queen's hand and joyously shook hands with his brothers and sisters. The Queen received him gravely, without effusion: as queen rather than mother. Meanwhile, archbishops and priests gathered around Napoleon's coffin, sang *Requiescat in Pace*.

The procession was fine, but excessively military: fitting for Bonaparte, not for Napoleon. All the organs of state should have been represented, at least in delegations. But the government's want of care was obvious. It was in a hurry to get the funeral over. Philippe de Ségur who, as one of the Emperor's former aides-de-camp, marched behind the carriage, told me how on the river-bank at Courbevoie this morning, with the temperature in the low forties, there hadn't been so much as a heated waiting room: the two hundred old men who'd served the Emperor had to wait an hour-and-a-half in a sort of Greek temple open to the winds.

Same story with the steamships that accompanied the body up the river from Le Havre—a trip otherwise admirable for the serious and respectful behavior of the river-dwellers. Not a single ship had been properly furnished or provisioned. No beds. Orders not to disembark. M. de Joinville was forced to sleep in a large room on a table, while others slept underneath. People slept on the floor, the luckier ones on a bench or chair. The powers-that-be were ill-tempered, and the Prince complained bitterly: that in this affair, the people showed its greatness, the government its pettiness.

Trying to reach the Champs-Elysées, I crossed the suspension bridge, paying my penny to do so. True generosity, considering that the crowd which fills the bridge doesn't bother to do so.

The various regiments and legions are still at war in the Avenue de Neuilly, which is decorated (or rather dishonored) along its whole length by more of those awful statues of the Famed, and by triumphal columns mounted with unbalanced golden eagles perching on pedestals of grey marble. Kids have fun punching holes in the marble, which is only painted canvas.

Each column carries, between two sheaves of tricolored flags, the name and date of one of Bonaparte's victories.

A sort of mediocre opera backdrop perches on top of the Arch of Triumph: the Emperor stands on a chariot surrounded by his Faithful: Glory on his right and Grandeur on his left. How can a statue possibly convey Grandeur? Does one make it bigger than the others? This is monumental Incoherence.

This decor faces Paris. But going round the Arch, seeing it from the back, what you have is nothing more than a stage-prop. On the Neuilly side, Emperor, Glories and the Renowned are no more than crude, round-topped shapes. On which subject, I add, the subjects of the statues on the main avenue of the Invalides were an ill-assorted lot. The published list offers the most bizarre sorts of combinations. One bears: Lobau, Charlemagne, and Hugues Capet.

A few months back, I was strolling on these same Champs-Elysées with M. Thiers, who was then prime minister. He would have pulled this thing off; he would have taken the task to heart. He was a man with ideas; he senses Napoleon, he loves him. He told me stories about the Emperor. M. de Rémusat had sent him his own mother's unpublished memoirs. With hundreds of little touches.

The Emperor was a good man, and a tease. Teasing is the wickedness in good men. Napoleon's sister Caroline wanted to be a queen; so he made her Queen of Naples. The poor woman no sooner had a throne than a swarm of problems arose; that throne gave her wrinkles; it made her fade.

One day, Talma was lunching with Napoleon—the Emperor would only receive him at lunch—and as they were seated, lo! The Queen of Naples arrives, pale and weary. The Emperor looked at her, then turned to Talma, who was much embarrassed between these two majesties, and said, "You see, my dear Talma, they all want to be queens, and they all lose their beauty thereby. Look at Caroline. She's a queen; look how ugly she is."

As I walk by, they've just finished taking down the draped-in-black stands and ballroom seats put up by speculators at the top of the avenue. On one of them, opposite the Beaujon Garden, is written: "Seats available. Austerlitz Stand. Inquire at M. Berthellemot, Confectioner."

On the other side of the street, under an acrobats' tent with two dreadful, painted insignia—the death of the Emperor, his feats at Mazagran—another board announces: "Napoleon in his Tomb. Threepence."

Workmen pass by singing, "Hurrah for the great Napoleon!" "Good old Napoleon!" Peddlers walk about offering some mysterious hot drink from a copper tea-kettle in the shape of an urn, and draped in black. An old woman innocently pulls up her knickers in the midst of the tumult.

Towards five, the empty carriage plods back up the Champs-Elysées to be "put away" under the Arch at the Etoile. A good idea. But those ghost-horses are weary now. They shuffle along painfully, slowly, and only with great efforts being made by the coachmen. Nothing could be stranger than to hear those "whoa there's" and "ho's" coming from this fantastical, imperial train.

I come home along the boulevards. The mass of people remains enormous. Suddenly, it parts and turns aside with a sort of respect. A man walks proudly up their midst. An old hussar of the Imperial Guard, a tall veteran with a firm gait. He is in full uniform: bright red trousers, a white jacket with gold trim, a sky-blue dolmen, a busby cable-knit with flames, sword at his side, scabbard banging against his thigh, eagle on his knapsack. Around him little children shout, "Long live the Emperor!"

This whole ceremony had something of a magician's disappearing trick about it. The government seemed afraid of the ghost it was evoking. It both showed and concealed Napoleon. What was too great or too touching about him was set aside. What was real and great disappeared under decorations splendid and less so; the imperial parade was buried in the military; the army in the National Guard; the coffin in the cenotaph.

Better would have been to take the man frankly, to be honored by him, to treat him royally and popularly as emperor: to take strength where it all nearly faltered.

Today, March 11, 1841, is three months later, and I've just seen the esplanade of the Invalides again.

I went to see an old officer who was sick. The weather was of the very best, the sun hot and young; it was a day from spring's fullness, not its youth.

The esplanade is all upside down, cluttered with the ruins of the funeral. The scaffolding for the stands is gone, but the patches of lawn which they had covered are hideously furrowed by deep ruts made by the builders' carts. Only two statues still stand: those of Marceau and Duguesclin. Hither and yon are little piles of stone, the debris of pedestals.

Soldiers, invalids, apple-sellers stroll about in this poetic decay.

A happy crowd hurried by the Invalides to see the artesian well. Two chocolate-colored omnibuses stood in a quiet corner, bearing the following legend in big letters:

VISIT THE SLAUGHTER HOUSE WELL

Three months ago, it read:

NAPOLEON'S FUNERAL AT THE INVALIDES

The great courtyard was a scene of great charm, young and old rejoicing in the warmth of the sun on this visiting day. The curious were many. Gardeners were pruning the arborways and lilacs blossomed in the little garden-plots of the invalids. A boy of fourteen or so had climbed up on the next-to-last cannon—the very one that killed a policeman during the opening salvo on December 15—and sang his lungs out.

A veritable swarm of children, hardly if at all supervised by their maids, and each with his own soldier, fought miniature battles among the eighty mighty long-barreled cannons that Constantine brought back from Algiers.

As I was copying the inscription on one of those guns, a fresh, pretty little girl, all in white, filled its Turk mouth with sand from her tiny pink fingers. An inmate, upright on his peg-legs, and no doubt responsible for the guns, watched her with a smile.

As I was leaving the esplanade at around three, I saw a little group crossing it slowly. It consisted of a man, dressed in black, with crepe on his arm and hat, and three others—one of whom, a young man in a blue shirt, held a little boy by the hand. Tucked under the arm of the man in black was a whitish box half hidden by a black cloth: he carried it the way a musician carries the case containing his instrument. I drew near. The man in black was an undertaker; the box, a child's coffin.

This little group moved parallel to the Invalides, thus at a right angle to the path followed, three months earlier, by Napoleon's bier.

Today, May 8, I returned to the Invalides to see the chapel of Saint Jerome where the Emperor temporarily lies at rest. Every trace of the funeral ceremonies is gone. The quincunxes have been redrawn; only the grass has not yet grown back. A sunny day, mixed with cloud and occasional rain. The trees green and cheerful. The aged patients talk gently to a bevy of children, and cultivate the blooms in their tiny gardens. It's that wonderful time of the year when the last, late lilacs show their leaves and the first laburnums bloom.

Great cloud-shadows course across the main courtyard where, in a first-floor archivolt, sits a pedestrian plaster bust of Napoleon, and a sad equestrian Louis XIV proudly carved in stone on the great portal. All round the yard, just under the roof parapets, there remain, as a last vestige, long, thin strips of black cloth painted, in threes, with the names of the great generals of the Revolution and the Empire. The wind is beginning to strip them away, here and there. But on one, whose tip floated loose, I read the following three names:

SAURET—CHAMBURE—HUG ...

The end of the third name has been torn off by the wind. Was it "Hugo" or "Huguet"?

Some young soldiers entered the church. The church itself was naked and cold. A huge grey cloth masked the dome. Behind, one heard dull, lugubrious hammering.

I walked around a bit reading the names of all the warriors buried there. The whole length of the nave, high up above us in the vaulting, gently floated the flags wrested from the enemy. Between hammer-blows, I heard a sibilant whispering in a far corner: an old woman was confessing.

The soldiers left, I behind them.

They turned right and we got mixed up with a large, well-dressed group going the same way and wound up in the inner courtyard and the little door into the dome.

There, in the shadows, I found three more leaden statues, come from God knows where, though I know I saw them when still a child, in 1815— during the general mutilation of buildings, dynasties and nations. These three statues, of the worst possible Empire taste, cold as allegory, woebegone as mediocrity, stand there in the grass alongside the wall in a jumble of cornices, like so many tragedians hissed off the stage. One represents Strength: the figure holds back a chained lion. Nothing is so out of place as a statue without a pedestal: it's like a rider without a horse or a king without a throne. Soldiers have a battle, or death; kings have empire, or a tomb; statues are either upright in the sky or lie on the ground.

207

A statue on its two feet, like an ordinary man, astonishes the comprehension and importunes the mind. One can't fail to notice it's made of plaster or bronze, and we know neither material walks. One wants to say to the poor, unhappy, man, "Come on, up with you. Walk. Go wherever you're going. You've got ground underfoot. What's keeping you?" For statues as for men, a pedestal is a narrow, tiny and honorable area: with a precipice on every side.

Having passed the statues, I turned right and entered the church. Several young women went in alongside me, and the sentinel, old, bent-over, silent and still in the shadows, let us pass. His worn wooden leg rested on a marble fleur-de-lys sticking up out of the pavement.

To enter the chapel where Napoleon rests, one walks on a mosaic of fleur-de-lys. The rest were in a hurry; I entered slowly.

A dull, white light from above, studio light, not church light. Under the cupola—where the altar was and the tomb will be—rose the giant scaffolding, cut off from the nave by a great, grey cloth, which had served for the dismantling of the baldaquin built under Louis XIV. Nothing's left of it but the shafts of the six wooden columns that supported the superstructure. These columns, lacking capitals or tops of any kind were held upright by six sorts of logs serving as pedestals. The gold leaf, whose spirals had once seemed to make the columns serpentine, had all gone, leaving black patches. The men working within the scaffolding looked like caged birds. Down below, others were ripping up the paving, and still others strolled about the church, carrying their ladders, chatting and whistling.

To my right, the Saint Augustine chapel was full of rubble. Great chunks of that splendid mosaic in which Louis XIV had planted his lilies and his suns, now hid the feet of Saints Monica and Alipe, who looked down, shocked and scandalized, from their niches. Between the two windows, Girardon's "Religion" cast a grave eye on this disorder. Beyond the chapel, great slabs of marble, which once tiled the dome, were stacked up against the wall, half concealing a white warrior reclining below a pyramidal heap of black marble set into the wall. Under the warrior, the floor tiles parted enough so that one could discern three letters:

UBA

The tombstone of VaUBAn.

Opposite Vauban lay Turenne, who'd been shown greater respect. There was no pile of ruins leaning up against this sculpture machine. It was more pompous than funereal, better at the opera than in church—so in keeping with the noble, cold etiquette that marks the art around Louis XIV. No hoarding or excavation kept the passer-by from contemplating Turenne, served up as a Roman emperor, dying of an Austrian bullet up above a bronze bas-relief of the battle of Turheim, or from reading the memorable date of 1675: in which year Turenne died, the Duke of Saint-Simon was born, and Louis XIV laid the foundations of the Invalides.

To the right, against the scaffolding of the dome and the statue of Turenne, between the silence of this sepulcher and the banging of the work-men, in a tiny, deserted chapel, I could just make out, through a white arch and behind a railing, a set of gilded statues laid there, pell-mell (and no doubt taken off the baldaquin)—seemingly conversing furtively about the devastation that surrounded them. Six angels, winged and luminous, six golden ghosts in the sinister light of a pale ray of sun. One showed the others the dark, mourning-hung chapel of Saint Jerome; with terror in his voice, he pronounced the word "Napoleon." Up above, on the cornice of the chapel's little dome, a great gilt, wooden angel, eyes to heaven, played on a bass-viol, his posture very like that Veronese gave Tintoretto in the Marriage of Canae.

I had arrived at the threshold of the Chapel of Saint Jerome.

A big archivolt with a violet portière, somewhat weedily stamped with golden frets and palms; at the top of this curtain, the imperial shield painted on wood; on the left, two sets of tricolored flags topped with eagles—more like cocks dressed up for the occasion; various invalids, pikes in hand, wearing their Legions d'Honor; a vast, silent and recollected crowd advancing under the dome; in back, eight or ten paces away, a wrought-iron grille painted bronze, with dull, weighty ornaments—lion-heads, gilded N's that look like applied tinsel, the imperial arms, the hand of Justice, and a scepter topped with a figurine of a seated Charlemagne, crowned and with an orb in his hand; behind the grille, the chapel interior, very August, formidable, grabbing, a hanging lamp, a huge golden eagle, wings widespread, belly shining from a votive light and wings from the reflected sun; over the eagle, under a giant, blinding sheaf of enemy flags, the coffin itself, ebony feet and bronze handles visible; on the coffin, the great imperial, Charlemagne crown, the laurel-leaf Caesar diadem, the pall, of violet velvet, sewn with beads; before the coffin, on a credence, the Saint Helena hat and the Eylau sword; on the wall, to the right, a silver roundel with the word "Wagram" and another with "Austerlitz"; all around, on the walls, more violet hangings, more bees, more eagles, and, the coffin—a fresco in which the Angel of the Last Judgment blows his trumpet into Jerome's dormant ear: all this I saw at a glance, and all this is engraved in my memory for life.

209

His hat, low, long at either end, barely used, with a black hat-band from which emerged a tiny tricolor cockade, rested on his sword, whose gauntlet of chiseled gold faced the chapel entrance, and whose blade faced the coffin.

Here, the petty sat with the grand. Petty were: the violet cloth stamped rather than woven, painted board making do for stone, hollow metal offered as solid bronze, this wooden shield, those N's like painted straw, these little canvas columns concocted into granite, those cock-like eagles. Grand was: the place, the man, the reality; this sword, that hat, this eagle, those soldiers, these people, that coffin of ebony, that ray of sunshine.

The crowd stood there as before an altar with God present. Yet when it quit the chapel, a hundred yards down the road, off it went to look at the kitchens and the great cook-pot. Such is a crowd.

With deep emotion, I studied the coffin. I recalled that it less than a year ago, in July, a certain M.*** had visited me. He was, he said, a master carpenter, my neighbor in the rue de Tournelles. He wanted my advice on a valuable and important project he was then undertaking. As I am greatly interested in this lesser architecture which we call "furniture," I had acceded to his request and followed him to his workshop. After walking through several crowded rooms, and when he'd shown me a vast inventory of pieces in oak and mahogany—desks with tooled beading, tables with curved, twisting legs (amongst which I admired an old, Renaissance cupboard inlaid with marble and mother-of-pearl, a charming piece, though much damaged)— he led me into an enormous, bustling workshop, all hurry, noise and work, in which some twenty craftsmen worked on various bits of wood. In a corner, I'd spotted a sort of large, black, ebony case, perhaps eight feet by three, with great bronze rings at its extremities. I drew near to it, and he said, "This is just what I wanted to show you." This black case was the Emperor's coffin. I saw it then; I was seeing it again today. I'd seen it empty, hollow, wide-open; now I saw it full, inhabited by a great memory, and sealed for all time.

I remember studying its interior at length; and a curious white vein in the ebony plank. I recall thinking: "In a few months the lid will be sealed, and my eyes will have been closed for three or four thousand years before other human eyes will see what I see now, the interior of Napoleon's coffin."

I then picked up the various pieces of the coffin that had not yet been fitted, and weighed them in my hand. The ebony was exquisite. And heavy. The artist, wishing to give me an impression of the whole, bade six men to put its lid on. I could not approve the banal shape of the coffin, which is that given today to all coffins, altars and wedding gifts. I would have had Napoleon rest in an Egyptian mummy-case, like Sesostris, or in a Roman sarcophagus like Merovingus. What is simple is also grand.

The lid was inscribed in large letters, "Napoleon." I asked him of what metal the letters were made. "Of bronze," he said. "But we have gilded them." I replied that the letters should be made of gold: before a hundred years were up, the bronze would have oxidized and eaten into the wood. How much would gold letters cost the state? I asked him. He replied, "About twenty thousand francs, Sir." That same evening I went to see M. Thiers and told him what I'd seen. "You're right," he said. "They should be in gold. I'll see to it." Three days later, on the 15th of July, the Treaty was signed. To this day I don't know if M. Thiers gave the appropriate order, whether it was executed, or whether the letters on the coffin are of gold.

I left the Chapel of Saint Jerome as four o'clock rang, and as I left, I said to myself, "Sticking to appearances, what we have here is a cheap, tawdry, breakable 'N' to replace the marble 'L's' with their crowns and fleurs-de-lys. But in fact, that's not the case. The day will come when Louis XIV will get his dome back, and Napoleon will have a sepulcher of his own.

[from Choses Vues, *abridged and freely translated—K. B.]*

Investigations

Harold Rosenberg

Notes from the Ground Up

Contrary to the suggestion contained in the term, the "middle-brow" is not a half-way person. The notion that all he wants is to mediate between the inventor of difficult truths and a public unprepared to receive them is a delusion—a delusion, one has reason to suspect, fostered by the middlebrow himself.

The fact is that the middlebrow is a fanatic and has his own truth.

It is the truth of those seeking revenge, of the insulted and the injured. For the middlebrow has been scorned by both the ignorant and the educated; by the ignorant for showing off his education, by the educated for yielding to ignorance.

You will not grasp the vengeful middlebrow truth if you reduce it to the proposition: knowledge is a commodity that can be purveyed at a profit. This is the middlebrow's working maxim.

Beyond it, however, he has another principle which he keeps to himself: KNOWLEDGE IS NOT POWER BUT CAN BE A TOOL OF POWER. In this is reflected the full depths of his malice and of his hope.

Appalled by the enormous implications of his secret credo, the middle-brow dons the disguise of the Middle Way. Should the spotlight fall on him, he will deny any knowledge of the conspiracy . . . Look squarely into his smiling, reasonable pan, however, and you will have no trouble spotting that it is a mask which he can replace in an instant.

Underneath his make-up of the impartial "communicator" who wants nothing more out of life than to enable you to understand what great minds think, this shrewd, ambitious, and fearful creature is scheming to win everything for himself, including respect for his incredible mental fabrications. Were he to have his way, both highbrows and lowbrows would be extinguished and his breed alone survive as the type intended by the evolution of the human brain.

Ideas as tools can never conquer, for there are men who are haunted by ideas.

By embracing the idea as a living presence, such a man fills it with his own self, which wrecks its working parts from within, a kind of monkey in the machinery.

No idea will function efficiently if someone is going to insist on taking it with absolute seriousness. The idea of freedom began to work poorly when John Brown appeared, the idea of Communism when the Hungarian students momentarily rescued it from the textbooks.

American literature is becoming more sophisticated about persons who manipulate ideas and are manipulated by them, e.g., spellbinders, hucksters, PR (public relations not *Partisan Review*) people. Yet despite the thirties and its casualties, it has still to learn how to deal with people haunted by ideas.

One reason our literature fails to rise to the comedy and tragedy of the idea-haunted intellectual is that the American intellectual, stuck with the nineteenth-century concept of personality, fails to recognize his own case. His belated romanticism apprehends life as a struggle to preserve his uniqueness from damage by "the material weight of society." It never occurs to him that this uniqueness, such as it is, can only be the effect of his idea and that it is that which he ought to defend at all costs. Instead, it is for the illusion of self that he struggles, even against his idea. For the sake of his constantly vanishing ego—and just because it is always vanishing—he will forsake not only his family, his love, his vocation, but even his deepest conviction, lest it dilute the original man in him. So he wars against everything, like a swami turned inside out, and, naturally, he loses—how could he win?—and must console himself with the old song and dance about crushed genius, coupled with oratory to the effect that lunatics and vipers have the truth on their side while their keepers are perverts and idiots . . . Keep talking, reply the keepers, so long as the social principle remains in our hands we can afford to let personalities fall to the ground.

It is possible to get sick of outlaws. Especially if their only interest in being outlaws is to assume a position in a debate that heard its last word a century ago. As for the real world, it has entered into an age of infighting.

One also gets sick of victims, whether their injuries were inflicted upon them privately or as members of a group. The problem is to rush them to a hospital and to clean up the conditions that brought them to their sorry pass. We should wish to eliminate the victims through philanthropy and social justice. If, instead, we cherish their complaints as literature, this is to cover up our indifference with esthetic hypocrisy.

But where would our official literature be without hypocrisy? Without JB, soap opera of the Common Man as victim—to Brooks Atkinson an epic, of liberalism, no doubt. Fake pity whose alternative is fake self-pity: beätkinson or beat.

Ahab was justified, though a victim, because in payment for one mere leg he assumed the right to assert in action his idea that to be a free individual meant that no one could take him for a sucker. In a nation of Confidence Men this was a pretty good idea, though to make a universal of it Ahab had to extend his principle to include nature and accident, which made his idea grotesque.

In any case, *Moby Dick* is a drama of *the refusal to be a victim*, of the going over of injury into freedom by means of an original concept. The Fitzgerald Trauma is something quite different.

Ahab, like Raskolnikov, was outlawed by his idea. Having his leg bitten off inspired him; without this inspiration he would have been a mere handicapped sea captain. Had he complained about his accident, or attempted to explain it by unsafe conditions in the fishing industry, all the worse for him. "Aw, stop whining," they would have told him on the bench.

As it was, his amputation became the pretext for a string of aggressive formulas, derived from capitalism but transcending it:

Every loss a profit.
Impossible to break even, but only a slave lets
himself be subtracted.
Freedom means 1 = 1: minus a leg, plus a world.

Ahab outlawed by his idea cannot be rehabilitated. To the sociologist, as to the doctor, he is a hopeless case. Since there is nothing they can do for him—actually, he's making out much too well—he has become a proper subject for the researches of poetry. Yet in no way does his ordeal reflect discredit on medicine or sociology, as does suffering in reactionary fiction, where every limitation of science is gleefully seized upon as an argument on behalf of superstition, as if medicine were worthless unless it could grow back legs eaten off by fish.

In the Fitzgerald Trauma, inherited by Faulkner and numerous descendants, the heavens are closed like a scar. Misery aplenty, but no storms. The hero fights to get even. Who will deny that, had it been up to him, Gatsby or Joe Christmas would have chosen to live without his handicap?

218

Although, being a romantic, he might have preferred to have it; the blemish made him mysterious, a personality, "unique"—and provided him with a "cause." Still, there was a problem: to "pass" or not to "pass."

What haunts this hero is not an idea but the image of another social self, a tonier one, a whiter one, which he might be were he not prevented. He wishes to be somebody else, and an abstract somebody at that. He is an outlaw out of conformity—like one who lifts a pair of silk gloves at Tripler's—a conformity made passionate through frustration.

Thus his pained presence gives pleasure and reassurance to those on the inside, or who think of themselves as on the inside—he is a witness to their being desirable (which they are not to themselves). Why have Fitzgerald and Faulkner become so popular since the War?—I mean, not in literary circles where, apart from their mental qualities, they deserve to be appreciated for their verbal and visionary gifts, but with the Broadway, movie, and paperback masses. As the literature of hunger gave savor to the giant meals of the Victorians, so today the literature of the outcast is the great binder of Philistine mental life, which has no trouble recognizing itself in both the excluded and the excluders of any social order.

But are Gatsby and Christmas genuine human outcasts, as Ahab by his idea? Why shouldn't they pass? There are so many things to pass into, every one of them as good as Long Island elite or Southern pure white. (It's the deepest insult that I'm supposed to take Gatsby's predicament seriously, as if getting in where he wanted to be were what I ought to be doing myself or agree that my life is worthless.)

But no, to the author, the heavens, and the earth too, are closed like a scar. As he himself is romantically committed to being "crushed by the material weight of society," so must his hero. To keep the latter's case from being settled amicably (perhaps with the aid of the "social dynamics" that those hybrid big-city intellectuals are so fond of talking about), it is necessary to insist that his hero's blemish is more than skin-deep. The author is on the side of the flaw against his hero.

This is another way of saying that he's against man, in favor of an image of purity (worth) that lacks any idea. No wonder Faulkner had Christmas *sacrificed* by a human vermin whose beastliness he covered with a seraphic refulgence. While Fitzgerald practices upon Gatsby a species of persecution, with the aim of demonstrating his solidarity with those who assume the right to despise him for what he *is*, like a Communist under a cloud who proves himself by putting the finger on his comrades. His tale succumbs as to a fate (of course, he's personally on Gatsby's side) to the enemy's definition of him and of itself. His work groans and leaps with the hardships, elations, and stoical afterthoughts of social climbing, the laws of which are in United States literature today universally mistaken for the metaphysics of identity.

The ostracism of Gatsby and the damnation of Christmas repeat the old theme of romantic revolt—but in reverse. Instead of attacking society, the author tries to fuse himself into it as its backbone. One might say, he doesn't revolt against it, he revolts toward it. The more it repels him, the more he needs to be in it. If he does attack it, it is only after he has invited its presence, like the fellow in the story, who says: "Throw that bum out." "He isn't here." "Well, bring him in and throw him out."

The reason for the reversal is that social changes have destroyed the old romantic situation. How can one *revolt* against a social environment in America today? Whatever the prejudices and snobberies of those in charge, they no longer exist as structural concepts of an accepted order, but rather as sneaky, private vices, as in the rest of us. These manners you may despise, but for revolt the object of your struggle needs to have authority over you; and this authority, no section of American society, whether Philadelphia, a

219

new Four Hundred, or the worthies of a Jewish middle-class suburb, possesses over any individual who refuses to accord it of his own free will. Revolt today has no more content than buying a bus ticket; any genuine attack on society must occur on the level of abstraction, that is, must be directed not against people and their manners but against the system of power and its mystifications. The drama of reform is as dead as the drama of nature; the struggle against the aesthetic or moral qualities of a class or community is no more meaningful than the struggle against the sea or the desert. It is for the popular media that such literature is destined, regardless of the "seriousness" of the author. The only true wrestle is with the abstraction: the credo, the slogan, the symbol, which the rebel must find in his own self.

Added to the emptiness of mere revolt is the fact that human beings have the right to be snobbish and prejudiced, as they have the right to be stupid; so that the non-revolutionary rebel writer who makes a specialty of his acquaintances' deformities is bound to appear as something of a nag or a bit cracked. He loves his neighbors too much, in being so disturbed at their weaknesses; and they can get along better without his heckling— especially in literature, where the deploring eye cramps the characters' behavior on the page or fixes it into something monotonously whacky. With a little less love and solidarity on the part of their scribes, the braves of Long Island's North Shore or of Mississippi county seats might have supplied some living grotesques as solid as those of Dickens or Gogol. Fitzgerald and Faulkner, however, hesitate to throw to the dogs of comedy these citizens upon whom they depend for "values."

220

From the passive absorption of social snobbery and prejudice, comes our latest literature of dispossession, with its stylized intransigence, devoid of radical content and eager for a goodnight kiss. Modeled on the mental case, into which the romantic rebel degenerates when the object of his rebellion has lost its contours, it has an inherent rancor and peevishness inseparable from wounds inflicted by social discrimination, actual or imagined.

New waves of social climbers—American literature can depend on them for continuous distraction from the ardors of thought. In the United States, social climbing—which includes climbing *down*; e.g., a writer becoming a fisherman, a farmer or a bum—achieves a profundity and complexity unmatched elsewhere. In a nation founded on the concept that salvation is a matter of geography, who you are normally depends on where you are; and there is nothing to prevent one from moving. With individuals constantly climbing around one another, the question is never settled, and you can't blame people if they try to get past themselves by a detour. Still, the striving to get on an invitation list is not the equivalent of an idea.

A Guide To Profundity, or Twelve Ways of Interpreting the Twentieth Century as a Disaster.

The Nothing, once the secret of adepts, has become a platitude.

The Nothing of the Existentialists represents the presence in the center of contemporary experience of the proletarianized mass of civilized societies—a cultural proletariat produced by the "decomposition of all classes."

With this notice, I invite the university metaphysicians suffering from the current "crisis of philosophy" to turn their unwanted energies toward a realistic study of society, giving particular attention to existing agencies of "nothing," in both their liberal (class-destroying) and their nihilistic (mind-destroying) functions.

Such a turn toward sociology on the part of the "existing thinkers" of the philosophy departments will at least keep them away from literature, which has already suffered enough at the hands of learned "disciplines," plundered by science and in search of a new subject matter.

Is proof needed that the void of the Existentialists and the mystics is an *historical* phenomenon? Today, anyone who looks into himself is certain to discover there the debris of his class heritage in a desert of freedom and aimlessness without limit. Montaigne, however, found something else than the ontological zero. "There is no man (if he listen to himselfe) that doth not discover in himselfe a peculiar forme of his, a swaying forme, which wrestleth against the art and the institution, and against the tempests of passions, which are contrary to him."

Comparing Montaigne's "moment" with our "moment," Montaigne's wins, because his being "wrestleth," and because the principle of struggle is stronger than the determination of history.

Too much reflection on "the degradation of modern man" leads the oddest people to put on the air of aristocrats.

*   *   *

"The individual" is an idea like other ideas.

When we speak of the ideas that prevail in a given time and place we do not have in mind the concepts people talk and write about, but something that has much more resemblance to prevailing winds. Under the influence of the idea, different actions incline in the same direction. The idea always reveals itself in *collective* phenomena, although no one can put an idea into words without making something unique of it.

Hence, regardless of what he thinks, anyone who speaks or acts is an agent. For that very reason, to submit consciously to being an agent is to throw one's life away. It was not necessary, and besides he has substituted his own thought for the prevailing idea as the controlling force of his actions. Were he really devoted to the idea, he would have been restrained by the fact that in his mind it could only keep becoming more and more unique.

An idea that can be *adopted* is only the distorted reflection of another idea which in its reality is inexpressible. The idea of Communism, for example, is such a surface idea; underneath it, a world solidarity may actually be in the process of formation. But this universal idea will never be thinkable in universal terms; and before it comes into being, how many Communisms will have to be overthrown!

If world solidarity is the fated idea, everyone is an agent of Communism, but the Communists are those who throw their lives away. The idea of solidarity will prevail, but in the meantime all theories of solidarity are superficial and false.

"In the meantime," however, is History; which means that our lives are governed by ideas of solidarity that keep marshaling their armies for the bloody division of the world as the means for making it one.

Yet what reason is there to accept the notion of a universal idea? More likely, no idea can conquer the world, any more than the world can conquer an idea. More likely, all ideas that come into being continue to live on side by side.

George P. Elliott

Critic and Common Reader

One of the sadnesses of the age is that the idea of the Common
Reader has fallen away so far. The word "common" itself has dwindled.
Henry Wallace's common man has little to do with Dr. Johnson's common
reader: "I rejoice to concur with the common reader; for, by the common
sense of readers uncorrupted with literary prejudices, after all the refinements
of subtlety and the dogmatism of learning, must be finally decided all claim
to poetical honors." Perhaps it is true that modern times have so fragmented
and troubled us that nearly all actual readers have been made into specialists
of some kind, or else use literature as a drug for killing time and dulling
anxiety. Even so, the ideal of writing for the mature, experienced, cultivated
Common Reader ought not to be allowed to perish—that Common Reader
whom Virginia Woolf considered herself to be when she wrote her superb
essays. Editors of books and magazines too often think of markets: fashion
magazines, sex magazines, little magazines; historical book club, science book
club, detective story book club; the Catholic novel, the Jewish novel, the
novel of Southern decadence, the avant-garde novel. To be sure, the world
being so incalculable a place as it is, things often won't stay in their cubby-
holes; it was pleasing to see how *Lolita*'s popular success confounded everybody hopelessly. All the same, the way of thinking of readers as specialists

has affected even writers, until they think of themselves as "aiming at a market." This wouldn't matter much if it didn't begin to have some effect on good writers, for some of whom popularity has become a proof of mediocrity. For some literary intellectuals nowadays, the only market worth aiming at is the company of the best, into which, so they are persuaded, ordinary folk can never be admitted. A few even seem to think that commoners are a sort of reverse Midas: their touch turns gold back into something base. *Finnegans Wake* is their book of books, impermeable and unalloyed; not even Auden, Barzun, and Trilling had read it through, so they confessed, when they recommended it in January 1956 to the members of that highbrow book club, The Readers' Subscription.

For literature has its fire-belching dragons guarding hoards of what they say is golden treasure—Yvor Winters, for example, or Northrup Frye, or Robert Graves. Word of them gets around, and travelers show you little pieces of pure gold which they claim to have gotten from the hoard of one of the dragons. So maybe some day you make the journey to his marvelous cave, wait till he is off guard, and rush in. And indeed there are pots of stuff that shines like gold; you pocket a few pieces and steal away; and if you were very lucky, maybe they are gold as fine as there is in the world. But probably not; probably what you get for your trouble is copper or brass or gold-plated lead. (Not that the dragon himself is a phony; he really believes that his hoard is pure bullion, that it was gold when *he* had it, that it was your touch that debased it.)

But the common reader lives in a more sociable country. He is like a citizen of a free and upright republic, in which most of the power is wielded by the patricians, who correspond to the writers and critics. Yet these very patricians are no more than free citizens themselves in the eyes of the law, and they must not forget, even during an age of Caesars, that the power they exercise comes from and reverts to the people. For when the state becomes too corrupt any longer to require responsibility of its citizens, some require it of themselves. They are worth writing for, always.

But how can a critic be a Common Reader? He reads all the time, he practically reads as a profession, and when he's not reading he writes about what he's read, and when he's not reading and writing, he talks about books, either as a teacher or else with his friends. He knows a great deal, about literary history, the lives of writers, the arts of writing. What's common about him? Very little, most of the time. There aren't many good critics, not nearly so many good critics as good poets—which is as it should be. All the same, since we now live in an age when critics flourish as never before, I think it worthwhile to look at the vocation of critic with some attention.

To define a critic negatively, by a critic I do not mean an esthetician, for he is interested in theories of beauty and in general principles, being a philosopher. Nor a literary historian, for he, being a historian, is interested in cause and effect among works of literature and between them and social forces. Nor an anthologist, for he is usually little more than an encyclopedist and archivist. One could, however, make a sort of case for some anthologies as being fine works of criticism; there are not many contemporary books of criticism which seem to me to be superior in their kind to Walter de la Mare's wonderful anthologies, *Come Hither, Behold This Dreamer*, and *Love*. Nor a scholar, though by a curiosity of history there exists a topsy-turvy world where scholars have more status and power than critics, and both have a hundred times more than writers—in the universities, where most literary people earn their living. In the looking-glass world of academic importance, knowing about literature is much more marketable than having your own opinions about it, and both fetch a higher price than writing it. But true scholars, who are usually humble about their calling, see themselves as servants to literature; the recovery, editing, and publication of the Boswell papers is a pure example of scholarship doing what it best can, bringing a text to readers, and the scholars involved, who did the work because they enjoyed doing it, merit the gratitude they have been accorded. But there are two main categories of literateurs who, to my thinking, should not be confused with critics—book reviewers and exegetes.

A book reviewer, because he hasn't time to allow his experience of the book he has just read to mellow and grow (or to wither and rot), is not a full critic, for when a critic talks responsibly about a book, one of his important considerations is how thoroughly the book has become an enduring part of his mind. My case about reviewing versus criticism has been made for me by as eminent a reviewer as the country has ever produced. Edmund Wilson, in an interview last year, to the question "What do you think of the standards of literary criticism today?" gave the following answer:

"I don't think about those things AT ALL! Literary criticism is a department of literature for me, and when I read literary critics I read them as literature; the others I can't read at all. I never think of myself, for instance, as a literary critic; I think of myself simply as a writer and a journalist." (*New Republic*, March 30, 1959)

An exegete is not a critic either, for his concern is to explain and reveal (originally he dealt with holy writ). He prefers a work of literature in which meanings are hidden, or else he claims there is no other kind. He looks at the structure of a short story not because it is beautiful but because he believes some of the meaning is to be found in the structure itself. He looks for ambiguities, irony, allegory, symbolic values. Take the tiger in Blake's poem. I have heard it identified as sin, evil, the destructive power of the universe, Satan, and Christ. Once I demurred—to the man who called the tiger Christ—and suggested that the tiger is a tiger. Oh, the embarrassment with which he told me, "Yes, yes, on *that* level to be sure." Imagine a great and grave poet troubling to write about a mere tiger! This incomprehension on the exegete's part comes, I think, from his own disinclination to enjoy a

poem for *its* sake; in his hierarchy, understanding is superior to enjoyment. He, looking at a poem, sees more significance than poetry; he may see the poem as a sort of hat-rack for meanings to hang on. "The meaning is the beauty"—an energetic statement like "beauty is truth, truth beauty," emitting more heat than light. So how can he believe that a poet looking at a tiger sees, overwhelmingly, a tiger? Did you ever *look* at a tiger? Did you ever try to imagine what a tiger *is?* The grandfather of the contemporary school of secular exegesis (commonly known as the New Criticism) is I. A. Richards, who wrote one of its books of secular theology, *The Meaning of Meaning;* and the most influential handbook in the technique of modern exegesis is entitled *Understanding Poetry*—not experiencing or enjoying it, but understanding it.

At this point I am afraid I am splitting imaginary hairs. Of course Cleanth Brooks has written some very fine essays in criticism, just as Richards has written not only some splendid criticism but also a few good poems. And T. S. Eliot, who is a critic if ever there was one, reviewed books by the dozen and furthermore some of his more celebrated essays were written as book reviews. And as for scholars, Dr. Johnson, who invented the Common Reader in the first place, was a critic *and* a scholar.

Essentially a critical essay, whatever else it may contain, is a creative form of writing; it does not aim to impart information to a reader, so much as to generate attitudes and emotions in him. Its subject is less an idea than an experience of literature, whether of a single story, or the total work of a poet, or a group of novels, or dramatic tragedy as a type. An essay which aims to communicate something of a valuable experience, or to re-create in the reader an experience analogous to it, is obviously a work of literature itself, though the experience used may be one of literature. It is quite possible for more to happen to a man when he reads *Don Quixote* than in a month of ordinary living, and if he then tells you about what happened to him, he is essaying criticism. To be sure, a good critic will be more learned than an ordinary reader; he will be possessed of a highly developed literary style; his judgment will be sound, though whenever he feels a conflict between that soundness and a fidelity to his own quirky experience, his experience wins; his discriminations will be fine; and he will be specially capable of joy in words, and in the sorts of experience which words can get at. All the same, because he both aims at the audience a poet aims at and at the same time *is* that audience, the critic may be any sort of specialist he wants to be, from esthetician to literary journalist to expert on place names in the *Morte d'Arthur;* but he must also, to avoid temptation, consider himself that imaginary creature the Common Reader.

II

The moment a critic despairs of his true calling, all sorts of temptations invite him to pervert his talents. Much the most interesting of such perversions are those of esotericism; the fires and roars of the dragons are pretty impressive, and there is some gold in their hoards. But the blatant perversions from the critic's true way are those of vulgarity, of acting stupider than he is.

Suppose that a man who has the capacity for true criticism drifts instead into vulgar criticism. Is it a case simply of selling out? It may be, in which event it is just another form of hypocrisy. But most of the time when a critic turns vulgar, he does some thing much subtler and more dangerous than selling books hypocritically: he confuses excellence with recognition. Maybe he does it because he wants money and fame, maybe he does it out of sincere conviction, maybe he doesn't even know he's doing it; but his motives are of very little importance compared to the confusion he causes.

One form of this is to use popularity for more than it's worth in gauging literary excellence. Only a sales-manager up to his gills in cocktails is imbecilic enough to think of popularity as *it*, and only a desert saint who's sure of his supply of manna can hold that there's never a connection between excellence and popularity. But in between, you're apt to come on statements like the one made by John O'Hara when the 1959 National Book Award for fiction was given to Bernard Malamud:

> "I believe it should be the duty of the National Book Award jury to reward the all-out professional author and not dig around like a truffle hound to rescue some unknown writer from obscurity. He's most likely not a readable writer. In this country the good writer does get read. I don't believe that there are any better writers than Hemingway, Steinbeck, Faulkner, Cozzens, and I—pining away down in Brown County, Indiana, or in an espresso joint on West Third Street in Greenwich Village." (*New York World-Telegram and Sun*, March 6, 1959)

228

This general view has been put somewhat less petulantly. George Orwell, who shared with most people a lack of enthusiasm for poetry, makes the main character of *Keep the Aspidistra Flying*, choose between writing poetry and affirming the aspidistra, which for him means creating a family and writing advertising copy. In the next to last chapter, he takes the manuscript of his long poem out of his pocket, "a great wad of paper, soiled and tattered," "the sole fruit of his exile, a two years' foetus which would never be born. Well he had finished with all that. Poetry! *Poetry*, indeed! In 1935." And he stuffs it down a sewer drain. There's a legitimate and formidable question here: If in fact ordinary people don't read it, how can you possibly say it was written for the Common Reader? There's an allied question, which is even trickier: How can you know when a book is very good? Later on I shall deal with them both at once.

A more important confusion which a critic can fall into concerns authority and excellence. Well, this is a dilemma everyone's hung up on, more or less, at one time or another. You can't go through school without knowing the "received" opinion toward Shakespeare; thousands upon thousands of children have been kept from liking Shakespeare's plays by reason of heavy-handed authority; but, before a group of even halfway literate people, it takes a revolutionary to maintain that he doesn't like Shakespeare, and a very Trotsky to maintain that Shakespeare is no good. It is simply absurd to reject wholesale the recommendations of authorities. After all, it is because of them that most of us know the good writers are there at all. Eliot spake: and behold, there was Donne. Authority tells you to read *War and Peace*, so read it; you can't read all the books, and it's probably good; you'll probably like it or learn to like it. Mickey Spillane was for a few years the most popular writer in the United States; but authority tells you his thrillers are garbage; very well, if you read one of them as a way of killing time and don't pretend you're doing something worth doing, little harm will befall you, though no good. But if it is absurd to reject authorities outright, it is repulsive to kowtow to them. Suppose the *Aeneid*, which they tell you to read, preferably in Latin, bores you in English. You don't have to be obnoxious about not liking it, but at least don't pretend to others that you do and certainly don't tell yourself that you do. It is far better to enjoy *King Solomon's Mines* by H. Rider Haggard than to like the *Aeneid* just because you think you ought to.

There are also a couple of vulgar traps for those who wield the authority. For one thing, the man of authority may himself become popular; so much the better; but then he may acquire a taste for popularity, and especially he may acquire a taste for being rubbed up against by popularity's half-naked little handmaiden, flattery. "How true, how wise, how beautifully put. What do you think of James's late novels?" Well, maybe this man of distinction has never thought about James's late novels, or even read them, for that matter; but he's pretty sure to know what the two main, going opinions on them are. For some more of those melting looks of adorers he's willing to spout some likely opinion or other; maybe he'll feel in the mood to complain that the late James loses himself in the subtleties of his own style whereas the earlier James . . . Maybe he'll take the other line. Either of them can, expertly taken, produce good results. I even saw both at once, in the hands of two critics who were agreeing to disagree, generate in the sitters-by blending purrs of adulation for both experts simultaneously.

A more important vulgar trap for those with authority consists in their acquiescing to become a part of that whole system of imposition for which "Madison Avenue" is a nickname. For whatever complex of reasons, most of them dreadful, readers seem to have become increasingly passive in

229

choosing their books. People generally seem to be allowing themselves to be told what to do, what to think, how to enjoy themselves. An external symptom of this tendency in book-buying (and therefore, presumably, in book-reading) is the decline of bookstores in the country and the rise of book clubs. When people bought their books in a well-stocked store, they more often than not chose for themselves and much more often chose non-best-sellers. Now that people buy most of their books through book clubs, they restrict their choice to one of a few guaranteed selections and they are apt to prefer a best-seller. Well, since book clubs are what people seem to want—or can be persuaded to want—and since there are well-oiled machineries for satisfying this want, obviously some authorities are needed to choose the masterpiece of the month and to assure and reassure the customers of its masterpieceliness. Let us imagine the history of such a judge.

Suppose him to be a professor at Columbia. Why Columbia? For excellent reasons. Columbia has a lot of prestige, not as much as Harvard, to be sure, but enough. And it is in New York. This means that our professor, who is personable, goes to some of the more important literary parties, where business and liquor are plentifully combined, and makes contacts. It also means that some of his students are likely to become reviewers, editors, publishers—men of power, the men who choose the book club judges. Further, suppose our professor to be a sound scholar, to which much popular prestige attaches, to have his own taste and to have the courage to persuade you of its soundness. In other words, here is a man who could be, and sometimes is, a critic and who deserves respect and commands it. But a masterpiece a month must be chosen, and he is asked to help choose it. Now the office pays well, it entails a certain fame, and it certainly offers power in a form that appeals to professors. The rationalization runs along lines something like these: There are so many books being published that ordinary people can't be expected to choose wisely; you are a man with the courage of your own taste and with the qualifications to choose well; you are beautifully situated to know what is going on in the literary world, of publishing and criticism as well as of writing; book clubs serve a real social purpose by saving people money and by giving writers a large audience; there is no question of bribery, of pay-offs by publishers; your choice will be made on the basis of your own judgment and only of that. Why not? And sometimes it works quite well. Our professor gets one of Thomas Mann's best novels to a lot of people who very well might not otherwise have read it; he feels good. But there are other masterpiece-of-the-month clubs with panels of honorable judges, and it turns out that the current supply of masterpieces is limited, especially of masterpieces of the kind which several score thousand readers nowadays are apt to enjoy. Still and all . . . Everything possible is done to make him believe: *If you choose it, it must be pretty good.* And he can coast along in this slick confusion for an indefinite time. The money-men who run the show, the experts in the techniques of imposition, the masses who are grateful to him for telling them what is worth reading, the honey-gold tongues of flattery, all help him not to think too carefully about why he chose, or allowed to be chosen, such books as *The Enemy Camp*, which may on literary grounds be worth reading but which is not a masterpiece, or *Aku-Aku*, which may be worth reading, or *Only in America*. The professor's regard for Horace and Catullus and Juvenal, Chaucer and Malory and Spenser, remains undiminished; his opinions about them are entirely unconfused; perhaps he is still capable of reading them as fully as he once did, perhaps not. What shall we call our power professor? A pretty good name for him would be Jacques Van Doren Highet. A name like that could sell 50,000 copies of the Graustark national epic in the original Fenugreek.

231

III

The errors of esotericism, as I conceive the matter, are closely connected with, and sometimes derive from, a dangerous ailment among literary folk. It is not a new disease, and it's seldom fatal; yet it is important enough to be worth mentioning. It holds that we should settle for nothing less than masterpieces—*we* being readers, critics, writers, teachers, anyone concerned with literature. You hear this view stated or implied in a thousand forms. It was Cyril Connolly who made the case most obnoxiously. "The more books we read . . ." (this is a different *we*; count me out)

> The more books we read, the sooner we perceive that the true function of a writer is to produce a masterpiece and that no other task is of any consequence. . . .Writers engrossed in any literary activity which is not their attempt at a masterpiece are their own dupes and, unless these self-flatterers are content to write off such activities as their contribution to the war effort, they might as well be peeling potatoes.

These two sentences occur on the first page of *The Unquiet Grave*. Since the book itself is no masterpiece—and I hope for Mr. Connolly's sake he was not attempting one—it provides as neat an instance as you could ask for of "Do as I say, not as I do."

Last year, I heard an eminent poet in his forty-first year assert that, between the time when Pound and Eliot burst on the scene until just recently, when there appeared an American and an Englishman both around thirty, there had been no new poet in English. The ailment has a melancholy form which afflicts writers sometimes, comparing everything you write to the best that has been thought and said; in very severe cases, like that of Matthew Arnold the poet, who "threw his gift in prison till it died," the writer quits writing altogether.

And this is what I have against the masterpiece-or-nothing theory: it is against life. It is literary Calvinism with a vengeance: a book is either one of the elect, and there aren't many of those, or one of the damned. But a man who is full of life is not so keen on this butchery of experience. Sometimes he is up to reading *Paradise Lost*, to be sure, but most of the time he is not; he finds Dostoevsky a marvelous but awfully rich diet; when he sees *A Doll's House*, he is stirred deeply, but sometimes he doesn't feel like stirring. He sees no reason to cast the novels of Kingsley Amis, Ramón Sender, or Jean Giono into outer darkness; he has moods in which he finds the poems of Stephen Spender or William Carlos Williams just about great enough for him; he is unabashed in his enjoyment of both *Pygmalion* and *My Fair Lady*; and the reason he gave for liking Charlie Chaplin's movies was that they were fun.

232

There are sound critical reasons to distrust the masterpiece approach to literature. One of them is that it violates a sense of history, of the context into which a book is embedded and out of which it has emerged. Scholarship has done us—all of us—a fine service by insisting upon our exercising historical imagination to the limit of our knowledge and power; I am sure that such a writer as Chaucer has been recovered for the Common Reader in good part because of the development of this faculty, which was long slighted. But if exercising historical imagination permits one to enjoy all sorts of works which otherwise would be lost, how much truer it is that books contemporary with the reader may speak to him with a living voice in tones he recognizes. And here, the *Meisterstück-über-alles* attitude is especially pernicious. I resent, more than I will say, being told that until three or four years ago there hadn't appeared a new poet in English since the 1910's. I do not benefit from such an attempt to demolish a whole delightful shire of my experience, a shire which includes poetry by Auden, Eberhart, Schwartz, Miles, Dylan Thomas, and a dozen more. Maybe there's not a great poet among them; I don't really care; I don't like to read in order to judge and pigeonhole. But they have told me in poetry about the world I live in and myself, they have given me pleasure, they have become part of me. Just as I would hate to have for neighbor a man who will love only saints, so I wish all the nothing-less-than-masterpiece monsters would get back up into the hills where they belong and guard caves.

Still, one should be glad the literary cultists are there, for they keep things toned up. Their roarings can be heard for miles, and they can make sitting in a chair with a book in your hand a risky adventure. But if there's anything they have no use for, it's Common Readers. The impulse to make a cult of Shakespeare must be terribly frustrated by his egregious popularity, in all ages, in many languages, among all classes of mankind. I suppose this impulse, hard put to find something inaccessible about Shakespeare, generated the absurdities about who *really* wrote the plays. At any rate, the squabbles over authorship are not engaged in just by crackpots, unless you think Freud was cracked. He believed that Shakespeare's plays were written by the Earl of Oxford. (He was persuaded to this view by a man named Looney.)

Cultism is a matter of attitude, of being in on a secret which you, you dolt, aren't in on, and cultists commonly find treasure among the obscure and/or difficult. Yvor Winters is a master at this sort of thing; according to him, one of the most considerable nineteenth-century American poets is Jones Very; one of the two or three supreme poets in English is Fulke Greville; and as for the greatest poem there is, he names *Ebauche d'un serpent* by Paul Valéry. But he doesn't stop with naming this poem; he goes on to exalt the type to which it belongs, the short poem.

> The epic and the poetic drama, for example, have long been dead, and I did not kill them. . . .The novel, for the most part an abortive form from its beginnings, is dying rapidly. . . .The writers of the short poem have done very well, if one regards them over a long period, and they are definitely alive today; but I am convinced that greater achievements are possible in the short poem and that we would have a better chance of such achievements if we could bring ourselves to

understand the nature of the form and the fact that this form is the greatest form, of all forms the one most suited to communication among those who are wholly civilized and adult. (*Function of Criticism*, Alan Swallow, 1957)

Well, since Mr. Winters assumes (perhaps somewhere he states it) that literature is the highest form of human activity, that makes Valéry's poem the greatest achievement of the human mind, anytime, anywhere.

Or there are paper dragons like Tiffany Thayer, who kept his hoard in a thimble; he led the Fortean Society, which is dedicated to the books of Charles Fort. Fort believed, among other things, that the firmament is composed of a sort of perforated gelatin and that spooks abound. Or there are very ambitious dragons like Robert Graves; he maintains that *all* poetry is hidden from the many, is essentially occult; if it isn't occult, it isn't poetry: QED. Or there are Frye-types who think that some works of literature, or even literature itself, provides the key whereby the secret meaning of life may be unlocked.

The most bellowish dragon I know of nowadays is Hugh Kenner. His roars are so hard on the ears that they prevent one from attending to what he's roaring about; I was kept off Pound and Wyndham Lewis very effectively by Kenner's lashings and gnashings, and I'm glad I got to Eliot, Joyce, and Yeats before Kenner got to me. This is from a book review of his:

234

> To be the best poet practising in England is, these days, to share a meaningless eminence with the wittiest statistician in Terre Haute or the handsomest peacock ever hatched in Idaho. It is therefore virtually useless to locate Mr. Tomlinson with reference to his contemporaries. (*Poetry*, February 1959)

I know that Kenner's hoard contains some 24-carat treasure, and I do hope it's gold he's got in his Tomlinson pot. But I'm afraid, after wincing through this review, it'll be some time before I even glance at the book he thought he was recommending. (You remember that other dragon who said there'd only been one British poet in the past forty years? Well, Tomlinson wasn't that poet; that was Philip Larkin. And this dragon is himself a poet who has recently been called, by a lesser dragon, the only English-writing poet of the twentieth century deserving to be ranked with Yeats. Someone should make a daisy-chain of dragons.) My favorite quotation from Kenner comes in the form of a simple declarative sentence which means exactly what it says. The 'Vortex' he speaks of was a group of friends, consisting of Pound, Lewis, Eliot, Ford Madox Ford, and Gaudier-Brzeska (whoever he was) "with Joyce a saluted ally," and with Yeats standing in the wings, where he was called on by Pound every Monday evening. The Vortex lasted from 1914 to 1916. I am quoting out of context, but nothing in what he says before or after modifies the dragonism of this statement:

> That World War I dissipated the Vortex, may yet prove to have been its most far-reaching effect. (*Gnomon*, McDowell, Obolensky, 1958, p. 147)

IV

By this time, if you, dear reader, have not developed a considerable opposition to what I've been saying, you're a lot more placid than I am. For example, I share the general critical opinion that Blake and Yeats are very great poets. Yet they are esoterics if ever men were. I have heard that on theosophical bookshelves Yeats's preposterous book *A Vision* stands not far from Mme Blavatsky's *Isis Unveiled*. Preposterous, yes, but he took *A Vision* seriously and it's conceivable that one would enjoy more of his poems, and enjoy them more thoroughly, for reading it. Is it not true that there are coigns and chasms of unknowledge everywhere man looks—in the physical world, in all that lives, within his own mind, in literature? Any Common Reader who ever opened his eyes at night knows this, and furthermore he puts more trust in a Blake than in writers who spread the answers out in smooth array for him to savor. Still, the occult as such does not charm him, and he balks when the cultists push at him too hard.

I am not easy in my position, for I know the truth is hidden; I know that to expose it in clear daylight is to dry it up and change its hue. I know that most of us lead our lives badly, do not want to change, do not want even to be reminded that we should change; we need prophets like Blake. I know that such men as Robert Graves and Yvor Winters have splendid and passionate minds and have written not only some of the best literary criticism I have read but also genuine poetry. Furthermore, I think poetry itself is

235

mysterious both because poetry uses familiar words in an esoteric way and because words themselves are mysterious and full of risk. The Word . . .

Earlier, I posed two questions, which I hope now to answer. The first is: If ordinary people don't in fact read or like a book, how can you say it was written for the Common Reader? You can't. But you can say you are convinced from reading that book that, when time and Authority offer it to the Common Reader, he will like it. Blake illustrates this contention; he thought he was writing his poetry for everyone; it has turned out that he was right, for at least part of it, the short poems rather than the Prophecies. Pindar, however, presents the problem in a different way. He has the reputation of a great poet, yet twenty-five centuries have not sufficed to give him popularity. He was an aristocrat writing for aristocrats, and he has been read almost exclusively by the literary elite; yet they, a good many of whom like to concur with the Common Reader, insist with persuasive vigor that Pindar is one of the supreme lyric poets. What to do? The difference between Pindar's Odes and Blake's Prophecies, is this: if a Common Reader should do the hard work necessary to understand either, he would probably find that he admired and enjoyed the Odes but not the Prophecies. So at least I

judge from my own experience, and that of many others not of the elect. And in this is implied the answer to the other question: How can you know when a book is very good? You can't, not in the ways you can know the sky is blue or the earth round. The surest you can be is for a great many readers both common and aristocratic to agree that it is good; when aristocrats alone like it, as with the Odes and the Prophecies, about the best you can do is to judge the tone with which they speak to you of it; if the speaker is courteous and seems to want you to share his enthusiasm, as Eliot did when he wrote on Dante, trust him; but if he is rude and seems contemptuous of you for being so stupid, beware. If he concludes an essay as Winters concluded the one I quoted earlier, beware.

> If my arguments are merely brushed aside, I shall win by default within twenty years. If I am right, there will be no great harm in this, and it will not be the first time I have won an argument in this manner; but if I am wrong, it will be unfortunate. (*Function of Criticism*, p. 75)

The publishers of the first collection of Shakespeare's plays put the case well:

From the most able, to him that can but spell: There you are number'd. . . .Reade him, and againe, and againe; and if then you do not like him, surely you are in some manifest danger, not to understand him.

Literature is a part of the Common Reader's life—a part only, but of it—and it gives him power, and confidence in his power, to communicate. He does not challenge those who know more than he; he gives way to those who have more energy than he; he is not contemptuous of those beneath him. Literature brings knowledge and it may bring wisdom, it may even instruct in virtue, it has changed a man's life more than once; it may divert you from trouble for a while like a game, it may untie your knots with laughter, it can purge you for a time of great dread, it has power if you will to elevate you to something like ecstasy. Yet, no matter how much pain literature may awaken in you—outrage you with images of violence like the *Iliad*, horrify you with Oedipus' gouged eyes, instruct you in the innermost ways of sin like Dante, rend from you inconsolable sobs like Lear's death, figure forth your most private inquietude like Dostoevsky—still it also produces delight, if only the delight of ordered thoughts and of language used well. Lovers are poets, and experience of literature is something like love: it quickens its lover to intense life, it is not everlasting, but at the time it is of eternity, it is incalculably precious, its power is measured both by its delight and by its anguish, it is there for all who want it, each makes it himself. It is everybody's language shaped with love.

237

Harold Rosenberg

Seven Numbered notes

1. SCALE. It is desirable at times for ideas to possess a certain roughness, like drawings on heavy-grain paper. Thoughts having this quality are most likely to match the proportions of actual experiences. Under the influence of methodology and scholarship our concepts tend more and more toward the microscopic and the cosmic. Objective techniques are unable to guarantee that things and events will keep their true relations of size. To get these right, the thinker must be aware of his own self and use it as a measure. But if this awareness is an honest one, it is bound to dispel evenness and excessive finesse.

2. EDUCATION. Aristocrats have a talent for memoirs, the declassed for religion and sensibility, the poor for mathematics and musical performance. As the mind descends the social scale, it becomes increasingly abstract.

     The present epoch takes its style neither from the well-born nor from the disinherited (as did the 19th century) but from masses who came into the world without possessions. Hence computation, horn playing, and nonfigurative art are the most faithful reflections of the age . . . The political leaders, however, identifying themselves with the property holders of all periods, are hostile to generalization and to rhythm, and demand that everyone force himself to recollect the happenings that brought the leaders to power.

3. THE CULT OF PERSONALITY. Bureaucracy is the social realization of the arithmetical point of view, i.e., the point of view of the mass that is ruled. The sage of bureaucracy is the statistician. But counting depends on the existence of the single unit. Hence bureaucracy must have one Person as its idol. Should there be more than one, each would insist on his individual difference and statistics would become impossible.

4. GEOPOLITICS. The global revolution of today is thrusting man into outer space, as the national and class revolutions of the 19th century drove Europeans across the seas to people the American prairies.

5. MANUSCRIPT FOUND IN A BOTTLE. "By refusing to stay fixed in a single place and in a lasting relation to those above him, man in our time is violating his essential nature."

6. THE END OF MEANINGLESSNESS. Life has meaning only within a context. Taken in themselves, actions lack definition and things change into one another as in dreams, which is why those who have observed it most nakedly like to say that life is a dream.

Today, of course, dreams themselves have been arranged to constitute a context. Thus one gifted with a persistent loss of the sense of proportion is thought to have a firmer grasp on the meaning of life than one who is *square*.

Conceiving life to be its own context, modern dream and nonsense literature has closed the door to meaninglessness. By means of this *tour de force*, everything in life becomes full of significance while life itself is meaningless.

The notion that life provides the meaning of life is nihilism in disguise. The literary masterpiece of this mood is Tolstoy's "The Death of Ivan Ilych." In the "Death," the context of Ilych's existence as a typical, successful Russian functionary, far from providing the meaning of his life, is presented as falsifying it and reducing it to zero; only when Ilych is pulled out of this context by a fatal illness does he throw off the lie imposed upon him by the facts of his life. Why not say flatly, then, that the void of death is the only reality, and that as against this reality life is meaningless? No, Tolstoy will not say it. On the contrary, Tolstoy would have it that life is infinitely meaningful, but on the condition that every actuality in it be seen as illusory.

As among our contemporaries, each concrete situation contains the hidden import of being a negation or inhibition of life. But, again, if life thus repels all content, it is meaningless. And Tolstoy does say this, though he says it dramatically, not as a philosophical conclusion. For when he has painstakingly plucked out Ilych strand by strand, fiber by fiber, from his casing of court sessions, card games, family routines, when he has released him at last into the dark current of being, he finds nothing for his hero to do and with the sure instinct of the storyteller gives him up and lets him die. Ilych has achieved Life—that is the end of him. So that whatever Tolstoy may have wished us to understand, it is now apparent that he was delivering a corpse to the dissecting room of the Absurd.

In Tolstoy's day, the intuition of nothingness had to be given the appearance of meaning—the Nihilists, for example, assumed the role of revolutionary liberators—as the early model auto had to appear as a version of the carriage. Ilych's death howl was also his birth cry. Had he lived in the West, he could have survived his nameless malady and taken passage for the South Seas. Had he been born a few decades later, the ex-judge might have married a circus performer and set himself up as a Surrealist or a Zen Buddhist.

For Ilych, unfortunately, neither time nor place was apt for affirming Life as a *professional point of view.* After canceling all civilized contexts, Tolstoy had found only one that seemed harmonious with pure being: the peasant's context of nature and toil. In living for life, the peasant made the void positive: when the servant rested Ilych's feet on his shoulders, the dying magistrate felt a great communion and was comforted and enlightened. The peasant was the model on which Ilych, had he been cured, would, like Tolstoy himself, have had to be rebuilt. Unluckily for Ilych, Tolstoy had gotten there before him and was thoroughly aware that this peasant and his life-itself context was a poetic fiction. The Russian peasant lived in a cruel context of forced labor; it was the wheel of hardship and hunger, not the cycle of the ripening seed, that set the meaning of his life, as the round of dinners and court cases set the meaning of Ilych's. Between the context of soil drudgery and dependence and that of rich proprietor, Tolstoy had made his choice, keeping the peasant shirt as an emblem that all the meanings of life could be subverted by the notion of life itself as the meaning. But this shirt was not for Ilych: a great writer can be frivolous in his living, but in his fiction things have to be taken seriously.

Released from the geometrical proportions of the social context, Ilych had no place to go but the grave; the only organic context is death. The actual peasant, on the other hand, had to go the way of the October Revolution, which tore him out of one context and enclosed him in another: the context of life is History.

7. THE MEANING OF LIFE. Organic life was the absolute context of Tolstoy's fictional peasant, as Heaven and Hell were the eternal context of the medieval soul. History, though its reality is the constant displacement of contexts, can also serve as an absolute context of fictions. But the dimension of History is Time, which is an indefinite dimension. No one can stay in History forever; it threatens all who are in it with a lapse of meaning, and this threat impels them to make every effort to remain in it as long as possible. Yet to enter History even for a moment is sufficient to differentiate one from those whose lives have meaning only to the census taker.

In our time, life has meaning only for those who get into History; all the rest are mere "mass," confined to the arithmetic of birth, labor-and-consumption, and death.

Hence the primary passion of contemporary man is to enter the historical context. For this he will sacrifice anything: principles, vows, love, life itself. To win a place in History—and lengthen his stay in it—all is justified. Nay, he is obligated, he owes it to his humanity, to stop at nothing in order that his allotment of time shall not be absorbed into animal nullity.

History is made from moment to moment, the open door into it is news. Before a person can become part of the permanent record, there must be tidings of him, as when the messenger arrives in the play and adds the action off-stage to the development of the plot. The effort to make the person into news, an effort on which hinges the issue of life or death in the deepest sense, has now become conscious of itself as an art, the art of "publicity." The art of inserting into the common attention and (hopefully) memory, the image which individuals have chosen to represent them is the most rapidly rising of professions and has already eclipsed the clergy in importance. The frenzy for publicity is nothing less than a manifestation of the craving for life's meaning. One's name in the papers, one's picture in the weekly, is reassurance that one has a place in the human record, and the success of totalitarian movements has owed much to the fine gradations of public notice by which the least of party members is joined to the leader.

It is the grossest idealism to mistake publicity for a mere tool of success or exhibitionism. The appetite for wealth or for flattery is a limited appetite: it can be satisfied by status and is not inconsistent with quiet enjoyment. Publicity, on the other hand, must keep pace with time; it is an effort within a metaphysical situation, which it strives to affect; and its results are gauged with an anxiety inseparable from that which accompanies the consciousness of death.

Since it is the quantity and duration of public attention that counts for meaning, the hunger for it cannot be appeased by the act done or the thing made. A good deed or a masterpiece produced in concealment is sufficient only for one convinced that life is meaningless, some unlikely knight of the unmarked grave. Cheops could devote his life and fortune to building a golden ship which, buried in a mountain, would carry him around the circle of the heavens. To fabricate today an object to be kept forever from the eyes of men would be evidence of an apathy toward values, if not the height of perversity.

Except for men drunk with immediacy, the human world is divided into two species: those who wear above their heads their reflections in the mirrors of anticipated memory, and the hundreds of millions of unseen ones destined to be the eager onlookers of attention-getting feats. In Freudian terms, one might think of two generations rather than of two species: the oversized infants of the front pages and the little gray Fathers and Mothers who watch over their cradles (since, after all, those who succeed in entering into History emanate from the lost hordes).

Crime in our time flourishes as the most popular medium of transcendence into the seen; as the Nazis proved, it is a way into History that is available to anyone. Murders and robberies are prompted, in the first instance, by the greed for meaning; it is a commonplace that were the showcase of the news to be closed to them crimes would be cut to a fraction. One who cannot endure the certainty of his own extinction will by a crime seize a moment of public time in order to rescue himself from the abyss, as when a clerk in a small New Jersey bank steals $20,000 and is arrested two hours later contentedly drinking beer in a bar around the corner ... For the extraordinary criminal there is, of course, the chance that the act by which he creates himself in the mind of others may earn him a longer historical duration.

A criminal, a statesman, an athlete, an artist—once he has mounted into the sphere of visibility—is aware of himself as a double being moving simultaneously within two substances: the senseless material of mere fact and a golden jelly of significance that extends outward across a field of Names.

The meaning of life is to attain the intoxication of floating in the shining aspic of potential lastingness while being conscious that one has already been changed into a phantom.

Louis Simpson

On Being a Poet in America

245

I swear I begin to see the meaning of these things,
It is not the earth, it is not America who is so great,
It is I who am great or to be great, it is You up there, or any one,
It is to walk rapidly through civilizations, governments, theories,
Through poems, pageants, shows, to form individuals.

Walt Whitman

A poet must have talent. No, this is not a joke—or rather, it is half a joke, like saying that one would like to be rich—but nevertheless it is true that most poets are a little short of talent. Don't ask me how the poet gets it. I am only making up a story. Ask God such questions. Talent is the one thing that cannot be bought, borrowed, or stolen. Many pretend to have it, but no one is deceived for long, least of all the man who is pretending. Give him a check and his face gets longer; give him a prize and he bursts into tears. For he knows that it is all a joke; inside himself he is standing without pants, naked, and the children are pointing.

Then maybe he ought to be not too much of his time, of his place. Perhaps he should be born in a log cabin in Ontario, where an old trapper has left the collected poems of Heine in German; and he will translate them alongside a dictionary as he grows up, in the long Canadian nights. Or he should be the third son of a realtor, embezzle his father's money, and have to emigrate to Brazil. There he will discover Rimbaud. Perhaps he should simply lie in bed in the Bronx till he is thirty, with his aunts and uncles bringing him his socks and urging him to get up, and arranging jobs for him—certainly, if he did that, jobs would be offered to him—and until he was thirty-one he would not write a word. That would be an original start, and above all poets must be original.

He should not behave like a poet. That is, he should not pattern himself on the famous dead or the influential living. There are many kinds of reputation. Some have glossy fur, black snouts, and sharp little claws; others are like storks, tall and full of wisdom; others are striped like tigers. And they all belong in the zoo or in the museum. The poet will avoid them by all means.

He will not serve other men. That is the occupation of a valet.

II

The astonishment that anyone reads anything you write, and that anyone takes it seriously, as though it actually existed. And then, your resentment. What right do they have to read your mail?

When anyone says anything either for or against a poem you've written, you feel like saying, "Listen, I work for a living. If I write poems that's my business."

Then, the internal writhing when anyone calls you a poet. And the look of dismay on the face of the person to whom you are introduced in this fashion.

III

"To have great poets we must have great audiences too." This tag from Whitman, which adorns or used to adorn every issue of *Poetry*, is about as close to the opposite of the truth as you can get. To have great poetry all that is needed is great talent. There can be no such thing as a great audience for poetry. An audience for bad writing—yes!

The mark of the bad writer is that he is popular, especially among people who "don't usually read poetry." To please, a writer must produce standard, name-brand goods. Everything such minds produce is predictable and trite, and therefore easily recognized by the "average reader." Originality is not welcome—at least, not until years have passed, when it has been diluted and become fashionable, and is no longer original. Those who hope for a "renaissance" of verse, to be measured by gate-receipts or the number of volumes sold, expect what simply cannot be. For the poet's task is to use his imagination, and imagination goes beyond what is already known—that is, beyond an audience. The poems of thirty years ago may be popular now— an audience has been prepared for them; the sentimental writing of today may be popular—for it flatters the stupidity of the audience. But real poetry cannot be popular in its own time. The poet knows this and hopes to be read by his fellow poets and a few intelligent readers.

Consider the most recent fashion in verse—the beat writing of the late fifties. It was sentimental—the whimper of the junkie, the whinny of the fairy, the whine of the man who, despising himself, threw the blame on society. Those writers were like the pale clerics of the 1850's who wrote sonnets expressing their respect for flowers and maidens, or their distress at some Darwinian idea. As for their audience. . . .The girl from Bennington arrived in New York equipped, mentally at least, with bent spoon, eyedropper, and needle, as her great-great-grandmother had returned from the Seminary with her own painting of St Francis and the determination to be a Christian martyr. In a year or so, such poetry-readers turn to other forms of titillation. The girl who was crazy about beat poetry married an advertising man, and if you meet her nowadays she tells you that advertising is the real American art form.

What was the appeal of the beat? It appealed to a certain devitalized, androgynous type—the male or female spinster. It was exciting to those who felt that they had not "lived." If you've had a joyless existence, junkie-business could seem terribly close to "real life."

And then, there was support of this kind of writing by certain influential literary figures. Maybe they felt that they themselves had failed as poets; they had fallen short of a career in the grand style; they were not Eliot, nor were meant to be. So to revenge themselves on the world they recommended bad poetry.

As Proverbs says: "The man that forsakes the law praises the wicked."

I remember reviews or articles by Richard Eberhart, Karl Shapiro, Louise Bogan, Marianne Moore, among others, ranging from faint praise to outright enthusiasm for beat writing. But not one of these critic-poets dealt with the content and purpose of beat writing. To a mind that has been subjugated for years to the dicta of modern criticism, everything must seem merely a problem in words, mere aesthetics. Many a beat poem recommends sticking a needle of dope into your arm. But to Mr. Eberhart and Miss Moore lunatic asylums are probably only an interesting figure of speech.

The critic-poets of the twenties separated their own writing almost entirely from the life around them; they were no longer able to judge anything in terms of reality. Poetry for them had neither content nor effect—it was just words. So when they were confronted with beat writing they talked about form, or lack of form, but none of them criticized the content. Having no convictions of their own, they were able to swallow any camel.

Then, of course, there were the mass-media people, who hate poetry as they hate any kind of imaginative life, and were glad to exploit the sensational beat scene, and to hold up the beat as an example of what poetry really is. The copywriter, as he got drunk on the 5:17 back to Danbury, could think, Maybe I'm a bastard, but at least I'm not a lousy artist, thank God!

And the beats, who had no character, lent themselves to this exploitation. If Dylan Thomas could not resist publicity, how could these, who were so much lesser than he, resist the spread in *Life*, the half hour on TV? And soon the beats had their imitators—Norman Mailer, for example, in the role of aging juvenile.

The beats were liars. They hardly ever told the truth about anything. They were filled with hatred and contempt for everything that was not like themselves—and that was most of the world. They were like the maniac in Kierkegaard's book who proceeds to slay his child because Abraham was ready to sacrifice Isaac. They evaded the ethical and went directly to what they claimed was revelation. But in truth they had not set foot on the first step of the ladder.

So much for those writers and that audience.

IV

The fifties also saw another kind of poet arrive on the scene. It was as though the "creative writing" workshops of Kenyon College, Sarah Lawrence, Iowa, and a hundred other factories, had released their apprentices all at once. The children of Empson, I. A. Richards, and Brooks-and-Warren had come of age. These "neatniks" could write a volume without embarrassing themselves. They could turn anything into good verse. They absorbed even Dylan Thomas. Alongside poems in the manner of Wallace Stevens, there would be strong hints that the poet had had sexual experience. In those days I wrote two pieces about these poets. The use of the sonnet form doesn't help any, but the content is historically true, and I may as well reproduce them:

SNIVEL

Snivel, his brains tuned to a tinny pitch,
Proceeds to be a poet. Why, by God?
Fame is his first infirmity, an itch
To be exceptional, however odd.
Wasting no time, he starts with middle age
And plasters up a Tower, just like Yeats.
The fashion changes—Dylan is the rage—
He hastens to assure he fornicates.

The book is out. He mingles with a few
Collectors of prestige, prestige collectors.
And then the party's over—one review
Sends Snivel to Parnassus' outer sectors.
He takes a teaching job, and travels once
Each summer to a writers' conference.

SNITCH

Snivel is melancholy; Snitch is worse.
Snivel steals from the dead, Snitch from the living.
He asks to see, you let him see your verse,
And listen to his flattery with misgiving.
And sure enough, a week or two goes by,
He brings a poem, asks for your advice;
You look it over, something strikes your eye—
Your own. You must admit, "It's very nice."

Though by foul means and fair Snitch courts the Muse,
The lady still continues to resist.
And now he is a writer of reviews,
An editor and an anthologist.
As some who lose a mistress take a wife,
He settles for the literary life.

V

The novelist George M. once told me, "I've been lectured on my artistic integrity by more damn people. And I meet them a few months later and they're in advertising."

True. Once at Columbia, a few minutes before I went in to take an exam in Chaucer, I met X. in the corridor. X. was a teacher in those days. I complained to him about the Chaucer requirement (I was pretty nervous). Why Chaucer? I said. Why not Tolstoy, or Sophocles?

He flew into a rage. It was people like me, he said, who were the trouble with Columbia. We expected the university to give us a degree just because we wrote poems. We didn't know the first thing about scholarship. I was astonished—in fact, he seemed slightly insane. Then I told him to go and peddle his fish.

About a year later, X. quit teaching and went into public relations where, I am told, he is making a pile of money.

Or consider Y. A few years ago he wrote a poem saying, "Where are all the young poets nowadays? They are all in the Universities." The burden of his song was that he himself was above teaching, or getting fellowships, or writing for the quarterlies. Then this apostle of the pure life proceeded to get himself a Guggenheim and a professorship.

As George said, you meet them a few months later, and they're in advertising.

VI

There is only one law for the poet—tell the truth!

For years you try to write, and at last you are faced with two alternatives—either write what is acceptable, or tell the truth. If you write what you really think, you will find yourself in a lonely place. But if you are serious about it—and if you're not, you aren't a poet at all—you must get to that place sooner or later. The sooner the better.

In America, success is the worst temptation for the writer, as it is for other men. At several points in my life I have seen rising clearly before me an opportunity to *belong*. I have met some of the more important literary men of my time, and they gave me to understand that they would be glad to help me in some way. But a voice within me, like Socrates' sign, said, "Flee for your life!"

I know too much about literary life. I know by what means, by what steady cultivation of his betters, by what obsequiousness in print and out of it, the mediocre writer gets himself a name. As Huxley said, fame, the last infirmity of a noble mind, is the first infirmity of the ignoble. The need of fame has turned many a decent man into an envious, spiteful, vanity-ridden, self-deluding wretch. And what does he have to show for it? A handful of reviews.

The poet's task is to tell the truth. And, of course, he must have talent. His only real satisfaction is in the writing of poems—a dull-seeming procedure in which he sits down facing a blank wall, and smokes, and from time to time scratches on a sheet of paper. There have been plays about piano-players and painters, but the writing of poetry is least suitable for dramatic representation.

It is getting harder and harder to write a poem. That is, I can start one well enough—but how to finish?

A few years ago I was able to begin and finish a poem. I found that

251

the poem was directed by certain external forces toward a certain end. But one day I found that ideas were better expressed in prose. No, it was more than that. I found that I no longer wished to please. The reader has certain stock responses to ideas, and certain responses—not very strong perhaps, but operative nevertheless—to metaphor, meter, and rhyme. A poem that satisfies his stock responses is "good"; a poem that does not is "bad."

I found myself wanting to write bad poems—poems that did not depend on stock responses. I wanted to write poems that would not please. For the last three years I have been learning to write this new kind of poem. The most important change is in the content (whether one writes "in form," or "out of form," is not an essential question—it is a matter for simpletons to worry about, and of course it is the only question that reviewers usually feel competent to discuss).

Instead of statements which reassure the reader by their familiarity, or shock him by their strangeness—instead of opinions, there are only images and reverberations.

I can never finish these poems. I wrestle with them and leave off when I am exhausted. Frequently, all that remains is a handful of phrases.

252

The difficulty is that, to write this new kind of poem which springs mainly from the subconscious, I must work not at technique, but at improving my character.

How easy it is to settle on a certain style, to write a certain poem over and over again! Most verse-writers do just this. They publish a new book of the same poems every four years, and when they have repeated themselves often enough they win the Pulitzer.

There is this to be said for not being a professional man of letters— you can do as you like. What have you got to lose?

Work is all well and good, but what you pray for is inspiration. That is, one day when you sit down and wrestle with a poem, you find that you are wrestling with an angel. Then all the phrases flow together; the unfinished poems lying in the back of the closet rise and fly together. They are changed into something that you have not logically conceived. At such moments, which are rare enough, you are not writing but assisting at the birth of truth in beauty.

Of course, to some people this is all nonsense. To a deaf man, music does not exist; to a blind man, there are no constellations in the sky.

VII

No, poetry is not dying, and verse is not a dying technique. Those who have said that it is, perhaps wishing that it might be, were writers of prose, and some of them were critics. They have congratulated themselves prematurely. A great deal of criticism is nothing to brag about, if the criticism has been an end in itself. And criticism in the last forty years has been largely an end in itself, a bastard kind of art, a kind of theatricals for shy literary men. I have known critics who were actors at heart, giving their own impersonations of Raskolnikov, or Donne, or Freud. Next week, *East Lynne*.

What is most disappointing about criticism is that when you examine the critic's method, under the appearance of sweet reasonableness there are only prejudices and taboos. The critic's art depends on an exertion of his personality, an unstable quality. Now, poets and novelists and playwrights also use their personality, but from this they extract certain definite objects— the poem, the novel, the play. They deal in facts. But the critic deals in opinions.

An age of prose? All that prose has been a symptom of culture, and the culture was not directed to any serious purpose.

253

NEW LINES FOR CUSCUSCARAWAY AND MIRZA
MURAD ALI BEG

> "... *the particular verse we are going to get will be cheerful, dry and*
> *sophisticated.*"
>
> T. E. Hulme

O amiable prospect!
O kingdom of heaven on earth!
I saw Mr. Eliot leaning over a fence
Like a cheerful embalmer,
And two little Indians with black umbrellas
Seeking admission.
And I was rapt in a song
Of *sophist*ication.
O City of God!

Let us be thoroughly dry.
Let us sing a new song unto the Lord,
A song of exclusion.
For it is not so much a matter of being chosen,
As of not being excluded.
I will sing unto the Lord
In a voice that is cheerfully dry.

VIII

When you are dealing with poetry itself, all these other matters—the question of an audience, fashions in criticism, the envy and malice that lie in your way like stumbling blocks—these all vanish. And the question of how to write also vanishes.

Yes. But why don't I say what poetry is, rather than what it is not?

The kind of poetry I am talking about has not existed in America for a long time. Perhaps it has not yet existed. There are starts toward it in Whitman, in Hart Crane. But mostly we have had a poetry of culture, the dry verse recommended by Hulme, or we have had sentimental verse.

What we need is the total poetic intelligence that existed in Rilke, in Yeats, in Blake. We need poetic brains. If Frost had caught fire, what a poet he would have been! But always in Frost there was a drawing back from ultimate commitment. The swung birch always carried him back safely to earth; he stopped in the woods for only a few minutes, and then he went home. This was wisdom, but it was not the greatest poetry. What we need is a poet of original, and purely poetic talent. That is, he would make up new ways of seeing things; he would push metaphor to the limit. And if such a poet were also interested in ordinary life, we would have great American poetry. Such a poet would not have to justify his existence in America; the rest of us would have to justify ourselves to him.

254

Herbert Blau

The Public Art of Crisis in the Suburbs of Hell

About the time I started taking the theater neoclassically, for instruction as well as delight, I had just been hired to teach at a state college in California. While God and Man were being betrayed at Yale, the loyalty oath was being legislated in Sacramento. There were dark perturbations on campus, but in those pre-Birch-and-Goldwater balmy days, the accent was still on behavioral benevolence and the clinical technique of the doctrines of perfectibility—Dewey-*ism*, replete with reading laboratories and remedial writing. In the canons of "student-centered teaching" (liberal dogma caressing jargon in social contract) to call a student illiterate if he was illiterate was worse than calling a student a nigger if he was a . . . well, you see the issue, words *do* fail. And there was reason in the surveys of "student needs," and something to remedy; even now, the laboratories continue, but with "stricter standards." The "goal": to get back to the subject through the student's problems. In such an atmosphere, no wonder the story arose about the freshman who, after a semester of self-searching—in psychology, creative arts, humanities, and even the social sciences, by Rorschach, true confession, by IBM—came to his instructor in English about a term paper, and said: "I don't know what to do, I can't find a subject, I've run out of problems."

The Sputnik, that great blast into the future, was grist for the New

Conservatism. Could Johnny dare remain illiterate—lo! the Word made flesh, even among the psychological adjusters—if Ivan wasn't? Yet in the backsweep toward the McGuffey readers, there still survive, up to the college level, Home and Family Living, Bibliotherapy, Group Dynamics, Collective Fun and Creative Togetherness, and deans who now believe in fraternities (those Platonic ideas of what the NAACP is calling "tokenism") as processes of Integration. And there is the semantic theory that all problems are merely verbal.

Sometimes this takes the form of reconciling opposites by canceling them: "They're saying the same thing in different words." Or, appearing to take opposites into account: "If Macomber could only communicate with Mitty, Mitty would understand." Yet even if Cow$_1$ is not Cow$_2$ (and I'm prepared to argue this), it is my contention—and the contention of the Theater when it is not betraying its nature—that there are these possibilities, too: either Mitty is never going to understand Macomber; or, if Mitty comes to understand, it will be precisely what he understands that he won't like. Khrushchev, I contend, understands Kennedy. "We will bury you," he says, with minimal malice—sounding, for all the shoe thumping, like a genial and unobscurantist Genet.*

"O words," says Ionesco's Jack, "what crimes are committed in thy name." Which can be taken two ways: words fail men, men fail words. We are—from the logical positivists to Antonin Artaud—too hard on words. Where words fail, they may fail at different limits. Lest we compound our crimes: Don't hesitate to call a spade a spade because somebody says it's a phoneme, or a well-wrought urn. You can't say the same thing in different words. Different words, different things. Communication will not solve the world's problems, it may cause some of them. How sad to discover, for instance, that foreign students, after four years in American colleges, go away hating us for somewhat better reasons. As the world grows smaller and smaller, it also looms woefully large, so that while one of our recent Nobel prize winners, an expert on atomic particles, assures us we'll never see the end, we see all too clearly the scaly dragon of Communist China raising its sullen head; and we know, I fear, precisely what it wants. I think of Beckett's

A day or so after I wrote this, Premier Khrushchev said about President Kennedy's *Izvestia* interview: "When Mr. Kennedy becomes a Communist, we shall speak a common language."

tramp, ruthless for recognition: "You're sure you saw me, you won't come and tell me tomorrow that you never saw me." There is a terrible innocence in the messenger from Godot, who says neither yes nor no.

As for the freshman, who had not yet developed techniques for seeing the whole world in a grain of sand, he was probably wrong, you can't run out of problems, one of the greatest being that when you examine the whole world in a grain of sand you see that, Lao-tse, Swedenborg, Blake, and Alan Watts notwithstanding, a grain of sand is not an empire. The least character in Shakespeare knows that: "I cannot draw a cart, nor eat dried oats./ If it be man's work, I'll do't." Or the other captain, who says about the military expedition of Fortinbras (who is not all that perfect a man of action): "We go to gain a little patch of ground/ That hath in it no profit but the name./ To pay five ducats, five, I would not farm it. . . ." Neither captain has entirely resolved the relationship between fact and fancy, but they each make reasonable claims upon the real. "Seeming, seeming." We may have to contend again with that old appalling possibility (suggested by Beckett and Shakespeare alike) that illusion$_1$ is no better than illusion$_2$.

Now the theater knows all this by instinct. Local habitation of illusion, the theater has conflict in its bones, and instead of doing away with it or pretending it doesn't exist or submitting it to panel discussion, it demands that conflict be brought to crisis. It is, indeed, the public art of crisis. (And that goes for the new "antidrama," more crucial about crisis than any we have going.) In public life a condition of insupportable tension, like that of the Cold War, may be made livable by the illusions of greater production, more conspicuous consumption, the strategy of controlled depression, and the whole Disneyland of shelter programs and stockpiled weapons. In popular art, it leads to what Dwight Macdonald (himself not exempt) calls Masscult and Midcult, culture for the brainless and culture for the middlebrow and half-educated, such as Frank Baxter's TV Shakespeare or the suburban-egalitarian-theater-party "Jews-and-Negroes-are-just-plain-white-Protestant" orthodoxy of Broadway. (From *Under the Yum-Yum Tree* to *A Raisin in the Sun*, from *Gypsy* to *Gideon*, Paddy Chayevsky's latest chapter from *The Greatest Story Ever Told*, one might do a study of public opinion on Broadway called "The Audience as Pavlovian Rat.") In real art, the same condition of insupportable tension, felt in privacy and cutting to the brain, is brought to even greater tension in the interest of *truth*, however unsayable, indefensible, or unbearable.

For people who don't understand the crucial concerns of the drama, who only think they believe in the dark at the top of the stairs, who are sure some guidance counselor or social worker or humane lady in slip or unbuttoned blouse will turn on the lights (or off; on or off, Love will out), there is secret wonder over the fact that neither Hamlet nor Oedipus was wise enough to consult a psychiatrist. But can you imagine either one of them going through a period of adjustment? "Why seems it so particular with thee?" asks Gertrude, after the unnerving if common saw: "All that lives must die,/ Passing through nature to eternity." "Seems, madam! Nay, it is. I know not 'seems.'" Hamlet, a born New Critic, creates problems with a runaway tongue. A self-made Academy, he tries to keep the language alive by his talent for paradox and his insistence on the seven types of ambiguity as modes of salvation or, depending on your illusions, therapy. Hamlet knows all about "the tyranny of words," but when the wind is southerly he can tell a hawk from a handsaw. And his advice to the players shows he believes words to be the life of the design and that he distrusts those, himself included, who dishonor the words in their charge.

258

The dramatic character is beyond adjustment, as he is beyond bargaining—which is to say, whatever his social role, as dramatic agent he cannot be bourgeois. Lord of the bourgeois, the Troll King says to Peer Gynt: "Man, to thyself be—enough." But Peer, Don Quixote of Free Enterprise, is full of the momentum of a century ringing down the grooves of change; he cannot rest. Until he comes home roundabout or is gathered in the artifice of eternity, the dramatic character insists on following things out to their inevitable end, or to that unmathematical and ready middle of experience that resolves "To be or not to be" in "Let be." The motive: what? Will? Moral purpose? Fate? History? Providence? The Dignity of Man? Or all these working interweavingly and impossibly together, as in the mat-making incident of *Moby Dick*, chance, in the indifferent blade of the pagan Queequeg, having "the last featuring blow at events." The cost: mainly self-destruction—calamity, catastrophe, the fall of the sparrow, accidental slaughter, a plague on both your houses, the shadowy waters, the dark root of the scream, the mill race, Birnam Wood, and the bleeding eyeballs. The effect: catharsis? Maybe. More likely woe and wonder, the hieratic emotion of what the jazz addict means by stoned.

The excess of the instinct for bearing things out to the edge of doom turns tragedy to comedy. We are in such a bad way now, with our cormorant Cold War. "What is right for us is comedy," says Duerrenmatt, the Swiss dramatist:

> *Our world has led to the grotesque as well as to the atom bomb, and Hieronymus' madness is with us again, the apocalyptic vision has become the grotesquely real. But the grotesque is only a way of expressing in a tangible manner, of making us perceive physically the paradoxical, the form of the unformed, the face of a world without face; and just as in our thinking today we seem to be unable to do without the concept of paradox, so also in art, and in our world which at times seems still to exist only because the atom bomb exists: out of fear of the bomb.*

Dread prolonged is laughable—a commonplace long before Baudelaire, but a collective fact of our time. Or, as the banished Edgar, resting from his role as Mad Tom, puts it in *King Lear*: "the lamentable fall is from the best;/ The worst returns to laughter."

If comedy is what happens when tragedy fails, tragedy is what happens when comedy fails. Duerrenmatt knows that the tragic (if not tragedy) may come out of the comic "as a frightening moment, as an abyss that opens suddenly"—as when Buster Keaton, directing the Rebel artillery with a sword that flies off the hilt, notices his comrades falling, mysteriously, one by one, about him. Discretion being the better part of valor, he runs, brandishing his terrible sword, blade leaving hilt in a high lyric arc, impaling a Union sniper. At the limits of the credible, the absurd, an *O altitude!* in reverse. "The point about tragedy," says Harold Pinter, "is that it is *no longer funny*. It is funny, and then it becomes no longer funny."

Whether crisis produces woe, wonder, or laughter, it is always in the interest of some Higher Self, one's god, or oracle, or essence, the deified *persona*, the grand mask of the comic animal. If it is not true, as the Greek choruses intoned, that Wisdom comes of suffering, then, maybe, as the Renaissance proclaimed with death's-head intuition, "Ripeness is all." Ripeness: maturing, coming to fruition, the image drawn from nature, suggesting fulfillment of the human, achieved only in crisis and hastening, teleologically, to an end. "Blest fig's end," says Iago. One forgets there follows upon the wondrous idea of ripeness in *King Lear* a sense of its absurdity, in Gloucester's equivocal remark: "And that's true too." Something like the enigmatic comedy of the gesture, no less spiritual for its scatology, of Leonardo's young Saint John the Baptist.

If in Socrates it is the unexamined life that is not worth living, in Shakespeare it is the uncontested. Even in the sonnets, the boughs do not quiver in the cold, they *shake against* it. The serenity of *The Tempest* and the green world of *Cymbeline* follow the blood and blackness of *Macbeth*, the dazzling scrofula of *Troilus*, and the misanthropy of *Timon*. Even when terror undergoes a sea-change, strong in the memory of the Brave New World is the mudcaked animality of Caliban and all the assimilated rage of the great tragedies, up to the very horror of that "kill, kill, kill, kill, kill, kill!" Even from his grave, Shakespeare speaks like a dramatist:

> *Good friend for Jesus' sake forbeare,*
> *To digg the dust enclosed heare;*
> *Blessed by ye man yt spares these stones*
> *And curst be he yt moves my bones.*

That last warning struck me all the more when I saw the same epitaph in the parish church of Chipping Camden, the curse removed, as the eighteenth century revised away the "multitudinous seas incarnadine" and the almost unimaginable horror of Cordelia's death. I had visited Holy Trinity in Stratford on a day in late autumn. Leaving the grave, I returned to the churchyard, a perfect sonnet of morning frost and bare ruin'd choirs. There, looking toward the Avon, I saw in the middle of the gentle river—like a footnote from the Underground—a large sign in red block letters: GREAT DANGER, WEIR BELOW.

Great drama is committed to that DANGER, and to the mystery of that WEIR. The dullard Kuligin, in Chekhov's *The Three Sisters*, tells the story of a schoolmate who was "expelled from the fifth form because he could never understand *ut consecutivum*. Now he is frightfully poor and ill, and when I meet him I say, 'How are you, *ut consecutivum*?' 'Yes,' he says, 'that's just the trouble—*consecutivum* . . . and then he coughs. . . .'" The anecdote is part of that whole mystique of malfunction and irrelevance that gives Chekhov's studies of provincial life a longevity that *Middletown* and the Kinsey reports never have. Words, words, words. "Balzac was married in Berdichev." (*Pause*.) Nothing is more real than nothing, says Beckett after Democritus, defining the formal principle of the following sequence:

ANDREY: In Moscow you sit in a huge room at a restaurant; you know no
    one and no one knows you, and at the same time you don't feel a
    stranger. . . .But here you know everyone and everyone knows you,
    and yet you are a stranger—a stranger. . . .A stranger, and lonely. . . .
FERAPONT: Eh? (*A pause.*) And the same contractor says—maybe it's not
    true—that there's a rope stretched right across Moscow.
ANDREY: What for?
FERAPONT: I can't say, sir. The contractor said so.
ANDREY: Nonsense. . . .

For all his virtues in the enlightenment of a *non sequitur* reality, such a
passage makes about half of Ionesco obsolete. Moreover, though Nothingness
is confirmed, neither Andrey nor Ferapont is denied; the one's intelligence
and the other's innocence come to the same end. The drama occurs at that
impasse of human relations, no less human for the impasse, where the rest
is silence, for the time being. History remains, a vague possibility. "It doesn't
matter, it doesn't matter," says the doctor, reading the newspaper and humming "Tarara-boom-dee-ay!" "If we only knew, if we only knew!" says Olga,
the music of the military band fading. Andrey pushes the perambulator in
which Bobik is sitting. *Consecutivum*—that's the trouble, not stasis. WEIR
BELOW.

261

    However it ends, drama begins with those who won't "Let be." "*L'aud-
ace, encore l'audace, et toujours l'audace.*" Not all heroes are up to Danton's
ethic, and if Hotspur is not entirely right that "out of this nettle danger we
pluck this flower safety," at least we pluck from the drama's dedication to
danger the courage to live in peaceful coexistence with the irremediable.
"What do we do, Kate, when the visions fail us?" "We kneel down and
pray, Mr. Blake." The prescription is lyric, the response dramatic. No mere
quietism here, that voice expects results. In drama—how often have we
heard it?—action is all. Though it may return us, inevitably will, to the
mystery of that weir.
    Andrey's lament to Ferapont is echoed by a village woman, cautioning
her child at the end of John Whiting's *Saint's Day*, a bizarre, incoherent,
and lovely play set in the English countryside: "Stella! We are strangers here,
Stella." The child is performing a "grave dance" around a corpse who bears
her name. It is impossible to say what it means, nor to resolve it, nor is it
necessary. Among the new wave of English dramatists, socialist or angry or

both, Whiting has not been searching for causes, because he believes all causes are failures. There is an Eliotic fall in the assertion of one of his characters that "it is not a question of finding but of losing the pieties, the allegiances, the loves"; but the final consideration for Whiting is not a matter of ideologies or postures or platforms, rather, literally, life and death. With or without the Bomb, "our fear is that the unknown hand is already at the switch." The sin of previous generations, with their passion for social exposé (the play's chief character is an octogenarian muckraker, now disgraced), was misinformation on the human condition, the failure to remind us as we convert history to the service of men that "the purpose of any memory— of any experience [is] to give foundation to the state of death." Truth and glibness mixed. Whiting knows that one of the chosen voices of intellectuals in this century is that which seems, prematurely, to have passed through nature to eternity. We have grown too chummy with Yorick's skull. The sin of the present generation is the disaffiliation it brings on, and which Whiting shares. *Saint's Day* reflects in action, and in a certain anarchic failure of form, the cost of setting limits on obligation, the risk of neutrality on aesthetic grounds, and the catastrophe of partial commitment. "There is always the responsibility—it must rest on someone."

Where courage fails, society like nature revenges itself. Disaffiliation invites the demonic. Indifference, recoiling into action, becomes the dupe of accident, as after the grave-yard scene of *Hamlet*. The result: promiscuous slaughter. Today, in mass withdrawal from the horror behind, we are almost passive before the horror ahead. Camus said the great philosophical problem of our time is suicide; the great practical problem is how to avoid deferring to solutions that are suicidal. Or, as Gerard Piel, publisher of *Scientific American*, said recently in San Francisco, we become victims of "the authors of frauds by computers. . . ." Nothing will come of nothing. Yet where to begin? Every profit a loss, every deterrent a possible disaster. Our reality is creepy. Literally. Think of the boon of penicillin bugged by the counter-revolution of staphylococcus. Would that the mystifications of modern society were even so imaginable as that weir. One hears the splashing of Grendel's dam everywhere, within and without. Whatever there is of "onto-logical anxiety," it passes over to the structures we create, so that we find paranoia and schizophrenia in institutions. Heorot quivers in the cold. Is there some grim poetic justice in the fact that Mies van der Rohe's bronze consummation of the Bauhaus, which aimed to turn the blight of industry to art, was built for Seagram? The whores sing in *The Rise and Fall of the City of Mahagonny:* "We must have whiskey, O you know why!"

In our time, who can avoid serving the enemy? (I am not alone in having enjoyed the discomfiting benevolence of a grant from one of the mortal enemies of my childhood.) If Ionesco's *Rhinoceros* had had the full courage of its excellent conceit, Bérenger would have gone on protesting his humanity while changing, willy-nilly, into a beast. The comedy would have been realer, if more repellent, by denying egress to those in the market for evasion. We all go under. It is the way we go that counts. One hopes he will go when he goes like Ahab's Pequod, taking a living piece of heaven with him. But there we have it—that skeleton-beneath-the-skin-sensibility, part of the higher criticism and one of the clichés of chaos, missing the issue in its own way, dodging crisis. (It is curious that President Kennedy, after the Cuban rout and the Berlin hostilities, picked up the tone of the disciplines of despair, the realistic promise of his Inauguration speech returning, somewhat, on a tour through the Midwest.) If T. S. Eliot taught us anything of value, it is to learn to live with illusions by improving their quality. Not what do we do as we go under, but what do we do while we're here, I'd say, on the assumption that the going under (yes, Old Possum, we must still give foundation to the state of death) will take care of itself.

"Nothing to be done." That's hardly the way a play should begin. However, a generation of incinerators, Hiroshima, and deterred deterrents lies between *Waiting for Lefty* and *Waiting for Godot.* And one of the illusions we've had to improve the quality of is that social problems are social. They are that, perhaps, but more than that—and it was not Dag Hammarskjöld but Jean Genet who gave us the better report on the Congo, a virtual prediction of the murder and dismemberment of thirteen Italian soldiers. (Recommended reading: *The Maids* as a minority view of our relations with Cuba.) It may be all right in wish fulfillment to get rid of social evil, as Giraudoux's Madwoman does, by pushing all the capitalists into the sewer, but it's another thing to get them anywhere near it so it can be done. Odets was saying: "Come on, let's do it—*now!*" But it was done when it was done, and done imperfectly. The New Deal was negotiated by experts, but it was improvisation nonetheless. Giraudoux, an elegant ironist, was saying, "Wouldn't it be nice if . . ." Which is a way of putting the real issue into somebody else's head. Genet takes the issue murderously out in the open, "Look out, it's going to happen, it *is* happening—those knives are real."

263

Only Genet, like the Envoy in *The Balcony*, is a master of obfuscation, and a pervert to boot. Can things be really that bad? We muse over it, fingering the selvage of our illusions, safe as only voyeurs can be.

"Security some men call the suburbs of hell,/ Only a dead wall between," says a Genet-like character out of Jacobean drama. Look at our situation in Berlin, that dead wall. Any first-rate dramatist would nose out one of the greatest ironies in the crisis, the fact that when the Krupp munitions empire was put up for sale, nobody had enough money to buy it out. So it was restored to its proper owner and recently celebrated its 150th anniversary. The *New York Times* reported, "Everyone"—ministers, ambassadors, employees, and two thousand invited guests—"had kind words for the House of Krupp." Theodor Heuss, former president of West Germany, was the main speaker. He said there was nothing "basically sinful" in the firm's past. Only "hatred spurred by war" had created an image of Krupp as an "annex to hell" while huge munitions firms abroad were seen "in the hands of heavenly angels." I don't know what company Mr. Heuss keeps, but outside of Shaw, and except by indirection in defense planning, I've never heard a good word for munitions makers anywhere. For propriety's sake we generally keep them out of the way, like the Mummy in Strindberg's *Ghost Sonata*. May choirs of angels sing around them all, for as to a more proper disposition of the House of Krupp, I'm not qualified to offer an alternative. I'm not sure, in fact, there is one. I do know that the theater cannot afford to put up, however, with the weird proposal that Germans, denazified, are just like other people; no more than it could put up with the equally astonishing idea that nobody is incapable of becoming a Nazi. I am. I insist upon it, like Bérenger, *yet* there but for the grace of God and historical circumstance go I. There is an enormous conceptual difference between the Karamazovan idea that "we are all murderers" and that we are *nothing but* murderers. If the theater brings conflict to crisis, it's because our conflicts are aggravated by the plague of choice, the most tortuous of which is, indeed—in an age where everything, not only the nefarious but the benign, conspires against it—the choice to remain human. Which includes facing up to crisis without hypocrisy and without snap judgment.

Where drama really takes place, judgment stops short. The Eichmann trial, which sent Portia packing back to Belmont, demonstrated this in an unexpected way. One could be predictably stupefied by Eichmann's discriminating between the assertion of one witness that it was 4,000,000 and another that it was 5,000,000 Jews he was responsible for killing. What monster was this? Yet when the prosecutor Hausner asked Eichmann whether he was guilty, the trial took a sharp turn into the special stupefactions of drama. Eichmann, with wondrous control it seemed, started to distinguish between moral and legal guilt, whereupon Hausner raised a finger at him and thundered: "Answer yes or no!" I don't know to what perverse instinct I may be testifying, but *at that moment* loyalties were annihilated for me, and I was with Eichmann.

Drama being a perpetual present moment, it may cut *you* to the brain. You are there, defenseless, guilty creature sitting at a play. What you lose by way of status and self-possession (*Einfühlung* or *Verfremdung*, drama sucks you in), you make up by full exposure. You are confronted with—what else?—yourself. That doesn't mean everybody else is excluded; if they were, you could escape the issue by claiming discrimination. The theater is nothing if not universal. Yet in a real Theater—I am not speaking of that politic convocation of worms where people meet for self-edification and digestion's sake—there is no safety in numbers either. Death or a lemon pie, you must face the issue. You are responsible for your foolishness as for your atrocities, and you may be horrified at the way one brings on the other, as when Lear asks his daughters to say they love him. And there is sorcery in the way, facing it all, brought nearly to exhaustion as *Lear* brings you, you become more available to yourself.

"You live badly, my friends. It is shameful to live like that." The charge may be gently reproachful, objective, as with Chekhov. It may be partisan and partial, as with Arthur Miller. "Attention must be paid!" You may hear a false accent in the voice, but you pay attention because the play insists on forcing its conflict to crisis, as when Biff forces Willie, already half-beaten, to confront himself. Whipping out the gaspipe, Biff says: "All right, phony! Then let's lay it on the line." The drama might be deeper if Miller did the same for Biff, who is clear about his failure but a little woolly about his aspirations. Still, we may be thankful for half-truths in a world of manifold illusions. Real drama, at some point, insists on laying it on the line. O'Neill's Hickey won't let the bums be content with their pipe dreams, to the misbegotten limit of his own delusions; nor, for all his massive clumsiness (about which we are sometimes too facile), would O'Neill be content with his own. If there is evasion in the confessions of *Long Day's Journey into Night*, it is beyond O'Neill's control, and he knows it, painfully: "The

265

makings of a poet. No, I'm afraid I'm like the guy who is always panhandling for a smoke. He hasn't even got the makings. He's only got the habit. I couldn't touch what I tried to tell you just now. I just stammered. That's the best I'll ever do. I mean, if I live. Well, it will be faithful realism, at least. Stammering is the native eloquence of us fog people." It's pathetic, but we have nothing more honest in American drama.

Though recently, we have acquired another sort of voice. "I'm crazy, you bastard," says the psychopath in *Zoo Story*, at the dead level of conflict. In drama, either that's my bench or yours, however we may be taught, and believe in, the value of sharing. There is a sense in which that line speaks for modern art, which has at its best been predicated on theories formulated by sinners, strangers, apostates and traitors, perverts and sickmen, and by all the holy demonism that is our romantic legacy.

It's a wonder we don't run away. Some do. Given the strategies of demonic art, the drama takes their flight, with Ubuesque pride, as a mark of *its* efficiency. Which speaks in the language of excommunication. It's funny, but then it's no longer funny. Ubu mourns, and becomes Clov. The laughter turns elegiac. A friend of mine once objected to Beckett's *Endgame* because "you can't call the characters on the telephone." True. But if you could, you'd only be talking to yourself. *Endgame* is the crisis of exhaustion playing itself out in the suburbs of hell. It has the eloquence of the blood below the eyelids of the nearly dead. It comes into the world of men and affairs like a scarcely audible bell out of the enshrouding fog—no less alarming for its remoteness. It is just such a story as Horatio might tell if he tried to fulfill the impossible burden placed on him by Hamlet in those exquisite dying lines: "Absent thee from felicity a while,/ And in this harsh world draw thy breath in pain/ To tell my story." How tell it? Where that story really took place, Horatio never was. To tell it, he'd have to re-enact the play, he'd have to *become* Hamlet. But wasn't it he who said, "'Twere to consider too curiously to consider so." Failing to tell the story, he'd become Hamm.

In such a play, rehearsing visions of greatness around "the insane root," the magic is blacker than we might like; but you can't run away because where in the world would you go? No modern drama comes closer to making you feel what Socrates meant when he said: "There's a doctrine whispered in secret that man has no right to open the door and run away; this is a great mystery which I do not quite understand." I don't presume to understand it either, but it is a mystery which informs all the great drama I know, and which constitutes for me the true condition of theater. It is this sense of the theatrical event that must have kept the audience in their seats at the first performance of Euripides' *Trojan Women*, one of the bravest plays ever written. In full daylight, Euripides said to the assembled Athenians, a people proud of being the most civilized in the world, that they were essentially a bunch of barbarians. They had just finished the siege of the innocent island of Melos, which they had assaulted for commercial reasons. Not content with victory, they had sacked the place. The play's prophecy of retribution on the Greeks (it dealt with the Trojan War, but the prophecy was writ large and contemporary) was actually fulfilled in the Sicilian expedition, virtually the end of the Athenian empire.

All the traditions of the Greek theater permitted Euripides to deal with such a crisis, because that theater, as we have been told, was central to the culture. Now that theater is only marginal, it may have to clamor more to get at the issues, but it will be worthless if it doesn't. The so-called Theater of the Absurd has been fighting a guerrilla war. It is the form of the Resistance, coming up out of Kafka's Burrow. Its passion is bare survival, and it uses every bean-bag, brass knuckle, and Molotov cocktail that can be salvaged from the wreck of theatrical history. It has the scapegoat *noblesse* of the Underground. And it awaits the time. The theater, it knows, needs more than piddling heroes and tight little emotions; it needs actors who, honoring that other, more inhibited, underground activity of the studio, *can* tear a passion to tatters; and it needs plays with a wildly civilized insurgence. It must seize with exuberance the task of being the public art of crisis in an age where crisis is a social and moral norm. And it must not merely escape into the apparatus of ritual and incantation, compounding the spiritual plague by making a ceremony of it. One can be as square in ritual as in realism, and the best of those dramatists whose guardian angel is Artaud, avoid the deadbeat of an easy demonism. The theater needs to learn again to contend with the world out of which history is made, men creating events, events determining men; a world of *Realpolitik*, sneak attacks, and holy wars, no less hieratic for its industry and no less hallucinated for its systems and categories, bureaucrats and dossiers.

As a public form, the theater has an illustrious history that is by nature opposed either to false silence or false security; it is a place where, strictly speaking, secrets are illegal. It knows about crisis as other forms don't because

267

it is virtually a State of Crisis—material, time-serving, collaborative, and adulterated by competing aesthetic claims as by competing temperaments. More than any other form, it calls constantly for its own purification: Eleanora Duse wants to kill all the actors; Gordon Craig wants marionettes and towers of light; Jacques Copeau wants to sweep the boards or take young blood into the country to kiss the soil again. They never succeed, but they live out the issues. Because it aspires to function, however marginal it may temporarily be, at the dead center of the community, the theater is more subject to compromise and adjustment than other forms. That is its shame and—when, somehow, in the strange bipartisanship of personal will and cultural ripeness the theater's inherent corruption is mastered—the source of its formal glory.

The theater has greater possibilities than other forms because it takes greater risks. This is a question of nature as much as choice. As it moves toward popular acceptance (and note the way even antidrama is becoming fashionable), it must beware of an excess of its own communal instinct. It must not be cabined or confined by demands for conformity, even to its own techniques of outrage, and all the other conspiracies of social approval; nor must it be tamed by good will and benevolence. God bless the medium, it is individual and protestant to its corporate bones and cannot help but look for trouble. For every saint in search of purification there are a thousand who think they love the theater and unwittingly, or pusillanimously, betray it.

You who work in the theater: learn to trust the trouble as it sings! For the real theater, intimate with catastrophe and memorizing another Golgotha, cannot be appeased by either false optimism or facile anguish or official realism. "After all, life—public or private—can often be carried on," says the Prime Minister of England, "with reasonable satisfaction on what a cynic once called a healthy basis of mutual distrust." In the theater, distrust is distrust, there is finally no hidden agenda. The theater is responsible to that distrust—where it comes from and what it does, its real sources, its real motives, its real consequences. Those declared, the theater leaves us—as far as humanly possible—to our own resources.

Raymond Tallis

A Dark Mirror:
Reflections on Dementia

In a famous passage, the French poet Henri Michaux asserted that
"more than the excellent skills of the metaphysician, it is the dementias . . .
the breakdowns in mental skills, which are truly suited to 'reveal' us to
ourselves." His intuition still guides many neuroscientists, for whom lesions,
things that go wrong—both naturally occurring and induced—are a prime
source of our understanding of the central nervous system and of the basis
of our ordinary mental functions.

What does dementia tell us about ourselves? What we feel, or fear,
dementia says about us may inform our attitude towards those who suffer
from dementia. The challenge offered by dementias is more intimate than
the unravelling of a scientific mystery, developing treatments, or meeting the
"burden of care." It is a fundamental challenge to our sense of who or what
we are.

This challenge—to think about our own nature—is implicit in another
famous passage, this one from William James' *The Varieties of Religious
Experience*:

> *Whilst in this state of philosophic pessimism and general depression of
> spirits . . . I went one evening into a dressing room in the twilight to*

procure some article that was there; when suddenly there fell upon me without any warning, just as if it came out of the darkness, a horrible fear of my own existence. Simultaneously, there arose in my mind the image of a patient whom I had seen in the asylum ... who used to sit all day on one of the benches, or rather shelves against the wall, with his knees drawn up against his chin, and the coarse grey under-shirt, which was his only garment, drawn over them, enclosing his entire figure. He sat there like a sort of sculptured Egyptian cat or Peruvian mummy, moving nothing but his black eyes and looking absolutely non-human.

This image and my fear entered into a species of combination with each other. That shape am I, *I felt*, potentially. *Nothing that I possess can defend me against that fate, if the hour for it should strike for me as it struck for him. There was such a ... perception of my own merely momentary discrepancy from him that ... the universe was changed for me altogether. I awoke morning after morning with a horrible dread at the pit of my stomach, and with a sense of the insecurity of life that I never knew before, and that I have never felt since ... I remember wondering how other people could live, how I myself had ever lived, so unconscious of that pit of insecurity beneath the surface of life* (pp. 116–117).

So far as I can tell, James seems to have been describing a severely handicapped young man with intractable seizures; but the object of his fear and pity could just as well have been a patient with end-stage Alzheimer's Disease.

That shape am I, potentially, is the fundamental intuition at the heart of a humane approach to dementia. It indirectly drives our usually highly abstract scientific endeavors. If we are deeply interested in, say, the damage caused by beta amyloid to vascular endothelial cells, or the phosphorylation of the tau protein—subjects restricted to science—it is because, ultimately, we identify with the person in whom aberrant beta amyloid or defective phosphorylation has brought about one of the most intimate and comprehensive catastrophes the flesh may be heir to.

This concern, the sense that we live under the sign of a common vulnerability—or, as William James put it, "the perception of my own, merely momentary discrepancy" from the victim—provides an ethical framework for clinical decision-making and implicitly shapes our law-making. We know for certain that a not insignificant proportion of those reading this text will some day assume "that shape." This knowledge will, if we allow it to, open on to two further intuitions: a sense of the extraordinary miracle of our ordinary consciousness and our ordinary volition, a sense whose obverse is a recognition of their vulnerability and fragility; and a feeling for an acceptable framework of law, ethics, and social comportment with respect to those who suffer from the condition of being demented.

The special tragedy and instructiveness of the dementias derives from the fact that they attack the self at the highest level. All fatal diseases do that eventually, but the dementias begin there, in the upper reaches of consciousness, and only later unpick simpler, more basic skills, such as the ability to navigate around a room or to handle and manipulate objects. By definition, dementias are "acquired global impairments of intellect, memory and personality *without impairment of consciousness*." Thus, they are especially "suited to 'reveal' us to ourselves" in the way suggested by Henri Michaux. Because the conscious level is preserved, our normal expectations of the sufferer remain intact. It is a human being we have before us; that this being has been overturned strikes us all the more forcibly.

271

We are accustomed to the interruptions and discontinuities of consciousness that occur in sleep. This accommodation enables us to assimilate even coma to our ordinary experience: we are used to these states of "present absence," of bodily continuity despite psychological discontinuity. True, the existentialist philosophers tried to work themselves up into a state of morbid horror at the fact that most of us are obliged at least once every twenty-four hours to lapse into a condition in which our will is suspended and we are subject to complex hallucinations; the rest of us, however, accept this with equanimity and welcome sleep. But we are all deeply disturbed when we encounter the dementing process in someone whom we have known as an ordinary human being like ourselves; when we encounter a person seemingly awake, relatively unchanged in physical appearance, who proves to lack the ordinary apparatus of wakefulness, the personal presence, to which we are accustomed.

So, what is it that dementia reveals to us about our nature?

Above all, it is a striking reminder that what we feel most essentially and intimately to be ourselves—whatever it is that is central to our sense of who and what we are—is contingent upon things (mechanisms, processes) that largely lie outside our knowledge, and entirely outside of our jurisdiction. It is through luck, not judgment or endeavor, that each of us is now severally thinking about dementia rather than suffering it, that the rooms about us make sense to us as scenes of purposeful activity rather than as a meaningless blur of lights and voices, a sea in which we are cast adrift. And this perception is underlined by the more detailed knowledge we have gained over the years about dementias.

Consider the well-known and seemingly innocent observation that the degree of impairment of the so-called higher mental function is proportional to the neuropathological changes observed at a post-mortem. To put it more dramatically: the tangle count determines the extent to which I cease to be myself and have lost that many-layered being-for-myself that constitutes both my familiarity with myself and a familiar world. This is entirely consistent with the general frame of understanding of neuroscience. And yet it is at once devastating and totally mysterious.

It is devastating because it makes painfully explicit the implicit assumption that a normally functioning central nervous system is a requisite for ordinary consciousness and the ability to impose one's will on the world through voluntary action. Since none of us has much of an idea how the nervous system works, and certainly could not run it if it did not run itself, we are in a permanent state of implicit dependency: our doings and our knowings depend on its happenings. This raises questions about our status as free agents, and it underlines the mastery of the dependency of ordinary consciousness upon neural activity.

Among philosophers, the currently favored account of the basis of higher mental function—indeed, of all consciousness and awareness—is that it is in some way due to, or caused by, neural activity in certain areas of the brain. There are, however, many objections to this widely-received notion. The difficulties are many and deep.

In brief, the first problem is that the relationship between objectively observed neural activity and the subjectively experienced contents of consciousness is far from clear. Some have suggested that neural activity and conscious experience are two aspects of the same events. This so-called dual aspect theory, however, has been largely rejected—because most people are not happy with the notion that a single event can have both a physical front-side and a mental back-side.

Others have suggested that the neural activity *causes* the mental activity, just as banging on a table causes a loud sound. Under this interpretation, there are two types of events: neural activity, which is the material cause, and the contents of consciousness (sensations, memories, thoughts, etc.), which are the immaterial effects. This essentially dualist account runs dangerously close to making mental events mere epiphenomena; they are digressions from the causal net, and have no role in bringing about other events. In this scheme, immaterial effects simply lie on top of the material, causal chain, and have as little influence on the latter as phosphorescence lying on the sea has on the movement of waves.

This is obviously unattractive, since it contradicts our firm belief that our conscious experience to some extent drives our behavior. If—to counter this objection—it is claimed that the mental phenomena themselves have causal efficacy and are able to bring about material events (for example, the neural activity essential for voluntary action), then we are faced with an unexplained, continuous causal chain or net, a material nexus of which we are a part, that passes into and then out of a mental phase. That is, the single, causal chain passes into the brain and, somewhere in there, it enters into and then exits from a "mental phase."

Given these problems with alternatives, most philosophers and neuro-scientists (when they have an opinion) prefer to espouse the idea that neural activity is *identical* with conscious experience: in the same way as molecules of H$_2$O are identical with drops of water with their phenomenal properties of liquidity, wetness, etc. In this light, objectively observed neural activity and subjective experience are the same thing, perceived at different levels, captured in different theoretical paradigms, etc.

Unfortunately, there are many seemingly insuperable difficulties with this notion. For a start, the idea of something being perceived or described at different levels rather presupposes consciousness and cannot therefore be the *basis* of consciousness. That is quite a difficult argument and may, for all I know, be a specious one. More specifically, the twin-levels, or twin-levels-of-description theory, fails to explain why some neural activity has the property of being consciousness while most neural activity—for example, that which takes place in the cerebellum, the spinal cord, the peripheral nerves—does not. Nor, most crucially, does this thesis account for the fundamental characteristic of conscious experience: its intentionality, its character of being something. For my consciousness of the cat refers to something outside myself. How, it remains legitimate to ask, do these neural discharges in my

273

brain refer back to the object that triggered them off? The inward causal chain that leads from the perceived object to the relevant area of the cortex fits well with our conventional materialistic and scientific framework; but the outward intentional link that reaches out from neural activity to the object of perception most certainly does not.

In short, it simply does not seem intuitively satisfying to explain human consciousness in terms of nerve impulses which, seen in the sober light of day, are only fluxes of sodium and other ions across semi-permeable (or, less charitably, flea-bitten) membranes. Even if the neural theory of consciousness could be modified so that it did manage to explain sensations—on a one-to-one or a one-to-many basis—that would not explain the unity of the conscious moment (which presumably involves huge quantities of activity in different areas of the nervous system); nor would it explain the coherence of conscious activity over time needed for the moment of understanding; nor, *a fortiori*, would it account for the coherence necessary to create and sustain the understanding self.

Just how far we are from comprehending such an ordinary fact—the coherence of the self in neural terms, a coherence which we see as though back-lit by its disintegration in dementia—is shown by the eccentricity of some recent theories advanced by some extremely respectable figures.

274

One of the front-runners is the idea that the global nature of consciousness is made possible by the micro-tubules in neurons which (they conjecture), because of their peculiar biophysical properties, are able to host quantum coherence (micro-tubules are the internal skeleton of the cytoplasm). This coherence, they argue, can extend across an appreciable part of the entire brain. Unfortunately, this notion—in which an entire system containing a large number of particles behaves like a quantum state of a single particle and provides the basis for the unitary sense of the self—would, even if it were itself coherent, fall foul of two facts: that micro-tubules are also present in many human and non-human biological tissues that are not conscious; and that quantum coherence occurs outside of living tissue.

And so we have a dilemma. On the one hand, evidence from the neuropathology of dementia strongly suggests that our higher mental function and everything we think of as our real selves depends upon the integrity of neural pathways in certain areas of the brain. On the other hand, the same evidence indicates that it is impossible to conceive of consciousness, particularly at the higher levels of integration, in terms of neural activity.

This latter impossibility is not surprising. Is it not difficult to imagine how the first person, the subjective viewpoint, could emerge in a material universe which seems to exist only in the third person? Is it not even more difficult to see how our world, and ourselves as viewpoints sustaining our individual worlds, could be dependent on the functioning of a small something in that world? Those two handfuls of porridge as the wetware of the brain?

Yet it is equally and extraordinarily difficult to ignore what the neuro-pathology of dementia tells us about the dependence of our ordinary lives as conscious agents on the integrity of the brain. It seems we are forced to conclude that: (a) consciousness is due to neural activity; and that (b) consciousness cannot be due to neural activity.

One way we might reconcile these two seemingly valid and incompatible views would be to deploy the ancient distinction between necessary and sufficient causes. Thus, for an event to take place, a necessary cause has to be present. Absence of that cause will ensure that the event will not take place. But its presence will not guarantee that the event will take place. For instance, I must be on the same road as a certain car to collide with it, but my mere presence is not a sufficient condition of the collision. A sufficient cause is one that, if it is present, will guarantee that the event will take place.

275

Using this distinction, one might argue that the integrity of the relevant neural pathways is a *necessary* but not a *sufficient* condition of consciousness: just as having legs is a necessary condition of walking, but walking itself requires more than legs—for instance, a nervous system. But without being able to specify just what that "added something" might be that is required to ensure consciousness, I suspect that the challenge issued by dementias to our self-understanding at the deepest level remains unanswerable at present.

Besides raising questions about the nature of consciousness, dementias ask even more difficult ones about the nature of volition and human agency. The correlation between neuropathological changes and impairments of higher mental function emphasizes the dependence of the latter on the structure of the brain; this would seem to make higher cognitive activity—including the formulation of the intentions we believe drive and shape our actions—an *effect* of events outside of itself. More specifically, the very passivity of the person with dementia, caught up in and forced to live out processes over which he or she has no control, challenges our notion of ourselves as autonomous beings shaping our own lives and even our own activities.

If we are agents, it would seem we are such only by courtesy of systems and structures of which we have little inkling and which we certainly cannot will into being or keep from failing. The most intimate ground of our choosing, the most proximate layers of our self-presence, are due to and rooted in processes we do not choose and from which we are absent. Even in our deliberate activity—for instance, in reading this text—we are apparently the overt effects of hidden material causes.

This, too, is hardly a revelation. The very fact that we are embodied means that our voluntary activity is imposed upon, or wrested from, a complex mesh of mechanisms of which we have only the slightest knowledge, and which we ourselves would not be able to run if they did not run themselves. The peculiar dialectic between "I do" and "it happens" is most vividly and puzzlingly illustrated when we consider the higher mental activity that drives voluntary action. The inescapable conclusion is that not only is consciousness dependent upon the brain, but *even the higher reaches of consciousness implicated in our most deliberate and seemingly free activity* are likewise dependent.

276

The neuropathologically-caused loss of higher mental function leading to the unraveling of all learned behavior, and in particular to the loss of the planning and purposive activity that fills daily life, and its replacement by purposeless wandering, illuminates the mystery by default: for how is it that the automata of the brain can underpin our human ability to choose and to act in accordance with free choice? How does mechanism dovetail with deliberate action? How does voluntary activity ever arise in an agentless causal net (nature, the physical world) of which the brain is a part? In short, how does a network of material causes secrete human agency? Dementia reminds us that human agency has to be fashioned in a sea of causation in which we are soluble fish.

The notion of agency—of the individual as a cause rather than an effect—is inseparable from that of explicit purpose, of the expression of the rational will. Purposive activity requires us to relate ourselves to things that are *widely scattered across time*, to larger frames of reference than are encompassed by the present moment of the instant of consciousness.

An early casualty of dementia is memory, information transmitted through personal time, by virtue of which the present moment is steeped in and informed by, answers to and reaches out to, other moments. Our standard understanding (which is also not without its problems) considers memory to be the back-bone of the self, the grounding of responsibility and, consequently, of our sense of who and what we are. Memory is that in virtue of which our current account of experience is transformed into the deposit account of our evolving personhood (habits, traits, character, aspirations), and the stream of experience leaves an alluvium of self. Memory is essential, for it ensures that the agenda of any given moment amounts to something more than a mere response to current stimuli or to instinct-mediated needs.

To be in such a state of immediate responsiveness to stimuli or to the unreflective pursuit of instinctive needs is to be in the end-stage of dementia. The sufferer passes through a variety of stages *en route* to this end-point, but ultimately people with dementia tend to live entirely for the present moment, although for them the present may represent an era from their own distant past.

The poet Philip Larkin expresses this lack of temporal depth in his unflinching and compassionate poem, "The Old Fools." He speaks of the sufferers sitting "through days of thin continuous dreaming / Watching light move." He speculates that this is perhaps like

> *. . . having lighted rooms*
> *Inside your head, and people in them, acting.*
> *People you know, yet can't quite name; each looms*
> *Like a deep loss restored*

and reflects that

> *That is where they live.*
> *Not here and now, but where all happened once.*
> *This is why they give*
> *An air of baffled absence, trying to be there*
> *Yet being here.*

The loss of temporal depth manifests itself in the fraying of the long-range internal connectedness that is so necessary for us if we wish to be the kind of responsible agents able to operate effectively in our complicated world. The temporal world of such an agent—you or me—is a huge and complex one. My writing this text is, in all its many stages, from idea to writing and revising, a remarkable tribute to the complex inner organization of my life (in this respect, like the organization of any other life) and its extendedness across time.

As dementia progresses, this temporal depth evaporates. With the gradual cessation of the process through which we lay down episodic memories, it soon becomes impossible to be a responsible agent—at least in the way we take for granted in our expectations of ourselves and of others. Eventually, sufferers can no longer take any kind of intelligent or sensitive interest in others; they can no longer remember the lives of others and are condemned to an involuntary egocentricity. The new facts go first, then the long-standing ones: first what the childrens' children reported last Thursday when they visited; then the fact that they visited; and, finally, what names are to be applied to the not-quite-familiar faces they bear.

Under such circumstances, we can no longer think of people suffering from dementia as responsible agents in any real sense; nor are they living lives which are in any way comparable to our own. They have descended into an intolerable solitude, one which consists of disconnected moments, the "thin, continuous dreaming" of which Larkin speaks. There may be, of course, flashes of wit, tatters of clarity, moments of ordinary affection, and these give us an occasional glimpse of what has been lost. Sufferers also make great efforts to restore the coherence and plenitude of daily meaning. But often these attempts are desperately misguided. There is a terrible pathos in the way they sometimes try to make sense of a senseless discontinuity by accusing others of bringing about the endless muddle, by plotting against them, by putting them in a situation which, since they cannot understand it and have not chosen it, they assume has been imposed by those "others." These others are usually their nearest and dearest, those who have done the most to assist and comfort them; they have now become the focus of anger and fear.

Finally, the connections between one moment and the next are lost; temporal depth evaporates entirely—and since such depth is necessary to make sense even of a single, given moment, the aura of meaning and recognition is withdrawn from things. All that remains is sensation warmed on the embers of significance.

Dementia, therefore, is an indirect reminder that to be human is to be explicitly extended in and across time; that the backbone of the self, the ground of personhood, is memory—itself the basis of what philosophers call "psychological connectedness."

Locke was the first to argue that sameness of consciousness—rather than the persistence of the body or of an immaterial substance such as the soul—was the basis of personal identity. This sameness, this connectedness over time—sustained across an extraordinary interdigitation of preoccupations, themes, locations, situations—is mediated by memory: memory implicit in habits, explicit in deliberate recall.

Of course, sameness and connectedness are only relative. I am the same person as my seven-year-old self, but we have little in common in terms of explicit memories. He could not, for instance, remember any of the things that have happened to me over the last forty-eight years because they had not yet happened to him. And there are many things that were uppermost in his mind that I have completely forgotten. But there is a sufficient overlap between the different stages of my life to sustain the objective fact and the inner sense of continuity—rather as the continuity of a long thread inheres in the overlapping of shorter filaments. At any moment, I may be mobilizing only a small part of my huge bank of memories, that massive archive of the available past; we do not require continuous, summative recall to secure psychological connectedness and the preservation of identity. All we need is sufficient recall: so that we may give meaningful context to the present, make the present "our" present, give it temporal depth—the implicit depth of recognition and the explicit depth of specific reference back.

This continuity is the necessary prerequisite to my status as a responsible agent: one who makes and fulfills promises, undertakes and discharges commitments, and is answerable for events in the past. The synchronic and diachronic unity of consciousness is the basis upon which each of us has a complex concern for his own future and a complex responsibility for his own past. All of this is eroded with dementia: as new memories cease to be laid down, the ability to connect the current account of daily experience with the deposit account of the past is lost, old memories fade, and the sufferer is no longer able to discharge his role in life, he loses habit, character and traits.

I underline this loss of psychological continuity in dementia because, for most of its course, the dementing process advances, yet physical continuity is preserved and, with it, until the late stages, a procedural memory that continues to make it possible for the victim to negotiate within a shrunken world, one largely reduced to the here and now. Even in the late stages of dementia, an individual—unlike someone who is asleep or in a coma—can find his way around a room, can identify an assailant, real or imagined, and respond in some fashion to what is said.

This dissociation of those aspects of identity that are usually indissolubly bound leaves us with a dilemma as to how we should view the sufferer. In an advanced state of dementia, patients are often seen by their families as being only the physical shells, or relicts, of the persons they once loved. It is at this point that we cross the boundary separating metaphysical mysteries from ethical and legal challenges. When, in dementia, the aura of recognition is eventually totally withdrawn from people, places and things, and experience becomes a series of disconnected moments which lack temporal depth, we are compelled to ask: In what sense is the sufferer still a person? Although he or she retains a viewpoint on the world, the sufferer has ceased to have the characteristics—in particular, continuity experienced through time—which we associate with personhood. We cannot, however, say when personhood ends; psychological connectedness remains a matter of degree.

280 The philosopher John Harris defined a person as "a creature capable of valuing its own existence." At what point does one cease to be such a creature?

This is no idle question. For when an individual suffering from dementia ceases to be a person, it may no longer be ethically imperative to strive, on his behalf, to extend his life. As Harris points out, "The harm you do in withdrawing life support is the harm of depriving someone of something they value." If they are no longer able to value their lives and you deprive them of those lives, you may be undermining their earlier wishes about their destiny and their earlier views of what they valued. This may well be ethically unacceptable, for as Ronald Dworkin has argued, "Making someone die in a way that others approve but he believes to be a horrifying contradiction of his life, is a devastating, odious form of tyranny."

It could be argued that personhood does not require temporal depth, that any conscious being values its own life—irrespective of a psychological connectedness that can tap into its past or formulate a future. But I have argued that valuing one's own existence in the way that humans do requires temporal depth in experience; mere sensations are not enough. If we are not obliged to prolong the lives of people with advanced dementia, those who have ceased to all intents and purposes to be people, are we obliged to care for them? What then of the rights of an individual who, in advanced dementia, seems no longer a true person? Do such individuals, who can exercise neither responsibilities nor duties, have any claim on us? On our instincts to care? On the public purse?

My answer is a resounding "Yes!" and comes from the intuition with which I began: *that shape am I, potentially*. The answer also derives from our separating two things: the ability to value one's own life in the way we typically associate with human beings; and the ability to experience pain, even in the very advanced stages of dementia. It is even arguable that physical experience, unmuffled by temporal depth, unmitigated by an inner agenda, may well be sharper rather than blunter in sufferers from advanced dementia. Though we may be uncertain how to tap into their feelings without the aid of speech, it seems reasonable and safe to assume that those things which make us uncomfortable—cold, dehydration, starvation, harsh words, uncaring attitudes—will also make them uncomfortable. We should conclude from this that they are entitled to a high level of comfort—a very high level, considering that they are so completely thrown into the present moment. Despite the sufferer's loss of a sense of duty and the diminution of his sense of responsibility, despite the fact that we withhold blame from him when he hits his wife or defecates on the floor, we accept such an asymmetry in retaining rights because we recognize *that shape, potentially, am I*.

With advanced dementia patients, different considerations affect life-prolonging as against comfort-securing treatments. If such individuals are unable to value their lives in the way that persons do, how are we to value their lives on their behalf? Directives set down in advance, such as "living wills," may not help. If we believe that personal identity resides in psychological connectedness and this has now been radically broken, then the individual who drew up that advance directive is no longer the same individual. Under such circumstances, how legitimate is such a directive? It is presumably less illegitimate if I become "no longer a person" than if I become another person; but it is still not unquestionably legitimate.

Questions such as these lie at the crossroads between the metaphysical mysteries of dementia and more practical considerations: the legal and ethical framework within which we determine the rights of people suffering from advanced dementia; the non-clinical decisions we make on their behalf; and more generally, the way in which we (professional and non-professional carers) comport ourselves towards individuals who have lost much of what constitutes being alive in the human sense, and yet are very much both human and alive.

Because the metaphysical stance cannot help us with these practical considerations, it sometimes seems frivolous. Nonetheless, we should meditate on the poignancy of dementia, which creates lives that have outlasted their customary meanings, and on a disease that progressively removes human significance from human lives.

In advanced dementia, mere existence has out-endured significance. The rich foliage of daily meanings—of communications, preoccupations, hopes, plans, responsibilities—has been burnt off, leaving only the naked branches of simple needs and mere existence. Action has given way to reaction; reaction to mere happening; life to living death. But the very absence of the layered meanings of daily life makes us aware by default, in advanced dementia, of the richness and mystery of ordinary consciousness, of what Philip Larkin called "the million-petalled flower of being here."

Dementia acts as a dark mirror which reflects the extraordinary and inexplicable mirror of our own consciousness. We should be grateful for this. As an inscription in York Cathedral says: *Lucem demonstrat umbra*. Darkness shows forth the light.

Lives

Josephine Herbst

A Year of Disgrace

I n the early months of that year John Herrmann and I were living in
a penthouse on lower Fifth Avenue. The address led visitors from the Midwest
to expect elegance. But when a stout uncle from Minneapolis arrived, he
refused to budge beyond the second landing, and bellowed up the vast
stairwell to us, as we leaned down from the top, that he was no Alpine
climber. The three rooms perched precariously on top of a solid iron-faced
monster reminding us of the lookout, called a crow's-nest, on the high masts
of seagoing ships, and, during windstorms, with rain battering the windows
and hammering on the flat tin roof outside our bedroom, the place shook
as we liked to imagine an old windjammer might have shuddered in a gale.
The furnishings were sparse. There were six chairs and a round table that
trembled to the touch. Two cots covered with plain gray blankets were
narrow as a ship's bunk. A dresser, painted black, had six drawers that stuck
when you tried to open one in a hurry. In the kitchen, there was a smallish
bathtub covered with a lid that served as a table, a washbowl with a cold-water
tap that was also a kitchen sink, and a decrepit gas stove. The toilet was in
the outside hallway.

The place was a sublet from a novelist, Leonard Kline, who had
retreated to the Connecticut countryside in a last-ditch effort to escape

alcoholism but who was to spend a year in the village jail instead. For he had drunkenly chased a visiting friend around his house with a shotgun and killed him. The rent was $45 a month and we felt we were lucky to have it. That it was bare was an advantage. We had a great many books, some in French and German, that we had brought home from Europe two years before. A shop around the corner had dug up some pine boards for us and we had made bookshelves that gave the main room a look of being lived in. A little model of a Breton fishing boat made out of a solid chunk of oak and fitted with a small square-rigged red sail stood on top of the bookshelves. Painted a dark blue, with its name, *Le Pouldu*, on the prow, it was the first object to strike the eye when you came into the room after the long climb up the six flights of stairs. John had made it during the year we had spent in an old farmhouse in Connecticut.

We had given up our house in Connecticut a few months before coming to New York in the late fall because our money had run out. After living in Europe where money had gone a great way, every dollar shrank from what it had been "over there." But the two of us could still get by in the country for $600 a year if you took it easy and asked for no more than the essentials. Nobody we knew was out to save for anything except to buy time. If the country was in high-gear prosperity, none of the young people we knew were sharing it. Of all the young writers Scott Fitzgerald was almost alone in going after money and he seemed never to have enough.

The owners of the house in the country had magnificently loaned us a big coal stove, bedizened with shiny medals and scrolls of steel. It stood in the living room where we also slept. We called it the *Kaiser*. In the dark of night the coal glowed through transparent isinglass doors with the fateful assurance of a charcoal burner's fire in a deep German forest. There was a wood range for cooking in the kitchen and a big pantry stocked with enough to start a small grocery store, for we were three miles from town and had no car. A farmer sold us a quarter of a cow he had butchered, and it hung, during the winter months, frozen stiff as a board in an icy unused room on the second floor. With a saw we could hack off choice cuts for stews or pot roasts. A big ham and a side of bacon were strung on nails from the ceiling of the kitchen. With snow up to the window sills and the roads a sheet of ripply white where the wind brushed the contours in tiny gusts of drift, we were often as isolated as we might have been on a long voyage beyond sight of land. For a week at a time the mailman, muffled to the eyeballs, in an old buggy drawn by a meek horse breathing frost, could not get through.

With both stoves going and the falling snow blocking the windows inch by inch, we gave ourselves up to the splendors of isolation. During the day we worked at our typewriters, John in the main room, I in the kitchen, where I could keep an eye on the cooking. Dark fell early and the light from the Aladdin oil lamp cast a mellow glow the color of a ripe pear. With a jug of hard cider drawn from a fifty-gallon keg in our basement we began to read aloud through the long and wonderful evenings. The reader sat in the one comfortable chair near the lamp while the listener lay at ease on the big double bed spread with a bright patchwork quilt. We took turns reading and it was often two o'clock before we could bear to put the book down. We read Shakespeare's play about Henry at Agincourt and squabbled about Henry's treatment of Falstaff. Or we read the Song of Solomon. A lot of Dickens. Sometimes the next morning at breakfast we would compulsively pick up the book again, but break off, guiltily, for a day was for work, not for reading. That winter we read Turgenev's "First Love" and Goncharov's *Oblomov* for the first time, and it is astonishing now, when I think back on it, how we retreated all those snowbound months as one might into a storm cellar, to the literature of the nineteenth century, or pushing on beyond Stendhal, once more involved ourselves with the *Iliad*.

The setting of that room is so vivid, I can see it all, and myself lying on the bed with red slippers dangling from my feet and my head propped upon one hand. I can hear the soft plop of snow on the window and see how the pear-colored light fell on the reader's hands. There were times, when we came to a work I already knew, when I let the words flow over me like water, hearing and not hearing, while some other self burrowed in the dark sorting out those thoughts that were so manifold and evanescent, or reviewed the past, yesterday or the year before, or speculated on the present. Everything fused, fleetingly, in a flux and ferment, fired by a spark from the words being spoken while you waited, expectant, for the passage that jubilantly intoxicates the heart. The room would stand still, in the shell of a dream, and you hardly dared breathe for fear the spell might be broken. Sometimes, late at night, a terrifying screech would echo from outside. The first time we heard it we threw open the door while the snow swirled past us to melt on the floor. The sound was like the cry of a woman in torment, but when we crunched out to see if some human creature had

287

floundered in the drifts, there was only the creak of a broken limb of an old tree, while beyond, high in the night, the demoniac cry echoed again: a screech owl.

On some nights we might spend the hours reading the plays of Heinrich von Kleist or those of Carl Sternheim so we could keep up our German, for we had both spent several years in Germany, I in Berlin, John in Munich, before we had met in Paris six months before we were due to sail for home. We met one April evening at the Café du Dôme on a day I had come up from Italy and two weeks later we had gone to Le Pouldu, a little town on the coast of Brittany, where Gauguin had once lived and paid for his room with a painting. The way we had met, accidentally, after living in the same country at the same time without crossing paths, seemed one of the marvels of chance events. In the Connecticut farmhouse my thoughts would turn to that summer, at the very moment I would be sitting before my typewriter, and an entire scene from a past time would be suspended before my eyes, enclosed within some magic circle, something apart from any of the life that had gone before or that might ever come again. It was one of the wonders of that isolated winter that nothing one looked at was blocked off in terms of time, and one's mind grew accustomed to work in a particularly ample environment. In terms of space, because the frosty windows and the sweep of snow as bare as a desert floor confined one physically, the ever-present time vistas could come and go, offering a hard stretch of sand on the Brittany coast where I could see us once more racing in the late afternoon when the fishing boats would be coming home, or again, walking under the larchwood trees where the light flickered as delicately as shadow birds as we stepped along a leaf-sodden path to Quimperlé. Or a sudden sound would bring the creaking of the oars of the fishermen as they rowed down the river to the sea past our hotel at four in the morning under a phantom mist as opaque as old silver straight into the kitchen, and I would whirl in my chair, startled as though a gun had gone off, to find nothing.

Nor was it only in the daylight of the winter that a scene from another time might push up from the underground. In the depths of night I might wake to hear John call out in muffled German. Or I might wake from a dream where I had been jabbering French, charmed to have heard myself so fluent in a language that in real life, in Paris, had come awkwardly to my tongue. Or I might wake suddenly in dim morning light, in a panic, not knowing in which of the many rooms I had known I now found myself, and in a brief spasm, clutching at now this, now that, or induced by an early fog pasting a clammy damp on the windowpanes, retreat back to that room in Seattle where, at the end of the Great War, the high notes of the Funeral March from Chopin's sonata had pierced to the vitals, for you knew that on the street a long line of hearses was somberly passing, carrying the boys who were dying of flu in the nearby camp to the railroad station with an honor guard to be shipped back home. In a few brief seconds a host of impressions would whirl wildly as falling leaves, then everything righted, the body beside me was comfortingly there, and the drift had settled down into the autumnal colors of the patchwork quilt that covered us.

In late spring some Connecticut rivers flooded, backed up into inland brooks, and then ebbed, leaving huddles of sticks, old leaves, and the owlish glitter of a tin can. A trickle of young people drifted into the countryside. You could have an abandoned farmhouse for the asking, with little more required than "to fix things up" or to paint a few walls. Some of the land had been taken over by Polish farmers whose coarse vitality could better cope with the smitten soil than the tremulous hands of an old New England bachelor, now content with collecting wormy apples for a barrel of hard cider. Katherine Anne Porter rattled around in a stone house in a maple grove and Nathan Asch scrambled with his wife into a leaky dwelling where a tub to catch the drips was a deathtrap to the unwary. One day a taxi driving all the way from New York dropped at our door a tall young man in tails with a wilted white carnation in his buttonhole and a girl with tawny hair and golden skin who came toward us in her chiffon evening dress extending one hand from a wrist heavily bandaged. The young man was someone John had known in Detroit; the girl a showgirl from *George White's Scandals*. They were sick of the messiness of New York, they said, and wanted us to find them a house in the country to live in. Her first account of having cut her wrist "opening a tin can" was changed in a few days to the truth; she had slashed it with a razor blade and had been "a fool." Ted had found her "dripping with gore," had rushed her to a doctor, and at dawn they had walked out into the empty early streets to hail a taxi for the getaway. Ted was an ad writer who vaguely wanted "to write." The girl didn't want to write anything except an occasional letter; she loved making curtains and little dresses, puttering about the kitchen, setting the table. Besides, she was being "written up," so she confided, by "Bunny Wilson, who is putting me in a book." Like everyone else who appears as a character in the work of an author, she didn't think much of it, though she was bursting with pride at being considered a worthy subject. "The way he makes me talk," she exclaimed, "You'd never believe it!"

But when I came to read *I Thought of Daisy* it seemed to me that the very exaggerations, of her idiom, for instance, that had repelled the actual Daisy, had evoked a protean Daisy as a Leonardo drawing may suggest the image of a woman more provocative than the full-fleshed Gioconda. But I could understand her dismay, perhaps at no more than finding herself in the company of Edna St Vincent Millay, whose chameleon presence had suggested now a sibyl, now a firebird. But Wilson himself astonished me, emerging in his novel as a sort of Proustian Swann, challenging my first impression of him on an evening when I had gone to see him in his apartment on Washington Square to ask if he would be willing to join a protest against the seizure by the Customs of a novel by John Herrmann, printed by Contact Editions in Paris, and which Morris Ernst had volunteered to defend in the courts. I had been deceived by the plump but graceful figure, the scholar's high brow, the luminous brown eyes, and the face, delicately larded with a baby-fat that might never wear off. I had imagined the squire, the don, or oddly enough, even the choirboy; but not the amorous, complex nature he was attempting to unveil.

290

And often, during that summer when our house opened from two rooms to six and our garden could have fed a huge family, it seemed to me that each of us in the valley called Merry-all relived some personal adventure as it might have been related in fiction. For surrounded by a company devoted to the art of fiction either as writers or readers, the source material of one's own existence stirred and came to life, was burnished and glistened, if only for the moment when the faces turned toward you ready to laugh or become bemused. You might be encouraged to ribaldry in recounting some old love affair or, in an attempt to be "honest," rob yourself of a subtler truth. One narrator might unconsciously distort for the sake of the paradox while another might painfully try to trace in the most dissimilar adventures the threads that implied an inner harmony. I might remember the Pears' Soap of childhood, its color as translucent as clear quince jelly. Katherine Anne could recall being bathed by the nuns and how the long gown considered appropriate for "modesty's sake" floated out on the bathwater like the pad of a water lily. Or the English painter, Ernest Stock, might spring a quotation,

> When antelopes surmount eagles in flight,
> And swans be swifter than hawks of the tower,
> Then put women in trust and confidence. . . .

thus tempting us to take note of a graver wound than the exterior scars of the shrapnel in his leg, earned in the War when he had been shot down in a plane. As he ran around in shorts we were not sure he was not trying to expose the one scar in token of the other, but he won no more than comment from a Polish farmwife who scoffed, "Look at him now, running around in underpants, showing off them bony knees!"

He might drop on the grass to sketch our corncrib, empty except for a mouse, or come suddenly as night fell, pale as an Orestes pursued down the coast of Calabria by the Furies, to beg to spend the night. When I had gone to bed upstairs in the dark, I could hear the voices of the men as they wet their whistles with hard cider in the kitchen, drone on and on. After midnight, they sounded to me as soothing as a guitar played outside the window.

It was an interlude of time as clear and uncertain as a drop of water. It hung, trembling and iridescent, like a fresh green grape. To eat it made a fever in the blood. Should the fever be fed or starved? Where were the sources of energy: in work, in love, in the ground itself? We could try them all, reaching into the bin that seemed to have no bottom. Sometimes the hands alone held restorative powers and one wished only to be rid of paper. To get close to the sky, skin, taste. To refurnish with a walk at night, or with a wild Polish dance where the shy country women danced, pinching up their stiff skirts in delicate scarred hands. To get up in the morning when the dew frosted the red cabbage, to pounce upon the cutworms ready to wilt the tender pea-stalks; what savage energy could leap out at the discovery of the cannibal soon to end his feast between two flat stones! What a miracle currant jelly was and how I gloated on the little jeweled array of glasses sitting in the sun. Nathan Asch, his hair dabbed with the yellow paint with which he was renovating the interior of his house, found an old waffle-iron, scrubbed off the rust, and invited us to waffle feasts with maple syrup. Daisy and Ted went in for pork roasts studded with garlic. Katherine Anne picked a bushel of dandelions to make delicious wine, as subtly intoxicating as champagne. John and Ernest Stock made little models of a Breton fishing boat and competed on a pond with the pomp of a Bermuda race.

Then Ernest persuaded our company to let him pour plaster of Paris around a hand so he could make a cast which he then filled with some bright silvery substance. When the casts were chipped off, a gallery of oddly assorted hands held out their empty palms. They seemed to be idling for use of the amputated, or destined as offerings to some little shrine where the faithful, in thanksgiving for delivery from sudden death, bring replicas of a leg or arm, or hang up a tin miniature heart or lung near the image of a saint.

Detached from myself, my own hand belonged to someone else. Posed like an empty cup it asked for too much. A counterswing of weather blighted the cucumbers. Opening a dark closet we found our city shoes greenish-white with mildew; long scars had been dragged in our winter clothes by the moths. The apples warned us that summer had ended and that we could no more indulge ourselves with the winy autumn than the cows should have afforded to guzzle the rotting fruit from the ground. A herd came running past our house one afternoon, racing madly from tree to tree, tails flying, a beery foam bearding their muzzles. Gorged on apples under the mile of trees lining the road, beginning to bloat, they were rounded up at last by the desperate farmer who herded them drunkenly reeling, bawling piteous cries, past our

door. Some died in the night.

The late shimmering of the Queen Anne's lace began to look like frost. Nathan Asch packed his wife off to Duluth, where her father, a rich banker, might be persuaded to give them a loan for the duration of their wait for his novel to be published. Then he hitched a ride to the railroad with his black cat Moses sourly peeping from a basket. Katherine Anne vanished with the mist one early morning on a milk truck. Ted and Daisy, deep in debt for pork roasts and goodies, fled anonymously. Ernest Stock washed his hands of Connecticut, where the landscape had never equaled the downs of England anyhow.

We came back to New York with what we called "the loot": manuscripts of two novels, a basket of currant jelly, and summer tan. No matter what happened no one could take away what we had made. It might be ground to dust but it had come alive. It was to take two years before either book saw the light of day, but in the twenties a young writer expected the run-around for a first venture. But no one waited for a first novel "to be taken" before beginning new work. Now it was only a question of what next.

We found a room in an old lodging-house and went to Julius's place in the Village, that in spite of Prohibition, boasted a long bar backed by a high mirror in an elegant walnut frame. John was carrying *Three Lives* with him and had barely laid it down when a man standing next to him, with a soft brown hat jauntily slouched over pale yellow hair, edged his drink nearer and clearing his throat began, "I see you are carrying Gertie with you." A book like *Three Lives*, a bluebound contraband *Ulysses*, a copy of *transition* or *This Quarter*, was enough for strangers to strike up a conversation that might lead to the drinking of *Bruderschaft*, a flirtation, or a love affair. Like the speakeasy, a good deal of avant-garde literature was considered unpalatable by the law and nothing could be more appetizing to the young than the forbidden. That the law was on the side of what the literary left in its new-found exuberance called the Philistine made a rallying point for the young for whom freedom to write was synonymous with freedom to love. Nor did it matter that some of the experiments were as obscure as a Chinese ideograph; even the duds generated an atmosphere tingling with the possibility of a chance encounter with the magical phrase. It was with something like pride that the editors of *transition* had announced in Number 7 that Numbers 3, 4, 5, and 6 had been confiscated on grounds of obscenity or other pretexts. Ezra Pound had written that his *Exile One* had been appraised by a Boston Customs Inspector as "stuff written by some narcotic fiend. Nobody has thoughts like those except under the influence of drugs." Brancusi's sculpture was taxed by the port of New York on the ground that it "wasn't sculpture but metal." A few weeks later they passed in the Hope diamond free, on the ground that it was a work of art.

293

Holger Cahill knew just the place for us; he even had the key to the sublet on Fifth Avenue. We promptly walked around to look the place over, climbed the six flights of stairs, and agreed at once that it was a regular crow's-nest and just the thing. Cahill was living in a "corner" of a loft on Fourteenth Street. The loft, big as a skating rink, had been taken by a young couple, friends of his, who had fitted it with tall screens separating living from sleeping quarters, a potbellied stove on an apron of zinc, pots of ivy at the windows; they, in turn, had taken Cahill in. He had transformed it in his imagination to a Dostoevskian "corner" and fairly gloated on his situation; temporary, of course, until the suitable thing turned up. Like everyone else we came to know that winter, he had come from somewhere else. His young boyhood on the plains of North Dakota had been his Nemesis; the arched blue sky, the wavering sea of wheat unbroken by the spar of a single tree. Family disasters had pitched him to wandering; he had bummed rides on trains, met up with migratory First World War farmhands and tramps of the jungle, hit Midwest cities and worked on small-town papers, inching his way, nibbling his education from books and papers, chewing his destiny fine, and, burned up with curiosity, stung by the itch to see it all, to know it all, had managed to get himself to China where his imagination had been taken over as the imaginations of others may be taken over by the Greeks or Etruscans. Back in New York, he had filled in his sketchy education at the Rand School, at Columbia, and at Cooper Union. Through his contact with social critics like Thorstein Veblen and Horace Kallen he began to fuse his native talents with his experience, and now, though an assistant to John Cotton Dana at the Newark Museum, he had found time to write a first novel, soon to be published. He was complaining that night that most writers were ignoramuses on the subject of art unless, like e. e. cummings, they could draw or like John Dos Passos painted water colors in the manner of *Manhattan Transfer*. As for most painters, they blacked out when it came to literature, he said, adding mournfully, "We have no Apollinaires, no Baudelaires." He might have added, "We have no

cafés," for the speakeasies with their heavy white cups holding dago red hardly filled the bill.

I don't suppose all of his story came out on the first evening. But it was a mark of the time and the place that a first encounter might last all night, overflowing from the speakeasy to the street, from the street to someone's room, to pitch you finally into a dawn exhilarated, oddly at peace, for wasn't it of engagements like this, long talks and walks, that you had dreamed in the Midwest town before the War when the sky had pressed above your head like a burnished brass bowl and the long secretive dark express trains zipped into the horizon? You had dreamed of it as surely as you had dreamed of love. A book told you it was so, long before you had the chance to prove it, and when some knowing librarian, seeing you flounder in the bookstacks, had put into your hand books beyond your years to prove to you, beyond the shadow of a doubt, that explosive, wonderful, witty talk existed somewhere as surely as it did in the pages of *The Way of All Flesh*, *Sanine*, or *Madame Bovary*. More than the theater, or the bright thoroughfares of big towns, more than the chance to see "real" paintings in big galleries, was the hope to verify the book by the human encounter.

Perhaps it was in those early days, in the little town, that "the word" had come to seem a holy thing. But "the word" can be used or misused by anyone. It can be flogged to death. Common denominator though it be, it may become the little stick of dynamite. It can drown the brook in a rumbling mountainside. We saw it happen. The Great War began in 1914 with no more than the incredulity of the elders—"Why, they can't let it go on. It's barbarism"—but it led right on through muddled unwillingness, to sluggish hesitation, to jingoist cries, to rhetorical betrayals; until beneath the public harangues other voices spoke and you heard them: D. H. Lawrence, Barbusse, Romain Rolland, Emma Goldman, John Reed—dissenters, dissenting among themselves, but reminding you that what you hoped to live for, lived. An underground aliveness burned and stirred, made signals in the dark.

A good deal of social existence eddied around "corners" where in little nests scooped out of old tenements, in basements, the newly arrived youth had stripped themselves to modest requirements. Though we had put distance between ourselves and our origins, and now, as through a telescope, imagined we might view the planets that had presided at our birth, we bore the stigmata of an early upbringing. It would take years to value the long shadows on the grass, the smell of homemade bread, the hum of telegraph wires in the winds of an empty prairie. Now we chose to remember the rustling long skirts, the heavily flowered hats of mothers or older sisters whose tiny pinched waists had betrayed the stays of a cruel medieval corset and whose notions of beauty might lead to an elegant vase from Tiffany, where, under the spell of an artful design, the true functions of a rose were lost in the whorls of an erotic daydream. So the sword of Picasso's analytical cubism had ripped the plump cushions on those enormous divans that had suggested, but only suggested, a harem, for the stiff braided designs, the heavy knots of beads and sequins, could only invite a mystique that seized on the erotic as a defense against life, not as an invitation. "The lovely and the beautiful" became for our generation a term of contempt; the grounds for complacency held by the parents, despised. As the Paris Surrealists had discarded Anatole France for a more distant Lautréamont or Rimbaud, some of us pried open the Pandora box of the past to see what had once lived there. You might rescue the old daguerrotype of a great-uncle whose bold profile of the arrogant blacksheep was more seductive than the direct gaze of a grandfather, seated in a genteel armchair, his hand on a Bible. Or, as Cahill discovered, finding his Icelandic forebears to be more fertile to his imagination than his father who had deserted his mother, or his mother, who had seemed to desert him when she married again.

Nor had all the newcomers flocked from the Midwest; some had moved up from the South. Allen Tate and Caroline Gordon held out in a basement apartment on Bank Street with rent free in return for janitor service. Allen stoked the furnace while Caroline looked after the stairs and hallways, hiring neighborhood colored women to scrub and clean. Ford Madox Ford's imposing white walrus presence was stationed on the top floor, where a fireplace burned chunks of coal all day long. Besides writing, keeping their apartment tidy, and cooking, Caroline acted as secretary for Ford that winter and even found time for a stray job of editing or proofreading. Like the rest of us, she was ready to try her hand at anything.

Katherine Anne Porter was living on the third floor of a rickety house on Hudson Street called by its witty tenants, Casa Caligari. Creaking up the stairs you half expected to see a skeleton wag from the ceiling, but instead, a door opened on the second landing to a view of a child strapped to a high chair while it gobbled its bowl of bread and milk. It was Dorothy Day's little daughter, a rare sight, for children were few and far between for our generation. When you came to Katherine Anne's room the prospect opened surprisingly to a domestic pavilion with gingham curtains at a window, a flowering primrose, a small cookstove with a coffeepot sizzling away, a gray cat on a cushion in a child's rocking chair. Her footing was as precarious as the house was shaky, but she could make light of it, wittily tossing the jacket of a book she had reviewed into a wastebasket or pinning up the jacket of Holger Cahill's *Pagan Earth* with a drawing by John Sloan in a place of honor. She was promising herself to do a review of the book but she never got around to it.

Nor did we get around to many of the things we had promised ourselves we would do when in the country we had taken a long view of the time to come. Brute necessity gobbled up time and energy. With no money, we had taken the first jobs that had been offered. John had a wardrobe that might have qualified him for a "young executive," as his well-to-do father sent him custom-made suits of the finest British material. My once smart Paris clothes were no longer so smart but would do for hanging around big laundries to get information from the working girls about their "conditions" for a research outfit. I could laugh at myself as a "big collar-and-cuff" woman, but selling books at Brentano's rubbed your nose into the fact that the best sellers might be no more than best sellers. In the grip of making ends meet, everyone was compelled to commit follies. Down to ten dollars I could throw it away on a delectable hat. Katherine Anne Porter invested in a chair with a delicate frame and a striped upholstery of blue and lilac veined satiny material that gouged a hole in her "capital" bigger than what remained. A young man might phone his girl, "I'll bring you asparagus in a taxi." A youth with literary aspirations, freshly out of college, might decide to have a grand fling before settling down to brass tacks, and with no other obligations than to salute the captain of a cattleboat, reporting hourly, "The cattle are all well, sir," get a comfortable bunk with good victuals, ten days' sail on the high seas, and a week in Paris.

Mobility was not only in the blood but was a fact. The youthful juices had neither jellied nor atrophied and if some of the young played with the recklessness of a gambler, with no more of a stake than talent and a fanatic's will, if the risks were high, what did you lose? The bottom had dropped out of the old world and it was a truism that the "old men had not only bungled the peace" but had screwed up the works. President Harding had been a stooge, the highest government officials had been crooks, and Coolidge, lulled by a booming stock market, took long naps every afternoon in the White House. The biggest city in the world had a play-boy for mayor who had danced the cancan in a homosexual dive in Berlin. Disenchantment was not only a necessity, it was a joy.

It was in this kind of setting that the early stories of Hemingway—then playing a lone hand in Paris—made so grave a mark. His young Nick might be the remains of the solitary trapper, but now he was educated, and through with everything, nourishing the residual grit of anarchism as a last hope. Don't get held by anything. Avoid getting connected. Break it up. What a pleasure! His young love ends: "It isn't fun any more . . ." "Everything's gone to hell inside me." It was really honest. Don't be sentimental and hold on to something that is dead. Beat it.

Every generation wants to be spoken to in its own terms. Young people of the twenties had been brought up in schools and universities where contemporary literature was a buried subject. You were given Longfellow and Whittier rather than Whitman. Who had heard of Melville until Raymond Weaver of Columbia began to unearth him in the twenties? But provincial towns had taken education seriously, had made impassioned readers of those with the inclination; we knew the classics, read Virgil in Latin, knew Plato and if not Greek, the translations. We had acquired taste through mad love, an extracurricular hit-and-miss encounter that had skinned and scarred and set a mark upon the forehead. We knew we were in a period of evolution and called it a transitional time. What period is not in transition? We named it as if it had never happened before, feeling ourselves actors in a rare moment, caught in a situation that would require not only flexibility but intensity of purpose. If more of the young were involved in an artistic movement than in political awareness, it was because politics had not yet put the bite on. Who believed in the vote? Women had been given the vote, but if they were now "emancipated" it was not through suffrage, but by jobs, birth control, even Prohibition. If a fine martial spirit existed between the sexes, it was a tonic and a splendor after so much sticky intermingling and backboneless worship of the family and domesticated bliss. We were a stiff-necked generation, defiant, each ready to defend his side, her side, against assault. You had to stand up for yourself, in literature as in love, and both worlds at their best had a wild salty savor.

A sense of fatalism fed the anarchistic heart, but fatalism does not always degrade. It may inspire elation. A pessimistic outlook was countered by a buoyant confidence in the precious moment. If we had abandoned the safe lives our parents had fancied so valuable, we seemed to have gained an insight into the creative fissures of the world. The fires and smoke steamed up from volcanoes, old and new. What had Baudelaire *really* said? Was Poe a phony? Stendhal, newly translated in the twenties, became a contemporary: a young man speaking for the age. A young writer in New York might hang a death mask of Nietzsche on the wall, remembering that young Russian poet in mittens and overcoat who had scribbled away beneath *his* freezing death-mask of Pushkin.

The little magazines, so different from the academic organs they were to become, tempted, teased, provoked, and ridiculed. The editors of the *Little Review* might publicly disagree, one stating that Hart Crane had better drop dead, the other claiming him as the finest of the hour. Irresponsible in any academic sense, the little magazines steered wildly, invited hugely, and didn't care a rap if they printed a shapeless imitation of Joyce by a youngster from Davenport alongside a hunk of the actual Joyce. A writer might flit with ease from the pages of the *Little Review* to the *Dial* or on the same day send one manuscript to *transition* and another to H. L.

Mencken. Or be aware that in the publishing house of Charles Scribner's Sons, Maxwell Perkins would be sorting the wheat from the chaff, and, reading the little magazines, would know your name before he knew you. Whether it was the more solid, dignified *Dial*, whether it was the little magazine, the stage was set for an international set of players; the era that gave the Model-T Ford to the farmers opened the world to its literary young on a scale never before ventured and not equaled since.

Ungratefully, rudely, some of the young made a swift bypass around their immediate literary progenitors, skirting Anderson and Dreiser in search of the unknown. In France, the Surrealists had brutally ditched the "sugary" Anatole France; in Russia the process had begun earlier, and four young writers of whom Mayakovsky was one, had delivered their manifesto, "A Slap in the Face of Public Taste." Delivered with all the confidence of youth and with youth's delight in shocking its elders, it had advised its readers among other things:

> *Throw Pushkin, Dostoevsky, Tolstoy, etc. overboard from the steamer of modernity.*

299

> *He who will not forget his first love will not recognize his last.*

> *All these Maxim Gorkys, Bloks, Sologubs, Remizovs, Chernys, etc., etc.— all they want is a villa by the river. That is how fate rewards tailors.*

And in the same mood it was a pleasure to chant:

> *There's not a single gray hair in my soul;*
> *With nice old men I have nothing to do!*
> *The world shakes with my voice's roll,*
> *And I walk handsome*
> *And twenty-two.*

Or, stimulated by a flaming punchino, some of us might recite in unison the maddening, repetitive lines from Kurt Schwitters' "Revolution in Revon," beginning with "Mama, the man is standing there," and ending with "They must be curious trees indeed, where the big elephants go walking, without bumping each other!" Or reel off the intoxicating Dadaist verse of

Hans Arp (later to become Jean Arp) whom we familiarly referred to as "the trap drummer."

Literature had not yet been boxed off from life. Nor had a body of critics nominated themselves as "the elite." You might write reviews for the literary supplements without having to qualify as a professor. A good deal of reviewing was done by practicing writers, while painters like Léger and Picasso, Max Ernst and Klee, explained themselves. The reader had not yet been herded to pastures chosen for him by the book clubs, nor did top lofty foundations presume to supervise culture from a doubtful pinnacle. The young writer had a private life where he could grow, change, develop. Or quit. You might not be a Dante; but Dante was dead. Your milieu was your own and nobody who was not alive could say the special words that needed saying to interpret it. You discovered on your own the worthy dead without the aid of scholars who also had not yet begun to gang up on the living.

With fingerprinting the image of man dwindled to the guilty worm but in the twenties we still were able to discern something of the divine. Two young people writing in different styles, using different materials, could afford hospitality to one another's work. Those who had socialist inclinations, those who ran gaily down the stairs with a manuscript no one would ever print, those who liked to read "The Waste Land" aloud to a girl, even though she fell asleep, those who were oddballs, those who fancied the wits of the Algonquin were reincarnations of the eighteenth-century London coffee house customers—all mingled in a sort of ridiculous, gorgeous, open-house limbo. Young women, who in an earlier era might be getting the kids ready for schoo,l fancied themselves as Aspasias and counted the number of their "affairs" as their mothers might have added up the household linen. Without a reader's guide you could make what you pleased of a sentence from Joyce: "What bird has done yesterday man may do next year, be it fly, be it moult, be it agreement in the nesto," or you could relish plain lines by Alexander Blok: "Excuse me sir, we don't allow that. You're picking over all the crayfish. No one will eat them." We could even suffer with laughter the tortured exercises of some of our contemporaries who, intoxicated with Joyce or under the spell of Freud, examined minutely their own often quite uninteresting interiors.

Pound could afford a world view that in 1927 would advise: "Lenin is more interesting than any surviving stylist. He probably never wrote a single brilliant sentence; he quite possibly never wrote anything an academic would consider a 'good sentence,' but he invented or very nearly invented a new medium, something between speech and action (language as cathode ray) which is worth any writer's study."

But you had to eat. Pay rent. Nobody thought then of leaving the university in order to dive back into it as an instructor. Pound, aided and abetted by Mencken, had presented the academic world as a Black Hole of Calcutta. Better to try your luck on Wall Street selling bonds. When neither the Brentano job nor my laundry enterprise proved enough to keep us afloat, John left the city as a traveling salesman for a publishing house on the big short trip to Midwest cities and I landed a job reading for a pulp-magazine outfit.

There were a dozen magazines going full blast, a dozen editors, a dozen desks, a dozen bottles of bootleg gin concealed in a lower drawer. You had to have the stuff to wade through the day. Our publisher liked to remind his employees, some of whom were bright boys out of Yale and Princeton, that there were advantages to be had beyond the stipend, and with the air of a big foundation establishing a fellowship, held up Dreiser and other "big names" who had made a start in similar enterprises. When the visiting authors, curiously prim, elderly bodies, who wrote with lubricity about chorus girls and Rotarians on the loose, complained that the editors interviewed them "reeking with gin," we were scolded by our publisher and forced to add peppermint drops and cloves to the bottom-drawer arsenal.

301

Cooped up in a small office with a meek woman in black who read for a true-confession magazine, I might mix up her monologue with the manuscript I was trying to read and suddenly feel that I had fallen into a bear trap where the stinging bottle-flies of words, written or spoken, were the real menace. Nothing could stop her; her voice was the voice of an endless soap opera that now and then disengaged itself from a recount of her love life with a Japanese "poet" to sing of the virtues of Katherine Mansfield, whom she was studying seriously, so she said, for that day of days, when she would ditch all this for "her own work." And, as if to prove her claim that she "could write" she might drift into a descriptive passage, filled with periods and semicolons, dashes and pauses, and in which she offered herself as a crucified relic of love with the flourish of Brutus extolling the death of Caesar.

But is there such a thing as the twenties? The decade simply falls apart upon examination into crumbs and pieces which completely contradict each

other in their essences. The twenties was not at all the museum piece it has
since become where our literary curators have posed on elevated pedestals a
few busts of the eminent. Even individual characters cannot be studied in a
state of static immobility. It was all flux and change with artistic movements
evolving into political crises, and where ideas of social service, justice, and
religious reaction had their special spokesman. You might be invited to
look forward to the social millennium or to the mechanical millennium;
you might beat a retreat to Jeffersonian agrarianism. Mencken and Pound
could exchange insults and compliments, Mike Gold of the *New Masses*
lunch amiably with an editor of the *New Republic*. Ernest Boyd might
travesty the new poets for Mencken, but the new poets were not defenseless,
and in a body as committed to their intentions as the Surrealists were to
their idea of Infinity, held together for attack and pursuit, even contemplating vengeance of another order, for Allen Tate was of the opinion that
verbal reply was too honorable, and that it would serve Mencken right to
be dealt with as a scoundrel, waylaid in the dark and beaten up in a dark
alley.

Styles in manners had shifted as well as styles in women's clothing
since the early days of the twenties; by 1927 you could make two dresses of
the material it would formerly have taken to make one. Hats with brims
became helmets out of which the face pressed, egglike, from a nest too tight.
What had happened to early friends to whose inspired account of Nijinsky
you had listened respectfully? The swan of Pavlova, the incomparable, had
evolved to other swans and the oldsters who, with moist eyes affirmed that
the great artists were vanishing, were bores. How could that be when *Jurgen*
had given way to Joyce and Proust? And what did you care for Eliot's
pronouncement that the novel was dead? It was as tiresome as the premature
announcement of Lenin's death had been. At that very moment, an ear to
the underground could hear the murmur of new voices, or catch D. H.
Lawrence in flight.

The very stuff of conversations had shifted. In the early twenties,
before I went to Germany, I had often visited the apartment of Alex Gumberg
on Union Square, where the talk veered around the Russian Revolution and
the Civil War; where the heroes were Lenin and Raymond Robins. Now,
in 1927, on my way home from the pulp mill I might drop by at the Tates',
and standing in the doorway listen idly to the conversation that went on
uninterrupted by a new presence, and wonder just which war was being

discussed. But in a few moments a name would flash and I knew this was our Civil War; the heroes Lee and Stonewall Jackson.

Or I might come upon a poker game in the same apartment during which Allen would be wearing "for luck" a wide-brimmed black hat that looked to me suitable for a Kentucky colonel, and Hart Crane, glancing briefly from the cards in his hand, flashed a beam from blue eyes that made his upstanding brush of white hair seem to belong to another man. Malcolm Cowley, with the rosy face of a farm boy, down for the day, drawled a hello, as Caroline darted from the kitchen where she had just torn their big yellow cat from the lamb chops freshly delivered by the butcher boy. Some of the young people who had lived abroad liked to talk of their days in Europe as an expatriate adventure, but the real expatriates were the Southerners in New York who came with a bloom of other lands more remote than modern France with its bright band of Paris Surrealists in their blue suits and white ties, their nonexistent means of livelihood, their pursuit of the mystical experience—"eager to discover the formula and the place." The Surrealists were even a sort of seismograph vibrating not only to the unseen but to the underground tremors of an explosion to come. But the Southerners reminded you of the fluctuations of time, and coming upon Allen Tate, suddenly, as he sat in his apartment without seeing you arrive, you seemed to be looking at a figure, enhanced by a fair skin and a noble bulging forehead, that could have belonged to an exiled dauphin of France, dreaming of the forfeits history had demanded. Caroline, sweeping by, with an energy that stifled the air, touching with a quick hand, now a cat, now a book, imposed upon your imagination some grandmother who had once had her hands full with a thousand supervisory chores and had stood looking out over plowed acres with the authority of a commander.

But if you passed the Tates' door and mounted the stairs to the apartment where Ford lived, you might enter his place to a voice murmuring, and come upon Ford, sitting in an armchair with his bare feet in a steaming footbath while before him stooped the slight delicate form of Biala, his adored companion, who, forgetting her own painting, commiserated in tender tones, "Oh, the poor feet," as she laved the misshapen bunions and broken arches of a man whose voice, often wheezing and whistling, reminded you of the poison gas and the trenches of a war our generation thought it could never sufficiently remember. And the presence of Ford, sitting stoutly erect, his florid face illuminated by pale blue eyes and furnished with a little mustache, sometimes military, sometimes straggling, was so real and so of the world that passing down the stairs again, you hardly stopped at that other door where some charming ambassador from the South might have newly arrived: Robert Penn Warren, very slim, with a plume of red hair, or Andrew Lytle, a squire from the eighteenth century, sandy, bemused.

For Ford could remind you by a poignant presence of the price you paid, not only for war, but to be alive. And with that reminder I could stiffen myself for the long climb to our crow's-nest, where I now kept a solitary vigil, and see the little boat *Le Pouldu*, with its sail dropping, as a puny but indestructible adversary to that other boat pictured in a reproduction called *"Au Bord de la Mer,"* by Chirico, which I had pinned to the wall, and where a classic archway opens only to space and the sky holds a cluster of pearly clouds that might be no more than the puffs from a shell exploded from the futuristic battleship posed naked on the dry land of an empty quay.

It was not always your contemporaries who reminded you of your contemporary world. Nor, though you might snatch at a new *transition* as a member of an underground might pore over a secret leaflet for a possible direction to action, could you always respond with a throb of conviction. There was a scatterbrained diffusiveness about some of these outpourings that aroused suspicion. Was modernity becoming a cult? Could "the word" become an idolatrous symbol of the inane? But a single issue might mingle sense with sensibility, or pose questions that forced sterner answers than the question might imply. Reading the editors' "Revolt of the Philistine" you might agree, without exactly knowing why, that it was, indeed, a "year of disgrace."

"The Philistine is as much the serf of living forces around him as ever," the editorial ran. "Dominated by his egotism and his sentimentality, he is incapable of hatred or love. He is not interested in the arts, save in their scandals. Dully he travels through his little world, devoid of any fresh impulse, hypocritically ecstatic at cultural phenomena, and, after his little sensation, goes back to his cocktail swilling and his self-sufficiency. His loves are whoremongering impulses, for he lacks the courage of his emotions."

In April, John came home. He looked thin, his dark eyes enormous in a paper-white face, but he was jubilant. He had stopped off at his hometown in Michigan, where he had acquired another unnecessary suit and had, at his mother's insistence, seen a doctor. "I'm a wreck," he said joyfully, laughing as I had once seen him laugh at the Fratellini clowns in Paris. "Is it something to laugh at? What do you mean?" I asked him coldly, for I was terrified. "Yes," he said calmly, "it is: (a) I am a wreck—my blood is thinning to water; (b) I have to take a long vacation; (c) we go to Maine and buy a boat. I know just the place. This trip was good; the haul was good. We can do it."

So we took misfortune to be a godsend, and, as if to send us off with trumpets, the long heralded première of George Antheil's *Ballet-Mécanique* occurred at the Carnegie shortly before our departure. The Antheil performance was a signal for the gathering of the clan. Pound had been beating the drum for the young composer for years, and in 1924, in Paris, we had been present at a private concert where Joyce, in dark glasses, half reclined in a long chair, conspicuously set apart from its fellows. Eyes were upon him, when at the close, the composer sat modestly, his hands in his lap, while Joyce lifted two long pale hands, and extending them at arm's length began a slow clapping that was the signal for the younger members of the audience to break out into wild applause. If the frantic response had struck me as comic, it might have been because the music had merely stirred me to confused wonderment. But my lack of enthusiasm didn't prevent me from wanting to attend the Carnegie performance.

We had spent that Sunday afternoon on Long Island Sound sailing in the 35-foot Alden ketch of our friends John and Liza Dallet. A contrary wind had delayed landing and there was no time to rush home to change clothes before the concert. We had not bought tickets in advance, but were now glad of it as we were hardly dressed suitably for anything but standing room. With our hair windblown, in sweaters, mine spotted where coffee had spilled upon it, we stood eagerly at the rear of the auditorium where we could watch the well-dressed audience, some of whom were smiling small patronizing grimaces as they fluttered their programs. Antheil looked wonderfully youthful with pale bangs cut straight above level eyebrows as he sat erect before one of the jumbo pianos in a company that presently broke into a din of saxophones, xylophones, trombones, drums evoking a maddened collision of braying steamboats, screeching factory whistles, with a yelp of human joy wriggling through a murderous crash of cymbals. The sound stunned the senses. A gentleman in formal attire rose from his seat, and, hoisting a cane to which he had tied a white handkerchief, began a slow and insulting exit. Titters broke out, followed by indignant hisses from the faithful. The performance closed to thunderous applause, hoots, catcalls. One dignified customer with white whiskers waddled majestically up the aisle braying lustily. The audience milled in the lobby; reporters darted about, button-holing Nathan Asch, who in dark, formal clothes proudly refused to answer questions, saying with a smile of lofty modesty, "I don't care to make a statement. I'm part of the movement." William Carlos Williams, in from Rutherford, grabbed John's arm, insisting we must come backstage and say a word to Antheil. And meet Pound's parents who had come, loyally, all the way from Idaho for the occasion. The green room was choked with enthusiastic cohorts, but I only remember Pound's parents, two frail, beautiful old people with white hair, both very slender, with spots of bright color in their cheeks, who stood shaking hands as if they had been parents at the wedding reception of a favorite son.

What did the music mean? I longed to be moved as all our friends seemed to be, including John, but it seemed to me I had heard no more than a hallelujah to the very forces I feared. My longing for a still small voice, for a spokesman not for the crash of breakers on the rock but for the currents, down under, that no eye could see, made me feel alone, but not an alien, and I looked at John, too, coldly, as one who had joined forces with some mysterious enemy. Was Antheil to be the symbol of an opposition to the Philistine? In a corner of my heart a slow movement of the pulse began to turn my attention elsewhere.

But we were not to depart on the receding waves of sound from the Antheil concert, but on a far more somber note. After seven years in prison, the sentence of death had been finally and irrevocably passed on the avowed anarchists Sacco and Vanzetti, on April 9th. What had we expected, those of us who could not believe in their guilt? At the start, only a nucleus, such as had formed around Dreyfus, had persisted, broken into factions, reformed, persevered, until gradually through the years a widening breach in an impassive society had brought many people of assorted temperaments, beliefs, backgrounds, and convictions to the conclusion that the fish peddler and the cobbler were innocent of the crimes of which they had been accused. Who can tell the source of a belief that may be concealed from the believer? So, some who might never be presumed to care were first caught, as by a flying thistledown, when they heard that Vanzetti was reading Dante's *Vita Nuova* in his prison cell. Their hunger strikes might have stirred a man who could remember the Irish rebellion. Did the seashells Vanzetti liked to hold in his hands call to some? Or his words?: "Nothing is worse than the false belief of self-goodness or greatness. It is that which permitted Nero to kill his mother without remorse."

But once in Maine, only the 23-foot ketch that John named the *Josy*, counted. It had been a ship's longboat, fifty years old, a double-ender, of stout oak, that we had picked up in a shipyard at Boothbay Harbor, fitted with masts, a red mainsail, a white jig and jigger. An old sea captain who had sailed to the Banks in a Gloucester fishing schooner for fifty years had built a cabin on her and had rented us his own tiny house, modeled like a ship, with a galley, a main room with a five-pointed mariner's star on the ceiling, a cookstove, and two small staterooms with built-in bunks. He had decided to give up his house to us on the day he found out that we adhered to sail, not power, and, taking a few dented pots, a handful of shabby coats, and a long flannel nightshirt, had marched off to "bach it" in an empty neighboring house from which he could supervise all of our seagoing activities. The little house was so skeletal, so trim, so smudged with human usage, its walls so deeply ingrained with the smoke from hundreds of fish frying and the fumes from the kerosene lamps, that it was like a ship long hardened to weather, ready to ride a gale or float upon the night, far out on the steadiness of an empty sea.

For someone like myself, born inland, never so happy as when crumbling earth with my hands for the planting of seeds, the sea and the waters emptying into it offered an occult science. But John had been sailing small craft on Lake Michigan all his life, could read the esoteric language of a chart, and knew navigation. And for months before we made the voyage in outside waters that was to terminate in the port of New York, our daily journeyings back and forth on smaller ventures, to Boothbay or Wiscasset or beyond to Monhegan Island, required the careful study of the tides—no longer a picturesque seething of water against rocks, but a signal to come or go. You had to wait for the moment when you might float home on the tide's dark swell under a full moon as you had to halt on land when a black cloud, no bigger than a great bird, gave the secret sign though the sky was blue. Nor could you play tricks with the sea. Like someone taught never to point a gun at anyone even though it is not loaded, we studied the water and skies with respect. The ketch was tiny, had no power, but neither power nor bigness mattered. Seaworthiness was all. The *Titanic* had foundered; the

Josy could ride out a gale. And to back up his assurance, not for himself, but for me, John had the lore of small craft in his memory, could recite names and dates: how Captain Slocum, singlehanded, had sailed his sloop around the world; how a frail tallmasted bark had clawed out a hurricane with master and mate lashed to the rigging.

And in May, when it was reported that a young man flying solitary in a tiny aircraft might be passing directly over us on the long flight to Paris, we and the farmers in their fields watched the sky, bemused by a gull, once deceived by a local plane that, dizzied with the course plotted over the Atlantic, swooped and whooped over our heads like a small boy at the edge of a ballfield where his hero is making a home run. When the news came that Lindbergh had landed at Le Bourget, the joy was contagious. The fish peddler delivering our mackerel gave a little prance to show that the wings of Mercury were in his heels; a farmer stooping in his field to hoist his plow stuck in the mire, stroked the shiny blade as he might a plane's propeller. We, too, were thrilled. Were not a bird of the air and a small black leaf floating on the water contiguous?

A new kind of world had opened up; a new lingo. The old Captain could sit on a mossy bank mending a fishnet while he recovered his lost voyages where the ice had frozen on the halyards as thick as your arm. He could call back his wives: one divorced, one dead. And he could spit with a careful wiping of his straggling mustache, delicately colored with chewing tobacco as he discounted the appraisal of the landlubbers who thought it folly for us to make the attempt down the coast in "that tiny boat with no power." "Always trust sail," the Captain said. "She'll ride like a gull. A seaworthy craft. Power can leave you helpless as a bug in mid-ocean. Why you can't even shake hands with the captain of a power boat; they're too dirty."

What couldn't the Captain's hands do! They were small, brown, and flexible. The tips of the fingers felt like velvet; the cords on the backs of the hands could thong out in spurts of energy or lie supine under knotted blue veins. The handclasp was oddly gentle; a confiding giving that let the hand lie in yours a second with a modest pressure upon withdrawal. Attacking a fish, his hands flashed with a quick jab of the knife he always carried with him in an oiled leather sheath. Never go without a knife. Never go without chewing tobacco. Keep matches dry. Though he was eighty years old, "widder women" were still after him, he boasted, eyes twinkling, an amorous gleam fondling the hull of the sleek black *Josy*. On a joint expedition to Monhegan, his little sloop, frail as a matchbox, could outride the *Josy* by virtue of his skill. Or he might stand outside on a morning after I had washed all the windows of his house, waiting for me to come out to call, "You got her shined up like a lighthouse. Saw your light last night from way up the road. Could sail by that beam, you could."

We might walk to the river's edge on a dark night for nothing more than to see how bright our light was, how truly like a lighthouse, and how pleasant to follow its long delicate beam where it tangled in the grass down the hillside, beckoning us home. In other ways the house had a magnetic quality; it could attract to us forgotten images, mislaid incidents, and bring flying through the air odd assortments from the past. John might remember the old fellow who had kept a bicycle shop where flyblown postcards of a lady in bloomers paddling for dear life on a bike named "Tiger" and a couple seated on a tandem provided a picture gallery the kids never tired of staring at, and how he had once astonished them by taking an opera hat out of a pasteboard box, advising them to touch it and see if it were not as "sleek as a seal." Or I might find myself recounting how my younger sister and I used to walk in the rain in Seattle during the War and how one night she stopped, the conversation died, as she put the question for which I knew no answer: "What would you do if your husband came home *in a basket?*" For what possible extremity were we preparing ourselves? Was a legless husband the worst that might happen? In the Captain's house it was awesome to sort out the bits of drift that floated out from other days, to piece together this with that and to feel a rush of blood to the head with the complexity of the material, its richness, its mystery. Or to wonder how to make it come alive in words, in what pattern, what form. John might confess that he wasn't really a *von* Herrmann as he had first claimed in Paris, but only Herrmann, or we might laugh ourselves silly remembering the time he had introduced me to a fellow-Detroiter with the remark that I had "been with Mencken," intending to refer to the two years I had read manuscripts on the old *Smart Set*, and how his friend, not to be outdone in sophistication, had leaped at the notion that I had been not a reader but a mistress.

Or we might wish we had brought more books with us, and fishing in our memories, be chagrined that we could bring up the last lines of Cowper's "On the Death of Mrs. Throckmorton's Bullfinch" but not Hamlet's soliloquy. On an evening when the Captain might drop in for some bootleg beer John magnificently recited with dramatic effect the ballad beginning, "A bunch of the boys was whooping it up in the Malamut saloon." The room would take on the liveliness of a theater with the Captain now and then politely opening the door to eject a long squirt of tobacco juice into the outer darkness. He was once inspired to contribute himself, resurrecting ten stanzas ending with:

> *And I would give all my greenbacks*
> *For those bright days of yore*
> *When little Nellie Gray and I*
> *Slid down the cellar door.*

There were moments when the Captain with his bright blue eyes reminded me of my mother, only to have her fade in what seemed to be an impersonation of my father, who had taken me to the train when I was bent on leaving home, saying simply, with utter trust, "Jo, I don't know what you're after, but I wish you all the luck in the world." The Captain, too, wished us all the luck in the world, though he might not follow us into that outer space where we would be shortly going. For we had to part. It was coming to mid-August; the season for good sailing down the coast would soon be ended. We hauled up the last lobster pot, cooked the six beauties in the iron tub in the yard to a brilliant red. The acrid smoke stung the eyes, hung on the air with a pungent pine fragrance. The Captain shared our last meal with us while we poured the melted butter on and broke open the last bootleg beer. The lamp chimneys shone from a last washing in soap suds. The floor had been scrubbed. "Why, I don't know what to make of my house," mooned the Captain. "It's clean as a breadknife."

The *Josy* was lying in the Sheepscot, loaded, ready to go. We boarded to make a last-minute check of our equipment. A roll of charts to cover the voyage down the coast; the one covering the first leg of our trip was laid out, ready for use. The Coastal Guide was in its rack. The compass, the foghorn, the anchor. A can of kerosene to fuel the riding lights. A powerful flashlight. Fishing tackle and a net. A homemade bobbin of wood to mend the net, smooth and polished by hand, with *Josy* carved in the shank. A life jacket for me stowed in the cockpit. A collapsible stove called Not-a-Bolt to set up for outdoor cooking in the cockpit; a foot-square, sheet-iron cube, with a pipe to puff the smoke away, it was a wonderful sight cooking an omelet, frying ham and eggs, or boiling potatoes. The dinghy held a pile of kindling wood, split fine for a quick fire; an old raincoat kept the wood dry. There was a Sterno for use in the cabin in bad weather. Clothes were crammed into a sailor's seabag. We both had seagoing slickers and were going to need them. Our gear was stored in the forward hold or under our bunks. The bunks were spread with woolen blankets, without sheets. We carried canned goods, sea biscuits, coffee, eggs, tea, canned milk. A pack of cards and a cribbage board.

The Captain stood on the shore of the Sheepscot while we shoved off, with an old gunny sack around his shoulders, for a fine mist was coming in. When the *Josy* stuck on a nest of reeds, he rushed into the water to give her a push, his old shoes with the leather slashed to accommodate his bunions making a quacking sound. "She'll pick up a breeze once you hit the channel," he shouted, for we had suddenly caught the current and were moving out. Then he climbed the bank and stood, waving. He grew smaller; he stopped waving. Lifting a hand, he held it open-palmed toward us. Then he dropped the hand to trudge up the hill, but paused, turned, lifted one hand once more, shyly, shoulder high, keeping it steady as he might have held a lighted lantern. The island came between and we lost him.

We never did get to New York. We hit squalls, were becalmed on a steamy open sea without a breeze in sight; then squeezed into Porpoise Harbor before a hurricane broke and jigged around for two days in company with sardine fishermen and big yachts from Bar Harbor, crouched in our tiny cabin, playing cribbage or heating canned beans over a Sterno. When the sun broke through the third day, we were the second boat out of the harbor. The first was a sardine fishing boat whose crew tossed us a rope so we could get out the narrow mouth under their power. The seas were running high but she went out like a bird. The crews on the big yachts were just beginning to stir on deck. When they saw us flying out over the shiny water they gave us a big salute. That little ketch was a beautiful sight! Big yachts would alter their course to come up beside her to ask what make she was. Some thought her no less than an aristocratic Alden ketch, she was so dainty, so shipshape, so well-made with her shiny black hull, her white cabin with little portholes, her beautiful red-and-white sails.

We got her as far as Cohasset, near the Cape Cod Canal, before we beached her. We had to. It had taken three weeks to get her that far and our money was running out. We hated to leave her, loyal as she was and high-spirited as a horse. But in some ways we were eager to be quit of her. One may love reality better, sometimes, after a long detour by way of dreams, and now that more than summer had ended, we wanted to be free of her. The day we decided not to make the run to New York but to try get her to the other side of Boston was marked in a way we couldn't ignore. For it was the day we sailed through a thick fog across Casco Bay to Portland and very nearly didn't make it. Sacco and Vanzetti didn't make it; on that same day, after the stroke of midnight, they were executed.

If we hadn't wanted to get to Portland that night we might not have tried to sail in so thick a fog. But we wanted to be where we could hear the news. For some reason we half expected a last-minute miracle. At eight in the morning the fog was so thick you couldn't see the dock in the little harbor where we had spent the night. But at nine it began slowly to lift and we sculled out of the harbor to make the first lap around the buoys. The Coastal Guide warned that it was a tricky passage in any weather, filled with shoals and hidden reefs, sudden islands and mysterious currents. We laid the chart out on the cabin; wiped off the gluey mist from the compass. Because it was so calm I was more at ease than I had a right to be. Out of pure ignorance. On other days, in the deep trough of an iron wave, I had been sick with fear, petrified in the cabin, where stretched out on a bunk I would expect to be plunged to the bottom in the black coffin of the *Josy*. John, of course, was an expert swimmer. I could not swim, but neither could the old Captain. I could never get into my head that to a true skipper the sound of breakers is a signal of dread. To me it intimated blessed land.

As the sails were so languid, barely moving, the breeze so light, we tacked back and forth with the patience of a spider stitching a fine web. The lazy, needlelike movement sometimes lulled me to sleep, but only for a moment. Waking was always the same. You were inside some vast cocoon and it was sticky with a wetness that soaked the skin. It clung to your hair like damp bees. We might have been alone except for the sound of the foghorns mooing in the distance of watery pastures. But the fog warped the view of immediate objects; the masts soared to twice their size to be caught in the swathing vapors; as in one of the crazy mirrors at Coney Island, John's six-foot stature elongated to a giant's. Sitting calmly, in the red cotton jacket of a Breton fisherman, his hand on the tiller, he held his head alert as a bird's, listening. Once we came about fast at the sound of breakers, and edging off saw the fanged tusks of a great slimy rock loom green to port. But mostly we sat listening with the rapt attention of devoted music lovers at the Carnegie to an unseen choir; the ponderous chugging of an invisible

312

steamer, the moan of the bell buoys, the piercing spectral whistle off Cape Elizabeth. By identifying the sounds we could mark the stages of our passage. Once a motorboat sheered past us out of the fog. A man with a long pole stood upright as a gondolier in the prow, feeling in the water ahead as a blind man might use his cane. Startled at the sight of us, they veered sharply, and lifting a hand in a silent salute, passed as rapidly as an apparition.

At five o'clock we were still moving through the white visceral matter of some monster sheep's brain. We had eaten our dry peanut-butter sandwiches; drank our thermos of coffee, smoked cigarettes. The coils of fog took on a violet pallor; a gull suddenly broke through to zoom over us. Then a sudden roar of warning breakers forced us about fast. The rudder skidded on the water, flopped, and snagged on the butt of the hull. The pin had twirled heavily to the bottom. John lifted the rudder out and flung it in the cockpit. "Take the tiller out," he said. "I'll have to steer now with the oar."

"Are we going to make it?"

"I don't know," he said. "With a breeze no bigger than your hand, we must have been drifting. I've tried to allow for it. We may be heading straight into port. We may be heading out to sea, past Cape Elizabeth. If we are, there will be nothing to do but ride it out all night. If we don't get a blow, it's all right."

But at six o'clock the light changed suddenly as though someone had lighted up a room back of a curtain. "The sun must be shining somewhere," John said. "And look, there's a bunch of gulls riding." The next second, straight ahead of us, the fog rolled up as slowly and steadily as a curtain in a theater, and there were the roofs and houses, the ribbons of streets of a town glittering in pure sunlight: Portland!

We moored the *Josy* in the harbor. It was like putting a faithful horse into its stall. Took down her sails, locked the cabin, got in the dinghy, rowed ashore, tied up the dinghy. Too tired to think of sleeping aboard, we hunted up an old hotel where they gave us an enormous room with two narrow beds stranded in the watery blue waste of a worn carpet. We ate spaghetti in a dockside EAT joint. Two soiled-jacketed stewards off a boat were shaking dice at the end of the counter. The counterman was a stout Italian in a clean white apron. When I complimented him on his spaghetti and asked if he ever made it with butter and garlic sauce, his face lighted up, and leaning on the counter he confided, "You like it? No call for garlic sauce. Meat they want, ham and eggs," and shrugging turned up a tiny radio a bit higher. Sports

313

news was coming through. A voice said that fog was heavily blanketing the entire New England coast. A sardine fishing boat had been rammed by a freighter. The Coast Guard had rescued several small craft.

We went outside and walked around. Waiting. The fog was coming in again, in huge puffs like smoke. One minute you could see to the corner, the next, no farther than a foot away. We pushed open the door of a drugstore, hunting postcards; wrote one to the Captain. "It was like going into the eye of a needle to make it," John wrote, adding, "she's a good little ship." I added, "He's a good captain or we wouldn't have made it."

There were several hours to go. We felt our way through the fog to the harbor, located the dinghy, but the *Josy* was hidden from sight. "I hope her anchor holds and it doesn't blow," John said. Then, "I suppose we should have gone to Boston. Not that it would have done any good." There wasn't much we wanted to talk about, but the way people do who are waiting together in a house where someone is sick unto death, we wanted to say something. "I never expected anything from Coolidge," John said. "Nor from the Governor. Nor all the rest. Except Brandeis and Holmes. I never will understand why they did what they did." His voice held the hurt of a son who has been betrayed by a father.

"There's never any place to sit down in America," I complained.

"You aren't supposed to sit. You're supposed to be up and doing."

"You remember how Sacco said, 'Kill me or set me free'?" I said.

"I guess they'll kill him all right," John said. "They seem to think they have to purify the city with a sacrifice. Like in old Athens where they led out two of the most debased citizens, as an offscouring, they called it. To get rid of a pestilence or a famine. What was it they called them? Pharmakos. First they gave them cheese and a barley cake. Then they beat them with branches from the wild fig tree, then they burned them. Scattered the ashes into the sea and to the winds as a general cleanup. That's the way they did it."

"You think we are any smarter?"

Once we visited our hotel room. It was a gloomy vault. Once we stopped in front of a ship chandler's shop, rubbed the mist from the window, and peered in at the fascinating array of ropes, bobbins, compasses, barometers, hardy utensils for Shipmate stoves, heavy boots, slickers, fishing nets, and life jackets.

"Let's go back to the Italian's," John said. "He had a good face." We climbed on stools. The Italian gave a pleased little sign of recognition. Two truck drivers were noisily arguing over ham and eggs. We drank our coffee hastily from the thick cups. The radio signaled midnight. The truck drivers, still arguing, threw down their money and left without shutting the door. John got up to close it. Now the voice came on. The prison would have to go dark, the lights out, to kill them. It went dark. Then lights on again. Then dark again. The Italian had been standing still as a statue. Now he took off his apron and hung it on a peg. Rolled down his sleeves over strong thick-muscled hairy arms. He reached up to turn out a light, hesitated, his hand still on the switch, looking at us. We were sitting quiet without saying anything. It was time to go. Then he looked around in a swift running glance, as if he might be overheard, and softly as if he were on tiptoe, came to the counter and leaned heavily on it, looking me straight in the eyes. His face was tense but calm; one of his eyebrows was nicked with a scar. He spoke in a quiet voice, confidentially, "Electricity. Is that what it's for? Is that the thing to do? Seven years they waited. Not bad men. No. *Good* men."

We must have said something. But what, I can't remember. All that I knew was that a conclusive event had happened. What it meant I couldn't have defined. Looking back from this distance I might add explanations that would signify. But I don't want to do that. I want to try to keep it the way it was, back there, on the early morning of August 23, 1927, when we walked out on the foggy streets, feeling very cold in our sweaters and reached out to take one another's hand for the walk back to the hotel. Without saying a word, we both felt it and knew that we felt it; a kind of shuddering premonition of a world to come. But what it was to be, we could never have foreseen. Not the density of fog, the bewildering calls from deceptive buoys, the friends lost in the mist, the channels marked for death. The port harder to find than the eye of any needle.

We were tender with one another when we came to our damp room. John punched the beds. "This one isn't so hard. You take it," he said.

"No," I said, "I don't want to take it. You did the work today. You take it." In the night I woke to find him standing at the long window. A dog was barking. "What's wrong?" I called to him, getting out of bed.

"We're drifting," he answered. "Hear that dog? We're drifting on the rocks. The anchor must be dragging." The fog swirling through the open window made the room a ship at sea.

"No," I said. "We're not on the boat. We're in the hotel. Come to bed."

So far as I am concerned, what had been the twenties ended that night. We would try to penetrate the fogs to come, to listen to the buoys, to read the charts. It would be three years before we took down a volume of *Kunstgeschichte* from our shelves to be replaced by a thin narrow book in red, entitled *What Is To Be Done?* by V. I. Lenin. Then in a few years it would be taken down to be replaced by another. And so on.

How could I have known that night in Portland that once we had beached the *Josy* at Cohasset I would never see her again? But I never did. Years later, John went to look for her, alone, and found her bashed in by a heavy tide, the planks rotted, her skeleton white as bone. He wrote me about it. For by that time we had parted, and I no longer saw him.

Antoni Słonimski

Memories of Warsaw

I was born on a street that no longer exists. On my return to Warsaw, after the war, I could still find the front wall of the house I lived in. I recognized it by the second-floor windows and iron balcony. Nothing more was left of No. 6. Through the arch of the scorched and corrugated entrance door, I could see grass-grown ruins and rubble—a sight typical of the Warsaw of those days. Even though the past was fresh in my memory, my imagination had to do some hard work to dig up from the shapeless mass of stone the picture of the old walls, where I lived through the little dramas and joys of my childhood.

In the old days, the apartments of the well-to-do were guarded by bolts and bars, door-chains and servants, so that even people living in the same block of flats could have no easy access to them. Only poor tenants, those who occupied the fourth floor, back yard, or basement flats, would be on close terms with each other. They would help each other out with washing tubs, saucepans, a pinch of salt, or a match, and would assist one another in sickness or childbirth. The solidarity of the rich manifested itself in a more complex way—on the social or political level—in the banks or offices, the press or the legislature. But in everyday life it was normal for the lawyer of the first-floor apartment not to be on speaking terms with the factory owner or doctor of the second. My father was an exception to this rule. Neither the front nor kitchen door of our home was ever locked.

None of the family ever used the front door. The kitchen was our real drawing-room. Spacious and inviting, it was the kingdom of Franciszka Veronavska, our cook. This fat, jolly, olive-skinned woman looked the very picture of her name. I don't know whether it was Uncle Józef who invented the story or whether Frania's family had really come from Verona to settle in Poland. But the fact was, that she alone spoke any Italian in the house, or Yiddish for that matter. Frania had been brought up by my grandfather and had stayed with him as his maid for several years. She must have picked up her Italian from Uncle Józef and her Yiddish from the children she played with in the yard.

Frania had a lovely singing voice. I was particularly fond of a song she used to sing to the tune of "*Santa Lucia.*" It began like this: "The storm is raging, the night is quiet, and freely heaves the sailor's breast." It was much later in life that the originality of those words suddenly struck me. I mean "the raging storm on a quiet night." But when I was a boy, this seemed quite natural. Another natural thing was to see on the inner lid of Frania's box a picture of the Japanese General Nogi in a garland of Catholic saints, pagan cupids, and doves carrying rosebuds.

In 1905, the Russo-Japanese War roused high hopes of independence and of a revolution in Poland. It was to this exalted cult of Japan that General Nogi owed his promotion to the status of an almost Christian saint. Simple people are not very fussy about old and new cults. I have seen something of this in quite recent times. Our housekeeper paid her Party contribution to the May Day celebrations by decorating the statue of the Blessed Virgin Mary at Warsaw's Bernardine Church with flowers.

This war engendered the myth of Japanese power. The first successes of the Japanese forces captured our imagination. Within a few months, the Japanese people rose to the stature of some universally powerful demons. My father used to tell a story how this new mythology won ground even in the small coffeehouses of the Jewish Quarter and how the battle of Tsushima was summed up there. The narrator would relish the Olympian calm of the Japanese Admiral, savoring the suspense in which he held his audience. "... Admiral Togo is sitting in his cabin over a bowl of sour milk with potatoes. His aide comes in and says: '*Vashe Vielitchestvo* (Your Majesty), we can see the Russian fleet on the horizon.' The Admiral doesn't turn a hair—just goes on eating sour milk with potatoes. His generals and captains come flying in and shout: '*Vashe Prevaskhaditielstvo . . . Istvo* (Excellency!) the Russian fleet is here!' But he is just enjoying his sour milk with potatoes as if nothing happened. So they begin to scream that the Russians have opened fire. Then he gets up, wipes his mouth with a napkin, goes on deck, and sinks the whole Russian fleet."

Another story I adored was that of the siege of Port Arthur. Some officers of the Russian navy take cover in a fortress, after having abandoned their warships in the port. One of them follows the battle through his field glasses and announces, from time to time, as they are sunk, the names of the battleships, cruisers, or destroyers. Meanwhile, the cash box has been brought in—for cash boxes were always prudently removed to some fortress—and the officers start dividing the money among them. "*Catherine the Great*," shouts the officer with the field glasses, "hand the cash over! *Boris Godunov*—hand it over!"

My father enjoyed the reputation of being one of the wittiest men in Warsaw. I remember his brilliant saying illustrating the limitations of empiricism. "We know by our own experience that it's always somebody else who dies." He had a harmonious and simple view of the world. In his day, science was accessible to the intelligent mind. He could understand Newton and Darwin. The natural sciences were not in a separate box from mathematics or the humanities. Specialization had not yet reached the point when an eminent physicist can be an ignoramus in biology or the other way round. Physics had not yet gone underground and had not developed into an occult science. The priests of this sect had not yet acquired a jargon inaccessible to their colleagues of other university faculties.

Quite frequently my father used to take us to the theater and the circus. We worshipped the circus. In those days, its magnificent pageant was a pure joy. The circus established a tradition of accuracy and precision. There was no room for humbug there. Whatever was done in the circus had to be done to perfection. No tricks could save the man who didn't know how to do his *salto mortale*. A bad juggler was sure to drop the lamp that kept revolving on top of a billiard stick, while a bad acrobat was in danger of breaking his neck. Not as in the other arts, alas, where one can get away with a sham performance. Gradually, however, even circus standards began to deteriorate. Some clever bluffing crept into such acts as the International Wrestling Tournaments, which were a favorite attraction with circus goers.

A dose of national antagonism was considered an extra thrill in a fight that held the house spellbound. Managers of such tournaments would arrange fights between Jewish and Polish wrestlers and their final face-off would usually take place on a Saturday evening. In case of some irregularity, the fight would be repeated on Sunday. I remember Pinecki, whose nelsons were a terror to his adversaries, fighting the Jewish wrestler, Wildman. When Pinecki took the giant Wildman in a double nelson and the latter began to pant and wriggle in this deadly embrace, the Jewish public in the gallery started booing and shouting: "Let him go, let him go!" The referee got up, raised his arm to calm the gallery, and said: "Gentlemen, Wildman is no baby."

II

My father firmly believed that if Poland regained her independence, she would automatically get rid of all social injustice. My vision of the world was a bit more complex. I dreamed of leading Polish cavalry squadrons into

battle, of winning crushing victories over Russian, Spanish, Tartar, or German regiments—as the mood of the novel I happened to be reading would inspire me. I did not deny myself the joy of brief expeditions to America, in order to put to rout a couple of Indian tribes; in my dreams I would massacre crowds of African Negroes or save some of them with Tom Sawyer. The spell of some book would make me take on an attitude I would abandon when reading another. As a pupil in the third form, I'd be in turn a blasé aristocrat, a noble and upright prince, a coarse cavalry sergeant, a North Pole explorer, or a highland sage, which—as the day went by—did not prevent me from becoming some bloodthirsty Iron Hand, chief of a great Indian tribe. My vocabulary, too, would undergo unpredictable changes. Seeing Frania come into the nursery, I'd either emit the wild screams of a Red Indian or address her with cold dignity, saying: "My good Franciszka, your master is sailing off to school, be good enough to wait with the meal for his speedy return."

Once I came across an anecdote in an old magazine about the Earl of Bedford and King George II. This story enchanted me. The Earl, who was a quarter of an hour late for his audience with the King, came into the audience hall when the clock on the mantelpiece was striking one. He went up to the mantelpiece and, with a single blow, smashed the clock. "What has the poor clock done to you that you struck it like this?" asked the King in amazement. "Why, Your Majesty, it was the clock that struck first," answered the Earl.

I was so taken by the Earl's wit, that I decided to carry the story into life. One day, I was purposely late for tea and waited behind the door to make my entry just before the clock was to strike the hour. I entered, with a stick I had taken from the hall, at the right moment, on the stroke of the hour, one might say; but there was no stroke coming.

"Don't stand there," somebody said. This upset my plans. But mercifully the clock did finally begin to strike. I gathered all my strength and smashed the dial with a single blow.

My exploit was followed by a dead silence. Instead of asking me, as decent people would, "What has the poor clock done to you that you struck it like this?" everybody began to shout at me. Then they took away the stick, and when I finally did stutter out in tears: "It was the clock that struck first," I was told to stop being a nuisance and ordered out of the room.

My first literary attempts were marked by an insufficient understanding of the words I was using. I was just attracted by their sound. Under the influence of Mickiewicz's poem "Farys," I grew Oriental-minded and started in my black oilcloth copybook a poem under the title "Harem." I remember the first two lines of that poem which, incidentally, were also the last: "Why is there no room for me / Poor Harem in this worldly sea?" I had no doubts that Harem was a masculine name.

I went to school rather late. Until I was ten, I'd spend half of the day at play in Ogród Saski, a public park in our district, then come home and bury myself in books till late evening. I used to get them from a public library in alphabetical title order, as they were set down in the catalogue. The first novel that fell into my hands was a book called *Basil and Sophie*, whose author signed himself A. B. I struggled through it, not understanding a single word of the sentimental and involved story. It's quite surprising that this book did not turn me against literature for the rest of my life, though it did give me a certain dislike for the written word, a feeling I never quite got rid of. But in books my first real passion—as that of the majority of boys—was for Jules Verne. My father shared my enthusiasm for adventure stories and I had to hide or steal back from him every new Jules Verne I got hold of. I was also constantly rereading the two volumes of Stanley's travels, kept on a shelf in my father's waiting-room. But I was not the only one in the house to be fascinated by the African continent or Stanley's travels. Besides myself, there was Redhead.

Redhead was quite an institution in my father's house. He would sit for interminable hours in the waiting-room, until father had seen his last patient. He first started coming to collect interest on loans, to talk over payment rates or some new loan. Though he had long stopped doing this kind of business with father and though father had paid him off every penny, the old Jew kept on coming to the house out of habit. He had grown fond of talking to father and had developed a love both for father's jokes and for things that were almost indecent for a moneylender to care about. Apparently Redhead's wife once came to see my father and complained that he had utterly demoralized her husband. Redhead had given up making money and had taken to reading Walter Scott and going to the "bioscope." This "wasted" usurer showed an unhealthy curiosity for the map of Africa, which he saw in our waiting-room. He once pointed to a white patch on that map and asked who this bit of land belonged to. He knew, of course, that red-colored spaces belonged to Great Britain, yellow ones to France, that blue spots meant German property and green ones the area of Italian interests—for all this was written in the righthand corner of the map. But he wanted to know to whom the vast white patches belonged.

"To nobody," Father answered him curtly.

"How big is this land? Bigger than Radziejówka?"

Radziejówka was a large estate where Redhead's father was tenant-dairyman.

"Bigger!"

"How much bigger?"

"A hundred thousand times."

"Is it bigger than the whole Warsaw province?"

"A thousand times."

The poor man could not get over this fatal bit of information. He walked about in a kind of stupor, repeating to himself: "A hundred thousand times bigger than Radziejówka and belongs to nobody!" His mental order and his faith in the laws of landed property had received a severe blow. My father maintained that Redhead fell sick and died after a few months with the words "to nobody . . ." on his lips. In point of fact, Redhead neither fell sick nor died just then, but it was true that father had entirely "depraved" him: he lost his bite and ruthlessness, faculties without which the moneylender's profession easily degenerates into a money-losing profession.

But father's way of life did not always have a disastrous effect on the people he came in touch with, though his attempts to help people sometimes had rather disappointing results.

III

My education at that time was a very peculiar affair. The books chosen at random and my idle days in Ogród Saski kept me in shocking ignorance of the so-called school subjects until I was nearly ten. The only proper lessons I had—or was supposed to have—were also of a peculiar nature. Our French governess, Mademoiselle Prochin, did not bother to teach me the lovely language of Racine. But what she did do was to make me read aloud the court reports and accident columns of the *Warsaw Courier*. Each time a thief was caught and brought to trial, Mademoiselle Prochin knelt down to thank God for taking such good care of the wealthy classes. For the good lady had some savings in State Loans tucked away in the lining of her navy-blue jacket, which no one ever saw her take off, as she was obsessed by a dread of theft. She died a few years later in her bath. The necessity of taking off her jacket on that occasion must have been too much for her.

Our home was not at all a banal middle-class household. It was a strange mixture of light-heartedness coupled with financial difficulties and a leisurely life above our means. Its slightly bohemian atmosphere made up the colorful and enchanting background of my childhood.

Under these circumstances, it wasn't really surprising that when my brother got the measles and I was promptly packed off to Grandfather's, two whole months went by before anybody noticed my absence from this happy-go-lucky home.

Life at Grandfather's was quite different from that at home. Grandfather was already a very old man when I came to stay with him. He had been born in 1808 and was ten years older than Dickens and Karl Marx and almost forty years older than Edison. The fact that I—now in my sixties—can record an eyewitness's account of Napoleon's troops marching into Lithuania, makes me feel slightly dizzy. It wasn't much of an account but Grandfather said to me: "They had such enormous caps."

He lived in a world that knew no motor cars, no airplanes, no films, and no radio, not to speak of atom or hydrogen bombs. In Grandfather's times, doctors used to wash their hands not before but after an operation. A trip to Paris from Rome took as long as in Napoleon's times, that is, as long as in Caesar's.

My grandfather was completely developed at the age of sixteen. The environment into which he was born supplied him with a set of beliefs and principles, with the "wisdom" of a long chain of ancestors, consisting mainly in an observance of rules laid down for a comparatively small nomadic tribe that had inhabited or had wandered along the Mediterranean coast of Asia Minor some thousands of years ago. And quite an effort was needed to devote one's life to the futile study of the old and frequently misinterpreted books.

It didn't look as if this already married Talmudist would have the slightest chance of breaking through the vicious circle of barren mental speculations and the ignorance of a small township in Eastern Poland. I don't know what made my grandfather rebel against the life and thought of his environment. But the fact was, that his mind caught the contagious bug of curiosity and, prompted by a great hunger for knowledge, Grandfather began to read forbidden books of a secular nature. He taught himself mathematics and astronomy, then went on to discover the laws of chemistry, never suspecting the existence of such a science. Finally, equipped with a small bundle of necessities and an equally small scientific baggage, he set out one day for Warsaw, which was a long way off. There, another refugee from ignorant Talmudism, the inventor of the counting machine and my great-grandfather, Abraham Stern, had attained the honor of becoming a Fellow of the Royal Society of Sciences.

His daughter, my grandfather's second wife, was an educated and advanced young woman, who spoke French and had mastered the art of embroidering pretty flowers and cupids. I remember that one piece of her embroidery had a dove beside the flowers and cupids.

The young savage from the Godforsaken township was tamed and began a life of intellectual adventure, success, and disappointment. His papers, attacking ignorance and superstition, and his rebellious thought stirred the imagination of other young victims of Talmudism and helped them to get away from their backwater. The punishment for reading or possessing my grandfather's writings was expulsion from Jewish orthodox schools. And so this fish out of water, whose fate seemed to spell only hopeless struggle and a life of agony, developed into a humanlike creature.

Apart from the incident with the Napoleonic troops, the story of my grandfather came to me later in life. Uncle Józef used to tell me all over again—at my request, because I loved the story—how Grandfather met the German and Russian astronomers. It happened when he was still living in the Lithuanian township of Zabludowo. A party of astronomers came to this dark corner of the world to observe the eclipse of the sun. Some parts of our globe seem to be particularly suitable for that purpose. Sometimes it's Timbuktu, sometimes Zabludowo. Anyway, the scientists from Petersburg or Berlin probably saw no difference between the two localities. The Jewish township must have seemed to those men from the capitals of the world a very exotic spot indeed, and the customs of the natives no less peculiar than those of some African tribe. It must have been something of a surprise to them to see a boy in a long black gaberdine hanging around the workers who were putting up the telescope all day, keenly observing its parts and asking questions, that showed a knowledge both of the instrument and its use. One of the Germans asked my grandfather the reason for this fascination.

"I'm fascinated by the telescope, because I've never seen it before. Observation itself isn't particularly exciting, since it's only an empirical confirmation of well-known facts," said Grandfather and went on to explain accurately the eclipse of the sun in scientific terms.

At that time, astronomy was the domain of a small group of specialists and the ease with which the Jewish boy used mathematical formulas must have given quite a shock to the German scientist.

"How do you come to know all this, Mr. Słonimski," he asked, throwing in the "mister" for politeness' sake.

"Every Jew around here knows it," came the quiet reply. The epilogue of this story appeared in a Berlin paper in a lengthy article by the German scientist: "The Secret Science of the Lithuanian Rabbis." The article explained how mathematics and astronomy came from Egypt and Chaldea, via Arabian scientists, to the Lithuanian Jews.

My two-month stay at Grandfather's created a lasting friendship between me and Uncle Józef. He was the "washout" among Grandfather's sons but also the one best loved by his father. Uncle Ludwik was an important St Petersburg economist; my father was a popular doctor and a no less popular Warsaw wit. But Uncle Józef, though he invented a new international language and a new shorthand system, though he knew sixteen languages, played the violin most beautifully, and could turn out a good drawing, stayed with his father until old age and had to earn his modest living by giving French and Italian lessons and by translations of commercial prospectuses. He had the peculiar charm of all failures—a charm composed of a certain dose of infantility, a faith in lucky accidents, a kind of wise simplicity, naïveté, and kindness. He might have been one of those wonderful cranks that people the pages of Dickens's novels.

All his savings went into hopeless propaganda for his "Lingua Neo-romana," which was no match for Esperanto, and into the publication of handbooks for that language. The idea of language-handbooks for self-taught students was not only new but logical and right as well. Uncle Józef thought that this gap ought to be filled. He simply noticed that there were no such books for, say, Swedes wanting to learn Polish and vice versa, or for Portuguese desirous of learning Yiddish. So he went on to publish such handbooks. But since there weren't many Swedes in Warsaw wanting to study Polish and still fewer Portuguese who'd ever take to studying Yiddish, my uncle's handbooks were doomed from the start.

IV

Transplanted to school from the free and easy atmosphere of my home, I felt miserable. Fear dominated my emotions. I was in a state of panic that I might be asked about things I had done my best to learn, but for the life of me could make neither head nor tail of. Homework assignments were worded very much like legal forms and I have never been able to master the art of filling them in properly, as was and is the case with most intelligent people. I used to be terrified of the robust boys who terrorized those from lower forms, and I was afraid I might be considered a coward. I took literally such threats as: "I'll rip your guts open with this penknife" or "I'll tear your eyes out with a corkscrew"—the latter strongly reminiscent of the sadistic vocabulary of some of Sienkiewicz's characters. Then I was haunted by a sinking feeling of injustice. I noticed that good marks went to boys who were no good at study but terribly good at cribbing. I myself would get bad marks when I had done my homework thoroughly, and satisfactory ones when I was not prepared. It all seemed just a matter of luck.

What did the school of my childhood teach its pupils? Above all, fear, I think. It taught us to flatter the stronger boys and to deceive the teachers. In this respect the boys showed endless ingenuity and the school might have been some Ecole des Sciences Politiques in its high standards of cheating. Cribbing and prompting had a long-standing tradition of methods, tested by generations of pupils in various schools—but there was always enough room left for ingenuity in the application of old tricks. A clever student knew how to talk the teacher into telling the boy what he did not know. In this subtle game the boys had the upper hand because they knew their teacher better than he knew each individual pupil. It is really something of a miracle that not all the graduates of such schools became swindlers, forgers, or criminals of some other kind. And yet the school I went to was the best and most advanced in Warsaw. In reality, social conditions were more to blame than the school.

Apart from fears engendered by a feeling of personal danger—that one of the rough boys might cut my tongue out with his penknife or that I might be left for another year in the same form—I was obsessed by a dread of a different, spiritual category, as it were. My father was received into the Catholic Church when he married my mother, a very devout Catholic, who brought us up in the spirit of strict Catholicism. I feared Hell and eternal damnation, yet I began to have my first doubts about religion. Two kinds of doubts, as a matter of fact. I wasn't so much preoccupied with the danger of being burnt at the stake for noticing a certain discrepancy between the natural sciences and the Scriptures, for I knew that this was a practice long discarded—but I was really worried about hellfire.

V

In my youth, I had no real idea of the poverty and degradation of the working classes. It was something one heard about but never imagined as real. One avoided thinking of this unpleasant and embarrassing thing just as one avoided the Jewish slums or Warsaw's fetid back streets and industrial suburbs. At times, however, real men and women from the great masses of the nation came to the capital's nice central district and so penetrated into middle-class awareness. This was accompanied by an unpleasant feeling but without further consequences. Such a morally unpleasant episode was my friendship with Maniek.

Maniek was the nephew of our cook-and-maid-in-one, Frania. Frania's sister had been married as a young girl to an industrial worker. Maniek used to come daily to play with me. I would lend him my books and toys. We planned together, in minutest detail, an expedition to the Pacific islands. We worked out the exact amount of food needed on this voyage, what the ship's cargo ought to be, and we drew up a list of the crew, striking off the names of those boys who, ignorant of their fate, had incurred our disfavor during play.

Maniek drew the plan of the boat in pretty red and black lines and also the plan of our route. He was very good at drawing. My sister's album contained a scarlet rose, in a place of honor, and a pair of no less scarlet hearts pierced by a golden arrow—all in Maniek's hand. One day Maniek did not come to play. Frania said he had gone to work. I did not get the real meaning of this but with the callousness and lack of loyalty appropriate to my age, I shared all the secrets of the Pacific expedition with another boy. After a few weeks, I began to have an uneasy conscience and went to see Maniek. He was out. He never came home from the locksmith's before six P.M. He was a full-time apprentice.

A few months passed before I had a relapse of uneasy conscience. This time Maniek was in, but I saw at once that he wasn't glad to see me. I thought that my long delayed visit might be the cause of his coldness. Maniek was no longer my closest friend and playmate. He was somehow a different being. He was morose and ironic. When I asked him whether he had done some new drawings, he stretched out his hands as if calling for help. They were the coarsened, swollen, tar-stained hands of an adult worker.

As a grown man, I used to be called up yearly for a refresher course of military training, from which I would always manage to get exempted without much trouble. I had, however, to appear before the authorities to get the necessary papers, which would enable me to get back to work and normal life. On these occasions, I'd meet with my working class contemporaries. In my early thirties, I still had the appearance of a young man, whereas workers, craftsmen, or petty clerks looked like men of a different generation. Their graying temples, tobacco-stained mustaches, and bent shoulders bore the stigmata of their hard lives. Embarrassed and impatient, I'd stand among those aging men, avoiding the eyes of my contemporaries, who had been robbed of their youth.

VI

It is customary to call old times "merry," just as old Warsaw is spoken of as "merry Warsaw", and the "Paris of the North." Indeed, so it appeared to me when I was seventeen. Today I have some serious doubts about that "merriness." It may well be that Warsaw impressed the provincial Russian merchants, who spent their nights in her cafés chantants, as a merry city. When I look back now on this "Paris of the North," I see dark streets paved with cobblestones and smelling of horse urine. Fetid garbage carts roll along these streets. The wind carries that particular Warsaw "perfume" from the slums of the Polish proletariat to the poor Jewish district. It barely touches the bit of town, called the city's center, where a few night clubs and elegant shops create the illusion of a European city. I detect a strikingly exotic quality in the landscape of that Warsaw, for it reminds me of the main street in Mukden, which I had once seen pictures of.

In that "Paris of the North" first-class private clinics had no running water in the sickrooms, hotels with private bathrooms were a great rarity, and street corners were lined with crowds of shabby hucksters and with regiments of prostitutes in kerchiefs, who would melt away at the sight of a policeman.

Holiday crowds were conspicuous by their ugly and pretentious clothes. A mixture of vanity and poverty was characteristic of Warsaw streets. Money may have been scarce for children's textbooks or pencils, for soap or books, but it had to be found for a fashionable overcoat or yellow shoes.

Skepticism was and remains an unchanging feature of the true Warsavian. Words like "stuff," "monkey trick," "moonshine," and "cock-and-bull story" have long held their rightful place in the Warsaw vocabulary. My barber was a very distinguished adherent of this philosophical school. I once looked at a French illustrated magazine with some photos of Briand's funeral. My friend, the barber, glanced at them and said: "He's grabbed enough for himself and then kicked the bucket." This true son of Warsaw was against all political changes. When a new government came into power, he shook his head with dismay. "That's bad," he commented. "The old crooks have had their share of monkey tricks and done all right for themselves. But the new ones'll be pinched with greed. They'll suck us dry."

The great men or women of the nation were never sacred to the true Warsavians. I remember two Polish housewives exchanging remarks on the funeral of the great Polish writer Stefan Zderomski. Seeing all those troops and delegations with wreaths and flags, one of them grinned: "That's not a poor man's funeral, is it?" Did the simple soul mean to say that every poor man in Warsaw ought to be buried with equal pomp, with schools, ministers, troops, and delegations walking behind the funeral procession? That wasn't her point. She was simply expressing her conviction that money is the root, not of all evil, but of all success in life.

VII

The traditional interest in science, which ran in my family, was, after my great-grandfather, grandfather, and father, continued by my brother Peter. He started collecting butterflies and all sorts of beetles at a very early age.

There were aquariums and vivariums with frogs, fishes, and snakes on the nursery windowsill. We took possession of an old sideboard to keep my brother's collections in it. There was a note on the inside of this piece of furniture saying: "Collections of Doctor, Professor P. Słonimski." Under the threat of removing a "mammoth's tooth" from the collection, I forced him to add in pencil: "And A. Słonimski." I soon switched to a passion for stamps, whereas my brother remained faithful to the natural sciences till the end of his life.

When Peter went to study at Lwów University, he left his frogs behind. Father didn't know how to feed them, so he wired to Peter: "What do frogs eat?" Peter wired back: "Nothing." Maybe frogs can do without food in winter but not when they are in a warm room. The sad fact was that our frogs became quite transparent and could hardly move, poor things, clinging pitifully to the glass walls of the vivarium. We knew, of course, that frogs feed on flies, but how was one to get them in the winter? We managed to get a couple of flies in the kitchen and our frogs simply devoured them. From that day on, Father kept on asking all his patients if they had any flies. This created some misunderstanding.

"What do you mean, flies?" one asked indignantly. "I have pains and aches and a stinging along my side, but flies?" Father explained the matter and some flies were found, after all, in that patient's kitchen. Father took a supply of this precious food home and kept on returning in a cab for more, which he brought home in a cigarette box.

The living conditions of my father's patients revealed a singular hierarchy of these people's needs. Food came first; the next item on their list of necessities was clothes, but their accommodations were bad. It isn't true that people in those days kept coal and potatoes in their bathrooms, simply because very few flats had any bathrooms at all. Everyone went to public baths, and to attract the public one of them bore the name of a famous operetta star. I remember a very posh party, given by a well-known poet in his apartment. There were French wines served by a butler in white gloves, but there was no water closet. The guests had to run downstairs to the house porter and get the key to a public convenience in the yard.

In middle-class homes the best room was not much used. It was the sacred "salon," which had a piano, some kind of palm tree in a pot, and a set of drawing-room furniture in covers. The family spent their lives in the narrow and dark back rooms. Windows were opened rather reluctantly, to avoid possible drafts. I once overheard the following conversation in a tram-car.

331

"I've broken with the Kolasinskis, it's too drafty there." This was said by an elderly, genteel-looking, and very irritated lady. My father fought by hook and by crook this Warsaw habit of closed windows. He had a story about a patient of his, for whom he prescribed just a dose of fresh air. Father threatened never to visit him again if he kept his room so stuffy. Next day, when Father arrived, the windows were still shut but the room was filled with the strong odor of a spray that was supposed to simulate a forest smell.

"What does it smell like now, Doc?" the patient asked proudly.

"Like dung in a forest," said Father.

The rapidly expanding technical civilization contributed to a growing interest in the natural sciences at the beginning of the century. The sudden upsurge of technical knowledge and man's new victories over Nature fired the imagination and molded a new world outlook. It opened exciting perspectives not overshadowed by fear and terror. When the Russian pilot Utotshkin rose in his biplane over Mokotów Common in Warsaw and stayed in the air for one minute and fifteen seconds, I felt an enchantment equal to the joy of the alchemist Sconitius who, after stirring a mixture of iron, copper, and other materials, suddenly noticed a gold sediment at the bottom of his cauldron. But my joy was as deceptive as his. The mere fact that a machine heavier than air could float above earth made a terrific impression on my generation. We did not ask then what causes and what people this wonderful invention might some day serve.

VIII

When I think of the Warsaw of my youth, I am amazed that this comparatively small city contained so many characters and eccentrics.

The first genuine eccentric I came across in my childhood was my father's friend, the poet Antoni Lange, a well-known translator from the Sanskrit and a less-known author of numerous papers, schemes, and inventions. Each time he came to see my father, he had a brand new and brilliant scheme for making a large fortune. He once sent a long memorandum to the Russian War Ministry, explaining the necessity of supplying the Russian army with one million chairs. The memorandum made it quite clear that such a big army cannot be a standing one. The stools suggested by the author, with drawings illustrating his idea, were like shooting-sticks. Despite its obvious absurdity, the memorandum was given serious consideration in St Petersburg by officials, or rather by officialdom, for the simple reason that such big supplies also meant big bribes.

Lange invented his own system of winning at roulette. For that purpose he made a couple of reconnaissance trips to Monte Carlo. He was accompanied on those journeys by his nephew, the wonderful poet Boleslaw Laśmian, who later went off and became a notary in a provincial town. Lange's trips ended in frantic telegrams to my father or some other friend, in which the hapless inventor begged for money. When he first went from Paris to Monte Carlo, Lange was in luck and won a considerable sum, large enough to start a real gambling career. He was a complete innocent at roulette and began his play by putting some money on number one. Number one won. He pushed his winnings on to number two and number two won. He proceeded logically to number three and won again. When he played number four, number twenty-seven won. Lange raised a hue and cry and demanded his money back, on the obvious claim that it was the turn of number four to win. His brilliant discovery was that, in order to win, one simply had to put money on consecutive numbers. He must have been rather surprised that no one thought of this before him. It seemed so simple and logical. From that time on, Lange became a passionate gambler.

But what it means to be a real gambler I understood only later, when I heard Fiszer's story. Franciszek Fiszer was a friend of my father's, and in later years also a friend of mine. He used to tell the following story: A certain rich landowner used to play cards at the railway buffet, whenever he would have to wait for a train. One day he had to wait for several hours but had nobody to play with. He asked the barman to suggest somebody. The barman said that he could provide two regular cardsharps. "I'm not playing with cheats," stormed the squire. Having wasted his time for another half hour he went up to the waiter and said: "Send in those crooks, I'll play with them, but for cash." The barman came back after a while, saying that the crooks were broke, because they'd been cheated by some bigger Warsaw cheats. "With pennyless crooks, nothing doing," panted the squire. After another half hour his morale was completely broken. He went up to the barman and said: "Send them in, I'll lend them some cash." "This man," Fiszer used to say with admiration, "was a real gambler."

Fiszer occupies a special place among Warsaw characters. He was not only an eccentric but one of the wittiest men alive. He was famous for his brilliant and instantaneous ripostes. A certain writer of mediocre talent once said to him: "Don't you think, Franciszek, that I have Dante's nose?" "Then why don't you write with it?" Fiszer howled back without a moment's hesitation.

I used to love Fiszer's story about a party given in honor of the Czar, during a visit to Poland. "There were forty-eight kinds of soup brought from Paris in special barrels," Fiszer would say. "Two hundred and fifty kinds of meat dishes. The feast went on for three days and three nights. When we left the Royal Castle after this gorgeous party, we were attacked in the courtyard by a squadron of Circassians who beat us with the flat of their sabers."

"Why did they do that?" I asked, taken aback. "Why, to beat the conceit out of us, of course," Fiszer replied indignantly.

To Fiszer, Warsaw was not only the most beautiful but also the only city worth considering in Europe. Somebody was once raving about Paris and Fiszer interrupted him angrily. "Horrible city. Dirty, dark, stinking sewers. Not even gaslight in every street." "How can you say such things," came a protest. "When were you last in Paris?" "Immediately after the siege, of course," said Fiszer with great pride.

Speaking of Warsaw characters, it is impossible to omit the distinguished actor and eccentric Wladyslaw Grabowski. He once played Sir Andrew Aguecheek in *Twelfth Night*. Under the influence of too much liquor, he refused to speak his lines but went on announcing instead: "Now it's me." Or *"tiepier ya"*—in Russian—for greater fun. He went on doing this all through the act. The actors managed somehow, and the audience sat patiently till the intermission. But the performance had to be stopped and there was a scandal. Grabowski was sacked. Some time after this incident, I saw him come into a restaurant where I was sitting. He came up to my table and delivered the following oration: "My soul is *tabula rasa* and Volga's in my eyes," meaning that they were full of tears. "I've lost faith in man. If a drowning person came to grovel at my feet begging a stamp, I'd refuse!" The picture of a drowning person groveling at somebody's feet and begging for a postage stamp was so ridiculous that I could never forget it. I asked Grabowski why this drowning person should want a stamp. "To write a letter about his accident," was his earnest reply.

334

There were many inimitable characters among Warsaw painters. Witkacy alone calls for a special study. I used to be a friend of this extremely interesting writer, painter, and philosopher. At one time, I was even third on his list of friends. Witkacy had such a list and would shift his friends up and down that list, notifying them each time he changed their position. After I had criticized his play *The Pragmatists*, he sent me a card: "We hereby notify you that you have been shifted on our list of friends from number three to number forty-eight—beneath the painter Chwistek." This place was on the very outskirts of Witkacy's friendship.

The gallery of Warsaw originals was limited almost entirely to the intelligentsia and middle classes. Our aristocracy, cosmopolitan in the worst sense of the word, added nothing to the specific color of Warsaw. The underworld, especially Warsaw burglars, was in many respects superior to the aristocracy. Its members could not, of course, compete with the magnates in wrongdoing, but they made up for this in originality and lent a special kind of glory to the capital. When burglary by tunneling was discovered at the Odessa branch of the Russian National Bank, the directors of the bank issued a special bulletin, stating categorically that the job was done by Warsaw and not by local burglars. This was a serious argument, and public opinion felt convinced that the directors could not be blamed. The inferiority of the bank authorities to Warsaw burglars was obvious to everyone.

IX

Much as I liked to travel—and I have done quite a lot of traveling in my life—it was not the journey but the home-coming that counted. I always came back hungry and thirsty for Warsaw. Until the tragic parting.

On September 5, 1939, my wife and I left Warsaw together with the Tuwims. Our destination was a small township on the other bank of the Vistula, where we intended to endure the first phase of the war. Our reasoning was simple. The German tanks—as everyone knew—were made of cardboard and wouldn't be able to cross the Vistula; they'd fall apart if they tried. At Kazimierz, my wife took a room and paid one hundred zlotys rent in advance. As our information about German tanks was not quite accurate and the Germans crossed the Vistula on that very day, we had to leave Kazimierz at once. At Krzemieniec, my wife took a room and paid only fifty zlotys in advance. Half an hour after this transaction we were on our way farther east. At Zaleszczyki, on the Rumanian frontier, we had no time to take a room at all.

335

At this stage, our adventures did not differ much from the flights and pursuits of Sienkiewicz's novels, describing seventeenth-century wars. On the face of things, this too was a war from books for juveniles—a war of small events, jolly, friendly skirmishes, fought with completely unfounded optimism, in which the soldiers never lost their good appetite. A wave of air-raids followed in our wake. They were not serious air-raids compared with the destruction wrought by later ones, but the effect of two or three bombs dropped by German planes on some small and peaceful town was like a thunderbolt.

On arrival at any of the small towns we passed, we'd always find the same scenery of sluggish provincial life, with all the restaurants and shops doing normal business. Then in a very short time, as in some quick-motion film, everything would be in chaos. Frightened horses would be neighing pitifully, barbers in their white pinafores would be all but floating in the air, as if they'd come off some Chagall canvas. At such moments, the poet Stanislaw Balinski would start dividing out his family heirlooms among us.

Then, all of a sudden, good news would come from the front, rumors of victories by some general or other, and we'd be in good spirits again. We commemorated one such victory by drinking a bottle of Napoleon brandy. But gradually—at the sight of the muddle in which our troops retreated, the utter lack of organization and the undisguised panic of the civil authorities—I began to resist the fool's paradise and took a rather pessimistic view of the military situation. At one of the frontier villages, a local official ordered us to turn back, because of some bylaw "that in time of war, civilians are not allowed to approach the frontier." This, translated into plain language, meant that in time of war only troops had a right to flee the country. This was not very far from the actual state of affairs. After many ups and downs we finally arrived at Zaleszczyki, and a few hours before the arrival of the Soviet troops crossed the famous bridge leading to Rumania.

I was leaving Poland with a heavy heart but also with a firm belief in our speedy return to Warsaw. England, France, and America were quite sure to put the Germans in their right place. The thing was to get to the Allied forces and to put oneself beyond the reach of the Nazis.

It was by no means a small thing to get from Rumania to France. One had to pass through Italy, and in Italy the Gestapo was given a free hand, while the Italian police was said to have a list of anti-Fascist writers and journalists and had in fact arrested some. As my anti-Fascist stand had once been the cause of a diplomatic *démarche*, I had reason to suppose that I might be on that list. I had insulted Dino Grandi in print. In answer to this, the Italian Embassy made a diplomatic *démarche* to our Ministry of Foreign Affairs. When, on the Italian-Yugoslav frontier, the police came into our compartment and began to check documents, I had to use all my self-control not to show my anxiety. The policemen began to talk excitedly. It turned out that they were excited about my companion, Count Sobański. He was fair with a reddish tinge and was taken for a Jew. I succeeded, without much difficulty, in convincing the police that this aristocrat and papal count was no Jew. I say "without much difficulty," because, on the whole, the Italians closed their eyes to the documents of Polish refugees.

Then came the long-awaited moment. After a series of tiresome train stops and document checks, we crossed the French frontier. At last we had reached a nation that was fighting the Germans. Safe at last! Between us and the enemy there was the Maginot Line. We had faith in it as we had in many foolish things.

On our first day in Paris, we met Artur Rubinstein on the Boulevards. Artur and his wife were old friends of ours. As usual, he was very sweet to us. He took us to a splendid restaurant and gave us lunch and some money. The truth was that we had been living from hand to mouth. We had left Warsaw, as we thought, for a very short time and took just a little money and one suitcase, intending to return as soon as the German army would be dispersed—that is, in a couple of weeks at the most.

In all our peregrinations through Poland—whether by car, cart, or on foot—we were at all times blessed with sound sleep and excellent digestions. It was as if some atavistic force, latent in normal and peaceful times, became active in us when danger was imminent. In a Paris hotel, where I was safe— or thought I was—I spent my first sleepless night in weeks, in a comfortable bed. As soon as I could relax, I was in the grip of restless thought, which poisoned my sleep. I was tortured with anxiety for my wife and myself and for friends and relatives in Poland.

The disasters of the first war months were something we could bear. Warsaw was still near and nothing could shake our faith in our ultimate victory. How little we had foreseen that dark night at Bordeaux, when a tiny Polish ship, without a single lifeboat, without a convoy took us to our last place of refuge, to the country that went on fighting Germany all by itself—to England.

When I saw the first German planes over Warsaw, when from my gay and peaceful window I detected in the white summer cloudlets the first bacilli of the war epidemic, I never thought that these might mean the beginning of an almost fatal disease. It never occurred to me that the order and conventions of my life—as I had lived it until that moment—were falling to pieces, that I was, in fact, entering on a new and terrible reality, that those planes were writing in the skies the death sentence of millions of people, that they announced the annihilation of Warsaw.

Despite their uncertainly and bitterness, despite their painful disappointments and struggles, the twenty years between wars had a lasting quality for me, and were as much my own as my very body. I saw their blemishes, their sicknesses, as I might call it, and I did my best to provide a cure, but the thought of their death never really reached the deeper levels of my consciousness.

When on a misty summer morning—after the fall of France—we reached the shores of England, I was richer for one more bitter experience and I looked upon the flat, seemingly defenseless coast of Cornwall with diffidence but also with a newborn calm and relief. My wife and close friends were here with me and I was about to enter a country for which I had much sympathy and admiration. The danger was still grave but I felt I could stand up to it now in conditions of human dignity, freed from the debasing agony of the hunted animal that never left me during my last few days in France.

Particularly nightmarish was my last night on the old Continent. The tiny Polish boat was to sail before dawn and had inadequate food supplies for her passengers. Late that afternoon, I went to town to get some bread, wine, and fruit. It was much further from the wharf than I expected. Most of the shops were closed. Those that were open had long queues in front of them. I was so worried that I could hardly wait for my turn and wanted to rush back. But with the obstinacy of a gambler who stakes his last penny, I went on queuing, though a feeling of disaster overtook me. When at last I did leave the shop, it was quite dark. Sirens sounded the alert and there was no question of getting a taxi. I started almost to run, sweating, stumbling in the dark, and forcing my way through a maze of unknown streets. I stupidly trusted my memory and didn't even know the name of the wharf where our boat lay. How was I now to find a small Polish boat in the pitch dark of a blackout and in a port that stretched for tens of kilometers? That boat was now the most desirable spot on earth and the only place of safety for me.

I knew in what despair my wife, Janka, would be; I knew the boat might sail any moment, and I was lost in ever new—or perhaps the same— streets, littered with packing cases and ropes. It was getting very late. Through the narrow gap in the blackout of a window there shone a faint light. My hands felt a door and pushed it. It wasn't locked. I entered an empty pub where the half-clad *patron* was busy washing up. I told him of my troubles and fortified my demand for help with a hundred-franc bill. The *patron* refused to take the money. He dried his hands quietly, took me by the arm, and led me outside. We were a few steps away from a wall with a gate in it, which the Frenchman found as easily as if he had done this many times. Behind that gate I was able to discern the outlines of a boat. I called out my wife's name. Somebody answered in Polish. I shook hands with the kind Frenchman and went up the narrow gangway. The engines of the ship were already rattling under full steam. The lower deck was crowded and the lights hurt my eyes. I was still holding two bottles of wine and a bag with bread

338

and grapes. On that night, when the French state fell and with it almost all our hopes, my wife, her face stained with tears, and I ate those grapes with a feeling of complete happiness and blissful peace.

X

The last war had taught us how relative any feeling of safety can be. How unsafe governments and armies, strategic frontiers and truths resting on agelong traditions can be. The fine weather and the almost uncanny gaiety of the 1940 summer in England roused in me a feeling of mistrust. The sharper edge of this mistrust pointed to our own authorities—the Polish Government in Exile.

It was a state in miniature, a symbolic country reduced to the space of a few London hotels and offices, lending itself to observation like a small ant hill in a vivarium. Its leaders usually met in the small dining-room of a little Jewish restaurant in Paddington. Government meetings and negotiations took place in the adjoining cabinet. When members of the Peasant Party threatened to leave the cabinet, it could simply mean that they intended to have dinner in the dining-room. General Sikorski once honored the restaurant with his presence. The owner—a Polish Jew—met the General with bread and salt on a salver. Apparently both these items were put in the bill later.

At that restaurant I used to have interminable talks with the émigré leaders of the time. I remember one such talk with Stanislaw Grabski, a former Socialist and an outstanding political figure, then an old man. I asked him why, though in his youth he had been editor of *The Worker*, the Polish Socialist paper in Berlin, he had changed his views. The professor, who was a little deaf, probably had not heard my question. He put his hand to his ear and said: "What?"

"Why did you give up Socialism?"

"Socialism? I don't remember!"

This answer took me quite by surprise. But it did, I think, give a fairly good idea of the trends of the time.

I was not such a complete stranger in England as were most of my fellow countrymen. I had been to England twice before the war. I had friends and acquaintances there. And yet in all my life I never knew such utter and bitter loneliness, a feeling of not belonging, as during my ten years' stay in that country, where I mixed with interesting and kind people, where I lived in conditions of comparative safety, in a city distinguished by a glorious past, in a land that has the loveliest countryside in the world.

My loneliness was to a great extent due to my early break with the Polish émigrés. One might have expected new friends to take the place of old ones, one might have thought that by leaving the émigré ghetto I would have found a way into the circles of Anglo-Saxon intellectuals, for whom I have always had great sympathy and admiration. In theory—yes. But not in practice. When I recollect today those times and try to find the real answer to my loneliness in London, I have to go back to Warsaw. I was not really lonely, I simply wasn't myself in England. I had left my soul in my country, or to be precise, in Warsaw. I had left my literary work there, my readers, my usefulness, my sense of existence. Were all these reasons devoid of vanity? Who can tell? For I was a popular figure of the Warsaw streets and cafés, whereas in London I was only a man in the street. In London I could only hope for compassion.

I had left behind something difficult to define: devotion and memory. There was a yearning in me for my father's city and for old friends, a feeling of solidarity with those who had stayed at home. That may be the reason why I instinctively and almost from the start opposed all émigré policy, which kept us away from home. That is why, despite some serious doubts and no less serious apprehension, I resolved to make the jump into the unknown and go back to Poland.

On my return, people asked: "Have you really come for good?"

"Not for good," I replied. "For better, or for worse."

Translated from the Polish by Cecylia Wojewoda

Saul Bellow

Mozart

In preparing this essay I have found myself sizing up Mozart as if I were thinking of writing a novel in which he might appear as a character. I was not aware at the outset that this was what I was doing. It was only after I had written half of it that I recognized what I had done.

Mozart is immediately accessible to the naive. Others obviously require preparation. It is no criticism of twelve-tone composers, to choose an obvious example, to note that they oblige us to give some thought to the formal assumptions they expect us to share. Mozart, however, can be loved freely and naturally by amateurs. It is because I am an amateur that I have been invited to discuss Mozart, and I intend to make the most of my amateur standing, bypassing the problems which intrigue and vex the learned specialists I have read in my efforts to get a handle of my own on this subject.

My best course is to convert ignorance into an advantage.

What follows is a confession, supplemented by such tentative ideas as are bound to flutter out when any of us makes an open declaration of this sort.

I shall begin by saying that there are corners of my existence which from the first were furnished by Mozart. It does not seem to me that any other musical tenant ever had to be moved out to make room for him. I had an older sister—much my senior—who played the piano. She did not play particularly well. She was a perfect metronome (metrognome) of a pianist, but she did familiarize me with Mozart.

There was a manufacturer in Chicago by the name of Gullbrantsen and in his advertisements, painted on brick walls, an infant was shown pressing the pedals of a piano. The legend was: "The richest child is poor without a musical education." This was a warning taken seriously by parents in the Midwest. I was given violin lessons at an early age. Many of the music teachers were refugees from Revolutionary Russia. Mine was a stout gloomy man from Odessa seeking a prodigy, a second Heifetz or Menuhin or Elman to make his reputation. Obviously I lacked the gifts he was looking for, and he would snatch the bow and whip my bottom with it. He was so peevish and futile that I was more amused than hurt. I did, somehow, learn to fiddle adequately and until middle age I was on the lookout for amateur musicians like myself and had the pleasure occasionally of playing Mozart sonatas arranged for duets and trios. In my student years I was an unpaid usher at the Auditorium Theatre; the Ballet Russe de Monte Carlo and the San Carlo Opera came regularly to Chicago. Samuel Insull, the utilities tycoon, gave

the city an opera house (before he fled to Greece and had to be extradited.) International celebrities were brought to Orchestra Hall by Hurok the Impressario. There were excellent teachers of theory and music history and first-rate performers at the south end of the Loop. Although I was not trained in a conservatory, I absorbed a considerable amount of music, and while I preferred books to instruments, there were odd corners of my existence reserved for Handel, Mozart, Pergolesi, etc.

I have now explained my amateur standing and will go on to the confessions I promised. But what does one confess today, when the worst of the sins have become venial? It is the violation of orderly processes of thought as prescribed by the higher rationality that throws you into sin. To be unscientific is in our time a grave mental offense.

Some of my speculations on Mozart are notably unscientific. I often puzzle over the nature of his genius. How was it that it should appear so early and develop so swiftly and be so complete? Was it because his father was an educator of corresponding genius? Nobody ever suspected genius of any sort in Leopold. Neither do the educational or genetic contributions of his mother strike his biographers as exceptional. Mozart, to borrow a figure from William Blake, was a piece of ground already spaded and seeded. It looks, in other words, as if he had brought it all with him. And then I think of other prodigies born into mathematical or musical families. The mature forms assumed by these exceptional creatures are not to be accounted for by environmental or historical theories. They resemble the flowers or the insects, they have powers which astonish and physiological refinements or resources of intelligence too curious to be explained by probability theory or the ponderous slowness of time, or by trial and error. What they suggest is the intervention of invisible purposes. "To a certain extent," writes Alfred Einstein, "it is true that Mozart was only a visitor upon this earth. Mozart as a man was nowhere truly at home: neither in Salzburg, where he was born, nor in Vienna, where he died."

At the heart of my confession, therefore, is the hunch that with beings such as Mozart we are forced to speculate about transcendence and this makes us very uncomfortable, since ideas of transcendence are associated with crankiness or faddism—even downright instability and mental feebleness. These are the charges and the guilts you open yourself to when you confess that you find it impossible to dismiss such speculations. To some reasonable minds this might lead to the limiting of art—art in which religious or other "undesirable" tendencies survive—to ceremonial or traditional observances. On occasions like the present one—occasions of cultural piety.

Music, I assume (amateurishly), is based on a tonal code containing, inevitably, expressions of the whole history of feeling, emotion, belief—of essences inseparable from what we call our "higher life." I suggest also that this is where we tend to go when we have gone as far as we can in the new modern positive orthodoxies that keep us within bounds—the assumptions which our education and the business of the world have trained us to accept as normal, practical, and indispensable: the founding postulates of our scientific and technological achievements.

From all this a Mozart gives us an orderly and also emotional exit—an endlessly rich and exalted release.

I don't want to make too much of this notion of a profound originality coming from God-knows-what source. I invoke it as a corrective to the earthbound psychology that rules our minds in this century. It does no harm to be reminded that this psychology is painfully limiting to the intelligence and is often little more than a convenient way to dispose of troublesome intimations of a forbidden nature. The miracles which fascinate us are the scientific and technological ones. These have changed space, time, and nature.

To positivists this is an object world ruled by ideas. A contemporary environment is made up of such embodied ideas—ideas of residence, transportation, seeing and hearing at a distance, etcetera. By means of such ideas (and they are highly sophisticated) the earth itself has been humanized. This is simple enough to see, and externally self-explanatory. Press this switch and you will see people, you will hear them speak. Few of us, however, can explain the techniques by which this is accomplished.

Years ago I read a curious book by Ortega y Gasset called *The Revolt of the Masses*. In it Ortega explains what a Mass Man is—he is not invariably a proletarian—educated professionals may also be mass men. This is not the place to explain what Ortega was talking about. Only one of his arguments concerns me here: he says that the Mass Man is unable to distinguish between a natural object or process and an artifact, a second-nature object. He takes it for granted, as part of the order of things, that when he enters an elevator and presses the button he will go up. When mechanisms fail, when, for instance, elevators do not rise or buses do not arrive, the spirit in which he protests reveals that he understands elevators or buses to be free commodities like daylight or the universal availability of breathable air.

To congratulate ourselves, however, on our educated enlightenment is simply an evasion of the real truth. We the "educated" cannot even begin to explain the technologies of which we make daily use. We speak of electronics or cybernetics—but it is all in vain. Natural processes are beyond us, too, and despite our talk of lipids or carbohydrate metabolism, we understand virtually nothing about the physiology of digesting or the transmission of nerve impulses. Face to face with the technological miracles without which we could not live our lives, we are as backward as any savage, though education helps us to conceal this from ourselves and others. Indeed it would utterly paralyze us to ponder intricate circuits or minicomputers, or attempt to gain a clear understanding of the translation of the discoveries of particle physics into modern arms.

These, however, are the miracles for which we have a very deep respect, and which, perhaps, dominate our understanding of what a miracle is. A miracle is what brings people to Australia in ten hours. And we owe this to the scientific revolution.

What I am calling to your attention is pitifully transparent. No other generation in history has lived in a world miraculously transformed by such artifacts. Ortega y Gasset notwithstanding, we are by and large no better at distinguishing nature from artifice than his Mass Man. Worse, we have lost Ortega's old-fashioned confidence in our powers to explain what nature is. Can we say that we can see through the metabolic internal blizzard that converts matter into energy?

Our assignment, in one sense, is simply to man the artifacts which technology provides in ever more sophisticated and esoteric variations. But what of the music of *Don Giovanni* or *Cosi Fan Tutte* considered as miracles—as comprehensive revelations of what *eros* can be in two such different outpourings of sound?

I suppose almost everyone would feel that just as the principles behind a product of technology can be fully grasped if we determine to study the method laid down for us by intelligent beings whom basically we resemble, we will be able also to give a full account of these operas. But when we try to do that, the music brings us to a standstill. There is a dimension of music which prohibits final comprehension and parries or fends off the cognitive habits we respect and revere. We appear to feel that we are riding the crest of a wave of comprehension that has already overcome nature, and we are committed to the belief that there are no mysteries—there is only the not-yet-known. But I think I have made myself clear. We are as ignorant of fundamentals as human beings ever were. Self-respect demands that we appear to be with it.

And perhaps what I have been saying is related to the growing importance of Mozart, for as the twentieth century concludes, his romantic rivals seem less great than they did fifty or sixty years ago. The most accomplished of contemporary music historians, writers like the brilliant Wolfgang Hildesheimer, feel that he is the sort of man we find singularly familiar, and Peter Porter some time ago in an *Encounter* essay (June 1983) wrote that Mozart "seems a modern man," closer to ourselves than Bach, "a personality in sight and comprehensible to our temperament." He goes on to say that there is enough evidence (by which he means documentary evidence—correspondence, personal reminiscences, data brought to light by researchers)—"to induce a great sadness when we consider Mozart's life. It will not look like a triumph, it refuses to allow us to escape an uncomfortable if anachronistic sense of guilt; no arrangement of facts or twisting of fiction, from the sugary distortions of Sacha Guitry to the demeaning simplifications of Peter Schaffer's *Amadeus*, will fit Mozart out in the garments of vindication or apotheosis. He is so very unlike Beethoven, a titan of a very different sort."

Now "modern" is a curious term—it can be used to degrade as well as (or more often than) to elevate. It can mean decadent, degenerate, nihilistic, abysmal, at one end—or it can signify a capacity to overcome contemporary disorder, or to adumbrate a stage in the formation of a new superiority, or to begin to distill a new essence. It can mean that the best of contemporary minds show qualities of power, subtlety, scope, and resourcefulness, of infinite plasticity, adaptability, of the courage to cope with all that world history has dumped on the generations of this present age. "The human mind," E. M. Forster observed, "is not a dignified organ." And he called upon us "to exercise it sincerely."

In Mozart's case "sincerity" is a marginal consideration, since he was not obliged to seek the truth in German, French, Italian, or English. His objective was not sincerity, it was bliss. But as we will all understand immediately, the view that the mind is not a dignified organ is modern. It is exactly what we expect. It is this casualness, irony, levity that we seem in our time to take for granted. The starchiness of nineteenth-century ideals, or the pompousness of twentieth-century dictators, are rejected and mocked as dangerous and false. Reading about Mozart's personal life we recognize that he was informal, to say the least, *sans façon*. He struck no attitudes—the very idea of "genius" was alien to him. From his letters we see that as an observer he was singularly modern. Let me give a few examples of this. Here is his description of the Archduke Maximilian, a brother of the Emperor and the new Archbishop of Cologne:

346

> *When God gives a man a sacred office, He generally gives him understanding; and so it is, I trust, in the case of the Archduke. But before he became a priest, he was far more witty and intelligent and talked less, but more sensibly. You should see him now. Stupidity oozes out of his eyes. He talks and holds forth incessantly and always in falsetto—and he has started a goitre. In short, the fellow has changed completely. (1781—aetat. 35)*

And here is his description of a Dominican monk from Bologna:

> *... regarded as a holy man. For my part I do not believe it, for at breakfast, he often takes a cup of chocolate and immediately afterwards a good glass of strong Spanish wine; and I have myself had the honor of lunching with this saint who at table drank a whole decanter and finished*

up with a full glass of strong wine, two large slices of melon, some peaches,
pears, five cups of coffee, a whole plate of cloves, and two full saucers of
milk and lemon. He may of course be following some sort of diet, but I
do not think so, for it would be too much; moreover, he takes several little
snacks during the afternoon . . ."   *(21 August 1770)*

Mozart has the novelist's gift of characterizing by minute particulars.
He is not respectful, neither is he severe—not even when he writes "stupidity
oozes out of his eyes." His manner of seeing comes directly from his nature,
perhaps from a source close to the source of his music. The two styles, the
verbal and the musical, have something in common. He often comments
on the voices of the people he describes. The Archbishop holds forth in
falsetto. The poet Wieland whom he meets in Mannheim in 1777 "has a
rather childish voice" and a defect of speech "that makes him speak very
slowly" so that, he "can't say half a dozen words without stopping." As for
singers, he comments extensively on them: "A fine singer, a baritone, and
forced when he sings falsetto, but not as much as Tibaldi in Vienna."
"Bradamante, in love with Ruggiero . . . is sung by a poor Baroness . . . She
appears under an assumed name . . . has a passable voice, and her stage
presence would not be bad, but she sings off-pitch like the devil."

He has a keen modern appetite for personal impressions, Einstein
notes. About landscape—though he is a great traveller—he rarely writes.
"About art he did not express himself at all." Einstein adds a little further
on that in Rome "the most beautiful flowers did not interest him, for he
was sitting at home covering paper with music." From Rome Mozart had
written to his sister jokingly that these beautiful flowers were being carried
past in the street: "so Papa has just told me."

To be modern is to be mobile, forever en route, with few local attachments anywhere, cosmopolitan, not particularly disturbed to be an outsider
in temporary quarters. On his journeys Mozart composed in his head. He
was mobile by temperament. Nissen, one of his early biographers, records
that Mozart's sister-in-law remembered that in his last years "he looked at
everything, whether he was merry or sad, and yet he seemed at the same
time to be lost in thought about something entirely different. Even when
he washed his hands in the morning he walked up and down, never stood
still, knocked one heel against the other and was always reflective. . . . He
was always enthusiastic about new entertainments, riding and billiards, for

example . . . He was always moving his hands and feet, always playing with something, e.g., his hat, pockets, watch-chain, tables, chairs, as if they were pianos . . ." (Hildesheimer, p. 265).

What *was* permanent, evidently, he carried within. In 1788 he writes from Vienna, "We are sleeping tonight, for the first time in our new quarters [in Währing], where we shall remain both summer and winter. On the whole the change is all the same to me, in fact I prefer it. . . . I shall have more time to work."

Einstein tells us that Mozart and his wife changed their residence in Vienna eleven times within a period of ten years, "sometimes after so little as three months. Their life was a perpetual tour, changing from one hotel room to another, and the hotel rooms were soon forgotten. . . . He was ready at any time to change Vienna for another city or Austria for another country."

Nor was art a "project" for him, as it was to be for others in the nineteenth century. Nor did the thought of being a genius fortify him. He shed superfluous externals, and he appears early in life to have made his reckonings as to what could be dispensed with. This was done with intuitive rapidity and sureness—the clear signs of a pure and faultless freedom. To a modern, the posturing of romantic geniuses has become hateful. It smells of public relations and image-making. In this line we think of Wagnerian megalomania, histrionics, cultism, and politics. Mozart has none of these defects or designs. He does not care about politics. "Power," in the classic modern sense, holds no appeal for him. Scheming is utterly alien to his character. And on the practical side he is utterly without foresight. His recent biographers agree that the management of his own affairs was disastrous. From these failures he withdrew into work. Among his Viennese contemporaries, says Peter Porter, summarizing the conclusions of Hildesheimer, he was judged to be unserious and improvident by nature. But this negligence or inability to foresee consequences (how could he fail to understand that *Figaro* would antagonize the Viennese aristocracy and that it would punish him by boycotting his concerts?) is something like the Roman flowers, the endless procession of carriages on tour, the landscapes he ignores, the many changes of residence. These transient experiences are a background or horizon. *The Marriage of Figaro had* to be written, the withdrawal of patronage consequently *had* to be endured. And so with other snubs, defeats, and disappointments. He fell in love with a woman who would not have him and made do with her sister. Of the lively interest he took in Constanze we know from the boisterous sexual candor of the letters he wrote her. Was he making the best of things—or are his fantasies about his genitalia and hers also on the transient horizon, a pleasant subject for correspondence—*not* after all the main thing?

We today have a particular fondness for Mozart's adolescent levity about sex (and what Porter speaks of as his "coprophilic fun and his . . . infantile sexuality"). But Mozart's own contemporaries were habitually freer in this regard than we are. His mother, too, used plain language. The nineteenth century gave us an interregnum of puritanism. I have often thought that "repression" and "inhibition" as described by Freud, refer to a temporary shift of "moral" emphasis. Students of English literature are familiar with this move from the open sensuality of Fielding and Lawrence Sterne to Victorian prudery ("propriety") in Dickens or Trollope. Rousseau's *Confessions* or Diderot's *Les Bijoux Indiscrets* confirm this. What the twentieth century has is a "liberation," with all the excesses and exaggeration the term connotes. It would be wrong to take Mozart as a herald of the "freedoms" we "conquered" at mid-century. He was not at all the pioneer "swinger" of Peter Schaffer's *Amadeus*. Seventy years ago my Russian-immigrant uncles, aunts, and cousins were still speaking freely and colorfully about bodily functions and things sexual—"country matters," as Shakespeare called them in *Hamlet*; such lewd *double entendres* are common in his plays. Specialists in Tudor and Stuart literature have collected them. Bawdry has a long pedigree. Conversation in the courts of Elizabeth and James I was not what we came later to call "respectable."

Mozart's lewdness in his letters to his "Bäsle"—a first cousin—might have been recorded, Mr. Porter says, for a textbook on infantile sexuality. But it is nothing like our modern street-language, which is seldom funny and tends rather to become routine. The high-spirited obscenities of the eighteenth century disappear from the romantic literature of the nineteenth— perhaps as a concession to the self-improving bourgeois reader with his peculiar ideas of gentility.

Yet it is no use pretending that Mozart was not curiously erratic. There is plenty of evidence that he acted up, that he clowned, performed tricks, made gags. He had a liking for low company, too. A certain Frau Pichler who wrote historical novels observes, [*ibid.* p. 271], that neither Mozart nor Hayden ever "demonstrated in their personal intercourse any unusual intellectual power at all, and scarcely any learning or higher culture. In society they displayed only a common temperament, insipid jests, and [in the case of Mozart—S.B.] a thoughtless way of life; and yet what depths, what worlds of fantasy, harmony, melody . . ." etcetera, she writes.

As this same lady once sat at the piano playing "Non più andrai" from *Figaro*, "Mozart who happened to be present, came up behind me, and my playing must have pleased him, for he hummed the melody with me, and beat time on my shoulder; suddenly, however, he pulled up a chair, sat down, told me to keep playing the bass and began to improvise variations so beautifully that everyone held his breath, listening to the music of the German Orpheus. But all at once he had had enough; he jumped up and, as he often did in is foolish moods, began to leap over table and chairs, miaowing like a cat, and turning somersaults like an unruly boy." Hildesheimer speaks of such outbursts as "physical necessities, automatic compensation for a transcendent mind . . . they are the results, as well as the reflection, of mental distraction."

To think about Mozart's personality and the circumstances of his life is, to me, very pleasant—his boisterous humor is so very contemporary. Still, we can no more understand him than we can understand our contemporary selves. We come away from books like Hildesheimer's study of Mozart, confessing that the riddle of his character is beyond us. It stands concealed behind his music and we will never get to the bottom of it. When we say he is modern, I suppose we mean that we recognize the signature of Enlightenment, of reason and universalism in his music—we recognize also the limitations of Enlightenment. We have learned from history that enlightenment, liberation, and doom may go together. For every avenue liberation opens, two are closed. Within Mozart's cheerful daylight secularity there is always otherworldly darkness. And the freedom he expresses is never without sadness, a deep submission to melancholy. We are endowed—so I interpret him—with comprehension but what we are required to comprehend is too much for us.

Hildesheimer is persuaded that both Mozart and Beethoven carried what he calls "a metaphysical aura." Beethoven was aware of this and he cultivated and exploited it. Mozart, not knowing that he had such an aura, "exaggerated his physical presence with continual diversionary tactics, which became routine." He was clownishly demonic. He was a "stranger" who never understood the nature of his strangeness. Beethoven asserts his greatness; Mozart does not. He is not concerned with himself, rather he is intent on what he was born to do. In him there are few indications of ordinary *amour propre* or common vanity, and no signs whatever of *grandezza*.

Now all this talk of "metaphysical auras" can be irritating, I know. Still, when people who are clearly sensible insist on speaking of metaphysics and auras we had better control our irritation prudently and ask ourselves why clear-minded, well-balanced people are obliged to forsake the positivist common sense on which we all rely. It is the music itself that drives them away from the rules of intellectual respectability. The music presses us to ask why it is so continually fertile, novel, ingenious, inexhaustible—why it is able to tell us so much more than other languages can tell us, and why it is given so readily, easily, gratuitously. For it is not a product of effort. What it makes us see is that there are things which must be done easily. Easily or not at all—that is the truth about art. Concentration without effort is at the heart of the thing. Will and desire are silenced (as many mystics have understood) and work is transformed into play. And what we see in Mozart's earthly record is the preservation of what matters amid distractions and harassments. Shall we make a sketchy list of these: lodgings, taverns, salons, cold and stupid aristocrats, unpaid debts, petty tyrants like the Bishop of Salzburg and his flunkies, endless travels, irrelevant landscapes, bad music, disappointments in love . . . ? Even the burden of a natural superiority which breeds rancor in others and must therefore be dissembled.

Against this, there is the understanding that work should be transformed into play—perhaps as Wisdom puts it in the Book of Proverbs—"The Lord possessed me in the beginning of his ways, before he made anything from the beginning. I was set up from eternity, and of old, before the earth was made. . . . I was with him forming all things: and was delighted every day, playing before Him at all times; playing in the world. And my delights were to be with the children of men" (Prov. 8:22–3, 30–31).

We can't speak of Mozart without wondering "where it all comes from," without touching on certain "eternal," "mysterious" questions. Many have credibly argued that he is "modern" ("one of us"), and yet it is the essence of the "modern" to demystify. How is it that our "modern Mozart" should *increase* mystery? We are inclined to think of mystery as woolly or amorphous, yet Mozart, working in the light, openly, is all coherence. Although he does not use a cognitive language we can, up to a point, understand him fully. His sounds and rhythms correspond to states of feeling which we have all somehow learned to interpret. This musical mode of speech is different from the semantic one that allows us to specify or denote. We feel moved to go beyond such speech, either in the direction of the pure exactness of mathematics or in the direction of the higher affects of sound or sight. The latter, the affects, are all the more powerful because they go beyond the definitions of speech, of intelligible discourse. This music of Mozart is the speech of affects. What can we call it *but* mysterious. In it we hear; through it is expressed our sense of the radical mystery of our being. This is what we hear in *Cosi Fan Tutte* or in the G-Minor Quintet. Of the latter more than a few writers have told us that they hear in it "the prayer of a lonely man," "the Garden of Gethsemane"—"cutting pain," says Albert. I prefer the term "radical mystery" to these religious interpretations. Radical mystery leaves Mozart freer to go into the problematic regions of existence in his Mozartean way. And all we can say about it is that it is "from beyond."

A few remarks now about the conditions of those of our contemporaries who listen to music. They—or, rather, we—can't be taken for granted. They are not what they were in the eighteenth century. I have already referred to Mozart as modern and drawn the usual unflattering picture, distorted if you like, of man in the present age. A strange creature—cerebral but not too intelligent, he lives in a special realm of consciousness but his consciousness is inadequate. Applied science and engineering have so transformed the external world that it affects him as something magical. We know of course that it isn't magic, it is highly rational—a kind of rationality that might as well be magical. Self-respect demands that he (the pronoun includes us all) make gestures of rationality to signify that he is capable, at any rate, of keeping up. But you would agree—I think we are all ready to confess—that this "keeping up" is very tiring.

Civilized man does not give himself a good press. I don't say that he deserves to hold a good opinion of himself. Philosophy and literature have been particularly hard on him from the beginning of the modern age, and by now "Eurocentrism" has become a terrible reproach. We reproach ourselves even for the few decencies, bourgeois relics, with which we cover our shame. We hear from all sides that we are "inauthentic" and that we are, every one of us, impostors.

All of this, I think, comes from *us*. It is *we* who set up and *we* who knock down. If we are impostors, we are also those who expose impostors.

This "being human" is our very own show. All that mankind is said to be, pro and contra, comes from mankind itself. Everything that we can possibly conceive is made into fact, and it all comes out of bottomless reservoirs of our invention and fantasy. Everything has to be tried out. Funnily enough, the same mind that takes in "Dallas" or rap music is also accessible to Homer and Shakespeare.

These are not merely diverting speculations. The awful truth is behind them. In this century, although briefly, slavery reappeared in Europe—in the wartime factories of Germany and in Siberian mines and forests. Only a few decades later the finest kitchens and bathrooms in history were produced in the West, a wide-scale consumer culture such as the world has never seen.

But there is no need to make an inventory of the times. It is demoralizing to describe ourselves to ourselves yet again. It is especially hard on us since we believe (as we have been educated to believe) that history has formed us, and that we are all mini-summaries of the present age.

When I say, however, that the mind that takes in the "Dallas" melodrama is capable of absorbing Homer and Shakespeare—or Mozart, since he is the focus of our attention—I am saying also that we have transhistorical powers. The source of these powers is in our curious nature. We have concentrated with immense determination on what forms us externally, but that need not actually govern us internally. It can do that only if we grant it the right.

But we as individuals, in inner freedom, need not grant any such thing. This is a good moment to remind ourselves of this—now that the great ideological machines of the century have stopped forever and are already covered with rust.

What is attractive about Mozart (against this background of rusting ideological machinery) is that he is an individual. He learned for himself (as in *Cosi Fan Tutte*) the taste of disappointment, betrayal, suffering; the weakness, foolishness and vanity of flesh and blood, as well as the emptiness of cynicism. In him we see a person who has only himself to rely on. But what a self it is, and what an art it has generated. How deeply (beyond words) he speaks to us about the mysteries of our common human nature. And how unstrained and *easy* his greatness is.

353

G. V. Desani

With Malice Aforethought

There are a lot of people—G. Gurdjieff, Ramakrishna Swamis, J. Krishnamurti, Ptr Dem'yanovich Uspensky, Ramana Maharishi, Zen masters, Meher Baba, Sri Aurobindo, Aldous Huxley, the holy Mother of Pondicherry, to name a few—who want you to go in for self-realization.

Self-realization is the absolute condition for happiness. To know this truth is growth, maturity, enrichment.

A fortunate self-realized victim might find comfort and fulfillment in martyrdom, in torture, and—at the receiving end of—flogging, assault, crucifixion. A self-realized adept doubtlessly finds fulfillment in martyring, torturing, flogging, assaulting, crucifying.

For the majority of beings this esoteric knowledge is not easy come, not easy to grasp when come, and—as *all* achievement—its arrival is conditioned by time, chance, destiny, luck, God, anti-God.

I discovered my true nature and become a self-realized being very early in life. When I was a boy, I used to pinch little girls (how many of you, my friends, have not done that *and* dropped wriggling worms down their little backs, what do you think?) and *enjoy watching them squirm.*

Not yet twenty, I became a businessman. I was a travel agent. (I had a one-room office and an elderly widow's savings. Travel agency was her idea. She wouldn't part with her savings for any other. She thought it was a "nice business" for an up-and-coming young man.)

I drew full pay but procured no client for the first eight months. (I might have been wool-farming in a sheepless country.)

At the beginning of the ninth, I got a customer—an old classmate of the widow (and her thirty-five-year-old nephew, by the name of—). I booked her a run of the East African coast on a tramp of tramps—a converted Arab dhow. (The old woman was gone on such words as *Mombasa, Kilindini, Cape Delgado*; and the scum of the earth—the captain of the dhow—had a fifty-fifty split arrangement with me.)

The woman—past her sixties, when I booked her—was never the same after her return from "the holiday." (The scum of the earth, the dhow, the seas, the sun, the manners of the crew, and dysentery all helped.) And "the boy" (the nephew, by the name of—) was wearing monocles of raw and bruised beef around both his eyes—so the bags about his eyes from little hernias seemed to me—as he took refuge in a nursing home.

His aunt was counted by death exactly a month after. (The dysentery bug was Arab and strong.) The widow followed her. I quit business and saved her savings.

356

By all reckoning, the two old women, and the nephew (by the name of—) cut a caper, or what do you think?

I enjoyed doing business with them.

Man, by nature, is happy. Search for happiness is folly. Happiness must be realized within. This is an esoteric secret. Indian Vedantin knows this secret. *Sat-Chit-Ananda*, he says. *Ananda* is Bliss, Joy, Happiness. (See Upanishad books, chapter so and so, page so and so.)

One reason why we do not realize our true nature is our preoccupation with others: because we do things *for others* (instead of doing them for ourselves), *help others* (instead of helping ourselves). This perversity—trying to run a stream against its course and current—results in effort, exertion, struggle. (All so-called religious and moral discipline is effort, exertion, struggle. It is anything but spontaneity. It is suffering. It is not happiness, my friends.) As soon as all that folly is abandoned, realization of Truth results. (The means of attaining this insight into Truth might be ever so trivial: squirming little girls, a duped widow, the departed dysenteric, or the nephew (by the name of—).

After realization, all service must be for the self. (All execution of such service is bound to be disadvantageous to others—who must be reduced, worsened, and eventually sacrificed.) And this course *must* lead to true spirituality (since it is the *Truth*): and it must lead to a further conquest, a greater freedom, mastery, to self-possession entire, and, only then, not before, my friends, will all be won!

To win *all*, the adept must not be satisfied with meeting the needs of his nature (self-realization, etc.). That is not *all*. He must forge ahead, be truly sovereign: be a man of metal (not flesh). Not satisfied with mere happiness (*Ananda*), he must be a Force unto himself, an adept in tempting, tiring, and confusing creatures: a hunter of men, a whipper, a scourge, a punisher of those who desire and accept punishment: those who seek escape from fire to a greater fire, in fast, pledge, Lent, discipline, crucifixion, death.

Thus, my friends, the adept—by laws of Magic-Eternal—gains *all*. He is never without his due: his *prey, feed, fodder*.

(These truths are not known to G. Gurdjieff, Ramakrishna Swamis, J. Krishnamurti, Ptr Dem'yanovich Uspenskv, Ramana Maharishi, Zen masters, Meher Baba, Sri Aurobindo, Aldous Huxley, the holy Mother of Pondicherry, to name a few.)

My night of achievement was rayless. There was an ebony gloss upon the darkness, too, I thought. And, with my heightened susceptibility, I could discern (a premonitory) amalgam of scents: the seasoned teak of the coffin, the woolen suit and the cotton tie (shrouding the corpse), the odor of palsied flesh (present premonitorily; the nephew, the name of—, RIP). Following these omens—having chosen to be a sovereign man of metal—not yet thirty, I was ready to forge ahead. Dispensing with all ritual, all ceremony, forsaking all vestment, naked, legs astride, face lowered, toward and below the navel— the posture prescribed—I invoked Him.

My aim was to be a Peer of the All-High: be second only to the tusky grandee, who wears the morning coat made of male hide and hair, the top hat of tarred female hide and hair, and sweats tongues of flame and smoke from his honeycombed hide, and hair: the solemn grandee who, forever, reviews the All-High's State of the Estate report: so many dead, devoured, sacrificed—war, pestilence, disease, ignorance, confusion—and so many on the way, fasting, laboring, struggling, courting the grave!

So resolved, on that night of achievement, I soon passed beyond the reaches of human mind: and beyond the range of the man-devil, warlock, werewolf, the comforter of witches, the leader of carnage, the master of whoredom.

357

I asked for a sign from Him.

In my library, in the fartherest corner—where the reading lamp stands—I was enveloped in a virgin radiance: an aquamarine light, cooling, comforting, consoling. Then the rays were gathered off me, became a girdle of a still purer splendor, throbbing with life, laughter, joy: all the smiles of babes that kick and gurgle when lying on their backs, when suckled, when kissed, when lying face down—all that *and* the jasmine, the rose, *and* the soul of sandal, the memory of myrrh!

In the girdle of supernatural light, my friends, then emerged dancers, dancers of fantasy, nymphs, creatures of such entrancing beauty, that I cried curses upon the poets, painters, sculptors, for never having known such *richness!*

Then the girdle was gathered, and became a swan: a swan of ultimate, immaculate, intrinsic beauty, symmetry, majesty. A swan of gold, and abreathing, its wings glittering from the rose of the morn and the magic argent of the moon!

Then the swan was gathered and became a hand of absolute perfection, a woman's hand joined to a wrist, and, on the wrist, I saw bangles of red and green, afired by an unearthly light, of the rarest ruby and the emerald!

The hand moved and *blessed me!*

Appalled, betrayed, cheated, I stood upright, my posture broken, and stamping, cursing, I cried, *"Deceit!" "False!"*

Wherefore, my friends, the true Symbols? The soothfast Signs? Wherefore the oozing, suppurating corpse? The fouled grave? Wherefore the Master's cloven hooves? His sulphurous smell? Wherefore His witch-kissed fundament? Wherefore the immense phallus of our Father?

Spitting on the Glory—the hand of Beauty which was blessing me—I invoked Him again, crying aloud my (aforesaid) thoughts, "Wherefore . . . ?" "Wherefore . . . ?"

Instantly, the hand became viscous—a splash of bloody red—and it coagulated a brownish muddy red, and in the middle thereof was an emptiness, and the emptiness was aflame with a malignant glare, an infrared, uneven glare, and it jumped off the emptiness and touched my bare flesh!

By that burning, searing touch, I knew it was He. Trembling from rage, and mocking Him, I said, "Have you come to me for *pity*, now, Beelzebub?" Standing straight, and facing Him naked, I defied Him. "Do

I expect *justice* from you, now, Beelzebub? Are you cultivating the *virtues*, now, Beelzebub?"

Father spoke humbly. "Did you say, 'Deceit!' and 'False!'—your reverence?"

"I said, 'Deceit!' Beelzebub! I said 'False!' Beelzebub!"

"What is false, your reverence?"

"Beauty is false, Beelzebub!"

"What is deceit, your reverence?"

"Joy, benediction, perfection, is deceit, Beelzebub!"

"You asked for a Sign, your reverence?"

"I asked for a Sign, Beelzebub!"

Gently, and pleading, our Father said, "The Glory was the Sign, your reverence!"

"Deceit! False!" I cried, blind to Truth.

The glare jumped toward me again and penetrated me viciously.

Scorched, scalded, seething, that very instant, my friends, I attained *all!*

I *was* His Peer, His son, His chosen, the chosen of the Great Magician, the perfidious Pretender!

"Hail, most-High!" I cried, assuming the posture prescribed, legs astride, face lowered, toward and below the navel. And I hastily read the oath and litany of the chosen. "I promise to protect, to serve, love, shield, shelter, the multitude. Thy food, Father! Thy weal, Beelzebub! Woe be to the multitude! The plagues of Egypt upon the multitude! Amen!"

Today, my friends, I am a man of religion, a convert, a reformed whore, a Magdalen. I endorse and support all doctrine, idealism, mysticism, symbolism, all *Sat-Chit-Ananda*, and profess love, chastity, propriety, decency, justice, charity, beauty, and I plead compassion for the creatures, for men, the multitude.

Sheltered, protected, and loved, the creatures are His *meat*, His *feed*, His *sacrifice!*

Deprived of safety, protection, caress, love—their *needs!*—the creatures seek other pastures, seek the anti-most-High, the First and the Last Enemy (the Adversary called God). They stray away from the world—which is the domain of our Father—and so many of His sheep—His *feed*, His *fodder*—are lost!

It is upon creatures, my friends, that our Father's *existence* depends. That is the cross He bears. Enthroned in their hearts, He lives, reigns, laughs.

359

In barren, broken hearts, what do you think? He is as dead. Ailing, eclipsed, and molested, aye, lost of His domain, forsaken by His subjects, deprived of His sacrifice, His church, is our Father!

So much is revealed and affirmed by the Sign, the Glory, the hand that blesses!

This truth, my friends, is revealed only to the chosen of Beelzebub. This truth would be realized only by the chosen of Beelzebub. This truth would be understood only by the elect of Beelzebub. And the purport of this *betrayal*—the publishing of this most secret commerce with the Master, which, by the laws of Magic-Eternal, the multitude must believe to be fiction, a G. V. Desani yarn peddled to earn himself cowries for pin-money—would be known only to the elect of Beelzebub. Amen.

Self-realization.

What do you think?

Rudolf Kassner

Sulla and the Satyr

Sulla's body was encrusted with a white scurf, or mange, with dark red spots protruding through it, on account of which the soldiers in camp nicknamed him Dusted Blackberry. From a distance his face looked like that of a corpse, or of a man who has come back from the underworld only because, in his view, nothing was to be found there, or at least he hadn't been able to find anything. His bright red hair stood up on his head like a sheaf of flames, and while he spoke or looked around him, his lustful glances shot from his face like two vipers from a stove they'd mistakenly entered along with a bunch of sticks collected in a forest.

That is how they were, his body and face: overgrown, precocious, their movements abrupt and hurried, yet also aristocratic and above the ordinary. And to this exterior corresponded Sulla's essential being, or soul, which was well aware that the body it inhabited was hideous, nay, repulsive and disgusting. Thus Sulla would tolerate no mirrors in his vicinity. There were two things in which his eyes were expert: shooting out glances to seize whatever they might rest on, and yet also avoiding mirrors, evading them; one might say that at the last moment his eyes would give mirrors the slip. This was why Sulla, or his soul, preferred not to be self-reflexively caught up and thrown back by other people, other souls; and thus it was that throughout his life he chose, in preference to people who claimed to be of his own kind, the company of dancers, bullfighters, singers, courtesans, and fairies, and that the actor Metrobius, who played female roles, one of the most vicious and depraved men of ancient Rome, also had to accompany Sulla on his campaigns in Greece and Asia Minor. It is as if the souls of all these people around Sulla had been blinded, bedazzled, and it was now their fate to live only by and for self-exposure. And this, too, was why Sulla gladly listened to flatterers and enjoyed being extravagant. In this respect he was different from the plebeian Marius, who believed that flattery would help him to acquire substance and scope; different, too, from other great men or men who wanted to be thought great. Sulla liked flattery because for him it was the only way to consort with monsters, or with bedazzled beings; and because Sulla was lecherous, lechery was the root of his being, the source of every expression of his being—flattery, mockery, scorn, extravagance, his generous bestowal of gifts upon friends and adherents, as opposed to the most horrible rapacity shown to his enemies and opponents, also the pleasure in killing or the direct and almost childish desire to obliterate any object standing in his way. Courage, or audacity, or even more, would be inept and erroneous appellations for Sulla's utter boyish insouciance in situations of extreme danger; his bravery, at least, was nothing like that of, say, Marius once again, whose courage was that of a great warrior or strong man. An ugly red fly settling in front of him, a toad, a spider, or the sight of an old woman, could strike Sulla for a moment speechless with fright.

One should put it as follows: Sulla was certainly brave, but he hadn't the slightest conception of courage in his soul, nor had he any such interior conception of virtue or purpose, or of a good end to things. His attribution of great significance to dreams is linked to this. One might say that for him, in any given situation, virtue simply evaporated; and his great victories, if they can be explained at all, like his victory at Signium over Marius the Younger, when Sulla lost only thirty men whereas twenty thousand were lost on the other side, seemed to come as results of chance. Similarly, for him as for children, reality disappeared at its edges and limits into dream.

After his great victories over Archelaus, Fimbria, Mithradates, and Marius the Younger, Sulla added the name FELIX—"Fortunate"—to his other names: Lucius Cornelius Sulla. Indeed, fortune was the only thing that Sulla believed in, and this was what he was always telling his friends and soldiers. He called fortune the child of Venus, mother of us all, and himself he called fortune's son. Sulla was indeed fortunate; but here again, to be accurate, we must say that Sulla was fortunate in the same way as Julius Caesar was great and Socrates or Seneca wise. Only the man who lives by fortune is in essence what he is—up to that limit where dreams begin; and only the fortunate man needs no mirror to make himself seem, to himself or to others, greater or smaller than he is, or any different. Only thus can we explain Sulla's almost childish attitude to his actions, so much admired in the centuries to come; only thus can we explain his having not the slightest internal conception of the virtue of courage, or of any other virtues, or of his own greatness, or of greatness in general. Greatness was something wholly external to himself; and that was fully consistent with the way in which he and other great men of the period regarded fortune.

One thing did sometimes preoccupy him as an anti-Platonist and negator of the world of Ideas: the language of men, their speech. He had noticed that it makes a world of difference for the human soul whether you say a thing or impose silence upon it: that speech is different from silence, and that, in this respect, words are different from things; also that the mastery or sovereignty which we exert, and the commands that we give, are rooted in this difference, occurring, as it were, in the interval between the spoken word and the unspoken word, much as fortune lives and moves between and among things.

363

On his march through Thessaly, having made peace with Mithradates, Sulla stopped for a while in Apollonia, to prepare for the sea crossing to Italy. It was here that a live satyr was brought into his tent. According to a Greek writer of the time, he was just like the satyrs portrayed by Greek sculptors: a human head with goat's ears, a human body with goat's legs. Soldiers had found the satyr sleeping on some yellow beech leaves in a gorge near the Temple of the Nymphs, an ancient shrine, and had captured him, trussed him up with rope, so that he looked, while lying on the floor of Sulla's tent, as if he'd been caught in a net like a huge fish or sea monster. But the moment the rope was untied he got free, gave everyone the slip, and ended up crouching against the wall of the tent. Crouching, he looked more like an animal than a human being, and smaller than he really was. While the people in Sulla's tent were standing around the satyr, much astonished and making a great deal of noise, one person tried to lure him away from the tent wall by offering him some fruit, which he tried to push between the satyr's lips. But nothing could induce the satyr to open his mouth. He only kept swivelling his eyes in fright: showing the white, which was very clear, like that of a freshly peeled almond, and surrounding a very dark center, like that of a human eye, looking at the people and then quickly looking away again, so that the white flashed.

When he seemed a little calmer, Sulla had him questioned, first in Greek, then in Latin, finally in the dialect spoken by fishermen and peasants in Apollonia and the coastal regions of Dyrrhacium: questions were asked about food, sleep, how he made love, if he had children or sons by the nymphs, if the nymphs had children at all and where, if there were many satyrs like him, and where they met, if he had come to the region with a troop of Pan worshipers, or with worshipers of other gods, if he had ever heard anything about the gods and their dwelling places. Since the satyr gave no answer to any of the questions, even seemed not to understand them, and since his eyes seemed unable to form any image of what was going on around him, one of Sulla's friends suggested that they should bring in one of the courtesans who were in the camp, so that she could entice him to make love and so inveigle him into making utterances that would be spontaneous, natural and appropriate to himself. This suggestion was welcomed with loud applause and laughter, and meanwhile some of the people approached the satyr more closely and began to tweak his ears, stroke the fur on his thighs, trying to tickle his little tail behind, and Metrobius, the aforementioned actor, made as if to force him to commit improper acts such as humans practise among themselves. Then, suddenly the satyr uttered a great cry, followed by other cries, equally loud, coming in bursts, a cry with many sounds mixing in it: a human cry, the bleating of a goat, the whinnying of a horse, and other sounds, so that the whole press of people suddenly scattered in terror. The soldier who had been sent to bring the courtesan had left the tent door open in his hurry. Seeing the opening, the satyr was outside with one bound of his goat's legs, an officer sped after him and had already put an arrow to his bow when Sulla grabbed his arm and drew it down, preventing him from releasing the arrow. But the satyr had vanished: everyone looked, but he was nowhere to be seen. Only the fields, pastures and woods echoed, now here, now there, with the satyr's cry; nobody could have told exactly where it was coming from; it was as if the cry had been dispersed all over the surrounding countryside. Or was the cry really not round about in the pastures and gullies and woods, but only in Sulla's ear and in his terrified soul? And did the soul of the Imperator never again lose or forget the sound of that cry, during the short time he still had to live?

Sulla was now victorious over all his enemies; tens of thousands were killed for revenge or for their properties, possessions, and money; Rome had been filled with the stench of corpses rotting in the streets, the putrid blood of murdered men was blocking the gutters and the ruts of chariot wheels. The populace was lavishly fed by Sulla for many days on end, so lavishly that the remnants were thrown into the Tiber. Bullfights were organized; there was one particular fight in which a hundred lions, sent from Africa by King Bacchus, bled to death in the arena. The dictator's triumph lasted for two days; men from the oldest families of Rome, with wreaths on their heads, had followed his triumphal chariot shouting his praises as father and savior. Sulla, whose additional name Felix, the Fortunate, had now been confirmed by senatorial decree, and was living in his villa at Puteoli. He was suffering from a terrible disease, which the ancients called the louse sickness: worms and maggots of various sizes worked their way out through the flesh, as if the body were rotting. But, in spite of these torments, up to the last moment, his two lifelong passions never left him. Indeed, it was shortly before his death that they seemed to be trying to coalesce in his soul, as if Sulla could now feel the same tickle of joy and pleasure in killing a man as in the arms of a courtesan or one of his boys. It was also at this time that the dreams, which Sulla had always got soothsayers to interpret, ceased entirely to visit him in sleep. Then, one day he discovered that the chief magistrate of Puteoli, Granius by name, had neglected to pay the taxes which he owed to the city, and was waiting until Sulla should die—everyone was living in expectation of his death. Angered by this, Sulla had the man brought before him, a strong man, with the neck of a bull, and commanded his servants to strangle him while he, Sulla, looked on, having his pleasure in the strangling and suffocating. It was done, but suddenly it was as if the cry which Granius could not utter, though so many slaves had a terrible grip on his throat, that the cry which should have come out of Granius's bull neck had entered into Sulla's throat, and he, Sulla, suddenly began to roar and bellow in bursts, meaningless noises, following one after another in quick succession, loud and meaningless and in bursts like the cry uttered by the satyr in the camp at Apollonia, and while uttering this cry Sulla broke a vein in one of his lungs and reeled and fell in a great pool of his own blood and that same night he died.

Translated by Christopher Middleton

This essay first appeared, as one of a group of "Parables of the Pagan and the Christian Soul," in Rudolf Kassner's Das Buch der Gleichnisse, *Leipzig, Insel Verlag, 1934.*

Seymour Krim

What's This Cat's Story?

After literally twenty lousy years of agonizing, poeticizing, fan-
tasying, doubting, speculating, sidestepping, I am going to try and devote
the writing time left to me to the openly and explicitly creative expression
that I always wanted to do from the age of seventeen to thirty-seven. As I
flatly say a so-long to the (to me) alien world of literary criticism and the
artificial one of the "essay" I do not know whether this new work will be
the traditional form of novel or play or a necessity-inspired homemade freak
of my own devising. Yet I do know I must bring it into being or my
seemingly tumultuous days will have been wasted (the bitterest word in the
language) in cowardly rationalizations.

367

But I had to live through two decades of the wildest confusion to
reach this point of commitment. I traveled all the byways and intellectual
traps of contemporary literary life to arrive where I should have begun—
and that is by giving everything you've got—but I hope to put the experience
of this nightmarish pilgrimage into my writing. Not hope to. I have to (and
since it is now part of me it will come out regardless) for my mess was not
unique and is almost a typical blood-specimen of my generation.

Let me start at the beginning. I began to "write" at the age of thirteen
and followed the usual pattern gone through by a dozen of my friends in

the same line. Namely writing for the high-school magazine (in my case the DeWitt Clinton *Magpie*, up in the Bronx), coediting a mimeographed literary sheet called *expression* (man, were we swingingly lower-case back in 1939!) because of the kid stuff in the official one and getting temporarily kicked out of high school for selling it in the john. Then going on to college—I deliberately followed Thomas Wolfe's big romantic boots to the University of North Carolina—and writing for the magazine there. After quitting college at the end of my first year, I returned to New York and had the usual erratic round of uptown editorial jobs: editing a Western pulp magazine, working as a snotty silly kid reporter on *The New Yorker*, ducking the war in the OWI, writing publicity for Paramount Pictures, writing the commentary for a national newsreel (a job handed to me by the stylish poet-painter Weldon Kees who is presumed to have committed suicide in San Francisco several years ago, although his body was never recovered from the Bay) and living off the advance for a novel that I never finished in the flush 1947 days when Don Congdon was giving away Simon & Schuster's money to young writers. He had come over from *Collier's* as their whiz-bang boy editor and I, plus a few of my friends, managed to get in line for the $1,200-advance-money handout.

In case you know nothing or little about how American writers live (which includes the various art-sanitariums like Yaddo and the Huntington Hartford Foundation where I and my brother pack of hungry artwolves made the free scene for wasted months at a time) the above is normal until the writer unwinds and starts turning out the novels and stories that he presumably wants to write. But I never unwound. I had natural sock as a storyteller and was precociously good at description, dialogue, and most of the other staples of the fiction-writer's trade but I was bugged by a mammoth complex of thoughts and feelings that prevented me from doing more than just diddling the surface of sustained fiction-writing. Much of this was personal; some of it was due to the highly critical (how can you write when you haven't yet read "Bartleby the Scrivener," etc?) period I came of age in; and some of it came from grave troubled doubts I had that the novel as a form had outlived its vital meaning and was being perpetuated by the dishonesty and lack of imagination of its practitioners. Taken together, all these facts finally threw me off the narrowly uncertain balance I had to begin with and sent me shuddering down the tunnels of introspection and pretentious, cosmic type thought that more or less paralyzed me for a decade;

until I ultimately vomited up my wretched life and found myself no longer even an amateur writer but a bona fide all-American 1-out-of-every-16 psychotic.

During this period of so-called paralysis—for it was that as far as the no-crapping-around, definite, creative birth of a real object was concerned—I sought out the best intellectual minds I knew and absorbed, absorbed, argued, learned, was criticized, and slowly found myself turning to literary criticism as a way of writing and thinking. Behind this choice-necessity (for I desperately needed some way to express even a little of myself and with it a mental center from which to operate), lay my painstakingly conscious effort to think through literary problems that before I had instinctively sensed with a built-in radar. But by now my self-conscious intellectual glands had become immensely swollen because of the people I hung around with and at the age of twenty-eight or so I could no more go back to my former glorious naïve conception of "the writer" than to knickers.

My most articulate friends were Jewish intellectuals (I'm Jewish but not a card-carrying intellectual) and they made me toe the ideational line like a spinster aunt going over her maid's cleaning with a white glove poised for dust. I was not permitted the excesses or romanticism I had kidded myself with before, and if life were eternal this education would be recommended by me as a must for any kind of mature achievement; but life is lived in time, time is short, and the burden of mortality is heavy, and a writer has only so much to say and should get to it without wasting his precious (to him) hours with scanning the heavens when his fly needs buttoning.

I did not know this during those days in the Village in the late 1940's, when I was part of a highly intellectual but not necessarily artistic group of brilliant minds who roved with almost illegal freedom over the entire domain of the thinkable and utterable. Some of these minds—like Isaac Rosenfeld, Dave Bazelon, Manny Farber, Weldon Kees, Willie Poster, Chandler Brossard, Anatole Broyard (with the occasional appearances of Delmore Schwartz, Saul Bellow, Alfred Kazin, James Agee), and the inimitable Milton Klonsky—were in literature partially or completely; some—like Will Barrett, Herbie Poster, Clem Greenberg—were more interested in "ideas" than expression. All of us were broadly part of the *Partisan Review* and *Commentary* worlds where ex-Trotskyites, ex-anarchists, ex-Stalinists (everybody seemed to be an ex-something) mingled with fancy Ph.D.'s and metaphysical poets to produce that contemporary eclectic monster who is as much at home with surrealist poetry as with British radical politics, with baseball and boxing (the big sport for intellectuals then) as with the foolproof technique for banging a girl. There was a tremendous charge in all this to me when I was accepted into the group and soon I was trying to graft this interstellar burst of new ideas onto that emotional-instinctual drive of my being which had originally led me to want to be a writer.

I had come from an entirely different background and self-taught tradition when I got my intellectual initiation in the late forties. I was intelligent enough but my touchstones until then had been strictly literature and, humanly enough, *American* literature (because that was what I wanted to write). But overnight it seems I became internationalized. I saw how parochial my small Hemingway-Wolfe-Dreiser-Faulkner standards were in the midst of these swinging world-dominating intellects and I was put in the impossible position of trying to write a piece of emotionally real description about some homely thing that happened to me and relate it to the interplanetary discussion I'd had the night before (tea-high, shouting, laughing, ideas zooming, then falling into Ratner's at 3 A.M. for chopped eggs-and-onions) on Kafka, Trotsky, and (yeah, my dear Klonsky!) the poetry of Marvell. This contradiction between my own limited hut of experience and the skyscrapers of new thought obviously cut deeper than just literature. Soon I was spinning like a human top as a result of this fantastic dazzle of diamond-bright gab and revelation and almost every standard I had previously thought was impregnable began to crumble the longer I looked at it. I didn't know then that this is the fascinating, tempting, delusory (I'm learning! I'm growing! I'm developing!) thruway to nowhere and that self-providential man was made to draw the line when common sense flashes its light.

II

The phantom of great European-inspired ambition drove all of us in my new group to the most miserable heights and voids of despair, like Hitlers in our own warped little Berchtesgartens. The reader shouldn't forget that the casual small talk of the people I greedily learned from was Kierkegaard, Kafka, Melville, Blake, Lawrence (Joyce was considered a misguided second-rater) and with such standards running wild and demonic in our lusting heads there can be little wonder that some of us cracked under the intense pressure we placed on ourselves or perished (perhaps there is no direct provable connection but the deaths included Isaac Rosenfeld, the very well-thought-of Bob Warshow, my editor at *Commentary*, James Agee, Kees' and just recently his good friend Willie Poster's suicide) or sucked nightly on Christ's vinegar sponge because we could never attain the impossible.

Driven by this illusion of great power and omniscience—getting daily more intoxicated by handling the tools of thought which made mincemeat out of famous names admired by the square public—I aggressively moved over the line into book-reviewing. Marjorie Farber, a peripheral member of our group and then an assistant editor of *The New York Times Book Review*, eased me into the Sunday section in 1947 and I showed off in print like a cramped colt led onto a fast track. I was never completely at home in book-reviewing and literary criticism during my twelve years doing this kind of writing (although I think I brought to certain novelists the insight that could only come from a constipated brother) but it became a dreadful ego-habit. Having tasted the blood of print I couldn't stop; criticism was very much in the air, was hip, impressive, the sign of rank; fiction was for brainless impressionists (thus ran my snobbery) and even though I felt split about reviewing from the start and kept telling myself it was only a temporary filler, the drug of seeing my glistening thoughts in print hooked me and I didn't have the courage to stop.

371

I felt I had to keep writing for publication (you've got to be printed no matter what or how!) while I sweated out the private war of trying to reach a unity between my experience and the murderously suggestive new ideas that were being fired at me and even beginning to shoot up of their own accord in my head. My dream was to make peace finally between my imagination-experience and these radical ideas, and out of this come forth with a high art of my own making which would combine the sensuousness of great literary style with the startlingness of an unprecedented approach. It would come, it would come—I *knew* it (in my blindness). Meanwhile reviewing was the only way I could almost consistently get printed, although later on I was to experience my share of rejections as neurotic and status-conscious editors began to torture themselves into regarding reviews as finely wrought poems! This made and makes reviewers overwrite and overstrain their case to glitter more than the competition and I too was to be such a shameless performer after getting my lumps. Even in noncommercial writing one learns to sell out!

But at this point I moved on to *The Commonweal* because they then had a tolerant and sympathetic book editor named Bill Clancy, who sensed I was not a native or orthodox critic but nevertheless brought out of me some of the best I could do because he had a taste for fullness of expression rather than the narrower, stricter conception of criticism then at its height (more or less going back to Eliot and made into a very subtle instrument by the scholarly Blackmurs, Tates, Ransoms, Trillings, and so forth). Along with *The Commonweal* I began to hit *Commentary* and had one small piece in *Partisan Review*—both places then giving the avant young writer the most superior feelings of having made it for keeps when actually he was aping his elders' manner in most cases and being dishonest to himself and his own generation in the way he expressed himself.

I was never comfortable at *Commentary*, which I felt then (and feel to a large extent today) could be no true ally of literature because it had to watch its step like a nearsighted cripple with asthma as far as what it published; it is sponsored by and beholden to the American Jewish Committee and tried to navigate a course between the impossibles of freedom and a cautious, worrying, in-groupy conception of "responsibility" (translation: the current line of the New York radical-highbrow corporation, which loves to be pretentiously eloquent about avant-garde heroes after they're dead and helps freeze them out when alive because their black charm never fits the latest abstract recipe for profundity). Even writing for a Roman Catholic magazine like *The Commonweal*, I literally had much more freedom of expression than in *Commentary*, where I and a number of writers I know had their most alive thoughts squeezed into gray sentences of qualification, humorlessness—overedited, unoriginal, because of the staff's tiptoeing fear of making a booboo. It took the heart out of a young American-Jewish writer to do a piece for them—the ton of worry that preyed on you when you sat down to the machine made sunny days automatically gloom-ridden—and the eventual non-you solidity that could finally be wrung out after six rewritings by knowing their Teutonic idea of a distinguished piece of work was not compensated for by the crucifixion of self and the joylessness of the labor. It was truly immoral to the whole act of writing.

Commentary, taking its cues from the universities and the various respectable academic and/or ex-radical pros like Richard Chase, the Trillings,

William Phillips, Leslie Fiedler, Dwight Macdonald, became a suburb of *PR* in literary evaluation and both magazines were rigid with fear, with *reactionary* what-will-T. S.-Eliot-or-Martin Buber-think? as far as the natural roaring young independent went. I feel sorry (premature as it may read to some who feel only the competitive sweat and panting breath of the race) for the hotshot young critics today like my friend Podhoretz, Steven Marcus, the various smoothie sons of the older literary generation who were taken in or foolishly slicked their way into the smart-money fold. Unless they chafe now and discover their own style, thoughts, even magazines, they will not speak to me or for me in the stupendous days of the future that lie ahead. And it will be our mutual loss for we are of the same generation and face the same problems as their benefactors do not.

As for the influence of *Partisan Review* on American writing during this time in which I was trying to establish myself ass-backwards, I will say little—an entire book is needed from one of its actual martyrs. It has lost its impact today for the whole beat shock-troop of young expressers as historically it had to and humanly it was fated to while it tried to span the world at the fantastic cost of patronizing (not caring enough, being too snob-clannish, overcerebral, Europeanish, aristocratically alienated) its own country and the terrific reality of our life here. On the mere factual level it led more writers to disappointment—overevaluation of themselves, illusion, smugness, fancying they were extraordinary philosophers or prophets when they were just ultrasensitive Americans who didn't always write well in their own language—than it ever saved or gave a point of view to. But was the creation of a monstrous historical period wherein it thought it had to synthesize literature and politics and avant-garde art of every kind with its writers crazily trying to outdo each other in Spenglerian inclusiveness of vision, like the Olympics. Yet obviously it printed many significant things and there was no place quite like it; and in my circle it was a hip badge of prestige and real in-ness to appear in its consciously big-gun pages. For people of my age and bent however the whole *PR* phenomenon along with the *Kenyon Review*, the *Sewanee*, the *Hudson* (to be discussed more closely), and all the others unfertilized into being by the Anglo-Protestant New Critical chill was a very bad, inhibiting, distorting, freakish influence. These magazines made us ashamed to be what we were and the cruel acid of their unreal standards tore through our writing and scarred our lives as well; in our prose we had to put on Englishy airs, affect all sorts of impressive scholarship and social-register unnaturalness, and in general contort ourselves into literary pretzels in order to slip through their narrow transoms and get into their pages. Sometimes I got the impression that the editors wanted to relax the entire torture-chamber that literature had become but didn't know where to begin. Whether I was right or wrong this masquerade prevented direct writing for most of the sweating muscle-bound contributors and became a weighty suspicious bore for the normally intelligent reader who couldn't rationalize it the way the insiders did.

By now as far as my so-called career was going in my late twenties and early thirties, I was publishing an occasional short story but gaining a small steady reputation as a good critic—not a brilliant textual beagle or a Coleridgean literature-shaker but unanonymous enough for a few party-met strangers to know my name and work. In spite of the kick in this I hated the critical reputation (a kid in the White Horse tavern one night actually shouted out in a beer-voice that "Krim is one of the best critics in America" and even though I knew this was drunken bar-talk I cringed inside and suddenly felt that my very goddamn being was a sham) because I knew it was horribly unfair to my truer, realer, imaginative bounce as a writer. What I didn't know was that each time I dug into myself to try and write an "important" piece of criticism I was committing myself to impossibly high standards that made me feel less than ever like giving out with my own untested jazz. I was weekly and monthly mutilating the best part of myself, setting up endless self-defeating dialogues and fancy but illogical rationalizations within, squirming always in the pain and defensiveness that goes with cheating the self of what it really wants—and all for the perverted boot of being a small name on the scene and keeping my hand in the pussy of petty success no matter what. Seen coolly, it was disgusting self-murder but there was no one to tell me this because almost all of my friends were caught up in the same narrow pocket, becoming increasingly exacting, fussy, competitive, narrow-minded, and less human in their writing and standards.

374

III

I should have gotten out of criticism, said to hell with it, but one turned scared at the thought because where could you go? Until the beats came along and revived through mere power and abandonment and the unwillingness to commit death in life some idea of a decent equivalent between verbal expression and actual experience, the "serious" New York literary scene was becoming a prison, to the point of shutting off the real, gamy, lowdown communication that must go into writing if it's to have even as much meaning as the telephone. But such obvious realism was of no interest to me then. I was hooked in the life, as hustlers say, and even though I knew it was fundamentally wrong for me I felt I had to follow it through until my creative work "matured" (illusion! perfumed bullshit!) and swept me off the bed of nails that criticism had become.

I was afraid to quit because then I would have nothing except the crumbs of the very few short stories I had managed to grind out. Thus I graduated to *The Hudson Review*, the very latest and coolest and technicalest of the swank highbrow quarterlies. My editor was Fred Morgan, Park Avenue and Princeton, and even though the money-family thing is not one of my euphorias I strutted a little within to find myself in such *Fortune*-acknowledged (the name, the loot, the leatherbinding-monogrammed-cocktail-glass montage) company and able to hold my own. On the cover of the *Hudson* were the names that impressed all of us (Yvor Winters, R. P. Blackmur, Ezra Pound, Robert Graves, Wallace Stevens) and I was now to be among them. So I punished myself to produce a couple of critiques that whatever their merit had no relationship in the pain of composition to what I could have said given the encouragement to loosen up, be real, fail richly rather than succeed as a miser and tightrope-walker. I succeeded and became one of the *Hudson's* second-string boys until I lost favor, but in so doing I again made a cramped miniature of my spirit, chorus-lined my self-respect, tidied up my originality, emasculated my real iconoclasm. I was sucking the sugar-tit of local snob success and didn't want to let go for nothing, dad, not even for the cry of perplexity and sadness that came up from the being of the man who had once wanted to be a big stubborn writer in the grand tradition that laid waste to crap and lying everywhere.

Fred Morgan, co-founder and editor of *The Hudson Review*, was and is a formal decent guy (approximately my own age) particularly so in view of the heavy-moneyed life he had to duel with to find a way of his own; but his allegiance to his near literary fathers—Blackmur, John Crowe Ransom, Eliot, Pound, the whole overstudied list of recent saints who are not guides for today and should never have been sanctified since literature is no church—made him uneasy among the very equals in age and experience whom he should have embraced in his magazine. The young need the young more than they need the old and honored; great writers take care of themselves and don't need monuments and schools since their influence is always present; but the brilliant kid writer can be crushed or turned into a foolish acrobat unless he gets an enthusiastic response from his own *contemporaries*, not elders whom he has sensible mixed feelings about no matter how generous they are. Love your own kind and the love and faith of even your enemies will eventually come to you! But if you choose instead to rely on the judgment and values of another generation as I think Morgan did—out of caution and overrespect and measuring his qualities against theirs as if they were the standard—you will inhibit your most vital contemporaries and get their most studied show-off writing, not their best. An editor's spiritual job (and I have had two excellent ones, Bill Clancy and Jerry Tallmer of *The Village Voice*) is to inspire the writer to top himself with each new effort and this is done by the writer's knowing the editor has complete confidence in him. An editor who has no confidence in a writer should tell him so very early in the relationship so that both can relax. Tact in this very close business is less important than faith and eventually degenerates into hostility and an insecurity that ruins the writer's relationship to his work: show the writer you are completely behind him or very early in this tight intimacy have the courage to be frank. But all of this implies a security of belief and a personal four-squareness (or four-hipness) which in this time of upset and ambiguity and daily reversals of personality is uncommon.

In this way did I fitfully work, masochistically and unjustly spending whatever was precious within me on criticism—I'll show these intellectual pacesetters I can lick them at their own game!—when I wanted desperately to return to the rollercoaster of open creativity. But, went my inner monologue, what *is* creativity in this time? Semantically the word means "to bring into being, to cause to exist." Didn't an insight—ah how we loved insights and illuminations in my old gang!—bring a new thought into being, wasn't a thought a window into reality, and didn't ever new truths about this vast clutch called existence mean that you were doing the holiest work you could? It was not only thinking like that which kept me and mine ("I write criticism like hammered steel," one poet who wrote comparatively little poetry told me proudly) chained to critical-analytical prose; it was truly a passionate sense of *intellectual superiority*, a fanatical personal pride that used the mind and its accomplishments as the test for true aristocracy in the modern world.

I formerly had believed in the aristocracy of fiction; but in this community of hip intellectuals I was justly in their eyes a naïf. I reformed to my ultimate personal unhappiness. I fell in stride, saw or tried mightily to see a more subtle and extensive creativity in criticism, shaped and directed my protesting mind into abstract ideas and became another of the young avant-garde gigolos who moved with patent-leather nonchalance from French symbolist poetry to existentialism to psychiatry to—you name it.

I had become a truly contemporary intellectual in the eyes of my pleased older friends, which meant in the scheme of values implicitly held by all of us a suave master-speaker (and theoretically thinker) in practically all literary and ideological areas. In simple actuality I didn't have the formal training for this glib seasoned role nor could 99 per cent of my friends have had as much background as they would have needed; yet when we picked up a copy of *PR* and saw (or wrote!) an essay on Toynbee next to one on Wallace Stevens, followed by one of Robert Lowell's obscure early poems wedged against an article comparing Einstein to Picasso, it was necessary to keep up, both to oneself and the killing standards of the super-intellectual community, by patiently tackling and trying to understand each of these offerings. I drove my mind to inhuman lengths to absorb and make mine each different intellectual challenge until I later sounded and sometimes wrote like a bastard encyclopedia. In the meantime my brain had the impossible task of trying to integrate this deluge of suggestive, sometimes profound thought with my personal experience and the vivid fantasy-life of the potential novelist. Because I was stubborn I kept adding the one on top of the other without restraint until I too thought I carried the entire world in my head and felt that I was the living embodiment of the contemporary god-writer, the omniscient one, the heir of all the ages and the true king of the present— out of my way slobs!

I now come to an unpopular topic but one that has to be opened up. Most of my friends and I were Jewish; we were also literary; the combination of the Jewish intellectual tradition and the sensibility needed to be a writer created in my circle the most potent and incredible intellectual-literary ambition I have ever seen or could ever have imagined. Within themselves, just as people, my friends were often tortured and unappeasably bitter about being the offspring of this unhappily unique-ingrown-screwed up breed; their reading and thinking gave extension to their normal blushes about appearing "Jewish" in subway, bus, racetrack, movie house, any of the public places

377

that used to make the Jew of my generation self-conscious (heavy thinkers walking across Seventh Avenue without their glasses on, willing to dare the trucks as long as they didn't look like the ikey-kikey caricature of the Yiddish intellectual); thus the simple fact of being Jewish when fused to the literary imagination gave a height and fantastic urge to our minds which in many cases outran reason. I may be reducing the many causes for this terrible display of intellectual egomania to an oversimple basic cause—for surely the overworshipped genius-standards of the literary and artistic climate as a whole goosed the entire phenomenon—but if I can generalize on the basis of my own experience it was the nagging ceaseless knowledge of knowing you could never erase the brand of being chosen to the classic outsider's role that drove us mentally upward without rest.

We were Americans who loved our country and its experience (being writers, who thrive on the real), but we were also Jews who because of Christian society's traditional suspicion and our own heartbreaking self-awareness became almost *fanatical* within ourselves to try and triumph over this blotch of birth by transcending it in brilliant individualism. It was an immodesty born of existential necessity if you will, and it was reinforced (as I've said) by the constant references in the conversation of my group, in *PR*, in *Commentary*, and the other reviews to none but the highest figures in Western literature, art, and thought. When I re-live it in my mind now it seems like a hallucination. But it was a specifically real personal and cultural phenomenon; and it is being carried on to this very day in determinedly intellectual quarters that seem ultra responsible from without but in fact are crippling natural genuine expression by their cruelly pretentious standards—born in this case out of the soul-pain of a hooked beak and a dead uncaring Jewish god who left the mess stamped on our face and beings and neurotically spread from there into huge defense-plants of fierce intellectualization that use the name of reason but not its pure spirit.

IV

It is ironic that what was once an unquestioned good—such as the stubbornly highbrow magazines printing nothing but the best, most honest, most imaginative non-commercial literature and criticism—became a king-sized disaster. It encouraged (not fulfillment of writing ability on the just level that the writer had in him) a competition with the past and the cultural heroes of the present which put inhuman pressures on the vulnerable young life-giver. If he couldn't be "great" in the sense of those spiritual movie-stars Eliot, Yeats, Proust, Kafka (the chief figure in my group), he felt like a failure in the airless climate in which we all sweated and squirmed. I knew gifted, fresh, swinging writers who told me in moments of confidence that they knew they weren't "major" and their voices were futile with bitterness when they confessed this supposed Big Secret; as if the personal horn each could blow was meaningless because history wasn't going to faint over them. (History, the god of my grotesque apprenticeship, the holy mirror of our me-worshipping egos which made monomaniacal animals out of essentially decent men—I'm not kidding!) I found in my group that this sense of measuring yourself against history prevented the most loaded talents from opening up and developing as only the practicing writer can—by publishing and exposing work to other *human beings*, the so-called public. The self-deceiving snob-god of "genius," reinforced, as I've said, by obsessive references only to the giants of literature and thought, grew like a tumor in the minds of myself and my friends until we carried it like hospital cases. In most cases including my own it prevented the writer from penetrating his own *special vein* of material, developing his own point of view, becoming adult and realistic about the tangible earthly tricks of his craft. Much of this fundamental understructure of writing was snottily put down and dismissed next to the tremendous ego-thrilling zoom of salting one's work with great or hidden meaning, Atlas-like trying to lift the most pedestrian and shabbiest material to a religious or epical height.

379

I can't stress strongly enough the insecurity that was pounded into the naturally talented writer with a feeling for people and story and good dialogue by such a scripture-quoting, perfectionist environment as the one I both wrote for and lived in. To be profound was not only a value in this world (the only one worthwhile) it was almost a necessary card of admission; it was as if a person who had the wit to be intelligent should realize that the age demanded nothing less than genius as the bare minimum and good taste itself required brilliance. As I look back on it from the vantage-point of what I have since been through, it seems that our demands on life itself had gotten dementedly out of hand, for even a half dozen of the most original works of this century—which my group did not and will not produce—could not have justified the height of our arrogance or the depth of our frustration caused by this sleepless mental anguish (like a drill on a NY street) to produce monsterpieces that would stun the universe and immortalize ourselves. The conceit of man, I have reason to know, is boundless. A willful ignorance about the limits of being alive plus a farfetched intellectual ambition—encouraged by our special literary organs who with each issue poured salt on the bitter wound that Man wasn't yet God, what a drag!—helped cook more lives and work during this period (1947–1957) than it ever exalted or inspired. The brutal fact is that it uninspired, depleted, broke down, sterilized, and pissed upon the very work it was supposed to encourage with its priestlike airs.

What had happened was that each outstanding single achievement of the immediate past—by a D. H. Lawrence, Picasso, Stravinsky, Hopkins, Melville (yes, the indoor ballplayers' Hall of Fame all over again)—was linked with the other to create a vocabulary of modernity; familiarity with great work was as casually expected of a person as familiarity with the daily paper; and this stitching together of luminosity provided the background for conversation, friendships, feuds, affairs, with such things as status in a living room or victory in argument being in large part dependent on one's immer-

sion in the new Hip Bible of greatness. In other words, these genuine achievements were turned into serviceability which took the form of coming out of the mouth at gatherings where it was used as a weapon for personal advantage by highly articulate and severely critical minds. And in this arena I nursed my private dreams of writing—not talking. Yet verbal aggressiveness, mental agility in conversation, knowledge and insight as shown by the deftness with which they sprang to the lips were actually much more valued among my friends than homegrown *literary* originality, which took grubby hard work and had to be done in private without glitter. The stuttering crudenik who couldn't make a show in public and didn't fathom or like Kafka—but who had a small, hard, true American imagination of his own sans the big-city timetable of Who's Who in World Culture—would have been slaughtered if he stuck his head in a jumping Village cellar apartment where my teachers and I mapped and re-mapped the universe by the second.

To make an enormously charged, complicated, tragic long story shorter, let me merely say that mine was as severe a critical-intellectual environment as can be imagined and being without true shape or definition as a writer (except for the stubborn urge to force a unity between my personal experience and these new dimensions of abstract thought) I was strongly influenced by my friends. I did not develop my story-telling abilities—in fact they began to seem, as I've said, simple-minded to me—and got in ever deeper into the speculative manipulation of ideas for their own jewel-like sake. In the meantime, in the tossing hours before sleeping so to speak, I would torment myself with those vain attempts to make a bridge between my newly found critical hipness and the emotional material that was begging for release and could only get out by smuggling its way into my criticism. If I had been more restrained in my own ambition and more sure of the worth of what I had to communicate as a mere human-type writer I would have been less knotted and uncertain about what to do. But all of the minds I most respected were almost without exception (one was the prose artist Michael Seide, not a member of my "group") as omnivorous in their intellectual greed and no one ever bothered to take me aside and say: "Why not be truly original, Krim, by cultivating your own natural garden and doing some catchy limited work that is your just inheritance and is right there under your nose."

It wasn't until I was thirty-three and had to scream my way to the inevitable climax of all the foregoing inner wrestling, doubt, confusion, backtracking, fantastic imprisonment of the me-self dying for release—not until I spewed up every hunk of foreign matter in my psyche and bloodily broke through to my own raw meat via the whistling rocket-ride of what is called insanity—that I began to think for myself because I had to. Baby, this wasn't any bullshit about beautiful words and dream-masterpieces any more—this was life and death and all that cellar-deep jazz! It was difficult to swallow the fact that I would probably not be a great writer because not only had I envisioned (in fact known) that this would eventually come true, a few people had even used the magic word during my twenties and I graciously took it in stride. It was just a question of time I then thought, and in the meantime T was ticking away and I was caught in the same vapor of twists and doubts that I'd been in since my early twenties: imagining a revolutionary prose in my mind while sweating over criticism for my ego's kicks. But when I almost threw the switch during the suicidal depression that followed my "breakdown" or, more truthfully, the massive mutiny against my living lie—then pulled myself out of it cliffhanger-style—it seemed stupid from that time onward to revert to the hypocrisy of keeping up an act as far as writing went. The criticism I did after this was much more straight and finally led to the series of uneven but definitely more

381

initiative-taking articles which I did for *The Village Voice* (1957–1959) and *Exodus* (1959–1960). The coverup of a stilted conception of writing is always ripped by the iron hairs on the dogged face of life.

V

I stand now at the end of any pretense with formal literary criticism (even if broke in pocket and adulation and blocked on my own road) but I will carry with me always the infection with abstract ideas that no one in my environment escaped. When I feel over-extended and almost drowning in the sea of speculative thought—hangover from endless nights spinning the world with my brother-gods in the most brilliant untaped talk of the century—and know I must call a halt for my own psychic preservation, then does the common sense of Gertrude Stein's shrewd remark (disregard her quaint egotism) strike home every time:

> *I know that one of the most profoundly exciting moments of my life was when at about 16 I suddenly concluded that I would not make all knowledge my province.*

But this kind of focused chastity can only be a pastoral memory for me and mine—the seeds of oceanic thought were sewn too beautifully in the ripest season and we must struggle with the bastard harvest in our heads. It is too late to duck the responsibility for what we so superhumanly craved; to wipe out the engrams grooved in our brains would need a Frankenstein-type operation. We became what we admired in that joke of jokes always heaped on sinners who now crave a leaner diet. Yet should such a communication as this be dug up in a future period I would insist that the reader try and appreciate how extravagant the whole conception of making volume-long footnotes to the writings of others became, how superior to the unclothed novelist or poet, the cunning super-intellectual critic normally felt because of his safe armchair perspective (*sub specie aeternitatis* my ass—he was wielding power and making the law). It was a period and still is in some dated quarters where the *display* of Mind—disembodied from its blistered feet, overloaded, intoning a language unlike the language of life—deballed the value of imagination and offbeatness and, found it "juvenile" or "irrational" because it met no preconceptions now that literature had become a science. The neatly articulate became a convenient mother to hold onto because of the threat of the unknown in a time that was subterraneanly groaning in labor; university-groomed goodygoodies clutched their rehearsed, Eliot-stamped script with self-satisfaction and coolly called it reason, sense, sanity, at the very moment that its snotty repressiveness was driving many unknown souls to mental suicide or murder; and those of us who finally rebelled and refused to punish our beings any longer in imitation of this iceberg version of truth became ultimately what we had always secretly wanted to be— individuals thrown back on our own clumsy resources, free to err, live, die, speak the truth or a half-truth or a lie, but free, free, free!

My style as a man and writer was shaped by the prevailing superior tone of this strangling decade that I now condemn. Even the wide-open creative work that I hope to do will never entirely shake off the odor of condescension and literary verbalism that was the norm in my circle. But I cannot hide a small penny of satisfaction at the lesson which reality has taught or at least offered to my peers who defied it. What ultimately happened was that their emphasis on rare theoretical intelligence lost its value under the impact of life itself; men and women who had trained themselves to be profound (peculiar as such a statement sounds it was true, and monstrous when you stop to think about it) found in later years that they did this at the sacrifice of their total personalities and had overevaluated the *PR* style of symphonic thinking to their final literary frustration and personal unhappiness. Real life as it is lived in this time must inevitably flood in upon those who would short-change it and *all* of us from my group have been justly lowered in our appreciation of ourselves and—if my experience is any judge—more respectful of the power of brute 1960 reality than in its flash intellectual transcendence. If extreme cerebration was part of the mental manners of my period, one still shouldn't forget that a needy and sometimes adolescent romanticism was hidden beneath this fascinating agility with ideas; the desperate and often simple needs of the being went on as they always do, under and quite disproportionate to the big ideas that were borne aloft on the fuel of maniacal frustration-ambition. I found in myself that I gave mental size to emotions that in themselves weren't worth such fuss, out of a need and desire to impress my scene with the image of my worth— converting bits of trivia into big-sounding phrases that used our mutual vocabulary and therefore were kosher no matter how intrinsically minor or

383

childish the emotion was in itself. I'm positive my friends were guilty of the same distortion to some extent.

The path ahead is hardly an easy one for me now. Nor would it be for anyone who came from the intellectual-literary climate that trained me or had for years (as I did) judged and fantasied himself in the platinum currency of literary greatness that was tossed around like nickels by my genius-intoxicated friends and the magazines we wrote for. In a real way—assuming I had the choice, which I don't—it is not "greatness" that I want now; my heart and mind are tired of the inhuman selfishness and egomania that I associate with its self-conscious quest. In itself it has lost its meaning for me, completely unlike what I would have imagined ten or even five years ago. I realize of course that the choice is ultimately nature's and not one's own but having lived among superlatives for so long, I am weary of pursuing what is not natural.

The writing I want to do now is inspired by the pertinent, the immediate, the actual of this very minute; that would be sufficient greatness for me if I can give it full voice. My longtime secret dream of a consciously heroic style and attitude towards American experience which I envisoned as being

legendarily all-inclusive and Proustian-Whitmanesque (a conception of mine for one monumental grand work which I lovingly nursed through the years when I was chewing stones) has been ground down by the steel heel of present-day necessity into a more immediate goal and I am grateful now to be given a second chance to gun out some leveler messages about reality. I believe my imagination is still my most unique possession as a writer and I want to use it to its uttermost to make such statements about the life of my time as I am particularly geared to do. The critical form which I forced myself to approximate over the years has left its cast on my mind for good, but I have learned or am learning how to cut its magisterial bondage to "judiciousness" and "responsibility"—believe me there is deeper responsibility in the human soul than playing supreme-court justice, and that is to make the life that others can judge!—and use whatever organizational, reasonable, analytic powers it encouraged as the mere mucilage to hold living thoughts together. I remember the ironic inner laugh I had recently when a good but literarily unsophisticated friend of mine defined me to my face as a "Jewish intellectual" rather than a Jewish *writer*—the brand has probably taken permanently in spite of all my protests and the attempt I have made here to show the way in which my innocence was raped (willingly) by the obviousness of intellect instead of the subtlety of soul. We violate ourselves ultimately and much as I can point factually to the historical period that worshipped abstract sky-writing and lured me into imitating its ways (I thank stubbornness my voice had its own concrete human sound at times), it was the mush of my own being that permitted this plastic surgery in the image of what was outwardly impressive.

I can only trust now to remake myself as a writer in the light of the truths that I can clearly see are *mine*, won by experience and temperament and personal vision, without forcing myself to engorge the thoughts of a thousand other minds or mind-binding myself in the suicide of absolute perfection. There has always been a place in writing for candor and frankness, for conscience-freeing personal honesty, which I would like to extend with my actual American experience. (Whitman, Dreiser, James T. Farrell, and Henry Miller have already hewed this most marvelous trail over here but it can be taken into exciting new country). There is a higher one for the birth of unexpected new truths based on this same ruthless love for what is. I am now committed to trying to combine the two, to creating a people-participating living experience about our mutual lives with my certainty that the foundation at least is real because it has been lived and not merely engineered to make a career for myself.

385

But all this assumes there is time. And yet time is just what I don't have, what is an uncertainty, what becomes more uncertain with each day. The years that have been wasted in living for the future, when the great work would come and one would just have to transcribe it, are never to be recovered; it is a bitter thought but one that I and my equally grandiose friends will pay for with increasing remorse as "The September Song" plays on the jukebox in the background. The trivial literary deeds (shreds of stories, memoir, unsatisfying critiques, a painful few overworked poems) that were to be a prelude to chords unheard on earth before may be all that many of us will have to show when the time comes for us to justify our presumption. My tears—both for myself and my brilliant friends—must turn to ice however when I contrast our ease of opportunity with the struggles of the men we quoted and the oceans of spirit we squandered in vanity that called itself by other names: exploration, speculation, experimentation, High Art. That time is dead! We killed it! It can only return in the immense concentration of all this lost mortality that one of us can get into his work and unlike what I once would have proudly hissed out, that person is not likely to be myself; and even if this past is recaptured or justified in words of "eternal life" can they compensate for the waste that the rest of us squatted in while competing with God? I saw what I used to think was the cream of a generation get increasingly sour because they theorized more than they worked, criticized more than they praised, and not only demanded but accused life for not giving them the key to the universe—with the tacit encouragement of their unrealistic elders who flicked off a Thomas Wolfe for being a greedy romantic and could tell you in a flash what *hubris* meant but who sinned quite as much as Wolfe. Not in the bad-boy area of sensuous excess but in the much more arrogant and sinister and fatal realm of mind where vices are perpetrated that make those of the appetite mere child's play.

I must end this unburdening of my being with some simple logic. The world and living are obviously much more difficult than they appear and ask by their very nature for our respectful intelligence and full humanity; if we don't give it, the just knights of retribution squeeze it from us when we are begging on our knees and all the literature we mouthed so fancily degenerates into a few humble words. What I am trying to say is that my period and its spokesmen used too many words to say too few things that matter today in each daily twenty-four hours in which you and I are spending our ultimate mortalities. Theirs was the elaborate rhetoric of ideas but when in time of crisis one went to grasp them for *human* use there was nothing specific and tangible in the hand. I resent as a person as well as a writer having been misled by such a self-absorbed, removed, Radio City Music Hall intellectual exhibition that failed to direct its statements to each very real individual who comprised its audience; or as Tolstoy might have said with the simple nerve of truth, what good was it? It is no longer enough in my opinion to deal in brain-seductive abstractions that are not directly related to the people who eagerly read you and take seriously what you say. Published writing is becomingly increasingly a crucial public act in our stripped down, pressurized environment and its immediate goal should be to penetrate like a bullet the mind and emotions of each contemporary who reads it. This is basic in a time when people are hungry and desperate for straightforward communication about the life we are all leading in common; inflated or overarticulated theory becomes a smug amateurish luxury under the hammer of the world we live in when tomorrow might be your or my last day.

I was confused and torn apart by the amount of material I was expected to absorb reading the more abstruse literary quarterlies—I who wrote for them!—and if this was true for a professional avant-garde writer like myself what can one say about the bewilderment, the lack of human time to pit against the elaborate obscurity of much of the work (was it worth it in the mortal countdown?), the absence of everyday experiential clues, the feeling of being a failure unto self of the unprofessional reader who wanted to know and experience this "apex" of modern communication but most often felt shut out in the cold? Literature is not worth the suffocation of life and the unnecessary alienation of your public if you have any respect for being alive yourself; it can't possibly be superior to existence and yet we often wrote about it as if it were exclusive of its human source. No single person can waft aside the chain of history and what I have described in these pages is now a historical accomplishment, with the overtones of the highbrow era being filtered down to thousands of college students throughout the US who read the magazines I used to write for and think the thoughts I used to flatter myself with and who will soon begin the same tortuous journey as myself if they want to be "serious" literary intellectuals and writers. No, we cannot dispose of history; but we can change it by a recognition of where it has led us. In fact change only occurs I believe when we stand against the last wall and realize that there is no place to go except in a completely different direction. By the value of one man's life to himself and his conviction that others must feel comparably, he has said goodbye don't bother getting up I can find the door myself.

Saul Bellow

Ralph Ellison in Tivoli

Some forty years ago I came into a small legacy and with it I bought a house in Tivoli, New York. "House" is not the word for it; it was, or once had been, a Hudson River mansion. It had a Dutch cellar kitchen of flagstones and a kitchen fireplace. There was a dumb-waiter to the vanished dining room above. The first floor had a ballroom but according to my informants, Tivoli's townspeople, no one had danced in it for eighty years. Tivoli had been the birthplace of Eleanor Roosevelt. The villagers were the descendants of the servants and grounds-keepers of the Dutchess County aristocrats.

I shan't be going into the social history of the township or the county. There were great names in the vicinity—the Livingstones, the Chapmans and the Roosevelts, but I didn't know much about them. I had sunk my $16,000 legacy into a decaying mansion. To repair the roof and to put in new plumbing, I drew an advance of $10,000 from the Viking Press to write a novel called *Henderson the Rain King*.

There was a furnace of sorts and a warm-air system that took the moisture out of your nostrils. I was too busy with *Henderson* and with my then wife to take full notice of my surroundings. The times were revolutionary—I refer to the sexual revolution. Marriages were lamentably unstable and unserious. My wife, tired of life with me in the gloomy house, packed her bags and moved to Brooklyn.

I was naturally wretched about this. I now found the solitude (and the decay of the house) insupportable. Determined to save my $16,000, I threw myself into the work of salvage. I painted the kitchen walls and the bedrooms, as much for therapeutic reasons as to improve the property.

Then Ralph Ellison, who was teaching at Bard College, accepted my invitation to move in. I have always believed that this was an act of charity on his part.

We had known each other in Manhattan. I had reviewed *Invisible Man* for *Commentary*. I was aware that it was an extremely important novel and that, in what he did, Ralph had no rivals. What he did no one else could do—a glorious piece of good fortune for a writer.

Both of us at one time had lived on Riverside Drive. We met often and walked together in the park, along the Hudson. There we discussed all kinds of questions and exchanged personal histories. I was greatly taken with Ellison, struck by the strength and independence of his mind. We discussed Richard Wright, Faulkner and Hemingway. Ralph, it was clear, had thought things through for himself, and his ideas had little in common with the views of the critics in the literary quarterlies. Neither he nor I could accept the categories prepared for us by literary journalists. He was an American writer who was black. I was a Jew and an American and a writer, and I believed that by being described as a "Jewish writer" I was being shunted to a siding. This taxonomy business I saw as an exclusionary device. Ellison had similar objections to classification. From his side, he saw the Negro as one of the creators of America's history and culture.

That was okay with me. We found each other sympathetic. We got along splendidly and went fishing together for striped bass in Long Island Sound.

Ralph drove into Tivoli in his huge old Chrysler. He himself serviced it, coddled it, tuned it, and it ran as smoothly as it had when it came off the assembly line. The trunk, when it was opened, gave me my first hint of Ralph's powers of organization. For hunting there were guns, there were decoy ducks; for fishing, rods, lures and a wicker-work creel; there were tools of every description. Ralph was able to repair radios and hi-fi equipment. I envied him his esoteric technical skills. Where I saw a frightening jumble of

390

tubes, dials, condensers (I can't even name the parts), he saw order. In my trunk I carried the spare wheel, the Jack, a few rusty tire irons, rags and brown paper bags from the market. His trunk with its tools and weapons announced that he was prepared for any emergency, could meet every challenge to his autonomy.

He did not come alone. He was accompanied by a young black Labrador retriever who jumped from the Chrysler, eager to play, pawing my chest. Ralph had bought the dog from John Cheever, who was then, briefly, a breeder of black Labs.

The ballroom now became Ralph's studio. It ran the entire length of the house. He set up his typewriter and his desk and we found a book case for his manuscripts. You couldn't see the Hudson from the ground floor. Instead you had the Catskills to look at.

In the ballroom, Ralph kept African violets which he watered with a turkey baster. It was from him that I learned all that I know about house-plants.

But the important thing was that the gloomy house was no longer empty—no longer gloomy. All day long I heard the humming of his electric typewriter. Its long rhythms made me feel that we were on a cruise ship moving through the woods—the pines and the locust trees, the huge hay fields plowed, planted and harvested by Chanler Chapman. Chanler, before I could be aware of it, became Henderson the Rain King. He drove his tractor like a real king, knocking over fences, breaking stone walls and pulling up boundary-markers.

Ralph and I brought the house under civilized control.

He came down to get his breakfast in a striped heavy Moroccan garment. He wore slippers with a large oriental curve at the toe. He was a very handsome man. A noteworthy person, solid, symmetrical and dignified but with a taste for finery. Ralph was never anything but well-dressed, and he liked clothes of an Ivy League cut. In the days before everybody had elected to go bareheaded, he wore what used to be called a porkpie hat of very fine felt. By comparison, I was a stumble bum. He put on his carefully chosen clothes with aesthetic intent. I often amused him by my (comparative) slovenliness. He studied me, silently amused—deeply amused by my lack of consideration for my appearance. Day in day out I wore the same blue jeans and chambray shirt.

Our meals were simple. We ate in the kitchen. I learned from Ralph how to brew drip-coffee properly. He had been taught by a chemist to do it with ordinary laboratory paper filters and water at room temperature. The coffee then was heated in a *bain-marie*—a pot within a pot. Never allowed to boil.

We saw little of each other during the day. I kept a vegetable garden and at the kitchen door I planted herbs.

At cocktail time we met again in the kitchen. Ralph mixed very strong martinis, but nobody got drunk. We talked a great deal, before dinner, before the martinis took hold. Over dinner, Ralph told me the story of his life—told me about his mother, about Oklahoma City; about their years in Gary, Indiana, and later in Cleveland, where he and his brother hunted birds for the table during the Great Depression. He described to me his trip, in freight trains, to Tuskegee; and how he learned to play the trumpet; and how he had come upon certain essays by André Malraux that changed his life. Often we rambled together about Malraux, about Marxism, or painting or novel writing.

There were long discussions of American history and of nineteenth-century politics, of slavery and the Civil War and Reconstruction. Ralph was much better at history than I could ever be, but it gradually became apparent that he was not merely talking about history but telling the story of his life, and tying it into American history. His motive was in part literary—he was trying to find the perspective for an autobiography. In this respect he much resembled Robert Frost, who had made a routine, an entertainment of the principal events of his life and polished or revised them again and again when he had the right listeners. But Frost was his own hagiographer. He would tell you how Ezra Pound had received him in his London flat, sitting in a hip-bath and treated him—Frost—like a ploughboy-poet. "I was no Bobby Burns," Frost often said. He was trying to establish *his* version or picture of a significant chapter of literary history and to spray it with a fixative of his own.

Ralph's purpose was very different from Frost's. He took pleasure in returning again and again to the story of his development, not in order to revise or to gild it but to recover old feelings and also to consider and reconsider how he might find a way to write his story.

He and I had our differences. I am not inclined to be sentimental about those Arcadian or Utopian days. He didn't approve of my way of running the place. I had complained also that his dog relieved himself in my herb garden. I asked, "Can't you arrange to have him do his shitting elsewhere?"

This offended Ralph greatly, and he was outraged when, in a fit of nastiness, I took a swipe at the dog with a broom for fouling the terrace. He complained to John Cheever that, with my upbringing, I was incapable of understanding, I had no feeling for pedigrees and breeds and that I knew only mongrels and had treated his *chien de race* like a mongrel.

Cheever was broken up by this. Well, it was very funny. Cheever never spoke of it to me. I learned of Ralph's complaint when Cheever's diary was posthumously published.

When I told Ralph that perhaps it would be a good idea to thin out the locust trees along the driveway he said, "Well, they're your trees."

Immediately I telephoned a woodsman with a power-saw. I don't recall that there was such a saw in the trunk of the Chrysler. But in my place, Ralph would have cut the trees himself. Nor would he have consulted anyone about it.

But the main cause of trouble between us was the dog. Ralph believed that I had taken against the dog.

I have begun in old age to understand just how oddly we all are put together. We are so proud of our autonomy that we seldom if ever realize how generous we are to ourselves, and just how stingy with others. One of the booby traps of freedom—which is bordered on all sides by isolation— is that we think so well of ourselves. I now see that I have helped myself to the best cuts at life's banquet.

393

But our boiling paranoias do simmer down, and later on Ralph and I resolved our differences. His dog was after all handsome, intelligent, lively. I didn't hold it against him that he was a thoroughbred, a *chien de race*. We made peace and parted on the best of terms.

Ralph and I later agreed that our Tivoli life had been extraordinarily pleasant. It's no longer a shored-up ruin. Its new proprietor has turned it into a showplace. But Ralph and I, two literary squatters, comically spikey, apart though living together, had been very lucky in the two years we spent together in what I called the House of Usher. We did not form a great friendship. What we had was a warm attachment. He respected me. I admired him. He had a great deal to teach me; I did my best to learn.

Since that time I have brewed my morning coffee precisely as he had taught me to brew it.

I often summon him up. He is wearing his Moorish dressing gown and the leather slippers with turned-up toes. Sometimes, while pouring water from the measuring cup with one hand, he rubs his nose with the other, rubs it so hard that you can hear the cartilage crack.

Leonard St. Clair and Alan Govenar

Stoney Knows How: Life as a Tattoo Artist

Mama didn't raise no crazy children. She just kept me on the
merry-go-round too long. That's it! A guy asked me one time, "How long
have you been in the show business?" So, I told him, "I was born under a
sideshow platform and mother was fined two dollars for missing one bally."
That was a rib, see? I wasn't born in the business. That's just a joke. I
followed my Uncle Albert.

Well, my first shop in Tampa was in Ybor City. That's the Latin
Quarter of Tampa, all Cubans. I set up right beside a chicken-plucking joint
and I knew that I was going to do all right. I'd heard of Ybor City all of
my life. They pronounce it Ibo, but it's spelled, Y-B-O-R. It's been there
since the pirate days. So, I got acquainted with this Cuban cop. He was a
nice guy. He told me, "Stoney, why don't you move downtown?"

"No," I says, "This is Ybor City."

He says, "You better move downtown."

I says, "Why?"

He says, "I'm damned Cuban myself and I know them. You're mama's
boy until the day mama dies. You can be fifty years old and you're still
mama's boy. You're going to tattoo a forty-year-old Cuban one of these days
with something that eighty-year-old mama don't like and mama's going to

come down some evening and smile and say 'Hello' to you and under that apron she's going to have a meat cleaver. She's gonna say, "You damn son of a so-and-so, you tattoo my baby boy. He cannot go to heaven," and boom!

I says, "I'll take your advice, sir." So, I moved downtown. I got along many, many moons after that without any trouble. That cop came down and visited me often. He said, "You see, what I tell you. You're learning these Cubans now. I know. I'm one of them." I tattooed him many times.

The shop I had wasn't near as big as this. The best tattoo shops I ever had, the ones that made me a lot of money, were little short ones. Some of them were between two buildings. You couldn't hold more than five or six people in them at one time. Yeah, you don't need a big shop, but me, being crippled up here in this town, with me closing early and everything, I've got to have a big one. I've got these dogs here. These dogs are life-savers, you know that. I have to have them.

I didn't live in my first shop in Tampa, but in my last one in Tampa I did. When I had my first shop in Tampa, I lived in circus winter quarters, carni winter quarters. Oh, that's good. You can live in a top, a tent, or you can live in a trailer; live any way you want to. Carnis lived neat and clean, you know. I've lived in wagons that look better than what I got around here. That's right, there was a sink in there, electricity. You've got folding dressing tables and everything that the actors, the performers, use during the season. You just let a platform down on a chain and it's got makeup and everything you need. In the winter, you use that platform to cook on. You can live decent, buddy, don't matter where you're at. You just have to have a little upstairs.

I lived better when I was in show business. I wore better clothes. I liked the clothing styles better in the thirties. You had wide-bottom trousers and nice pin stripes, good clothes, buddy. You had sharkskin. You had gabardine. Today, it costs you twenty or twenty-five dollars for a good shirt. Why, a lady in Mississippi used to tailor my shirts for me with pearl snap buttons all over them. She only charged me five dollars a shirt, and they had five dollars worth of material in them. You had to have them dry-cleaned. You can see in these pictures what I wore. There's one of them. There's one of them. There's one of the shirts that lady in Mississippi made. I used to look like a miniature Tennessee Ernie or an Elvis the Pelvis with a mustache.

I didn't mind traveling some in the winter time. I'd follow all the winter shows, you know, penny arcades, freak museums, stuff like that. A lot of the show people worked in the freak museums. There were tattooing, freak and novelty acts, sword swallowers, electric chairs, just about anything you'd see in the sideshow. Now, I only work the arcades and the museums in the winter. I couldn't get that sawdust out of my shoes until 1950.

I could be making good money in Biloxi or Phoenix City, Alabama, but as soon as that sun came out, I'd have to leave and jump on the show, knowing that it was going to be a couple of months before I did any good. I'd jump all the way up here and freeze to death. That's right, open with Gooding around here in the rain, but I still had that merry-go-round and that calliope in me, buddy. I just had to hear it.

I've worked in quite a few arcades. A lot of the times I'd have to give up a percentage. I've set up right in the windows like that window there, except that they were a little larger, you know. I'd set up right in the window. They could see you from the outside. You pay the arcade a percentage, but if you are bringing in a lot of business and there's a big demand for you and you've got your own advertising, the next year, the man's liable to let you set up for free because you're an asset to the business.

In the arcades they usually had dart games, little games, you know, little eating stands, pitch-'til-you-win, fortune telling machines, a little bit of everything. You could book anything in there: penny and nickel and dime machines, diggers. You know what diggers are? They're the machines where you drop in a coin and you get to control a little steel claw that reaches over and picks up a prize or a silver dollar. Now, you think that's legitimate, but that's hot as a pistol, buddy. I've seen them close joints that were legitimate, and the joints next to them were as hot as a pistol. They do the same thing at this fair. That's the kind of fools they are. The fair committee doesn't know what's crooked and what isn't. Us old circis and carnis, we know the score. I've seen them close bingo where somebody won a prize every time, and right beside that bingo joint was a digger.

When I tattooed in Tampa during the winter, I usually worked in an arcade. One of them was called the Orange Arcade. The one where I worked right up in the display window was called the Dixie Arcade. It was run by a big arcade man, Bernie Mattson, a big Jewish fella. He had arcades on carnivals at that time. Bernie got to where he liked me so well that after the first winter with him, he says, "Don't give me a percentage, Stoney. You're an asset to the business." I brought in quite a few soldiers then. McDill

Field was in Tampa. It was Army in Tampa, but there was never another in that arcade. If you book with a carnival, you don't have but one. You get what we call the X. You go see the boss and say, "Now, I'm going to tattoo in here. Don't let anybody else come in and tattoo."

At that time there were only three or four tattooers in Tampa all winter, but there was only one permanent one, Al Kemp. He's dead now. He was there from 1921 until he died in 1961. He was an old tattooer. He and I tattooed right across the street from each other, but we didn't get along when I just set up there for the winter. He never came across the street to visit me, but when I moved there permanently in 1957, he came over ever day. He knew he had to put up with me then. I had to put up with him, too.

The number of tattooers varied in Tampa in the winter time, but there was never but one in the summer, and that was Al Kemp. A lot of circus and carni tatooers settled in Tampa in the winter. The highest number that I ever knew was four at one time. Wait a minute now: Al Kemp (he was permanent) and me, two; Sailor Katzy was there (he was the tattooed man and sideshow operator that the big snake killed); Sailor Don Nubey was four. Wait a minute. I know of five at one time. The fifth one was Walter Ally. He was half Hindu. His father was a great tattooer. His mother was a tattooed lady. She was tattooed to look like Bertie Gibbons. Walter's mother went by the name of Artoria. She was a beautiful woman, buddy, and she looked just like Bertie Gibbons. Bertie Gibbons was the wife of an old tattooer and show man, Red Gibbons.

Sailor Katzy had a little zoo right outside of Tampa, Showtown, USA., just south of Tampa. He drank a lot. He was tattooed all over, one of the most completely tattooed men. It looked a lot better then Lyle Turtle over there. Katzy knew the sideshow business, but he was a little boisterous. He liked to say, "Hey, look, hey Hi!" He waved that kind of bally and stuff like that. He loved glory.

Me and several other showmen figured one of his cobras would get him one day. The cobra is a very slow snake. That's why there's a low death rate on him. He's a slow striker. Katzy drank too much and would fool around with the cobras, showing off. We thought the cobra could get him or the lions. He'd show you how to get in there and clean the cage and twist the lion's tail and everything. A lion will only take so much of that.

So, Katzy ordered this pretty good-sized boa, about twenty-two feet long, and he called him a python. He was a pet, but still, he wasn't a little snake. Well, Katzy was painting outside one day, half high, and his wife was down at the other end, cleaning the lion's cage. Sailor didn't have his shirt on, just pants. He was painting, had paint thinner on him, and he noticed that his snake, the pet, was trying to shed in the glass cage. Well, not being out in the wilds, they have a little struggle sometimes crawling around in there. So, Sailor went inside of the cage building with the paint thinner on his hands. There was nobody there to see it, but when they found him dead, he was on the outside of that building. Either he brought the snake outside to help him shed or the snake coiled around him and dragged him outside. Anyway, they found Katzy under a palm tree. They don't know whether he brought the snake out there, but they do know that the paint thinner on his hands irritated that snake's new skin and the snake's instinct did something, coiled him around his chest and throat. The snake squeezed the air out of him, strangled him, you know.

All right, the ambulance came immediately, and they called Sailor's wife. Sailor ordinarily was so brave. He didn't ever have a knife. If he had had a knife on him, he could have cut that snake and got him before, easy. They rushed the body to Tampa General hospital, but Sailor was already dead. His wife had to leave the hospital real quickly because she heard that the sheriff had started back to kill that snake. She wanted to beat the sheriff. She didn't want them to kill that snake. She knew it was a freak accident. Nothing against that snake. It's instinct. That's right. She stopped them from killing the snake. She went and got Doc Hartwick, a good snake man, and he helped her get the snake out of the tree. Yeah, she used that snake for several seasons after that with big blow ups, "This is the one that killed Sailor Katzy."

She got letters of condolence from all over the world, including Russia, and from some of the ignorant. Well, I shouldn't say that. I'm ignorant as all hell myself. Yeah, she got some typewritten letters, the hunt-and-peck kind, the kind that shows you how hard the person hit the keys. You can usually pick out the hunt-and-peck kind by the holes in the paper, where the keys went through. One letter was from a woman somewhere in Georgia, some religious fanatic, who wrote a long letter. I can't remember her words exactly, but it went something like this: "This is the work of the devil. You know it is. You're capitalizing on this snake killing your husband, making

399

a living off of it. This snake will kill again and we hope you be next." What that lady didn't understand, was that it would have been Sailor Katzy's request that his wife make a living off his death.

During those years, there were a lot more tattooed men and women than there are now. And there were more tattooers. I say tattooers. I won't say pork-and-beaners like we have now. For example, when you go into California now, you'll find a few tattooers, men like Bob Shaw and Doc Webb. I'll even include Painless Nell even though Nell and I don't have the same ideas. Yes, those people are tattooers. They know the game. They're out of the Old School. The rest of the tattooers that you find out in California are just pork-and-beaners. They're trying to glorify tattooing into something it's not. Let me tell you something, good buddy. When you have things going around like that card I gave you the other day from that woman who calls herself something that she's not, it's going to hurt the business. If they want to make themselves into gods or something, they're not good tattooers. They've been at it a year or two and don't care hell or high water. They want to get their names in print. They want to be famous.

I don't think it's something great to be a tattooer. This is my living and I try to keep it clean. I don't want to be called "Sailor Stoney." Katzy did that one time and I called him down on the front, and told him, "You're going to stop saying that on the front. When they get on the inside and look at a little shrimp like me, they'll say, 'Sailor in whose Navy?' You don't call me Sailor Stoney. You just call me Stoney, or St Clair, the tattooer. That's all." That's where we put it again: not the best, just as good as the rest.

I had a little sign over the ticket box which said, "Tattooing by Stoney. Stoney knows how," and I had a big banner with a little guy like me, hump-backed, sitting in a tattoo shop, tattooing a lady named Louise Williams, one of the nicest tattooed ladies in the business. Katzy had a banner put up there that cost approximately fifty dollars with a sailor, sitting on a stump in a jungle, with nothing but pastes on, a frown on his face, and about fifty little pygmies all over him with hammers and chisels, cutting little pictures on him.

Sailor Katzy's name was actually Alfred P. Henley. He came originally out of Knoxville, Tennessee. He was a wonderful builder. He could build an electric chair that could fold up. The thing was larger than a real electric chair. You know, there's a gimmick to it. Electric current goes through a girl's body. It goes through her body, but it's not a killer. Well, you could fold that electric chair flat and it wouldn't be more than five inches thick. I copied it. I built one just like it. Yes, Katzy was a builder!

He was a boisterous man. He had an immaculate wardrobe. His wife did too. He married a girl who was a wonderful worker out of Arkansas, Stuttgart, Arkansas. He got the name Sailor because he'd been in the Navy. He sailed all over the world. He was a shellback. That's when you cross the equator and take the initiation and all that. He said that he got the name Katzy because he and his brother were so ornery when they were growing up in Tennessee, so mischievous that they were like the Katzenjammer kids. So, they called him Sailor Katzy.

Katzy's wife had only one tattoo, and Katzy put it on her. It was a beautiful little scenery on her leg, had a sunrise, a little water, and "Katzy" written in a ribbon under it. I'll tell you, Katzy loved blood when he was tattooing. He could plow them up. He tattooed with his needle sticking out approximately a quarter of an inch; well more than an eighth of an inch. He used to let the needles glide on his finger like Charlie Wagner used to do. See, the needles stuck out from the end of the needle bar and he used his little finger as a guide to keep the needles from going the wrong way. If he tattooed like me by bearing down, the machine wouldn't go, the needles would hang on the skin. It works for me. I don't draw much blood. You've seen me tattoo long enough, you know. Katzy didn't think he was tattooing unless it bled good. He did some pretty tattoos, but he couldn't draw good designs. I drew a lot of designs for him, but he knew the art of tattooing. They all bandaged their work then. I did back in those days, too. I didn't know about this Monsell's Solution. It's an anti-coagulant—ferric sub-sulfate.

Yeah, Katzy held his machines like Charlie Wagner. You know, I tattooed with Charlie Wagner. Charlie Wagner let me work in his shop through sympathy. I was broke. It was in the winter. I wanted to make enough money to go down to Florida and get with a show in winter quarters.

I worked in Charlies's shop twice. Four months was the longest period of time I ever spent with him. Charlie Wagner had the biggest name in the tattoo business. He built machines, sold them for three dollars apiece. He tattooed a lot of people, but it was on the Bowery. The environment got to him. Charlie got to drinking a lot, taking everything in his last days. You

401

can't mention tattooing without someone from the Old School recognizing the name Charlie Wagner, but they only know what they've heard or read. Charlie Wagner died years ago. He was a friend of O'Riley, the man who invented the electric tattoo machine.

The first time I met Charlie was in 1929. I had been tattooing about a year. Yeah, he liked me. Charlie was all freehand. He never used a stencil. He sold them sailors what he wanted to. "Oh, you don't want an eagle today. I'm not putting on eagles." A sailor was sitting there, about half drunk one day. "Yes I do. I want this eagle right here." "You don't want an eagle." Charlie went to fooling around, mixing colors, put a heart on the guy. He had a gimmick, though. If he made a mistake or did something wrong, he'd make it up to you. You see that five-pointed star. That was his type. He'd give you about five of those around your tattoo and says, "No extra charge."

He'd square the joint, see, by a lot of extra work. He was fast, buddy, fast.

That's where I got the name for being the fastest. I copied that from Charlie. I knew how to run a machine across that guy's arm. I was the world's fastest for a time. Katzy gave me that name too, and Katzy didn't like to brag about anybody but himself.

I used to order machines from Charlie Wagner for three dollars, and if he sold you a secondhand one, he'd include eight or ten extra bars, a little piece of solder, and several screws just in case you needed them. He used to send me old labels off apple crates, anything. "Think this would make a nice design?" He'd do anything just to be friendly.

You had to like him, yeah. When I was working in his shop, he used to tattoo sailors under the stairway. Now there were four barbers in there too, you know, leased under Charlie. It was a barber shop, selling leeches, haircut for a dime, nickel for a shave. You had to run an oil mop over the floor. You couldn't sweep it. There were splinters all over the place. The whole front of the shop opened up, windows and everything in there.

I was sitting there one day and Charlie was tattooing under that stairway. A piece of plaster fell and part of it went into his colors, and Charlie says, "Think nothing of it. That's just a coincidence. We use zinc oxide in these colors anyway, and that's what that plaster's got in it. It can't hurt a thing." He lifted that piece of plaster out of there and squared it with the sailor. I'm not lying buddy. That's the truth.

Most of his customers were sailors. On the Bowery, most of the civilians were winos. Why, you could get beer by the bucket across the street. They had fifteen-cent night clubs there, fifteen-cent cover charge. One Saturday night, we were closing up and there were four or five winos laying asleep in the shop. Some of them were setting up, others were laying down. It smelled like rotting apples in there, buddy. Charlie says, "Well, let's go!" We started out the door, and he had a big railroad lock he was going to put on the door.

I says, "Hey buddy, you're going to lock those men up in there?"

He says, "Sure."

I says, "I got equipment in there."

He says, "God damn it, so have I and I was here before you. I pay the rent on it. Them guys can't get out until I come in the morning anyway." He locked that door and the next morning, I met him down there around ten o'clock. Them winos were there with smiles on their faces, all rolling Bull Durham cigarettes, smoking. They were clean. They had used our straight razors, had shaved, used the barbers' bay rum. They had even taken ties out of their pockets and put them on.

We opened and the winos sat around for a while and then caught the streetcar they wanted. We gave them money for the streetcar. I don't know, I think it was a nickel or a dime then. Anyhow, Charlie told me, "Now they will ride that car until they can get off at the best running corner. They'll bum all day for money to buy some more wine." If Charlie didn't want them in there, and they were sleepy, he'd give them a dime to catch a streetcar and they'd sleep all day on the streetcar.

Charlie was an amazing man, but he was a little crooked. I wasn't. If you dropped a dollar on the floor, Charlie would never let you know it, let you know you dropped it. Of course, I put the flowers on myself now, but you know me. That's the way I am. You've been around here long enough. You know me. That's my policy.

Charlie was a great tattooer, but he eventually got a little sloppy, got to where he didn't even care. He could draw anything freehand, buddy. He didn't use a stencil. Charlie kept VD all his life. Oh, man, he was a woman's man. He was careless. He didn't care about anything. I think Charlie was from the Bowery. I think that's where he was born. I can call the number, buddy, 11 Chatham Square, yeah, in the Chinatown section of the Bowery. I'm not sure when Charlie died, but I'm going to make a guess. I think it was in Biloxi. I believe it was in '49 or '50. It was in the *Billboard*. A lot of tattooers called me, corresponded with me, told me about Charlie's death. Yeah, Professor Charles Wagner. I believe he died from sclerosis. Charlie took anything from paregoric to Jamaica ginger.

There were six or seven tattooers on the Bowery then. The one that did the nicest, cleanest work was a woman, Mildred Hall. Some people called her Hull. I got a picture. She was in love with one of Charlie's customers who was covered with tattoos. His name was Tom Reed and he was a no-good son of a gun. Mildred made a lot of money and he helped her spend it. She was a good tattooer. I've got her picture in this album over here. Yeah, Mildred Hall was so in love with Tom Reed that she took pills and killed herself, left him some money too. Charlie taught Mildred how to tattoo. He taught a lot of people to tattoo. He'd get drunk and teach a lot of people he should not have taught. He ruined himself that way. They set up down the street from him. He had too much competition.

Tattoos cost a lot less then. A cheap battleship cost fifteen dollars then. Now it costs a hundred and fifty dollars or more. Charlie used to put them on for thirty-five cents, sixty-five cents; some days, free. I'm telling you the truth. Ask any old tattooer, they'll tell you, "Oh, you've been to Charlie Wagner. Charlie Wagner ruined you. Yeah, he tattooed you for thirty-five cents.

I tattoo now with my right hand. I draw with my left hand and write letters with my left hand. I used to use both of them when I was drinking years ago. I had to use pads on my hands, heavy pads, cause I was working off an alternating current which heated the machines. The machines used to get so hot that I had to switch the machine from one hand to the other every once in a while. I burned my left hand bad back when I was smoking cigarettes. Some matches went off in my hand. I tattooed with my right hand for a couple weeks until my left hand healed, but I got to where I liked my right hand best. Now I only tattoo with my right hand.

I started using little stars as a trademark for my tattoos in about 1940. I tattooed another tattooer, Pete Holmes, in Mineral Wells, Texas, and he used a star. Pete was a good tattooer. So I thought that stars looked good around a tattoo, but instead of using only one star like Pete did, I used two stars. Now, there's a trick to putting those stars on. You see, if you put those stars on while the dye is spraying, you can't tell what you are doing by the motion of your hand. Then when you wipe off the excess dye, they say,

"Oh my goodness, look what he just did. This man knows what he's doing." That's a little trick. It's a two-second job. It looks good and they think they're getting more for their money. I haven't heard from Pete Holmes in a long time. I think he's dead. I know he's not tattooing any more. Let's see, I use the star, sometimes two stars, and there's a youngster in Texas who uses the star. Yeah, the chickens went home to roost, got back in Texas.

Tattooers used to stay in close contact with one another during those years. Every once in a while, they would fall out over something. Some yokel would double-cross them. The youngsters are the ones who did the double-crossing, see? The youngster knows he don't know it all, but when he starts to ask a question, he feels inferior. He don't want to ask it, so he goes ahead and fouls up.

Now, you know before the guy sets down to get that tattoo. You know what kind of fight he's going to put up. That's the way Beatty did it. He would sit and study jungle animals two or three months before he would go into the cage with them. He knew what kind of fight that guy was going to put up when he got to him. It's the same way with tattooing. You know if the guy's going to be nervous. You know how much he's interested in his tattoo. You put two and two together. You know what kind of tattoo he wants. You try to put it that way to please him. A lot of tattoos you couldn't put on me for five thousand dollars. I don't want to, but I give the guy what he wants as long as it's within the bounds of decency.

You can usually tell when somebody walks in the door if he's going to get a tattoo. You get what we call punchers, guys who hit the design sheets with their fingers. He's usually the guy who does all the talking. He says, "Oh, man, oh, man . . ." He points to the designs with his finger, showing them to the other guys. You can hear his fingers hit the board. He says, "Smoke that over. Check that out." Nine times out of ten, that guy is not going to get a tattoo, but he may pay for another guy to get one. He wants to see someone else get a tattoo. H wants to do the talking. Look at that design sheet over there. See the fingerprints. You can tell where the puncher is going to punch. Yeah, look at that dirt. Now, that won't come off. That sheet has fingerprints all around it and I've only put that tattoo on once.

You can tell where a damn man's mind runs when he's punching at a certain design. It's the same damn thing if you're a policeman and you've been at it for a long time. During certain phases of the moon, you'll take

405

special precautions around a black area because you know a criminal watches the moon. You get in one profession and stay at it a long time, you learn a lot, buddy.

I used to cover my design sheet, but I got lazy. I don't cover them any more. I'll tell you something. I leave pencil marks around the designs so they can tell that I drew them. I drew this sheet this morning. See the pencil marks on it? I do that purposely.

I don't draw that often. I may go six months and then draw another sheet. Yes, I've gotten lazy about that too, but when I do get started, why, I can turn out three sheets in one day. That's right. I used to turn out three sheets in no time at all, but that was back eight or ten years ago. I've got so many designs up there now, it's almost a waste to draw any more. You see, if I draw new sheets any more, I just lay them in that pile over there. They can look through them over there, if they want to.

Did I tell you about the three who came in here from the university? It was quite a while ago. They asked me what the sensation was, you know, what it felt like to get a tattoo. Well, I knew when they walked up the sidewalk. They had shorts on. I knew damn well that they were not going to get a tattoo. It was all right for them to come in and look, as long as they behaved themselves.

So, the one with the thick steel-beam glasses and last night's makeup still on says, "Can we just look around?"

"Go right ahead." You'd have to swear that that one son-of-a-bitch was fruit juicy. He was that queer, gay as New Orleans. Well, I got to studying. I got to figuring.

"Oh, isn't that gay?"

I knew damn well if I got a customer that they would want to see it done, but then they would start ridiculing it. I wasn't going to stand for that, if I was good enough man to let them look at my pictures. So, they stood it as long as they could and one of them came over here. His face looked like a Sherwin Williams advertisement. It had so much paint on it.

"Do you give some kind of shot before you tattoo them?"

I was praying I wouldn't get a customer. I says, "No, I hit them over the head with a hammer!" That didn't faze him. That was an insult, but it didn't bother him. They went back over there, and looked about twenty minutes longer. I was getting madder than a wet hen. Finally, one of them walked back over toward me.

He got his nerve up and said, "Could you explain the sensation, how it feels?"

I says, "Did you ever jerk off with a handful of barbed wire?"

He went back over there and says, "Let's go." He dropped his wrist and looked back and said, "Have a good day."

I haven't seen him since. Yeah!

Tattooing is an art to itself. It doesn't go with anything else. There are too many dumb clucks around that think that tattooers tell fortunes or something like that. Tattooing is older than Christ. It's like the sign says out in front of my shop: ancient as time, modern as tomorrow. Then again, I don't know what you would call art. The crap I see today on canvas and paper, I don't call art. Chimps can do better than that.

Oh, buddy, did I tell you about this nurse that started farting? Well, these two nurses came in last spring from Toledo. One wanted a cockroach on her, the little short one wanted a cockroach on her butt, and the other wanted a butterfly. So, I tattooed the biggest one first with the butterfly. The little one was one them types you couldn't say shit in front of, but if you turn your head, she's a mean son of a bitch. She'll pick her nose and eat just like that, see? So, I tattooed the biggest one. She was all right. The other made me mad. When it was her turn, she said, "Oh, oh, I'm ashamed," and went over and locked the door and pulled the curtain herself. I was just acting real dignified like a damned doctor. She says, "Do I have to take my pants down?"

"Mam, you have to take yours off because you're shorter."

"Oh."

So, I got that little bench over here. I was just being mean because she was mean. I broke her bare ass down like a shot gun and I started tattooing her. Well, after about a minute or so work on her ass, she started farting, "Boop, boop, boop." It sounded like these little logging engines in the woods calling for water for the corn. I just lifted the machine and didn't say anything.

"Please excuse me. That's nerve reaction." Now, here's where I put my foot in my mouth. I says, "I know there's some kind of action back there." I started laughing to myself and it was twenty minutes before I could finish the job. Yeah, that was a good one.

Josephine Herbst

The Starched Blue Sky
of Spain

Apart from a few news accounts, a few descriptive articles, I have never written anything about Spain. It had got locked up inside of me. There was one thing you couldn't do when you came back from Spain. You couldn't begin to talk in terms of contradictions. Everyone I knew wanted the authoritative answer. There were characters who had never left New York who were angry with me because I couldn't say for certain that the Trotskyist leader Nin had been murdered. Other characters raged because I refused to accuse Nin of leading a Fascist plot in complicity with Franco. What was wanted was black or white. I wasn't even useful for speech-making, as I might make a slip and refer to a church where horses were munching hay on the high altar. Religionists might be offended. And by the time I had returned to America the situation had moved to the big courtship phase. To win, everybody had to be wooed. But everybody can't win; nor did they.

If I didn't write, if I didn't speak, it wasn't that I felt ignorant. But it may have seemed to me that what I had brought back was too appallingly diffuse. Like the twigs I used to see the old women in Germany pick up in the forests to tie in little bundles to lug home on their backs. Each twig was precious; it had come from a living tree and would make living fire. I had all sorts of curious oddments; like a pressed flower that grew under a broken olive tree, a bit of quartz from an old cave that had been carved out by the Moors for twenty miles, and where families huddled beside little candles during weeks of air raids. I even had a tiny bluish feather that a young Czech soldier had given me one night as we sat by a road in pitchy darkness near the Guadarrama Mountains.

Why do you write a book? Why do you fall in love? Because. It is the one conclusive answer that comes from the bottom of the well. Later you may dress it up with reasons; some of them may very well apply. But *because* is the soundest answer you can give to an imperative. I didn't even want to go to Spain. I had to. Because. It didn't make sense to Max Perkins when I visited him in his office five days before I sailed. He looked at me as one might at a child who has answered the query, "Why do you want to run out in the rain and get all wet for?" with nothing more than *because*. "What's the matter with all of you?" he asked. "Hemingway's gone off, Dos Passos is there, Martha Gellhorn's going. And now you. Don't you know that Madrid is going to be bombed out? It won't do you any good to go around with the stars and stripes pinned on your chests or on your heads. They won't see or care." Now, the unknown is dear to us, and contrary to opinion, security is not the heart's true desire. Death is no deterrent but its forms may terrify. So for the five nights before I sailed I dreamed of spectacular flames and falling balls of fire in visions never to be rivaled by any reality I was to encounter. As a preview, these visions had even a salutary effect. On my first day in Madrid the heavy shelling sounded oddly unconvincing; curiously like one of those torrential thunderstorms we used to get in the Iowa of my childhood.

Don't expect an analysis of events; I couldn't do it then, I can't now. I have my opinions but what I can only call my convictions go to deeper levels where opinions hardly count. What's more, those convictions have to do with me, as an individual, and apply to more than events. I can hardly think back upon Spain now without a shiver of awe; it is like remembering how it was to be in an earthquake where the ground splits to caverns, mountains rise in what was a plain. The survivor finds himself straddling a widening crack; he leaps nimbly to some beyond where he can stand ruminating upon his fate. I suspect that it was the question of my own fate that took me to Spain as much as it was any actual convulsion going on in that country. I certainly didn't run to it as crowds do to a fire. I was respectful and frightened. I had gone through more than one metamorphosis since I was young and had to go to New York. Because. I had lived for three years in the Germany of the twenties—*because*—battening off the ill fortunes of the country which ordained me a dollar princess with no more to spend than three hundred dollars a year. I had a sprinkling of Spanish, not Castilian, but Mexican. Spain was Cervantes and Goya. It took a kind of crust to go to Spain. There was little food in Spain; I would be eating. How was I to pay my way by justifying my presence?

If the pen was ever mightier than the sword in a time of crisis, it didn't seem to me that the typewriter held a ghost of a chance against the new weapons. I didn't believe that I could write anything deathless or even sway to any appreciable extent the rigidities that had made for the fantastic nonintervention pact.

Was it possible that I was going in order to live out that early nightmare when as a little girl I read what even Iowa newspapers had carried about the Chicago Iroquois Theatre fire? The element that stuck had been the stampede; the fact that grown men had trampled women and children in their effort to escape. My mother had been horrified by that fact, and almost only that fact; "better to sit quietly in your seat and perish than to have to live the rest of your life with such a memory." For years I could never go to a theater without a secret rehearsal of how I hoped to behave. Nobly, of course. But could anyone be sure? Put to the test I had more than once proven to be a physical coward; as a child, during two household accidents I had nimbly run from the house and raced around the block expecting to see the place burst into flames. The sight of blood sickened me, though I took care to let no one know. But the difficulty at finding any root answer to the question of why I or people like me went to Spain is endless. I could just as well claim that the basic reason was that I was a vivid dreamer who had all my life been conscious of the power and art of flying as a peculiarly enviable happiness, and that to soar lightly above trees and over the tops of mountains was a delight so secure that, from early childhood, it had made demands upon actual existence which refused to believe that the impossible might not happen. There *were* miracles; I could testify to it. And there were intimations of possible miracles in Spain.

If I seem to be going into subterranean regions, it is because these regions, as related to myself, are what I know. I don't know anything really about Spain except what came through me and my skin. I believe that my own deeper feelings about myself and the way those feelings attached themselves to

411

the fact of Spain applied to many more than myself. In a certain sense I hoped to find in Spain an antidote to the poison I found in Germany, when in 1935 I went back to a country familiar to me to write a series of articles for the *New York Post* and to try to discover if there was any actual underground movement. The Germany I had known had vanished. Once traveling on a train to Munich an old man got into some conversation with me, and on parting, said: "Write me a postcard when you get to Paris. I never get any mail any more. People are afraid to write to one another now."

In another sense, I was probably trying to find some answers to the confusions in my own mind. The thirties had come in like a hurricane. An entire young generation had been swept up in a violent protest against the realities of events. But the answers were numbing. The slogans were pieces of twine throttling something that was struggling. Phrases like the "toiling masses" did not answer terrible questions. There were always people, real people, each an individual spirit with its own peculiar past. The Spanish war was doubtless the last war in which individuals were to enter fully with their individual might. But what a welter of conflicting views this implies! The soldier is not only fighting *against* an enemy but also *for* something beyond.

412

But no war can be the purifying fire. Individuals cannot fight as individuals and conflicting visions bring a conflict of will and design. Before I left Spain, the disintegration had begun with a squalid internecine brawl in Barcelona. I have never had much heart for party polemics and it was not for factionalism that I had come to Spain. I did my best to find out "the facts," I even went to Barcelona in May where barricades were still in the streets. We shall never see that kind of outmoded fighting again. No more barricades! They were even outmoded then and proved nothing. I can't say to this day what really happened in Barcelona, in all the diversity of conflicting causations, but I do know for certain that it was no anarchist plot, hatched up in conjunction with Franco. If the enemies of Franco had split into groups and were killing each other, it was not because each group was not equally determined to defeat the common enemy. Was the aim of the war a revolutionary one, which would strike at the terrible wrongs that had led to the uprising, or was it "a war for democracy" which, to the intransigents, implied no more than a restoration of the *status quo?* By that time, abstractions had taken over on the Loyalist side; on Franco's side, the superiority of weapons was surely winning.

My entry into the Hotel Florida in the heart of Madrid was surprisingly cozy. Hemingway came toward me in a kind of khaki uniform with high polished boots. I was dragging my knapsack; a white dust from shells exploding in the streets had coated my hair and felt gritty on my hands. He threw his arms around me and gave me a big kiss. "How are you, Josie? I'll never forgive you for letting that sixty-pound king off your line." Three years before, on a fishing trip in Key West with Hemingway and Max Perkins, I *had* let a kingfish get off my line, and secretly had been glad of it. Now here, in the Hotel Florida, in a war, was the fish, looking me in the eye. I didn't feel ashamed for my lack of skill; I had never set myself up as a fisherman. And at the moment I was grateful for the reference which seemed to bring the world together and hold the disparate parts in conjunction. Hemingway was at home, if I wasn't, and that was something.

I don't know what the Hotel Florida had looked like before the war, but it now had a stripped appearance with its bleak stuffed chairs abandoned in the lobby. On the clerk's desk was a little box with an invitation, "Take One," and the one and only thing to take was a little brochure advertising the Hotel Plaza in Havana, Cuba. There was a lift, but to save the electricity it didn't run. I had a room on the fourth floor, and on that floor Hemingway had a suite of two rooms, one of which was occupied by Sid Franklin, his devoted friend and sort of *valet de chambre*. There was a tall wardrobe in Hem's room and it was filled with tasty items; ham, bacon, eggs, coffee, and even marmalade. These tidbits were the fruit of Sid's ability to scrounge around, and as someone who knew Spain, had been admired in Spain as a valiant bullfighter, he could lay his hands on essentials no one else could have touched. As I was to find out, everyone hoarded a little of something. A few of the correspondents had even brought along little electric coffeepots. I had come in with a package of tea, some chocolate bars, and six packs of cigarettes.

As I think of the Hotel Florida now, I can see it only as a misty sort of unreality. I never seemed to be there, even when I was actually there. Something inside seemed to be suspended outside, waiting. Or listening. Or hovering around, in places I had managed to be or in places that I heard of and to which I hoped to go. There was a disembodiment about my own entity which didn't even disturb me. I soon got used to it. There was a kind of distinct core inside me around which the disembodied elements might

413

cluster as around a magnet and they came and went around that magnet, sometimes swarming and buzzing. What I remember clearly was the way the floors opened up upon a deep well of a rotunda so that walking around on your floor you could look down and see to the first floor, where people might be sitting, midgetlike, below.

After I had been to the front lines at Jarama I used to sit there in the early mornings when the boys on leave would have a chance to drop in to see me. I had my tea and the only thing the hotel could furnish was hot water. With a bit of dry bread saved from supper the night before, I would sit munching and talking to the boys. Often Dos Passos was there doing the same thing. Then the odor of ham and coffee would slowly penetrate to our level and from the fourth floor Hemingway would lean down and call, inviting us to breakfast. It was a terrible temptation. Everybody was hungry all the time and the smells incited to gluttony. I would be haunted all day, hating myself for being haunted. I hated it that I also felt virtuous for not going. For doing the right thing. For you couldn't run off from your visitors. Tomorrow they might be dead.

Though food was on everyone's mind, I never heard anyone complain of the lack of it or because some of the dishes served at the restaurant on the Gran Via stank to high heaven. The restaurant was in the basement of a building nearly opposite the Telephonica, where you filed your dispatches and got permits for transportation. Gas was very limited and it was hard to get a ride to anyplace. Hemingway had two cars for his use, with a gas allowance, but then he was undertaking the movie *Spanish Earth* and needed to be going back and forth to this village. It didn't always make for good feeling among some other correspondents, particularly those who were not on regular assignments and had only a short time allotted to them. I didn't feel so good myself seeing those cars go tootling off. Other people came out of the hotel and set off briskly, but where did they go? Martha Gellhorn sailed in and out in beautiful Saks Fifth Avenue pants with a green chiffon scarf wound around her head. Everyone knew where they were going, what they were doing, except me. Everyone talked learnedly during the evening meal on the Gran Via about the number of shells that had come in, the number of people killed. In a chaotic situation to get hold of a few simple facts is consoling. If you can speak of them in terms of measurement it is one way to control them. In Germany, during the inflationary period of the twenties, it had been the egg. I had lived with Germans in Berlin and every day the egg was the center of conversation. "What is the egg doing today?" Why, the egg was a hundred thousand marks. Soon it was a million.

I had been assured at the press bureau that I would get to go places, but for days I was suspended, wondering, where? In a situation like that it becomes second nature to hide one's ineptitude. You can't admit that you aren't bustling about, knowing exactly what it all means. If I had been a regular correspondent, I would have been obliged to show something for each day. But I was on a special kind of assignment, which meant I would write about other subjects than those covered by the news accounts. The people I wanted to know were the Spanish, but it seemed to me that I was out on a rim where the atmosphere often struck me as frivolous. There were some first-rate correspondents in Spain and there were also some curious characters like the journalist from England who had written a book about trawling. He had pale-blue eyes and pale hands that wandered helplessly over his food. If he caught me in the lobby he would make an attack and fill me with factual information, none of which rang true. Or he would propound his sleeplessness. "I couldn't get to sleep last night. I kept thinking over and over: Out of the barbed wire of the war comes communism." Then he would stand back and wait for me to be electrified by his slogan. When I didn't electrify he would trail off disconsolately.

I did a lot of walking around looking hard at faces. There was nothing in shopwindows except a few sun-drenched relics of other days. There was almost nothing to buy except oranges and shoelaces and all this seemed wonderful to me. The place had been stripped of senseless commodities and what had been left was the aliveness of speaking faces. The heavy shelling usually came in the afternoon and if you got caught in it, the only thing to do was to duck into some café. No one anywhere was well dressed, not even the tarts. There were no mantillas or black lace or shrinking girls with duennas. In the evening on the way to the restaurant the pavement was likely to be all hummocks and busted-up rubble. You picked your way with a flashlight. In the morning all this stuff would be swept up and new patches of cement would cover the holes. This went on, day by day, with the regularity of washing up the supper dishes.

I was just coming back from a stroll to the Puerto del Sol one morning when Sid Franklin called me from a little car. It stood in front of the Hotel Florida and held himself and Joris Ivens, who was shooting the film for

Spanish Earth. They were going to the village, and just out of the air, like manna from heaven, offered to take me along. Not to their village, but Murata, the village near the front lines at Jarama. I jumped in just as I was.

Some of the fiercest fighting had taken place at a tangent up the Tajuna valley toward Murata not long before. The Fascists had made a dangerous push against the road to Valencia in January and every available mixed brigade with its international troops had been rushed to the line. To have lost the battle would have been to seal the doom of Madrid, and there was no time to spare any man who could be thrown in. There were over four hundred Americans in the Abraham Lincoln Brigade who had barely had time to learn to shoot a rifle or to handle a machine gun. Raw as they were, they went into the battle and most of them came out alive. But shortly before I got to Murata, the Fifteenth Brigade had been ordered to launch an attack to take Pingarron Hill, the dominating terrain of the Tajuna valley. The attack had failed and of the four hundred Americans, one hundred and eight were left.

The village of Murata didn't look like the center of a storm as we entered it. There was a town hall and a church and some empty spots filled with rubble where houses had been. We passed through the town and began to mount into the hills. They stood in rounded hummocks or looked like jagged claws and seemed to be covered with an olive-colored pelt. Halfway up we wheeled into the courtyard of what had been a farmhouse. A cart stood nearby, its shafts broken. There was a big wooden rake with a cat sitting under it. A rick of sodden hay was being pecked by a few straggling hens. The house was languidly open. Sunlight poured into plain white-washed rooms where some cots were covered with neat blankets. No one was around. We could hear a murmur, and pushing on, entered a big kitchen. It had an enormous table, white as bone, and sitting at it were two young men in the cinnamon-colored uniforms of the International Brigade, peeling potatoes. The potatoes were very small and angry looking and lay in a pallid earthy heap on the white table.

I said who I was and fortunately the young men knew my name, mostly because of some articles I had written about Cuba. They didn't seem in the least surprised to see me there. They weren't even surprised when Joris and Sid simply drove off and left me. I offered to help with the potatoes and they gave me a knife. We talked about the weather. There must have been some communication with Brigade headquarters in a big solid house, not far off but hidden behind a hill, for in a little while, a young man on a motor bike heaved into the courtyard and said I was to come with him to see the General. I had no notion then, nor have I now, whether he was a "good" general or a "bad" one. We spoke German though he was not German; but neither was he a Russian. A Frenchman came in, spoke a few words, looked sharply at me, and went out. The General smiled, stamped a little card, and told me one of the boys would take me to the front lines. He hoped I would go. I could stay for a few days if I liked. It was fairly quiet now. They might order me out if things changed. But I could sleep at the little café in the village. One of the boys would see I got there.

It was too good to be true. From melancholic inertia I felt I was walking on air. The young man with the bike walked back with me. A loud clatter came from the kitchen. They were chopping up onions. Then one of them brought around a tough-looking open car with good, heavy tires. On the way up the crooked road the driver explained that this had been an old donkey road. They had leveled it out some to get supplies and an ambulance up to the men, but it was still bad. When we got to the top there would be a stretch of open ground we would have to cross before we came to the dugout leading to the trenches. The English battalion was to the right and on the left were the Poles. There was a mixture of Spaniards in all of them, but it didn't always work out so well; they didn't like the same kind of food, for one thing.

Looking back from the top, the view was beautiful. You could see the town hall and the church of Murata and you could see olive orchards and vineyards spreading softly along the hills toward the valley. The ground where there were no trees was harsh and brutally rocky. A man plowing in the distance was steering his plow as if it were a boat around obstacles in a bay. The view in the other direction toward the front lines was wavery ground; many of the olive trees looked as if they had been split open with an axe. The inside pulp was pinkish and blue with the look of quivering flesh. Blackened twigs lay scattered around the trunks. The ground itself had little plowed-up runnels that burst now and then into star-shaped pockets. I never saw this hilltop as a whole scene, but only in its parts as they met the hurrying eye, because it took all of one's concentrated energy to get across this emptied space. The birds had deserted it. You could hear distinctly

417

the rattle of a machine gun, then the olive tree near you shivered in a gust of wind. A bullet had passed by. Some leaves fell lightly. The thing to do was to walk swiftly toward your objective. We went in a straight diagonal without talking. Then suddenly we fronted an open dugout and dipped down to it.

A little group around a bare table with a telephone on it stared at us. The men had a wonderful red-brown color, and in their cinnamon-colored uniforms with the baggy trousers gathered into stout boots their youthful bodies seemed to have been fitted out with armor to mask their innocence. It is wonderful to have people glad to see you. These boys had been in the line for sixty days. It was by no means so tranquil as it seemed. They were expecting an attack any time. To have a newcomer, not a soldier but a woman, suddenly pounce down into the dugout was a refinement of warfare they hadn't expected.

There was a camp cot, a cabinet with first-aid equipment, some chairs, and copies of a mimeographed sheet that they got out once a week. It was called *Manana*. The boys had some hot coffee and gave me some. Even when we went along the line of trenches where soldiers were manning machine guns or lying beside rifles, I felt buoyant, and for the first time since I came to Madrid, not afraid. If you kept your head down, you were safer here than in Madrid so long as the attack hadn't begun. There was some firing all the time. But the front line of the enemy was very close, a few rods distant.

Boys who could not bear to shoot a rabbit back home had ancient guns that didn't work thrust into their hands on the night of the big offensive. Others tore the pins from grenades too soon, wounding themselves. Some went in with nothing but stones and tried to dig a shelter in the earth with cartridges. A wounded man might call only to the dead, who lay like shipwrecked sailors on the spurting earth. The nucleus of Americans left from the big offensive was holding tight together, but they must have felt, during the prolonged stalemate, where men died one by one, that the real war was going on elsewhere. Or that only the enemy would remember them and on some dark night swoop down and take them by surprise.

The long line straggled in a zigzag and one morning I went up with two doctors to the British sector, where some of the men had refused to be inoculated against typhoid. The disease had broken out all along the line. The Americans had taken the shots without a murmur; the Poles stubbornly refused; even some of the British surprisingly resisted. The doctors were impatient and fearful of the typhoid threat. They thought the presence of a woman might shame the boys into submission. Sitting on a rock, I smoked a cigarette, while some twenty recalcitrant British soldiers filed out to a little plateau. It seemed to me an exposed position; you could hear the whine of bullets through the olive trees. The men were ordered to take off their tunics, and, stripped to the waist, the pale cage of their ribs looked pathetically vulnerable. The tanned faces, the ready-looking brown hands, didn't belong to the stemlike bodies that held some of the translucency of the Indian pipe that grows only in dark woods. One of the doctors went into a routine pep talk and got out his needle. Some of the soldiers shuffled uneasily out of the line; others stood, hesitantly.

One of the younger men came toward me, and calling me "Doctor," began to tell me why he didn't want it done. At first he said his mother was against it. Then he admitted that the reason was that they were due to get out of the line. If they took the shot, they didn't know when they'd get out. They had already been in sixty days. They had been promised relief; it hadn't come. This was a kind of strike to get what had been promised. Then they had the notion that the shot would cripple their arms badly. Suppose you got a surprise attack? Suppose it was the Moors coming at you? Would you have a chance, hand to hand, with a bad arm? You always kept a bullet for yourself if it was the Moors. That was better than to let them get you and cut you up alive. All this was said quietly.

419

The boy had very blue eyes and sometimes the eyes seemed to be laughing. I couldn't help but look at the pale bluish skin of his body where the veins shone. It seemed to me the clothes were a masquerade and that he wore them as Indians might war paint. The cinnamon-colored uniform gave his body an appearance of health; underneath, the skin shivered with a kind of phosphorescent light.

If I sometimes felt that the scene where I stood or sat was a stage set due to vanish the next moment, it was because the players, with their sunburned faces, were the actors of the moment who were concealing some of their real life in their role as soldiers. But none of them was trying to live up to any heroic image of the soldier; their modesty was one of their most engaging traits. They disparaged exaggerated reports of victories which had been printed in the very papers that seemed to them pledged to nothing less than "the truth," and they warned me not to deal with blood-and-thunder stories. They could laugh at some of the letters from home while admitting it was wearisome to get repetitious slogans like the cries of cheerleaders roaring away to enhance a game they were not playing. And it seemed at the front that too little was done by the homebodies in America, France, and England who might have gone out on prolonged strikes to protest the infamous nonintervention pact or might even have dipped down more substantially into their own pockets. Doubtless many of the soldiers in the International line were under the old spell of "workers of the world, unite" in the full belief that the true causes back of the war in Spain were revolutionary, and that, *this time,* a great new world might once more have a chance. But the mirage of the future did not blind them to the present; it induced the opposite to an easy optimism. To be stupidly optimistic does not give courage; the longer you stand on the bank and tell yourself how brave you will be to swim the swollen river, the harder it will be to dive in. Someone might cite the story reported in one of the papers about the Cuban pitcher who was said to be throwing grenades into the enemy lines like baseballs, when the truth was he hadn't had a chance to get near enough to throw anything. What the Cubans had wanted to tell me was that once there had been sixty-four of them. Now there were twelve. Please to remember them. Remember Pablo Torriente Brau, a good newsman from Havana.

There were not only living soldiers in the little groups where we talked. The dead were present by their absence. The dead often seemed as real to me as the man who might be talking of his friend, the battalion adjutant, born in Tennessee, who never had raised his voice when he talked to the men. Please remember Douglas Seacord. Remember Tomlison, who had commanded a machine gun company. Please remember. Not the dead as corpses, or even how they had died. But for the simplest ordinary things; for the way one rolled a cigarette, or another had squatted in the dust to make good maps of their position with his finger. Or some man might suddenly want to talk about his little boy, and how he stood in his crib, shaking the bars, laughing, and looking at his father, "just as if he knew me."

But as I was to find out, talk at the front was different from talk that might come from the same soldier once he was on leave in Madrid. At the front, he was pulled together, as if for a spring. He couldn't play around with his fears, but had to keep them down, like the folded blades of a knife, deep in the pocket. So you also never heard much talk about military tactics as you did among the noncombatants at the Hotel Florida, where there was a certain amount of vainglory in knowledge of the how and when. Nor did you get ghoulish accounts of the dead. What you sometimes got was a spurt of criticism of decisions, even open condemnation of some brash and willful leader. Privately, they even called one such man, who was sometimes headlined in heroic terms, "the murderer," later, on the Teruel front, against orders, he actually led a little band into what turned out to be an enemy ambush and death.

We might even get on the subject of dreams, and leaning on his arm, a soldier with hazel eyes and an auburn cowlick would begin, "I had this funny dream" and then tell how he saw a wide river flowing into a bay. The water looked thick. It was lapping this rock, kind of. Then it seemed to be lapping at things floating in it. They looked like clots of something, old rags, kind of. Then he saw that the bay and the river were blood and the clots bodies. The bodies were dead. You could see he was sorry he had told the dream the second it was over; he fumbled in his breast pocket for something, and to take his mind off, I told him I dreamed of bread. It was true. At the Florida I was always having this dream of coming home from school and smelling my mother's wonderful homemade bread. In the dream I would head for the pantry and have time to lift the white towel from the beautiful golden loaves before I heard the thunder. I had to leave the bread to shut the windows so the rain wouldn't come in. Then I woke up. There was no bread and no thunder. Only the noise of the early bombardment.

421

They loved this story and I had to repeat it several times. There may seem to be something childish in all this, but these were not childish men. It just happens that a kind of childishness, in the sense that the child knows how to savor joyful things, is a source of instinctual happiness, and even in this crucial situation, they had not lost the art or the heart for this kind of search. The Spanish soldiers had it to an even greater degree. When I saw them in their front lines at the Casa del Campo they were often playing the fool.

Back at the Hotel Florida was nothing at all after the front. The atmosphere at the restaurant on the Gran Via was not exactly effete, and yet it now struck me as tiresomely superficial. There were little cliques and it did not console me that characters who had paid no attention to me were now inclined to gather me to their bosoms because of what they considered my feat in establishing myself at Murata. At night I no longer dreamed of bread. My inner room looked out on a little well and I could see shadows fall on the wall opposite when there was a moon. I longed for my room in Murata and its cold stone floor where the chill shot up your leg like a toothache if you put your bare foot down. The shadows on this wall were barren; in Murata I could look out on the little empty street where late at night a dog might wander or a single figure come to a doorway and stare up at the sky. When I thought of the long trench, the earth-work seemed like a wave that would be certain some day to fall. At the Florida, I would lie in my bed rehearsing the times I had walked through the trenches at Jarama. I could see the young Spanish boy leap to his feet with the cry *"Salud"* and watch other figures tidying up their little nooks as I approached. I could feel their hands, for to each you gave your hand as you passed by, and each hand was different. Some had a cool hardness; some clung, spasmodically tightening their fingers. If I had come like news of an outside world in which they still had a place because they were not forgot, they reminded me of some inner necessity for which I was struggling for some kind of answer. At the Florida, I could lie still, remembering some of their observations, which often had delicate poetic insights. I had looked over the top of the earthen wall where the land rolled with the inevitability of a sea to that distant port which might disgorge some night the crawling creatures who came on their bellies like monsters of the deep. There was something primeval about my visions of that hilltop where the earth was often streaked with the slime of dead things. Then I would tell myself that this primeval world was in me, and that the boys on the line would bear up to the wave when it came better than I could.

All I wanted was to get out again, somewhere, to people who were "in it." Once more, I had to wait. Others were also waiting in a state of discontent. A well-known journalist from London, with a pinkish dome around which were wound some miraculous wisps of pale hair as long as my arm, was obsessed with "atrocities." He had been in the Great War and had been a prisoner in Germany. There was an unhealthy glitter in his eyes as he told me that people rounded up as spies were shot regularly. He had been out to see the nicks in a high white wall against which they stood to die, and he had even surreptitiously counted the nicks. Dos Passos was worrying about his friend, Professor Robles, who had translated his books into Spanish, and who had been arrested as a spy, and Hemingway was worried because Dos was conspicuously making inquiries and might get everybody into trouble if he persisted. "After all," he warned, "this is a war."

Two of the boys from the Jarama front came to see me, and not finding me in my room, went to Hemingway's room, where they picked the lock of his wardrobe. They stole two jars of jam, which put Hemingway into a rage. The rage didn't mean a thing. Hemingway, like a good many others, was undergoing some kind of transformation, and part of the reason he had come to Spain was doubtless because the forces of that process were already at work. It wasn't only that he was giving up his wife for Martha Gellhorn. He had answered a definite call when he came to Spain. He wanted to be *the* war writer of his age and he knew it and went toward it. War gave answers that could not be found in that paradise valley of Wyoming where he had fished or even in the waters of Key West when the tarpon struck. What was the deepest reality *there* was in an extreme form *here*, and to get it he had to be in it and he knew it.

He was a real friend to the Spanish; he had donated an ambulance and had come as a correspondent. He was promoting the film, *Spanish Earth*, which was to show life in a village and what the war meant to the Spaniards. But in annexing new realms of experience, Hemingway was entering into some areas that were better known to people like Dos Passos, or even myself. He seemed to be naïvely embracing on the simpler levels the current ideologies at the very moment when Dos Passos was urgently questioning them. On another level, Dos was absolutely right in refusing to believe that his friend could be guilty of treason; the bonds of friendship were not to be broken that lightly. You could feel the irritation growing between the two men and even wonder at the origin.

There was a kind of splurging magnificence about Hemingway at the Florida, a crackling generosity whose underside was a kind of miserliness. He was stingy with his feelings to anyone who broke his code, even brutal, but it is only fair to say that Hemingway was never anything but faithful to the code he set up for himself. He could give an ambulance, but would not be able to stomach stealing jars of jam on the sly. It wasn't soldierly. When I laughed at the whole thing, he was indignant. Part of his exuberance came from the success of his love affair. But even his love affair was not exactly a benign influence in a wartime hotel. The corks popping were not for you, and late at night on the stairs, after a trying day, some of the correspondents would be sitting talking about nothing much, just to put in time or to take the edge off jerky nerves. Now and then the divine odor of cooking would seep through the hallways, and Hemingway, bursting with vigor, would bustle around and confide in me that he had shot a hare and a partridge and that the good Spanish maid on our floor was cooking them for him. His feat would be presented as a virtuous act and I was inclined to agree with him, even if I only shared the good smell. For as someone who could broil trout over a fire in the woods and had raised food in my own garden, I felt as he did, that there was a special virtue in the food that you had got together with your own hands. I would find myself compulsively narrating my own exploits in the food line. Our mouths would water.

There were days when you sat around brooding or lived only for that brief hour at noon when the bars opened for the sale of beer. Other days crammed the meaning of a lifetime into a few brief hours. One morning just before clear daylight I was awakened by two terrifying thuds. A heavy wall of water seemed to be crashing down with an iron force. But the havoc was in me where the flood was swishing and my heart had become no more than a helpless chip. My hands shook as I tried to find my clothes; then I gave up, and throwing on a dressing-gown, ran into the hall, where there was a strange sound like the twittering of birds at dawn in the country. People were running toward the rooms at the back, doors banged, and when Hemingway, fully dressed and fit, called out to me, "How are you?" I opened my mouth to say "fine," but no sound came. I rushed back to my room with the insane protest that had popped up—"but I didn't come here to die like a rat in a trap"—mocking me. For what had I come, if not possibly that? I managed to dress and to walk out again, and seeing Claude Cockburn with a coffee-pot in his hand, walking with his head bent, pale but impeccable, I rushed up to him and took it from him.

We went to a room toward the front where the banging was heaviest. Thousands of rats seemed to be scrambling for their lives in the plaster of the walls. We got the coffeepot plugged in, but there was no coffee. Someone else brought coffee and someone else some stale bread. A toaster came from somewhere. Dos Passos, fully dressed and composed, even to a necktie, came in. A French correspondent in a vibrant blue satin robe emerged carrying an armful of grapefruit, which he passed out to each of us, bowing to us in turn. Who would give away a precious grapefruit if this was not to be our last hour? No one ate the fruit, but each one, when the shelling was finally over, stole off with the loot. Hemingway blew breezily in and out. There was conversation, but I don't know what about. It was consoling to see everyone behave so well and to wonder if, within, the turmoil in others had been as hard to quell as it had been in me.

When the shelling was over some people ran at once to the street. Hemingway came back with the report that the Paramount Theatre had got it, including the big sign advertising Charlie Chaplin's *Modern Times*. A team from England was out picking up shrapnel. An old man was displaying some handsome brass fragments that were clearly part of a German shell. A workman left his job of clearing up debris to join a little crowd that had gathered around him. The workman began to argue with him that it was his duty to give up his prize to the English to take back with them as propaganda. The English stood politely waiting. The old man was torn between duty and desire; one moment he held the piece out toward them, the next he drew it back. Then he fondled it, and abruptly put it in his pocket, muttering that he had to show it to his daughter. The entire square was a mass of rubble of a pinkish gray color that looked like the entrails of animals in an abattoir.

425

Though the day had barely begun no one knew what to do with what was left of it. The big lobby was gritty with a pasty kind of sand. Some got consolation in talking about the merits of shelling as opposed to an air raid. Others analyzed the position of the hotel, which was in a suicidal spot, in the direct line of fire aimed at the War Ministry and the Telephonica. Though our lives had been spared, everyone was touchy. Hemingway asked me why I was so glum, and I answered angrily that I didn't feel like a Girl Scout and I didn't care who knew it. Then he relented and invited me to his room for a snifter of brandy. But what he really wanted was to urge me to talk to Dos Passos and to tell him to lay off making inquiries about Robles. It was going to throw suspicion on all of us and get us into trouble. This was a war. Quintanilla, the head of the Department of Justice, had assured Dos that Robles would get a fair trial. Others in authority had told him the same. He should lay off. Quintanilla was a swell guy; I ought to get to know him.

His request was terribly disturbing. I had known all along that Robles had been shot as a spy. I had been in Valencia before coming to Madrid and there had been told, in strictest confidence, and for the reason that Dos

Passos was an old friend of mine, that the man was dead. Some of the Spanish were beginning to be worried about Dos Passos's zeal, and fearing that he might turn against their cause if he discovered the truth, hoped to keep him from finding out anything about it while he was in Spain. I had no way of knowing whether Robles was guilty of the charges against him, but he had been in America, had been a professor at Johns Hopkins, was well known for his enlightened views, and there was the chance that he was the victim of personal enemies or even of some terrible blunder. The trouble was that I had sworn to keep this secret, just as my informant had been sworn by someone higher up. The circumstances seemed to me more pressing than any promise. I could not believe Quintanilla so good a guy if he could let Dos Passos remain in anguished ignorance or if the evidence was so clear as not to admit contradiction. I felt that Dos should be told, not because he might bring danger down on us, but because the man was dead.

So I put my drink down and said: "The man is already dead. Quintanilla should have told Dos." Hemingway was surprised. What were we to do? Because of my promise I felt I should not be brought into it, but Hemingway might admit that someone had told him; someone from Valencia who was passing through but whose name also he must withhold. Perhaps he agreed with too cheerful a readiness. I don't think he doubted for a minute that Robles was guilty if Quintanilla said so. But I did. Hemingway was to have an opportunity to talk to Dos that very day, for the three of us had arranged to go to Brigade headquarters where the Russians were installed. I had been fearfully curious, but now I wasn't even certain that I wanted to go. I didn't know how Dos Passos would take the news and I even dreaded to find out.

Rafael Alberti and his wife, Maria Teresa, were to go with us, and in fact had arranged the meeting, but probably because of my own state of mind, their ebullience, and their chatter, which went on with the vivacity of bright canaries, did not strike a sympathetic note in me. I felt I would rather read Alberti's wonderful poem *"Sobre los Angeles"* quietly at home than go twenty steps to meet him in his sparkling military boots and with his camera in hand, and his propensity for arranging groups for pictures, then leaping into the center of the group at the last moment while he thrust the camera into someone else's hand.

What I remember most, as we drove along the road through the countryside, was the sight of the Guadarrama Mountains, blue with purest white snow at the crown, and beyond a sky even more intense in its blueness. A bird, an actual bird, was flying above us, wheeling, and no words for it could be better than those written by the very man who was prattling away so volubly in the car that was taking us to the former castle of the Duke of Tovar.

> *Se olvidan hombres de brea y fango*
> *que sus buques y sus trenos,*
> *a vista de pájaro,*
> *son ya en medio del mundo una mancha de aceite,*
> *imitada de cruces de todas partes.*

> (Men of pitch and mud forget
> that their boats and trains,
> to a bird's eye,
> are a stain of oil in the middle of the world,
> bounded by crosses on every side.)

427

    No place could seem more remote from the front than the castle when we drove past the big square tower with its guard of soldiers and entered a patio where the walls of the alcaldía were lined with shining blue and white tiles and where big oleander trees in earthen pots were spaced like sentries at regular intervals. When we went in through an enormous kitchen we seemed to have stepped into a Brueghel painting; the coppery pans above the huge fireplace—actual cooking was going on—seemed reflected in the deeply sunburned faces of a dozen soldiers, who were lifting spoons and forks around a table where dishes of food sent up an appetizing steam. High windows let in sunlight through delicate starched curtains that parted to show the nodding tops of blooming lilacs.

    It was as if we had stepped back into another age, and where only our oddly assorted presences served as dissonance. The Russians had luncheon for us in a noble room where paintings of ancestors in ruffs and swords stared haughtily down at us, and where the Russians themselves, two attractive men with soft voices, actually did not seem inappropriate substitutes. The division commander, next to whom I was seated, even spoke German, though

I do not remember that I could find anything that seemed worth saying. Most of the talk was in French or Spanish, and though I knew from Dos Passos's abstracted air that Hemingway had told him, he kept up his end of the conversation with considerable spirit. In the garden afterward, another officer who had not been at luncheon wanted to talk German with me, and though it was about world politics and the decline of capitalism, I felt I had heard all this before. With a little coffee cup in his hand, Dos came up to me, and in an agitated voice asked why was it that he couldn't meet the man who had conveyed the news, why couldn't he speak to him too? The only thing I could think of was to tell him not to ask any more questions in Madrid. It would be better to wait until he got to Valencia and then see someone like Del Vayo and find out what he could.

Except for the chirping of Maria Teresa, who with coral earrings, a brooch, and filmy scarf suddenly made me feel that I looked as austere as a nun, the ride back to Madrid was silent. Hemingway bolted from the car the second it landed at the Hotel Florida, and the Albertis shot off, leaving Dos Passos and me standing on the street wondering what to do until it was time to pursue what would probably be a forlorn sausage stuffed with sawdust at the Gran Via. Dos suggested we walk to the Place Mayor, which was part of the old but not a grand section of Madrid, and which I did not know, although it was one spot that had been a favorite of his in other days. It wasn't far distant and was still beautiful. Some of the houses were mere shells with the light from the setting sun illuminating their flushed skeletons. Houses with the top sliced off still held occupants who continued to water the plants in the windows and to keep the bird cages in which little birds were hopping and chirping out in the open air.

But the best thing about the square was the horse. It was only a statue of a horse, but of such a spirited creature with such a mighty tail and mane that it suggested all the vitality of some great horse-ancestor who has sired a race of triumphant winners. Its flanks glittered a coppery rose and upon its side had been painted in bold red the brand of the anarchist syndicate CNT. In the hand of the rider—for it had a rider, though of not so much distinction as the horse—had been thrust a little anarchist flag. A woman with eyes black as jet and with a knob of black hair throbbing at the nape of her neck leaned out a window. Some kids whooped from behind a pile of rubble. An old man, tilted in a chair against an empty shell, called out cheerfully: *"Salud."*

At the Gran Via we had barely gone down the steps when the Englishman who had once been so happy writing about trawling, came up to me and in a flutter said, Who did I think had arrived *now?* I was beginning to think he was like those factotums in Victorian novels who stand at the door of the ballroom and bawl out the names of the guests. Celebrities fascinated him, and he not only announced but foretold. He had foretold the arrival of a Duchess and of a Lady something or other. Now he was waiting to get my reaction to the Dean of Canterbury. "So he's arrived. What of it?" I said, knowing full well I annoyed. The trouble was that I had already cast my eyes on the black-frocked Dean, a well-meaning man, no doubt, with a large, pink, saccharine face, the head of a Humpty Dumpty, bald, and fringed with a little babyish skirt of lacy hair. His secretary was impounded on my floor and ran around in a long funereal skirt, with a bunch of keys dangling at her waist like some bailiff out of Dickens. No doubt about it, the day had brought out all my most contrary impulses. But I didn't get a chance to indulge them.

Sid Franklin, on one side of me, began to relate how he had come to be a bullfighter and that on killing his first bull he had puked. On the other side, the UP correspondent, Hank Gorrel, was reminding me that it would soon be the seventeenth day of heavy shelling and that the press bureau might have to move from the Telephonica. The evening ended by going to a movie with Hank. It was Marlene Dietrich in a spy movie and the glamorous creature was finally led out to be shot. Perhaps back home it might have gone down, but here in the heart of Madrid with shells beginning to crash down once more and some people rushing out, others hissing, *shush*, and angry calls to the back where a big black curtain was carelessly left open by somebody hastily exiting, the whole drama was hilarious. We laughed until the tears came. "What a production!" Hank exclaimed. "How could anyone in their right minds think they could get away with it?" Then he went on to say, soberly, that war was a production, and he feared that he had been typed as a war correspondent. This was the third time he had been shot into a big production and if you asked him, we were only seeing, here, a prelude to the biggest smash production of all.

In Madrid it began to seem more and more a tight squeeze and though it was actually a front with the lines not far off in the Casa del Campo, it often seemed utterly remote from the more meaningful scenes you might witness in the villages. For in Madrid, no matter what you might see, or

429

where you might go, you were obliged to rotate around the axis of the Florida and the Gran Via, and with characters coming and going, even to a movie actor from Hollywood, the atmosphere began to feel, as the correspondent with the pink dome confided to me, "more and more like Bloomsbury." But for all that, individuals went about their business, soberly, and Herbert Mathews, of the *New York Times*, not only kept to the line of duty but strolled around, discovered tiles that had been designed by Goya taken from a wrecked mansion, and began patiently to collect a few. When you passed Hemingway's room, you heard the busy sound of his typewriter pecking away.

As for myself, I soon found out that the first requirement was not to make a nuisance of myself or to press for any privileges, but the odd thing was that this very condition seemed to invite the miraculous chance. Even Pink Dome went out of his way to invite me along after he had wangled a car to drive to a village where raw Spanish troops were being drilled in three columns up and down the street. The trumpeter who set the signals was very young and handsome in a red shirt with the neck open and short sleeves and wearing a cap cocked to one side above stiff curls that might have belonged to one of those carved wooden Angel Gabriels that I had once admired in the medieval churches in Germany. The troops were tagged out in all sorts of costumes; smocks, old ragged shirts, faded corduroys or old frayed pants, but they marched with a proud pomp that brought praise from Pink Dome, who fancied himself as something of an expert from the Great War and insisted on peering down the barrels of their guns, which he pronounced clean but in need of oil. One of their officers, also in ragged pants, said there wasn't any more oil. But when the trumpet blew, the men marched with fine straight backs, proud swinging steps, while their leaders, brisk and happy, watched to see what Pink Dome might say. At the bugle call to halt, they all stopped on the instant, wheeled on a dime, and were pronounced by the British expert to be excellently disciplined.

I was more interested in them when they were at ease, or loafing amiably inside a church where the altar now held an assortment of kits hanging by straps and ammunition, and where a horse, a horse! turned a powerful neck from munching hay to stare at us with mild eyes. There was a big iron kettle outside from which the men were ladling stew, and they even offered us some. It tasted better than anything we got at the Gran Via, as seemed only fitting. Not far away in another village, the same thing was going on, and this time the men were exercising on what had been a threshing field, which still held the firm beautiful color of a golden loaf of bread. As they wheeled and turned in the lovely ambient air, the blue and red of their smocks bellied out with the exuberance of little flags. All the color seemed to have drained upon the field that sparkled with gold and blues, reds, and greens and made the womenfolk, some of whom stood watching on the sidelines, seem like little black withered fig trees. But that was only the superficial view, for though they were in the perpetual black clothes of women always in mourning or always at work, their eyes snapped with an inner fire.

More than once I wondered at what we had assumed to be the vaunted independence of the American woman when I saw the proud authority of the Spanish woman upheld by something more than reliance upon any externality. Or, as on the night I stayed in the caves above Alcala de Henares, where the old, the children, and a few of the less able-bodied women remained during the day while the rest trudged down the steep mountain to work in the fields even when they were under fire, and when I saw women of sixty come proudly home, erect, magnificently wrathful as they shook their fists at far distant towers of enemy smoke piercing the sky, or burst out into gorgeous obscenities oddly mixed with symbolic religiosity that reduced my memory of fashionable ladies back home, with their little stereotyped lavender curls and their mincing high heels, to a parody of a potential they had forfeited.

431

In that ancient cave that the Moors had carved so fabulously out of living rock, the people of the ruined Alcala de Henares had set themselves up, each in his little household, and at night songs echoed along the corridor as they cooked suppers over tiny fires. A baby had been born the day before I was there, and lay in a little crypt with its mother on a mound of hay covered with a worn blanket. It was very tiny and looked in his new raw redness more like a little image carved from wood than an actual child. The entire community was proud of his arrival as if he had been blessed by fire and would certainly survive to reap the benefits of their struggle. Though there was ominous foreboding elsewhere, which events were to confirm, among the people of the villages you got nothing except the will to win. Those who didn't want to win had run away or were concealed in some hypocritical setting biding their time.

But there were times when I sometimes wondered how much they actually relished the presence of so many foreigners, even though they were soldiers. The Spaniard is so proud, and so deeply self-reliant, that it must also have been a wrench to be brought to a pass where outside help was needed. There were conflicting reports about the reaction among Spaniards to this foreign invasion, and there is no doubt that it differed with different communities. The soldiers of the International Brigade had great delicacy in handling the situation in the little towns near which they were billeted, and often found the simplest ways to win the confidence of some townsmen who in turn might win over all the rest.

I know that once when I had managed to get myself transported to the little village where they were making the film *Spanish Earth*, and the others had driven away and left me, I felt it was outrageous that I should be willing to linger to eat into the villagers' scant supplies. For food was so precious, and it would have been different if I could have come without empty hands. On that day, once I was alone, I wandered along the little street where some of the houses had been flattened in earlier air raids, and which seemed so empty because every able-bodied man was at the front, and the old men and most of the women were in the fields working to cultivate the crops. At the edge of the village a few goats were cropping the scant grass and the children were gaily playing a game that looked like drop-the-handkerchief. Only it was a little rag. I sat down and idly took out a notebook in which I often made little sketches of the terrain. There were some hills that looked shaved off to a level not far off and in their flattened sides were holes that might have been made by some gigantic bird and which reminded me of the swallows that used to build in the clay banks along the Missouri in Iowa. Some little flowers grew modestly in a scratchy sort of way and I picked a few, pressing them in the notebook. But I had not been long idly sketching and mostly to compose myself, while I figured out what to do, when I felt the presence of somebody, and looking up, saw that a circle of children had gradually drawn near me and were watching me intently. One small boy had so beautiful a head that I found myself trying to draw it, and when a little girl edged near me, she screamed out that it was Pedro! I was flattered that she could see a likeness, and before I knew it, I was taking orders from them and they in turn were ordering each other to stand in line and "to be next." It was like a funny kind of photograph gallery and with such gusts of laughter, and even mockery at my failures, that before I knew

432

it I had let them marshal me around the village where nothing would do but that I "do" old Uncle Ramon who was huddled in his chair in the sun, and then go after Grandma whose hands were deep in the washtub.

It ended by my staying in the mayor's house for a few days—the mayor was of course at the front—and going with his wife to pick up twigs to make a fire to cook with. There was literally nothing to make a fire with except clippings from grapevines, which were hoarded like precious jewels in a sort of casket of dried branches. Someone had killed a goat a short time before, and it was delicious cooked in olive oil with garlic over a tiny fire of twigs. As for eggs, the mayor's wife and I trudged all around the village to collect a few and even went to those holes in the hillside that looked as if made by huge birds, where people lived, in caves hollowed out, and where some old woman, standing at the door, would advise us to hang around a few minutes as the hen was on the nest and would be off shortly with an egg for us. The nest of course would be within the whitewashed den, which was kept neat as a pin and had been scooped out in such a way as to catch the warm rays of the sun. There would even be a goat making himself at home alongside the hen, or a homely donkey amiably coming up to look over the newcomers.

Caves like these were not just wartime provisions, but features of a country where the life blood had drained down a few funnels to the rich. The owner of the manor had fled to Franco, leaving his wealth of grapevines, which it was the duty of the villagers to cultivate for his profit. That he had abandoned the village did not mean they were to abandon the vines, and they had harvested the grapes, sold them in the usual way, and had bought a pump with the proceeds which was to pump the waters of the river to an area of land which might be irrigated to make the gardens the villagers had never had. They were at this work, now, and the seeds had already been planted, the little life-giving rivulets were watering onions, melons, and vegetables that some of the kids of the village had never so much as tasted.

One night, driving out from Madrid to the Guadarrama under a quarter moon, which was the only light allowed, I had a chance to see what pains some of the soldiers of the International Brigade took to reconcile the villagers to their presence. Not a chink of light shone from the squat dark houses and our feet rattled noisily as we walked over the rough cobbles and opened a door. A battery crew of Germans were eating supper on a table spread with a white cloth. Pitchers of wine glowed under the beaded lamp,

433

which swung from a useless chandelier, now shrouded carefully in green netting. They were all hard at work on a platter of eggs, with coffee in pink cups steaming beside their plates. The faces had a curious uniformity: I can only describe it by saying that they looked confident and joyful. One has to remember that these men had been summoned, as it were, from the shadow of a cellar. The whistle that the very air gives to every child at birth had been stopped up with dirt. Now they had cleaned the whistle and whether for a little while or for years they might be allowed to make the music of the living, didn't perhaps matter so much to them as the fact of the NOW which had restored them to visibility where they were actual men. They were no longer like sleepwalkers whose actions are mechanical and meaningless and who are haunted by menacing noises and phantoms of the dark. Inescapable as their private troubles may have been, *here* at least, as if they had been on shipboard sailing from port to port, they could do nothing about them, and the saving grace was to use the NOW as if it were literally the forever.

So it is not so far-fetched to say that this one evening had a celestial quality, and that the little girls of the village, in their skimpy white dresses, sang like angels. Or that the schoolroom, packed with many different nationalities, had the benign air of those paintings called "The Peaceable Kingdom" made by the Quaker Hicks in Pennsylvania when trying to reconcile the animal world to the human, the invading whites to the Indians, and the Lion lying down beside the Lamb. If the soldiers' chorus of Yugoslavians with their leader rounding his *O*'s and leaning forward with his hand transformed to a baton reminded me of the frescoes in Italy where Fra Angelico's band of musicians resembled the choirboys who sang in the big cathedral, it was because everything during this evening reminded me of something else, and that something always vibrant and living. It was a kind of enchanted world which was being kept suspended, like the colors in a soap bubble that may burst all too soon, but while it lasts reflects in gorgeous illusion every smallest object in the little universe where it will soon explode to nothing.

There was even an accordion solo—"*Solo Mio*," of course—and a German recited a long narrative poem, filled with witty idiomatic allusions that nobody could understand except the Germans. But everybody applauded like mad and a mother stoppered up her bawling kid's mouth with a wine-soaked hunk of bread, which he blissfully chewed. The Czech soldiers sang Goethe's "*Röslein, Röslein, Röslein roth*" with the tenderness of men who were actually serenading a real sweetheart, and the evening was pitched so high that when the clown burst out, with a face whitened by flour and wearing a pink skirt over his uniform, and dangling a silly pocketbook from a stout wrist, it was almost unbearable. The audience moaned with pleasure. People at the back of the room clambered up on their chairs. Someone fell with a squeal. It took a lot of shushing and hissing to quiet people down so they could listen to the violin solo played by a handsome Hungarian who had been the first violin in the Budapest orchestra and who was followed by two comic Rumanians, stamping and singing—of all things—"Who's Afraid of the Big Bad Wolf"!

Afterward we went to another house where the girls of the village had arranged roses and ferns in a little silver dish for the center of the table and where the soldiers, pressing around, produced a few bottles of champagne. Then they brought out photographs of groups taken with different nationalities all congenially intermingling, as if the photographs could substantiate forever the hope they had tried that evening to sustain. The Germans made me accept packages of Lucky Strikes inasmuch as they insisted I "belonged" to them because I knew through my own skin what Germany had come to be like.

435

My room at the Florida was hardly bearable when I got back to it, and it was all I could do to keep from opening the door and shouting "Dry up!" at the little group on the stairs who were intoning monotonously: "I've been working on the railroad/All the livelong day."

If the next morning was so quiet that everyone at lunch at the Gran Via had relaxed to an almost ordinary temper, the peace was short-lived. I was about to leave the restaurant when Hemingway called me to his table, where he was sitting with Virginia Cowles, who was there for King Features, and Pepe Quintanilla. When I heard his name, I looked hard at him, as the man who had not told Dos Passos the truth about Robles, but his looks were as disarming as anyone's looks can be. In the old days he would have been called a police officer, but now he was head of the Department of Justice and the question was, could any court actually dispense justice? So I sat down, a little gingerly, as he went on with some amusing tidbit about Spanish artists in Paris, who in the good old days had hung around La Rotonde and had a little factory, painting Grecos by the yard for rich South Americans. They had five times stolen blocks of building stone to lug home to turn into sculpture.

The next second he was talking about Maneas, the anarchist miner, who had simply taken up a butcher knife on one of the first crucial days when they hardly had anything to fight with, and calling to the members of their little group—who were lying low on the roof and whom he had accused of being intellectuals who would never fight—yelled: "Come along, you bastards" and running straight at the enemy, had fallen with a bullet in his chest. But it was his kind, said Quintanilla, who had saved the day in Madrid, by calling upon everyone to do the impossible. Crazies, crazies, he repeated, smiling and shaking his head. There were lots of crazies. Sometimes kids. Like the time twenty soldiers ran out of ammunition and sent the kids back for it and when the kids brought it back, they refused to give it up. The men had to fight the kids to get it and then fight the enemy. Crazy. There was the lieutenant who wouldn't give up his three bars for the one due him as a newly-made captain. What, give up three for one! Nothing doing. Of course he couldn't read or write. In Spain that's one great trouble. At this point a shell fell and sounded as if it had dropped right outside the restaurant. Quintanilla kept on talking, telling little stories, but each time a shell fell he counted. By the time he came to ten—interrupting what he said each time to count—he was flushed and the rest of us had become very quiet. The lights in the restaurant were lowered and everybody except those at our table left. Even the waiters left. By the time Quintanilla had counted fifteen they all came back, for some reason or other, standing around near the door to the kitchen.

We suddenly find we have no more cigarettes. A waiter leaps forward and offers Quintanilla the last of his tobacco out of a pouch, pouring it into a paper and rolling it carefully. Quintanilla's fingers, as he takes the thin cigarette and puts it in his mouth, are delicate and transparent looking. The shoulders of his coat are awkwardly padded, his hair is thinning, but his gray-green eyes are not only completely alive but can emit warm sparks.

"I only carry one card to permit me to ride on a streetcar," he says. "Sixteen. The rest I keep concealed in an inner pocket. At home there are eight guards. I know how men die, all right. It's worse if it has to be a woman. Seventeen. One officer shat in his pants, huddled in a corner. He had to be carried out to be shot like a dog. Eighteen."

Hemingway interrupts and says he has got to go.

"Nonsense," says Quintanilla. "No one goes."

"*El Rubio*," says Hemingway quietly, thinking of Martha back at the Florida.

"Nonsense," repeats Quintanilla. "Work, I must work," says Hemingway, half out of his seat.

"Crazy, crazy, no," says Quintanilla, and beckons to a waiter to bring cognac. When it comes, he pours some for everyone, and the waiters, standing near the door, who seem to have been waiting for this, bolt their drink and then vanish.

"There is no work once you get hit," says Quintanilla. He turns toward Virginia Cowles, who has been sitting quietly but looks very pale. A little blue line shows around her mouth. She is young and pretty; dressed in black with heavy gold bracelets on her slender wrists and wearing tiny black shoes with incredibly high heels. I often wondered how she navigated over the rubble from the Florida to the Gran Via. Now he pats her knee reassuringly and says: "We will all go to my house. I will divorce my wife and marry you. There are plenty of beds, plenty of room, even for Hemingway, an old man who is still green."

"I am only thirty-eight," says Hemingway.

"An old man but still green," insists Quintanilla. Then he takes out a picture of his son and shows it proudly. "I have a son," he tells Virginia, and "you won't have to make another. Just be my wife. My wife can be the cook. I have lived with her so long that it is just like mailing a letter and my only worry is will the stamp get on."

"Your wife is a magnificent woman," says Hemingway.

"We will kill a sheep and have wine. We can have a fine time. You can be the lover and I'll be the husband. Twenty-five."

"I'm afraid when you get tired of me you'll make me be the cook," says Virginia. We all burst into laughter, happy to hear our voices.

"I think it is letting up," says Hemingway. "I've got to go."

"No," says Quintanilla. "Twenty-seven." The plaster has been tinkling rather pleasantly like ice in glasses inside the walls. Above a big window crashes. Twenty-eight. Then comes a long pause and we all get up and gingerly go up the basement stairs leading to the street. It looks fuzzy in a fume of cloudy dust from where the explosions hit, and empty, except for two soldiers with a girl between them, humping along, arm in arm, down the middle of the street, over the hunks of rubble through the steamy rose-tinted mist. Quintanilla pokes his head out, screaming: "*Hombres,*

hombres, go back, keep away. Go back." But the *hombres* pay no attention to him and crookedly, as if they were drunk, zigzag arm in arm, where not a hundred feet ahead of them a shell suddenly cracks down, sending up a cloud of steamy dust and a clatter of falling stones. "Crazy, crazy," moans Quintanilla. "Simply crazy. It happens like that. They walk right into it. Wait, we must wait."

We went below again and waited some more and by this time no one counted and the stories had ended. "If we only had a cigarette," said Quintanilla. Then we got up once more and decided to chance it. The street was murky and plowed; a little man in a white apron was out with a bucket of water and a broom grimly washing up a big pool of blood. Even our hotel had got a direct hit this time and the balcony had been chipped off. But no one had been killed. A nervous aviator from the front said he wished he were back in his little two-seater.

Some correspondents were going to take a leave to England. New ones arrived. H. L. Brailsford from London, whose writings I had long admired, came and sat like a little gray chipmunk waiting for a car to take him places. One of the Hungarian commanders came from the front bringing a ham in a tin and packs of Camels, and suggested that we buy champagne. But when Sid Franklin stuck to us like a burr he ordered wine instead. Then they got into an argument. The Hungarian called bullfighting a barbaric business. Sid said it was an art, a great spectacle when well done and he earned much money at it. "And what about your opinions?" asked the other. Until he came here, he had never been interested, Sid explained. Now he was trying to make up his mind.

"You ought to let it go," said the Hungarian. "It's too late to make up your mind."

"If the Fascists win, it will put us back a thousand years," said Sid.

"If you have got that far, how can you stop? The bullfight is a sham fight. You should fight in this war in a great cause. The important thing is a *Weltanschauung*, but for that we pay. One pays for everything. For *everything*." He seemed to have turned to stone and sat cold and stoic, staring at the table.

With his eyes on the ham, Sid whispered to me, asking me if he could buy some of it. I looked at him in astonishment and began to laugh. "Are you crazy? Of course not." More than once Sid seemed to rub someone from the front the wrong way. But there was no one at the Hotel Florida who did more to keep up morale just by a kind of buoyant mindlessness that was wonderfully contagious. He could smile when everyone else was glum or crack a joke or bargain for perfume or jewelry to take back home in a little shop where the shopkeeper might bring out a hoard of treasures that no one else was ever allowed to see. He couldn't understand why I wouldn't invest in furs. "You'll never get such a bargain again," he insisted and made me go to a shop where the owner dug out some beautiful skins that were of the unborn lamb. "Just look how they shimmer," Sid said. "Beautiful. And wonderfully cheap." He couldn't understand why I didn't even want them. "I couldn't" was no answer for him.

He even liked to get off cynical remarks in front of some of the boys from the Jarama front who might have only one evening in Madrid and must sometimes be thinking that evening might be their last. A kind of nervous anxiety had overtaken them; they were almost longing for the dreaded attack. One night Sid was rattling away about women and saying that sex was no more than a drink of water. "Take it or leave it," he said airily. He could be funny too about the rounding up of the whores, and that one of them had been sent scuttling from the hotel with her pajamas in a paper bag. But this particular girl was one that everybody liked; one of the boys from Jarama even tried hard to imagine that he had fallen in love with her. He felt it was unjust that the girls should get it in the neck; that they should be treated as spies without making any difference between those who might be and those who were loyal. Somehow he had imagined that here, of all places, things would be ordered differently.

439

Sid's contention that what everybody wanted was security, didn't go down well either. "It's not true," one of the Jarama men whispered to me. "What they want is happiness. And something to believe in." But the word "happiness" confused him, even pained him. He squeezed his eyes shut and asked me if I would walk out with him. "I need air," he said.

This fellow was in a position of command, but my lack of interest in military details kept me from even noting what his distinction was. He wore the same uniform as everyone else, but he was responsible for a good number of men and it was the men who "were like children, and looked to him" who were now on his mind. "Someone gets it every day or so. Just a nick here, a nick there. They look to me to see what to do. I don't know what to tell them. The lines are so close. They'll attack with grenades sooner or later. Or we will."

Then he dropped it and took up Sid. He didn't like that kind of talk;

all that drink-of-water stuff. He had loved his wife. "You should see my kids, a girl and a boy." But he didn't know when he would ever see them, or what they would be told about him if he were killed, for his wife had left him.

We began to walk and somehow the talk about the boys in the Jarama line and his wife waiting for her kid to be born all got mixed up together. The night in the trenches while they waited for an attack seemed like a hideous counterpart to the night when his wife had waited for the doctor who didn't come. When she had the girl, she had gone to the hospital, but with this one, hard times had struck. He got paid in paper scrip that no one wanted. There was a doctor lined up, but when her waterbag burst two weeks ahead of time they couldn't get hold of him. In the middle of the night, they were all alone, with her pains coming hard. She gripped his hands so tight that he could feel it to this very moment. It was so dark; he kept looking out the window. His eyes just gnawed the dark, trying to make a hole for the doc to get through. He tried to get another doc but there wasn't time. Time—it squeezed you up and wrung you dry and limp. Then she said, I can't help it; it's coming. He rushed to wash his hands. Then he thought he heard a step and ran to the door, but no one was there. Then the boy came. A fine fellow. He tied his cord. When it was all over both doctors came. One was smoking a big cigar.

I had stumbled over a pit in the pavement; when he caught hold of my hand, his own was wet. I could not see his face, only feel how he felt, and that he was sorting things out from a jumbled mass of experiences if only to make some order to help him to live. Did I remember that fellow at the front, the dark guy with a cut on his cheek? He had been killed and it was an awful thing to say but it was a kind of relief. You know what? He actually liked to kill, and it was all they could do to keep him from killing the prisoners they sometimes brought in. Why that fellow would actually cry, and bite his hand until the blood came, and say, but it's so nice! Can you beat that? Some of the prisoners might be giving themselves up, and just hoping we would catch them. A Spaniard knew one such man who had been brought in. They had come from the same village and he knew it was true that this fellow had been trapped by the Fascists and forced to fight for them. This prisoner said there was a lot of discontent in their lines; and they only got meat once a week. Why wouldn't there be discontent? You couldn't tell him that the ordinary guy wanted to see Franco win. Look who ran after him. The rich. Had I seen any of those big houses? Some of the wounded boys were convalescing in them. Wonderful joints. But what could the owners be like when they had these photographs stoked away in some little drawer, bunches of them, of some swell dame that one of the Spaniards said was a fashionable duchess, taken stark naked with a naked man, and in poses you'd never expect to find except on those dirty postcards they were selling you in Paris.

Or sometimes late at night sitting on the stairs at the Florida, talking to whoever might be there, we would be interrupted by the rap of high heels and see some of the "girls" being herded along the hall. "Just when she was giving a little comfort to some poor guy," remarked one of the men.

Though spies began to be on everyone's mind, no one could imagine who they might actually be. You never saw one. The "girls" locked up for a night would be certain to filter back, if not at the Florida, then elsewhere. But I noticed when we made trips out of the city and our car was stopped for the password, that the only papers they were interested in were mine, as the one woman present, and that when on the first of May they stopped the car and poked a head inside to look carefully, saying, "the first of May," that our prompt answer, "unite and fight," the password for the day, satisfied them about everybody except me. They had no suspicions about me except that I was a woman, and as such was a possible threat. But what concerned me was that I was a noncombatant and as such it was probably time for me to move on. I even told myself that I was eating too much, though it was very little and I had lost twenty pounds.

Unite and fight seemed so terribly urgent that no one could believe the news from Barcelona. What? Barricades? With Loyalists fighting their brother Loyalists and not Franco? But some of the correspondents had warned all along that even if Franco won, a Civil War was certain to follow. There were rumors and counter-rumors. H. L. Brailsford was stunned, and as he had more background than almost anyone else, it was a comfort to talk with him. Though he agreed that when you are at war with a deadly enemy it is better not to begin fighting among yourselves, yet it is well to remember that it takes two to make a quarrel and that people do not begin building barricades unless they have received something that they regard as provocation. The Spanish anarchists had been persistently denigrated in the foreign press for some time, and he intended to go to Valencia and look up some of his friends among the anarchists and get to the bottom of it. The war had come to a point where the anarchists were probably asking questions. Were they fighting for the same old stuff or for a redress of ancient wrongs? When I asked him if he believed what they were putting out about POUM he shook his head. "It sounds bad," he said. "That's one reason I can't believe it." But when I cornered Claude Cockburn, whose paper, *The Week*, had always had so much information no one else carried that even prime ministers took it, he could only shrug and say: "They are putting out the usual line of accusations; they claim they've got documents to prove collaboration with Franco."

When Brailsford told me he had wangled a car and if I wanted to go with him to Valencia, to come along—I was ready to go that instant, if only because I didn't want to say any goodbyes. Except for one more item, I wrote no more in my journal. But I couldn't resist putting down a conversation at a little filling station halfway to Valencia, when a young Spanish officer came up to the car, and beaming, asked me if I did not remember him. The day I had been at Guadalajara and looked through the periscope? It was on a day when I had visited the German battalion and had deployed through a beautiful field to climb a whaleback mountain on top of which a lookout had been established. From that point you could see directly opposite across the valley to another whale with gun emplacements and another lookout— the enemy, doubtless—looking at you. It had so innocent a look, enhanced by the sound of a gramophone playing some light-hearted music, that you couldn't believe that this terrain sprinkled with tiny delicate flowers, was a deadly place which would be paid for, inch by inch, with human lives. The young officer had been in charge of the lookout, and now he was being sent to a school for more training. He was happy and proud. As we were talking, a simple townsman came up and listened in, enchanted. "A commander?" he questioned the young officer, politely. As there were women soldiers in Spain it was not so strange a question as it seems. "No, no," answered the officer in a low intimate voice. "American?" The officer nodded, and we went on talking about his school. When he spoke to me he raised his voice as one does to the deaf. It is the way people do to someone who is not completely conversant with the language. The townsman was beaming and listening with all his might. Once more he plucked at the soldier's sleeve. "But she understands everything!" "Everything," repeated the soldier, condescendingly, *"muy intelligente."* *"Valiente,"* breathed the small townsman, *"muy valiente."*

442

But I was far from understanding everything. About the most important questions, at that moment, I felt sickeningly at sea. As for being *valiente*, who wasn't? If I wrote it down in my journal, it was to put heart in myself, if only to say, come now, be *muy intelligente*, be *valiente*. Just try.

Saul Bellow

Saul Steinberg

A dinner with Saul Steinberg was one of the standing attractions of a visit to New York. We flew into La Guardia from Midway in Chicago and after a short shoeless pause at the Lotos Club to ease our feet, timing ourselves fitfully (Steinberg was a stickler for punctuality), we walked to the East Seventies along Madison Ave.—for the window-shopping—and at 7 p.m., while the elevator man waited to make certain that we were the parties expected, I rang the door bell. There were art treasures in the apartment and there was also Mr. Steinberg's privacy to guard. You felt at times that the elevator man had a second skill: that he was also a bouncer, and he was furthermore on Steinberg's payroll. Plainly Steinberg didn't want to be disturbed by unwelcome callers.

You entered. Steinberg, quietly beaming, sat you down on the sofa. On the low table before you a bottle of white wine, a dish of salted nuts, several wine glasses were waiting—always the same arrangement. The underlying assumption was that you had a dionysiac character, apt to be disturbed. Orderliness and regularity would keep you in balance. The pictures, most of them his own, several by de Kooning, were hung with the same intent— to regulate, to maintain order, harmony, and calm. My wife claimed that this had an effect even on the temperature of the room. "You don't need a thermostat," she said. The bottom of every frame was mathematically aligned within a fraction of an inch. "This brings you to your senses," she said, "no matter how upset you may have been when you rang the bell."

In earlier times as a special treat we occasionally had the critic Harold Rosenberg—a large, robust-looking ill man, very tall, with legs of unequal length—dining with us. Supported with his stick or with his game leg laid on a hassock, Rosenberg would develop some idea or other while smoking or drinking, the emphatic words coming from the back of his teeth. In his writing he described Steinberg as "a writer of pictures, an architect of speech and sounds, a draughtsman of philosophical reflections . . . a master pen man and calligrapher, aesthetically delectable." He added somewhere that Steinberg's work was his "line." In the sense of organized gab. As a man might approach a woman with "a line of gab," Steinberg seduced his viewers. For a long time Steinberg and I had known each other in the ordinary oblique way of knowing—at dinners, cocktail parties, on the beach at Amagansett or at one of Rosenberg's impromptu seminars.

But some thirty years ago on a crowded street in downtown Nairobi he and I met. On both sides there was some difficulty in making a positive identification. The streets were filled with men in tunics or togas or droopy drawers, women in turbans and flowered dresses. But both Steinberg and I were wearing bush-jackets like all the other jackets sold at tourist shops, with deep, zippered pockets for passports and currencies. We had also bought the soft-soled suede boots called "yellow buggers," but what identified us positively as Americans was the long-billed baseball cap each of us wore. Two men known to have independent imaginative powers had made the identical GI-costume choices. Laughing, we sat down together on the curb-stone.

I had come to Africa with Peltz, an old Chicago school chum. Peltz, who had been here before, was, so he said, the intended mark of a gang of con artists who pretended that they had an unlimited supply of semi-precious stones. They had proposed that Peltz should set up a company and that this company should buy them the necessary mining machinery and trucks. Peltz and I had discussed the deal with an English lawyer who advised us to leave town. "Get away from Nairobi awhile," he said when he saw copies of the letters Peltz had sent to his associates, "lest you end up in a courtroom."

"Why don't we go to Murchison Falls," I said.

"Just my cup of tea," said Steinberg. "I've always wanted to go but I never found the right company."

We flew at once to Entebbe and there we rented a Volkswagen van and hired a driver, who immediately offered to supply us with hashish. Wasn't hash what Americans wanted? We drove into Kampala where we took over the penthouse of the best hotel. The water-pressure at the very top of the building was not sufficient and we had to fill the bathtub from the fire-hose in the corridor.

Idi Amin was already active in politics but he hadn't yet taken over the government. His name was unfamiliar to travellers but, as we were soon to learn, he was already throwing opponents to the crocodiles.

In Kampala we were just beginning to experiment with hashish. My friends were high on it. Steinberg was madly happy. I was deeply depressed by the stuff and soon stopped using it. I recall very little of the early stage of our journey. On the main street of every town you saw foot-operated sewing-machines one after another and philosophical-looking unsmiling black tailors, who took no interest in you whatever.

Our driver brought us at last to the Paraa Lodge below the Murchison Falls. The huge waters crashed non-stop like a world congress of washing machines and then circled below as if considering what to do next—the hippo mothers and their calves showing nostrils and ears above the surface. The crocodiles, cruising under an agreement millions of years old, gave them a wide pass. Steinberg later sketched this scene, and there now hangs on the wall behind my desk a Steinberg drawing of a hippo looking very like a NY Department of Sanitation truck. This huge beast came every morning to the Paraa Lodge with her calf and together they overturned the large garbage cans and rummaged in the kitchen waste. In the sky, the moon is like a thick slice of canteloupe and beneath it runs an ornamental edging of crocodiles with open jaws.

The management of the Lodge arranged a meeting for Steinberg with a young English biologist employed by the government of Uganda whose specialty was crocodiles. He described to us the duties of his job. Now and then he had to kill one and report on what the animal was eating.

"They must be hard to kill."

"There's a spot behind the ear where you shoot them—they aren't vulnerable elsewhere. Human remains? Yes, from time to time you find some in their stomachs. And I am also directed to taste the croc meat—that's part of the examination."

Steinberg spent an entire afternoon questioning the young man: Do you taste it cooked or raw . . ?

"Either way, I don't think I could," he said.

The Paraa lodge had a motor boat that cruised the river and we went sightseeing in the morning, before the heat had built up. One of the guests was a young woman travelling alone—quite a pretty Scandinavian in poplin. Steinberg sat down with her. Such young women, Swedish or Danish, generally speak English. Peltz said, "Will he get anywhere with her?"

I thought it unlikely. She was not responding.

The boat approached a sand bar where crocodiles had laid and buried their eggs and seemed to be dozing in the sunshine and as we drifted by a croc braced herself on her short legs and in a combined swift movement came to her feet and rushed at the boat. The speed of these creatures, because of their Gothic construction and their look of clumsy torpor, takes watchers aback. They pull their prey to the bottom and drown it. The animal tried to board on Steinberg's side of the boat. The young Danish traveller had one elbow on the gunwale, and she went down. Steinberg also fell into the aisle. I thought, "This is it! Killed in Africa by a crocodile!" The creature had forced its head into the seat. Remembering the young Brit naturalist who said that you had to shoot behind the ear, I saw us at the mercy of this overpowering monster. I thought, "Steinberg will be killed. I'll have to write his obituary. But we'll all be killed. There's nothing but an oar to defend yourself with."

But with his oar one of the boatmen pushed against the sand-bank and the croc slid or fell back into the water. All the men laughed at this innocent fun. Steinberg helped the Danish lady to her feet, but there was nothing he could do to please her.

The heat on our hands and faces had a weight of its own. You wouldn't have cared to cool yourself in the water, the domain of the hippos and the crocs. By the time we docked it was evident that Steinberg had gotten nowhere with the lady from Copenhagen. This was my first glimpse of Steinberg the man of the world with his trim moustachios and his highly correct, goggled profile. It didn't make any difference that he had failed to impress the lady, because he was obviously having a wonderful time in male company. The hemp, as I have said, made me sick, but Peltz and Steinberg were preternaturally cheerful and you could glimpse the multiple projects generated in each of us by the heat, the unceasing white bombing of the

449

tons of falling water, and the ambling animal tons of elephants, wildebeests and hippos.

On the way back to Entebbe the hashish our driver bought in the backrooms of bars was smoked in our hotel parlors. Steinberg thrived on these evening smokes. But when the trip ended, when we had paid the driver and said goodbye to him, Peltz carried off the remaining hash to Europe while Steinberg resumed his regular, orderly, non-narcotic life. He and I flew to Addis Ababa, where we stayed in a near empty hotel on a fancy but empty boulevard. On the main streets there was nothing at all to see. They were utterly vacant. We visited the Emperor's Zoo. As he was called the Lion of Judah, he kept a zoo of lions. Their cages were little bigger than hen coops and the animals were underfed and down in the dumps. I've never seen lions so blue, so defeated. In these cramped cages they were in arrears with their grooming.

On the boulevard there were no cars, no buses or taxis—no shops, no people. Instead of buildings there were partitions of scrim and behind these partitions we saw people with dysentery squatting, entire communities, men and women, young and old. They took no notice of us, and we with-drew. Nor did we discuss what we had seen.

What Steinberg had to say he said with his pens. Conversation seemed to make him awkward. Back in the States you felt, when you met him for drinks or dinner, that he had prepared himself, had gotten up a subject from his very special angle. You were careful not to disturb him by introducing terms of your own and spoiling his planned effects. He wanted to speak as elegantly as he drew. He was highly intelligent, but he did not presume to come on like an intellectual. His silent moments were shrewd but never ill-natured. His face, with its goggle-and-moustache symmetry, forgave you in advance for your errors of judgment. He could be clinically frank about his ailments, about the shots his doctors recommended or about the marital troubles or the boozing of our friends.

Steinberg never lost sight of the fact that the artist was required to become someone else by fixing his attention on the mystery of his individual identity. Thereafter he was known by his *nom d'artiste* as well as by his way of interpreting the world. Even the crocodile, by being a crocodile, was, in his armored essence, his scales, his jaws, his teeth, interpreting life, interpreting nature. Prior to the Steinberg we knew there had been a Romanian Steinberg, and after that an Italian Steinberg, and latterly an American Steinberg.

The modern writer who suited Steinberg best was Chekhov. He knew Chekhov's stories, his plays, his correspondence and had read a good many of the biographers. The Russian writer had crossed Siberia to inspect the czar's empire, to find out what it was really about. During the Second World War, Steinberg had been sent from the United States on a mission to China. Why China? I had often tried to find out what the US had wanted him to do there but I had never succeeded. Steinberg, however, was well paired with Chekhov. Both were tentative, peripheral, almost occult personalities directed by some obscure vocational force to find out what humankind was up to. The Russian writer responded to an impulse very familiar to the Roumanian-Italian-American painter, the cartoonist, the autobiographer who was obliged to invent the self who would be known to the world as Steinberg.

In the jungles surrounding Murchison Falls, Steinberg tried out his crocodile theory on the English gamekeeper. "Don't you think that the crocodiles are living out or illustrating their view of existence simply by being crocodiles?" he said. But if the young naturalist was not ready for such a thought who could blame him.

Certainly not Steinberg who thanked him kindly for the time he had so generously given.

In the last years, he seemed to be fighting a war against distraction, against the scattering of his substance. He complained that busloads of people were coming from Manhattan to see the houses in East Hampton and Amagansett where de Kooning and Jackson Pollock had lived. On the public address the tour guide said, "And this is where Saul Steinberg lives." Steinberg was therefore no longer able to sit quietly in his garden. He withdrew to his New York apartment. He practiced yoga. He sent us a photograph in which he sat, lotus-style—his cat in a similar posture in the foreground. Europe no longer attracted him nor did Key West, which had for a short while been his sanctuary. From time to time we had lengthy telephone conversations but friendships don't thrive on long distance calls. He drew closer, I think, to Norman Manea, the Roumanian writer with whom he had much more in common.

I saw him as a man whose vital connections had become, for me at least, indescribable. Our meetings were all good will and cordiality. His gaze was friendly and warm. I was something of a relative to him—a kind of cousin—but we were not able to exchange ideas. As a source of enlightenment I was not in a class with Harold Rosenberg, not an intellectual guide who

could explain to the artist what he was doing. I was a sort of kinsman from the urban wilds of Chicago. Each of us wished the other well. But when he, Steinberg, was seriously up against it, I had no relief to offer him. I learned with astonishment that he had died of cancer.

By what morality to be guided in cases such as his, one doesn't know these days. I have lost three friends this year to the same disease. It's something like a board-game—backgammon or parcheesi or checkers. Towards the end, the board becomes more and more bare.

In some of Steinberg's pictures you are offered a contrast between the solitary human figure and the boundlessness of sea and sky—of natural earthly emptiness and of outer space as well.

Poems

Poems

Howard Nemerov

Life Cycle of Common Man

Roughly figured, this man of moderate habits, *457*
This average consumer of the middle class,
Consumed in the course of his average life span
Just under half a million cigarettes,
Four thousand fifths of gin and about
A quarter as much vermouth; he drank
Maybe a hundred thousand cups of coffee,
And counting his parents' share it cost
Something like half a million dollars
To put him through life. How many beasts
Died to provide him with meat, belts and shoes
Cannot be certainly said.
　　　　　　　　　But anyhow,
It is in this way that a man travels through time,
Leaving behind him a lengthening trail
Of empty bottles and bones, of broken shoes,
Frayed collars and worn-out or outgrown
Diapers and dinnerjackets, silk ties and slickers.

*

Given the energy and security thus achieved,
He did . . . ? What? The usual things, of course,
The eating, dreaming, drinking and begetting,
And he worked for the money which was to pay
For the eating, etcetera, which were necessary
If he were to go on working for the money, etcetera,
But chiefly he talked. As the bottles and bones
Accumulated behind him, the words proceeded
Steadily from the front of his face as he
Advanced into the silence and made it verbal.
Who can tally the tale of his words? A lifetime
Would barely suffice for their repetition;
If you merely printed out all his commas the result
Would be a very large volume, and the number of times
He said "thank you" or "very little sugar, please,"
Would stagger the imagination. There were also
Witticisms, platitudes, and statements beginning
"It seems to me" or "As I always say."

Consider the courage in all that, and behold the man
Walking into deep silence, with the ectoplastic
Cartoon's balloon of speech proceeding
Steadily out of the front of his face, the words
Borne along on the breath which is his spirit
Telling the numberless tale of his untold Word
Which makes the world his apple, and forces him to eat.

Oonagh Lahr

The Advance on the Retreat

When the city had passed me, my feet took a course that was gentle
To a field that was empty, and full of the color of green
Spread with remembrance, enameled with various liking
Where even the ditches are clear enough trenched to be trusted
The hedgerows grow neatly, and cleanly the gate hangs on hinges
In order so careful it leaves no location for longing.

The city was daunting, and tortured with hope and with longing
The barkers were fierce there, and slopes too afraid to be gentle
The arches were falling, and every door shrieked on its hinges.
To relief of staccato, this world here's a cadence of green
The footing of silence on turf makes a pace to be trusted
While the grass has the ease and the spring of immediate liking.

The buttercups shine like small suns of intemperate liking
Which eat up the eye and yet manage to discipline longing
Fulfilling all promise of riches with gold to be trusted
They gladly and smugly reflect back a light that is gentle
And even their scissor-torn leaves are a sureness of green:
The soil of this meadow is scented, the air moves on hinges.

The way to the meadow is easy, there's oil on the hinges
The only requisite is: giving up loving for liking.
And yet of all colors I fear most this marvelous green
A color that harms you and cheats you with satisfied longing
With turning a passion that's fierce to a kindness that's gentle
(If the kindness of lovers were ever the kind to be trusted).

The cry of the city was: only despair can be trusted,
A point is well-taken when reason is shorn off its hinges,
And levity grows in a field which is sunny and gentle.
The days trickle past and at length I am stifled with liking
I seek for an answer which never can answer my longing
To mow with a sickle that's sharper than this tender green.

By staring at scarlet you find it's the obverse of green.
Look here and away, and which is the hue to be trusted?
To feed on bright scarlet with never a hope of belonging
You batter your head on a door without handle or hinges.
The entry to either recourse is too dear for my liking:
When wishhorses couple with nightmares they breed nothing gentle.

This tells me that gentleness is not the nature of green.
When I proffer my liking I know that it should be distrusted.
All blame but my own comes from hinging my loving on longing.

Alexander Pushkin

Count Nulin

Hallo, hallo! the horns resound;
The whippers-in in hunting coat
Are long asaddle; every hound
Tugs at the leash and bays full throat.
Out steps the master, on the stoop
Stands arms akimbo, takes their measure,
Nods his approval of the troop,
And beams with frank but lofty pleasure.
Inside his caftan, tight as a drum,
He buttons up a flask of rum,
Hooks to its loops of bronze his horn,
Tucks in his sash a Turkish knife . . .
Against a window-sill his wife,
In night cap, nightdress, and a shawl,
Leans gazing down with sleepy scorn
Of men folks and their dogs and all.
She sees: they bring his horse; he tries
The stirrup, grips the mane, vaults on,
"Don't wait for me," he turns and cries,

And in a moment he is gone . . .
      September, what with drizzling snows
(To use the epithets of prose),
What with its mud, uncertain weather,
Fall winds, and wolves, is, toward the close,
A dismal trial altogether.
But just this time of year arouses
The hunter in the hunter. Out
He gallops with triumphant shout,
Puts up with—at—what's to be had,
Gets sopping wet and roaring mad,
And with his trampling horde carouses.
      Meanwhile, the domiciliar spouse—
What can she do, bereft of *her* spouse?
Pickle the mushrooms, feed the geese,
And order dinner *à la russe?*
Wives do, of course, have household chores,
Like checking barn and pantry stores,
And housewife's eye is quick to spot
What's missing from the purse or pot.
      The rub is, our—to say Natasha
As does her husband (have I said?)
Would at this early stage be brasher
Than we are wont, and so, instead,
Natalya Pavlovna to you—
Our Natalie, then, 's not reflected
On what a housewife ought to do;
Her training has been much neglected,
That is, more stylishly directed
By Madame F—, with whom young misses
Acquire more brilliant arts than this is . . .
      So, at the window as before,
She's sitting now, with volume four
Of a most tender composition
About some *Armand and Elise*
(*Or Letters of Two Families*),
A classic of secure tradition,

Of measured, O how measured gait,
Most edifying and sedate,
Without romantical sedition.
   Natalya Pavlovna a span
Reads on engrossed as she began,
But, once distracted, leaves her book:
Outside her window, in the yard,
A dog and goat are fighting hard,
And quietly she turns to look:
Sees laughing boys crowd round about;
And closer, startled by their shout,
A rain-bedraggled turkey cock
Leading his discontented flock;
Three ducks that paddle in a pond;
A peasant woman, out beyond,
That through the puddles splashing goes
To drape a fence with new-washed clothes;
The weather's worse; she thinks it snows
At times like these, but cannot tell—
And now she hears a carriage bell . . .
   Whoever's known the life apart
Of mournful countrysides can tell
How uncontrollably the heart
Beats to the sound of a distant bell.
Some friend returned from times that were—
Or now they seem so—brave and sweet?
What—Heavens! what if it was her!
It's closer—how the heart does beat!—
   But passes, faint and fainter still,
And dies at length beyond the hill . . .
   Natalya, at a single bound,
Is on the porch to greet the sound.
She looks: along the farther bank,
Behind the mill, a carriage sweeps.
It's on the bridge, it's coming, thank—
No, there it turns. She watches, blank,
She watches and she nearly weeps.

But suddenly, O joy! That hill!
The carriage topples—down it went!
"Run Vasska, Filka, with a will!
Someone! There's been an accident!
Bring back the carriage to the shop!
Invite the gentleman to supper.
I wonder if he's hurt? Don't stop!
Run faster!"
      Natalie fluffs up her
Exuberantly curly hair,
Puts on a shawl, pulls curtains to,
Shifts, imperceptibly, a chair,
And waits—what else is there to do?
But here they come, at last they come.
Mud-crusted from long traveling,
And sadly battered out of plumb,
In limps a coach on tired spring.
Behind, a sprig of Russian gentry,
Limps too, but not his valet, *non!*
That hero cries, "Courage, *allons!*"
And helps his master through the entry.
      And now may I, while the door is wide,
And a room set specially aside,
And the Picard's busy to excess,
And the master's half a mind to dress,
Present, before our story starts,
Count Nulin, home from foreign parts—
Where he has squandered in advance
His next year's rents to sport in France;
And now to Peter's town he goes
To air his foreign ways—and clothes;
His store of vests and coats with tails,
His corsets, hats, fans, cloaks, and so on,
Lorgnettes, studs, links—and what these go on—
Gay kerchiefs, stockings sheer as veils,
A work by Guizot (worst of wretches),
An album of malicious sketches,

The very last Sir Walter Scott,
Bons mots from Paris, piping hot,
Some chansonnettes by Béranger,
Rossini and Paër to play,
Etcetera, etcetera . . .
      The table's laid, the meal is waiting,
The lady too (all eagerness),
When in the doorway, hesitating—
The count. She rises to express
Concern at all she heard and saw.
Count Nulin answers, *"Nichevo."*
They take their places at the table—
Count Nulin nearing hers a bit
And starting in at once, to wit:
He wonders how one's ever able
To stand our Holy Russia's snow . . .
Scolds Paris for declining so.
"But still the theater?" "A farce!
C'est bien mauvais, ça fait pitié:
Talma's quite deaf, *senescit ars,*
And so, alas, does Mam'selle Mars!
And yet, Potier—le grand Potier!—
Potier alone sustains the passion
And former glory of the scene!"
"Which writers now are most in fashion?"
"Why, D'Arlincourt and Lamartine."
"Some Russians imitate them, too."
"Not really? So our Russian thought
Begins to take on shape and hue?
God grant it yet may come to aught."
"Where is the waistline now?" "Quite low.
Down to—well, down about to these.
Permit me—your accessories:
Hum . . . ruching, figured goods, and bow—
All this is very good, you know."
"Of course: we see the *Telegraph.*"
"Ha! Here's a tuneful little thing,

A vaudeville," and he starts to sing.
"But, Count, you haven't eaten, half."
"Please, not another bite!"
      They rise,
The youthful hostess very gay,
The count with nothing more to say
Of Paris—to his own surprise,
All wonder at her charm, all eyes.
The evening passes uneventful,
With him not quite himself and her
Now radiant but, as it were,
Now downcast as if half resentful.
Before they know it, by the clock,
It's midnight and they both recall
A servant snoring in the hall,
The distant crowing of a cock,
The watchman at his iron plate.
Slowly the candles gutter. "Ah,"

Observes Natalya Pavlovna,
"It's time to go to bed. It's late.
Sweet dreams!" Reluctantly and vexed,
And half in love, he stands and bows
Above her hand, like us perplexed
At what her playfulness allows:
For she—the flirt!—forgive her, please—
Discreetly gives *his* hand a squeeze . . .
      Natalya P. prepares for bed
With garrulous Parasha's aid.
Parasha, I should add, 's her maid
Her confidante—when all is said—
Who scrubs and sews and carries tales,
And for her pains gets gowns of sorts,
And publicly at master rails,
And privately with master sports,
And lies to mistress at every turn.
Just now she's full of what she's heard
About Count Nulin's least concern;

The Lord knows how she came to learn
What now she spins out, word by word.
Natalya must—at length—remind her
She's boring, calls for cap and gown,
And bids her (being snuggled down)
Go out, and close the door behind her.
     Meanwhile Count Nulin too is ready—
With valet's aid—to go to bed. He
Lies down and calls for his cigar;
Which, thereupon, Monsieur Picard
Brings with bronze candlestick instanter,
And silver goblet and decanter,
And clock, and snuffers that spring shut,
And novel, with the leaves uncut.
     The book is Scott; he keeps his gaze
Upon it, seems to read on through it;
But constantly his fancy strays
After adventure dearer to it;
One question nags him: if, by chance,
This is another such romance?
What if the play need not have ended?
Yes, what indeed? The thought is splendid;
"She *likes* me, that's beyond a doubt,"
He adds, and blows the candle out.
     Unbearable, September heat;
The count will never even doze;
The Devil too's awake, and knows
How to inflame him with deceit:
For the lady smiles, or so it seems,
And beckons in his waking dreams.
How full her form, how gently rounded!
Her voice how—womanly—it sounded!
How warm with country health the faint
Young flush, still innocent of paint!
All this he saw, and sees anew,
This and a dainty little shoe.
He sees anew, or feels, that is,

How *her* hand gave a squeeze to his.
"You idiot! You missed your cue;
You never should have come away,"
He thinks. "You had your part to play."
But opportunity still knocked:
Her door (most likely) was unlocked . . .
And without more ado or thought,
Donning the dressing-gown he bought
In Paris, tripping over chairs,
And groping, our new Tarquin dares
What may ensue—rebuff, caprice,
Alarm—in search of his Lucrece.

      Just so, spoiled darling of the house,
The pet of some fond serving wench,
A cat slides off the kitchen bench
And edges closer to a mouse;
Approaches with its eyes in slits,
Back arched, and tail at nervous swing,
Unsheathes its claws from tiny mitts,
And makes at last its deadly spring.

      Love-sick Count Nulin, in the dark,
Feels, even so, his way ahead,
Driven by passion to the mark.
At every creak, in silent dread,
He trembles and his breath comes fast;
But—the forbidden door at last.
He finds the brazen knob; it turns;
The door swings back upon the room;
A taper at an icon burns
And faintly shows, within the gloom,
The bed, the lady—downy heap—
Who's gone to, or pretends to, sleep.

      He enters, hesitates, withdraws,
Then all at once falls at her feet;
And she . . . But let me briefly pause
And ask the notably discreet
St. Petersburg great ladies, please,

To contemplate her woeful plight:
What, with Count Nulin at her knees,
Should she awake and do by night?
    Wide-eyed and wondering, she gazes
Upon this vision of a lover
Who showers her with borrowed phrases
And reaches boldly for the cover—
Such onslaught startles and amazes . . .
But speedily she summons strength
And righteous anger to her aid,
And just—perhaps—a bit afraid,
Swings, at a buxom arm's full length,
A, yes, a slap—and what a stark one!—
Full in the face of startled Tarquin.
    Count Nulin seethes with lordly rage
At suffering such contumely,
And this could be a tragic page
That chronicles the brief sequelae;
But, luckily, Natalya's spitz,
Jealous of her repose and its,
Brings, with its frantic barking, stout
Parasha; and these fresh reserves
Upset Count Nulin's force—and nerves—
And, after one last fusilade
Of curses at the headstrong jade,
Put him to panic-stricken rout.
    How he, the lady, and the maid
Live out the balance of the night
The reader needs (and gets) no aid
In picturing to inner sight.
    Next morning, rising strangely quiet,
Count Nulin dresses languidly,
And, tie in hand, half fails to tie it;
Inspects his nails indifferently,
And yawns; and the accustomed brush
Forgets to moisten and to crush
His curls, he's lost in thought, but we

Shall never know of what, for tea
Is ready, and with haughty smile,
Concealing shame and pique the while,
He goes . . .
     The mischievous coquette,
Her eyes half veiled, but smiling still,
Biting her red lips redder yet,
Engages him against his will
In quiet talk of this and that;
And though he glowers, he unbends,
Jests, wryly smiles, begins to chat,
Forgets himself, and even ends
By being half in love once more.
     But what's that noise? And at the door
Who's this? "Good morning, Natalie."
"*Akh! Bozhe!* How you startled me!
My husband, Count. Count Nulin, dear."
"Most pleased to know you. Nasty weather,
We're having. At the smith's, I hear,
They've got your coach put back together.
Right by the garden, over there,
Natasha, we ran down a hare.
Hey, bring the vodka! Have some, do;
We send for it. A special sort.
Of course you'll stay to dinner, too?"
"I'm not sure, really, if—in short,
I should get on." "But, man, you must!
Come, come, you must; my wife and I
Delight in sharing our poor crust."
     But no entreaties mollify
The doleful count, deceived again
By hopes that first revive and then
Are dashed once more . . .

So, fortified
With one last dram, the valet brings
A heavy portmanteau outside;

Two servants fix upon the springs
A carriage trunk, and screw it tight;
The coachman drives up to the door;
The valet sees that all is right,
And now they're off . . .
      With which, my friends,
My story proper properly ends—
But let me add a few words more.
      The coach is barely out of sight
When Natalie begins to boast
About what happened in the night
And how the count was put to flight.
Of those who hear, who laughs the most?
Who most enjoys it with her? Guess.
Her husband? Never. No one less.
He, as it happens, doesn't feel
Such things are funny; swears the clown,
The milksop, shall be made to squeal:
If that's the way it is, why, we'll
Turn loose the dogs and hunt him down.
No; *Lidin* laughed: their neighbor he,
A bachelor of twenty-three.
      And so we reach our parting phrase,
A moral that the case allows:
Wives are no marvel nowadays
Who merely keep their marriage vows.

Translated from the Russian by Robert C. Stephenson

Anthony Hecht

Message from the City

It is raining here.
On my neighbor's fire escape
geraniums are set out
in their brick-clay pots,
along with the mop,
old dishrags, and a cracked
enamel bowl for the dog.

I think of you out there
on the sandy edge of things,
rain strafing the beach,
the white maturity
of bones and broken shells,
and little tin shovels and cars
rusting under the house.

And between us there is—what?
Love and constraint,
conditions, conditions,

and several hundred miles
of billboards, filling-stations,
and little dripping gardens.
The fir tree full of whispers,
trinkets of water,
the bob, duck, and release
of the weighted rose,
life in the freshened stones.
(They used to say that rain
is good for growing boys,
and once I stood out in it
hoping to rise a foot.
The biggest drops fattened
on the gutters under the eaves,
sidled along the slant,
picked up speed, let go,
and met their dooms in a "plock"
beside my gleaming shins.)

Yesterday was nice.
I took my boys to the park.
We played Ogre on the grass.
I am, of course, the Ogre,
and invariably get killed.
Merciless and barefooted,
they sneak up from behind
and they let me have it.

O my dear, my dear,
today the rain pummels
the sour geraniums
and darkens the grey pilings
of your house, built upon sand.
And both of us, full grown,
have weathered a long year.
Perhaps your casual glance
will settle from time to time

on the sea's traveling muscles
that flex and roll their strength
under its rain-pocked skin.
And will see where the salt winds
have blown bare the seaward side
of the berry bushes,
and will notice
the faint, fresh
smell of iodine.

Cesare Pavese

What An Old Man Has Left

What an old man has left. He's up early
and catches the last stars out; he downs
a drink; he beads out into the streets.
He knows none of the faces: that's the end,
as expected. He looks at them; he thinks
about them. That's no longer enough.
Even peaceably. This old man
rises with the dawn.
Out. Round and about.
He looks and no one sees. He thinks,
I was young once: how young the world is.
He's trailed by dogs, who don't know how
it is to go round in an old man's
skin, to show your ribs to the wind,
to be naked and frail: and to look
on those young bodies male and female
fresh from their beds: in each one the sap
running. They worry in public
and avoid his eye in their hurry.

They've each got a life. The old man's
not seen that: his terms are young and old.

That's life, all of it. Sure, the streets
stay the same, the a.m. is always good.
But let some lout knock him down,
trample him on the stones. That's only right.
He's thought of everything but fails
to recognize fate. Someday, he thinks—
it worries him—they'll be old.
Who's going to be there to catch
the expression on their faces
when they knock against things? Without him
watching, they'll be unknowns.
The fact is, the morning is when
things wake up; there's a share of the world
for each. And an old man has left:
surprising the dawn, that'll be left
and going down into the streets
into that quick crowd.

Michael Hulse

Winterreise

for Dorle, after our parting

I

I've been a stranger here from birth,
a journeyman on homeless earth,
an ancient out of time, a boy,
a saddened heart surprised by joy,
a lover in ideal vein
acquiring expertise in pain,
supposing love might still redeem
the unaccommodated dream—

a man of faith without a god.
I write this, Dorle, from Cape Cod.
The trees have fretted into leaf,
stating a natural belief.
The moonlit beauty of the lake
quickens the unforgotten ache.
Here, once again, I'm passing through.
And, once again, I'm missing you.

September I returned to find
you'd thought it through, and knew your mind,
and had to go. I'd feared you would.
It made no sense. I understood.
Since then I've loved you, hated, tried
to forget you, liked it not and died—
and now, like Luther, look at me
planting my little apple tree.

With lovers, gods, and history,
the trash of nationality,
the dross of time, we think the war
is won if we're in love or score
the pyrrhic victories of art
over the knowledge of the heart.
—Say, if my pain falls silent, who
will ever give me word of you?

480

We thought it out of ocean's reach,
our sand-love promised each to each—
hieroglyphics on the strand
which now I no more understand
than smoke unscrolling from the joss
writing its ideograms across
the void and vanishing: I swear
our love was smokescript, writ in air.

II

This spring I visited the grave
of a good friend who always gave
you all the greatness of the heart
and soul that you require of art,
one who lives on in minds made better

both by her spirit and her letter,
and brought you from that Highgate plot
this April's first forget-me-not—

if only consolation grew
with such a pure and peaceful blue!
Philosophy is all awry:
it simply waits for us to die,
making the odd assuaging noise,
providing us with clever toys
to while away the interim
from void to voided Elohim.

Our cancered friends who died too young
are words for silent music, sung
to a pitiless measure of the spheres:
we keep the time and count the years,
praying the substance that survives
will lend us grace to shape our lives.
Andreas. Karin. Come to dust.
As we too must. As we too must.

What is the point of all we make?
It never palliates the ache.
Even the Bach they play on Cape
Classical's subtly shifted shape:
without you, he's become a bore,
B flat and A C B, no more,
and Monteverdi hurts to hear
without my music lover near.

I see you bending to the keys,
the mistress of the harmonies,
your hair a curtain on your cheek,
the bone so fine, the flesh so meek,
inheriting with every tone

481

the world you justly call your own,
the Passion and the Pentecost.
—That touch of fire it is I've lost.

III

On this first sea-grey day of June
I spent the affectionate afternoon
with Jeff and Julie by the water,
watching their wide-eyed son and daughter,
pained to an exquisite degree:
the kids you wished to have with me
are limbo'd, powerless to be born.
Aborted. Unbegot. Forlorn.

These thoughts are good for nothing. Rather
follow the comedy of a father
trying to fly the children's kite
in breezes that refuse to bite
and act as if I weren't unduly
troubled by the grace of Julie,
a tranquil beauty through and through,
so disconcertingly like you.

My days are like the aftermath
of war.—I thought I'd found the path
out of the wild unholy wood.
I thought that I was home for good.
For childish notions such as this
the gods keep an ancient nemesis,
and when it hits, their age-old song
has a familiar chorus: Wrong.

Assuming I've three score and ten
to serve in all, like other men,

that leaves near thirty still to do—
so many years of missing you,
so many years of marking time
in this *monotonous sublime,*
of making sense where none is given.
My days are snowfall, blown and driven.

Three thousand miles away you sleep,
and that your dreams be safe and deep
and that you witness when you wake
a day but not a lifetime break,
I write this *gute Nacht* in snow
to tell you what I know you know:
Dorle, my friend, my infidel,
I love you. And so fare you well.

Cape Cod and Cologne

483

Texts

Edward Hoagland

Cowboys

Zino'd been the gator wrestler since he'd left the Army in the spring. Lemkuel's Hollywood was a pretty good carny. Offered lots of attractions but nothing too big for the trucks or expensive to use; easy to move; played it cool. The hard part for the wrestler was hopping on him and off because if you know about gators, you know they can't open their mouth once you're holding it closed—not the same as the muscles which shut it. That was when the gator's being calm was important. There's a powerful tail also, but this one forgot about his and, as it worked out, only had teeth to eat. Lemkuel told Zino to take some kind of spurs to him to jazzen up the show. Zino told Lemkuel to *hire* a freak.

Zino wrestled with the gator, and Spike, his friend, took care of the hyenas, controlled their jitters and made them laugh at the right times. The third guy who was with them, the paratrooper, took care of the carnival's elephant, gave the towers rides. He did a lot else and so did Spike and so did Zino but the point is they thought they were tops for handling animals, Frank Buck, Tarzan, and the cat's meeow.

Lemkuel's H. was showing Kimberton while the rodeo went on. That's eastern Oregon, cattle country, pretty famous for its rodeos. Lemky's H. was there a week day-and-dating with rodeo when all the people were in town.

Wasn't competition, really, just to get their slough-off, which made a new experience for Spike and Zino and the Trooper, in hick country not to be the grand attraction. May seem silly, but it had to matter, working in a lousy carny, sleeping anywhere, with on their shoulders stamped indelibly in cattle ink the numbers they'd been given by the border cops when the show had zigzagged into Canada to play the suburbs of Vancouver. Beside the rodeo Lemkuel looked almost the same as the gypsy, nut-game, hot-dog stuff that used to creep up near his midway to try for a smidgin of business. And Zino and his friends were on the bum and not true carnies to whom a fleabag three-truck show set up in a vacant lot in Harlem, New York, might be the greatest object of attraction in the city: if the general public didn't know this, so much the worse for it.

Spike was a Marine—had been in the Marines—and he was sure he was the toughest thing God made. No, he let the paratrooper be an equal to him. But Spike didn't cotton to playing second fiddle to that rodeo. Competing cowboys owned the town like Lord and Master. Five-thousand-dollar cars wouldn't draw a glance if one of them was strolling down the street. Cowboys never brag to strangers, excepting ways like flossy chaps or with their hats, but even silent ways irked Spike. He watched the cowboys all the time. He'd squint. He'd reconnoiter vantage spots where he could watch a bunch of bars and several streets, and not ascared of nothing. A Marine.

They're suckers, cowboys, course. Zino had sucker stuff he fiddled with, Chinese charms, and they spent when they won—cowboys don't get salaries, they win or starve—so he had no particular complaint. He was peaceable by nature. But usually in a town people would be asking *him* and hanging round and being excited. Here, this town, *he* was s'posed to be the fascinated one and dog *them!* In a bar the cowboys would be leaning on their arms with all their weight, on account of all their hurts and pains, favoring one leg or the other, and everybody'd want to buy them drinks, breathe their burps, listen for the pearls of wisdom—when the cowboy'd gotten drunk enough to condescend to talk. Women would be saying those fancy shirts they wore were cute as mink. And, because of the rodeo, ordinary, everyday cowboys who never gave Zino any trouble in the other towns got to thinking they were special. Seemed to take an hour to make a quarter off them.

Spike wore tee shirts covered with the carnival and a mauler-looking leather jacket with LEMKUEL'S HOLLYWOOD CARNIVAL written out in full on it, the whole shebang, and always threw out hints to people as to where he worked. Here it was like he had had on a Wall Street suit. People thought he was different from them, all right, but they paid no attention to him, didn't give a damn. The cowboys weren't starting trouble, either on the lot or off it. They kept their fights among themselves—stand still trading punches till one guy'd run low, and that would start the tumbling over tables and the throwing of crockery and chairs—bartenders were the ones they hurt, because they'd wreck a bar. But Spike lost weight about them, until finally Spike took Zino and the Trooper to the rodeo.

Zino'd served his time like anybody's brother as a draftee, not a Fighting Man. The gator wrestling redeemed him for the other two. And although Zino was proud enough of the carny as carnies went he knew you had to be a bum to work in one and once he'd started getting some breaks from the world he'd quit—so in the last analysis he wasn't proud; it wasn't like a service outfit to him. But Zino was curious, wanted a laugh. He went along for kicks. Spike was deadly serious. Spike suggested it while they were hosing down the bears. "Let's go to the rodeo." He emphasized the "go."

"When we're off they wouldn't be showing either," Zino said.

"That don't matter."

Spike thought about the thing all Sunday, and the next day, soon as they finished the morning chores and before the opening for the matinee, he asked again: "You comin'?"

Zino hardly knew what Spike was talking about—"You comin'?" was all he said—and yet he really couldn't be excused by that because he had a notion. Even if he didn't know Spike's plans he did know Spike. Cowboys were hayseeds, Zino figured. He'd never been worried by hayseeds before, and if a carnie can't handle the hayseeds he'd better go straight.

"We'll see about Airborne," Spike said.

Airborne was sleeping on top of his elephant. He liked height. Spike didn't hesitate to wake him. "Hey, you want to stir some cowboys up?"

Airborne was down—fast as that. Didn't wait to be elevatored on the elephant's trunk. He jumped. And then he scratched his elephant's tongue. She moved it under his hand like diddling a lollipop. "Do we got to clean?" Airborne asked Spike. Watching them was funny. Paint four dots on a piece of metal and you'd have how their eyes looked. Sergeants' eyes. Zino smiled.

Spike told him yes. It was risky. Lemkuel spotted people with nothing

489

to do; it would be safer simply to clear out—in that the carnival was like the service—but they always made him wash. Being a good soldier, Airborne kept his clothes and face and armpits clean, but anybody taking care of elephants stinks something terrible. Washing doesn't do away with it, but you try. Stinks terrible if you don't like elephants much, which women don't. They argued about the smell and scrubbed and fooled around so long they had to call in witnesses whose noses still could judge if it was there. Finally let him be. No one happened to think cowboys must stink too: they weren't going visiting women. It was habit, washing Airborne any time they left the show.

So now they waited while he got his boots. He'd always fuss. Like putting money in the bank, when you brought Airborne you started off by sacrificing. And Spike and him were buddies. The jump boots he had on weren't freshly polished—"These're getting crummy." The second pair was in an airtight plastic sack inside a box inside his trunk, each boot wrapped with felt to prevent scrapes against the other. And he was always changing boxes to find one which would "hold up." He blew at the boots to get off lint, then started in with rags and polish. Spike was sympathetic, but Zino told the guy to hang a sign Museum Exhibitions. When Airborne was through with the rags the boots were like you'd see on a colonel. He was only partly done. He spit and used his finger round and round and round laboriously. Then to cement the shine he lit a match. The shine burned in, he took a razor blade and shaved the white-gut laces newly white. They were permanently put in, a special, raised, jump-boot pattern; zippers on the sides were used for getting in and out. He polished the zippers. Zino made faces and began looking forward to going to the rodeo very much. Spike tapped his foot and whistled softly, stared at trees. Last, Airborne bloused his pant cuffs to the boots with two steel springs which shaped and made them rigid and with rubber bands. A sergeant's shine, a sergeant's boots. Zino snorted.

"Are we ready?" Spike asked, trying to keep from being sarcastic. He sympathized with soldiering and didn't want to side with Zino.

"Wait'll I look," Airborne said. "You didn't give me notice." Since he wore no shirt he centered his buckle and the fly of his pants with the line of hair down his stomach, and checked that the huge tattoo on his chest wasn't blurred by hair, was shaven. The head of a screaming eagle, his old outfit's emblem.

Zino kidded: "Did the gooks give you notice?" Spike still watched trees.

"Let's move out," Airborne said, satisfied and grinning. He snapped Spike a salute in fun, which Spike returned. None of this pussyfoot brush-your-fore-head-with-your-hand an officer would use: a leaping, whiplash, and electric motion, an enlisted man's salute. They stepped off with the thirty-inch step, Spike calling cadence, all regulation. Hup Haupereep Haup. Zino was the slick-sleeve but they weren't harassing him; he went along with it. Spike's lilt and chat and joyousness made it fun, as good as a band for stirring you up. Kosher sergeants: by the book.

Pretty soon Spike gave them Double Time, letting Airborne do the Airborne Shuffle. Spike was smart, though, cut it back to Quick Time before Zino thought about the silliness of running, then to Route Step, where they walked as they pleased without cadence. He was a battlefield Marine and he preferred this, quiet and alert, not civilian walking. Put them fifty feet apart on alternate sides of the road with a stride that could last for thirty miles. And as he walked Spike seemed to clothe himself in solemn battle-green, the aura of war, the time-honored burdens of pack, shovel, and littler gear and crossed, tall weapons—all half-joking; he wasn't a nut. But he started memories of maneuvers crowding upon Zino. The flares and hammering machine-guns; the trim traced mustaches of the officers, the clap of laughter when the top ones joked. The shadow of a marching file in the afternoon, long on the grass like a moving fence. The First Soldier during the hurricane telling them this was the United States Army and to feel some pride and quit their gripes, and late the worst night (not in the hurricane at all but when he chose to make it), in a jeep's headlights standing erect on one foot on a roadside post in his tee shirt and muddy pants and boots telling the two hundred of them: "Yes, you men are troops now. You done good. I don't swear at men under me, I just run them till their tongues drop out, and the man that falls had better show me blood on him and whites for eyes, because I'll look. But you're men now, you boys, and you're troops. And any of you that were men before are good men now, and troops. You've earned your sleep. Fall out."

491

Spike said over his shoulder: "Fix your knives." His hand made the start of a motion toward where a bayonet would hang. He smiled but, too, his lips pressured together; his hands were dandling a weight—in his mind, by God, he was carrying a gun! And a man's-best-friend, not an idiot-stick like Zino.

The rodeo arena was open-air, surrounded by stands, with a big dirt-floor shed at one end for everything to live in. As any place in show business, the way to the performers was through the most inconspicuous door an outsider found. It brought Spike under the stands and next to the chutes and following the chutes he came to the shed. Airborne got fiercely bubbly like the average sturdy sergeant about to be tested. Zino recognized the state and despite his own tenseness smiled. Spike was just alert.

"We gotta find where the crum-bums are hiding. What should we do, yell? Maybe we'd scare them. Maybe better if they think we're towners," Airborne said.

The animals looked out, the way they kept them. You could be used to the carnival zebras and bears and gators teed off and hyenas snapping and still not feel comfortable seeing past a couple of grape-vineyard slats those horns which even the steers grew, horns yellow like teeth and high, thick— long so you couldn't see both at the same time unless you stood back. Razor horns *mellowed* yellow. The steers were packed in the pens so crowded the horns were like a head-high mass of thicket. Then in another pen instead of horns there'd be the horses' heads, goggly, watching Zino, all turned in one direction and touching each other, like a school of fish, hanging still or moving as fast as fish in unison with ups and downs and quivers.

The bulls were by themselves and didn't make Zino nervous; they plain made him sweat. Their pen should have burst just from the numbers in it—couldn't have forced in a pitchfork of hay; how were they fed?—not to mention the boards being about as thick as one of their nostrils. Zino'd have circled a field a mile across that one of those bulls was in—and watched awhile to admire—couldn't have dreamed up a better bull in a nightmare! Not farm bulls: humped Brahmins for spirit, now standing as bulky and still as so many cannon. Twenty bulls in a pen the size of a kitchen. He dried his hands on his pants.

And calves for roping were squeezed in a pen like frogs in a pail, and hopping and making the noise for everything else. In narrow spaces between pens, besides the hay and cowboys' bunks, were dogs, cats, and special, privileged horses with blankets on their hinds and pails of water of their own. The shed held more animals than Zino would have expected to see spread on a whole horizon during a roundup. Right then, as soon as that, he felt sorry he had come. But Spike and the Paratroop were every bit as gutty, straight, and veteran-looking as before. They didn't bluff.

They kept a distance from the animals, not to excite them, and hunted for the cowboys, who were hard to find. Some were hidden in the horse pens, messing with the horses, and some were smoking in the hay asleep. Yes, asleep, smoking, in the hay. These weren't the first guys Zino'd seen smoke in their sleep but were the only sober ones who didn't do it for a stunt and had the nerve to lay in hay. Another bunch was in the rafters of the shed with fifths of liquor playing cards. Turned out to be the ones who at the time could walk without much pain, although their jeans were trussed against their legs for injuries. Zino and the sergeants watched them. Cowboys are really proud of two things, besides their horses and themselves—their boots and hat. And so they're always fooling with their hat, fixing it on their head or playing with it on their knee. And whenever their feet are dangling, straddling a fence or on a rafter, they'll kick them out, kick them back, and admire the spurs and boots from every angle. Dainty boots they wear, with personality, pointed slim and formfit curving—funny to compare beside the Trooper's giant stomper weapons.

Dogs let the cowboys know about the strangers, but nobody was interested. Spike had plenty of chance to look around and map his plan. There wasn't much to see except the animals. Saddles on some sawhorses. A kerosene stove (banked in hay) and pots and dishes. Cots with Indian or khaki blankets; saddlebags, knapsacks, suitcases, little private stuff, a mirror hung on the side of a pen. When Spike had learned the lie of the land he whistled sharply at the cowboys in the rafters, jerked his rifle hand for them to come. They didn't stop to ask a question. Like such a thing was natural they swung themselves around till they were hanging by their arms and dropped off down among the steers and skeedled out before they could get gored. The steers went wild. The steers thought it was raining men. The fence careened and cracked, but lasted. "They need some jumping lessons," said the Troop, meaning in technique. A cowboy pounded extra slats onto the pen where it was damaged. Zino noticed earlier repairs the same.

Spike played the situation fine. He took his time. He put his fists against his hips Commanding General-style and let the cowboys wait. Pat Patton's pearl-sided six-guns strapped at his waist would have looked swell and a cowboy Earp or Ringo trash.

When the cigarettes burned near their lips the guys asleep woke up a little. As this happened to each man Spike jerked his rifle hand at him to come. The ones in fooling with the horses showed up of their own accord, propped on their elbows on an animal's back. Most all the cowboys tried to make it. The guys from the rafters walked, bowlegged and teetery on those high-heel boots. Others got a stick and used the corners of their feet or hobbled on their knees, arms crooked out with pain. A few only were able to crawl on a horse for the view and put braids in its mane while they listened. That's how to tell a rodeo cowboy from a regular one. Oh, the regular, he won't walk like you and me. But the *rodeo*, most likely he won't make it to the can without a horse. It's the falls which do it, not the actual stock. A herd of horses couldn't give a hogtied cowboy half a bump.

Zino was six feet, Spike even bigger, and Airborne, if a finger shorter, was muscled tougher than a shark. They'd murdered the loggers and the apple pickers and the sheepherders and salmon fishermen through Washington—there are no rougher places than a carnival. They'd have given the cowboys a day's work in a fight. But Spike didn't seem to plan to. He just was there to talk.

The animals got restless and stampy. But the cowboys were attentive. Scratching their stomachs or tilting their hats around with their fingers, as they were always doing, or tinkling a spur; otherwise still and planted to listen. Spike had been practicing what to say all week, he'd been so mad, and now he had forgotten. He was confident, but he'd forgotten. Pinched his mouth and frowned. Each cowboy looked different from each other cowboy; couldn't treat them as a crowd. That's what bothered Zino. Each hat had its own independently airy-curvy brim, although always leveling sternly with the eyes in front, and its own variety of creases in the crown. And the necessity for hat-room made the cowboys space themselves so that each man was an island to be dealt with separately. And the faces weren't the same. Each had elements its own.

Spike would do this kind of thing in the Marines, he'd said—on pass go into town and tell the locals what was what—but now the feather-tinkling spurs were all they heard. Spike couldn't start, and Airborne couldn't either, being outranked.

Suddenly Spike grinned, squared his chest, pushed his lips against each other and his fists against his hips, pulled himself so straight he was a picture. Loud as ringing metal he began.

"You people! Get this clear! Because your soul may still belong to God but as of now your ass is mine!" (The tone: why sure, he'd talk recruit.)

"The shit has hit the fan. I'm going to take the swagger out of you! I'll bring some order here. I'll straighten you. You'll take the course. I'm going to run you through a grinder! Each word I say is going to be your Bible. *I'*m your law and you'll stand tall! When I say jump you'll jump for me, you people, till you wee and wet your whiskers! Except you won't have whiskers. You'll dry-shave."

Knots and lumps stood in his face, of strength. He stopped and looked at Zino and at Airborne like assisting cadre, then beyond them to the pens of stock. The cowboys got the same expression from him as the stock.

"I helped put up the flag on Iwo Jima that the people took the pictures of; I was on the hill. I was in on Okinawa, Bougainville. I was in the Philippines when the Japs gave in. And I know two things: Japs, they stink and you guys too. When I was going to school I hung from railroad ties when trains crossed the bridge. You couldn't do that now, but I was having fun and goin' to school. And I'm a better man with women." He grinned abrasively. "And I brought in the first Dakota well, my crew that I was in, which meant the state gets rich. And I knew Tony Zale like brothers. Not many guys have done the stuff I did, not you! Cowboys are for kids! Cowboys are for children!"

And Spike looked something fine. He'd dropped the boot camp patter, but his tightened lips still carried fight, stamped what he was as sure as hash marks up the arm. His voice would fill a company street, and if he'd coughed he would have shouted louder. Those cowboys should at least have been set back. But no, and not insulted. They were enjoying Spike, hunched smiling on their heels like wolves sitting. They held their hats and tippy-tipped their fingers on them as if they had Spike in a jar.

"S'pose I yell Hey Rube like show guys yell. You'd be skinned!" He grinned at Troop and Zino to share how smart it was. Nobody's used Hey Rube in shows for twenty years, but he said that. They weren't near hearing distance of the lot. The Trooper, he was next to Spike's left shoulder, one pace out and one pace back, in shining battle boots, the screaming eagle on his chest. Zino stood where he could make a run for it. Twenty cowboys to the three of them! But cowboys weren't the athlete he was. They're funny, cowboys. Blind drunk every night; chain-smoke, drink themselves blind. Because they only do the stuff they do for ten or fifteen seconds—stay on a horse—they aren't in good condition. Got no wind: never's a need for wind. And crippled. And always thinking about something. Watching you and sitting on their heels and thinking. These ones did. His back crawled.

Spike faced up to them, had suckled nails. "I'm from the carnival,"

495

he said. "Which means in every town the guys who think they're rough come down to make it rough. Everybody. Cops off-duty. And we handle them, *we* make it rough, we chase them through the town. I've always been with outfits like that. Our battalion used to trade the medics in for fightin' troops before we'd hit the sand. Our tankers emptied the tool box throwing wrenches before they'd die. No ammo and a Jap comin' in? *Give him the butt and the steel!*' he roared, so even the cowboys blinked. He knocked the hat off one. The guy was bald. "Skinheads!" Spike sneered. "That's why you wear them hats!" He kicked the same guy in the foot, which made him howl. "Sorefoots! That's why you wear them boots! 'Cowboys!'" He spat the word. "I think they call you that because you look as dumb as cows. Huh? Answer up! Umbrellaheads! Your cattle got your tongues?"

The cowboys grinned. Their mouths and noses got real wide.

"Slaps, open up the gate."

Horses poured forth like a dam had burst in a wall of dancing crazy water—brown as water—out the gate and racing to both sides. Zino bounced as the ground shook and the mass whirled round the shed. Singling out individual broncs was scarier still. They pinwheeled, their hooves topped their heads. Zino fell down in a ball and covered his head. Then he got up to try and survive. Spike was willing to run for it now, but too late. Zino stuck beside him like any raw replacement. The horses were everywhere, plunging and thrashing and kicking each other, fiend-faced, an oncoming merry-go-round brought alive. And now old Slaps got happy-go-lucky and let out a couple of bulls, which were charging but hadn't decided where. Spike couldn't maneuver because of the horses. Soon as the bulls spotted him and his men they'd be cooked, as it seemed.

The cowboys didn't bother with the bulls, only to dodge. The cowboys were after the horses. Cowboys are cripples but cowboys can move, just never how anyone else would move and most of the time they aren't balanced steady; every few steps they'll fall. These guys were using their hands to help. Sometimes they almost ran on their hands, skeedling next to the ground like crabs. The slender skin-colored boots seen at a distance made them look barefoot. Several men had a funny run, limping on both legs: each step was a stumble and to keep from falling they went at a run. And as much as they ran they threw their hats. Stalwart sailing hats so big. They must have thought it wasn't fun enough to rope the horses, because they dove and flopped and skidded, told each other wordless things and yipped and shouted at the horses, sailed and flapped and flung their hats to steer them. The hats were charmed. Never crushed or tromped on; kept their gallant complex shapes, as if to wear one was to wear a helmet. Of course Zino and the sergeants didn't care about the hats. They were trying to save their skins. But the way to live was stand right still and watch in all directions. This they did, in the middle of the tumult.

By and by the cowboys got the horses circling. Couldn't stop them, but they got them circling, and relaxed, dusted off their hats with careful swats or with their fingers, and began to eenie-meenie, picking out their broncs. Everybody was inside the horses' circle but the bulls, who charged in and out. The cowboys took it slow, rolled cigarettes, listened to the hooves and breathing. Then they limped along beside the circle—man might stop, change his mind about a horse, now go again—stumbled along and one by one grabbed onto a horse's head like hauling in a running catch and shinnied up as effortless as rolling into bed—so easy: course it wasn't. The horses sunfished, seesawed, wrenched around like puppets, when the bulls got near went off their rockers. A cowboy scissored with his spurs to liven up a dull one. Another man was having trouble, holding to a horse's neck, his body flat out from it like in the greatest jitterbug. Got smashed against a post and really caught a case of limps. Anybody else's legs would have been mangled. Once a cowboy sat secure, why he'd perch on the rump of the bronc, swing his legs up on its back and ride, with it bucking, like that, hold onto the hide with his fingers.

Mounted, the cowboys had some height. On the ground because of all their walking troubles, as well as legs bowed bad as wishbones, they seemed small. The horses became different too, more individual. Bucked in a circle tight jackknifes; lunged roomily and straight ahead. Or the mechanical, classic, easy buckers, rhythmic as a circus horse except the motions bigger. Affectionate horses acted happy. Complainers wagged their heads. The cowboys with horses broken fooled the bulls back in the pen.

Spike was catching his breath. He didn't seem to figure these new procedures had anything to do with him. Airborne waited for his orders. Zino only wanted to be gotten out of what they'd brought him into. Spike watched everything, part contemptuously laughing but also interested and entertained. There wasn't a trick he missed, hands on hips, scalp-close haircut, a Marine.

Still cowboys hadn't mounted, those banged up the worst. They crawled to the top of a pen, using their elbows for hands and their knees for feet. The rest of the horses were driven past and they got on that way, like straddling the chute. Men who wanted ropes and saddles went for them, and Spike began at last to feel outnumbered, started for the door, although to look at him he was a kid being dragged away. Now suddenly he ran— the three of them—a hard determined dash which would have bowled over anybody on the ground. Riders loped in front to cut him off and squeezed in from the sides and nudged up from behind. They crowded Zino and the Trooper in so close to him all three hugged each other. From then on Zino never knew what he was doing before it was half done. The cowboys talked a different language, hee*yah!* and wh*ooo!* and partly to the horses, and what they said was swallowed in the dust and noise. Their faces didn't seem to move, except the lazy smiles, so he never even knew who'd spoke. And he was running without stopping, the horses with their manes gone wild, and mouths, and hooves about to split his back. The dipsy lassoos teased. The cowboys doing it he couldn't even see, just occasionally, smiling lazy at their skill. Spike tried to slam a guy who'd been bucked off and they thought that was marvelous, as with some kind of monkey, though wouldn't let the cowboy make a fight; wasn't what they wanted.

The posse had no boss but one guy spoke officially. "Talk is cheap." He grinned at Spike. "You'll live, you fellas. Don't think we're out to kill you. Just havin' little fun. Dusty up that fella's shoes. Do what you're told until it's over." Which was bullcrap because they couldn't hear what they were told and had as much control of what they did as mice.

To start, the cowboys put a horse on either side of Zino and a horse behind and ran him into the arena. Only place to run was straight, until the horses turned him, and if he tried to stop the horse in back would stomp him. He couldn't fall down in the midst of the hooves and he couldn't climb the cowboys' stirrups because they'd whip him with their ropes. They had a race with Spike and him and Airborne—who could be got to go the fastest—although he didn't see his pals, was lucky seeing the sky. Yes, Spike raced too.

Then they cut it down to one horse and rider, made it like steer wrestling. Ran the man beside the grandstand wall and leapt on him from the horse. The hard thing was to land on target, instead of, when they'd do it with a steer, landing in the right position, heels braced out to plow the sand. One guy who missed Zino wrecked his knee; another struck the wall and was unconscious. And sometimes Zino had a couple of moments to fight them on the ground before the posse broke it up. "Don't spoil him," the posse'd tell the cowboy. Zino couldn't do much, with his breath knocked out; or else the cowboy would have hit the ground and be behind him. He slugged, ran, fell, was hit with those flying tackles off the horses, was bumped by the horses—once got hit with a horse's head; it tossed its head—socked like a club! His eyes were blind with tears of hatred and with sand. He gasped too hard to cry. The grunts of the horses pounding in turns and stops seemed to come from him. Knocked him down, knocked him down; he gave up fighting, just tried to dodge and let the cowboys bust themselves against the ground. If, as he'd heard, the crucial qualities in battle were the wind and legs to run, he proved as well as Spike and Airborne he could run.

Finally came a contest at roping and hogtieing. Cowboys who were last won because by then the captives simply waited for the rope exhausted. Even so the cowboys fascinatedly compared their times for roping calves with these for roping people, and tried to rest them up to make it fair. If a cowboy missed two throws the man might run right out the other end of the arena and be free. Didn't happen but it gave the roping purpose. And as much as catching the man the cowboy had to put the loop to bind his arms or else he'd lose out to the stopwatch busy in a fight before the feet were tied, because no posse helped him now. Spike and Airborne got some good licks in. Zino was too tired. A cowboy hung under a horse's belly while it galloped, roped Airborne from there. Zino didn't see. He reeled in circles. Always a goddam horse pulling taut the rope around his chest until the cowboy had him down and tied. Or else a goddammed horse's nose goosing at his kiester.

499

The three of them finished as crippled as the cowboys, without the broken bones. Lay on their backs. The cowboys looked enormous from the ground, and the horses had tremendous chests and necks and wispy little heads, and tall—they reared and stamped—bodies huge and long like walls. The cowboys' hats blocked out the sky. Black sideburns spread down their cheeks and hair between their eyes; expressions on their yipping mouths to dream about. The chaps, the spurs, the boots, jean jackets, hats—each item never would need boasting. Zino didn't hope to kill the cowboys. He wanted God to have them die. One made a horse cross over him, kick near his head. He didn't pray. He shut his mind.

Arthur Miller

Please Don't Kill Anything

T hat beach was golden toward sundown. The bathers had all gone home when the wind got brisk. Gulls were diving just beyond the breakers. On the horizon they could see four stubby fishing boats moving in a line. Then she turned toward the right and saw the two parked trucks and the fishermen hauling on a net. "Let's see if they caught anything," she said, with the swift surge of wonder that swept through her at any new sight.

The trucks were battered and rusty with open backs and the one they came upon had about twenty-five big, sand-sprinkled bass and small bluefish piled at the tailgate. A man in his sixties was sitting on the truck holding a rope which was wound around a winch at his side. He nodded to them pleasantly and drew on the rope to keep it wound tightly around the turning winch. At the water's edge another man kept watch over the net, piling it in a heap as it was drawn out of the water.

Sam glanced at the fish as they arrived at the truck and knew she would be startled. She saw them and her eyes widened but she even tried to smile in congratulation to the old man who drew on the rope, and she said, "You catch all these?"

"Yup," he said, and his eyes warmed at her beauty.

"These are all dead, aren't they," she said.

"Oh, ya," the old man said.

She had an excitement in her eyes as she looked, it seemed, at each individual fish to be sure it wasn't moving. Sam started talking to the old man about the probability of a good catch in the net now coming into shore, and she was drawn into the conversation and he was relieved that her eyes, the color of the blue sea, were calmed.

But now the old man moved a lever and the winch speeded up with a rising whine and he was exerting himself to keep the rope taut. The winch on the other truck also turned faster and the two net-tenders on the beach moved rapidly from the trucks to the edge of the water, hurriedly piling up the incoming net. Now they could see the curving line of cork floats only a few yards away in the water.

"Why do you pull so fast?" Sam asked the old man. "Are they fighting the net?"

"Naw," the old man said, "just want to keep her taut so they mightn't jump over and git away."

The waves were breaking into the net now but they could not yet see any fish. She put her two hands up to her cheeks and said: "Oh, now they know they're caught!" She laughed. "Each one is wondering what happened!" He was glad she was making fun of herself even if her eyes were fixed in fear on the submerged net. She glanced up at her husband and said: "Oh, dear, they're going to be caught now."

He started to explain but she quickly went on: "I know it's all right as long as they're eaten. They're going to eat them, aren't they."

"They'll sell them to the fish stores," he said softly, so the old man at the winch wouldn't hear. "They'll feed people."

"Yes," she said, like a child reassured. "I'll watch it. I'm watching it," she almost announced to him. But in her something was holding its breath.

A wave receded then, and with one pull the bag of the net was drawn out of the surf. Voices sounded from both trucks; it wasn't much of a catch. She saw the tails of small bluefish writhing up through the net ("it's standing on its head!"), and a great bass flopping and sea robin trying to stretch their curved umber wings and one flounder lying in the midst of this tangled rubble of the sea. She kept pointing here and there at a fish that had suddenly jerked or flopped over, and called out: "There's one! There's another one!" Meaning they were not dead yet, and, he knew, must be rescued.

The men opened the net and pulled out the bass and some bluefish, tossing the sea robin onto the sand and the flounder, and two blowfish which immediately began to swell. She turned to the old man on the truck and trying to smile, she called to him with a sharpness in her voice, almost a cry: "Don't you take those?"

He drew an old man's warmth from the glow of her face and the startling shape of her body under the striped jersey and the beige slacks. "They're no good, ma'am," he said.

"Well, don't you put them back?"

The old man seemed to hesitate as though some memory of guilt had crossed his mind. "Sure. We put them back," and sat there watching his partner who was picking good fish out of the net and tossing the winged fish right and left onto the sand.

There were now about fifty sea robin on the beach, some of them gulping, some perfectly still. Sam could feel the tension rising in her and he walked over to the nearest fish and, feeling a tremor of repugnance, picked it up and threw it into the waves and came back to her. The pulse of its life was still in his fingers. "If I had something to hold them with . . ." she began.

"You can't throw all those fish back," he said to her, knowing the old man on the truck was being astonished even now that he had thrown back one.

503

"But they're alive!" she said, desperately trying to smile and not to separate herself from him.

"No, they're dead. Most of them are dead, Sweet."

"Are they dead?" he turned and asked the old man.

"No, they ain't dead. Most."

"Would they live again if they had water?"

"Oh, sure, they come to," he said, trying to assuage her, but not moving from his place.

She took off her sandal and went to a fish which was writhing and tried to flip it into the water, but it slipped away. Sam came over and picked it up and flung it into the sea. He was laughing now and she kept saying: "I'm sorry. But if they're alive . . . !"

"It's all right," he said, "but they're mostly dead by now. Look." And he picked up one that was motionless; it felt flabby. He threw it into the water and it arched itself as it struck and she cried out: "There! It's swimming!"

Defeated and grinning, now that he saw the fishermen watching him with smiles on their faces, he went about throwing all the sea robin back into the water. He sensed that even with their smiles the men were somehow held by her insistence, and as he threw the slimy fish in one by one he saw each fish separately, each straining for its quart of sea, and he was no longer ashamed. And there were two fish left, both sea robins with white bellies and stiff umber wings and the beginnings of legs sprouting from both sides of their necks. They were motionless on their backs. He did not bend to pick them up because she seemed prepared to sacrifice them and he went back to her, feeling, somehow, that if he let those two die on the beach she might come to terms with this kind of waste. For he had had to open the window at home, once, to let out a moth which ordinarily he would have swatted, and while part of his heart worshipped her fierce tenderness toward all that lived, another part knew that she must come to understand that she did not die with the moths and the spiders and the fledgling birds, and now, with these fish. But it was also that he wished the fishermen to see that she was not quite so fanatic as to require these two last, obviously dead, sea robins to be given their chance.

He stood beside her again, waiting. He smiled and said: "You got a job cut out for yourself. There's twenty-five miles of beach we can cruise, throwing back fish." She laughed and drew his head down and kissed him and he hugged her, and she said: "Just those two. Go on, Sam. They might be alive."

He laughed again and picked up one of the fish, knowing that it was even more unjust for two to die when fifty had been saved, and as he tossed it to the waves a dog appeared. It was a big, brown retriever with sea-matted hair and it leaped into the waves and dipped its head into the water, raised up with the sea robin gently cradled in its mouth, and came back with great pride to lay it carefully at Sam's feet. "God, look how gently he brings it back!" Sam said.

"Oh, dear!" she laughed, and bent toward the stern face of the buff-eyed dog. The dog returned her a look of athletic determination. "You mustn't do that!" Helplessly she looked at Sam, who picked up the fish and threw it back. Again the dog leaped in and retrieved it and now with enormous élan and pride nearly danced back to Sam, lay it at his feet, and stood waiting for the next throw, its legs trembling with eagerness.

"Well?" he said to her, "there you are. There's a whole conspiracy against these two fish. This guy was trained to help man; man has to eat and something's got to die, Puss . . ."

As he spoke a silvery minnow slid out of the mouth of the sea robin at his feet. "Look at that now!" he yelled. "See? What about *that* little fish?"

"Yes!" she said, like an admission.

"You see? The victims make other victims."

"Well, hurry, throw him back anyway."

"But this character keeps bringing him back. This fish is doomed," he said, and they were both laughing but she had in her head a clock which was telling her that every second counted, and she started to bend toward the fish at his feet despite her repugnance at touching it. He moved her hand away and picked it up, threw it, and when the dog turned and went into the water for it, he ran a few yards along the beach to the other fish and threw it in.

"Now," he said, a little breathlessly, as the dog returned with the first fish, "now there's one. This is a positively doomed fish on the principle that man has to eat and this dog is part of the scheme to feed him." But now even he could not take his eyes from the fish which had taken to breathing rapidly, what with the shocks of being thrown into the water and being picked up by the dog and flying through the brisk wind. "This fish wishes you'd let him die in peace!" He laughed.

She looked around almost frantically, still smiling and laughing with him and saw a stick and ran, ran with the dancer's leaping stride, and the dog glanced at her, then watched her as she waved the stick and called to him. She threw it into the sea and the dog streaked into the water after it and Sam picked up the last fish quickly and flung it and it arched with life as it slid into a wave.

The beach was now clean and the fishermen were busy stowing their nets and the two walked away toward the road. "I'm sorry, Sam, but they were alive, and if nobody's going to eat them . . ."

"Well, the tide would have taken them out dead, Puss, and they'd have been eaten by other fish. They wouldn't have been wasted."

"Yes," she said. They walked, holding each other by the hand and she was silent. He felt a great happiness opening in himself that she had laid his hand on the fish which were now swimming in the sea because he had lifted them. Now she looked up at him like a little girl, with that naked wonder in her face even as she was smiling in the way of a grown woman, and she said: "But some of them might live now till they're old."

"And then they'll die," he said.

"But at least they'll live as long as they can," and she laughed with the woman part of her that knew of absurdities.

"That's right," he said, "they'll live to a ripe old age, and grow prosperous and dignified . . ."

She burst out laughing: "And see their children grown up!"

He kissed her on her lips, blessing her and her wish. "Oh, how I love you," she said with tears in her eyes. Then they walked home.

Wright Morris

The Scene

ome to the window. The one at the rear of the Lone Tree Hotel. The yellow blind is half drawn, and the dangling cord taps the pane like a finger. The view is to the west. There is no obstruction but the sky. The pane rattles like a simmering pot and between the window and the half-drawn blind a fly is trapped: the crawling shadow can be seen on the blind. Dead flies lie on the floor beneath the window and in the fly-tracked dust on the sill.

At a child's level in the lower pane there is a flaw that is round, like an eye in the glass. An eye to that eye, there is much to see on the empty plain. Is it a flaw in the eye, or in the window, that transforms this dry place into a wet one? A scud seems to blow on the sea of grass, and waves of plain roll up as if to engulf the house. Above it towers the sky, like the sky at sea, a wind blows like the wind at sea, and like the sea it is boundless and shadeless: there is no place to hide. There is, however, one difference: it is dry, not wet.

Drawn up to the window is a horsehair sofa, covered with a quilt. On the floor at its side, garlanded with flowers, sets a nightpot, full of cigar butts and ashes. Around the pot, scattered like seed, are the stubs of half-burned kitchen matches from which the sulphur heads have been chewed to sweeten the breath. They are also known to aid the digestion, and Tom Scanlon, the man who lies on the sofa, smokes the cigars, and chews the matches, stands in need of both. He is not there on the sofa now, but the sagging springs hold his shape. He is inclined to sit with his knees drawn up, sleep curled like a child. He has passed his life—if it could be said he has lived one—at the front and the rear of the Lone Tree Hotel. A young man, he liked the view from the lobby, looking out on the promise of the town—an older man, he settled for the comforts of the horsehair sofa in the kitchen, his snot-green eye close to the flaw in the glass.

Tom Scanlon's one good eye, a cloudy phlegm color, lets in more light than it gives out. What he sees, when he sees, are the scenic props of his own mind. His eye to the window, the flaw in the pane, such light as there is illuminates Scanlon. Nothing irked him more—when he was subject to irks—than to hear from his guests that the plain was flat, the light was strong, and that there was nothing for an eye to see. *He* saw plenty. No matter where he looked. In Scanlon's window is a spot rubbed clear by the sleeve of his coat, the size of a melon, and above it a line, like an eyebrow, made by the bill of his drayman's hat. The hat has wicker sides, a badge at the front, and a bill to keep his nose from smudging the glass. What Scanlon sees through the opening is his own business, but a stranger might find the view familiar. A man accustomed to the ruins of war might even feel at home. The plain surrounding Lone Tree, like the town itself, pitted with the cellars of vanished houses, resembles nothing so much as a battlefield. The plow that broke the plains is there in the field, but it is clear that the dust won the return engagement. All around Lone Tree one can see the scars and stumble over the reminders. The bleached bones of a steer, strips of barbed wire, abandoned sheds and machinery, and in the blowouts on the rise, lead bullets and arrow-heads. It is all there to be seen, but there is little evidence that Tom Scanlon sees it. The silence and emptiness of the plain generate illusions that require little moisture, and grow better, like tall stories, where the mind is dry. The tall corn might flower or burn in the wind, but the plain is a metaphysical landscape, and the bumper crop is what one sees through a flaw in the glass.

Down the tracks to the east, like a headless bird, the bloody neck still raw and dripping, a tub-shaped water tank sets high on stilts. Scanlon once saw a coon crawl out the chute and drink from the spout. Bunches of long stemmed grass, in this short grass country, grow where the water drips between the rails, and Scanlon will tell you he has seen a buffalo crop it up. A big bull of course, high in the shoulders, his short tail like the knot in a whip, walking on the ties like a woman with her skirts tucked up. Another time a wolf, half crazed by the drought, licked the moisture from the rails like ice and chewed on the grass like a dog out of sorts. On occasion stray geese circled the tank like a water hole. All common sights, according to Scanlon, where other men squinted and saw nothing but the waves of heat, as if the cinders of the railbed were still on fire.

It seldom rains in Lone Tree, but he has often seen it raining somewhere else. A blue veil of it will hang like the half-drawn curtain at Scanlon's window. Pillars of cloud loom on the horizon, at night there is much lightning and claps of thunder, and from one window or another rain may be seen falling somewhere. Wind from that direction will smell wet and Scanlon will complain, if there is someone to listen, about the rheumatic pains in his knees. He suffered greater pains, however, back when he had neighbors who complained, of all things, about the lack of rain.

In the heat of the day, when there is no shadow, the plain seems to be sucked up into the sky, and through the hole in the window it is hard to be sure if the town is still there. It takes on, like a sunning lizard, the colors of the plain. The lines drawn around the weathered buildings smoke and blur. At this time of day Scanlon likes to take his nap, and by the time he awakes the town is back in its place. The Lone Tree, a dead cottonwood, can be seen by the shadow it leans to the east, a zigzag line with a fishhook curve at the end. In the crotch of the tree, according to Scanlon, Indians once asked permission to bury their dead, and while the body was there the tree had been full of crows. A small boy at the time, Scanlon had shot at them with his father's squirrel gun, using soft lead pellets that he dug out of the trunk of the tree and used over again. The crows were not so obliging. When hit, they flew off with the pellets.

From the highway, a half mile to the north, the town sets on the plain as if delivered on a flat car, or a movie set brought in by trucks and thrown up during the night. Dry as it is, something about it resembles an ark, from which the waters have receded. In the winter it appears to be locked in a sea of ice. In the summer, like the plain around it, it seems to float on a watery surface, stray cattle stand knee-deep in a blur of reflections, and waves of light and heat flow across the highway like schools of fish. Everywhere the tongue is dry, but the mind is wet. According to his daughters, who

509

should know, the dirt caked around Tom Scanlon's teeth settled there in the thirties, when the dust began to blow. More of it can be seen, fine as talcum, on the linoleum floor in the lobby, where the mice raised in the basement move to their winter quarters in the cobs behind the stove.

To the east, relatively speaking, there is much to see, a lone tree, a water tank, sheets of rain, and heat lightning: to the west, a strip of torn screen blurs the view. The effect is that of now you see it, now you don't. As a rule there is nothing to see, and if there is, one doubts it. The pane is smeared where Scanlon's nose has rubbed the glass. The fact that there is little to see seems to be what he likes about it. He can see what he pleases. It need not please anybody else. Trains come from both directions, but from the east they come without warning, the whistle blown away by the wind. From the west, thin and wild, or strumming like a wire fastened to the building, the sound would wake Scanlon from his sleep before the building rocked. It gave him time, that is, to prepare himself. The upgrade freights rocked the building and left the noise in his head when they left, but the downgrade trains left a vacuum he sometimes raised the window to look at. A hole? He often thought he might see one there. A cloud of dust would veil the caboose, on the stove one of the pots or the lids would rattle, and if the lamp was lit the flame would blow as if in a draft.

510

One day, as the dust settled, he saw a team of mares, the traces dragging, cantering down the bank where the train had just passed. On the wires above the tracks, dangling like a scarecrow, he saw the body of Emil Bickel in whose vest pocket the key-wound watch had stopped at 7:34, proving the train that had hit him had been right on time.

From the west, when he needed something, might come Scanlon's brother Harold, an old railroad man good for a free ride in the caboose. He would get off the slow freight when it stopped for water, and walk the half mile into town on the ties. Before speaking to Scanlon, he would tap the cinders out of his shoes. Scanlon credited his brother with a good deal of sense, since he had had more brains than get himself married. For many years he had lived, with a dog named Shep, in a truck that had been wrecked at the Indian Bow crossing, the only disturbance being the clang of the new crossing bell. He and the dog lived very well on a pension of forty-five dollars a month. Hollyhocks and sunflowers grow in one of the tires knocked off the truck. What the highway traveler loses, or throws away, supplies Harold Scanlon with most of his needs: the coat he wears, winter and summer, he found on the radiator of an abandoned car. A tarpaulin blown from a station wagon serves him as an awning over the summer. When the weather is fair, he sits under the tarpaulin smoking his pipe. Until Tom Scanlon was hauled off to Lincoln and forced to spend the winter with one of his children, Harold would come to Lone Tree to dip his hand in the matchbox on the stove. Except for matches and tobacco he seldom felt the pinch of anything.

Back from the crossing, across the dry bed of the river, is a new cattle pen and cattle loader. The wood looks new. The wheel of the windmill creaks day and night. Clumps of the white-faced cattle can be seen on the slope or in the windows or doors of the abandoned sod houses. Harold Scanlon first thought he might settle down in one of them. Built into the slope, out of the wind, the door a little narrow for the cattle to enter, he spent several days in a soddy where the walls were still papered with calendars. The faded pictures showed rivers wide enough for steamers, and grassy slopes where cattle rested in the shade. On the rise behind the soddy were several graves, but Harold Scanlon didn't see them until the snow melted. A trough of snow lay in the shallow hollows until late spring. Flat on one of the graves was a stone with the name of MATTHEW BRADY, and under the name some prankster had scrawled *Kilroy was here*.

A man who might have been Kilroy once stepped off the freight when it stopped at Harold's crossing, and walked down the tracks as if to get a better view of the town. He watched the freight go slowly up the grade, then came back to the crossing to smoke his cigar. This man's name turned out to be Jennings Brady, and some of his people were buried on the rise. A big man, he walked with a slight limp, taking in two railbed ties with each stride, in the manner of a man who knew the feel of track cinders in his shoes.

To the west, the towns are thin and sparse, like the grass, but east of Lone Tree they have lawns, elm-shaded streets, and signs that point off the highway to parks and swimming pools. The town of Polk, just down the line from Lone Tree, is the home of the man who married Scanlon's eldest daughter. In the house where Walter McKee was born, grass still grows between the slats on the porch, and the neighbor's chickens still lay their eggs under the stoop. At the corner of the porch a tar barrel catches and stores the rain

511

from the roof. At the turn of the century, when McKee was a boy, he buried the long white hairs he pulled from a mare's tail knowing they would turn up next as garter snakes. In the middle of the century that isn't done, and a TV aerial, like a giant Martian insect, crouches on the roof as if about to fly off with the house. That is a change, but on its side in the yard is a man's bicycle with the seat missing. The small boy who rides it straddles it through the bars: he never sits down. He mounts it slantwise, like a bareback rider, grease from the chain rubbing off on one leg and soiling the cuff of his pants, rolled up to the knee. Gordon Boyd, McKee's boyhood chum, still bears the scar where the teeth of the sprocket dug into his calf. Bolder than McKee, he liked to ride in the city park, on the curving sidewalks, leaning forward to hold a strip of berry box wood against the whirling spokes.

      The shortcut in the yard, worn there by McKee, still points across the street and a wide vacant lot to the tree where McKee broke his arm. Taunted by Boyd he had climbed to where the sway and the height made him dizzy. Mrs. Boyd, a white-haired woman, had put his arm to soak in a cold tub of water while Gordon went for the Doctor on McKee's new bike. Over that summer he had grown so fast he could pump it from the seat.

512   The Boyd house, having no basement, had a storm cave at the back of the yard where McKee smoked corn silk and Boyd smoked Fourth of July punk. The white frame house still has no basement, and the upstairs bedroom, looking out on the porch, is still heated by a pipe that comes up from the stove below. When McKee spent the night with Boyd, Mrs. Boyd would rap a spoon on the pipe to make them quiet, or turn down the damper so the room would get cold. The old coke burner, with the isinglass windows through which Boyd and McKee liked to watch the coke settle, now sets in the woodshed crowned with the horn of the Victor Gramophone. The stove board, however, the floral design worn away where Boyd liked to dress on winter mornings, now sets in the corner where the floor boards have sagged, under the new TV. Since the house has no porch high enough to crawl under, Boyd kept his sled and Irish Mail under the porch of a neighbor. Along with Hershey bar tinfoil, several pop bottles, a knife with a woman's leg for a handle, and a tin for condoms, thought to be balloons, blown up till they popped on the Fourth of July, the sled is still there. The boys don't use the ones with wooden runners any more. The chain swing no longer creaks on the porch, or spends the winter, cocoonlike, drawn up to the ceiling, but the paint still peels where it grazed the clapboards and

thumped on the railing warm summer nights. Long after it was gone, Mrs. Boyd was kept awake by its creak.

The people change—according to a survey conducted by a new supermarket in Polk—but the life in Polk remains much the same. The new trailer park, on the east edge of town, boasts the latest and best in portable living, but the small fry still fish, like McKee, for crawdads with hunks of liver, and bring them home to mothers who hastily dump them back in the creek. The men live in Polk, where there is plenty of room, and commute to those places where the schools are overcrowded and the rents inflated, but there is work. At the western edge of town, an air-conditioned motel, with a stainless steel diner, blinks at night like an airport, just across the street from where McKee chipped his front teeth on the Civil War cannon. Once or twice a year, on his way to Lone Tree, McKee stops off in Polk for what he calls a real shave, in the shop where he got his haircuts as a boy. The price for a shave and a haircut has changed, but the mirror on the wall is the same. In it, somewhere, is the face McKee had as a boy. Stretched out horizontal, his eyes on the tin ceiling, his lips frothy with the scented lather, he sometimes fancies he hears the mocking voice of Boyd.

513

> *Walter McKee*
> *Button your fly*
> *Pee in the road*
> *And you'll get a sty*

Although he comes from the south, McKee goes out of his way to enter town from the west, passing the water stack with the word P O L K like a shadow under the new paint. Just beyond the water stack is the grain elevator, the roof flashing like a mirror in the sun, the name T. P. CRETE in black on the fresh coat of aluminum. The same letters were stamped, like a legend, on McKee's mind. The great man himself was seldom seen in the streets of Polk, or the rooms of his mansion, but his name, in paint or gold leaf, stared at McKee from walls and windows and the high board fence that went along the lumber yard. T. P. Crete's wife, like a bird in a cage, sometimes went along the tracks in her electric car, making no more noise than the strum of the wires on the telephone poles. It was this creature who deprived McKee of his friend Boyd. She sent him, when he proved to be smart, to those high-toned schools in the East that indirectly led to the ruin he made of his life. Destiny manifested itself through the Cretes, and the sight of the word affected McKee like a choir marching in, or the sound of his mother humming hymns.

Beyond the grain elevator is the railroad station, the iron wheels of the baggage truck sunk in the gravel, an Out of Order sign pasted on the face of the penny scales in the lobby. On the east side of the station is a patch of grass. Around it is a fence of heavy wrought iron, the top rail studded to discourage loafers, pigeons, and small fry of the sort of McKee and Boyd. Polk is full of wide lawns and freshly cropped grass healthy enough for a boy to walk on, but for McKee the greenest grass in the world is the patch inside the wrought iron fence. He never enters town without a glance at it. If it looks greener than other grass it might be due to the cinder-blackened earth, and the relative sparseness, and tenderness, of the shoots. But the secret lies in McKee, not in the grass. No man raised on the plains, in the short grass country, takes a patch of grass for granted, and it is not for nothing they protect it with a fence of iron bars. When McKee thinks of spring, or of his boyhood, or what the world would be like if men came to their senses, on his mind's eye he sees the patch of green in the cage at Polk.

Tall grass now grows between the Burlington tracks that lead south of town to the bottomless sandpit where Boyd, before the eyes of McKee, first attempted to walk on water. But not the last. Nothing seemed to teach him anything. On down the tracks is Aurora, home of LeRoy Momeyer, related to McKee by marriage, and Alice Morple, a childhood friend of his wife. In the park at Aurora, in the place of a cannon, sets the Burlington engine with the funnel-shaped stack and the pistons that once hissed steam on the legs of McKee and Boyd. East of Aurora is Lincoln, capital of the state, the present home of McKee and his wife Lois, Lois's sister Maxine Momeyer, her husband Bud, and their daughter Etoile, and Charlie Munger, the most famous gunman since Billy the Kid. North and west of Polk, in the sandhills, is the ranch of McKee's eldest son, Gordon, his wife Eileen, and their two boys. Tom Scanlon's youngest child, Edna, married Clyde Ewing, an Oklahoma horse breeder, who found oil on his farm in the panhandle. The view from their modern air-conditioned house is so much like that around Lone Tree, Edna Ewing felt sure her father would feel right at home in it. Tom Scanlon, however, didn't like the place. For one thing, there were no windows, only these gleaming walls of glass. He walked from room to room with his head drawn in, as he did outside. Although the floor and walls radiated heat Scanlon felt cold since it lacked a stove with an oven door, or a rail where he could put his feet. Only in the back door was there something like a window, an opening about the side of a porthole, framing the view, with a flaw in the glass to which he could put his eye. Through it he saw, three hundred miles to the north, the forked branches of the lone tree, like bleached cattle horns on the railroad embankment that half concealed the town. The false fronts of the buildings like battered remnants of a board fence. Even the hotel, with its Mail Pouch sign peeling like a circus poster, might be taken for a signboard along an abandoned road. That is how it is, but not how it looks to Scanlon. He stands, as if at the screen, gazing down the tracks to where the long-stemmed grass spurts from the cinders like leaks in a garden hose. The mindless wind in his face seems damp with the prospect of rain.

Three stories high, made of the rough-faced brick brought out from Omaha on a flatcar, the Lone Tree Hotel sits where the coaches on the westbound caboose came to a stop. Eastbound, there were few who troubled to stop. In the westbound caboose were the men who helped Lone Tree to believe in itself. The hotel faces the south, the empty pits that were dug for homes never erected, and the shadowy trails, like Inca roads, indicating what were meant to be streets. The door at the front, set in slantwise with a floral design in the frosted glass, opens on the prospect of the town. Slabs of imported Italian marble face what was once the bank, the windows boarded like a looted tomb, the vault at the rear once having served as a jail. A sign—

515

$5.00 Fine for Talking
to
PRISONERS

once hung over one of the barred windows, but a brakeman, who was something of a card, made off with it.

The lobby of the hotel, level with the hitching bar, affords a view of the barber shop interior, the mirror on the wall, and whoever might be sitting in the one chair. Only the lower half of the window is curtained, screening off the man who is being shaved, but offering a view of the street and the plain when he is erect, just his hair being cut. Tucked into the frame of the mirror are the postcards sent back by citizens who left, or went traveling, to those who were crazy enough to stay on in Lone Tree. The incumbent barber usually doubled as the Postmaster. In the glass razor case, laid out on a towel still peppered with his day-old beard, is the razor that shaved William Jennings Bryan. In Lone Tree, at the turn of the century, he pled the lost cause of silver, then descended from the platform of the caboose for a shampoo and a shave. On that day, a balloon, brought out on a flatcar, reached the altitude of two hundred and forty-five feet with Edna Scanlon, who was something of a tomboy, visible in the basket that hung beneath. The century turned, that memorable summer, and most of the men in Lone Tree turned with it, like the engines on the roundhouse platform they wheeled from west to east. But neither Scanlon, anchored in the lobby, nor the town of Lone Tree turned with it. The century went its own way after that, and Scanlon went his.

From a rocker in the lobby Scanlon can see the gap between the barber shop and the building on the west, the yellow blind shadowed with the remaining letters of a word: MI L NE Y. On the floor above the Millinery, is the office of Dr. Twomey, a cigar-store Indian with human teeth guarding the door. He stands grimacing, tomahawk upraised, with what are left of the molars known to drop out when the building shook from a downgrade freight. When Twomey set up his practice, the barber chair served very nicely as an operating table, a place for lancing boils, removing adenoids, or pulling teeth. A flight of wooden steps, without a railing, mounted to his office on the second floor, but they collapsed within a week or so after he died. A huge man, weighing some three hundred pounds, it took four men to lower his body to the casket on the wagon in the street. The stairs survived the strain, then collapsed under their own weight.

A hand-cranked gas pump, the crank in a sling, sits several yards in front of the livery stable, as if to disassociate itself from the horses once stabled inside. At the back of the stable, inhabited by bats, is the covered wagon Scanlon was born in, the bottom sloped up at both ends like a river boat. Strips of tattered, faded canvas dangle from the hoops. Until the hotel was built, in the eighties, the Scanlon family lived in the rear of the Millinery, and the covered wagon, like a gypsy encampment, sat under the lone tree.

Before the railroad went through, the Pony Express stopped in the shade of the tree for water. Scanlon remembers the sweat on the horses, and once being lifted to the pummel of the saddle, but most of the things he remembers took place long before he was born.

In the weeds behind the stable is a rubber-tired fire hose cart without the hose, two short lengths of ladder, and the iron frame for the fire bell. When the water pressure system proved too expensive, the order for the hose and the fire bell was canceled. On the east side of the stable, the wheels sunk in the sand, a water sprinkler is garlanded with morning glories and painted with the legend VISIT THE LYRIC TONITE. The Lyric, a wooden frame building, has a front of galvanized tin, weathered to the leaden color of the drain pipes on the hotel. It stands, like a souvenir bookend, at the east end of the town, holding up the row of false-front stores between it and the bank. Most of the year these shops face the sun, the light glaring on the curtained windows, like a row of blindfolded Confederate soldiers lined up to be shot. A boardwalk, like a fence blown on its side, is half concealed by the tidal drift of the sand—nothing could be drier, but the look of the place is wet. The wash of the sand is rippled as if by the movement of water, and stretches of the walk have the look of a battered pier. The town itself seems to face what is left of a vanished lake. Even the lone tree, stripped of its foliage, rises from the deck of the plain like a mast, and from the highway, or the bluffs along the river, the crow's nest at the top might be that on a ship. The bowl of the sky seems higher, the plain wider, because of it.

517

A street light still swings at the crossing corner but in the summer it casts no shadow, glowing like a bolthole in a stove until after nine o'clock. The plain is dark, but the bowl of the sky is full of light. On his horsehair sofa, drawn up to the window, Scanlon can read the paper until ten o'clock. The light is there after the sun has set, and will be there in the morning before it rises, as if a property of the sky itself. The moon, rather than the sun, might be the source of it. In the summer, the bats wing in and out of the stable as if it were dark, their radar clicking, wheel on the sky, then wing into the stable again. At this time of the evening coins come out to be found. The rails gleam like ice in the cinders and the drayman's badge on Scanlon's hat, bright as a buckle, can be seen through the hole he has rubbed in the glass.

If a grass fire has been smoldering during the day you will see it flicker on the plain at night, and smoke from these fires, like Scanlon himself, has seldom left the rooms of the Lone Tree Hotel. It is there in the curtains like the smell of his cigars. His daughter Lois, the moment she arrives, goes up and down the halls opening the windows, and leaves a bottle of air-wick in the room where she plans to spend the night. For better or worse—as she so often tells McKee—she was born and raised in it.

The last time Lois spent a night in Lone Tree her father had been found, wrapped up like a mummy, his cold feet in a colder oven, big as life on the front page of the *Omaha Bee*. The caption of the story read,

MAN WHO KNEW BUFFALO BILL SPENDS LONELY XMAS

although both his daughter and McKee were out there in time to spend part of Christmas with him. The story brought him many letters, and made him famous, but put an end to his Lone Tree hibernation. To keep him entertained, as well as out of mischief, his daughter and her husband, the previous winter, took him along on their trip to Mexico. There he saw a bullfight and met McKee's old friend, Gordon Boyd. In Claremore, Oklahoma, on their way back, they stopped to see Scanlon's youngest daughter, Edna, the only one of his children he liked. Her husband, Clyde Ewing, claimed to be one-fifth Cherokee Indian and an old friend of Will Rogers, whoever that might be. Ewing and his wife spent most of their time going up and down the country in a house trailer just a few feet shorter than a flatcar. It had two bedrooms, a shower and a bath, with a rumpus room said to be soundproof. In the rumpus room, since they had no children, they kept an English bulldog named Shiloh, whose daddy had been sold for thirty thousand dollars the year he was born. Scanlon never cared for dogs, and being too old to ride any of the Ewings' prize horses he was put in a buggy, between Ewing and McKee, and allowed to hold the reins while a white mare cantered. It made him Hmmmphh. The Ewings were having a family reunion, but Scanlon saw no Cherokees present.

While they were there, on the Ewings' TV, they got the report of a tragedy in Lincoln: a high-school boy, with a hotrod, had run down and

518

killed two of his classmates. An accident? No, he had run them down as they stood in the street, taunting him. On the TV screen they showed the boy's car, the muffler sticking up beside the windshield, like a funnel, the fenders dented where he had smashed into the boys. Then they showed the killer, a boy with glasses, looking like a space-man in his crash helmet. His name was LeRoy Momeyer—pronounced Lee Roy by his family—the son of an Aurora machine shop mechanic and the brother of Bud Momeyer, related to Scanlon by marriage. At the time he ran down and killed his classmates he was working in a grease pit at the gasoline station where McKee had used his influence to get him the job. Eighteen years of age, serious-minded, studious looking in his thick-lensed glasses, LeRoy was well-intentioned to the point it hurt—but a little slow. Talking to him, McKee fell into the habit of repeating himself.

"Mr. McKee," LeRoy would say, "what can I do you for?" and McKee never quite got accustomed to it. And there he was, famous, with his picture on TV. In the morning they had a telegram from Maxine Momeyer asking if McKee would go his bail, which he did. Two days later, as they drove into Lincoln, coming in the back way so nobody would see them, there was no mention of Lee Roy Momeyer on the radio. A man and his wife had just been found murdered, but it couldn't have been Lee Roy Momeyer. They had him, as the reporter said, in custody. Before that week was out there had been eight more, shot down like ducks by the mad-dog killer, until he was captured out in the sandhills, not far from Lone Tree. His name was Charlie Munger, and he was well known to Lee Roy Momeyer, who often greased his car. Between them they had killed thirteen people in ten days. One of them, Lester Hodge, was well known to McKee, and such mail as seven others ever received was delivered by Bud Momeyer, their mailman.

"Why the devil'd he do it?" Tom Scanlon asked.

"All we know is what he said," McKee replied.

"And what did he say?"

"Said he wanted to be somebody."

Was that what he meant? Anyhow, it was what he said. And it was what he was. Nobody thought or talked of anything else. Scanlon's daughter Lois kept the lights burning all night long, in her new house, and it did no good to tell her the killer was caught. If it could happen at all, couldn't it happen again? If one boy could do it, what was stopping another one? Didn't they all want to be somebody—anybody, that is, but who they happened to be? But it had one advantage. It made Lee Roy Momeyer seem pretty tame. They put *his* picture in the back of the paper, and what he had to say went almost unnoticed. Almost, but not quite. McKee found it and snipped it out. Just a simple statement in answer to a question put by a reporter.

"I guess I just got tired of bein' pushed around."

McKee filed the clipping under his desk blotter where he kept insurance statistics, and the increased chances for a long and happy life of a man of his age.

520

Mark Harris

The Self-Made Brain Surgeon

I ordered the illumination extinguished in the power pole, but on the following day the cruising Streetlight Bench replaced it. It was the Electrical Overhead who referred me to the Streetlight Bench, again I ordered the illumination extinguished, but the Fire Department took issue, one Inspector Mahaffey there, complaining that he required the light, it illuminated the alarm box on the corner. Not enough co-operation, too much efficiency, men are double-barreled. I arranged with the Streetlight Bench for an independent circuit, they installed it in the ground at the base of the pole. A buried brook ran underneath the sidewalk. It emptied in the reservoir. I could kick on the power pole with my foot when I went home, or off, however I desired. Several nights I went home very late, I was constantly afraid, the neighborhood was unfamiliar to me.

Complaints were initiated in the neighborhood when the light was observed extinguished, and I observed in the dark beside the pole. But where else could I have stood? From any other point I could not have obtained a full view.

It was not Mr. Kayzee who initiated the complaint, for he is not a man frightened by much. He possessed no gun, while his door he long ago took down off the hinges, so at night when he quits he drops and lashes a tarp, that's all. The hinges are there, but no door hanging, yet he has never been broken or entered.

His own illumination is all interior, except his beer sign, which throws a little blue light on the sidewalk. Late at night, when the fog blew in, it shone blue on the particles of the fog, and when the wind was right I could hear the foghorns. It was cold. Sometimes, when all was very quiet, I could hear his beer sign buzz, and yet I don't see how I could have heard it as far away as the power pole, but I thought I could. I became accustomed to the noises.

What you don't hear. Imagine if you could see as well as hear. I could hear the water running in the buried brook underneath my feet, babies crying and people arguing, dogs or cats barking or wailing, cars starting, doors slamming, brakes or honking, people whistling or singing, pianos or trumpets playing or blowing, bells ringing, radio or television, hammering or repairing. It is a great neighborhood for repairing, do it yourself. A man was repairing dents in bodies, one Lionel Hefley, age 44, residence 615 Twelfth, he was a moonlighter, he didn't really need the money but he needed the hammering. Nobody complained. Somebody shouted out a window one night: "Hefley, for Christ's sake, go to bed," then I heard the window slam, but it wasn't a peeve or beef, it wasn't anger, it is an understanding neighborhood, he needed the hammering. He was a patient of Mr. Kayzee's. Then, little by little, all around you the lights go out.

Sometimes he forgot to turn his beer sign off. He lives over his shop, when he switched his lights on upstairs he remembered his beer sign and came back down again. The mind is not such a mystery. If he had a patient he went in the back room. One night I went around the corner and down the alley. but I could not see in, nor was there entry or access there, although the Fire Department claimed that escapement was not impeded, one Inspector Farmholder there. What was he thinking? It was a small window, and I scraped it, but it was painted brown and blue on the inside, triangles all crisscross, and I could not see in, nor hear in.

One Mrs. Marinda Marveaux was a patient at that time, a housewife, age 24, residence 55 San Pedro, I stood aside when she left, the rear of the Marveaux house faces the rear of Mr. Kayzee's premises. Complaint was initiated by one Armand Marveaux, her husband. Another patient was his alleged bookkeeper, one Miss Denise Willerts, age 18, residence 689 Twelfth, a student at the Washby Office Machines School & Sales. Another patient was one Lionel Hefley, aforementioned.

Never was a job more lonely or depressing, it was too little to do for the hours, standing and observing nothing happening. It is a quiet neighborhood, night after night, go out and buy a loaf of bread, a half a dozen slices of meat for the pail tomorrow, two cans of beer for bedtime. Where is such a life leading? I was so depressed, talking out loud under the pole was next in store for me, babies cry, people die, one night there was a wake for one Mrs. Theresa McQuinn, age 78, deceased, residence 714 Twelfth. Mr. Kayzee closed early and attended the wake, babies cry, people die, get up, and go to work, everybody waiting for some piece of luck to carry them out of the neighborhood. In front of Mr. Kayzee's store they were always talking, the word I could hear was "Money." Yet when will such a piece of luck float by, and for who? You can try to promote your luck, you can bet the horses, fly to Reno for the weekend, hunt for your Lucky Dollar in the newspaper numbers, you can drink or take a pill, but half the ways of promoting your luck are illegal or harmful to your health, and the harder you promote it the thinner your lines become, you lose patience, your habits become irregular, you become irked and irritated. Finally you lose your job. Most of them figured it was luck enough to be working. You can borrow, you can gamble, but you can't really win, or even if you win you won't be satisfied, for winning once is only half of winning twice, in the end the regular life is best, come home, eat your dinner, put the kids to bed, read the papers, look at the television, go out and buy two cans of beer, come home and drink it, argue with the wife, turn out the lights, and go to sleep. It is that kind of a neighborhood, just the noises, not much.

523

He was born over the store. He was named Hopkins in honor of one Hopkins, deceased, who held the first mortgage on the store for his father. His father's name was full of *k*'s and *z*'s, such as Kzotszki, a foreign name, and when he was a young man he took out the *k*'s and *z*'s and called himself Kayzee. It was clever. I inquired of one M. J. Cavendish, age 84, retired, of 802 Twelfth (back): "What kind of a boy was Mr. Kayzee?"

He replied: "He was a studious boy, read books and ate fruit in the front of the store."

"Was he given to cutting up frogs and such?" I inquired. Information to this effect was divulged by Mr. Marveaux, complainant.

"Yes," replied Mr. Cavendish, "he was given to cutting up frogs and such. The boys all caught frogs in the buried brook. It ran diagonal to what is now called Twelfth. The boys caught frogs and the Kzotszki boy cut them up with a knife. He ate fruit and read books and cut up frogs and such."

In the old war he served in a medical detachment, 1917–1918, carrying, bandaging, and nursing. Following his military career he continued his career in his father's store, The Rite-By Market, 696 Twelfth.

Once every night I crossed the street and entered, purchasing a cigar. Cigarettes I kept lighting up and illuminating myself, maybe it was how I was observed, whereas a cigar could remain dead in my mouth for long periods of time and avoid illuminating myself. At that time I smoked three packages of cigarettes daily, I was on the verge of a nervous collapse. Once I cashed a small check, five dollars.

He always wore a white coat, and it was always clean, the sleeves turned back neatly, one turn at the wrists. He wore a badge of blue and gold three inches in diameter, like an election button. It was a joke:

US OFFICIAL
taxpayer

Every night he threw the coat in the hamper, the final action before turning out the lights, pinned the badge on the new coat, except on Thursday night he also set the hamper on the sidewalk prior to dropping and lashing the tarp. The liner of the hamper was removed on Friday morning by one Owen Segret, age 27, driver for the Pacific Linen Supply Company. The coats bore no stains or questionable matter other than ordinary, the pockets contained nothing informative, sometimes a coin or a register receipt. Segret returned the coins, if any, each following Friday when he replaced the new liner.

His books were kept by his alleged bookkeeper, one Miss Denise Willerts, aforementioned. In addition to Miss Willerts he was assisted by his wife, one Dorothy, age 59, residence same. She was formerly a nurse at Letterman Army Hospital, 1951–1956, and elsewhere. Also by a delivery boy, one Warren Ponce, age 15, residence 685 Twelfth, the boy and the girl are relations. I can't describe how. Her mother and Ponce's father were formerly husband and wife, their marriage terminated, the wives exchanged husbands, the husbands exchanged residences. It was the second exchange, since prior to the termination of their marriages Mr. and Mrs. Willerts were married to each other, and Mr. and Mrs. Ponce also. The Willerts girl and the Ponce boy now reside again with their natural parents. Eight other children are also issue, residing at 685 and 689, three born to Mrs. Ponce and living with same (two by Mr. Ponce, one by Mr. Willerts), while five were born to Mrs. Willerts (three by Mr. Willerts, two by Mr. Ponce), all eight now resident with their natural parents except August Willerts, age 14, resident in the Ponce residence, 685. Mr. Willerts was arraigned but never tried for alleged attempt to defraud, June 1946, in connection with a litigation involving multiple disability claims for alleged internal injuries suffered in a collision of two machines at the intersection of Junipero Serra and St Francis Circle *de facto* unoccupied when alleged collision occurred. He was represented by one Carlos Minna, age 57, an attorney, residence 113 San Pedro, also attorney for Mr. Kayzee.

In addition he employs one Alvin (Monk) Kuhnle, Jr, age 38, a painter seasonally employed, residence 134 San Pedro, who paints items and prices and occasional interior surfaces, who painted the blue door leading to Mr. Kayzee's alleged storage room, who painted the window in blue, with brown triangles within, and who paints the numerous signs or decorations such as MY MIND IS MADE UP. DON'T CONFUSE ME WITH FACTS or DON'T CRITICIZE YOUR WIFE. LOOK WHO SHE MARRIED or LOVE YOUR ENEMY. IT'LL DRIVE HIM CRAZY. These are the simple wisdom of ages. Kuhnle receives groceries and sundries in lieu of rates or wages. He was arrested in January 1953, for petty pilfer of the poorbox of the Church of Our Lady of Mercy, San Pedro at Thirteenth, charges were not preferred, he was represented by one Mr. Minna aforementioned and released in Mr. Kayzee's recognizance.

Except in the case of Kuhnle he pays standard rates or wages to Miss Willerts and Warren Ponce, withholding taxes and Social Security deductions according to law, and $599 to his wife *per annum*, whereby he claims her as an itemized business expenditure while also retaining her as a dependent exemption; it is legal.

Nothing was illegal. He possesses authorization to sell beer, wine, liquor, or one or all and has no record of violation, possesses a Fire-Sanitation permit to burn trash during daylight hours in an approved receptacle, permit to encumber pedestrian right-of-way with cardboard or light wood cartons

525

or crates or other pending removal by scavenger service, and permit to maintain storage space at the rear of his establishment not to impede escapement. I ordered a Fire examination of the alleged storage space, one Inspector Farmholder there, but he failed to observe contents as I directed, reporting only "adequate escapement." Co-operation is difficult. Persons in high stations are often negligent or indifferent.

I made numerous inquiries of nonperishable salesmen or truckmen dealing in such goods as bottled or canned beverages, packaged cereals or desserts or cake mixings, inquiring: "Does your business with Mr. Kayzee differ in any way from your business with other grocers operating establishments similar in size or kind?" I gained helpful information from all, especially one Jack Schindler, age 48, a salesman-truckman employed by the Twin Peaks Bottling & Distributing Company.

"I am forced to call daily on Mr. Kayzee," he replied, "whereas I don't call daily on anybody else."

"How do you account for this?" I inquired.

"Because he'll stock shelves or refrigerator facilities," replied Mr. Schindler, "but he won't stock storage."

"Why won't he stock storage?" I inquired.

"Because he's not a progressive businessman," replied Mr. Schindler.

"Doesn't he do a good business?" I inquired. Then I stated: "He lives."

"You're asking a tricky-type question," replied Mr. Schindler. "He does a marginal business, he owns the building, he eats off his shelves, sure. Sure, he *lives*."

"But he has a storage room," I stated, and then inquired: "Why doesn't he use his storage room?"

"Because he performs brain surgery back there," replied Mr. Schindler. He laughed. Over the freezer was a sign painted by Kuhnle aforementioned in the old English style: BRAIN SURGERY PERFORMED ON PREMISES. ALL WORK GUARANTEED.

Everybody knew so. It was a joke in the neighborhood. Who cares? Anything goes, everything and anything is taken for granted, it was no surprise I became depressed. Consider the neighborhood. It is a neighborhood of churches, including the Church of Our Lady of Mercy, San Pedro at Thirteenth, the largest Church in the Diocese, and yet you will hear a great deal of criticism of the Priests. All persons follow politics but do not trust the politicians. It is heavy with the residences of municipal workers, Police or Fire or other, and yet the Department is not respected. It is a Union district, and yet the leaders of labor are not respected. The taverns are full, illegal betting is freely solicited, graft and corruption are everywhere, violations exist, scores of residents draw unemployment but will not work though bodily able, it is a neighborhood joke. Scores of residents draw disability but are not sick, respectable physicians sign statements, and everybody knows but nobody tells. The outstanding industry of the area is minding your own business. Information is difficult to develop. I saw children smoking on the street, the adults turned their backs. I heard vile language from women and children. Do my own children do this, does the wife swear outside the house?

Whereas when I was a boy the future was arranged, my father allowed me my way, but never too much, I swore on the street but nobody heard me, I smoked under the stairway, we respected our elders, or if anybody heard me or saw me it was definitely by chance, I ran around a little, I fought a little, I pinched a stick of candy here or there, an item of fruit, I cut school, I window-peeped, I sneaked into ball parks and films, we all did. I wrote my name in the municipal cement. But we never doubted the future was arranged, and when the time came, we settled down.

The more I stood there, the more depressed I became. I wore dark clothes. I surveyed his premises from across the street beneath the power pole. For three nights I stood there late, while after the first few nights I became almost too depressed to remain, sometimes I kicked the power pole on and went home early, though I put in far short of the hours.

His knives depressed me, he was always slicing fruit, the blades reflected from his interior lighting. He sliced a little, he laid the knives down carefully for a customer, he wiped his hands on his coat, rang up the money, and picked up the knives again. Over the bread and pastries was a sign: ANYONE WHO REMAINS CALM IN THE MIDST OF ALL THIS CONFUSION SIMPLY DOESN'T UNDERSTAND THE SITUATION. But he was calm, there was no confusion, his hands were steady. He sharpened his knives on a whetstone, and when he spoke he spoke slow, and he was calm, a deep thinker. MAKE SURE BRAIN IS ENGAGED BEFORE PUTTING MOUTH IN GEAR.

On the east wall was a large sign:

GOOD RULES FOR BUSINESS MEN
1. Don't worry; don't overbuy; don't go security.
2. Keep your vitality up; keep insured; keep sober; keep cool; keep your dignity.
3. Stick to chosen pursuits, but not to chosen methods.
4. Be content with small beginnings and develop them.
5. Be wary of dealing with unsuccessful men.
6. Be cautious, but when a bargain is made stick to it.
7. Keep down expenses, but don't be stingy.
8. Make friends, but not favorites.
9. Don't take new risks to retrieve old losses.
10. Stop a bad account at once.
11. Make plans ahead, but don't make them in cast iron.
12. Don't tell what you are going to do until you have done it.
13. Speak up, for dignity is more than dollars.

Mr. Kayzee discovered these rules in the front of his Daily Reminder, a black book I examined, showing Domestic and Foreign Postage Rates, Table of Days Between Two Dates, Actual Rate of Income, Distances and Mail Time Between Cities in the United States, Distances and Mail Time to Foreign Cities from San Francisco, Common Stains and How to Remove Them, Rates of Interest in All States, Actual Time in Use in the Largest Cities of the World when it is Noon in San Francisco, Rules for Computing Interest, Points of Constitutional Law, Weights and Measures, Explanation of Weather Bureau Flag Signals, Help in Case of Accident, Approximate Weight of Substances, Presidents of the United States, Nicknames and Flowers of the States, Supervisors of the City of San Francisco, Assemblymen of the State of California, Population of Principal Cities, Legal Holidays in Various States, and other necessary information.

II

Complaint was initiated by one Armand Marveaux aforementioned, age 33, a plasterer, residence 55 San Pedro. San Pedro is only three blocks long, running parallel to Twelfth between Twelfth and Thirteenth, blocked at the east end by the reservoir, and at the west by the Nuns' Convent adjacent to the Church. The rear of the Marveaux house faces the rear of Mr. Kayzee's premises. As aforementioned, she crossed her garden, jumped over a rock wall there, it was not high, afterward returning the same way and entering her own house by her own rear door. She was in love with Mr. Kayzee, afterward she loved her husband again, all was proper, it was only transference. San Pedro was known in former times as Vivian Lane, honoring a noted prostitute, one Vivian. Certain older residents of the neighborhood still refer to it as Vivian Lane, such as Mr. Cavendish aforementioned. They are incorrect. Complainant complained that his grocer, one Hopkins Kayzee, was engaged in alleged illegal or illicit relationships with his wife, one Marinda, in the storage room of the latter's premises and was performing alleged illegal or illicit brain surgery upon the head of same.

I was at that time assigned to Convention Protection. "We are the Nation's foremost Convention City, boasting splendid luxury hotels, unexcelled fine restaurants, a wide variety of sophisticated nocturnal amusements and daylight summit vistas, an average Summer temperature of 65 degrees (Fahrenheit), the world's largest International Airport, and a Cosmopolitan Atmosphere blended with a Frontier Tradition whose spirit encourages mature restraint as the better alternative to an unrealistic strict enforcement." 529 It was the height of my depression.

I worked hotels and demonstration or display rooms with an old friend of mine, Archie Wilson. He also depressed me. Some months prior, coming home one night, he was attacked by hoodlums, his gun was stolen, he was beaten, his assailants were never apprehended. Requesting a change, I drew for a partner a young man of little experience, one Robert (Bob) McFee. Our work was limited to report. We were permitted to detain or arrest pick-pockets or confederates only. McFee took it in stride, everything and anything he took for granted, and yet he was a college man. Is this the respect my children will be taught in college? We reported or observed, but we could not take action, we could only survey. Whereas, with an arrest here or an arrest there, it could have been cleaned up entirely, Convention Protection done away with forever, but it wasn't done, the idea being: Allow it to be professional but prevent it from being organized, let girls work, let card players work, only keep it in singles or pairs and off the telephones, keep pimps or heavy operations out. What were we doing? Do you wish your city to be no more than a protected operation? You will attract to it the dregs of civilization from Reno, Vegas, Denver, or other points.

When I awoke I inquired: "How can I face another day?"

The wife replied: "Let it pass, it's the summer season," while McFee took the same position, stating: "Let it pass, you're already an ulcer type, let it pass, let it pass."

"How can I see and not speak?" I inquired.

"Who would you speak to?" the wife inquired, then stating: "Limiting and containing is all you can do, accept it, it's the summer season," until I bottled it up inside me but could not release it, for who could be spoken to? She was right. "Speak up, for dignity is more than dollars." Men cannot always speak up. Men shoot themselves in the head in the locker room, it is a common occurrence.

Lt. Kline said a little rest would do me wonders, he gave me a week away, we left the children with my mother, the wife and I flew to Reno. We allotted one hundred dollars to the slots, we attended the nude shows, we slept in a hotel, we approached the end of our allotted money on several occasions, we hit, we were rich again, we laughed, but I wouldn't live there. When I returned Lt. Kline stated it was better for me to work slowly, relax a little, avoid tension, keep to myself. "What's this?" the Lt. inquired. He laughed. "Whose wife? The grocer's wife or complainant's wife? Investigate the back room, work slow, relax a little, avoid tension; is it a storage room, or what is it?"

Complainant is the father of three children, Marilyn, Lucinda, and Marilinda. I rang the bell, the children and the dog came running, laughing or barking, and Marveaux himself behind them, I stated my business. "Finally you came," stated Mr. Marveaux, walking out on the porch and chasing the children back inside. Then he himself went inside, coming out again wearing an orange leather jacket, and he zippered it up. In those days I never forgot anything, if a man wore a jacket and zippered it up; it remained in my mind, my mind was a storage room of useless small facts, whereas I was out of touch with the big pattern of things. After he zippered up his jacket we walked down San Pedro and around the corner. "What right has any man got," inquired Mr. Marveaux, "to be tampering with another man's wife's ways?"

"No right," I replied.

"When your wife goes to the grocery store," inquired Mr. Marveaux, "do you expect the grocer to be asking her all kinds of questions or making her all kinds of suggestions regarding her sexual activities with her husband?"

"Certainly not," I replied.

"A grocer is a grocer," stated Mr. Marveaux, "a grocery store is a grocery store." We crossed Twelfth and stood under the light of the power pole, his hair was cut in sideburns, he smoked Oasis cigarettes, and his jacket was illuminated, shining orange. It was called The Rite-By Market. "Don't you think a grocery store is a grocery store?" inquired Mr. Marveaux. "Is he permitted to call himself a brain surgeon?"

"We must know the facts," I stated, and then inquired: "Does he actually call himself a brain surgeon?"

"He performs brain surgery," replied Mr. Marveaux.

I inquired: "He actually cuts people's heads open with a knife?"

"He tampered with my wife's sexual attitudes," replied Mr. Marveaux.

"He cut open your wife's head with a *knife*?" I inquired.

"It was brain surgery," he stated. "He shifted around her brain, causing her to alter her image of herself by brain surgery."

"With a knife?" I inquired, then stated: "If it was a knife she would have come home bleeding. Answer me," then inquiring again: "A *knife*?"

"Go read the sign," he replied. "See the knives."

I crossed the street, he remained where he was. I entered the store, I bought a package of cigarettes. Over the freezer was the sign aforementioned: BRAIN SURGERY PERFORMED ON PREMISES. ALL WORK GUARANTEED, and in his hands a knife, he was slicing an apple. He put down the knife, he placed his apple on the scale, he gave me my cigarettes, rang my money, gave me change. Then he picked up the knife and the apple again. I went back across the street and leaned against the power pole again. "It's just a joke," I stated.

"It's no joke," he stated. "He made a regular sexual fiend out of her. She was just an ordinary girl, after six years you don't suddenly develop along the lines of a sexual fiend unless somebody's been tampering with your attitudes. It was surgery."

"With a *knife*?" I inquired.

"Formerly it was now and then, take it or leave it, *comme ci, comme ça*, my background is French. She's also of French background."

"Answer me. Did she come home *bleeding*?"

"She came home a fiend. 'Where are you going?' It's seven o'clock. 'I'm going down to The Rite-By for a loaf of bread.' It's eight o'clock. It's nine o'clock. I'm all alone. Where is she? 'Where have you been?' 'I went

531

down to The Rite-By for a loaf of bread.' 'Since when does it take two hours to buy a loaf of bread?' 'He was slicing it. It was unsliced bread.'"

"Slicing it with what?" I inquired.

"A knife."

"*Was she bleeding when she came home?*"

"It was brain surgery."

"You can't leave the house," I stated, "at seven o'clock and have brain surgery and walk in at nine and not be bleeding."

"She never walked in, she ran in, she leaped in my arms after six years, she loved me, I was tired, I'm a plasterer all day. She had a new image of herself. Formerly she was who she was, now she is Marinda Marveaux, French lady of the night. 'Where have you been?' 'I've been in the back of the store with Mr. Kayzee.' 'Doing what?' 'Receiving brain surgery.' Everybody in the neighborhood is having brain surgery in the back of Mr. Kayzee. Ask around. Read the sign."

"Mr. Marveaux," I stated, "brain surgery is a job done by medicine men of long experience and training in many colleges, and you bleed. You lie around unconscious for many hours afterward, and they send you a big bill." Then I inquired: "Does Mr. Kayzee send you a bill?"

"Only for groceries," he replied. He leaned against the power pole, thinking of Mr. Kayzee. "He's a very fair dealer. I like him. He has done wonders for the wife."

"Then why did you issue complaint?" I inquired.

"I didn't issue complaint," he replied.

"You called the police," I stated.

"Well, it's all right now," he stated. Again he leaned, thinking, and soon he stated further: "I withdraw complaint. I'm not complaining any more."

It was Wednesday. Thursday I ordered the illumination extinguished in the power pole, but Friday the cruising Streetlight Bench replaced it. Monday they installed the independent circuit, I could kick it off or on with my foot, however I desired. The cigars depressed me. The noises depressed me. The water in the buried brook depressed me, flowing, flowing, flowing, flowing, babies crying, people dying, I could feel it in the vibrations of my feet. It never ended. I began going crazy from depression. It became foggy at night, and the people were a blur, sometimes it was difficult to view the movement or motion within his store. What was I accomplishing?

Miss Willerts, Mrs. Marveaux, and Mr. Hefley were patients on the first three nights of the week, Monday, Tuesday, and Wednesday. Thursday I went home early. I was cold. Friday night I cashed a small check, five dollars. He took the check and placed it in his pocket still wet. "Will that be all?" he inquired. I bought a cigar, that was all. "That will be all," I replied, and he stated: "I thank you very kindly." I turned around and started out, he further stating: "Oh, by the way Mr. Cop, last night you forgot to kick the power pole back on."

"What power pole?" I inquired. Then I stated: "You're crazy, Mr," and I continued walking. Yet why deny it? I had made many inquiries, I was illuminated by cigarettes, one way or another it was bound to get back to him, it was how the neighborhood is, he is appreciated, he extends credit and courtesies of every sort, he has lived all his life in the neighborhood, raised his children there, maintains his property, respects the peace, such a man is respected in that neighborhood or any other. I stated: "You've got no license to dispense."

He stated: "Maybe you're crazy, too."

"OK." I bent my head, I removed my hat, it was a joke. "Here's my brain. Cut." He laughed, I laughed a little also, he dropped and lashed his tarp and turned out the lights. "Don't forget your beer sign," I stated. He went back and turned out his beer sign, in his hand was his knife. In the storage room he took off his white coat, unpinning his badge, then pinning it on a fresh coat. The room was dark, his coat was white, he turned his lamp toward the window, and it shone against the triangles brown and blue. Behind him was a shelf of books made of crates standing side by side.

"What's the tapecorder for?" I inquired.

"To talk in," he replied. "I record their lives."

"Play me a life. Play me Mrs. Marinda Marveaux."

"I erased her," he stated. "Tapes are expensive. She is a woman who expected perfection, but men are not perfect, men are double-barreled. Smoke if you wish." He turned the tapecorder on, a small red light shone, the spools went around and around, reflecting on the ceiling. In former times I was hypnotized by the spools going around and around, but later I did not mind them.

"Turn it off," I ordered. He turned it off.

He gave me a sheet of paper, *Good Rules for Business Men.* "This is all I dispense," he stated. "This is all I dispensed her, these are the simple wisdom of the ages. I recommend especially Number 13, speak up, for people must tell their troubles to one another, they discover their own mind with help, the mind is not such a mystery. They cannot pay much. Poor people cannot go downtown to the high-priced men. Accept the world, it's a low-income neighborhood."

I inquired, "This is all you dispensed her?"

"That's all," he replied. "We discussed the imperfections of her husband, which are numerous, but also his qualities, which are also numerous: he is steadily employed, he does not drink, he does not gamble, and he beat her only once in six years."

"You've got no license or authority to dispense," I stated.

"Why not eat your apple?" he inquired. He ran a small electric heater, the room grew gradually warmer, the heater switched off, the hour still was early, I agreed to eat my apple.

I inquired: "Where can I wash my apple?" He took me to a lavatory adjoining, it was clean but cool, I washed my apple, it was good to return to the warm room again. "Since when," I inquired, "does it take two hours to dispense a sheet of paper? Tuesday night she entered your store at 7:09, you turned out your lights, you entered this room, she departed at 9:11."

"We also talked," he replied.

"Where was she?" I inquired.

"Sitting where you are," he replied. I was in a leather chair.

"Did she sit or did she lie back flat?" I inquired, for the chair leaned back for comfort.

"*Comme ci, comme ça,*" he replied. "However she desired."

"Where were you?" I inquired.

"I was right here," he replied.

It was a comfortable chair, my head rested on a barber-pillow, I leaned back, I sliced my apple, while outside the wind blew fog down the alley. "Go ahead and eat it," he ordered. "Enjoy something. An apple is an apple, don't be so cautious, the health of the apple overpowers the germs. Why are you so cautious? You screw the cap on your pen too tight, your pen clips too tight in your pocket, your writing is extremely small and cautious, your hat is a half a size too small, it leaves a red mark on your forehead. Do you think the world is lying in wait to steal your fountain pen?" He informed me that in former times he also was an extremely cautious man. He spoke in a soft, steady voice, I loosened my shoes, I loosened my tie, I smoked

534

cigarettes. In those days I smoked three packages daily. We discussed smoking. When I was a boy I smoked cigarettes under the stairway, I thought
nobody saw me, but Mr. Kayzee suggested that the smoke drifted up, I was
observed by my father and others, I agreed it was a possible theory.

"Take off your coat," he advised. "Take off your gun, too." He
possessed no gun, and he inquired whether I had ever shot a man or not. I
replied that I did not know, for I shot into the shadows twice after Archie
Wilson was attacked by hoodlums unknown. He inquired whether he might
hear the story of Archie Wilson in the tapecorder, I agreed, the red light
shone and the spools went around and around on the ceiling. Upon later
occasions I heard my own voice on the tape. My voice grew stronger in
later weeks, I became less depressed.

The hour grew later and later, and the wind died, but I did not leave,
although it soon was midnight, and I became afraid, stating: "I cannot go, you
must at least walk me to my machine, the hour is late and the neighborhood is
unfamiliar to me."

"There is no reason to be afraid," he stated.

"Even in a machine a man is not safe," I stated. "You dare not even
stop at the light at certain intersections, they are on you in a minute. Our
own municipal streets are no longer even safe."

"The front page of the papers," he stated, "is not the story. Don't be
afraid."

"I'm not afraid," I stated.

"Good," he replied, "because there is little to be afraid of."

"Then walk with me," I stated, but he refused. I could not go. I could
not stay. What could I do? "You do not know the number of crimes committed every night, we are under-staffed, we are not respected, we are without
power, young thugs are running wild, attorneys defend them, the judiciary
is far too lenient, social workers bleed their hearts out, the boy had a bad
beginning, excuse and forgive, meanwhile they leave court in a stolen machine
full of billiard balls in high stockings, the streets are not safe, I cannot go."
Yet he refused to go with me. He unlashed his tarp and lifted it, and we
stood on the sidewalk in front of the shop.

"Cross," he stated, "and kick on your power pole, walk to your
machine, do not run, and drive home," but still I could not do as he directed.
The wind was down, I lit a cigarette. "Consider," he stated, "that you were
observed smoking under the stairway, not only by your father but by all the

neighborhood. You were loved and protected by your neighborhood, although you thought it was filled with enemies. But the truth is, let a thief enter, let a man be lewd or molest a child, let a man assault, and the neighborhood will rise and crush him, then or now or anywhere or any time, the neighborhood defends itself. The police are few, the residents are many, the neighborhood is its own Department, it cures or mends, it regulates itself. There is some danger tonight, but there was always some danger every night, not more and not less-so cross."

I did as he advised, and I continued afterward for some time until my depression faded away. We said goodnight, I crossed the street, I kicked the power pole back on, I walked to my machine, I drove home, I advised Lt Kline on the following day complainant withdrew complaint, I ordered the independent circuit discontinued, I resumed Convention Protection at that time.

Louis Guilloux

Friendship

Jean Kernevel was a man of fifty, big, well-built, but with a bad heart.
His friends had long been anxiously noting his leaden complexion, his ink-blue lips, his yellow eyes, and on his face that grave look men have who know they are under sentence of death. From his look, one knew he was thinking: "Perhaps in a month, perhaps in two, but surely soon."

A bachelor, he lived at the edge of town in a room he had furnished with his share of his parents' legacy—an oaken bed, a round table, a cupboard with two doors, and a pinewood chest of drawers. The rest of the furniture, three cane chairs and an armchair, he had picked up secondhand.

His brother Léon, three years his senior, had gone to live in Paris after his military service. He had married there and never come back to his own part of the world. It had taken a war for the two brothers to see each other again and for Jean to meet his sister-in-law and his nephews. . . .His sister had married late and remained childless; on learning that her husband had been killed at Verdun, she had gone mad, and since that time had been shut away at the *Incurables*. For Jean Kernevel, this was a grief of which he never spoke, not even to his old friend, Fortuné Le Brix.

Next to Jean Kernevel, Fortuné Le Brix seemed small. Kernevel was a head higher than he. Nonetheless, Le Brix was a vigorous man, well set on his legs, and had never known a day's illness. He had abundant red hair, a sanguine complexion, cheeks crisscrossed with tiny violet veins, a strong mustache, and hands like shovels. A bullet wound received at the Somme had left him with a long scar on his left temple; his eye was a little pulled in that direction, which made it look as though he were squinting.

They were both the same age and had hardly been separated since their school days. They had been apprentices together; they had gone off touring together; and before the war they had worked together for the same employers. The war had parted them but a few weeks, after Le Brix's wound and evacuation, and they were soon side by side in the trenches again.

Back home, they had started a small plaster, lime, and cement business with a young and recently married friend, Dagorne. Good workers, all three of them, they had quickly made their mark and earned a good living.

It was Kernevel who managed the business. He had good sense and solidity. He could write a letter and handle accounts; he did not drink and never lost his temper. Dagorne was not without education either, but he was too young to carry authority. As for Le Brix: "Work," he would say, "any amount of work, by God! There's not a son of a bitch in the whole area knows stairs better than I do! But as for writing . . . that's no go! Every man to his own job and let's get on with it!"

In spite of his illness, Jean Kernevel had not stopped working. When he had no suppliers or clients to call on, he arrived on the job at the same time as the others, and left at the same time, too. But his work got done slowly, and during the day he occasionally rested.

When Le Brix saw him lay down his trowel without saying a word and saw him get down off the scaffolding and lie down in a corner on some sacks, he made a face and thought: "Old Kernevel's flagging. Lose him and lose all. The business'll be done for!" Meanwhile business went on.

They were offered the rough-casting and plastering of a little house being built five kilometers from town. The job was good and the road there easy. A few minutes away was the White Pigeon, where they could catch a bite. A stream flowed nearby, and Dagorne, a born poacher, immediately started talking about laying down nets.

Kernevel figured they had three solid weeks of work, which would take them to the end of September. Then the bad weather could come. They would go back to town and do work indoors. They were not afraid of being unemployed.

The job progressed. The weather stayed fine. At the end of work one Saturday evening, Le Brix had climbed up the scaffolding, as he always did before leaving, to make sure that nothing had been left behind. Kernevel was changing below. Dagorne was already on his way home. He lived out of town and on Saturdays he left an hour early. He arranged it so that he could catch up during the week.

His rounds done, Le Brix came back down into the yard. He was humming a dance-tune and keeping time by nodding his head. He was pleased to be going home, to stop and wet his whistle at the White Pigeon and tomorrow to be spending the afternoon at the Velodrome. Le Brix liked sports, bicycle races most of all. As it happened, tomorrow was a championship race. Bicycle aces had come from Paris.

As he came around a corner of the house, he suddenly stopped humming. At the end of the yard, Kernevel was sitting on some thick planks, his head in his hands. He was looking at the ground through his legs without moving. "Could he be worse?" Le Brix asked himself.

"Well, old man?" he asked, coming nearer. "Something not going right?"

Without raising his head Kernevel replied, "Not right at all, Fortuné."

"Where's it hurt?"

"It doesn't hurt," Kernevel said. "It's the weakness. My legs won't hold me up."

Kernevel was doubled over, his cap askew, his lips parted, like a man under the weather. His bike was next to him. On the handlebars he had tied his white overalls, rolled up into a package. His breath came heavily.

"Wouldn't you like to lie down?" asked Le Brix. "You could use your overalls as a pillow. Lie down and it'll blow over."

Kernevel shook his head and Le Brix crossed his arms. "A fine fix," he said to himself. "Here I am all alone with a sick man. And how do I get him home?" He looked around, as though hoping for help. But the landscape was empty. The nearest house was the White Pigeon.

"A good slug of rum's what you need," he said. "I'll just hop over to the White Pigeon."

"Wait! Stop, Fortuné! Don't go!" Kernevel cried out. His voice was so weak and worried that Le Brix, who had already taken a few steps, turned half around.

Heavily, Kernevel looked for his handkerchief in the pocket of his jacket. He could not quite bring it up to his brow and Le Brix only just had time to sit down next to him and catch him in his arms. "Good God almighty!" he thought. "It's the real thing! Is he going to die on me?" He took the handkerchief from Kernevel's hand and wiped his friend's brow.

Kernevel indicated that his tie and vest bothered him. Le Brix undid them, but his huge fingers slipped on the buttons and he got angry with himself.

"Don't move," he said. "I'll take care of you."

He sat Kernevel down on the ground, his back against the planks, and put the overalls he untied from the bike under his head. Then he dipped the handkerchief in a tub and moistened his temples.

"That do you good?"

"Yes, Fortuné."

Kernevel passed his hand across his forehead, stretched out his legs, and tried to sit up.

"It'll pass."

"Sure." Le Brix took him up. "I'm going to get you a shot of rum."

He went back into the house to get his bike. "Goddam, goddam, goddam," he swore when he was alone. "It would have to be Saturday night! Dagorne gone an hour ago and five kilometers to home!" Furiously he picked up his bike at arm's length and made as if to throw it far away. "Goddam it to hell! And a flat tire!" He started pumping it in a rage; then he checked his free-wheel and his brakes. "I might have to take him home on my back," he said. After that, he changed, and finally came out into the yard.

Kernevel was standing, ready to leave, his hand on his bike. Le Brix stopped short and shouted: "I suppose you think you're going to bike home!"

"Got to."

"You strong enough?"

Kernevel shrugged his shoulders and repeated, "Got to."

Le Brix knew it was no good contradicting him. He had always obeyed him. It had started early, at children's games; and it had been the same since, even at the front. This obedience was neither servility on his part, nor brutality on Kernevel's: it was born of long custom, of everyday experience, of fraternal friendship. But this time Le Brix wanted to speak his piece.

"What you want to do's crazy, Jean. Wouldn't it be better if I went and got a car?"

"You'll do nothing of the sort," answered Kernevel. "I'll get home on my bike."

He straddled the bicycle and Le Brix said to himself: "How's it all going to end? And if he drops dead on the way?"

Kernevel looked as if he were just learning to ride a bike.

"Ride next to me," Le Brix shouted.

Jean Kernevel did not answer: he gritted his teeth.

II

Fortunately, there wasn't much to it. All they had to do was let themselves be carried into town. The road was easy and as it was after half past seven, there were few cars. Kernevel had taken the lead. He rode hunchbacked, without saying a word. Le Brix could hear him pant. "He's done for," he thought. "But tough. Some character!"

It wasn't the first time Kernevel showed Le Brix this kind of courage. All his life he had shown it. At the front, a calm man—but then the front wasn't the same thing. It was just a matter of waiting. There was no choice. Whereas now, if he had wanted, he could have had a car.

The road crossed the moors. They went by the White Pigeon without stopping. With the night, some clouds rose in the sky. They didn't take the time to light up.

At a turning in the road, the town appeared, with its lights, in the plain. It was high time they got there. When Kernevel got off his bicycle, at his door, he would have fallen to the sidewalk if Le Brix hadn't held him up.

It was an old house, with long windows full of small square panes. The door gave onto a stone staircase: like a railing, a rope hung there, thick as a cable, black and shining, and ending in a knot. With one hand Kernevel clung to this rope; it tightened with a snap.

"Home, Jean," said Le Brix. "I'll give you a hand up to your room. You'll have to lie down."

"It's my bed I need, all right."

He stopped at every step to catch his breath. Two flights they went up that way; then Kernevel took a key from his pocket. "Here," he said.

The room was in order. The oaken bed with its batiste curtains was covered with a red eiderdown. By the bed were lined up the two chairs and the armchair, and in the middle of the room the round table, with its flowered oilcloth, bore an oil lamp. Kernevel let himself fall into the armchair and Le Brix lit the lamp.

"Poor old Fortuné," said Kernevel, throwing his cap on the bed. "Here I am home. I thought I'd never get here."

"Don't think about it, man. Get to bed now," answered Le Brix.

"Wait. Let me breathe."

He was spent and his hands trembled on his knees where he had placed them.

"When you're in bed," Le Brix said, "I'll go find you something to eat."

"I don't want anything. I want to go to bed and sleep if I can. You ought to go home yourself, Fortuné. You're wife'll be wondering where you are. She'll give you hell."

"Bah! It won't be the first time. I want to see you in bed before I start home."

Kernevel rose from the armchair. He took off his jacket. Le Brix started walking up and down the room.

542

He had rarely entered it. The last time had been a year ago; he'd helped his friend whitewash the ceiling. The wash had held up well, but the walls needed it badly. Kernevel had hung some chromos. Le Brix looked them over one by one. Then he went over to the chest of drawers on which Kernevel had arranged some photographs, framed in red velvet: of his father and his mother, of his brother as a soldier, and of his sister on her twentieth birthday. Le Brix greatly respected the orderliness that reigned in the room. It was Kernevel himself who took care of it every morning as his coffee was warming upon the wood-alcohol stove.

Le Brix heard a groan and turned around. Kernevel had bent over to undo his shoelaces and now had straightened up. "I can't . . ."

"You see!" Le Brix shouted. "Don't push it. Don't move; let me handle this."

He kneeled down and untied the laces on the great hobnailed boots Kernevel wore. The leather was reddened all over with mortar. Then he helped him off with his corduroys and his jersey and said: "Think you can get into bed alone?"

He pulled back the blanket and Kernevel got in without a word. But once he lay stretched out with his head on the pillow, tears filled his eyes.

"What's that for?" said Le Brix. "What's got into you? Come on, man: you mustn't worry. Don't think, sleep. I'll be back in the morning. You need anything?"

"Nothing, Fortuné."

"Tomorrow then, and sleep."

He shook his head and left. "There's a man who worries too much," he said to himself, shrugging his shoulders.

It was night. Le Brix lit his lamp and jumped onto his bike.

His wife was waiting for him. She was a short woman of forty, thin, dark, and shrill, but good-hearted and a worker. Her hair was dressed in the old way, with a chignon and a puff. She was well-known in the district: Marie, Le Brix's wife, with her two tiny black eyes always on the lookout. She was a charwoman.

When Le Brix opened the door, she was at the stove, watching over the stew. She turned around, ladle in hand. No sooner had he taken a step into the room than she began swearing at him.

"There you are, you drunkard!" she shouted. "And where were you? Here I was eating myself up waiting for you!"

She threatened him with the ladle. He did not answer, put his tools down on a chair, and sat down at the table in front of his plate.

The room was low-ceilinged but huge. They had lived there all the twenty-five years of their marriage. They were happy in this huge room that had seemed so empty when they had set up house, when all the furniture they had in the world was a bed, a table, and a charcoal stove. But day by day the room had been furnished. One day they bought a stove, which they put near the bed to keep them warm in winter. Another day, a cupboard; then chairs and utensils. Today they were so numerous that no one knew where they had been obtained, or how. There were boxes filled with God knows what, rusty tacks and tools. Against a whitewashed wall stood the black staff of a flag in its sheath: the red flag, stored with Fortuné Le Brix since the town had closed down the Labor Exchange.

Marie turned down the lamp that had flared up. "Here it is so late I can't see a thing," she said. "Oh, you wretch!"

He played deaf. And she went on insulting him. All afternoon she had counted on going to the movies that night, as sometimes happened on Saturdays. The idea had stuck in her head. It was a thought, a wish, and she'd enjoyed a private joke about it, for there was little likelihood that she would have any other kind of desires. On that subject she was firm. She had no children and she would not have any. It was too late and she no longer even regretted it as she once had, back in the days when she had quarreled about it with Fortuné, who was, notwithstanding, a warm-blooded man.

With the movies in mind she had hurried through her work and made the stew. Then eight o'clock had struck and no husband! Eight-thirty and still no one. And now he came in, after nine o'clock!

"Ah, so help me, you drunkard!"

Finally, he had enough of it. He struck a great blow on the table with his fist and got up. "Goddam it!" he said. "Now you're going to shut up, Marie."

From time to time, if she got too shrill, he would hit her one. Then she would quiet down right away.

"Look out, woman," he said, his hand raised. "Just bring the soup."

She looked him over carefully. No, he was not drunk. But his looks indicated that something serious had happened. She had seen those eyes before, when there had been an accident. Her anger dissipated. She put the soup pot on the table in front of Le Brix and took the bread and a bottle of red wine out of the sideboard.

"What's wrong?" she asked.

"Wrong, Marie," he answered, "is that Kernevel's done for. Do you understand that?"

She opened her mouth, but said nothing. Le Brix gulped his soup down noisily.

"Well," he said between two mouthfuls, "eat your soup."

"What kind of a story's that? Jean Kernevel?"

"That's what I said."

The whole meal long they exchanged not a word. When Le Brix finished, he wiped his knife, pushed aside his plate, and told how Jean Kernevel had had an attack on the job.

"He insisted on coming home on his bike, but I had to put him to bed."

Elbows on the table, Marie listened. She did not want to believe her husband. She wanted details and more details.

"It's just not possible," she said.

"And," Le Brix concluded, "just on a Saturday night, Dagorne gone home, damn it!"

"And . . . ?" she asked. "And the business?"

Furious, he answered: "Business, there's no question of business right now, Marie."

He rolled himself a cigarette, drank his coffee, walked around the room a while, and went to bed while Marie washed the dishes.

III

Le Brix woke up at daylight. Marie was still dozing. "And Jean?" he said to himself. "I wonder how he's feeling."

He got up gently, not to wake up his wife and dressed. From the cupboard he took a clean cloth, a piece of Marseilles soap, and went out.

The street was fresh and empty. He made good time to the wash-house: a covered wash-house, built along the road at the end of town and fed by a fountain whose water was perpetually pure. Sunday mornings, like many of his friends in the district, Le Brix went there to perform his ablutions.

In the wash-house, he took off his shirt. Naked to the belt, he shivered. Suddenly, kneeling on the ledge, he ducked his head into the water; nothing like it, he was wont to say, to wake up a man. He rose dripping, his eyelids burning, and groped for the soap he had put down next to him. Then he rubbed his neck, his arms, and his hair, in which lumps of plaster and lime stubbornly refused to budge. He tore them out with rage, grimacing with pain, and urged himself on with jokes and oaths. Finally, he rinsed and dried himself off, snorting.

Only Sundays was he able to undertake what he called the "great wash." The other days, eye on the clock, he barely had time to pass the tip of a wet cloth across his eyes.

Once ready, he strode out into the fields. After a great wash he always took a walk, to "react." Sometimes he went as far as the Mare Melée, and breakfasted there with a great bowl of black coffee and a slice of buttered bread. Then he would walk back slowly, smoking a cigarette. This time he did not go so far.

A wind blew right along the ground. The earth was wet. On the edge of a vale, he stopped momentarily; the spot pleased him. From there he could see a whole stretch of country, and rising from it, the belfries of two villages, and farther on, the gray line of the shore and the sea. . . .He started back. The walk had warmed his blood. He was hungry.

Marie was up, dressed in a jacket and a petticoat of thick white wool with red stripes. Her hair was carelessly braided and struck her on the back every time she moved. Breakfast was ready.

"Here," she said. "It'll do you good if you've been out walking."

"I took a short one. I'm afraid it's not going to clear up; it looks like rain later. Still, I should see Dagorne later."

"You certainly should," she said.

He swallowed down his milk and bread; then he went out and fed his rabbits. Behind the house, at one end of the yard, he had a little corner of his own. When he had fed his animals, he shaved. Then he fetched his Sunday clothes, smoked a cigarette, and polished his shoes, one foot on a chair.

"I'm going to Jean," he said.

"Don't go empty-handed," she answered. "Here's a pot with some broth in it. Warm him up. And tell him I'm making some more, fresh, and he'll get it tomorrow."

546   "All right."

His hand was on the door.

"And buy him something on the way. Some oranges if you like. And say 'hello' to him from me."

He nodded his head and left.

Ordinarily, Sunday mornings passed like the wind. He went lazily from inn to inn. There was no question of inns today. He went straight to Kernevel's, walking as he did on his way to work. As he walked, he kept on repeating to himself: "How'll I find him? I wonder if he's had any sleep." The more he thought about Kernevel, the more worried he grew. "Poor fellow," he thought, "and only fifty years old!"

IV

Kernevel was not asleep. The morning light bothered him and he shut his eyes. But he was not strong enough to get up and close the shutters.

It had been a bad night. After Le Brix had gone, he had grown drowsy; then, at midnight, he had been awakened by a pain in his side. He had been unable to get to sleep again: until daybreak he had counted the hours.

Since he had fallen ill, Kernevel had been through some bad moments, but he had taken even the worst of them without giving in. But this one was not like the others. "No," he said, "this time I've really had it. But if it lasts, what will the others do? How'll they get along?"

Thinking made him worry more. To finish the job they had in hand, three fit men putting in their ten hours a day were not too many. Now there would be only two and Dagorne would have to lose time seeing customers. "Will he be able to stand up to them?" Kernevel asked himself. "What a shame, it was going so well!"

He did not try to hide the truth about his condition from himself. He felt that if his illness dragged on he would have to go to the hospital. He was afraid of the hospital. His father had died there, and after his father, his mother. He told himself that when he went in his turn, it would be to die. It was not the fear of dying that made him afraid of the hospital. The fear of death he fought as well as he could; but he did not want to be abandoned.

It was a dark night. The noises outside had all ceased. Kernevel was alone in his bed, thinking. "Bah!" he said. "Sick men's fancies!" And to drive them away, he wanted to think some more about the business, about the work that couldn't wait, about his accounts.

He had his own way of running the business and there were lots of little details that he settled without telling his companions; they were hardly worth talking about. But suddenly, he was overtaken by scruples. His accounts were up to the moment and well-kept, but nevertheless there were some things that his partners would not understand unless he explained them. And if he should die suddenly, as could happen? And without seeing them again? This thought so tormented him that he turned over and over in his bed, moaning. Once he was gone and they looked at the accounts, they might think that he had cheated them of some money. He would not be able to defend himself, or show them that he had always been honest. All feverish as he was, he would have liked to get up and take out his notebooks; but he could not. "Ah," he thought, "I've really had it this time, really had it." At the same time, he was angry at himself for thinking his friends capable of such an accusation. But no matter how much he repeated to himself that such an idea would never enter Le Brix's or Dagorne's head, he could not rid himself of his anxiety. "As soon as I see them again," he promised himself, "I'll talk to them about the accounts." This thought calmed him a little.

He heard the street wake up, with joy. People called from one window to another. A man began singing at the top of his voice. Water thrown from a window fell into the street in one great splash. These were Sunday noises, so different from week-day ones. On weekdays, there was not much singing to be heard. Steps on the stairs told him that his neighbors were going out on a trip and were hurrying to catch the first train.

The day rose; it filled the room. Kernevel was looking at the light on the walls when Le Brix entered.

"I was waiting for you," he said. "I knew you'd get here early."

"Damn right!" answered Le Brix, putting the pot down on the table. "Did you get some sleep?"

"Not much. I woke up at the stroke of midnight with a pain in my side."

He was lying flat on his back and spoke without moving his head. His eyes were yellow, his complexion mud-colored and his lips puffed. "He's not getting any stronger," Le Brix said to himself. "Got to see a doctor, there's no getting around it." Nor would it be an easy matter. Kernevel wouldn't want to hear talk of a doctor . . . and yet!

"What's in the pot?"

"Some broth from Marie. You'll have some fresh tomorrow. She's making some. Where's your stove?"

"Open the cupboard. Right in front of you. But I'm not hungry."

"Got to eat."

Le Brix poured the soup into the pot in which Kernevel heated his morning coffee and lit the stove. Then he sat down by the edge of the bed and stayed there, his great, bare, clay-colored hands resting on his knees. He chewed on a cigarette, wondering how he could bring up the question of a doctor. Finally he said:

"Listen Jean, old man, I don't mean to say that you look worse. On the contrary, you look better than last night. But for the sake of your conscience, don't you think I ought to go get the doctor for you? Old Houdan lives nearby, you know that. And he's a good guy. What do you say?"

"It'd be a waste of time, Fortuné."

"Bah! It'd take a weight off your mind."

"I don't need a doctor. I know what I've got."

There was nothing Le Brix could answer. He knew that unfortunately doctors were pretty much alike; they served to kill you a little quicker, but that was all. He wanted no part of them himself; no more than he wanted a priest. On that score he'd already made his wishes known to Marie. But it wasn't his time yet, and regardless of the poor opinion he had of doctors in general, he was ready to admit that old Houdan was a fine fellow and devoted to his patients.

"Damn it, Jean, you're a stubborn character!"

"That's beside the point. The fact is, old Houdan can't do anything."

"Where does it hurt?"

"Nowhere."

The same question, the same answer as last night. The idea that Kernevel was not suffering disconcerted Le Brix. What could the matter be that he should be so sick and yet feel no pain? Nothing above board, that was sure! Wouldn't it be better to suffer one good blow and have it all done with?

The soup was steaming on the stove.

"Sit up, Jean."

Kernevel sat up painfully in bed. He took the bowl Le Brix handed him with both hands and swallowed a gulp. Le Brix, arms dangling, watched his every move with an affectionate air.

"All of it, bottoms up! That's where the best of it is!"

"Easy, friend, little by little," Kernevel replied. He put the bowl down on the night-table.

"Didn't you yourself tell me you had a pain in your side?"

"Yes, but it went away. I feel weak, that's all. You'll have to get along without me tomorrow."

Le Brix thought: "He's done for."

"I brought you some oranges," he said.

Kernevel jumped. During his father's last days, they had brought him oranges to the hospital. "Am I sicker than I think?" he asked himself. Le Brix took the oranges out of his pocket. There were a half-dozen of them.

"For when you wake up at night and feel thirsty."

"Thanks, Fortuné, you're a good man."

But his voice was so sad that Fortuné, crossing his arms, protested.

"What's the matter with you? Don't drop out now, Jean. Don't go soft on me now, goddam it! What's the point of turning sad on me all of a sudden? I'll be damned! Do I have to put up with stuff like that?" he said furiously.

Kernevel shook his head to indicate his indifference and said: "Bring me my accounts. They're in the cupboard, in the bottom drawer."

In the drawer Le Brix found two little notebooks with red edges, bound in gray cloth and kept shut with elastic bands. He handed them to Kernevel.

"These the ones you mean?"

"Yes, take them with you. Give them to Dagorne and tell him to come and see me. I've got some things to explain to him. Promise?"

"Count on it," Le Brix answered, stuffing the notebooks in his pocket. "I'll go and see Dagorne this afternoon."

"Good. Thanks, Fortuné. Now leave me. I think I'll rest."

V

550 Dagorne lived in a village on the Paris road. It was a good four-kilometer ride. After lunching, Le Brix took his siesta. He woke up on the stroke of half-past two and took a quick look at the weather. The sky had cleared. "Good," he said, "I'll walk there."

And he left.

The road went right past the Velodrome. He heard people cheering the racers and climbed up an embankment, trying to see them. But he could see nothing and he set off again.

He found Dagorne playing bowls in the village square, as he had expected.

Dagorne was a jovial man, but "staid." He was twenty-six and just beginning to fill out. High-colored and bright-eyed, his look of health was a joy to see. In five years of marriage he had produced two girls and a boy; they were expecting a fourth.

Seeing Le Brix, he stopped bowling and came up to him.

"A miracle," he said, drying his hands on his pants. "You mean to say you're not at the races?"

"I don't give a good damn about racing," Le Brix answered. "Come on over here."

He dragged Dagorne along with him.

"Now," he said, "this is the story: Kernevel's had it."

The two men stopped and looked at each other. Then they took a few more steps. The bowlers were calling after Dagorne: it was his turn to bowl. He made signs to them that he was not going back to the game.

"Let's go to my place," he said.

He did not live in the village itself, but two hundred meters away, in a little house standing by itself, built of gray stones and roofed with slate. A path led up to it, which they went along without saying a word.

Dagorne's wife stood on the threshold. She had a baby in her arms. She was a small woman, dressed all in black, pale and spotty, her hair pulled back and bound in a net. Her belly was enormous. She smiled when she saw them.

"You've decided to come and see us," she said. "Please come in."

She herself went in first and cast a quick eye about to see that everything was in order. The baby was asleep; she put it in the crib.

The two men went and sat next to the fire.

Two beds, end to end, took up the back wall of the room. The parents slept in one, the two girls in the other. In the middle of the room, right on the earthen floor, was the table, and in front of the chimney was the stove, which hissed. Although the daylight was already growing weak, the copper on the buffet shone.

"What will you have. Fortuné?" asked Dagorne.

"Nothing, thank you."

"You'll make me feel ashamed. Give us a little coffee, will you, Angèle?"

She got busy, fetched the cups out of the buffet, the bread and butter, and put the coffee pot on the stove. They said nothing.

"What's the matter with you good people?" Angèle asked. "Nothing wrong, I hope?"

They were startled. Women always seem to know everything, just by looking.

"Nothing exactly wrong," said Le Brix, "but nothing good, either."

And Dagorne added: "Old Kernevel's sick."

To herself she said that Kernevel must be really sick for Le Brix to trouble himself on a Sunday to tell her husband.

"Ah, poor Kernevel. I thought something bad would happen, the way his color had gone. And always thinking. It's his heart, I suppose?"

"He feels weak, he says. It doesn't hurt."

"His heart," she said. "That's bad."

They had taken out their knives and Dagorne set himself to cutting big slices off the round loaf. Angèle brought the coffee and a bottle of unpressed wine. It was very pleasant. The smell of the coffee filled the room. She opened the stove to stoke up the fire and a glow rose to the ceiling.

Le Brix ate with appetite. He was worn out from his walk. He was not used to it and four kilometers at a stretch hurt his legs more than twenty kilometers on a bike. Sitting there and feeling nice and warm and relaxed, drinking down his coffee and sometimes pouring it over his bread, contentment stole over him. Nevertheless, the thought of Kernevel would not quit him.

"It took him all of a sudden," he said. "Last night, on the job. I thought he was gone. But that's a man with will power. You know that, Dagorne? He came back on his bike, by God! I think that finished him off. He looked weak this morning."

They pondered. Angèle sat at a corner of the table and ate without appetite. If old Kernevel died, what would happen to the business? Of course, she felt sorry for the poor devil. It was a shame to see a young man like him, with so much life in him, taken off before his time. But with him gone, they'd never find another like him; and two-man businesses—well, they just don't work. Her husband would go back to working for someone else, like before. They wouldn't die of hunger, but it would be a narrow squeeze. No employer would give him what he now brought home every week. How would they manage it, with three children to bring up, and soon a fourth?

"Has he seen a doctor?" she asked.

"He won't have anything to do with one," answered Le Brix. "And besides, he's gotten ideas into his head. He cries."

Dagorne shook his head. A bad sign. Sick people are close to their end when they start crying. He'd seen it, often.

"He must feel pretty sick," he said.

"To my way of thinking, Dagorne, he won't pull through."

Le Brix regretted his words. Perhaps they should not have been spoken. The silence that followed embarrassed him, and he broke it:

"He's eating himself up, old man. You go and see him tomorrow, as soon as you can. He gave me the accounts. Here . . ."

He drew the two notebooks from his pocket and put them on the table. Dagorne took them and turned them around in his fingers. Finally he shrugged his shoulders and handed them to his wife.

"Here, put them away, in the drawer. It's no time to be settling accounts, now."

He poured himself a little brandy and offered some to Le Brix. "A bad sign," he said to himself. "A man who cries and can't keep up his accounts."

Angèle had come to sit by the crib. Her mind was still on the same subject.

"If you ask me," Dagorne said, "he's got to be sent to the doctor. You hear me. Fortuné?"

"That's my idea too," answered Le Brix. "Tomorrow I'll go fetch old Houdan."

Le Brix got up, apologizing for the trouble. Dagorne accompanied him as far as the village. On the square, he left him. He was off in another direction to fetch his two daughters, who had been picked up in the morning, as on every Sunday, by a sister-in-law.

VI

Monday morning, Le Brix got up with the sun and drank down his breakfast while Marie filled a canteen he had brought back from the trenches with fresh broth. He slung the canteen over his shoulder and leaped onto his bike. On his way, he stopped in at Doctor Houdan's, in spite of the early hour. The Doctor promised he would be there shortly.

Le Brix found Kernevel awake.

"Well, old man, so you won't sleep," he said. "I've brought you some fresh broth. I'll make your bed while it's warming up. You must need it. Get up."

"I give you a lot of trouble," Kernevel said.

"Forget it. We're here to give each other a hand."

Kernevel let his legs slip to the ground and, leaning on his friend's shoulder, sat down in the armchair and wrapped himself up in a blanket. Le Brix gathered up the eiderdown, the sheets, and the pillow and put them on the edge of the open window. He turned over the mattress and beat it flat with his hands. He looked like a baker at his trough. He went backwards and forwards endlessly and the huge nails on his boots sounded sharply on the floor.

"I feel like I'm back in the Army," he said.

"Those were good times, Fortuné."

"Good times, old man. Don't worry. I'll make you a bed you'll feel real fine in."

He stretched the sheets out to eliminate the wrinkles, and he beat the bolster and pillows with great blows. When he had finished, he said: "In with you!"

He helped Kernevel back into bed and made him drink his broth. This time Kernevel drank it to the dregs.

"That's better," said Le Brix. "How do you feel in a freshly made bed?"

"Fine, thanks to your good heart, Fortuné."

"Damn it, man, there's no 'thanks' to it. Just tell me, who would take care of you if I didn't, eh, poor Jean? Right now I'd better empty the pot."

Kernevel shook his head.

"No," he said.

"Why not?"

"Because I don't want you to do latrine duty."

"Why make such a fuss? Goddam it," he swore, "I sure as hell will."

He took the pot and went out to empty it in the latrine in the yard.

When he came back up Dagorne and Doctor Houdan, having met on the stairs, were sitting by the bedside. Without feeling ashamed, Le Brix put the pot back in the night-table.

Houdan was a little old man with sideburns and bifocals. He wore an overcoat with an astrakhan collar. He had put his bowler hat down on the table and was rubbing his hands together, a tic of his, meanwhile firing questions at Kernevel: How long had he been ill? How had this last attack taken place? How was his appetite? Did he get some sleep? Kernevel replied dully, and every time he answered a question Houdan said: "Yes, very good," nodding his head. Dagorne and Le Brix watched without moving. Houdan auscultated Kernevel and when he got up again he took a notebook out of his pocket and wrote out a prescription. He said:

"I'm going to give you a powder, which you'll take morning and evening. But what you need most of all is rest and no emotional disturbances, no worries." He took up his hat and made for the door. "It's a matter of patience," he said. "And if anything happens, send for me."

554

Le Brix joined him on the stairs.

"Doctor Houdan," he called.

"Ah," said Houdan, anticipating his question. "He's a very sick man. He'd be better off in the hospital."

Le Brix had been saying the same thing to himself. A hospital was a hospital, of course; everyone knows what that means. But at least one is cared for. He asked: "Will he pull through?"

"I don't know," answered the Doctor. "I can't tell you anything, except that he's very sick; and above all, that there must be no disturbances."

He went off down the stairs and Le Brix returned to Kernevel.

The visit had tired Kernevel. His hands were stretched out, open, on the blanket. Le Brix sat down. After a moment, Kernevel called out: "Dagorne?"

"Yes."

"Did you bring the accounts?"

"Here," said Dagorne.

"Did you look them over?"

"No."

"Oh," Kernevel said. "You should have. Come closer, Fortuné. Let's have a look at them together. They're all in order, you know. . . ."

555

They didn't know whether to laugh or be furious.

"Damn it, Kernevel," Dagorne broke out, "a fine thing to bring us so early in the morning! Some idea! Of course the accounts are in order; catch me ever going over them after you've done with them."

"I want you to."

Le Brix folded his arms.

"You haven't gone crazy by any chance, have you? If you ever say another word like that . . ."

But Dagorne quieted him down.

"Quiet, Fortuné. If he wants to, let's do it. Here," he said to Kernevel, handing him the notebooks. "Here they are."

Kernevel, notebooks in hand, started explaining to his friends. Here there were so many sacks of lime due. A harness they had made two months ago hadn't been paid for yet. A bill should be sent right away. He had not noted down so many bags of cement bought from a fellow tradesman because he owed them several cart-loads of sand. They should more or less even out. The man would have to be seen and the business settled. He would have gone himself if he hadn't been sick. And there were last month's accounts, too. Everything had to be checked.

Le Brix listened without understanding. He was too angry. Dagorne nodded.

Finally Kernevel shut the notebooks and said: "Everything's in order. You saw that, Dagorne?"

"Yes."

"And you, Fortuné?"

"Sure. You didn't have to make all that fuss about it."

Kernevel looked into Le Brixe's eyes. "It's not that I don't have confidence in you," he said, "but I don't want you to have anything to reproach me with."

It was after nine. They went off to work.

VII

Their hearts weren't in their work, and yet they had to get on with it. The quicker they got through with this job, the better it would be for all concerned. With a little money in their pockets, they'd feel safer. They were going to need it. Dagorne thought of his wife, who would be delivered soon: deliveries didn't come free. They worked until the very last ray of light, eating lunch on the job so as not to lose time going to and coming back from the White Pigeon.

Kernevel was no better. On the contrary. From day to day he weakened, he ate less, he grew thin. The nights were particularly bad. The fever kept him awake.

Every morning at the same time, Le Brix arrived with his canteen. He made the bed, forced Kernevel to take his medicine and swallow a little soup. He emptied the pot. As it happened, Le Brix was somewhat squeamish, a defect of which he was ashamed and which he hid. No one ever knew that more than once he had vomited up his breakfast carrying out the pot. But nothing in the world would have made him give in, and so long as Kernevel was ill, he kept it up. He would settle his stomach with a little glass of rum on his way to work.

Sometimes, in the afternoons, Marie would get to Kernevel's. She would bring him a brioche, some fruit, or apple-sauce between two plates.

She would light him a wood fire in the fireplace. Unfortunately, she never stopped talking and her shrill voice destroyed Kernevel, happy as he was to see her. He was a little ashamed and when he could no longer bear listening to her he would pretend to doze off. Then she would fall silent and creep off without a sound.

He would stay alone until evening. Le Brix then came to see him, and sometimes Dagorne. The work went on in spite of everything, and they would soon be back in town.

"Don't worry, Kernevel," Dagorne said, "I'll manage."

In fact, he showed himself quite capable of doing so, and Kernevel stopped worrying about the business. "Once I'm gone," he said to himself, "Dagorne will run it. They'll find a third man to take my place."

A week passed this way.

When Sunday came around again, Le Brix shaved Kernevel. For several days he had been telling him: "Your beard's grown too much. It makes you look woebegone. You ought to take it off."

His beard had grown thick, right up to under the eyes, and low on his neck. But what did Kernevel care about the state of his beard? Still, he let Le Brix go to it and Le Brix put the water on to heat and meanwhile cracked jokes: Kernevel's beard, he said, he was going to cut just as if Kernevel were some fat businessman! First he washed his friend's face; his movements were awkward and rough. But with the razor itself he showed himself to be more capable. And when it was done, Kernevel passed his hand over his cheek, now smooth, and smiled. It was the first time Le Brix had seen him smile since he had taken to his bed. He was so happy about it that he started rubbing his hands together like old Houdan and said: "Now you look like a human being. But thank God no one saw you an hour ago! What would he have thought?"

There was no doubt he did look better after the shave, but under the beard his cheeks were sunken and hollow. Kernevel wanted a mirror. He examined himself at length and rolled his eyes to see the yellowness in them. He gave the mirror back to Le Brix without a word.

All week long he had waited for Sunday, hoping to have company for a slightly longer visit. And now here was Fortuné, and even his company was a burden. It was without pleasure that he saw Le Brix come back in the afternoon, this time accompanied by Marie, all dressed up in a hat, and Dagorne. He would have liked to be alone. They stayed a long time and he was barely able to pry his lips apart to say anything; at the same time he was angry with himself for seeming so ill-tempered. He wondered why he was suddenly behaving that way.

VIII

After leaving Kernevel, Dagorne was the first who dared to speak.

"He's sinking," he said.

Le Brix spat out his cigarette into the gutter. "Yes, Dagorne, more's the pity."

"I know he has a sister at the *Incurables*, but doesn't he also have a brother?"

"Yes," answered Marie, "his brother Léon. He lives in Paris."

It was late. Each of them said to himself that he ought to be getting home, but each of them lacked the strength to quit the others. Le Brix said: "Let's go have a drink."

They went into an inn. The room was small, stinking, and jammed. They ordered cider. Marie took off her hat; it was giving her a headache. She wasn't used to dressing up.

"Don't you think we ought to let him know?" asked Dagorne.

"His brother?"

"Yes."

Le Brix grimaced. "You really think so, Dagorne?"

"It looks that way."

"A delicate matter," he said.

From his pocket he drew out his tobacco pouch and his cigarette paper; he passed them to Dagorne.

"It's not really our business," he began again. "I've thought about it, of course, but so long as Jean doesn't mention it, we have no business meddling."

"You've got to remember that they quarreled," said Marie.

"I don't deny it," Dagorne answered. "They may well have fallen out for all I know; but a quarrel then and a quarrel now . . . things have changed."

They drank and then put their mugs down on the table and looked at each other. Marie pursed her lips.

"That's not this year's cider," she said.

"You're right, woman. It's hard as hell. The bastards! Not like the cider we get at the Pigeon, eh, Dagorne?"

"Not even close," said Dagorne as he wiped his mouth with the back of his hand. "But to come back to the brother. If they have something to say to each other, they ought not to wait too long."

It was true. In a week, Kernevel had greatly deteriorated. The worst was to be expected. Why hide the fact? The first few days, they had hoped, in spite of everything. But when a man can spend a whole evening without letting out two words, what else could you conclude?

"I get your point," Le Brix said. "And perhaps it's a good one. As for us, we do what we can. But it's not the same thing, after all. We're just friends, and family's family. That's the way it is. And me, Dagorne, if I was like him, on the point of kicking off, don't you think I'd be happy to see my brother Adrien again?"

"You've got a brother?"

"Yes. You didn't know? He's ten years younger than I am. You might say I brought him up myself. He took off twenty years ago and no one's ever heard of him since."

"Perhaps he's dead," said Marie.

"What do you know about it?" Le Brix retorted. "You just let your tongue wag too much. To my way of thinking, he's not dead. It just happened that it wasn't in him to write letters, and that's all there is to it. He'll be like my uncle, my father's brother: he'll turn up after forty years. No one expected *him* to turn up! The proof of it is, my mother took him for a tramp."

"Ah," said Dagorne.

"That's no cock-and-bull story, Dagorne; you can ask Marie there. What's the use? That's the way it is with us. When you have to earn your living, there's not much time to think about others. Or rather . . . there is time, we do think about them. But when do you have time to write? No, Marie, I doubt he's dead. It's a hunch I have."

"And when the police came for him, for his twenty-eight days? Where was he?"

"Police!" Le Brix burst out with scorn. "A batch of good-for-nothings! You can tell them . . ."

"And when they came back, about the war, did they find him then?"

"Of course not. But he's a smart fellow. He thought of a way out. He thinks we're a bunch of pricks for playing along with it."

559

Excited by his own words, he had raised his voice.

"Don't talk so loud," Marie said. "People are looking at you."

"I don't give a damn!" he answered. "He's right, too: we did play along with the war like a bunch of pricks, and I'll say it again: it's just too bad if it bothers anyone to hear it! And if Jean Kernevel's dying right now, you can damn well say it's their fault. There's a man who was as healthy as I am before the war. He did his job quietly and he didn't ask anyone for anything. I'm not saying he was in seventh heaven, but he managed. Then they came to fetch him. Why? Me, I tell you it's their fault. They're a bunch of crooks. When I think of what he was . . . And look at him now!"

An old, long-standing anger rose within him. Whole days went by when he never thought of these things, days when they were as though forgotten. One has to forget if one is to go on living. But then other days, the memories came back to him, and for weeks they would not let him out of their grip. Nights, he dreamed about the front. He sat up in bed screaming.

"I thought I was still there," he would say to Marie. His shouts would have woken her up.

She would calm him as well as she could. "Go to sleep, go to sleep," she would repeat, "stop bothering us with this war of yours." But he did not dare go back to sleep for fear of tumbling back into his nightmare. He would pull his legs out of the bed and strike his knees with the sharp edge of his hand. Some clever fellow in the hospital had shown him how to get rid of nightmares that way. Nightmares, he said, came from poor circulation, and all you had to do to restore it was hit yourself on the knee.

"You'll have another one of your dreams," Marie said, seeing her husband getting excited. "You think Kernevel got what he's got at the front, eh? He wasn't sick when he came back."

Le Brix made a move as though to hit her. "That's women for you," he said. "So, he didn't get it at the front? I suppose you think the front cured him?"

She fell silent, fearing his temper. She wanted to go home. She said it was late, but Le Brix refused to go and ordered another round, but this time aperitifs, not cider.

"In the state you're in?" she asked.

"Don't you worry about it."

Dagorne, elbow on table, was wrapped in his own thoughts. His cigarette had gone out and he did not light it again. The room was emptying out.

"Listen," Le Brix said. "Having thought the matter out, I think the brother ought to be left alone. In the first place, as I told you, it's not our business. Then you've got to think of Jean seeing his brother arrive one fine day—do you think he'd have to think twice about that one? No, it can't be done. It would finish him off."

Dagorne had not thought of that. And yet what Le Brix was saying was plain common sense. "Does he know?" he asked.

"I don't know," Le Brix answered, "but I doubt that he really does. He'll be conscious to the end. Right now, I wish for only one thing: that he should die in peace, at home, that he not have to be taken to the hospital. He's afraid of the hospital, Dagorne. He hasn't said so, but I know. Come on, let's get home. It's night already and we should be on the job early tomorrow."

Marie got up first; her husband's haste to get out of the inn was a bad sign. Le Brix emptied his glass and as he pushed it back onto the table, he said: "And all this because of those sons of bitches. . . ."

IX

As the days went by, Kernevel thought less about death. In vain he told himself that death was near: he did not think it had come to that. Except for a pain that caught him occasionally in the ribs, sweating at night, and some fever, he was not suffering. But he would have been unable to stand up. In the morning when Le Brix arrived, he heard him as though in a dream. Often Le Brix had to go away without having made his bed. There were days when Kernevel did not even answer his friend's questions. The next time Le Brix came he would apologize and say: "I didn't answer you yesterday morning, Fortuné. I was resting."

Le Brix then replied that he had thought so, seeing as how his head had been turned to the wall.

The questions were always the same; and the answers.

"Did you get some sleep?"

"Some."

"Do you need anything?"

"Nothing."

Even his voice was changed. It could hardly be heard, and Le Brix thought of the years gone by, when they had toured France; he thought of the proud Kernevel of those days, his friend, and of the songs he used to sing on the scaffolding. Kernevel's father had taught them to him. He had sung them at full voice, sure of himself and sure to please. He had made all the girls fall in love with him. And now he was dying, moribund. Did he remember his youth? Two or three times Le Brix had tried to recall old memories to him, to talk of old friends with whom they had shared good times. Kernevel had barely answered.

One evening Le Brix had come, as usual, after work. Kernevel was dozing. Gently Le Brix had put a few oranges on the night-table and had left again without making a sound. Kernevel had not stirred. He had heard his friend, but thinking himself on the point of falling asleep, he had not called out to him. But sleep would not come. A few minutes after Le Brix had left, Jean Kernevel turned around on his bed and opened his eyes. The light was on. It was an end-of-October day, silent and softened with rain. He regretted having let Le Brix go. He would have liked someone with him. "What's the matter with me?" he said. "What's come over me?" Peace, a great feeling of tenderness, overtook him. He took a long look around the room and suddenly tears flowed from his eyes. They were not, as before, tears of regret. He was not crying for himself, or over his impending death. They were tears of joy. He did not know where they came from. He accepted them gratefully. He looked at the cupboard, the chest of drawers, and the table and his tears flowed abundantly. He did not dry them. "What's the matter with me?" he murmured. "What's the matter with me?" He had heard it said that at the moment of death, the dying have a moment's respite. "Is this it? Am I already going to die? Alone?" If this was it, then death was a great joy. He thought over his life, and regretted nothing. He felt he had possessed the friendship of all those whom he had loved, just as they had possessed his. The rest didn't matter.

He had sat up in bed, the better to see his old furniture, particularly the cupboard that had been his mother's, and before that, his grandmother's. Its brasses had become tarnished since he had taken to his bed. He reproached himself with not having asked Marie to give it a touch of polish. He stretched out his arm and reached out his fingers as though to touch these things once more. In the drawers of the chest were his father's pay-book and his service record. He thought of his father as a comrade. . . .

He fell asleep, and for the first time tasted real rest. His sleep was calm, without nightmares, and when, two or three hours later, he woke up, he sighed regretfully to think that his joy was over. His lamp was still lit.

X

Towards the end of the week, they ended their work in the country. They undertook another job in town right away. It was in a café, not too far from Kernevel's; they were re-doing some partitions. Dagorne brought the news to the sick man. When he returned, he told Le Brix: "He barely listened to me. You'd think he was no longer quite with us."

"It's just a matter of days, Dagorne," Le Brix answered. "And if you want the truth, man, then I'll tell you that it hurts me quite bad; yes, it hurts me quite bad, by God!" He threw down the trowel in his hand and broke out sobbing.

Dagorne put a hand on his shoulder.

"Fortuné," he said, "you musn't cry."

"I don't tell it what to do, Dagorne. Just think, I've known him all my life, and if it weren't for their goddam war . . ."

When Le Brix came to Kernevel that noon, he was sitting up in bed, his eyes feverish. As soon as he saw his friend, he raised his hands and cried out: "Come, Fortuné, come on in . . ."

"What's the matter, Jean?"

Kernevel grabbed his hands and squeezed them hard. "You're like a brother to me, Fortuné; tell me what happened."

"Where? What do you mean?"

"Out there, under my window. Less than an hour ago. Some kids were running around my sister and yelling that she was crazy. Why'd they do that? Fortuné, tell me!"

Le Brix tried to escape from Kernevel's grip, but Kernevel resisted and repeated: "Tell me what happened!"

"He's getting delirious," thought Le Brix. "It's the end. I ought to get Houdan."

"Kids, you say?"

"Yes. Why'd they make fun of her?"

"Bah! You've been dreaming, Jean. If you start worrying about things like that, you'll only shorten your days."

Kernevel let go of his hands. He stretched out on his bed.

"Yes," he murmured. "That's what I heard. Perhaps she found out I was sick. She wanted to come and see me. That must be it, Fortuné. Poor Céline, they must have prevented her."

"Wait a moment," said Le Brix, walking to the door. "I'll be right back."

"Where are you going?"

"Wait a moment, I said. I won't be long." Relieved, he left. He went to Houdan and found the Doctor at lunch. Nevertheless, he received Le Brix.

"He feels worse?"

"Delirious, Doctor."

"I'll be right there. Wait for me."

Together, they returned to Kernevel. While they walked there, Le Brix told the Doctor what had happened, how Kernevel had thought his sister wanted to come and see him.

"She's at the *Incurables*, Doctor. She can't possibly have gotten out."

At first Kernevel did not seem conscious of their presence. Then he opened his eyes and said: "Is that you, Doctor Houdan?"

"Yes, my friend."

"I don't feel well."

"It's a touch of fever. It'll pass. You need care. If you take my advice, you'll let yourself be taken to the hospital. You'll be better off there. . . ."

"Oh, well . . ." Kernevel turned his face to the wall.

"You'll have to get him there right away," Houdan said, lowering his voice.

"All right."

"Go have your lunch. He'll rest a little. He'll feel better in an hour and then you can take him. Get a car, unless you want to have the town ambulance."

"I'll get a car."

"Good. Well then, my friend, I have nothing more to tell you."

"Poor man," murmured Le Brix. "We thank you very much, Doctor, you know, for what you've done. . . .Goodbye."

Dagorne was eating at the Bons Enfants. Le Brix found him there. They lunched together.

"It's the end, Dagorne. He's in a kind of delirium from the fever. Old Houdan said to take him to the hospital. I'm going now."

"Right away?"

"Yes, right away."

"You want me to go with you?"

"No, you get back to work."

Le Brix found a car on the Square. "And if he should still have a fever?" he asked himself as he drove to Kernevel's. "If he should start talking to me about his sister again? Or if he doesn't want to go to the hospital? What do I do?" He regretted not having taken Dagorne with him. But how could Dagorne leave the job? Bah! He wouldn't need any help.

The car stopped at the sidewalk and Le Brix went up the stairs two at a time.

"You've come for me?"

"Yes, old man." He wanted to seem jovial.

"You'll be well taken care of there."

Kernevel could not stand up. "Where are my things?"

"I'll help you. Your things are all ready in the cupboard. There they are."

He took out the corduroy trousers, the blue jersey, the jacket, the vest, the boots still spotted with the mud from their last job, and helped Kernevel to dress. When he was ready and Le Brix had put his cap on his head, they went down the stairs.

Kernevel, supported by Le Brix and the driver, sat himself down in the depths of the car; he let himself down on the cushions.

"I'm off to my grave," he said.

Le Brix could not reply. He put his arm around his friend's shoulder.

Kernevel looked through his pockets. "I'm going to give you the key to my trunk. You'll find all my papers in there and a little money. The papers and the money are for my brother Léon."

"Yes, Jean."

"And you'll take my watch."

"Why? I've got one. No, I don't want anything."

"You'll take it in memory of me, Fortuné. That's the way I want it to be."

He lowered his head and Le Brix could not see his face. The car rolled along the paving. Kernevel waited for the noise to stop before going on.

"My work things Dagorne can have. We're about the same size and he'll manage. You take my bicycle."

"No, Jean."

"Yes, and my good trowel."

They fell silent. At the hospital door, they shook hands. Two attendants took Kernevel away on a stretcher.

Le Brix returned to work.

"Well?" Dagorne asked.

"He's gone. We'll go see him tomorrow morning."

But when they showed up at the hospital the next morning, they were told that Jean Kernevel had died during the night.

Translated from the French by Keith Botsford

Louis Guilloux's "Friendship" *appeared originally under the title* "Compagnons"—*Editions Bernard Grasset, 1931*

Sol Yurick

The Annealing

She lived from day to day and didn't much care which day it was.
If she laughed once or twice, laughed big that day, she had it made. If she
cried more than she laughed, she knew it wasn't her day. Sometimes it wasn't
her day, not really, for weeks on end. Sometimes, with that liquor sloshing
around in her, it was her day, her night, her everytime.

One day Minnie D. and Olivia Santiago had a fight. Minnie was big,
plump, easygoing, and golden brown. Olivia was black with purple shades
and hated niggers anyway, scorning them with a proud look on her black
Castilian face. She pushed all the time. Minnie D. was easygoing, a soft-
laughing girl with seven children out of five fathers, and a dead or deserted
husband posed stylishly in a Woolworth's gaudy frame. She had a lover,
Leroy, who never laughed, and beat her for her Relief money twice a month.
Olivia had six children. That morning she discovered she was pregnant again
and would have to get the Supplementary Relief, and that entered her in
that slut Minnie's class. She had a hard-working husband and she still
couldn't make it and so she started the fight. She passed Minnie's free-and-
easy kind of door with the two, three, malodorous garbage bags which Minnie
planned to bring down if she ever got to leave sweet Leroy lying all manlike
in the bed, not caring that it was all adding to the three or so generations

of stench accreting in the hallway. Olivia yelled at Minnie through the door, telling her, "No-good nigger get that garbage out of the hall," and tiraded her about how that was what the niggers were doing to honest, good people. And her Nelson, he worked hard at the job and made the money, and people like that, like that Minnie, they loused it up for everyone. Minnie, screaming. "You no-good spic bitch," came piling out of the door, wearing only a white half-slip, her plump, round good nature gone, her teeth bared, and her eyeball all yellow with blood and hate. Olivia was thin, but she was full of the great hate too.

They fought all the way down from the third floor to the ground floor and boiled out into the street. They pulled hair, twisted breasts; they bit, scratched, screamed, drooled; they kicked; they gouged. The neighbors came to the doors and stood, laughing and shouting encouragement, picking sides. The kids screamed with delight. One of Minnie's sons came tearing up the street, leaving the little card game he was playing in, to kick Olivia's oldest daughter in the slats. Ramon, Olivia's oldest boy, had to be held back from putting a flick-knife into this cool card player, Alonso.

They fought their way out to the middle of the street where, half naked, they tried to push one another into a greasy pool of oily water, pulling, snarling, while everyone stood around and said things like, "I put five to four on that fine fat girl. Man, look at her." Minnie, not laughing at all now, her great breasts shining with sweat, her slip almost gone, a few festive shreds holding on to the elastic cutting into her soft brown middle, kept swatting mightily. Olivia dodged, ducked, and kept trying to close in so she could sink her bright white teeth into Minnie's throat, or better, her breast. A joker, wearing a motorcycle fly-boy cap with a white visor, stood behind the crowd and stopped traffic like a policeman, or a general. All the windows were opened and everybody was having a ball, looking out. Leroy, the lover, hung out, yelling, "Give her one, Minnie, give her one good, you hear?" laughing to beat everything, and that was the first time he had laughed in three weeks, not since he had scored in a poker game, scored in a craps game, scored with a little lightskin girl way up in Harlem, scored. Hinton, Minnie's middle boy, whereabouts of the father unknown, not since he was conceived, stood in the kitchen and contemplated knifing Leroy. He didn't have the nerve. He was nine years old.

Some do-gooder called the fuzzy bulls, and they came tearing around the corner, sounding the siren loud so everyone would know they were

568

coming and could compose their little stories about they didn't know who, or what, or when. In that sunken Sump of Brooklyn by the Canal, everyone minds their business, Officer. The crowd scattered to the stoops and stood there like good little stupids, only seeing, peaceful, grinning because it was such a good fight. But Olivia and Minnie were in earnest and didn't hear a thing. Minnie, looking like a fat, good-natured hula dancer, swatted Olivia finally, catching her low and bringing on the miscarriage Olivia wanted so badly. If she hadn't felt so bad later, and her pride hadn't been hurt, she wouldn't have done a thing. The policemen stepped out of the car with that slow dignity they had, squaring their chests, hunching their shoulders, fingering their guns, swaggering as if to say, it will be your arse if anyone starts anything at all. The crowd fell silent, watching. Hard boys, cool boys, from the territory for miles around, had materialized on the rooftops and stood around, looking down into the streets innocently. The cops, they missed nothing at all.

"Who started it?" the cops asked. Minnie, panting and triumphant, shrugged her shoulders and said they were having a discussion that had gotten out of hand. Seeing that she had won and Olivia was smeared, her clothes torn, her face bleeding, filthy with oil and water, Minnie was inclined to laugh about the whole thing. Olivia hated Minnie more, but there were codes you never violated. Not there in the Sump. "Come on, come on," one of the cops said impatiently. The street became very still and the cops knew what that meant. They were hated for breaking up a very prime battle. It was like taking away red meat, chitterlings, a little cheap whiskey, or the TV when everything else was gone. Minnie shrugged and smiled an innocent smile, folded her arms, and tried, with some degree of dignity, to cover her vast breasts, which were exciting the men and boys in the crowd, not to speak of the cops. No one said anything, not even Olivia, and the cops told Minnie D. they could run her in for indecent exposure, for disturbing the peace, for any number of things. Minnie whined she wasn't doing nothing, Officer, and someone shouted, "Aw, let them alone," and Olivia stated it was just the friendly, if somewhat athletic, discussion between two friends. The cops, not caring if the bastards killed one another, muttered threats, told them all to go home, clear the streets before I run you in, but knew that in the middle of such a mob, running anyone in might be more trouble than it was worth, considering no one was hurt. Minnie, clapped on the back by a few of her kind of women, who knotted around her to hide her gleaming nakedness, left the field of honor, beginning to forget because it was past. Olivia, comforted by a few of her friends, was bleeding from scratches, from the nose, from her vagina. Her miscarriage had started.

Leroy, feeling full of fun, having enjoyed himself thoroughly at the fight, gave Hinton the last of Minnie D.'s Relief money, and told him to go and bring a bottle of something good to drink, and not to forget, or run off, or do anything wrong, you hear, Boy? And before Hinton had even gone out the door, he took Minnie and laid her on the bed to reward her bitter, bitter life with a little something sweet for victory's sake. Hinton lingered at the door, watching, till the unbearable groans and moans and screams started, and wished he had had the courage to stab Leroy when he had the chance.

Olivia, being bathed by her neighbors, chattered bitterly. When everyone had left, she sat down and wrote a revealing letter to the Relief people. She named names and stated facts, and even, in the heat of her burning, scorched pride, she overstated things. She wrote that Minnie beat her children and this was untrue. In fact, Minnie frequently interposed herself between Leroy's fists and the kids because she loved them. That kind of pain she could take, and did.

Mr. Jones, the Relief Investigator, came, responding to the complaint. Since it was not his normal time to visit, he came when Leroy was at home, lying half naked on the bed. Minnie D. told Mr. Jones that Leroy was a distant cousin and a good friend who sometimes stayed over. And when he stayed, he gave money for his food and brought little presents for the kids. Mr. Jones shook his head. Minnie was an old-time sore point with him. The kids stood around as they always did, not looking directly at the Investigator, but somehow managing to radiate hostility. It never even occurred to Hinton, wearing a torn shirt, and stinking, to see irony in what Minnie said about the presents Leroy brought for the kids. As for the oldest, Alonzo, he was too concerned about a rep with the boys, the clothes he bought out of stolen money, and his straightened, exquisitely marcelled hair. Alonzo and Leroy had a healthy contempt for one another. But no one was betraying, saying anything more to the Investigator other than that they needed money. The money grant wasn't enough. The complaint was a tissue of lies. Mr. Jones sighed. He had worked hard with Minnie, through "cousins" like Leroy. He had tried everything, all the proper socialwork techniques and a few improper ones. Mr. Jones had threatened. He had pleaded. He had appealed to Minnie D. as one Negro to another. He resented that she lived a life apart, wild, bounded by *now*, sloppy, meaningless. He pointed to himself. His wife teaching. His two affordable and neat children. His little house in Queens. His sense of tomorrow. All that, all of it, could be Minnie's too. She just told him her troubles.

Over the years, it had been a case of not knowing or caring that there was tomorrow. Mr. Jones knew the tomorrows and the promise in store for the world of man when all the inequities would be righted. It was a matter of managing, cleaning, meeting deadlines, marrying, saving, keeping appointments, and bringing up the children with a sense of the future. He couldn't understand Minnie D.'s recurring fall from grace. She drank. She had lovers and had children. She spent her money on the wrong things. Bright, impermanent things interested her. If Leroy didn't get the Relief money first, it was fried chicken for a few days and little food thereafter, unless she didn't pay the rent or the utilities. Once, they cut off the lights, but she cheerfully tapped the meters. They had fought it down the years, irresponsibility and procedure, Mr. Jones and Minnie D. But this time, Mr. Jones knew they had come to the end of it. It had been arrests, Children's Court, Domestic Relations Court, Child Placement, Foster Homes, Private Agencies, the Truant Officer, the Bureau of Child Guidance, the Mayor's Committee on Multi-Problem Cases, the Society for the Prevention of Cruelty to Children, the Department of Health, the Department of Buildings, the Office of Rent Control, Visiting Nurses, Homemakers—memos, endless memos. But misspending Minnie D. was always getting a little drunk here and there, getting hurt, going to clinics, to this doctor, that chiropractor, and the other faith-healer, or spending it on one bright blue silk dress she wore on Saturdays for the big nights when she left the children in charge of Alonso, who tied them up, and went uptown with Leroy. Well, she needed to laugh, didn't she? Mr. Jones, he wouldn't understand.

Minnie wondered who had done this to her. Somehow she couldn't connect Olivia Santiago with something like that. It was a simple fight and everyone forgot, now that it was over. Mr. Jones was hurt, annoyed at the presence of Leroy, who looked sullen. His look seemed to say, don't ask me no questions, Boy. Mr. Jones, perspiring in his Ivy League suit, his striped rep tie a little askew, asked as few questions as possible and made notes in his little book.

When he returned to the office, Mr. Jones worried about finding a way out. "Close the case," the Supervisor glibly said. He couldn't bring himself to do that. She would be back, getting Relief, in no time flat. He had an idea. He would frighten her with the insane asylum. A new discussion with his Supervisor seemed to indicate, as they say, a psychiatric interview. Yes, perhaps, Mr. Jones thought, it would scare her. Very little else did. In order to get approval for a psychiatric interview, Mr. Jones had to state the case a little strongly. But after all, he reasoned, wasn't chronic irresponsibility a form of psychosis?

He wrote a letter to Minnie D., telling her to be home on a certain day, or he would surely close her case and cease Relief. And to make it certain, he scheduled the interview for Check Day. Minnie D. didn't mind and told Leroy he would have to be out of the house then. Leroy, who had come back after three days gone, was willing to be gone for three days more. He had the need of a fix and wanted money since there were no Relief funds left. Of course, Minnie D. wasn't going to tell that snotty Mr. Jones she had spent the money on Leroy, gambled just a little, gotten drunk and laughed a lot, bought Hinton a red tie, and herself a foundation and baby-blue suede pumps, and it would be another month at least till the electric company bothered her.

572

The psychiatrist was a woman named Ostreicher. She was a German refugee of the thirties who had kept on cultivating her accent, but to no avail. She had never been able to get an expensive clientele. She was unable to write any books. Every time she came up with a new theory that would perhaps revolutionize psychoanalysis, Karen Horney, Erich Fromm, or Wilhelm Reich wrote a book about it first. She was bitter. She had to work for the city in order to make a good living.

She was perfectly on time at nine in the morning, and stood in the quiet sunlit street, littered from one end to the other, watching all the little children playing. She stood, waiting for Mr. Jones, a stolid, squat monolith in expensive tweeds. Her sturdy legs were stuck like the feet of conquerors into sensible English walking-shoes. Mr. Jones was ten minutes late and she was filled with hatred and loathing for the imperfect and incorrect Relief Department. When Mr. Jones appeared, she looked at him with contempt, feeling that somehow he didn't belong in those Ivy League clothes. One button of his button-down collar was undone. It seemed to her that Mr. Jones belonged with the clients. Because he was late, her day had already started badly.

Mr. Jones excused himself politely for being late. Dr. O. could not really accept it at all. She adjusted healthily to these things, of course, but she knew, being of the old Freudian school, that there were always the unconscious impulses. She asked Mr. Jones to fill her in on Minnie D. It seemed to her that Mr. Jones's memo was just a little too sparse. Neglect, irresponsibility, repetition of patterns—they were common things that were, true, neurotic, but not in and of themselves psychotic, you understand. Mr. Jones understood that. Of course, she, Dr. O., was glad to examine the woman. But then, wasn't it a waste of taxpayers' money if there were no bases of commitment? Mr. Jones hemmed a little, and hawed, and became committed under the stern, disapproving stare of the doctor. He had another thing to blame Minnie for. He tried to meet the Doctor halfway. He had had courses in psychology. He talked in very learned terms about the refusal to ventilate problems, hostility patterns, destructive patterns, recurrence of the death wish in the shape of the dead, the deserted husband, the five putative fathers, the Leroy-figure, long, black, lean and saturnine, who was capable, in equal parts on equal days, of largess or destruction. He beat the children. All the casuals who tramped in and out of Minnie's life beat the children. They were a noisome, smelly lot. And then, didn't it follow, because Minnie placed herself in those situations where she was permissive of the beatings, the neglect, the hunger, that she accepted, condoned, approved in effect? So he told Dr. O. that she did beat the children. Dr. O. nodded her head approvingly, noting everything Mr. Jones had to say. When he had finished, Mr. Jones was sweating a little.

573

He led the Doctor up the stairs, past all the paint-cracked doors, past and up the stairs through wells tilted crazily, ready to collapse everything to the bottom, past the numberless doors where the mad mambo music poured out, the sullen-sad jazz singers sung their blues of living, and through the great banal beat of the morning soap operas coming in on the TV. They passed the little stenchy cubicles shared by two families to a floor, and the graffiti gratuitously graven onto the walls, obscening the world and telling it, them, those, the fuzz, and everyone to go and . . . Outside Minnie's door, the light bulb had burned out, and the hallway was a pool of black limned with little lights where the cracks under the doors showed. Mr. Jones lit a match for Dr. O. to find her stolid way, stepping over the shards of lives, the dust, the dirt, the grainy grease, and avoiding the garbage bags Minnie hadn't gotten around to bringing down. In the sputter of the going-out match, they saw, emblazoned in unseen red, Minnie D.'s lipstick, Hinton's little rebellion. "Fuck Leroy," it said, and if ever the landlord got around to putting a bulb in the hallways, Hinton or some other one of Minnie D.'s kids was going to be whopped. They could hear the big booming sound of a radio coming out of Minnie D.'s door and her contralto singing a swinging song, full of life, full of today's happiness. It was Friday, the check was coming, and she had a little something out of the left-over bottle Leroy thought he had hidden. They were going to go out that night and none of the children was sick for once. Only the minor little cloud of Mr. Jones, looming no larger than a punitive fist on the horizon, was coming that morning. Today she had a little future and that was tonight. She didn't much care what followed tonight, only that she drank, she danced, she got loved by Leroy, and slept very soundly indeed.

She was wearing only a pure-white slip when she answered the door, and her skin glowed dark and rich brown. Plump against it they could see the counterpoint of brown skin, the breast and belly lines, the emphasis of the large, lazy, child-caring nipples, and the black pubic triangle. She had been seen by Mr. Jones, to his great discomfort, like this before. Minnie D. let them in. Dr. O. followed steadily, smelling everything out. When they saw the Doctor's face, they all stiffened because the inaudible alarm note went out. The children stood around, clean as Minnie felt she ought to get them, sullen and resentful, not looking at the newcomers, staring everywhere else, or at one another, or reading torn comic books. Only Hinton looked at them, wishing he had stabbed Leroy, wondering if he could take a knife and stab everyone in sight, especially now his mother-slut, Minnie D., dressed in her pure-white slip and naked underneath. Alonso, the oldest, the cool poker player, sat, impeccably wearing his gang uniform: white shoes, white pants, a blue Ivy League Paisley-print shirt, a stocking on his head to keep his marcel in perfect wavy form. Sitting aloofly, Alonso, on a three-legged kitchen chair with a bongo between his legs, kept up a constant little subliminal mutter like distant, dangerous drums. The youngest caterwauled in his crib and the radio boomed the bouncy, swinging accompaniment to what Minnie had been singing when they knocked.

Mr. Jones did the honors, telling Minnie D. that Dr. Ostreicher was really Miss Ostreicher, a social worker wishing to ask a few questions for a survey. Minnie D. regretted that she had only bothered to clean the kitchen, where Mr. Jones usually did the interviewing. Dr. O., standing there, looked them all over and knew immediately that it was a family beyond hope, beyond redemption. She looked at the soft brown skin of Minnie glowing delectably around and under the pure-white slip. "Put on your clothes," she snapped. Minnie D., trying to be pleasant because she was still on tonight's dust of having a ball, smiled at the hard, square-faced lady and said, "Won't you sit down?" Mr. Jones skittered a little over the floor, trying to adjust the kitchen chairs for everyone, and caught the hard, look-at-you-there-man contempt look of Alonso, who muttered the drums derisively. A roach scuttled across the floor, banana-peel bound. Miss O. said that she was Dr. O., not a social worker at all, and that she had come to examine Minnie D., and to put on some clothes. She cracked it out in her hard, let's-get-things-clear voice so that everyone shut up, even Alonso. He stopped the drum mutter against this hard, hard authority and tried to look cool and insolent, and make me, man; but she had. Minnie, not understanding what it was all about, smiled painfully, starting to come down out of her dream, and went into the other room to find something she could put on over the pure-white silk slip. "What I need a doctor for, Mr. Jones?" she called in her whiny voice from the other room. "Nothing wrong with me at all. I have my health, praise the Lord." Mr. Jones looked at Dr. O. as if to say, was that necessary? But, taking in the implacable, methodical face; the hard, square shoulders bunched up in the rough and ready cloth; the thick thighs curving through the rough skirt; the gray stockings—he knew it was necessary. He was a little ashamed to have been bested in front of the children, especially Hinton, whose disturbed confidence he had succeeded in winning with bright bribes of candy.

575

Dr. O. took out a notebook and put it on the table. She tapped a little silver pencil and waited, uncaring in the ring of hostile dark faces. She appeared to listen to the sounds of morning coming in through the alleyway windows. She watched a hard bar of untrammeled sunlight blasting onto the floor, shining on the caked cracks between the boards. She picked up a little silver vase on the table, containing dusty, artificial flowers, looked casually underneath, and saw Hotel Something-or-Other written on it. She put it down and gave a look of triumph to Mr. Jones, which was understood by everybody but Mr. Jones. "Get these children out of here," she told Minnie D. when she came in, compromising with propriety by wearing a tan, stained skirt, leaving her breasts unbound, and bouncing softly, rustling in white silk under Dr. O.'s avid, hating stare. Minnie D., trying to hold on to the remnants of a smile, shooed them all out, even Hinton, who never went outside at all. Alonso took off his stocking with careful insolence and slouched out, every line of his body, his neat clothes, saying, do me something, man, do me something. "Whew," Minnie D. said when they had all trooped outside, "raising a family is sure hard work," and smiled a propitiatory smile.

"No one told you to have so many children," Dr. O. said. "Could you turn off the radio and get the infant quiet?"

Minnie D. could feel something unreasonable forming inside her. Her cunning mind was good enough to tell her that there was something more to this whole bit. Mr. Jones had always been friendly, making his fusses about keeping clean and getting rid of Leroy. But the hard-faced lady with the icy eyes that kept looking at her in some certain way—she meant a little more. And when Minnie felt that way, she began to close herself up, get the look on her face that said nothing at all, answered sassy because they wanted something from her she didn't understand. She tried to get Leroy out of her mind.

"Put something on," Dr. O. told her. "You are indecent."

Minnie D. shuffled to turn off the radio, to find a blouse, to come back slowly to the metronomic ticking Dr. O. made with her little silver pencil to mark Minnie's movements.

"What you have a doctor here for?" she asked Mr. Jones.

"It's Central Office's idea," Mr. Jones told her, somehow caught and unable to say too much, ashamed because no one was acting very nice and he didn't know what to do about it. Two buttons of her blouse remained open, for spite.

"What day is it?" Dr. O. asked Minnie D., snapping out her question as if to say, why are you so evil, why are you so resistant? Minnie D. just looked at her as if to ask, what is your bit, why come on so salty? She didn't know. They bugged her more. She didn't bother to answer this silly, silly question at all. It was Check Day. Who need know any more? She looked coolly at the Doctor. The Doctor nodded. The interview was going along satisfactorily. "You don't know what day it is?" she asked Minnie D., looking at the deep cleft where the spiteful buttons didn't button, and at the way her haunches strained against the tan skirt.

"I know what day it is," Minnie D. told the Doctor.

"You do?" the Doctor said with benign hatefulness, nodding with the proper degree of meaningful gesture, and wrote this in the book too. Mr.

576

Jones, writhing inside to see it happen this way, poured his calm oil on the water. "Mrs. D., tell the lady what she asks for. She is on your side."

Minnie D., seeing the hard eyes take her apart and leave her nothing at all, knew this witch was never on anyone's side. "April 18th," she said, packing contempt into those little words. The Doctor was a little ahead of her and finessed Minnie D. by interpreting attitude. Then they relaxed for a little silence while the Doctor looked around the room with hate, with loathing, with don't touch me. Those sensible shoes under the heavy feet moved swiftly and crushed a roach making advances. "Where did you get this?" she asked with a policeman's triumph, holding up the little silver vase and spilling one red cardboard rose onto the greasy checked linoleum. Minnie looked sullen and shrugged it off.

"Why are you asking me these questions?" she asked.

"Where did you get this?" the Doctor asked and made minute notes on minute reactions. Minnie D. feared what the Doctor wrote in her little notebook. She could almost feel the happiness slip away completely, almost irretrievably, and feel the blackness come down on her, down like depression, down like candy and sweets and liquor taken away. She thought she could hear the rattle of the letter boxes being opened up and everyone crowing with satisfaction. They had made it for another two weeks without discovery, pulling out the window envelopes, hearing the satisfying rustle of cellophane ripping, holding their checks. It came drifting up the stairs. It was a feeling like dancing in the streets. All that laughing. And the shopkeepers rubbed hands because it was payday, and eager liquor-store people looked out, welcoming from behind their just-ordered cartons of whisky. And she felt a little sad, left out. She had to go down and get her check too. But she didn't hear what the Doctor said, only coming back to the little scene to see the Doctor writing it all down, whatever was asked and not answered. Client, having obviously stolen the vase, avoids all mention of it. Blocks out, blanks out, mild catatonic state, stares into space, has difficulty focusing attention. "What did you say?" she asked. Mr. Jones, the spirit of help, wondering how they had gotten this psychiatrist, started to ask the question again. Dr. O. stopped him with a gesture. "How much is five and six?" she asked Minnie D., sounding like talking-down-to, and treating Minnie D. like a child. Minnie D. was stung a little this time. "I'm no child," she said.

"And that depends on how you answer the questions," Dr. O said with galling sweetness. They sat for a while, quiet. Minnie D. struggled with

577

it. It was all different from dealing with Mr. Jones. When Mr. Jones tried to come on hard and asked his penetrating questions, she whined a little and cunningly, shrewdly avoided all pitfalls because she had been playing this game for so long a time. But she could sense that she had gotten off on the wrong foot with this hard lady and this lady was going to put her down hard or break a gut trying. She wondered what she had done to antagonize this lady. Here was a menace. The worst kind. She could see it. She could hear it. She could smell it. She knew it. She should play the good client and answer the questions, whine where she should whine about how hard times were and how hard it was to manage and how hard it was to bring up children, and know nothing else about anything. She knew what the Doctor was doing with her, but she couldn't help herself. She was beginning to play it as the Doctor wanted, play it to lose her head, play it with a little dignity, and the dignity of it was going to cost her the check and the night with Leroy. "I'm no child," she told the Doctor again.

Dr. O., with infinite and cunning patience, asked how much nine and five were, what day it was, did she hear strange voices? Was it winter, was it summer, what season of the year was it anyway, and how did she care for her children? Minnie D. drove herself out of her dream of tonight, her sleepwalk of now, and weighing all the factors, answered the Doctor. But she couldn't fight the black tide of anger that welled up inside her the way it had with Olivia Santiago. She answered the questions sullenly, so sullenly, and the Doctor wrote not only what she said, but how she said it. Mr. Jones began to feel it building up like angry crowds gathered in the dusty streets staring down the cops, or like the boys, leaning in their white, white pants on the corner and waiting for the action. Who knew? The action might be you any time. He knew. He saw what Dr. O. apparently didn't see. But that Dr. O., it didn't matter to her one way or another. She had looked upon the soft brown Minnie-flesh and she was disturbed. She had seen the sullen faces of Minnie D.'s children, the rotting building, the shouting and singing in the halls, the littered streets, the pervading smell of the nearby canal choked with garbage and dead flesh, the little silver vase with the artificial flowers marked Hotel Something-or-Other, and the helpless face of Mr. Jones, quick to jump to conclusions of neurosis and psychosis. She wasn't going to be stopped. Not Dr. O.

Minnie D. sat there, not looking at Dr. O., not even facing her, but looking away, yet sort of, toward, out of her shrewd peripheral vision, seeing it all and knowing it all. But that basic wisdom of hers was robbed by so many hungers and by the dream of tonight and Leroy. The timelessness of life, the ball tonight with this half-month's stipend, the thought of that check sitting there in the mailbox itched her as if she were tickled, or fingered. And what if that sweet rat, Leroy, sneaked back, took the check as he had before, forged it, and went out and had himself a ball, leaving Minnie with her squalling brood? Surely one of the neighbors would come in and give her a drink out of pity and good spirits, but what was that compared to a ball anyway? She sat there in her tweed, Dr. O. did, and was unrelenting and harsh and every time she spoke, she got Minnie D.'s back up so she could feel hair pricklings at the base of her spine, and all the way up to the nape of her neck.

She kept muttering, "Talking to me that way, like I was my bitty child, Hinton. I ain't no child," while Dr. O. kept obligingly putting it down, and she said challengingly to the Doctor, "Put that down in your little book. I ain't no child."

"Now, Mrs. D.," Mr. Jones said. But she kept up with her dangerous mutter.

"Is that the way the children are always dressed?" Dr. O. asked.

"What's the matter with the way my children are dressed?" Minnie asked, stung again. "What do you expect me to do with the little money the Relief gives me?"

"Now, Mrs. D.," Mr. Jones said, "you know that this is all I'm entitled to give you." She kept up the muttering. "And anyway, you have misspent the money so many times," he reminded her. "And what about Leroy?"

"Where did you steal this?" Dr. O. asked.

Minnie D. rose, angered almost beyond endurance, and screamed, "I didn't steal this." Leroy had given her this little present, together with the little clutch of paper flowers so cunningly and artfully painted like the real thing. Well, she thought, maybe Leroy had not gotten it the right way. But her man was a little like a child, meaning no harm, like her sulky Hinton, perhaps, or like her Alonso. And if the truth were known, there were more roaming the street who were worse, much worse. She didn't say this. She said, "If you keep on talking that way, I'll throw you out." But, she saw that if she went after Dr. O., she would get her hide whipped. Dr. O. was no Olivia Santiago, but she had shoulders like a man, legs like a man, and big hands that could handle her easily. She was a little afraid.

Minnie D. started for the door. "Where are you going, Mrs. D.?" Mr. Jones asked.

"I'm going to get my check," she said because she couldn't control herself, thinking about it down there in the rusted mailbox, tortured for it. "Sit down, Mrs. D.," Mr. Jones said. She started to explain the possibility of the check being stolen.

"Sit down," Dr. O. told her. "I am not finished with you." She opened her little black doctor's bag and took out a stethoscope. "Strip to the waist," she told Minnie D. Mr. Jones stood up to go into the next room. "You don't have to go," Dr. O. told Mr. Jones.

"I'm not taking off my clothes while there's a man here," said Minnie D. to the Doctor.

"Do as I tell you."

"Look, I'll go into the other room," Mr. Jones said. The Doctor shrugged her shoulders as if to say, what did it matter, and smiled her contempt for Mr. Jones, who kept hopping from one leg to the other. He went into the doorless other room and stood by the window, looking out, studying the depressing back alleys, seeing white rags fluttering on the clotheslines, pigeon flocks, kids climbing up and down the fences, a scene of domestic tragedy taking place in another window. A man was beating his wife silently and she got beaten without screaming.

With insolent grace, Minnie D. took off her blouse, slipped the shoulder straps off, and stood, half-naked, in front of Dr. O. She was a splendid savage, warm and defiant brown, big-breasted, full-breasted, her face frozen with black, sullen dignity. Dr. O. jabbed the silver weapon of her icy stethoscope between her breasts, making Minnie's skin goosepimple. Minnie jumped a little and lost that splendid, defiant look. Wielding the forever icy tip of the stethoscope, unconcerned, Dr. O. pushed, jabbed, probed, listened, and felt Minnie here and there, her hateful white hands prying over Minnie's body till she was ready to scream. Does this bother you and does that bother you and if Minnie answered with her voice full of obvious hate, the silver tip flickered out to touch her and make her shiver in punishment. Then Minnie sat while the Doctor whaled her with a rubber mallet to test her reflexes, hurting her a little, the way she used it. "Do you drink? Take drugs? Given to sleeping too much? Have sleepless nights? Special troubles when you menstruate? How often do you masturbate? Dream? Don't dream? And how many times a week do you have sex with men? With women?" the

Doctor asked, seeming not to care about the answers while she listened, tapping, toying with the silver vase, making Minnie jumpy, so that sometimes she answered without thinking and had to retract what she said. The Doctor took it all down, sitting there, pin-neat and mechanical, clean and well dressed, untouched by the stink of cooking greens and baby piss and deodorant. Minnie, who had never worried about it too much, sat there, half nude, finding that her uncontrollable hands and arms tended to cover herself up in the face of that long long stare the Doctor stared at her. "Come back, Mr. Jones," the Doctor called. Minnie struggled to raise her slip, put on her blouse, was fumbling around, clumsy, entangled in straps, cloth, and her own flesh. Mr. Jones saw and turned away as if he had overlooked something new in the fascinating, true-life scene being played out across the alleyway. Seeing how Minnie struggled with the blouse, Dr. O. wrote down that she had poor motor responses.

And before Minnie finished buttoning up, the Doctor asked again where she was, what city, what borough, what district, what planet, lashing her with questions, and did she beat her children? She played with the silver vase and let another flower fall to the floor, and Minnie kept getting more nervous. She tried a digression. "Why are you picking on me?" she asked the Doctor. "Why are you white folks against me?"

"But I'm not white." Mr. Jones said.

The Doctor didn't bother to answer, it being obvious to everyone, even to Mr. Jones, abstracted in his back yard, that being picked on was a delusion of Minnie's. She put it down. Paranoid delusion. Thinks she is not being helped by the Relief people and is being picked on by the Doctor who is, if anything, benign beyond belief. Ascribes it to racial prejudice. Accuses dark Mr. Jones of this too. Mr. Jones, feeling that everything was all right now, came back into the room and stood behind Minnie, leaning against the soiled stove.

And the Doctor started it again, asking questions sweetly this time, asking them with a let's-humor-her kind of patience that no one missed, not Minnie, not Mr. Jones. Minnie, she couldn't play it anyway because she knew that final flood of anger was going to come up, up, up in her and she was going to have to try and hit, kill that woman.

"It has come to our attention that you beat the children," Doctor O. said. Minnie said it was untrue. Minnie said she might hit them to keep them in line. Every mother did that. She never beat them. The Doctor looked at her for a second, and almost abstracted, hefted the silver vase a little bit with a questioning look on her face. Minnie, unable to take it any more, knocked it out of her hand. It fell, silver to the floor, scattering the paper flowers and a little water one of the children had put into it to make them grow. "Don't go bugging me," she screamed. "What you trying to do to me?"

"Nothing at all. Nothing at all," the Doctor said softly, looking like hit me, try and hit me. They sat there, silent, Mr. Jones horrified, not knowing what to do. "Did you think," the Doctor asked, "that those flowers would grow in that water?" Minnie couldn't even laugh at such a stupid question any more because the Doctor had wound her up too much. "If you don't get her out of here, something bad is going to happen," she told Mr. Jones. "Why don't you answer me?" the Doctor asked, softening the harshness of her low, hoarse voice. Minnie got up, went to the kitchen drawer, and pulled out one long bread knife and appealed to Mr. Jones: "Get her out of here." The Doctor sighed slowly, stood up, put everything into the little black medical bag, snapped it neatly to, buttoned the top button of her jacket, and said, "Let us go, Mr. Jones," and walked out.

582   Mr. Jones smiled weakly at Minnie D. and followed Dr. O. out into the hallway. He followed her down the stairs and to the front door. She turned and blocked him from the street, holding him there in the rancid hallway. "You were right, Mr. Jones." He couldn't seem to understand her. "She is obviously paranoid. We will have to commit her," Dr. O. told Mr. Jones.

"But . . ."

"I will write out the commitment papers for you. You will go back. I will send for an ambulance. And, oh, yes, the police."

"But . . ."

She took out a pad of commitment forms and began to write: "potentially dangerous . . ." Mr. Jones saw. "You drove her to it," he told Dr. O. Dr. O. looked at him. Under her pale eyes, he could only perspire and hate Minnie for what she had made him do. Dr. O. reached out suddenly and her thick hand quickly buttoned his undone collar. He felt the tip of her pencil touch his chin. Dr. O. kept looking at him and continuing to write a breviary of disturbances. Feeble hatred shook him. Dr. O. was beyond hatred. She tore, with a neat, ripping sound, three copies. One for him. One for the ambulance attendant. One she kept for herself. "Go up and wait for them to come." He turned and went back up the stairs. The wood creaked, ripping slowly loose from the walls.

They sent two policemen as a precaution till the ambulance came. The policemen stood around and looked at the patient suspiciously, fingering their nightsticks. They were ready to move fast because you never know how strong these looneys get when they blow their corks. Minnie D., bewildered, sat between them, not knowing what was wrong. The policemen noticed the fallen vase, the spilled water, an overturned chair, the implied violence, and watched her, making pleasant conversation with Mr. Jones. Minnie D. kept muttering over and over again, "What did I do?" When the boys in white came, dragging, as a matter of course, a strait jacket, she blew her top completely and jumped Mr. Jones, who was trying to tell her that everything would be all right if she kept calm. His tie was torn loose, his Ivy League suit was ripped, and she made a deep, bloody scratch up the side of his face. Like two accomplished pikemen lazily practicing their art, the police, dispassionately, almost sorrowfully, hit Minnie D. right and left, knocking her one way, catching her with the other nightstick to bounce her back, so that she bled bloody sideburns down both sides of her face. As she dropped, the attendants dressed her like a bad little child in a long, confining strait jacket. They sackmealed her down the stairs, her head drooping and bouncing on each tread, blood coming down on the steps. She screamed again and again and again. Leroy, who saw it all, wisely waited until they were gone and went to collect the Relief check to ball it up that night. He accepted. Mr. Jones went around to collect the children to place them in institutions and foster homes.

Minnie D., she lived it from day to day and almost cared what day it was because they were going to observe her for ten days and if she was good, they would have to say she is sane and let her go. But she looked around at the looneys, whom she was not like, remembered Dr. O. and Mr. Jones, and the way the policemen clobbered her right and left, and wondered about the children and Leroy, who had certainly taken all the money and spent it on drinks and some slut up in Harlem. Had a ball on her money while her children were there, everywhere, and she was here without reason, falsely accused. So she kept blowing her top whenever they talked to her. She couldn't feel it ahead for ten days to play it cool, because there is only *now*.

And in ten days, it was still now, and they put her away in the state bin for another six months, away from all the goodies, except for a little smuggled-in liquor she worked off in one way or another. And in time, how bad can it be? The anger died slowly and she whined to the doctor that she was all right again, she would be good, she had done wrong, which is most of all what they wanted to hear. They let her out in six months; they gave her back her children; they found her an apartment in another part of the Sump district. Leroy heard she was out, found her, and they set up housekeeping again. He beat her at checktime and gave her the kind of loving she needed, and in nine months, she had another Hinton-baby.

Dan Wakefield

An American Fiesta

When Henry James returned from Europe to cast a cold and discerning eye on the American scene, he observed of Newport, our highest social mecca, that "it is the only place in America in which enjoyment is organized." That was in 1907, however, and our national progress is such that the only place I can think of today where enjoyment is *not* organized is 100th Street between First and Second Avenues in East Harlem. We common men are plagued more and more by the curse of leisure that the rich have had to bear for so long, and we, too, have discovered the blessings of organized enjoyment. The latest national pastime to be organized is jazz, and, appropriately enough, it first was successfully done at Newport, that town where Americans originally learned how to make a ritual of pleasure. The new rites in fact have been so successful that the name of Newport today (and to borrow again from Henry James, "let me not be suspected, when I speak of Newport, of meaning primarily rocks and waves . . .") is more widely known through its fame as a mecca for jazz than as a mecca for society.

Every year since it opened in 1954, the Newport Jazz Festival grew in size and gained world-wide attention—and recently it nearly collapsed beneath the weight of its own success. On the Saturday night of this summer's fiesta several thousand beer-inspired troops, mainly collegians, who were turned away when Newport's Freebody Park had been filled to its 15,000 capacity, attempted to storm the gates. It took the combined forces of the Newport police, the National Guard, and the US Navy to quell the mob, and in the course of the battle 182 revelers were arrested and fifty wounded (though none seriously). The City Council voted in emergency session to close the show's remaining performances, and the Festival impresario, Louis Lorillard, darkly told the press that this meant the end of the annual rites.

But success dies hard in our land, and within a few short weeks Mr. Lorillard's death knell sounded premature. The Festival's board of directors sued the city for damages, saying that the crowd inside the park was perfectly orderly, and that it had been the city's failure to control the unticketed hordes which caused the trouble. The city of Newport has a vital stake in the Festival, for the pilgrims spend about a million dollars each year during the three or four days of the program. Some notion of how influential this is in the thinking of the city leaders can be gotten from the fact that while armed forces were battling the rioters in the streets, the Governor was rushing to the scene from Providence, and bridge and ferry service was cut off to the city, the Council measure to halt the Festival passed by only a vote of 4–3. Two weeks later, Mr. Lorillard was able to report that the councilmen were "taking deep second thoughts about banning the festival" and that the "Chamber of Commerce is coming out strongly for continuing it."

There were rumors that in the remote chance that the city carried through the ban, the Festival directors might camp next year in Yankee Stadium. In any case, the show would go on. It has by now, in its seventh year, taken its place in the ranks of such long-established American fiestas as the Rose Bowl, the Kentucky Derby, and Halloween, and no mere riot can kill it off.

I first tuned in on these new American rites by chance and by radio while sweating out a Sunday July afternoon in New York City in 1955, drinking beer and listening to the Monitor program. I had heard very little about the goings-on at Newport before that, but Monitor's breathless, on-the-scene announcers, who could make a handball game on Amsterdam Avenue sound like the Battle of the Bulge, convinced me that I had turned on something momentous. It was, they said, the second annual Festival, and the hostile older social set of Newport had not been able to stop it or stem the tide of incoming pilgrims. The beer-and-Bermuda-shorts atmosphere of gaiety was noted, music from performing combos was tuned in, and spot announcers chased their stars through the crowds to say a few words to the fans out in radioland when the sets were over. Attracted as I am to both jazz and fiestas, I determined to try to make it to Newport some Fourth of July weekend for the ceremonies, and have since succeeded in getting there and getting housed (a considerable feat) for the full duration of the festivals in 1957 and again last year. As a former observer of, and participant in, other American fiestas, ranging from fraternity Hell Week to the 500-mile Speedway race in Indianapolis (I didn't drive, I sold Coca-Cola), I feel qualified to speak about the fiesta aspects of this new native celebration in Newport.

When I got off the bus that takes the New York pilgrims from the train at Providence into Newport for the Festival, I was carrying a single suitcase, wearing a light blue summer suit of the type that every third male in New York has purchased for $27.60, and considered myself altogether inconspicuous. And yet, I was spotted and followed down the street by a group of children, who finally rushed up, yelled "Look at the Jazz Cat!," and ran off squealing, as if suspecting that I might chase after them wielding some instrument of the Devil such as a tenor sax.

Hostility on the part of the natives can of course be expected in any invasion, whether it be of a military or festival nature. Certain factions of the summer high society, rather than the year-round Newport "townies"— who profit from its business—have been appalled by the jazz intrusion, and tried to halt it. Ironically enough, the Festival began and was nurtured under the gilded wings of Mr. and Mrs. Louis Lorillard, since divorced but formerly leaders of Newport's younger society. Before any further comment about the intricacies of high society in Newport, however, I had better admit to my scant and largely imaginative understanding of it. My only personal brush with this particular layer of American life came during the 1957 Festival, when I was invited, along with several hundred other untitled individuals with press cards, to attend an open house after the Festival's initial evening session, at Quatrel, the "cottage" of the Lorillards on fabled Bellevue Avenue, a broad and tree-lined thoroughfare where the czar would have had his summer palace if he had ever come to America. I met the Lorillards in the receiving line, partook of the scrambled eggs and bourbon, attempted to spot the few true socialites among the crush of people like myself who were jamming the liquor line, and heard one beautiful girl with a voice like Daisy Buchanan's (full of money) pay homage to an aged Negro musician from

Kid Ory's entourage who was planted like a potted palm in a chair in a corner of the hallway. Aside from the literal, accidental touching of shoulders with the rich whom I happened to brush on my way to more bourbon on this generous occasion, I have no personal connection with or insight into the life of Newport society. The Lorillards' divorce unhappily ended these democratic mixers on Festival nights, and no other Bellevue Avenue cottage owner has since dared to open his doors to the free-loaders of the press. Most of my historical data on these matters, then, is based by necessity on the revelations of Cleveland Amory, chronicler of *The Last Resorts*, and Doris Lilly, society columnist of the *New York Post*.

Miss Lilly reported last summer that Newport is "probably the last frontier left to the 400," which shows us just how far things have gone in this age of the rising masses. Little wonder that the Bellevue Avenue crowd resents the occupation of their last crumbling capital by the jazzmen and their followers every Fourth of July; it is the final affront to their lost glory. The more elaborate of the summer places are relics now, many of them open to sight-seeing sans-culottes who can afford the minor entrance fees. Still others, left vacant, are looted of chandeliers and statuary by fraternity boys and other barbarians who come by night to sack the halls of the departed Romans. The end of Bellevue Avenue closest to the main drag of the town, where the stores and public buildings stand in old New England brick-and-spire dignity, is scarred now by a neon shopping center, that ultimate symbol of the end of taste.

According to Cleveland Amory, the death of Mrs. Hamilton McKown Twombly in 1952, at the age of ninety-eight, "marked the end of Newport's era of elegance." Fortunately, Mrs. Twombly didn't live to see the opening of either the shopping center or the Jazz Festival. Had she lived two more years to complete a century, she would have seen (or heard) the saints of the new cult of jazz come marching into the socially hallowed halls of the old Newport Casino. The shock of this spectacle to the old guard socialites can be guessed by recalling the extent of one of their few former recognitions of the doings of the cruder world beyond. When Mrs. Astor once announced that she was going to hold a "Bohemian party," a surprised Newport colleague asked her whom she was going to invite. Her answer was: "Why, J. P. Morgan and Edith Wharton."

But when Louis Lorillard and his wife, Elaine, announced in 1954 that they were going to have a Jazz Festival, they didn't mean that Wayne

King or Paul Whiteman were coming to town. It was Albert Edward (Eddie) Condon who thumped the chord on his banjo to open the first annual rites of jazz at Newport. This same Mr. Condon was riding the riverboats with a group known as Peavey's Jazz Bandits not long after the days when Pierre Lorillard was building a special pier over the reefs in front of his Newport mansion in order to bring his yacht to the front door.

The incensed old guard of the socialites were able to drive these invaders from the Newport Casino, and later from Belcourt, a fifty-room cottage that Louis Lorillard bought as a home for the Festival, but these gestures were empty, anyhow, since the crowds of pilgrims quickly grew to such proportions that the only possible place for the fiesta was Freebody Park, Newport's outdoor arena. The only act of defiance remaining to the socialites was to hold rival balls and dinners on Festival nights, but this obviously had no effect on the jazzmen, whose standing and reputation is based on how they blow, rather than where they eat dinner. Even the overtures of the socialites friendly to the Festival had been lightly regarded by the jazz performers. When Louis Armstrong, one of the reigning saints, was asked by a reporter why he didn't show up for dinner with the Lorillards on the opening night of the 1957 Festival, he answered frankly: "A long time ago I stopped going to dinner before I have to work. You go, you get full of that whiskey and you sound bad, and the people who ask you to dinner are the first to complain. I gotta work."

The "rival" parties thrown by the socialites can at best only serve to prevent defection from their own ranks. Yet the pull of the fiesta is such that more and more of the Bellevue Avenue people show up in the boxes at Freebody Park each year, joining with the masses (not only in the park but also around the world; the Festival provides the most widely heard program of the Voice of America) to form a scene that can be no better described than it was, in 1957, by Murray Kempton in the *New York Post:*

589

> "The American Jazz Festival opened last night for Karachi, Beirut, and Prague, and the rich people who come with their cocktail shakers to drink in the twilight while waiting for old men from New Iberia named Robichaud and Slow Drag."

What draws them all is certainly more than the Newport setting, for just as the success of the Rose Bowl spawned the Sugar, Orange, and Cotton

Bowls, the Newport event set off the chain reaction of the Playboy, the Monterey, the Boston, and a rash of other jazz festivals. According to *Billboard* magazine, last year's was the longest outdoor jazz season on record, beginning May 29 on a Hudson River passenger boat and ending in October with the festival at Monterey. Fourteen cities were host to these ceremonies, and the total number attending probably went beyond 100,000.

All these extravaganzas seem to have certain aspects in common aside from their praise of jazz. They differ from most of the other great American fiestas in that they offer no competition, and, therefore, no betting. But they are like the others in their Hollywoodian accent on bigness and bargains. A full-page ad, which ran in a number of magazines, for the first annual Playboy Jazz Festival in Chicago (it was originally scheduled for Soldier Field, but wound up in a slightly less awe-inspiring stadium) announced the event as "Colossal . . . Gigantic . . . The Greatest Jazz Festival on Earth . . . See and hear more great jazz stars in one weekend than most people see in a lifetime."

Newport, too, was always crowded with stars as well as pilgrims, and attempted to offer the fiesta fan everything short of salvation. Last year there was an afternoon of carnival variety in which the crowds had to choose between a regular jazz program at Freebody Park climaxed by a "Jazz Fashion Show," and at the same time, at Rogers High School, the world premiere of a jazz ballet, performed to the music of John Lewis's *Fontessa*, and based, as the music is, on the commedia dell'arte. One weary pilgrim, returning to his room at the end of the afternoon, speculated that "next year they're going to have a flood and set it to music."

The Festivals have often been criticized for this sideshow quality, which sometimes seems to overshadow the music, but its backers stoutly defend it as part of the fiesta nature of the event. (This year Charlie Mingus and other jazzmen disgruntled by this carnival aspect put on their own widely praised festival at Newport's Cliff Walk Manor—with the assistance of Mrs. Lorillard.) In an article on the Newport proceedings in *Look*, Maurice Zolotow wrote that "there is a wonderful atmosphere of release and fiesta, which, while often experienced in France, Italy, and Spain, is rarely found in the United States." I think the observation was valid, as far as it went, but any comparison with the European fiestas must end right there. The trimmings and presentation of the Newport Festival, and others like it, are peculiarly American. Can anyone imagine getting up in the morning after a hard night of celebrating the running of the bulls in Pamplona and rushing over to the local school-house to hear a professor discuss "The Roots of the *Corrida*"?

But I joined a faithful group of pilgrims at Newport last summer after a hard night of music and parties and went to sit in the auditorium of the local high school to hear Professor Marshall Stearns, the Cleanth Brooks of the blues, discuss "The Roots of Jazz." We Americans are not content to dance, sing, and cavort; we must also dissect. I do not mean to condemn this national impulse, but it has its surrealistic aspects. There was, for instance, the moment when Professor Stearns was telling us about the "field hollers" of the Deep South. He explained that each slave had his own holler, then he put on a record for illustration. After several scratching seconds there arose the wail of a human voice:

Oh, Lord, I'm not gonna stay here very long.

You could close your eyes and imagine that godforsaken, sun-beaten field and the single figure standing in it, turning his head toward the blank, wide sky, and raising that moan from the bottom of his soul. Then you opened your eyes and there was the ultramodern, ultrasterile auditorium of Rogers High School, and the tall, sport-coated professor at the front, lifting the needle from the record.

591

Besides the American inclination to study anything we enjoy, Newport's Jazz Festival displays the bent of our business world for sniffing out anything that smells of life and attempting to suck the blood for transfusion into its own endeavors. Last summer's Jazz Fashion Show at Newport was sponsored by such enterprises as TWA, Wolfschmidt vodka, and Studebaker; fashions were chipped in by American designers. The show, in honor of the latest product of Studebaker's artisans, was entitled "Newport Is a Lark," and featured one Irene Zastrow, who was chosen "Golden Lady of Jazz and Fashion."

What remained of the crowd took the fashion show with laughs; it was an afternoon crowd, and therefore, by the nature of the Newport proceedings, more sophisticated. The afternoon programs, which feature some of the more advanced groups, and often the best jazz of the festivals, are attended by much smaller, but much more devoted audiences. During one of these sessions last summer, one of the Festival impresarios remarked that "the evening is more of a social occasion. The real jazz fans come in the afternoon. And there just aren't that many real jazz fans."

Fiestas of course are social events, but there are plenty of social events that fail to strike the public imagination as Newport does. I think that the music which lies at the heart of the Festival hullabaloo has a special pull, particularly now. Jazz is a cult as well as a kind of music, and it offers the sense of belonging that any cult does—and a greater measure than most. During one of the afternoon sessions last year the drummer Art Blakey came to the microphone and said: "I don't know why there aren't more of you out there. Next year, bring your square friends. They're the ones with the bread, anyway. Get 'em out here and get 'em baptized—they'll love you for it."

I think he was right, and I think his terms were right, too. People are not "introduced" to jazz, they are baptized into it. We already have a man who is known as the Jazz Priest—Father Norman O'Conner of Boston (not to be confused with piano player Thelonius Monk, who was introduced to the Newport audience as the High Priest of Jazz).

The notion of jazz as a religion is hard to avoid, and I think it goes deeper than mere terminology. The enthusiasm, fervor, and belief of jazz musicians and listeners is greater than that to be found at any of our current religious rituals, with the possible exception of the Pentecostals, whom the "established" Protestant leaders look upon as a "fringe group." Aldous Huxley has suggested that the dying religions of our time put passion into their proceedings by the use of a drug called mescaline. Perhaps they might try jazz, too, which draws out so much more genuine emotion than most religious services.

I was struck by this kind of comparison more deeply than I ever had been last year at Newport when I returned from a lively afternoon session of music and happened to turn on a radio in my hotel room. The program was the reading of a Catholic Mass, and a priest was reciting to an answering chorus the words: "Hail Mary, full of grace . . . pray for us now and at the hour of our death."

The words were repeated, from priest and chorus, both of them droning in a singsong monotone. I listened for a while, fascinated and absorbed in the compelling monotony of the liturgy, wondering how many times they would repeat it. It went very fast, like the reading of an order by a sergeant, and with roughly the same amount of passion. I tried to take down the words, but they were spoken too fast and ran together. I happened to glance down at the desk where I was sitting and noticed a sheet below the glass along the hotel menu, which set forth instructions from Civil Defense to be followed in case of an air raid. It said that this was my home away from home, and that in case of an air raid alarm I should go out into the hall, sit down on the floor with my back against the wall, and await further instructions. It said that I should not attempt to get on the elevator, because only wardens were to use the elevators.

I poured myself a bourbon and water, then put on my tie and walked outside. The sky was that twilight color of blue that Henry James had half a century ago compared to the sky of Venice. Automobiles were moving toward the Festival Park. I followed them, walking down the street that leads off fashionable Bellevue Avenue toward the park. Hundreds of college kids had encamped on the island of grass in the middle of the street, drinking beer, shouting, chasing girls, singing, playing bongo drums, guitars, mandolins, and banjos. A guitar player was being given three "hip-hip-hurrahs" by the crowd around him. They shoved their beer cans up to the evening sky, the silver foam rising and spilling around them.

After the evening program a group of these kids gathered in the shadows outside the Muenchinger-King Hotel, one of them playing a guitar and singing a song about how everyone hates everyone else, and "What nature doesn't do to us, will be done by our fellow man." The last line was: "Someone will set the spark off, and we'll all be blown away."

The next night was Saturday, and Duke Ellington and his band were playing a new composition called "Launching Pad." Toward the end of the program, the great blues singer Jimmy Rushing was called to the stand. I was sitting at the time in one of the boxes, and glanced behind me to watch the crowd as they began to stand, dance, clap, and sway to Rushing's powerful rendition of the blues.

There is a power in the blues, as in the other jazz that has flowed from it, that we have in no other kind of native American art. It is the power of painful honesty, and painful, yet relieving, recognition—recognition of the truth that is denied by the covers of *The Saturday Evening Post* and the lyrics of popular songs that say "the night is like a lovely tune" and "we'll be together again." Jimmy Rushing was telling us

> *Walked all night*
> *Until my feet got wet.*
> *Walked all night,*

> *Haven't found my baby yet.*
> *Bye bye baby, bye bye...*

The park was alive in front of him, with him, and even in the boxes people were standing up and clapping to the music. It was the kind of revival meeting atmosphere I had expected and failed to find when Billy Graham brought his mild crusade to Madison Square Garden. I happened to be sitting next to Langston Hughes, the poet laureate of Harlem. After saying, with genuine delight, that "you can't beat the blues," he informed me that the man standing up in front of us clapping and blocking the view was Charles McWhorter, legislative assistant to Richard Nixon, and, like Hughes, a member of the Newport board of directors. Jimmy Rushing was singing.

> *Don't the moon look lonesome*
> *Shinin' through the trees...*

He meant it, too. And the rest of us knew what he meant. To me and Langston Hughes and Charles McWhorter and "Dizzy" Sal of India and Jimmy Rushing of Oklahoma City and Louis Lorillard of Newport and the girls from Vassar and the boys from Sigma Chi; to all of us the moon has looked lonesome shinin' through the trees. And all of us are hungry to hear it.

The crowds that started the riot this year were hungry too. Their pockets may have been full of money and their bellies full of beer, but they were hungry just the same. We have very few opportunities for shouting and singing and letting off steam, and when the chance arrives we hardly know how to act. Walking down the crowded streets of Newport last year where the college kids had gathered to sing and cheer and talk and drink beer, I thought of the lines of the blues that Big Bill Broonzy used to sing, and how much they were all about what was going on:

> *I feel like hollerin'*
> *But the town's too small.*

Our town today is the world; it gets smaller all the time, and we have more cause than ever before to feel like hollerin'. There may, of course, not be very much time left to holler, and the grotesque theme that lies beneath all our celebrations is how completely we have come to accept that fact. The women's section of *The New York Times* has instructed us on how to decorate our fallout shelters, and our young sing "folk songs" announcing: "Someone will set the spark off and we'll be blown away." I do not wish to show myself as a crackpot, however, and rather than further pursue this point I will merely follow the current trend and offer a "practical" suggestion. If any descendant of Big Bill Broonzy is around when the spark is finally set off, he might find this slight revision a more appropriate rendition for his blues:

> *I feel like hollerin'*
> *But the town is gone.*

Jara Ribnikar

Copperskin

We took the child from my sister-in-law, to live with us in Belgrade. We had no daughter of our own. Her family was poor. Being her uncle, I promised to put her on her feet. We made much of her. We did not let our sons so much as touch her. They were jealous, and got many a beating because of their malice. I had her learn the hairdresser's trade. I took strict account of her conduct—after work, straight home, and if she was unable to get home in time, she had to phone from the shop. At that time, not a thought crossed my mind of any relations with her. Once I took her to the movies, and she tried to hug me in the dark. Soon afterward it turned out that we were left alone at home because the family had gone to the country. They were also to visit my sister-in-law. I observed that the girl purposely undressed in my presence, and I tried to recall whether she had ever done this before, but I had not noticed. No, she had never taken such a liberty before. Every evening now she combed her hair before the mirror. Since her childhood, she had shared the bedroom with my wife and me, and it had never occurred to me to put her elsewhere when the others had gone, although there was sufficient room in the house. We went to see sexy movies; she asked to go. One evening, at the Partisan Theater, I came across a girl friend of mine, and she signaled me to come to her. My niece firmly

597

pulled me by the sleeve, "Come home, don't go with her." I complied. As soon as we got home, I left her with the excuse that I was going out for a drink, and went to my girl friend instead. She showed me a letter from Copperskin. "Where did she get your address?" I asked, amazed. "You just read it and you'll see. She must be spying on you. You're harboring a snake in your bosom." A fine letter she had written. I howled with laughter. "You bitch, leave Vasso alone. I'm going out with him and he's going to be my husband."

I went back home. She was awake. She was sitting before the mirror in her slip, combing her hair. When I entered she didn't turn. She combed and combed her hair as if she would keep it up like that until morning. I contemplated her shoulders, her bare arms, her bare feet, her copper skin; she was slender and round; her skin was luscious and dark, glowing as though it were oiled. I stood in the middle of the room looking. She kept combing her hair. I approached and roughly turned her round. She threw back her head, eased down her shoulder strap, dropped her lacy slip, thrust out her breasts, and asked, "Aren't I prettier than her?" I grabbed her, pushed her on the bed, and to tell the truth, I came to my senses only after it was all over. I did not regret having made a woman of the girl; I said better I than someone else. She lay peacefully by my side, sleeping. I bent over her, measured her breath. She was really asleep. I could not believe it. This was her first time—how could she! I wanted to wake her up and ask if she loved me. But I refrained. I smoked my pipe and so the whole night passed.

In the morning, she left as though nothing had happened. "Give me money for a snack." I gave her a thousand-dinar note. "You want to fatten me," she said with a smile. I did not go to work—I had the day off—and I went from bar to bar to kill her inside me, somehow, thinking of my sister-in-law, of the whole family. I smoked two packs of cigarettes. I tasted nothing. In the evening I offered to take her to the Majestic Hotel. She eagerly consented. We had supper. Everything went well. The next morning I had to leave. My job as a dining-car steward kept me away from home six days of the week. Now it was a problem. How was I to leave her? Who would take care of her? What would she do without me in the evenings? What if someone had designs toward her? Suddenly I started to suspect our next-door neighbor, a tall man working at the beekeepers' co-operative. I noticed that he always greeted her cheerfully on the staircase. Before I left I told her, "Straight home after work. Lock yourself in and do not open the door. There's a monster in the city, kills young girls, that's what the papers say." She embraced me fiercely and saw me off as far as the stairs. "When I get back I'll take you to the photographer's," I promised.

Those six days were as though I had a fever! I made a mistake in my accounts. Fortunately I myself noticed it. Nothing like this had ever happened to me before. Numbers obey me well, they add themselves up; I can think about anything else and do sums without a slip. I was worried. But then I remembered that I had her, Copperskin. And, as though I were the owner of a diamond mine, I felt buoyant, content, self-confident, calm, happy. I had Copperskin. I had her. She was beautiful. This I said to myself as an oath whenever I was seized by the shivers. This thought always gave me courage and relief until the next attack. Later I had terrible times, but not like this. She was in me like a disease.

Twice I brought her embroidered slippers. I gave her a bracelet, sweets, a whole dressed lamb; I dropped twenty thousand dinars into her lap. She was intoxicated with joy. I asked whether she had had supper. No, she said. And then I, tired as I was, dead as a dog, after six days' work and nights without sleep, and troubled with the disease she had cast upon me, *I* went out to buy her some broiled meat, because she did not care to go out. My veins bulged from all the standing, but wings carried me. I set the table and waited on her, as though I had not had my fill of waitering on my trip. She shone, laughed, exhilarated as a child, excited, hot. And we drank together.

599

One month later, when my wife returned and filled the house, she and the children, everything chock full from top to bottom, it was, I need hardly say, impossible to live together. I left for my run and then straight to that girl friend of mine. I tore my hair. I told her everything. "You're mad over the girl," she said. She understood. "You'll come to a bad end; she's too young." "You're already counting me among the carcasses," I shouted, "among old men and impotents." I cursed her. "No, you're not," she said to calm me, "you're not old; but she's young, too young." "I'll kill my wife and children, tell me how to kill my wife and children, I'll go mad and kill them, I must be with her." "You'll go to prison and the girl will go with someone else. It's obvious, she's the type." I grabbed her by the throat and flung her to the floor. But she had brought me to my senses. A good woman, she is. I made it up to her, sent her some flowers after this quarrel. She was right, that was no way to live.

Now my Copperskin was pregnant. It happened during my wife's absence. Before we found a doctor and arranged everything. She was already in her third month; the abortion was difficult. She lay there pale; I brought her some carnations and asked her how she felt. She smiled, "Like a cat," she said. The doctor said she would have had twins and asked whether there were any twins in our family. I'm a surviving twin—my brother is dead. I buried my head in my hands. She would have continued my line. "Don't grieve," she said.

As soon as she entered the house my wife guessed what the trouble was. She tore her hair and wailed over her: "Who is he, who is responsible?" She cursed Copperskin and seized a ladle, beating her with it, weak as she was and wretched; I couldn't stand it any longer and stepped between them. My wife looked at me and understood. She dropped her hands, stood several moments as motionless as a stone, went to the cupboard, gathered up the girl's things, brought them to the door. "Here, you bitch, you whore, get the hell out of here, get these rags out of my house," and so forth, as she threw piece after piece over the banister, dresses and underthings falling on the dark staircase; then shoes, knickknacks, combs, hairpins—all sorts of things. Doors began to open, people stood looking, and my wife, as though she had lost her senses, was throwing things about and cursing. I was lost, confused, I hadn't expected this; I stood there looking. And when I did pull myself together, I grabbed my suitcase, took Copperskin by the hand, and together we gathered up her things under a torrent of curses and vituperation. I kept silent, biting my lip and thinking that it was with that woman that I had lived and had children. Out in the street, the girl swayed as though she were going to faint. I took her to the nearest bar and gave her a glass of cognac. I hailed a taxi. Just imagine what a scandal it was! When I think of it, I was not far from the point where a man becomes a killer. I wanted to push my wife over the stairs, over the banister to go hurtling down with the girl's things. But no, I remembered the words, "You'll go to prison and the girl will go with someone else." I didn't believe she was capable of going with someone else. But what should I have done in prison without her?

We went to a friend of mine. He took us in and gave us the maid's room. The next day I bought a big mirror and hung it to make the room look larger, and so that she would be reflected everywhere. I didn't let her go to work, nor did I register her new address with the police; I was afraid my wife would hound her, or that perhaps her parents would do something.

600

But I soon heard that they had renounced her and that her old man had threatened to give it to me. Well, I wasn't afraid of him. Whenever I went out I locked her in. I kept her hidden from the public eye, and I brought her meat, cakes, fruit—whatever she wanted. I even got her a doll to play with when I was away.

I had saved up eight hundred thousand dinars and had promised my wife and children a car. But with Copperskin I began to spend this money lest she should be dissatisfied with me. We lived without a care. I bought her a fur coat—paid forty thousand for it. And underthings in every color— white, black, pink, violet, yellow, green: the rainbow. They cost me fifty thousand. How terribly beautiful she was! I wonder how I managed not to kill her. I must have been sick, sick in the wits, in the brain, hexed, infected by her. It gave me a thrill when she was furious in the street because some girl had said hello. Once in Revolution Boulevard before the crowd, she slapped me three times, shouted after a girl, "What are you staring at my husband for, you country bitch!" I laughed like mad and people stopped, looking after us; I was proud because she was so inordinately beautiful in her bright colors. Everyone noticed her from a distance. When I pulled her from the scene, she kept on crying aloud, "The bitch, whoever she is!"

We were happy. At least I was. Was she also happy at that time? Is it possible that she wasn't? I gave her gifts and gifts, and money too whenever she asked for it. But she liked dancing, especially those new dances, the mambo and all the others. I didn't know them. I took her to dances and she went from arm to arm. I was jealous at her partners' holding her while I could only look on. I told her I'd get a divorce and marry her if she would stop going to dances. She agreed and I soon got my divorce. I have friends everywhere, and my wife didn't make any difficulties. Now we lived as husband and wife; we didn't get married. That was not my choice. "You're my uncle," she said. "How can we? Let's wait a bit." There was a note of fear in her voice as she said it. She was afraid of her family.

My damned job. I had to go. One evening, a neighbor told me that Copperskin had been going out every night. "I don't go with anyone," she protested, "only with you." I hired a man to shadow her, paid him three thousand in advance and promised to give him as much again when he made his report. She had given him the slip in a building and stayed in it three hours. I paid him off and gave her a beating. It was the first time I had ever raised a hand to her. She wept and begged, "I didn't do anything bad, I'm not mixed up with anyone," and I beat her until the neighbors banged on the door, and I had to leave off. She threw herself on my chest, madly kissing me. There it was—she loved me while I tortured and insulted her. Shameful. I was hurting her; I begged her to forgive me and she did. I went to a tavern with her and ordered the singers to sing. The musicians played only for her and the whole place looked on. At two in the morning I took her arm and we made our way through the guests. How I'd like to walk again with her like that! I'd bring her in chains and tie her to a chair to listen to all those songs again and to watch me spend my last penny on her.

Meanwhile we moved from that small room and took a large furnished room with bath. I forbade her to work at all, even at home. I wanted her to be beautiful, rested, and only to love me. I had to scold her from time to time because of some trifle or other she had stolen. I don't know why she did it. She took a brooch from our landlady and I returned it. Once I was buying her some bananas; when we left the shop, she showed me two bananas she had taken. "Why do you do that?" She laughed. At the grocer's she would steal chocolate bars, at the taverns she would lift the toothpicks if there were nothing better. I kept my eye on her and always paid damages or returned the things. I scolded, but she only laughed, and sometimes I also laughed when I saw the trifles she took for no reason at all.

I went on working, but things didn't go well for me. I had almost used up my savings. I had been lucky with money once, but now everything went wrong. Once my weekly returns were stolen and I had to pay out of my own pocket. Such a thing had never happened to me before. Money sticks to me. I don't lose it; I know and feel where it is. Who could have taken it and how? It is true that Bora III, the respectable thief who goes about the country giving shows, removing watches, ties, billfolds, and wallets, was in the diner. He took a foreigner's passport and there was a row; he slipped my watch, but he gave everything back amid applause and was generously tipped in all kinds of currency. My money vanished the next day, when Bora was no longer on the train. But he had had a friend with him, and he, I felt, must have pulled the trick. I had no one to accuse. I pawned our radio. Copperskin complained and I promised to buy her a new one. I got the money for it by selling a set of silver forks and knives, old-fashioned things. I also promised to buy her a motorboat. I told her I'd take her out on the Sava and Danube. "Just imagine, water everywhere and above us, the sky." "Not at night, surely?" It surprised me. Why did she ask whether it would be at night? Did she fear I would drown her? She was no swimmer. I had been giving her lessons. One evening we were returning from swimming and she stopped for an orangeade. I waited, reading a paper. She came back followed by four young men. "They won't leave me alone," she said. I told them off. One of them hit me in the mouth and I fell, striking my head against the curb. When I came to, they were gone. Slowly, as though I were drunk, I got to my feet, while Copperskin shouted with laughter: "What a sock that tramp gave you!" At the clinic they put two stitches in my lip. I still remember how silent I was that evening, looking now at her and then at the floor, thinking. She asked what was troubling me; "I have a headache," I said. "Do you want to play a few games of casino?" she asked. We played. Then she went to bed and I smoked until dawn. Something had happened.

I left in the morning before she woke. I wasn't feeling well. I drank some bad brandy at a bistro and went to the café to find company. I was going through hell. I sat the whole morning with my cronies, telling them what had happened the day before, what she had done and what she had said when I came to my senses. Everyone had his own interpretation and piece of advice. At noon she burst in like a fury: "Where've you been, you bum; so there you are, sitting with tramps!" She insulted me and my friends; I shouted at her to be off; I took the wristwatch I had bought for her to show how I was punishing her and I told her to get out. She looked at me. I added, "To hell—out!" She left and I got drunk. I made the rounds of the cafés, eating nothing, accompanied by a friend, a mechanic—we often drank beer together. But some devil had gotten under his skin and he kept driveling about her; just when my thoughts were on something else, he would mention her. "Haven't you noticed, she's got a goiter, something on her throat," and such nonsense. I said there was nothing wrong with her throat; we began to quarrel, they threw us out, and we came to blows in the street. A crowd gathered round us to protect him from me. That made me terribly angry; I'd paid for his lunch and supper, he was a friend of mine. So what was the big idea, their trying to sit in judgment between us? I threw myself at him, but there were too many of them; I fought all I could and then tried to get away, but they threw me down and when I came to I was in the hospital.

I sent a nurse home with a note. She found the room locked; the landlady said my girl had left. I didn't believe it. I questioned the nurse to see if she had been to the right place. I sent her again. She came back with the same story. I tried to get up, but my head swam. She said, "You've got a skull fracture. You've also had concussion. Keep still," I gave her a thousand-dinar note and thanked her. She agreed to go again in two days to make inquiries. She brought me a letter from the landlady, in which Copperskin told me we would never see each other again because she was gone forever.

I rushed from the bed and grabbed some hospital trousers and a tunic. I wanted to go out into the street. They were hardly able to restrain me. They threatened to send me to the madhouse for observation, which frightened me into submission. The nurse was good to me, and also came at night to sit by my bedside. I offered her money for her services, but she refused. "I only want to make it easier for you, it's my duty." I poured out my heart to her. I couldn't go on without Copperskin. It was driving me mad. I would jump out the window. I had to learn at least where she was and what she was doing; I'd work out a way. The nurse said she would go to the police to ask them to look for her. That was how she calmed me. Everyone learned about my despair. When the doctor made his rounds, he asked whether I had found my beauty. I kept dreaming of being in a boat with her; I had the same dream several times: complete darkness, the stars invisible, the sky could not be distinguished from the water; she afraid, soft and wretched as when I beat her, asking me to row to shore. Tears streaming down her cheeks, and my heart aching because I must kill her. I already saw her floating down the Danube, her head in the waves, flung back, her hair on all sides. They say the drowned always come to the surface. I dreamt of her and a boat, the boat I never had and had never seen. Maria, the nurse, heard my nightmare voice and tried to soothe me. I was excited because I did not want to kill Copperskin; it didn't even occur to me to do a thing like that— all I wanted was to find her. To find her at all costs. My friends came to see me, my landlady having told them where I was, and they promised to help me. But there was no trace of her. I was out of my senses for days, weak, twisted in pain, and the people in the hospital kept telling me I had to be patient, that my head was much better, and that all I had to do was to wait just a little while longer. I have never known what it is to be patient and I have never seen patience reap much profit, either for myself or for anyone else. I lay there reliving everything. I recalled her as a child waiting by my side every Thursday while I counted my money and made up my accounts; she hovered about and always got a few coins. I remembered the first thousand-dinar note I gave her when she became a woman, the way she opened her eyes and mouth, like a fish. She was money-hungry. But still respectable, young; no, it was not for money, I do not believe she would have done it for money at that time. Illness was now injecting suspicion into my brain, illness was troubling me . . . dreams, the boat I had never bought. But I'll buy it if I find her! I'll buy her a boat and teach her to sail. So there, now you know, so cruise by yourself on the Sava and the Danube, with people looking on! Because I'm generous, I would tell her. Such were the thoughts streaming through my brain in the hospital bed, and at moments I was sure I should find her, keep her better than I had; at other moments I would go mad, smash everything within reach, batter my head against the bed, and, but for Maria the nurse, I should have long since been sent to the asylum. She refused to accept any money from me, saying that she liked me and would do anything to please me. I sent her home to bring the money I kept in a special locked drawer. I had over twenty thousand dinars there. She returned empty-handed. The money had been stolen, the drawer forced open. At my request Maria notified the police of the theft and charged Copperskin as the thief. Later I discovered she had taken my silk pajamas and three shirts.

605

The night the nurse told me about the forced drawer I dreamt I was standing by the window, when Copperskin appeared in the doorway, looked about the room, strode toward me, came up, stopped—I remained silent, she was leaning out the window as though looking for someone in the street. I drew a pistol and shot her in the back of the head; her thick tweed suit soaked up the blood, she removed the jacket, threw it at my feet, and vanished. Maria, coming in, advised me to put the jacket in cold water, but don't by any chance open the hot-water tap or you'll never get the stains out. Wash it during the night in cold water, all the blood will come out, don't worry, Maria consoled me; and I, sweating and trembling, told Maria no one would look for Copperskin: her parents had thrown her out and my wife had given us up. I awoke and felt sick. I was killing her again in my dreams without remorse, being afraid only for myself, scared to go to prison. I never knew myself to be like that, I told Maria; was it true that I loved myself more than I loved her?

"Dreams are false," said Maria, "you've still got a fever. Our patients have all sorts of dreams—don't take it seriously." Maria was wise and considerate, and it crossed my mind to wonder why I hadn't had the luck to meet someone like her. Such a girl deserved the very best in husbands.

The police searched for Copperskin. Fifteen days later they informed me that she had reached Novi Pazar. They asked if I wanted her arrested. I notified them that she was my common-law wife and that we would get married as soon as I was better. Although I could walk, I had to sign a statement that the hospital was releasing me on my own request, and so I left for Novi Pazar.

I found her immediately. At the hotel. The porter told me what room. I went in. She began to tremble at the sight of me, paled, and retreated right back to the wall. "Don't be afraid; I've come to take you back." She told me she had been abandoned by a wealthy Turk. He had promised to take her abroad. Then they stopped at a tavern near a station and he had left her on the road without anything. "What did you do then?" I asked. "Don't ask me to tell you—I can't."

I knew it. Then I remembered the porter's readiness to let me in to her. She had had an arrangement with him.

We returned to Belgrade, to our room. She had lice in her hair. I was so touched that I did not go to work for ten days. All I did was bathe and comb her, cleaning her hair of the lice, playing with her for days. She soon recovered and we began to go out.

But the day came when I could no longer stay away from my job. I locked her in and went to take my train, but I became so sick with sorrow and fear that they sent me to the doctor's at Mostar. He immediately gave me sick leave, advised me to see a specialist, gave me a chit, and forbade me to smoke. Instead of going to the hospital, I went straight home. My room was empty. I hurried to the center of town. I ran through the streets like a lost dog, going into shops and restaurants and through trolleys and buses, elbowing my way, colliding with people. And so from early morning until seven in the evening. And then I met her near the theater. She was with a big man whom I had never seen before. They were chatting away. I went up to them and slapped her several times. Her companion vanished. "Wait at the bus stop," I ordered, "I'll be right back." She went toward the bus stop. I went to a bistro and had four stiff brandies. She was not at the bus stop. I took a cab and drove through the city. I cruised all over the city, but I failed to find her. I went home. She was there, at home, at my house. I went into the hall and announced to the neighbors that I was going to beat her because I had caught her with someone else and that they were not to interfere if she screamed because I had an axe behind the door and I wouldn't hesitate to use it on anyone who came between us. I beat her with all my strength. She shrieked for help. I beat her with my fists until she couldn't defend herself and fell on the bed. I took her shoe and beat her with the high heel until she was bleeding and only groaning softly, reaching out her hands and begging, "Don't, don't beat me any more, please, I did wrong, forgive me, I can't stand it any more." But I kept beating her until she was silent, until she stopped begging. I lit a cigarette and sat on the bed by her side, smoking one cigarette after the other. I considered what to do. After midnight, when she slept, I lay down beside her and caressed her. She looked like a child, and I felt sorry for that beauty. Suddenly she pressed close to me, hugged me.

That night I decided to throw her out. Why should I let her run off again? I'd throw her out. When she was asleep once again, I packed the things I had bought her into two suitcases, locked them, and put the keys in my pocket. At seven I woke her. "Get out. You don't deserve to be with me," I said. "Me go? I don't want to go from you." My hands shook; I seized her by the throat. "I say get out, or something awful will happen." She got up, pale and broken, and began to dress. I had never seen her so perplexed. She saw that her things, except for two dresses, were missing; she looked for them, saw the two suitcases, and burst into tears: "Where are my things?" I did not answer. There was a lump in my throat. I frowned at her. She started wrapping her few remaining rags in brown paper as she wept; this scene afflicted me so profoundly that I fled from the room. I locked myself in the bathroom and waited. With that wretched parcel under her arm she went out. Then I threw myself upon the bed, tore the pillow with my teeth, and howled like a wounded beast. Horrible! I don't know how many hours I lay there.

607

Later, I went out to drink. Alcohol only intensified my grief. I did not sleep, and the following morning I asked for her at the police station. The officer on duty found out that she had slept at the Paris Hotel. I hurried there. I bribed the porter and he told me that she had sat for a long time in the hotel restaurant and then had gone upstairs with someone. I told him I was her husband. He looked at me with astonishment, but gave me her room number. She was alone. "Come back," I said. "Come back, I beg you. Everything will be as it used to be. Everything will be all right." "I'm not a fool," she said insolently. I hit her. She screamed and the porter came in.

Together we went to the police and there I demanded the twenty thousand dinars she had stolen, the silk pajamas, the three shirts, and all the trinkets. She promised she would bring everything back. The things were at a friend's. Indeed she did bring everything (except the money) to the bus stop as arranged. This surprised and overjoyed me. The world was becoming beautiful. She had shown me so much good will, I invited her home with me. I would forget everything because she was so young and did not know what she was doing. If I didn't help her she would go to the dogs. I don't remember everything I said. First she was silent, her head bent; then she looked at me, pierced me with the fire and malice of her dark eyes, and said: "I won't. And mark my words, you'll go mad for me. But I'll never come back. I'll be your last woman." And then, as though she did not know me, she turned her back on me and left without goodbye.

I stood paralyzed at the bus stop. I did not go home. I didn't tell anyone about this. I drank the whole night through with strangers. Next day I began again to search for her. Three days I scoured the city. I neither ate nor slept. I only drank, lest I lose all my strength. I was aware only that my feet were swollen, my head buzzing. On the fourth day, the police sergeant told me she had left for Novi Pazar.

608

And he called me not only Copperskin but also Copperface and sometimes Copperhead. As though I were a snake. But I see nothing wrong with that. It's no insult to be called a snake. A smooth snake, warmed by the sun, lying lazily as though the whole world belonged to it—lord of the earth. Of copper. Red, dark and yellow, the earth's richest colors. I say to myself, "I'll have a shop. I'll save for a shop." But think, you fool, what we all go back to. We go into the earth. And he, too, with his exclusive ownership. He wanted to own me as I thought of owning a shop. But possession is only an illusion. I should have knocked that out of his head, when he said, "Mine only and no one else's." No one and nothing belongs to anyone alone. We are all everyone else's.

He would never have admitted this. Yet he has also always been everyone else's. He likes to lie to himself. And I would pretend to be listening devoutly, believing in him. Well, now I won't pretend to believe—since I learned to walk I've known he was deceiving my aunt. She supposedly didn't know it, because the main thing was that he should cough up his crumpled notes so that she, the boys, and even I could have what we needed. Of course, he raised me. . . . I will never understand why you had to pay for me, unless it was because you saw the woman in me even at six. While she, yes, she loved her sister. And so because of her sister: "Let's do her the favor, Vasso, let's take the child." Because good is always repaid with good. Yes, she believed that madness: that good, whenever it is done, is somehow always returned when it is most needed . . . She who now hates me. And she who even beat her own children because of me when they were jealous . . . In their place, I'd have thrown the likes of myself out long since, the damned intruder, the parasite. I was like a milk snake sucking a cow. I've drunk up everything. Even their father and mother. Because she grew suddenly old when I went off with Vasso. I never want to see her. Never.

I sit in this hole, outside the city which I've learned to love as my own; more than my own. Lelitsa was right: that's what Belgrade is; everyone feels at home there. Probably because it seems that all doors are open. And even when I knew only two of the streets, names my aunt taught me so that I wouldn't get lost, I was at home. I was never afraid. We belong to each other, the city and I . . . I'd forgive his having called me Copperhead. I'd forget my bathing his feet like a slave. Not that he had demanded it; no, once I brought him the warm water on my own, and he was taken by surprise. But then it went on like that. A serpent queen bathing feet, serving. I had to. Some devil compelled me to do it. I trembled in his presence. I always felt that he could choke me with one hand if he only wanted to, or slit my throat. I expected something terrible to happen. "If you so much as look at a man, I'll get a club and wallop you two or three times, good and hard, and maybe once more until I'm sure I've broken your back, and then I'll stop. That'll be your life." And I turned to stone with fear whenever I remembered. One day he'll slit my belly open . . . He'll kill me. I can't go back. If that Turk had only taken me to Istanbul. But he slept with me and left me. Though I am beautiful, copper-colored, young . . . "If you had stayed with me you wouldn't have come to this bad end," Vasso said. I couldn't stay, I couldn't stand it any more. Sometimes he would lock me up for days. Once he kept me under key for six whole days. I was mad for fear a fire would break out and I would burn to death. I'm afraid it's my fate to suffocate in fire . . . "Don't lock me in." I knelt before him. "Don't lock me in, I'm afraid." He brought me sweets, meats, wines, cognac, silk, beads and earrings. "Everything for you, Copperskin, everything for you . . !" He would laugh as though he were out of his mind whenever he found me so frightened, tearful. "Don't be scared, you little nitwit. The key is at the neighbor's, I won't let fire eat you. I won't let anyone have you. Don't be scared . . . But the next time the key won't be in the same place, do you get me, it won't be there, so don't ask for it, you know, just by the way . . ."

And then everything would begin all over again. We would eat and drink, and go to bed and he wouldn't let me sleep all night long. "You sleep tomorrow." And this madness would go on for six whole days, and I never knew whether it was day or night, everything would be swimming in my head, and I could barely stand when I got up to prepare something to eat, and then he would decide to take me out to some tavern or other, worn out like that, after midnight. I had to get dressed to the teeth. He insisted. He would order dozens of songs, all at once. And everyone bowed to us, the guests gaping. We drank bonded wine. "We won't go by bus. That's not for you. We'll take a taxi." And so, dizzy with drink we would go back home, and then all over again from the beginning . . . Whenever he would leave for his run I would think: He's terrible, what can I do, what . . . I was locked in. No, I would have forgiven everything and submitted again if only he had not kept me locked up. That drove me mad and once I broke down the door and got out, and it was then that the trouble began. Everything as before, and beatings besides. God, was it possible to beat anyone so much? What are you doing with me? "Don't be afraid, I won't mutilate you. I won't break a single bone. I know, I'm careful." And then he would lock me up again . . . I got an idea. I dropped notes into the yard for the janitor (he had taken a shine to me); he agreed to take a note to Lela. Lela had her boy friend make a duplicate key and they unlocked the door for me. That is how I would get out of Vasso's jail. But he suspected something. I observed that I was being shadowed. I ran through the streets into different houses to give the man the slip. I wanted to kill myself. "I can't live without him," I said to Lela when she urged me to leave Vasso. She offered me a room in her flat and a job in her beauty parlor. I felt Vasso's knife in my belly. I can't. "You fool, he'll be the death of you." So what, I must, I don't know, but I must go back to him . . . I don't want to be destroyed. I can make it here in this crazy Novi Pazar. I'm young and pretty. I look at myself every day and I'm getting more beautiful. It doesn't matter if I've grown thin. And I'm still healthy. It was with Vasso that I was going to the dogs. I was melting away. I hated that whole house and he shut out the whole world. From the darkness, from the daily fear of fire, from his hunger for me, from all of it, I fled. I fled and wept. And then I met that Turk, who took me to the best hotel, bought me things on the way, fed me in luxury, told me he would smuggle me to Istanbul—"Such a beauty!" Could hardly speak, but could say, "You beauty." To Istanbul. He could, he said, because he was a diplomat, and he showed me some passport or other. I don't know, perhaps he was one. And then he threw me aside, left me at a whistle stop, just like a paper bag. Well, I'll never go to the dogs if I didn't then. They gave me a job in the first beauty parlor I went into. No, no, I'm not one to go to the dogs, I won't go downhill. Just to spite you, Vasso, I won't. Lela wrote that Vasso wandered about the city like a madman. He was on sick leave, not on the road any more. Some sickness of the head. He told her: "Let that whore know that she'd better stay out of my way, or I'll kill her." And I'll stay here. I don't especially need anything. Maybe someone will help me. My boss tells me to concentrate on my work, that I've got talent, that we might go to Zagreb to compete in the hairdressers' contest. What do I need Zagreb for? What's the use of all that training every evening just for a hairdo? I haven't got the patience. I haven't got the patience for anything. I can always earn my bread, that's sure. Everyone can put out more. Can't I? Can't Vasso? Or that Turk who deceived me about Istanbul? He was generous. No, no, I can't complain. He was good. I've still got some underthings, a beautiful blouse, and the most expensive set of sweaters he gave me. And he didn't torment me either. And five thousand dinars in my purse. "You may need it," he said as we left. The pig! He knew all along he was going to desert me, all the time he treated me to liqueurs, and we were laughing. That's how I earned my first money. So that's how it is! So that's how a woman becomes one! But I've got my job. I don't want to go to the dogs.

611

The carpet in the room covered the floor from the door to the wall. We couldn't hear a step. And in the restaurant people spoke in whispers. "You like everything fine and pretty. I'll take you to Turkey. I can do it through my contacts. I have a *laissez-passer.*" Whatever that is. He mentioned it several times. "I'll show you how I'll do it," he said. "I wink at the border authorities: 'My wife.' They shut both eyes." He laughed. He took out his wallet and showed me a sheaf of colored papers. All foreign notes. We drank. And breakfast in bed. Afterwards the train, first class, the best of everything. And then he shook me. To go for a short walk. Left me for just a moment— a call of nature. He found me a table in the restaurant. I heard the engine whistle, then it rumbled . . . He was gone. Gone . . . That's a man for you! What can you expect? Either he beats you and throws you out; or he plays with you and then ditches you. I fell in love with him so I could run away from Vasso. Vasso didn't know how to speak like a man; he was the silent type, staring at me as though I were a book, and kissing and making love to me. That he knew. Whole nights long until I grew stiff with exhaustion and then he'd begin all over again with me like that, half dead. He tormented me, deadly quiet and inexhaustible. As though he were not a man but something out of nature. Maybe plants do it like that, for hours, without a pause. Like that. And perhaps bugs. It's more like bugs, and not like us— me. Who could go on for hours like that? And he'd measure it in days . . . I was crazy. Really crazy about him, I know. I kissed his back and hair when he slept. Out of exhaustion, despair, out of fear I kissed him. During those first nights I was tremendously happy. Everything was mine. I was beautiful and I had a man. And money. Any dress I wanted. Any shoes, any gloves, anything, anything! He would say, anything you desire . . . Me desire? My aunt's old dress was what I knew about desire. *You* desire! Desire me! Desire! I thought to myself. Desire me more, still more, until your head bursts, until your brain and your heart melt, desire me . . ! I lay under a sheet. It was summer, and I waited for him. Desire, desire me! I implored, desire me more. I'll die if you don't desire me to madness. I felt I was sinking, that I was weightless, that my strength was dropping into an abyss. I lay as though I were no more, fixed by thinking and waiting. If he went to sleep, I kissed his back, his hair. But that rarely happened. And in the morning I felt it again—hard, charged with it. It was gleaming from me. "You'll desire me tomorrow," I whispered into his ear, "you'll desire me the day after. And I'm mad about you, I want more. I want to feel more. Soon."

612

Time is passing, but I'm still pretty, and I won't go to the dogs. But you'll desire me the day after tomorrow.

Translated from the Serbian by the author
and revised by Saul Bellow and Susan Glassman

John Berryman

Thursday Out

I have left an order at the desk for a car at six, and told the bearer to call me, with coffee, ten minutes earlier, but not trusting him I am up at a quarter of and thinking of washing. I am only thinking of washing, because there issues no water, neither from the left tap nor right, nor from either of the shower taps. After buzzing for the bearer I unbar the door to put my head out into the arcade and call him, without hope. He does not come. I dress, and pack. In a darkening mood I go out to the lobby to see about my car. There is no car, and nobody in the lobby. Shouts bring a bearded sweeper, who has no English and calls here and there about the offices, softly, in vain. For no reason I return to my room, where the bearer has turned up with tea, and we have an unsatisfactory interchange about taxis. There is no time for the tea and I forget about the water. The barber appears, eager to shave me. The sun is to rise at quarter past six.

I move rapidly out of my court, leaving the bearer gesticulating and the barber stoical, into the drive, which is jammed with cars without drivers. It is a fine day, already bright, and they were right at the desk last night about the sun. The only human beings in sight are a few pedestrians in the road, a man in a tonga, two passing in pedicabs. Again nobody is in the lobby and I can start only the alarmed sweeper, which does not please but does not surprise me, for this is almost the only hotel in India I have found for myself. It is true the lights in my room did not work when I arrived, though there was water, and the air-conditioning was merely a blower, and breakfast was an evil farce shared with unusually large lizards and roaches, and the bearer could never be found, but I thought: for twenty-four hours what does it matter? Worried, with my traveling-clock in my pocket (my watch many cities ago ceased running), I emerge into the road and get a pedicab, who turns at once in the direction opposite to all three of my earlier trips out to the Taj.

We have a kind of conversation about this, as he plunges north into the Old Quarter. I prevail upon him to seek advice, and we do so, of a distinguished-looking man, naked except a loincloth, standing calmly in his raised shop front toweling himself. His English is good and I am wrong; this is *also* the way. Soon we bear off right, come out into the deep green, mildly rolling country, with little ruins, that I know, and after twenty longish minutes we are here. Telling the boy to wait, I hurry along the enclosure and turn left toward the gigantic Gateway. The sun is full up, its light level on the great tomb, and my luck is better than it was yesterday except for the moon.

I walk down the steps and follow as usual the broader promenade to the right of the watercourse with its narrow walks, watching the building. I skirt the platform midway over the watercourse, and sit down on the bench I like best. This is in the far northwestern corner of the second court of the garden, or one court away, and off on the right, from the vast plaza up from which, on its colossal platform, the Taj rises. The view straight on is stagey and exhaustible; here is one reason photographs produce little sense of the monument. And a large scaffolding, as maniacal in appearance as other Indian scaffoldings, disfigures at present the southeast corner, which is least seen from where I sit. Many years in the world, besides, or partly in it, have taught me I see things better from the right; to be on the left, ends by making me feel wall-eyed. I sit here for a while. The light brightens but does not deepen, and the building less continuously changes than it did yesterday or last night. I sit here.

The central dome, two-thirds of a sphere, with its spire, withdraws, from this angle, is less flagrant and crushing among the lesser domes, and does not sit flatly on the immense central bay with its Saracenic arch but is removed. Its relation to the towering minarets at the corners of the platform—so removed, so intimate—is clearer too from here than from elsewhere.

I am perfectly happy. Sways the great work and steadies, flash from the high corner nearest me its gems, in the wide washed monsoon light of the risen sun.

Presently I make my way into the western plaza, under the overpowering marble mass, four or five times my height, of this side of the platform. People are waking, looking out immobile over the broad river, talking. The environs of the Taj are a sort of hotel in this weather, lightless but well patrolled, quiet. The watercourse platform, marble, with its benches and steps, this plaza, and the Taj platform itself, seem to be the places, not the gardens; a group of twenty-five or thirty—men of course—in keen, low conversation, smoking, thronged the northern steps last night when I wandered past at ten, late for India, waiting for the moon. Now as I come around to the front, to have the loose cloth slippers bound on my offending shoes, men are washing themselves busily in the six inches of scummed water. I mount by the inside stair to the platform, cross, and enter directly where the screen stands solid under the huge dome.

The light here is not strong, even now, though there is more of it than there was at noon. This is the most solemn place I have seen. The pattern thrown from the man-high screen on the tombs—hers dead center, his larger, close by it, left—lies light, not easy, like flowers, filtered through the high outer screens into and through this three-inch solid marble eight-sided massive screen encompassing the tombs. Each quiet shattering panel is six feet by ten in one piece, and dustless—no one has been able to tell me why. Acquaintance here begins with one's fingers, palm, upon the not believable, cool, not quite smooth, nervous, vigorous surviving inventions that create these lucid openings. From without, the building wants thought; in the chamber below, emotion; here, a gravity of sensual experience neither emotion nor thought. The tombs blaze, austere. Large, his larger, higher by a little, ascending through their terraced rectangles to the crowning casket-shapes that would hold, each, one of the bodies, they bulk to me in brilliant gloom, their black and reddish floral inlays in the rigid gray-white marble alive as not before. Half a small cylinder, recumbent, super-crowns his. The only mysteries here are the force of the commissioned imagining—a Venetian brain; the decades' effort of faultless carving; the enigmatic light falling over the symbols of their deaths. She had thirteen children and one more of

615

whom she died. She had a long wait for power, this Persian woman. He caused her husband to be murdered but then, after she was brought to Delhi, he would not see her and made her a very poor allowance. She embroidered and painted on silk, selling things in the harem. She became famous. There is a scene when, hearing of her at last, he visits her apartments, to find her simply attired among her gorgeous attendants. She was extremely beautiful. Some dialogue reaches us.

"Why this difference between the Sun of Women and her slaves?"

"Those born to servitude must dress as it shall please those whom they serve; these are my servants, and I lighten the burden of bondage by every indulgence in my power; but I, who am your slave, O Emperor of the world, must dress according to your pleasure and not my own."

Thereafter, he lived agreeably and passionately under her thumb, saying he required nothing beyond a measure of wine and an amount of meat, while she ruled, celebrated alike for wisdom and benevolence. They say the Emperor stared out, from his chamber across the river, in his last night's hours, upon the high pale form, long complete, of the Taj. In our world, it reminds me solely of the love Isotta degli Atti drew from Sigismondo, past their children, through the machinations, beyond the marriage, beyond the affairs. Cut flowers, real, lie on the grand base of her tomb, and upon its top, scarlet, white. I take one, white. Yesterday the State's watchman offered me one going out, I refused; last night, below, I picked up a little red one—where is it? I take one, white. It resembles a gardenia, smaller, but I know nothing of flowers. Jasmine—for eternal life—I remember dominates the fretwork of the true tombs below, and I have to go out.

There is no time to circle the platform once more, wondering, touching. I look up at the immense black marble inscription inlaid in the frame of the central bay, and descend. The boy who undoes my slippers has become a friend and wants no tip. Will I ever come back? It seems impossible that I shouldn't, the building has become so familiar and necessary. It must be impossible to take one's way without any regret off down the long garden, but I leave India today and my feeling is strong. We very hardly, Americans, relinquish things. I have not time even to go across to my bench, but I pause and turn. I was lucky to come at all, reluctantly, ill, without expectation, urged, my reservations out just allowing it; and yet this at the end, and the Ryoan-ji garden at the beginning, are the most remarkable things, single works, I have seen in Asia, and for the garden, so far as books, photographs, plans, study can prepare, which is not well, I was prepared. For the Taj, nothing prepares. There is the matter of its size, enormous, though even at this short distance it begins not to seem so, balanced amid its quartet of tapering minarets (but these are 137 feet high) and between—here knowledge enters, affecting vision—the thin perpendicular watercourse before, the broad horizontal river behind. Murray's states that a side is 186 feet, and the central bay of each is 63 feet high, and in certain lights, as now, the whole prodigious bulk floats on its giant platform. Then, notwithstanding this, it is perfect as a jewel, like a jewel, the work of a jeweler: a matter again for fingers, in the bays, the pearl-smooth gleaming inlays of jacinth, chrysoprase, agate, some translucent blue stone, semiprecious stones unknown to me, in most chaste scrolls. Nor even apart from these is the Taj white, but thousand-hued, like the word invented by Paul for the wisdom of God, *polypoikilos*, in marble veined and tinted, violet, gray, cream, tan, set off with black marble picking out the minarets, with huge flowing characters inlaid black alongside and above the front main bay.

In unshielded sun the tomb is glowing with its own removed life, as, after sunset last evening, when the overcast sky was almost lost, it held its light. Sumptuous it certainly has to be called; but such was not my ruling impression yesterday. Both the splendor and the grace stand at the service of something else, and this so strictly that my impression of severity, accompanying that of sumptuousness, overcame it. This is bound to be partly an effect—accidental for us—of art from which all images are of course excluded, whether of God or man; especially after the human and divine complexities of Buddhist and Hindu temples—it is a month only since I was at Bhuvaneshwar, two since I halted along the serried ten hundred life-sized figures gleaming in Sanjusangendo. But anyway the clear essence of the Taj has, it seems to me now, to be named otherwise.

The Ryoan-ji garden—sand, fifteen stones—is a work devoted wholly to thought (tumbling Zen thought, it's true), and purely symbolic. But here is a performance devoted wholly to death, and not symbolic at all, embodying no protest of any kind, inspiring no sadness. I suppose—I know—that pain—well-nigh infinite calculation—hardly endurable fatigue—exasperation, agony—went to the making of the vivid thing. They are incidental, like the awe inevitable below in the crypt in darkness or the wonder at the miraculous echo above, where my merest mutter stirred forth a low far thunder long in the dome. Some other word—tranquil—will have to do for the essence of this work entirely beyond our Western quarrel with time, free from all longing. The echo and the awe were by-products. No one I think ever looked on the Taj, since the Emperor, with sorrow or passion. There is something limited or missing at the heart of this, accounting for the nature of its beauty; for I suppose this is the most beautiful of man's buildings. Can I account for it to myself by the anomalous inspiration? If it is true that the work was designed for Shah Jehan by a jeweler of Venice, who took as his model Humayun's superb tomb, then new, at Delhi, I can imagine what is missing; and there exists evidence, very early, Jesuit evidence moreover, for the ascription. Geronimo Veroneo was the name of this transcendent genius, who dying when the Taj was ten years under way, half done, in 1640, is buried here at Agra, three or four miles away in the Catholic cemetery northwest: his executor, a Jesuit, said to another Jesuit who came here that year that Veroneo designed it. Will a man whose executor is a Jesuit have lost his faith? I long since joined those who see Islam as a Christian heresy. But the work is Mohammedan in inspiration, Mohammedan in end, and neither faith is really here present. Few masterpieces so little vague, so definite, make a sense so curiously nonassertive; it has no theology, it offers

618 neither hope nor consolation, and belongs—as against the Mahabharata, Sainte-Chapelle, the *Commedia*—among the sublime uncommitted works, with the *Iliad* and *King Lear*. I expect I am wrong about all this, as I turn away again, anxious already about the world outside, my plane, but we get teased into thought. That young man's formulation, Keats's, of a few men's ability—negative capability—to be tranquil and effective, *between* faiths or doubts, is one of our deepest; and I wonder at the tumultuous energy of quiet mind in this astonishing Italian, creating in other culture its supreme achievement, when I turn for the last time, on the steps of the Gateway, to glance back at the great calm building above the cypresses, in the less bright sky. It looks as if it had just been finished, or were being finished now. It is secular: the content of the inscriptions is nothing, was nothing: it is mere love that everything here is at the service of, love for one actual woman— a love without eagerness, or future.

I shut my eyes and bear the sight away.

My rickshaw boy is waiting and my troubles begin immediately. "Republic Hotel," I say urgently. "Republic. Where we came from," with gestures. "*Vite! Schnell! Molto rapido! Diritissimo!*" When at a loss in a language, as I am in Hindi—also in Japanese, Bengali, Oriyan, Gujarati, and

Mahrashta, to mention other tongues that would have been helpful on this tour—I fall back on languages in which I am also at a loss. In the right direction, but then there is only one, he sets off very slowly. His eye said nothing, nor did he shake his head (Indian for "yes," agreement, or comprehension) at the name of the hotel; he looked indeed as if he had not had an idea for three years and is not having one now. We drift toward Agra, where my plane-connection leaves at 8:10.

I encourage him freely to increase his pace, but it is where we are going that truly bothers me, particularly when he takes a turn I don't remember. The road is more uphill, too, than it was coming—a point neglected in my calculation—and he frequently gets down to wheel the pedicab. I would like to get down myself, but he won't hear of it. It is time for me to begin worrying about money; we are going so quietly, however, that the hotel gate is as far ahead as I can see. Is my clock right? Is this the right way? I should know it, or them, by now, but besides being dazed by the Taj I am still full of German and Swiss medicines against a virus I picked up long ago in Calcutta which then laid me flat in Ahmedabad. Pedestrians are getting thicker. Making him stop beside three who look like students, I implore help in going to the Republic Hotel, suddenly. "Republic Hotel," one of them says to him. An expression of sharp surprise comes into the boy's face and he shakes his head with assent. What was in his mind I will never know. The student says something else; we are off like a rocket. "*Meherbanii!*" I call back. I never use Hindi unless when it is unnecessary.

We are in at one minute past eight. I give him four chips and he acts as though I had bought the cab and then returned it to him. This leaves me about one rupee over my bill, if I am right about it (and I have reckoned in a lemon soda that it took me three-quarters of an hour to come by last night, and soda with both meals) and if I can get the bill.

I am wrong about everything. At the desk, which is now inhabited, my bill is ready. This has never happened to me in India before; campaigns are fought to a conclusion in desolate countries while a hotel bill is being prepared; the British taught these peoples paperwork and they have learnt the lesson. I have forgotten the service charge. One anna for matches does not signify, but the service charge brings the bill over forty rupees, or two more than I have. Knowing money is waiting for me in Delhi, and anxious not to over the mark as I leave the country, I am bare as a bone. The tiny shopping I did yesterday was ruinous. I explain this to the manager, identifying myself as a traveler on official business and offering to post or wire him the odd rupees from New Delhi later this morning. He is sympathetic but I can see the suggestion holds no attraction for him.

I feel stopped. If the Government had made my reservation, as always before, there would be no difficulty. For forty cents I am going to lose my plane, my planes. Then I see my ten-dollar bill, tucked in the back of my wallet.

"Ha," I say, extracting and virtually brandishing it. "You can change this."

"The bank," he says. "We no longer have authority to change money." He glances up at the big clock. "The bank opens at ten."

With ten dollars in my hand, I argue, like Tantalus. I put forward my desperation: I would be happy to stay in Agra for days, for ever, but with great difficulty, at last, the Government have got me a reservation out for Karachi this afternoon, by BOAC, and if I miss it there is no saying when I can have another; my family are waiting for me in Italy, and have been; dollars are money, this bill is excellent, here is my passport; good heavens! Etc.

620

I am irresistible, because all my arguments are true and because the money is clearly real and because Indians dislike governments as much as I do. "If I don't see your passport," he says at last, "I can do it. But not officially."

"I won't tell anyone," I promise intensely.

While he is making the calculation, I stand here flooded with gratitude. I love this abominable hotel and I love all India, and once again it looks as if I were really about to get out. But it is nine minutes past eight. "The airline bus!" I cry. "Oh that doesn't leave until later," he says looking up, "8:30 or 8:40." Then he is counting out the good chips and I am solvent once more. "May I have a receipt?" I ask. "Oh no," he begins. "Well that's all right," I say, understanding, voluble: "When my wallet was stolen from my room in the Grand Hotel in Calcutta—look at it, will you, it looks as if it had been under the Ganges for a month, it was put in a postbox, emptied of money, and the police returned it to me—it had three or four American dollars in it but not the ten, which I'd locked with my large rupee-notes in a bag—well, I can just say they got it all—" I feel I would like to tell him the story of my life.

Pulling up short, I pay the bill, he sends a bearer off for change, and

I shoot around to my court to be shaved. The barber is squatting patiently by my door, water has come on, this takes five minutes, when I ask him how much he shrugs and smiles and I overpay him absurdly. Farewell to the bearer and I give him eight annas, for nothing. Back in the lobby I collect my change, wait. My bag comes. At last coffee is brought round and I am drinking it from the top of a showcase when the plane-connection, a bus larger than a jeep, comes at 8:55.

What is so agreeable, withdrawn, timeless, as a ride to an airport? Some tourists have come in and are waiting in the little passenger-cottage that occupies what used to be the stage of a small amphitheater—this was an American air base during the war, like half the other places I have visited. The pocket-plane takes off, unsteadily, on time—as usual. The smiling, sullen hostess is wearing the usual blue sari which hampers as she crosses and recrosses the shin-high barrier mid-way the plane, brushing her bottom into my shoulder every time. This is not seductive but Indian indifference. She wears lipstick, and no gum-gum. I did not see the Fort, or anything else, but regret nothing but Veroneo's grave—which I determined long ago to visit if I ever went to Agra—but there was no time.

I should have liked to stand with reverence beside the grave of this man who exerted his ultimate strength of imagination in a monument, to be created in an idiom not his own culture's, to the love for a woman who had been another man's. We are in a cloud. I see the hostess is curled up behind us (the other passenger and myself) with a film magazine. I doze.

621

Thomas Pynchon

Under the Rose

s the afternoon progressed, yellow clouds began to gather over Place Mohammed Ali, casting a tendril or two back toward the Libyan desert. A wind from the southwest swept quietly up rue Ibrahim and across the square, bringing the chill of the desert into the city.

Then let it rain, Porpentine thought: rain soon. He sat at a small wrought-iron table in front of a café, smoking Turkish cigarettes with a third cup of coffee, ulster thrown over the back of an adjoining chair. Today he wore light tweeds and a felt hat with muslin tied round it to protect his neck from the sun; he was leery of the sun. Clouds moved in now to dim it out. Porpentine shifted in his seat, took a watch from his waistcoat pocket, consulted it, replaced it. Turned once more to look out at the Europeans milling about the square: some hurrying into the Banque Impériale Ottomane, others lingering by shop windows, seating themselves at cafés. His face was carefully arranged: nerveless, rakish-expectant; he might have been there to meet a lady.

All for the benefit of anyone who cared. God knew how many there were. In practice it narrowed down to those in the employ of Moldweorp, the veteran spy. One somehow always tacked on "the veteran spy." It might have been a throwback to an earlier time, when such epithets were one reward for any proof of heroism or manhood. Or possibly because now, with a century rushing headlong to its end and with it a tradition in espionage where everything was tacitly on a gentlemanly basis, where the playing-fields of Eton had conditioned (one might say) premilitary conduct as well, the label was a way of fixing identity in this special *haut monde* before death—individual or collective—stung it to stillness forever. Porpentine himself was called *"il semplice inglese"* by those who cared.

Last week in Brindisi, their compassion had been relentless as always; it gave them a certain moral advantage, realizing as they did that Porpentine was somehow incapable of returning it. Tender and sheepish, therefore, they wove their paths to cross his own at random. Mirrored, too, his private tactics: living in the most frequented hotels, sitting at the tourist cafés, traveling always by the respectable, public routes. Which surely upset him most; as if, Porpentine once having fashioned such proper innocence, any use of it by others—especially Moldweorp's agents—involved some violation of patent right. They would pirate if they could his child's gaze, his plump angel's smile. For nearly fifteen years he'd fled their sympathy; since the lobby of the Hotel Bristol, Naples, on a winter evening in '83, when everyone you knew in spying's freemasonry seemed to be waiting. For Khartum to fall, for the crisis in Afghanistan to keep growing until it could be given the name of sure apocalypse. There he had come, as he'd known he must at some stage of the game, to face the already aged face of Moldweorp himself, the prizeman or maestro, feel the old man's hand solicitous on his arm and hear the earnest whisper: "Things are reaching a head; we may be in for it, all of us. Do be careful." What response? What possible? Only a scrutiny, almost desperate, for any fine trace of insincerity. Of course he'd found none there; and so turned, quickly, flaming, unable to cover a certain helplessness. Hoist thus by his own petard at every subsequent encounter as well, Porpentine, by the dog-days of '98 seemed, in contrast, to have grown cold, unkind. They would continue to use so fortunate an engine: would never seek his life, violate The Rules, forbear what had become for them pleasure.

He sat now wondering if either of the two at Brindisi had followed him to Alexandria. Certain he had seen no one on the Venice boat, he reviewed possibilities. An Austrian Lloyd steamer from Trieste that also touched at Brindisi was the only other they would have taken. Today was Monday. Porpentine had left on a Friday. The Trieste boat left on Thursday and arrived late Sunday. So that (a) at second-worst he had six days, or (b) at worst, they knew. In which case they had left the day before Porpentine and were already here.

He watched the sun darken and the wind flutter the leaves of acacias around Place Mohammed Ali. In the distance his name was being called. He turned to watch Goodfellow, blond and jovial, striding toward him down rue Cherif Pacha, wearing a dress suit and a pith helmet two sizes too large. "I say," Goodfellow cried. "Porpentine, I've met a remarkable young lady." Porpentine lit another cigarette and closed his eyes. All of Goodfellow's young ladies were remarkable. After two and a half years as partners one got used to an incidental progress of feminine attachments to Goodfellow's right arm: as if every capital of Europe were Margate and the promenade a continent long. If Goodfellow knew half his salary was sent out every month to a wife in Liverpool he showed none of it, rollicking along unperturbed, cock-a-hoop. Porpentine had seen his running mate's dossier but decided some time ago that the wife at least was none of his affair. He listened now as Goodfellow drew up a chair and summoned a waiter in wretched Arabic: "*Hat fingan kahwa bisukkar, ya weled.*"

"Goodfellow," Porpentine said, "you don't have to—"

"*Ya weled, ya weled,*" Goodfellow roared. The waiter was French and did not understand Arabic. "Ah," Goodfellow said, "coffee then. *Café*, you know."

"How are the digs?" asked Porpentine.

"First-rate." Goodfellow was staying at the Hotel Khedival, seven blocks away. There being a temporary hitch in finances, only one could afford the usual accommodations. Porpentine was staying with a friend in the Turkish quarter. "About this girl," Goodfellow said. "Party tonight at the Austrian Consulate. Her escort, Goodfellow: linguist, adventurer, diplomat . . ."

"Name," said Porpentine.

"Victoria Wren. Traveling with family, *videlicet:* Sir Alastair Wren, F.R.C.O., sister Mildred. Mother deceased. Departing for Cairo tomorrow. Cook's tour down the Nile." Porpentine waited. "Lunatic archaeologist," Goodfellow seemed reluctant. "One Bongo-Shaftsbury. Young, addlepated. Harmless."

"Aha."

"Tch-tch. Too highly strung. Should drink less café fort."

"Possibly," Porpentine said. Goodfellow's coffee arrived. Porpentine continued: "You know we'll end up chancing it anyway. We always do." Goodfellow grinned absently and stirred his coffee.

"I have already taken steps. Bitter rivalry for the young lady's attentions between myself and Bongo-Shaftsbury. Fellow is a perfect ass. Is mad to see the Theban ruins at Luxor."

"Of course," Porpentine said. He arose and tossed the ulster around his shoulders. It had begun to rain. Goodfellow handed him a small white envelope with the Austrian crest on the back.

"Eight, I suppose," said Porpentine.

"Right you are. You must see this girl."

It was then that one of Porpentine's seizures came upon him. The profession was lonely and in constant though not always deadly earnest. At regular intervals he found the need to play the buffoon. "A bit of skylarking," he called it. It made him, he believed, more human. "I will be there with false mustaches," he now informed Goodfellow, "impersonating an Italian count." He stood gaily at attention, pressed an imaginary hand: "*Carissima signorina.*" He bowed, kissed the air.

"You're insane," from Goodfellow, amiable.

626 "*Pazzo son!*" Porpentine began to sing in a wavering tenor. "*Guardate, come io piango ed imploro . . .*" His Italian was not perfect. Cockney inflections danced through. A group of English tourists, hurrying in out of the rain, glanced back at him, curious.

"Enough," Goodfellow winced. "'Twas Turin, I remember. Torino. Was it not? '93. I escorted a marchesina with a mole on her back and Cremonini sang Des Grieux. You, Porpentine, desecrate the memory."

But the antic Porpentine leaped in the air, clicked his heels; stood posturing, fist on chest, the other arm outstretched. "*Come io chiedo pietà!*" The waiter looked on with a pained smile; it began to rain harder. Goodfellow sat in the rain sipping his coffee. Drops of rain rattled on the pith helmet. "The sister isn't bad," he observed as Porpentine frolicked out in the square. "Mildred, you know. Though only eleven." At length it occurred to him that his dress suit was becoming soaked. He arose, left a piastre and a millième on the table and nodded to Porpentine, who now stood watching him. The square was empty except for the equestrian statue of Mohammed Ali. How many times had they faced each other this way, dwarfed horizontal and vertical by any plaza's late-afternoon landscape? Could an argument from design be predicated on that moment only; then the two must have been displaceable, like minor chess-pieces, anywhere across the board of Europe. Both of a color (though one hanging back diagonal in deference to his chief), both scanning any embassy's parquetry for signs of the Opposition, any statue's face for a reassurance of self-agency (perhaps, unhappily, self-humanity), they would try not to remember that every city's square, however you cut it, remains inanimate after all. Soon the two men turned almost formally, to part in opposite directions: Goodfellow back toward the hotel, Porpentine into rue Raset-Tin and the Turkish quarter. Until 8:00 he would ponder the Situation.

At the moment it was a bad job all round. Sirdar Kitchener, England's newest colonial hero, recently victorious at Khartum, was just now some four hundred miles further down the White Nile, foraging about in the jungle. A General Marchand was also rumored to be in the vicinity. Britain wanted no part of France in the Nile Valley. M. Delcassé, Foreign Minister of a newly formed French cabinet, would as soon go to war as not if there were any trouble when the two detachments met. As meet, everyone realized by now, they would. Kitchener had been instructed not to take any offensive and to avoid all provocation. Russia would support France in case of war, while England had a temporary rapprochement with Germany, which of course meant Italy and Austria as well.

Moldweorp's chief amusement, Porpentine reflected, had always been to harass: All he asked was that eventually there be a war. Not just a small incidental skirmish in the race to carve up Africa, but one pippip, jolly-ho, up-goes-the-balloon Armageddon for Europe. Once Porpentine might have been puzzled that his opposite number should desire war so passionately. Now he took it for granted that at some point in these fifteen years of hare-and-hounds he himself had conceived the private mission of keeping off Armageddon. An alignment like this, he felt, could only have taken place in a Western World where spying was becoming less an individual than a group enterprise, where the events of 1848 and the activities of anarchists and radicals all over the Continent seemed to proclaim that history was being made no longer through the virtù of single princes but rather by man in the mass; by trends and tendencies and impersonal curves on a lattice of pale blue lines. So it was inevitably single combat between the veteran spy and *il semplice inglese*. They stood alone—God knew where—on deserted lists. Goodfellow knew of the private battle, as doubtless did Moldweorp's subordinates. They all took on the roles of solicitous seconds, attending to the strictly national interests while their chiefs circled and parried above them on some unreachable level. It happened that Porpentine worked nominally for England and Moldweorp for Germany, but this was accident: they would probably have chosen the same sides had their employments been reversed. For he and Moldweorp, Porpentine knew, were cut from the same pattern: comrade Machiavellians, still playing the games of Renaissance Italian politics in a world that had outgrown them. The self-assumed roles became only, then, assertions of a kind of pride, first of all in a profession which still remembered the freebooting agility of Lord Palmerston. Fortunately for Porpentine the Foreign Office had enough of the old spirit left to give him nearly a free hand. Although if they did suspect he'd have no way of knowing. Where his personal mission coincided with diplomatic policy, Porpentine would send back a report to London, and no one ever seemed to complain.

The key man now for Porpentine seemed to be Lord Cromer, the British Consul-General at Cairo, an extremely able diplomat and cautious enough to avoid any rash impulses: war, for example. Could Moldweorp have an assassination in the works? A trip to Cairo seemed in order. As innocent as possible; that went without saying.

628

The Austrian Consulate was across the street from the Hotel Khedival, the festivities there unexceptional. Goodfellow sat at the bottom of a wide flight of marble steps with a girl who could not have been more than eighteen and who, like the gown she wore, seemed awkwardly bouffant and provincial. The rain had shrunken Goodfellow's formal attire; his coat looked tight under the armpits and across the stomach; the blond hair had been disarranged by the desert wind, the face was flushed, uncomfortable. Watching him, Porpentine came aware of his own appearance: quaint, anomalous, his evening clothes purchased the same year General Gordon was done in by the Mahdi. Hopelessly passé at gatherings like this, he often played a game in which he was, say, Gordon returned from the dead and headless; that odd, at least, among a resplendent muster of stars, ribbons, and exotic Orders. That out of date, certainly: the Sirdar had retaken Khartum, the outrage was avenged, but people had forgotten. He'd seen the fabled hero of the China wars once, standing on the ramparts at Gravesend. At the time Porpentine had been ten or so and likely to be dazzled; he was. But something had happened between there and the Hotel Bristol. He had thought about Moldweorp that night and about the likelihood of some apocalypse; perhaps a little, too, on his own sense of estrangement. But not at all about Chinese Gordon, lonely and enigmatic at the mouth of that boyhood Thames; whose hair it was said had turned white in the space of a day as he waited for death in the besieged city of Khartum.

Porpentine looked about the Consulate, checking off diplomatic personnel: Sir Charles Cookson, Mr. Hewat, M. Girard, Hr. von Hartmann, Cav. Romano, Comte de Zogheb, &c., &c. Right ho. All present and accounted for. Except for the Russian Vice-Consul, M. de Villiers. And oddly enough one's host, Count Khevenhüller-Metsch. Could they be together?

He moved over to the steps where Goodfellow sat desperate, yarning about nonexistent adventures in South Africa. The girl regarded him breathless and smiling. Porpentine wondered if he should sing: It isn't the girl I saw you with in Brighton; who, who, who's your lady friend? He said:

"I say." Goodfellow, relieved and more enthusiastic than necessary, introduced them.

"Miss Victoria Wren."

Porpentine smiled, nodded, searched all over for a cigarette. "How do you do, Miss."

"She's been hearing about our show with Dr. Jameson and the Boers," said Goodfellow.

"You were in the Transvaal together," the girl marveled. Porpentine thought: he can do whatever he wants with this one. Whatever he asks her.

"We've been together for some time, Miss." She bloomed, she billowed; Porpentine, shy, withdrew behind pale cheeks, pursed lips. As if her glow were a reminder of any Yorkshire sunset, or at least some vestige of a vision of Home which neither he nor Goodfellow could afford—or when you came down to it, cared—to remember, they did share in her presence this common evasiveness.

A low growl sounded behind Porpentine. Goodfellow cringed, smiled weakly, introduced Sir Alastair Wren, Victoria's father. It became clear almost immediately that he was not fond of Goodfellow. With him was a robust, myopic girl of eleven; the sister. Mildred was in Egypt, she soon informed Porpentine, to gather rock specimens, being daft for rocks in the same way Sir Alastair was for large and ancient pipe-organs. He had toured Germany the previous year, alienating the populations of various cathedral towns by recruiting small boys to toil away half-days at a clip keeping the bellows going: and then underpaying. Frightfully, added Victoria. There was, he continued, no decent pipe-organ anywhere on the African continent (which

Porpentine could hardly doubt). Goodfellow mentioned an enthusiasm for the barrel-organ, and had Sir Alastair ever tried his hand at one. The peer growled ominously. Out of the corner of his eye Porpentine saw Count Khevenhüller-Metsch come out of an adjoining room, steering the Russian vice-consul by the arm and talking wistfully; M. de Villiers punctuated the conversation with mirthful little barks. Aha, Porpentine thought. Mildred had produced from her reticule a large rock, which she now held up to Porpentine for inspection. She had found it out near the site of the ancient Pharohs, it contained trilobite fossils. Porpentine could not respond; it was his old weakness. A bar was set up on the mezzanine; he loped up the marble stairs after promising to bring punch (lemonade, of course, for Mildred).

Someone touched his arm as he waited at the bar. He turned and saw one of the two from Brindisi, who said: "Lovely girl." It was the first word he could remember any of them speaking to him directly in fifteen years. He only wondered, uneasy, if they reserved such artifice for times of singular crisis. He picked up the drinks, smiled all angelic; turned, started down the stairs. On the second step he tripped and fell: proceeded whirling and bouncing, followed by sounds of glass breaking and a spray of Chablis punch and lemonade, to the bottom. He'd learned in the army how to take falls. He looked up bashful at Sir Alastair Wren, who nodded in approval.

"Saw a fellow do that in a music-hall once," he said. "You're much better, Porpentine. Really."

"Do it again," Mildred said. Porpentine extracted a cigarette, lay there for a bit smoking. "How about late supper at the Fink," Goodfellow suggested. Porpentine got to his feet. "You remember the chaps we met in Brindisi." Goodfellow nodded, impassive, betraying no tics or tightenings; one of the things Porpentine admired him for. But, "Going home," Sir Alastair muttered, yanking fiercely at Mildred's hand. "Behave yourselves." So Porpentine found himself playing chaperon. He proposed another try for punch. When they got to the mezzanine, Moldweorp's man had disappeared. Porpentine wedged one foot between the balusters and looked down, surveying rapidly the faces below. "No," he said. Goodfellow handed him a cup of punch.

"I can't wait to see the Nile," Victoria had been saying, "the pyramids, the Sphinx."

"Cairo," Goodfellow added.

"Yes," Porpentine agreed, "Cairo."

Directly across rue de Rosette was the Fink restaurant. They dashed across the street through the rain, Victoria's cloak ballooning about her; she laughed, delighted with the rain. The crowd inside was entirely European. Porpentine recognized a few faces from the Venice boat. After her first glass of white Vöslauer the girl began to talk. Blithe and so green, she pronounced her *o*'s with a sigh, as if fainting from love. She was Catholic; had been to a convent school near her home, a place called Lardwick-in-the-Fen. This was her first trip abroad. She talked a great deal about her religion: had, for a time, considered the son of God as a young lady will consider any eligible bachelor. But had realized eventually that of course he was not but maintained instead an immense harem clad in black, decked with rosaries. She would never stand for such competition, had therefore left the novitiate after a matter of weeks but not the Church: that, with its sad-faced statuary, its odor of candles and incense, formed along with an uncle Evelyn the twin foci of her serene orbit. The uncle, a wild or renegade sun-downer, would arrive from Australia once a year bringing no gifts but prepared to weave as many yarns as the sisters could cope with. As far as Victoria remembered, he had never repeated himself. So she was given enough material to evolve between visits a private and imaginary sphere of influence, which she played with and within constantly: developing, exploring, manipulating. Especially during Mass: for here was the stage, the dramatic field already prepared, serviceable to a seedtime fancy. And so it came about that God wore a wide-awake hat and fought skirmishes with an aboriginal Satan out at the antipodes of the firmament, in the name and for the safekeeping of any Victoria.

631

Now the desire to feel pity can be seductive; it was always so for Porpentine. At this point he could only flick a rapid glance at Goodfellow's face and think with the sort of admiration pity once foundered in makes detestable: a stroke of genius, the Jameson raid. He chose that, he knew. He always knows. So do I.

One had to. He'd realized long before that women had no monopoly on what is called intuition; that in most men the faculty was latent, only becoming developed or painfully heightened at all in professions like this. But men being positivists and women more dreamy, having hunches still remained at base a feminine talent; so that, like it or not, they all— Moldweorp, Goodfellow, the pair from Brindisi—had to be part woman. Perhaps even in this maintenance of a threshold for compassion one dared not go beneath, was some sort of recognition.

But like a Yorkshire sunset, certain things could not be afforded. Porpentine had realized this as a fledgling. You do not feel pity for the men you have to kill or the people you have to hurt. You do not feel any more than a vague *esprit de corps* toward the agents you are working with. Above all, you do not fall in love. Not if you want to succeed in espionage. God knew what preadolescent agonies were responsible; but somehow Porpentine had remained true to that code. He had grown up possessing a sly mind and was too honest not to use it. He stole from street-hawkers, could stack a deck at fifteen, would run away whenever fighting was useless. So that at some point, prowling any mews or alley in midcentury London, the supreme rightness of "the game for its own sake" must have occurred to him, and acted as an irresistible vector aimed toward 1900. Now he would say that any itinerary, with all its doublings-back, emergency stops, and hundred-kilometer feints remained transitory or accidental. Certainly it was convenient, necessary; but never gave an indication of the deeper truth that all of them operated in no conceivable Europe but rather in a zone forsaken by God, between the tropics of diplomacy, lines they were forbidden forever to cross. One had consequently to play that idealized colonial Englishman who, alone in the jungle, shaves every day, dresses for dinner every night, and is committed to St George and no quarter as an article of love. Curious irony in that, of course. Porpentine grimaced to himself. Because both sides, his and Moldweorp's, had each in a different way done the unforgivable: had gone native. Somehow it had come about that one day neither man cared any longer which government he was working for. As if that prospect of a Final Clash were unable by men like them, through whatever frenzied twists and turns, to be evaded. Something had come to pass: who could guess what, or even when? In the Crimea, at Spicheren, at Khartum; it could make no difference. But so suddenly that there was a finite leap or omission in the maturing process—one fell asleep exhausted among immediacies: FO dispatches, Parliamentary resolutions; and awakened to find a tall specter grinning and gibbering over the foot of the bed, know that he was there to stay—hadn't they seen the apocalypse as an excuse for a glorious beano, a grand way to see the old century and their respective careers go out?

"You are so like him," the girl was saying, "my uncle Evelyn: tall, and fair, and oh! not really Lardwick-in-the-Fenish at all."

"Haw, haw," Goodfellow replied.

Hearing the languishment in that voice, Porpentine wondered idly if

she were bud or bloom; or perhaps a petal blown off and having nothing
to belong to any more. It was difficult to tell—getting more so every year—
and he did not know if this were old age beginning to creep up on him at
last or some flaw in the generation itself. His own had budded, bloomed,
and, sensing some blight in the air, folded its petals up again like certain
flowers at sunset. Would it be any use asking her?

"My God," Goodfellow said. They looked up to see an emaciated
figure in evening clothes whose head seemed that of a nettled sparrow-hawk.
The head guffawed, retaining its fierce expression. Victoria bubbled over in
a laugh. "It's Hugh!" she cried, delighted.

"Indeed," echoed a voice inside. "Help me get it off, someone."
Porpentine, obliging, stood on a chair to tug off the head.

"Hugh Bongo-Shaftsbury," said Goodfellow, ungracious.

"Harmakhis." Bongo-Shaftsbury indicated the hollow ceramic hawk-
head. "God of Heliopolis and chief deity of Lower Egypt. Utterly genuine,
this: a mask used in the ancient rituals." He seated himself next to Victoria.
Goodfellow scowled. "Literally Horus on the horizon, also represented as a
lion with the head of a man. Like the Sphinx."

"Oh," Victoria sighed, "the Sphinx." Enchanted, which did puzzle
Porpentine: for this was a violation, was it not, so much rapture over the
mongrel gods of Egypt? Her ideal should rightfully have been pure manhood
or pure hawkhood; hardly the mixture.

They decided not to have liqueurs but to stay with the Vöslauer, which
was off-vintage but only went for ten piastres.

"How far down the Nile do you intend to go?" asked Porpentine.
"Mr. Goodfellow has mentioned your interest in Luxor."

"I feel it is fresh territory, sir," replied Bongo-Shaftsbury. "No first-rate
work around the area since Grébaut discovered the tomb of the Theban
priests back in 'ninety-one. Of course one should have a look round the
pyramids at Gizeh, but that is pretty much old hat since Mr. Flinders Petrie's
painstaking inspection of sixteen or seventeen years ago."

"I imagine," murmured Porpentine. He could have got the data, of
course, from any Baedeker. At least there was a certain intensity or single-
minded concern with matters archaeological which Porpentine was sure
would drive Sir Alastair to frenzy before the Cook's tour was completed.
Unless, like Porpentine and Goodfellow, Bongo-Shaftsbury intended to go
no further than Cairo.

633

Porpentine hummed the aria from *Manon Lescaut* as Victoria poised prettily between the other two, attempting to keep equilibrium. The crowd in the restaurant had thinned out and across the street the Consulate was dark, save two or three lights in the upstairs rooms. Perhaps in a month all the windows would be blazing; perhaps the world would be blazing. Projected, the courses of Marchand and Kitchener would cross near Fashoda, in the district of Behr el-Abyad, some forty miles above the source of the White Nile. Lord Lansdowne, Secretary of State for War, had predicted 25 September as meeting-date in a secret dispatch to Cairo: a message both Porpentine and Moldweorp had seen. All at once a tic came dancing across Bongo-Shaftsbury's face; there was a time-lag of about five seconds before Porpentine—either intuitively or because of his suspicions about the archaelogist—reckoned who it was that stood behind his chair. Goodfellow nodded, sick and timid; said, civilly enough: "Lepsius, I say. Tired of the climate in Brindisi?" Lepsius. Porpentine hadn't even known the name. Goodfellow would have, of course. "Sudden business called me to Egypt," the agent hissed. Goodfellow sniffed at his wine. Soon: "Your traveling companion? I had rather hoped to see him again."

"Gone to Switzerland," Lepsius said. "The mountains, the clean winds. One can have enough, one day, of the sordidness of the South." They never lied. Who was his new partner?

"Unless you go far enough south," Goodfellow said. "I imagine far enough down the Nile one gets back to a kind of primitive cleanness."

Porpentine had been watching Bongo-Shaftsbury closely, since the tic. The face, lean and ravaged like the body, remained expressionless now; but that initial lapse had set Porpentine on his guard.

"Doesn't the law of the wild beast prevail down there?" Lepsius said. "There are no property rights, only fighting; and the victor wins all. Glory, life, power and property, all."

"Perhaps," Goodfellow said. "But in Europe, you know, we are civilized. Fortunately. Jungle-law is inadmissible."

Soon Lepsius took his leave, expressing the hope they would meet again at Cairo. Goodfellow was certain they would. Bongo-Shaftsbury had continued to sit unmoving and unreadable.

"What a queer gentleman," Victoria said.

"Is it queer," Bongo-Shaftsbury said, deliberately reckless, "to favor the clean over the impure?"

So. Porpentine had wearied of self-congratulation ten years ago. Good-fellow looked embarrassed. So: cleanness. After the deluge, the long famine, the earthquake. A desert-region's cleanness: bleached bones, tombs of dead cultures. Armageddon would sweep the house of Europe so. Did that make Porpentine champion only of cobwebs, rubbish, offscourings? He remembered a night-visit in Rome, years ago, to a contact who lived over a bordello near the Pantheon. Moldweorp himself had followed, taking station near a street-lamp to wait. In the middle of the interview Porpentine chanced to look out the window. A street-walker was propositioning Moldweorp. They could not hear the conversation, only see a slow and unkind fury recast his features to a wrath-mask; only watch him raise his cane and begin to slash methodically at the girl until she lay ragged at his feet. Porpentine was first to break out of that paralysis, open the door, and race down to the street. When he reached her, Moldweorp was gone. His comfort was auto-matic, perhaps out of some abstract sense of duty, while she screamed into the tweed of his coat. "*Mi chiamava sozzura,*" she could say: he called me filth. Porpentine had tried to forget the incident. Not because it was ugly but because it showed his terrible flaw so clear: reminding him it was not Moldweorp he hated so much as a perverse idea of what is clean; not the girl he sympathized with so much as her humanity. Fate, it occurred to him then, chooses weird agents. Moldweorp somehow could love and hate individually. The roles being, it seemed, reversed, Porpentine found it neces-sary to believe if one appointed oneself savior of humanity that perhaps one must love that humanity only in the abstract. For any descent to the personal level can make a purpose less pure. Whereas a disgust at individual human perversity might as easily avalanche into a rage for apocalypse. He could never bring himself to hate the Moldweorp crew, any more than they could avoid genuine anxiety over his welfare. Worse, Porpentine could never make a try for any of them; would remain instead an inept Cremonini singing Des Grieux, expressing certain passions by calculated musical covenant, would never leave a stage where vehemences and tendresses are merely forte and piano, where the Paris gate at Amiens foreshortens mathematically and is illuminated by the precise glow of calcium light. He remembered his performance in the rain that afternoon: he, like Victoria, needed the proper setting. Anything intensely European, it seemed, inspired him to heights of inanity.

It got late; only two or three tourists left scattered about the room.

635

Victoria showed no signs of fatigue, Goodfellow and Bongo-Shaftsbury argued politics. A waiter lounged two tables away, impatient. He had the delicate build and high narrow skull of the Copt, and Porpentine realized this had been the only non-European in the place, all along. Any such discord should have been spotted immediately: Porpentine's slip. He had no use for Egypt, had sensitive skin and avoided its sun as if any tinge of it might make part of him the East's own. He cared about regions not on the Continent only so far as they might affect its fortunes and no further; the Fink restaurant could as well have been an inferior Voisin's.

At length the party arose, paid, left. Victoria skipped ahead across rue Cherif Pacha to the hotel. Behind them a closed carriage came rattling out of the drive beside the Austrian Consulate and dashed away hell-for-leather down rue de Rosette, into the wet night.

"Someone is in a hurry," Bongo-Shaftsbury noted.

"Indeed," said Goodfellow. To Porpentine: "At the Gare du Caire. The train leaves at eight." Porpentine gave them all good night and returned to his *pied-à-terre* in the Turkish quarter. Such choice of lodgings violated nothing; for he considered the Porte part of the Western World. He fell asleep reading an old and mutilated edition of *Antony and Cleopatra* and wondering if it were still possible to fall under the spell of Egypt: its tropic unreality, its curious gods.

At 7:40 he stood on the platform of the Gare, watching the porters from Cook's and Gaze's pile boxes and trunks. Across the double line of tracks was a small park, green with palms and acacias. Porpentine kept to the shadow of the station-house. Soon the others arrived. He noticed the tiniest flicker of communication pass between Bongo-Shaftsbury and Lepsius. The morning express pulled in, amid sudden commotion on the platform. Porpentine turned to see Lepsius in pursuit of an Arab, who had apparently stolen his valise. Good-fellow had already gone into action. Sprinting across the platform, blond mane flapping wild, he cornered the Arab in a doorway, took back the valise and surrendered his quarry to a fat policeman in a pith helmet. Lepsius watched him snake-eyed and silent as he handed back the valise.

Aboard the train they split up into two adjoining compartments, Victoria, her father, and Goodfellow sharing the one next the rear platform. Porpentine felt that Sir Alastair would have been less miserable in his company, but wanted to be sure of Bongo-Shaftsbury. The train pulled out at five past eight, heading into the sun. Porpentine leaned back and let Mildred ramble on about mineralogy. Bongo-Shaftsbury kept silent until the train had passed Sidi Gaber and swung toward the southeast.

He said: "Do you play with dolls, Mildred?" Porpentine gazed out the window. He felt something unpleasant was about to happen. He could see a procession of dark-colored camels with their drivers, moving slowly along the embankments of a canal. Far down the canal were the small white sails of barges.

"When I'm not out after rocks," said Mildred.

Bongo-Shaftsbury said: "I'll wager you do not have any dolls that walk, or speak, or are able to jump rope. Now do you."

Porpentine tried to concentrate on a group of Arabs who lazed about far down the embankment, evaporating part of the water in Lake Mareotis for salt. The train was going at top speed. He soon lost them in the distance.

"No," said Mildred, doubtful.

Bongo-Shaftsbury said: "But have you never seen dolls like that? Such lovely dolls, and clockwork inside. Dolls that do everything perfectly, because of the machinery. Not like real little boys and girls at all. Real children cry, and act sullen, and won't behave. These dolls are much nicer."

On the right now were fallow cotton-fields and mud huts. Occasionally one of the fellahin would be seen going down to the canal for water. Almost out of his field of vision Porpentine saw Bongo-Shaftsbury's hands, long and starved-nervous, lying still, one on each knee.

"They sound quite nice," said Mildred. Though she knew she was being talked down to her voice was unsteady. Possibly something in the archaeologist's face frightened her.

Bongo-Shaftsbury said: "Would you like to see one, Mildred?" It was going too far. For the man had been talking to Porpentine, the girl was being used. For what? Something was wrong.

"Have you one with you," she wondered, timid. Despite himself Porpentine moved his head away from the window to watch Bongo-Shaftsbury.

Who smiled: "Oh yes." And pushed back the sleeve of his coat to remove a cuff-link. He began to roll back the cuff of his shirt. Then thrust the naked underside of his forearm at the girl. Porpentine recoiled, thinking: Lord love a duck. Bongo-Shaftsbury is insane. Shiny and black against the unsunned flesh was a miniature electric switch, single-pole, double-throw, sewn into the skin. Thin silver wires ran from its terminals up the arm, disappearing under the sleeve.

637

The young often show a facile acceptance of the horrible. Mildred began to shake. "No," she said, "no: you are not one."

"But I am," protested Bongo-Shaftsbury, smiling, "Mildred. The wires run up into my brain. When the switch is closed like this I act the way I do now. When it is thrown the other—"

The girl shrank away. "Papa," she cried.

"Everything works by electricity," Bongo-Shaftsbury explained, soothing. "And it is simple, and clean."

"Stop it!" Porpentine said.

Bongo-Shaftsbury whirled to him. "Why?" he whispered. "Why? For her? Touched by her fright, are you? Or is it for yourself?"

Porpentine retreated, bashful. "One doesn't frighten a child, sir."

"General principles. Damn you." He looked petulant, ready to cry.

There was noise out in the passageway. Goodfellow had been shouting in pain. Porpentine leaped up, shoving Bongo-Shaftsbury aside, and rushed out into the passageway. The door to the rear platform was open: in front of it Goodfellow and an Arab fought, tangled and clawing. Porpentine saw the flash of a pistol-barrel. He moved in cautiously, circling, choosing his point. When the Arab's throat was exposed sufficiently Porpentine kicked, catching him across the windpipe. He collapsed rattling. Goodfellow took the pistol. Pushed back his forelock, sides heaving. "Ta."

"Same one?" Porpentine said.

"No. The railroad police are conscientious. And it is possible, you know, to tell them apart. This is different."

"Cover him, then." To the Arab: "*Auz e. Ma tkhafsh minni.*" The Arab's head rolled toward Porpentine, he tried to grin but his eyes were sick. A blue mark was coming out on his throat. He could not talk. Sir Alastair and Victoria had appeared, anxious.

"May have been a friend of the fellow I caught back at the Gare," Goodfellow explained easily. Porpentine helped the Arab to his feet. "*Ruh.* Go back. Don't let us see you again." The Arab moved off.

"You're not going to let him go?" Sir Alastair rumbled. Goodfellow was magnanimous. He gave a short speech about charity and turning the other cheek which was well received by Victoria but which seemed to nauseate her father. The party resumed their places in the compartments, though Mildred had decided to stay with Sir Alastair.

Half an hour later the train pulled into Damanhur. Porpentine saw

Lepsius get off two cars ahead and go inside the station-house. Around them stretched the green country of the Delta. Two minutes later the Arab got off and cut across on a diagonal to the buffet entrance; met Lepsius coming out with a bottle of red wine. He was rubbing the mark on his throat and apparently wanted to speak to Lepsius. The agent glared and cuffed him across the head. "No bakshish," he announced. Porpentine settled back, closed his eyes without looking at Bongo-Shaftsbury. Without even saying aha. The train began to move. So. What did they call clean, then? Not observing The Rules, surely. If so they had reversed course. They'd never played so foul before. Could it mean that this meeting at Fashoda would be important: might even be The One? He opened his eyes to watch Bongo-Shaftsbury, engrossed in a book: Sidney J. Webb's *Industrial Democracy*. Porpentine shrugged. Time was his fellow professionals became adept through practice. Learned ciphers by breaking them, customs officials by evading them, some opponents by killing them. Now the new ones read books: young lads, full of theory and (he'd decided) a faith in nothing but the perfection of their own internal machinery. He flinched, remembering the knife-switch, fastened to Bongo-Shaftsbury's arm like a malignant insect. Moldweorp must have been the oldest spy active but in professional ethics he and Porpentine did belong to the same generation. Porpentine doubted if Moldweorp approved of the young man opposite.

639

Their silence continued for twenty-five miles. The express passed by farms which began to look more and more prosperous, fellahin who worked in the fields at a faster pace, small factories and heaps of ancient ruin and tall flowering tamarisks. The Nile was in flood: stretching away from them, a glittering network of irrigation canals and small basins caught the water, conducted it through wheat and barley fields which extended to the horizon. The train reached the Rosetta arm of the Nile; crossed high over it by a long, narrow iron bridge, entered the station at Kafr ez-Zaiyat, where it stopped. Bongo-Shaftsbury closed the book, arose and left the compartment. A few moments later Goodfellow entered, holding Mildred by the hand.

"He felt you might want to get some sleep," Goodfellow said. "I should have thought. I was preoccupied with Mildred's sister." Porpentine snorted, shut his eyes and fell asleep before the train started to move. He awoke half an hour out of Cairo. "All secure," Goodfellow said. The outlines of the pyramids were visible off to the west. Closer to the city, gardens and villas began to appear. The train reached Cairo's Principal Station about noon.

Somehow, Goodfellow and Victoria managed to be in a phaeton and away before the rest of the party got on the platform. "Damme," Sir Alastair puzzled, "what are they doing, eloping?" Bongo-Shaftsbury looked properly outwitted. Porpentine, having slept, felt rather in a holiday mood. "*Arabiyeh*," he roared, gleeful. A dilapidated pinto-colored barouche came clattering up and Porpentine pointed after the phaeton: "A double piastre if you catch them." The driver grinned; Porpentine hustled everyone into the carriage. Sir Alastair protested, muttering about Mr. Conan Doyle. Bongo-Shaftsbury guffawed and away they galloped, around a sharp curve to the left, over the el-Lemun bridge and pell-mell down Sharia Bab el-Hadid. Mildred made faces at other tourists on foot or riding donkeys, Sir Alastair smiled tentatively. Ahead, Porpentine could see Victoria in the phaeton tiny and graceful, holding Goodfellow's arm and leaning back to let the wind blow her hair.

The two carriages arrived at Shepheard's Hotel in a dead heat. All but Porpentine alighted and moved toward the hotel. "Check me in," he called to Goodfellow, "I must see a friend." The friend was a porter at the Hotel Victoria, four blocks south and west. While Porpentine sat in the kitchen discussing game birds with a mad chef he had known at Cannes, the porter crossed the street to the British Consulate, going in by the servants' entrance. He emerged after fifteen minutes and returned to the hotel. Soon an order for lunch was brought in to the kitchen. "*Crème*" had been misspelled to read "*chem.*"; "*Lyonnaise*" was spelled without an *e*. Both were underlined. Porpentine nodded, thanked everyone, and left. He caught a cab and rode up Sharia el-Maghrabi, through the luxurious park at the end; soon arrived at the Crédit Lyonnais. Nearby was a small pharmacy. He entered and asked about the prescription for laudanum he had brought in to be filled the day before. He was handed an envelope whose contents, once more in the cab, he checked. A raise of £50 for him and Goodfellow: good news. They would both be able to stay at Shepheard's.

Back at the hotel they set about decoding their instructions. F. O. knew nothing about an assassination plot. Of course not. No reason for one, if you were thinking only about the immediate question of who would control the Nile Valley. Porpentine wondered what had happened to diplomacy. He knew people who had worked under Palmerston, a shy, humorous old man for whom the business was a jolly game of blindman's-buff, where every day one reached out and touched, and was touched by, the Specter's cold hand.

"We're on our own, then," Goodfellow pointed out.

"Ah," Porpentine agreed. "Suppose we work it this way: set a thief to catch one. Make plans to do Cromer in ourselves. Go through the motions only, of course. That way whenever they get an opportunity, we can be right on the spot to prevent them."

"Stalk the Consul-General," Goodfellow grew enthusiastic, "like a bloody grouse. Why we haven't done that since—"

"Never mind," Porpentine said.

That night Porpentine commissioned a cab and roved about the city until early morning. The coded instructions had told them nothing more than to bide time: Goodfellow was taking care of that, having escorted Victoria to an Italian summer-theater performance at the Ezbekiyeh Garden. In the course of the night Porpentine visited a girl who lived in the Quartier Rosetti and was the mistress of a junior clerk in the British Consulate; a jewel merchant in the Muski who had lent financial support to the Mahdists and did not wish,now that the movement was crushed, to have his sympathies known; a minor Esthetic who had fled England on a narcotics charge to the land of no extradition and who was a distant cousin of the valet to Mr. Raphael Borg, the British Consul; and a pimp named Varkumian who claimed to know every assassin in Cairo. From this fine crew Porpentine returned to his room at three in the morning. But hesitated at the door, having heard movement behind it. Only one thing for it: at the end of the corridor was this window with a ledge outside. He grimaced. But then everyone knew that spies were continually crawling about window-ledges, high above the streets of exotic cities. Feeling an utter fool, Porpentine climbed out and got on the ledge. He looked down: there was a drop of about fifteen feet into some bushes. Yawning he made his way quickly but clumsily toward the corner of the building. The ledge became narrower at the corner. As he stood with each foot on a different side and the edge of the building bisecting him from eyebrows to abdomen he lost his balance and fell. On the way down it occurred to him to use an obscene word; he hit the shrubbery with a crash, rolled, and lay there tapping his fingers. After he had smoked half a cigarette he got to his feet and noticed a tree next his own window, easily climbable. He ascended puffing and cursing; crawled out on a limb, straddled it, and peered inside.

Goodfellow and the girl lay on Porpentine's bed, white and exhausted-looking by street-light: her eyes, mouth, and nipples were little dark bruises against the flesh. She cradled Goodfellow's white head in a net or weaving of fingers while he cried, streaking her breasts with tears. "I'm sorry," he was saying, "the Transvaal, a wound. They told me it was not serious." Porpentine, having no idea how this sort of thing worked, fell back on alternatives: (a) Goodfellow was being honorable, (b) was truly impotent and had therefore lied to Porpentine about a long list of conquests, (c) simply had no intention of getting involved with Victoria. Whichever it was, Porpentine felt, as always, an alien. He swung down by one arm from the limb, nonplused, until the stub of the cigarette burned down to his fingers and made him swear softly; and because he knew it was not really the burn he cursed he began to worry. It was not only seeing Goodfellow weak. He dropped into the bushes and lay there thinking about his own threshold, sustained proudly for twenty years of service. Though it had been hammered at before, he suspected this was the first time it had shown itself truly vulnerable. A pang of superstitious terror caught him flat on his back in the bushes. It seemed he knew, for a space of seconds, that this indeed was The One. Apocalypse would surely begin at Fashoda if for no other reason than that he felt his own so at hand. But soon: gradually, with each lungful of a fresh cigarette's smoke, the old control seeped back to him; and he got at last to his feet, still shaky, walked around to the hotel entrance and up to his room. This time he pretended to have lost his key, making bewildered noises to cover the girl as she gathered her clothing and fled through connecting doors to her own room. All he felt by the time Goodfellow opened was embarrassment, and that he had lived with for a long time.

The theater had presented *Manon Lescaut.* In the shower next morning Goodfellow attempted to sing *"Donna non vidi mai."* "Stop," said Porpentine. "Would you like to hear how it should be done?" Goodfellow howled. "I doubt you could sing Ta-ra-ra-boom-di-ay without mucking it up."

But Porpentine could not resist. He thought it a harmless compromise. *"A dirle io t'amo,"* he caroled, *"a nuova vita l'alma mia si desta."* It was appalling; one got the impression he had once worked in a music hall. He was no Des Grieux. Des Grieux knows, soon as he sees that young lady just off the diligence from Arras, what will happen. He does not make false starts or feints, this chevalier, has nothing to decode, no double game to play. Porpentine envied him. As he dressed he whistled the aria. Last night's moment of weakness bloomed again behind his eyes. He thought: if I step below the threshold, you know, I shall never get back again.

At two that afternoon the Consul-General emerged from the front door of the Consulate and entered a carriage. Porpentine watched from a deserted room on the third floor of the Hotel Victoria. Lord Cromer was a perfect target but this vantage at least was unavailable to any hired assassin-in-opposition as long as Porpentine's friends kept on the alert. The archaeologist had taken Victoria and Mildred to tour the bazaars and the Tombs of the Khalifs. Goodfellow was sitting in a closed landau directly under the window. Unobtrusive (as Porpentine watched) he started off behind the carriage, keeping at a safe distance. Porpentine left the hotel, strolled up Sharia el-Maghrabi. At the next corner he noticed a church off to his right; heard loud organ music. On a sudden whim he entered the church. Sure enough, it was Sir Alastair, booming away. It took the unmusical Porpentine some five minutes to become aware of the devastation Sir Alastair was wreaking on the keys and pedals. Music laced the interior of the tiny, Gothic house with certain intricate veinings, weird petal-shapes. But it was violent and somehow Southern foliage. Head and fingers uncontrollable for a neglect of his daughter's or any purity, for the music's own shape, for Bach—was it Bach?—himself? Foreign and a touch shabby, uncomprehending, how could Porpentine say. But was yet unable to pull away until the music stopped abruptly, leaving the church's cavity to reverberate. Only then did he withdraw unseen out into the sun, adjusting his neck-cloth as if it were all the difference between wholeness and disintegration.

Lord Cromer was doing nothing to protect himself, Goodfellow reported that night. Porpentine, having re-checked with the valet's cousin, knew the word had gone through. He shrugged, calling the Consul-General a nitwit: tomorrow was 25 September. He left the hotel at eleven and went by carriage to a *Brauhaus* a few blocks north of the Ezbekiyeh Garden. He sat alone at a small table against the wall, listening to maudlin accordion music which must surely have been old as Bach; closed his eyes, letting a cigarette droop from his lips. A waitress brought Munich beer.

"Mr. Porpentine." He looked up. "I followed you." He nodded, smiled; Victoria sat down. "Papa would die if he ever found out," gazing at him defiant. The accordion stopped. The waitress left two Krugers.

He pursed his lips, ruthful in that quiet. So she'd sought out and found the woman in him; the very first civilian to do so. He did not go through any routine of asking how she knew. She could not have seen him through the window. He said:

"He was sitting in the German church this afternoon, playing Bach as if it were all he had left. So that he may have guessed."

She hung her head, a mustache of foam on her upper lip. From across the canal came the faint whistle of the express for Alexandria. "You love Goodfellow," he hazarded. Never had he been down so far: he was a tourist here. Could have used, at the moment, any Baedeker of the heart. Almost drowned in a fresh wailing of the accordion, her whisper came: yes. Then, had Goodfellow told her? . . He raised his eyebrows, she shook her head no. Amazing, the knowing of one another, these wordless flickerings. "Whatever I may think I have guessed," she said. "Of course you can't trust me, but I have to say it. It's true." How far down could one go, before . . . Desperate, Porpentine: "What do you want me to do, then." She, twisting ringlets round her fingers, would not look at him. Soon: "Nothing. Only understand." If Porpentine had believed in the devil he would have said: you have been sent. Go back and tell him, them, it is no use. The accordionist spotted Porpentine and the girl, recognized them as English. "Had the devil any son," he sang mischievous in German, "it was surely Palmerston." A few Germans laughed, Porpentine winced: the song was fifty years old at least. But a few still remembered.

Varkumian came weaving his way among tables, late. Victoria saw him and excused herself. Varkumian's report was brief: no action. Porpentine sighed. It left only one thing to do. Throw a scare into the Consulate, put them on their guard.

So next day they began "stalking" Cromer in earnest. Porpentine woke up in a foul mood. He donned a red beard and a pearl-gray morning hat and visited the Consulate, posing as an Irish tourist. The staff weren't having any: he got ejected forcibly. Goodfellow had a better idea: "Lob a bomb," he cried. Happily his knowledge of munitions was faulty as his aim. The bomb, instead of falling safely on the lawn, soared in through a window of the Consulate, sending one of the proverbial charwomen into hysterics (though it proved of course to be a dud) and nearly getting Goodfellow arrested.

At noon Porpentine visited the kitchen of the Hotel Victoria to find the place in a turmoil. The meeting at Fashoda had taken place. The Situation had turned to a Crisis. Upset, he dashed out into the street, commandeered a carriage, and tore off in search of Goodfellow. He found him two hours later sleeping in his hotel room where Porpentine had left him. In a rage he emptied a pitcher of ice-water over Goodfellow's head. Bongo-Shaftsbury appeared in the doorway grinning. Porpentine hurled the empty pitcher at him as he vanished down the corridor. "Where's the Consul-General?" Goodfellow inquired, amiable and sleepy. "Get dressed," bellowed Porpentine.

They found the clerk's mistress lying lazy in a patch of sunlight, peeling a mandarin orange. She told them Cromer was planning to attend the opera at eight. Up to then, she could not say. They went to the shop of the chemist, who had nothing for them. Barreling through the Garden Porpentine asked about the Wrens. They were at Heliopolis, as far as Goodfellow knew. "What the bloody hell is wrong with everyone?" Porpentine wanted to know. "Nobody knows anything." They could do nothing till eight; so sat in front of a café in the Garden and drank wine. Egypt's sun beat down, somehow threatening. There was no shade. The fear that had found him night before last now crawled along the flanks of Porpentine's jaw and up his temples. Even Goodfellow seemed nervous.

At a quarter to eight they strolled along the path to the theater, purchased tickets in the orchestra, and settled down to wait. Soon the Consul-General's party arrived and sat near them. Lepsius and Bongo-Shaftsbury drifted in from either side and stationed themselves in boxes; forming, with Lord Cromer as vertex, an angle of 120 degrees. "Bother," said Goodfellow. "We should have got some elevation." Four policemen came marching down the center aisle, glanced up at Bongo-Shaftsbury. He pointed to Porpentine. "My Gawd," Goodfellow moaned. Porpentine closed his eyes. He'd blown it, all right. This was what happened when one blundered right in. The policemen surrounded them, stood at attention. "All right," Porpentine said. He and Goodfellow arose and were escorted out of the theater. "We shall desire your passports," one of them said. Behind them on the breeze came the first sprightly chords of the opening scene. They marched down a narrow path, two police behind, two in front. Signals had, of course, been arranged years before. "I shall want to see the British Consul," Porpentine said and spun, drawing an old single-shot pistol. Goodfellow had the other two covered. The policeman who had asked for their passports glowered. "No one said they would be armed," another protested. Methodically, with four raps to the skull, the policemen were neutralized and rolled into the underbrush. "A fool trick," Goodfellow muttered: "we were lucky." Porpentine was already running back toward the theater. They took the stairs two at a time and searched for an empty box. "Here," Goodfellow said. They edged into the box. It was almost directly across from Bongo-Shaftsbury's. That would put them next to Lepsius. "Keep down," Porpentine said. They crouched, peering between small golden balusters.

On stage Edmondo and the students chaffed the Romantic, horny Des Grieux. Bongo-Shaftsbury was checking the action of a small pistol. "Stand by," Goodfellow whispered. The postilion horn of the diligence was heard. The coach came rattling and creaking into the inn courtyard. Bongo-Shaftsbury raised his pistol. Porpentine said: "Lepsius. Next door." Goodfellow withdrew. The diligence bounced to a halt. Porpentine centered his sights on Bongo-Shaftsbury, then let the muzzle drift down and to the right until it pointed at Lord Cromer. It occurred to him that he could end everything for himself right now, never have to worry about Europe again. He had a sick moment of uncertainty. Now how serious had anyone ever been? Was aping Bongo-Shaftsbury's tactics any less real than opposing them? Like a bloody grouse, Goodfellow had said. Manon was helped down from the coach. Des Grieux gaped, was transfixed, read his destiny on her eyes. Someone was standing behind Porpentine. He glanced back, quickly in that moment of hopeless love, and saw Moldweorp there looking decayed, incredibly old, face set in a hideous though compassionate smile. Panicking, Porpentine turned and fired blindly, perhaps at Bongo-Shaftsbury, perhaps at Lord Cromer. He could not see and would never be sure which one he had intended as target. Bongo-Shaftsbury shoved the pistol inside his coat and disappeared. A fight was on out in the corridor. Porpentine pushed the old man aside and ran out in time to see Lepsius tear away from Goodfellow and flee toward the stairs. "Please, dear fellow," Moldweorp gasped. "Don't go after them. You are outnumbered." Porpentine had reached the top step. "Three to two," he muttered.

"More than three. My chief and his, and staff personnel . . ."

Which stopped Porpentine dead. "Your—"

"I have been under orders, you know." The old man sounded apologetic. Then, all in a nostalgic rush: "The Situation, don't you know, it is serious this time, we are all for it—"

Porpentine looked back, exasperated. "Go away," he yelled, "go away and die." And was certain only in a dim way that the interchange of words had now, at last, been decisive.

"The big chief himself," Goodfellow remarked as they ran down the stairs. "Things must be bad." A hundred yards ahead Bongo-Shaftsbury and Lepsius leaped into a carriage. Surprisingly nimble, Moldweorp had taken a short cut. He emerged from an exit to the left of Porpentine and Goodfellow and joined the others. "Let them go," Goodfellow said.

"Are you still taking orders from me?" Without waiting for an answer Porpentine found a phaeton, got in and swung around to pursue. Goodfellow grabbed on and hauled himself up. They galloped down Sharia Kamel Pasha, scattering donkeys, tourists, and dragomans. In front of Shepheard's they nearly ran down Victoria, who had come out into the street. They lost ten seconds while Goodfellow helped her aboard. Porpentine could not protest. Again she had known. Something had passed out of his hands. He was only beginning to recognize, somewhere, a quite enormous betrayal.

It was no longer single combat. Had it ever been? Lepsius, Bongo-Shaftsbury, all the others, had been more than merely tools or physical extensions of Moldweorp. They were all in it; all had a stake, acted as a unit. Under orders. Whose orders? Anything human? He doubted: like a bright hallucination against Cairo's night-sky he saw (it may have been only a line of cloud) a bell-shaped curve, remembered perhaps from some younger FO operative's mathematics text. Unlike Constantine on the verge of battle, he could not afford, this late, to be converted at any sign. Only curse himself, silent, for wanting so to believe in a fight according to the duello, even in this period of history. But they—no, it—had not been playing those rules. Only statistical odds. When had he stopped facing an adversary and taken on a Force, a Quantity?

The bell curve is the curve for a normal or Gaussian distribution. An invisible clapper hangs beneath it. Porpentine (though only half-suspecting) was being tolled down.

The carriage ahead took a sharp left, moving toward the canal. There it turned left again, and raced alongside the thin ribbon of water. The moon had risen, half of it, fat and white. "They're going for the Nile Bridge," Goodfellow said. They passed the Khedive's palace and clattered over the bridge. The river flowed dark and viscous under them. On the other side they turned south and sped through moonlight between the Nile and the grounds of the viceregal palace. Ahead the quarry swung right. "Damned if it isn't the road to the pyramids," Goodfellow said. Porpentine nodded: "About five and a half miles." They made the turn and passed the prison

647

and the village of Gizeh, hit a curve, crossed the railroad tracks and headed due west. "Oh," Victoria said quietly, "we're going to see the Sphinx."

"In the moonlight," Goodfellow added, wry. "Leave her alone," Porpentine said. They were silent for the rest of the way, making little gain. Around them irrigation ditches interlaced and sparkled. The two carriages passed fellahin villages and water-wheels. No sound at all in the night save wheels and hoofbeats. And the wind of their passage. As they neared the edge of the desert Goodfellow said, "We're catching up." The road began to slope upward. Protected from the desert by a wall five feet high, it wound around to the left, ascending. Ahead of them suddenly the other carriage lurched and crashed into the wall. The occupants scrambled out and climbed the rest of the way on foot. Porpentine continued on around the curve, stopping about 100 yards from the great pyramid of Kheops. Moldweorp, Lepsius, and Bongo-Shaftsbury were nowhere in sight.

"Let's have a look about," Porpentine said. They rounded the corner of the pyramid. The Sphinx crouched 600 yards to the south. "Damn," Goodfellow said. Victoria pointed. "There," she cried: "going toward the Sphinx." They moved over the rough ground at a dead run. Moldweorp had apparently twisted his ankle. The other two were helping him. Porpentine drew his pistol. "You are for it, old man," he shouted. Bongo-Shaftsbury turned and fired. Goodfellow said: "What are we going to do with them anyway? Let them go." Porpentine did not answer. A moment or so later they brought the Moldweorp agents to bay against the right flank of the great Sphinx.

648

"Put it down," Bongo-Shaftsbury wheezed. "That is a single-shot, I have a revolver." Porpentine had not reloaded. He shrugged, grinned, tossed the pistol into the sand. Beside him Victoria looked up rapt at the lion, man, or god towering over them. Bongo-Shaftsbury pushed up his shirt-cuff, opened the switch and closed it the other way. A boyish gesture. Lepsius stood in the shadows, Moldweorp smiled. "Now," Bongo-Shaftsbury said. "Let them go," Porpentine said. Bongo-Shaftsbury nodded. "It is no concern of theirs," he agreed. "This is between you and the Chief, is it not?" Ho, ho, thought Porpentine: couldn't it have been? Like Des Grieux he must have his delusion even now; could never admit himself entirely a gull. Goodfellow took Victoria's hand and they moved away, back toward the carriage, the girl gazing back restless, eyes glowing at the Sphinx.

"You screamed at the Chief," Bongo-Shaftsbury announced. "You said: Go away and die!"

Porpentine put his hands behind his back. Of course. Had they been waiting for this, then? For fifteen years? He'd crossed some threshold without knowing. Mongrel now, no longer pure. He turned to watch Victoria move away, all tender and winsome for her Sphinx. Mongrel, he supposed, is only another way of saying human. After the final step you could not, nothing could be, clean. It was almost as if they'd tried for Goodfellow because he had stepped below the threshold that morning at the Gare du Caire. Now Porpentine had performed his own fatal act of love or charity by screaming at the Chief. And found out, shortly after, what he'd really screamed at. The two—act and betrayal—canceled out. Canceled to zero. Did they always? Oh God. He turned again to Moldweorp.

His Manon?

"You have been good enemies," he said at last. It sounded wrong to him. Perhaps if there had been more time, time to learn the new role. . . .

It was all they needed. Goodfellow heard the shot, turned in time to see Porpentine fall to the sand. He cried out; watched the three turn and move away. Perhaps they would walk straight out into the Libyan desert and keep walking till they reached the shore of some sea. Soon he turned to the girl, shaking his head. He took her hand and they went to find the phaeton. Sixteen years later, of course, he was in Sarajevo, loitering among crowds assembled to greet the Archduke Francis Ferdinand. Rumors of an assassination, a possible spark to apocalypse. He must be there to prevent it if he could. His body had become stooped and much of his hair had fallen out. From time to time he squeezed the hand of his latest conquest, a blonde barmaid with a mustache, who described him to her friends as a simple-minded Englishman, not much good in bed but liberal with his money.

649

Herbert Gold

Death in Miami Beach

T he state of madness can be defined partly as an extreme of isolation of one human being from everyone else. It provides a model for dying. Only an intermittent and fragmentary awareness of others interrupts the black folding of the layers of self upon each other—this also defines the state of that dilemma known as "mental health."

There is a false madness induced by the accidents of isolation which prisoners, travelers, and the very ill may sometimes experience without giving up their return ticket. Surely you out there all know what I mean from your own troubles and painful decisions. To say that it is false madness does not soften its extremity. The mask of existence fits harshly on your skin, but it is in fact your only skin; and when harshly your skin is peeled off—beneath it you are naked and your naked isolation is no joy to you.

During a period of work on a long job of writing in the winter of 1958, I deliberately withdrew myself from all those who knew my name and traveled by automobile in slow stages through the deep South to Miami Beach, Key West, Havana, and finally back up toward Detroit. No one asked me to write a novel, no one asked me to go away; but I did anyway. I was tempted by the prospect of dreaming through my story amid a pleasant chaos of sun and sea, all other responsibilities suspended, and so I arranged it for myself.

Work is very fine, but after the day's work, isolation, silence, and death seemed to follow me through the zazzy carnival of Miami, the casual resort indolence of Key West, and the smoky, blistered elegance of a tourist's Havana. In Havana, from the rooftop of the Ambos Mundos Hotel, I could see Batista's police loafing with their weapons in front of public buildings; occasionally there were bombs; once a body happened to be left in the street and people hurried by as if they knew nothing, nothing, nothing at all but the next step before them.

At Key West, a few days before Christmas, I visited the turtle slaughter-house. It is one of the few tourist attractions on this spot of island, "North Havana," raised far out into the sea off the coast of Florida. Visitors take their kiddies by the hand and lead them to see the nice turtles.

Before being killed and canned, the turtles swim in dense kraals, bumping each other in the murky water, armor clashing, dully lurching against the high pens. Later, trussed on a plank dock, they lie unblinking in the sun, their flippers pierced and tied. The tough leather of their skin does not disguise their present helplessness and pain. They wear thick, sun-hardened accumulations of blood at their wounds. Barbados turtles, as large as children, they belong to a species which has been eliminated locally by ardent harvesting of the waters near Key West, but the commercial tradition still brings them here to be slaughtered. Crucified like thieves, they breathe in little sighs, they gulp, they wait.

At a further stage, in the room where the actual slaughtering occurs, the butchers stride through gore in heavy boots. The visitor must proceed on a catwalk; a misstep will plunge him into a slow river of entrails and blood. Because it was near Christmastime, the owners of the plant had installed a speaker system for musical divertissement of the butchers, and while the turtles dried under the sun or lay exposed to the butchers' knives, Christmas bells tolled out, electronically amplified, "God Rest Ye Merry, Gentlemen," or the Bing Crosby recording of "*Adeste Fideles.*"

These commercial details are not intended to support a special plea on behalf of the humane harvesting of Barbados turtles. In fact, let me grant that I sought out this scene and visited the abattoir without having any proper business there at all: merely curiosity and the need to confirm my imagination about it. I should be judged for vulgarity by the man who chooses out of purity not to follow me, not by the man I saw lurking outside, with a face ravaged by the horrified fascination which makes it impossible for him to visit his dreams. What had I done which he could not permit himself? Was I filthied, was I weakened by pleasure but obscurely nourished, was I fed on coveted turtle joys after trampling in turtle blood? Had I asked permission from the butcher and plied a knife with my own hands on the belly of one of the slow, unblinking, dragon-headed, ancient sea-beasts? And did it arch its graceful dragon neck in reproach as I stabbed? He stared at me like a jealous lover, imagining my wickedness, rabid and hopeless, wanting to bury his head in the reek on my hands.

Most of us turn from the vision of death only out of weakness, and this is no turning from death. Serve up your turtle steak, gourmet friend, with no protest from me; I'll eat at your table. ("A nice rendition," one gentleman said of Bing Crosby to his wife. Turtle is tasty, somewhat gamy meat. Protein nourishes the brain—brings oxygen and freedom.)

A few days later, in Miami Beach, I participated in two trivial accidents. My hotel was in one of the oldest, therefore least expensive, parts of the town, only a short block from the sea and a short block from restaurants and therefore very convenient to my casual schedule: breakfast at Whelan's, a stretch of writing, a long swim, lunch, a pleasant bit of loafing on the beach, then perhaps some sunbaked work at my typewriter on the tar roof ("solarium"), and another swim before dinner. I had the habit in the morning of disregarding the elevator, hurrying down a back stairway of the Webster Hotel, through an alley, and so shortcutting to the drugstore. One day, wearing tennis shoes, I felt an evil slide and crunch underfoot, and knew first by the shrinking in my heart and then by simple inspection that I had stepped on a small animal.

653

It seemed to be a variety of tropical cockroach. It had been perhaps an inch and a half long, longer with its wings spread, and it had strayed from the raised platform nearby where the hotel stored its rubbish. Now it lay twitching, legs scrambling in the air without moving, and a yellow ooze seeped from its body within the crushed carapace. I suppose it was already dead despite all this nervous movement. I went for a walk, told myself that this was a silly matter to be fretful about (I was merely isolated), and finally took my habitual breakfast: orange juice, scrambled eggs, toast, coffee.

An hour later the dead beast was glued by its own innards to the paving of the alley; the Florida sun was moving through the sky above it. But now there was also a row of ants leading to it, another leading away, like twin caterpillars dissembling their unity of purpose. They were not merely eating, of course, they were carrying off the meat to their hill someplace. But the dead roach still twitched, and when the tickling jaws struck, it fluttered, squeezed, blindly pushed in its place. The ants went scrambling away, each carrying its minuscule steak.

All afternoon the shell of the roach lay there. Its row of legs no longer waved of their own power, but there were still tremors as the eating ants tugged at it. Unfatigued and busy, they were determined to wipe this slate clean.

Shortly before dark I again came down the back stairway. Now the familiar arena had changed. Another foot had struck, more strange and haphazard than my own. The shell of the roach was destroyed; there were also dead ants freckling the stone; stillness and death. The ants were suddenly individual in death; the undulating columns were erased. And the work of eating was permanently interrupted for both eaters and eaten.

The next morning when I walked through the alley no sign remained. A sweeper had done her work; there were straight, mechanical striations— a friendly broom. Good. But I bent to look for some sign or memorial to the departed beast on this stretch of alley which I now knew very well. There was none. Marks of broom; new arrangements of pebbles and dust; history here had entered upon an epoch which was strange to me.

Then finally a homely death entered what might pass for society in my isolated Miami Beach—the world of the soda fountain at Whelan's, where strollers came into an air-conditioned place to shake off the sand of the beach, sip a Coke, buy lotions and plastic sunglasses, and sometimes order a quick meal.

I was taking my breakfast, according to my habit, on a stool at the counter. By this time I was acquainted with Frank, the short-order cook, who had emigrated from Second Avenue in New York twenty years ago for his health and, for sweet health's sake, still managed to cover the leathery pouched skin of age with a fierce Miami tan, despite his long hours in Whelan's service. It relieved the silence to exchange a few morning words with a man who by now knew my face: "Two scrambled light."

"Same as yesterday, Mister."

"Yes, like yesterday." (Triumph in my voice: He remembers me!) "Whole-wheat toast. You got marmalade today?"

"Marmalade." Frank knew my face and my eggs.

Other eaters, like me, were forking up eggs and grits and sipping their

Cokes or coffee when the woman entered. She was blotched with sunburn, had a swollen nose, and a mouth open so wide for noise that all her features were distorted. Emitting emergency alarm signals, turning her head and staring, demanding passage, demanding attention, a shouting vehicle, she pushed a stumbling old man along with her. "Ohh," she screamed, "a Bromo! For God's sake a Bromo! My husband is dying, a Bromo, for God's sake!"

The man's face was blue and he seemed barely conscious. He swayed stiffly as she steered him toward a stool near me.

"Oh, a Bromo right now, please!" she wailed.

Frank, behind the counter, looked sideways at her, pretended the impossible—that he did not hear her—and went on making a bacon-lettuce-and-tomato sandwich on whole-wheat toast, light on the mayonnaise.

Two or three of us jumped up to support the old man. His skin had a thick purple glow that said death to all our eyes.

"Oh, have mercy, a Bromo for my poor husband!" the woman screamed. "He didn't do nothing to you! For God's sake why don't you give it to him?"

Floundering, I watched Frank finish the bee-ell-tee, slide it onto a plate, and hand it to his customer. The hotrodder bent his head to the spilling sandwich and ate as if his life depended on it, thrustingly. In the meantime, the pharmacist, a short man in a white coat, sweating profusely despite the air conditioning, came bustling from his cubicle and said, "Heart attack? You want I should call a doctor, Missus?"

"Ohh, please, dear God, a Bromo!" she shouted.

"I'll call a doctor, he'll be right over."

"Bromo for a dying man! Why don't you give it to him? Mercy, mercy!"

The pharmacist was on the telephone and the howling woman subsided in shrill spasms. Her husband swayed on the stool, his eyes shut, while his wife leaned sobbing against his back to keep him from toppling onto the ground. She refused to let anyone touch him in order to lay him out on the floor—someone's idea—as if this ministry would commit him once and for all to the hands of death. Naturally, my innards shrank from this; the layers of the self closed tight; the flower of feeling was shut, sealed. I wanted to rush in some place, rush away; strike, destroy, *run*; kill Frank, kill the hotrodder, because a man was dying and nobody could do anything. Thus righteousness substitutes for being straight with the world. I was sly and scared. Thus I occupied myself with rage at my friend Frank, who pretended to hear nothing and stubbornly refused to make the glass of Bromo Seltzer.

During the five minutes before the doctor arrived, the scene altered rapidly and tensely. Of course, all the breakfasters but the determined hotrodder stopped their eating. The kid in the leather jacket asked for pretzels with his Coke for sustained strength behind the wheel. The rest of us drifted, lurking behind the sick man on his stool. His wife wept and cursed and heaved out her sobs because no one would supply a Bromo.

Then abruptly the man shook himself and opened his eyes and tried to stand up. He stumbled; his wife pushed him back onto the stool. He shook his head and mumbled. Then rapidly the purple color diminished; his eyes stopped their blind rolling; he began to talk with his wife. He was returning to the living. He and his wife had a whispered consultation. She nodded rapidly at him, like a bird.

Suddenly she alighted and flew out the door. The man, left behind on the stool, said hoarsely, "Lemme have a glass of water, will you, pal?"

Frank gave him the water.

Now the doctor entered, rolling his sleeves down and carrying his black bag open. He had apparently run a block in the tropical morning heat.

"Haha!" said the formerly dying man. Just like that: "Hahaha! Hi, Doc!"

"You're the sick man?" said the doctor. "Let's see now—"

"Hahaha! Don't touch me, Doc," said the old man, leaning away. "Listen, Doc, it's a funny thing. My wife gets herself all excited—aggravated."

"You mean you're all right?" the doctor said.

"Just like a little attack was all I had, hahaha," said the old man.

"You're okay?"

"Look, Doc, I ain't been eating right, you know, enjoying myself, hahaha. A little attack. I get them sometimes. Like a little attack is all."

"Okay," said the doctor firmly, "you don't want me to look at you? Okay." He nodded briskly to the pharmacist, said, "I've got a patient in my office," and trotted off again into the heat.

The old man smiled and gazed without malice at Frank, who had refused him the Bromo. Instead of leaving a tip he left him one word of explanation before he headed off after his wife. The word was deposited on the counter behind him with an apologetic smile: "Constipation."

Eggs in the plates of all the late breakfasters were left cold and shiny.

The hotrodder alone had finished his sandwich, Coke, and pretzels, and left whistling. Angry at last, I discharged an unformulated hostility on Frank: "Why the devil didn't you give the man his Bromo?"

His reply seems an obvious bit of logical disquisition at this remove, but there in the shadow of panic and crisis it struck me with the force of revelation. Rubbing a dirty cloth on the counter—formulating and reformulating a smear of grease before me—he said, "If he was dying of a heart attack, what good would a Bromo do him? And if he was not dying, what good is a Bromo?"

"Yes, but."

"So I have to do my job, but I don't have to listen to nuts."

"But you didn't say anything! That woman was hysterical."

He looked at me with undisguised pity for my ignorance. "That's why I didn't say anything. I been in trouble for saying things before, I learned."

He went back to work; the pharmacist was back in his cubicle, counting pills into a bottle; the doctor had returned to his office. It was eleven o'clock and Frank took down the sign about the breakfast special. A man came in frightened to ask for the special, and Frank pointed to the sign, which was upside down on the counter, and said, "It's five minutes after eleven already. But I'll give it to you." The look of despair faded from the man's face.

657

In a few days I finished my own job and began the long drive out of the false Florida summer into the northern winter, my wheels passing over all sorts of unfelt beasties, my gullet accepting steaks and chops, my heart leaping with no better welcome to death than before. In Detroit my daughter asked me, "What's God's last name? How big is the whole world? Where do you go when you die?"

The foregoing inconclusive words were written two years ago. Now I have seen fit to return to my cafeteria-and-old-folks slum on lower Collins Avenue, and ostensibly for the same lure of cheap sun, sky, water, beach, boredom. I write, I swim, I stroll on Lincoln Road, I eat steaks and pizza, I sniff the sea with my sunburnt beak, I suck in my belly and run barefoot on the sand, I sleep, I write. In front of one of the new hotels I found a nude in plaster, beckoning, with her hand lifted as if hitching a ride. All aboard, you masturbators. Some of the fruit juice and hamburger stands have disappeared; new ones have opened. The Ellis Department Store, Here Since 1919, is closed, looks ransacked, has a box of Fruit of the Loom T-shirts spilled in the window and a US Federal Court bankruptcy notice affixed to its sealed door.

I met a waitress in a restaurant which advertises nine-course dollar dinners. She has a pretty, lively, thirty-five-year-old girl's face, with all the black brightness of eye a man could want; she turns out to be Corsican and we speak French; an artillery sergeant brought her to Florida and apparently tired of her brightness of eye. She has a rattling Corsican accent, likes Edith Piaf records, and gives me extra shrimp bits in my shrimp bits salad. So some things change. Last time I heard no Edith Piaf and earned no extra forkfuls of shrimp. The sirloin steak she brings me spreads its wings and seems ready to flop off the plate. My gut talks French and I take ease in the flattery of food. I wait and at last she slips into my booth with me and sighs. It is eleven o'clock, time to begin real life. Her history is sad. I feel obliged to offer some recompense for the evil done her by men and luck, and so I listen, wondering how her eyes can remain so bright as the disasters and disillusionments unroll.

When I said good night, she replied with a funny, rapidly fiddling, diddling, twenty-one-fingered gesture at her mouth. I asked what it meant.

"Fun and glee!" she said, "fun and glee! *Maintenant je suis une vraie Americaine.*" Her eyes burn like stars, but like the stars, she has darkness between them.

A day and a night and another day. The first week passes.

I eat salty bagels in the sun, I listen to the teenage girls after school with their curious mixture of Florida cracker and Bronx accents, I go back into the damp of my room—the peculiar dank assault of cheap tropical bedrooms—and think my novel through once again, examining the pile of manuscript with my intentions in motion like a column of ants working over the struggling body of an insect. And when the life seems to weaken, I leave it and go out onto the beach or into the street.

Madness consists partly in an extreme of isolation? Partly. But the demented tumble down from their associations and memories into other associations and memories; they are sent away into the future with a map of the past which conforms to no agreed past and to no other map—and yet it is their only chart, their history and route, their needs which are unfailingly present. The lonely traveler also brutally inflicts absolute possession of his movements upon the endless day, and the novelty of what he sees joins him in yet another way to his deepest desires and dreads. He returns, he never lets go. There is no escape even in isolation; there is no isolation, merely interrupted and distorted association, until death claims us. Then every man is an island entire of itself.

In love, we seek freedom and purity even more than the comfort of diminished isolation. Those few fortunate ones who have the talent can bear the paradox of love. The rest of us are harassed by our contradictory demands—*join me, make me free*. With age and aging, the model of all voyages (learn and grow, diminish and become weary), comes final approach to the ultimate simplicity which love seeks to confound—death. A paradox forever out of balance to answer a grave black simplicity: *we are ill used*. The facts we make for ourselves disappoint the intentions with which we make them. The opposable thumb, which is said to be responsible for civilization and history, gives us no answers here, though with it we can grasp our pens and break insects in our hands. Finally we die, opposable thumbs and all.

In the meantime, I visit my story. We exchange visits. I laugh over it, frown and worry over it, and urge it forward. Then I leave it for the Miami streets. The book follows me; it does not let me visit unaccompanied; it enters me instead and I try to shake it off as an adept at voodoo fights against possession by the importunate god. The opposable thumb is of no use in this contest; both the prize and the weapons have reached beyond tools, even tools of thinking; I am the quadruple god's horse—dream of love, hope of meaning, joy of power, relish in being. Too much burden on one soul. Who asked me to feel sorry or glad for others? They were merely pious who asked me. Why follow their orders? I decide: *I won't*. But I cannot escape my self, which also gives orders. The flower of feeling opens; the flower shuts; it obeys the freshness of weather. All emotion flowing from health or illness partakes of the pathetic fallacy, identifying moral value with the gifts of nature. My feet want to run; I am wearing Keds, and feel light on the foam rubber soles; but the heat of the sun holds me to earth.

There is a hotel on Washington Boulevard which specializes in "economical, comfortable living for the retired." It is a huge dark building like the Women's House of Detention in Greenwich Village, but without the bars on the rooms, and there are purple lights playing on the palm trees outside, soft music piped throughout the grounds, and the frequent blare of a loudspeaker: "Missus Goldberg to the telephone! Missus Goldberg! *Sadie, answer the phone!*" when the children call from New York. The streets of the neighborhood are filled with chattering or mournful elder statesmen, mostly losers after sixty years of continual negotiation, men with chagrined pouches slipping sideways beneath their eyes, women with hair bursting onto their cheeks and upper lips, as if all at once, near the end, they have decided to make a final try at being better men than their husbands.

To walk through the crowd during the hour following their afternoon naps is to wade in senility. There is a deep sea lack of light despite all the sun and brisk resort clatter; you gasp for life and run to look in a dusty window. Narcissus wants to be just thirty-five, "*nel mezzo del cammin di nostra vita*," and not seventy, not seventy! The crowd flutters by. "She thought she could be my daughter-in-law! A girl like that! To be my daughter-in-law! And you know what? Now she is." "I used to be in business. I had a good business. It was a nice store, good location. Furniture. I should have kept my location." "What does the weather report say? Does the weather report ever say anything but the weather?" "Moishe died. He had an attack. Well, we all got to go."

Is it the same voice, the same rhythm? It is the same crowd—grief, isolation, death. There almost always seems to be an ambulance pulling up or pulling away.

It is fine to tell a story, which feels like affirmation, but afterwards, after the morning's writing, then what? Writing is an expression of affirmation, power, longing, but not a proper cause of these emotions in the writer. He is a guide into delight and dread because he can escape victimization (he thinks); he has left a little trail of paper behind him as he threads his way into the maze, and can find his way back (he believes—though the roar of the maze sets up a disarray in anything as fragmentary as his intentions about return). He tracks the minotaur with an open mind. "Maybe I'll like it," he says, "and maybe I won't. At least I'll see." He initiates passion only because he has it—otherwise self-delusion and covetous self-therapy. And so it is not good to be alone for long, entirely alone.

But at least for a time, until they dim out, loneliness sharpens the eyes. I feel like a safecracker; loneliness has also sharpened my fingertips, and my entire body throughout feels the clicking tumblers as I yearn toward the combination. I come to focus, I work. But afterwards, then what? I have retreated from the distractions of Manhattan. There are no telephone calls. No friendship, no duties, no hazards of pique or pleasure. I shall work till the battery runs down, frozen and stilled by this busy emptiness under the sun. I ask myself: Can the silent column of ants reconstruct the living roach at its leisure underground? No, only a tree can make a tree, only a winged roach can make a winged roach. A column of ants works by an invisible will which resides in no one of its jointed parts, but only a swollen green ant can breed an urgent ant.

As I walk on Lincoln Road, the smart shopping area of "the Beach," I ogle the oglers, the sunburned sun-worshippers basted with oil, cream, tonic, and lotion—the touts, boxers, fairies, grandmothers, exiled Cubans, local hotrodders and their gumchewing molls, sportsmen, natty invalids in gabardine, drunks, stockbrokers, antique collectors, Semites and anti-Semites all taking the air together on Lincoln Road. Hill people, swamp people, and ex-pugs sell newspapers flown in from all over—New York, Chicago, Los Angeles ("Smogsville!" cackles a refugee). And New York is harried by flu and Chicago is black with coal and damp. And here we all are on Lincoln Road, with a delicious breeze, courtesy of the steakhouse pumping cool air into the street. So let's buy the hometown paper to see how miserable we might have been, for others are.

On Lincoln Road, fair Lincoln Road in Miami Beach, the Negroes have been freed; freed of existence, that is; only a few black ghosts slip discreetly by. Even if they were not so discreet, they would be invisible, though for a new reason: they are going some place, namely, to work, or at another hour, home. For them, Lincoln Road is a mere artery for transit, while for the others, Lincoln Road is parlor, sunroom, promontory into health and beauty. For the visitors, Lincoln Road is a slow matter, a recipe for yearned-for slowness, sloth, strolling ease, delicacy of control. The cocky Broadway chapparoonies are wearing their new pleatless "Miami-Tailored Daks." Their bellies do the work of belts, hiding the place where belts would be. Now I'm so slow I don't need a belt, the pants proudly announce; I'm just walkin' along, just struttin' down the avenue, just here and pleasant with myself, and when I take a breath, the expandable elastic waistband expands with me. In the men's room of a bar off Lincoln Road, hung with photographs of wrestlers, there is a curious vending machine which is decorated with a crown and raised scepter and submits a product called DE-LA: "Say Delay, a light lubricating ointment designed to aid in the prevention of premature climax. Odorless. Safe. Stainless. Easy to apply. Directions on package. 50¢ coins only. Machine does not give change."

Machine makes comment, however. Machine is trying to tell us something.

661

The Negro girl who cleans my room gets yelled at, screamed at all morning. "Stupid, stupid, stupid! A single room only gets two towels, one face, one bath!" She smiles slyly to herself as if she knows where the manager's DE-LA is hidden. This is the southland, I am reminded, where we have grits for breakfast. But it is not quite dat ole Dixie, boss, which changeth not, nor can age alter it. It is Miami Beach. The Sholem Aleichem Literary Society ("Managed by Tourists—Managed for Tourists") has a For Rent sign on it. "Owner Will Remodel for Any Business."

I decide as I walk: I'll write my book till the battery runs down, though distraction seems necessary; other duties, friends, "real life."

The sirens of the police ambulances work up and down the Beach all day and night, announcing the news as they carry away the attacked, the fallen, the stroked, the perished. A population of the aged sheds its members at the merest trifle of an excuse—a bottle of cold pop in the sun, a skipped nap, somebody raising his voice suddenly—or no excuse at all. It touches life and someone dies. It treads carelessly and someone dies. The sirens whir and howl and Negroes courteously open the back door for the corpse. For some reason people smile at the ambulance as they stroll, sucking ice cream. Perhaps they dream of an accident, a distraction: *Siren meets white Thunderbird, boy of forty cut off in his prime, had a girl in there with him, not his wife.* Perhaps thinking: *Not me this time.*

One of those impossible coincidences. Today I met Dr. Meyer leading his blind wife. He was our family doctor in Cleveland, addicted to practical jokes, who always said he wanted to do research, and in fact he had some sort of connection with one of the important drug laboratories. When he retired from practice, he announced to my parents over a bottle of wine that now he would begin his true life's work. I had decided that his practical jokes, bought in Jean's Fun House on East 9th Street—buzzers, false flies, stomach noises, leaky cups—were a symptom of childish anger at adult responsibility. But now that he could retire from practice and try his hand at research . . . It turned out that his wife had inoperable cataracts; she went blind fast, and he went sour, quiet, mean; and they left Cleveland for Miami Beach, where I saw him leading her, walking with the stiff, frightened step of the unaccustomed blind. He is shrunken; only today do I notice that he is a small man—when I was a boy, he was immense. At present, and forever until the very end, his life's work is to steer his wife to the beach in the morning and sit with her to describe what he sees. He has replaced both practical jokes and dreams of a laboratory with loyalty to his wife, but virtue has made him a furious runt.

Fantasies of thighs, breasts, bellies as I nap on the beach. I awaken, sticky with salt. My nose is peeling. Shall I visit the Corsican waitress again tonight? Shall I ask the Meyers to dinner? But I have made this disappearance into Miami Beach in order to avoid the troubles of others and of myself. I swim again. I doze again. I dream of sex with a woman I overhead describing the proper way to kill a chicken "so it don't suffer. You ask anyone, they'll tell you. And there's nothing like fresh-killed chicken. You can't trust the butchers."

A man in the coffee shop later said to the cashier: "I been sick, that's why you ain't seen me. Doctor said coronary thrombosis. You ever heard of that?"

"Naw. Lots of people got coronaries, but that thrombosis, that's a new thing. The docs keep finding new things so they can charge us."

"Well, I'll tell you, it left me feeling pretty weak."

I went one night to see a road company version of *My Fair Lady* at the Miami Beach Auditorium, which more frequently provides hospitality for wrestling or boxing matches. A maggoty, bored imitation of Rex Harrison, a thick Eliza without any bounce. The audience is quietly taking in the famous sight. They write on their postcards home: Tonight we saw a Broadway show, but the girl was fat.

Crazy Louie on the beach—a frantic grandfather with Latin records, maracas, castanets, silk Cuban shirts, feathers, straw skirt, rubber Halloween masks, a huge earring loosely hooked to his ear by a bent hairpin, thick glasses sliding down his nose, leathery withered legs, dancing and dancing, all sinews and grins and shakes to some inner song while the portable phonograph goes rattle-and-scrape, screech, rattle, and scrape. Amazingly, the crowd which regularly gathers on the sand nearby seems to enjoy his music; some of them shake, too, dreaming of the days when they had lust to squander on their legs. Dr. Meyer's wife smiles as he describes the scene. "Are you smiling, Meyer?" she asks. He says yes, but is lying. Crazy Louie bangs his castanet under her nose and screams "*Olé!*" and she jumps. At last Dr. Meyer smiles.

Then he tells her that sometimes the beginnings of arteriosclerosis can be detected at age twenty-five. "Cuts off the blood supply to the brain. The psychiatrists think they're smart, but they can't do anything about the histological system. The brain dries up like a scab."

"Meyer, you shouldn't use such language."

"You mean histology?"

"I mean scab, Meyer."

Crazy Louie is dancing and cackling, kicking sand. The old ladies in their bathing skirts fan themselves contentedly as he enters his Afro-Cuban apocalypse. On the beach there is a rural, village tolerance of madness. Louie doesn't do any harm. His children sent him down. He is new since my last visit.

And where are my old friends?

The cockroach in the alley is long gone, of course, and its grandchildren unto many generations. But I have found cheap sun again for my sinus, and white ocean breaking against the distractions of Manhattan in winter, spring, summer, fall. I think of a friend, a Jewish chauvinist, arguing with his girl: "When your people were still living in trees and hitting each other with sticks, my people already had sinus trouble."

The Spinoza Forum is gone, replaced by a motel. Dr. Wolfson still goes to the beach every afternoon. But the neighborhood is changed. He has nothing to say to me except that raw beets, honey, and tangerines keep a man virtuous and healthy, no matter what his age.

The woman who knew Thomas Wolfe—did I forget to mention that last time?—and swam as if she wanted to die, and worked as a B-girl . . . gone. She wanted to reconstruct some cabin-in-the-woods dream of perfection, but she could never find the missing pieces. Life is not a jigsaw puzzle; once it has been scrambled, the old picture is gone.

The racing-car driver with whom I chatted a couple of times at breakfast—gone.

The column of ants at the cockroach—gone.

The drummed-up acquaintances—even their names forgotten.

The hotel clerk who wanted to explore in Guatemala—perhaps he is exploring in Guatemala. The new manager of the hotel has never even heard of him.

And the man who died—dead.

I know this for certain, for I have finally discovered an old friend. Frank, the gray bozo behind the counter at Whelan's, is still there. I had taken up new eating habits and did not return to Whelan's during my first week in Miami Beach, but then I did and found him, still building hamburger platters and scrambling eggs. At first he did not remember me. He never knew my name. When I reminded him of the incident about the man who died, and of our long breakfast friendship, a look of irritation captured his face—demands were being made on him—but then his cross mug creased into a smile. He did remember me! He only needed to be reminded!

"You know that old fool," he said. "Later really did die. He's dead. Later died."

There was a new cat in the store. A new special on toothbrushes. A new pharmacist.

I had a hamburger on our old friendship, and Frank put an extra slice of tomato on the side to *prove* that he remembered me. But why should he? He had been an experience for me—the same now, with balder eyebrows— but what was I to him? For me he existed as an example of something, a moment of frightening history, a troubled memory which I had set down in words. I had needed a friend then, but he did not. I was frightened by death then, and worse, by a way of receiving death, but he was not and perhaps never admits that he might be.

Why does he stay in Miami Beach ?

Yes, for a job. Yes, for the sun. But why there?

All right, then why not there?

Why do I go back?

Why did I go back? What happened to those dead and dying ones? They died and were dead; they were swept away. I thought, the first time I went to Miami Beach, that I had made a free choice to be isolated, but I discovered that everyone comes to the state of isolation in time—though not freely. What I did out of apparent health and youth, in the pleasure of work, those others did in sickness and age, in the anxiety of boredom. But eventually work is done, health turns to decay, youth turns to ripeness turns to age; feebleness and dying must precede death except for fighter pilots, who are anachronisms. Miami Beach is an extension, adult education course in how to die, pursued with great seriousness by the enrollees. The old folks work at it with deliberate and modest intensity, in group sessions, complimenting each other on their tans, their sport shirts, their postgraduate skill at finding a proper weather. The young vacationers flush in on packaged tours, immerse themselves in the ceremonial indulgences of resort hotels, eat, swim, and enjoy their honeymoon wrestling, take in Eartha Kitt or Leo de Lion, sigh with boredom and excess, buy bottles of Man Tan at the air terminal ("Arrive With Fresh Sun On Your Cheeks!"), and flee back to real life with a secret conviction that this is leisure? Strictly for the birds, brother.

That first time in Miami Beach, I was a curious observer, obscurely moved, with the face of a man who fearfully unwinds a rope as he visits his dream of the turtle slaughterhouse. The second time (the last time!), two years' change had begun to discover my implication to me; I broke the rope; the model of death is real; the dream of dying is real. The tanned, reduced, heliotropic Doctor Meyer recognized me despite his wife's blindness ("Hannah! Look who's here!"), and when I spoke to her, she gropingly embraced me. This was why I went back—to feel Mrs. Meyer's arms hotly convulsed about my neck, as if I were still a boy in Cleveland, and to know that I was not. I was not a young man from Cleveland visiting Miami Beach as he had toured carnivals, the war, the Caribbean, Europe, and taken the boat ride around Manhattan. I was a winter visitor, tired of town, come for the sun, who had been there before.

Am I now satisfied with what I found? Which is: "Later really did die. Later died." Just as in the alley two years ago, in that swept space where there was no longer any roach and no column of ants, history enters upon new epochs which begin to grow familiar to me.

G. V. Desani

Mephisto's Daughter

Being an old sinner, one of the worst living in this part of Western India, I have access to a member of Mephisto's family. My first meeting with the Old Ugly's daughter happened when I was seventeen. She tempted me with the latest super-duper watch, Swiss-modeled, 1,000-jewel—all proof and break-proof. It was made from the metal cooked in the Furnaces, and hammering it for two hours didn't hurt it. It didn't even scratch the crystal. That was years ago, and I was told never to speak to girls.

Her father, Master Mephisto, lives in a sticky honeycomb, the size of the Taj Mahal, with his arms and legs permanently stretched to the four corners of the honeycomb. His daughter—that is, my friend—lives not far from him, also inside the honeycomb, and she calls him *Abba Huzoor*. There are burning hills and valleys fuming about—no stokers are needed to stir up these flames, ha! ha!—and there Mephisto suffers mightily. He has smothering in him flames of overwhelming desire, the urge for domination—undreamt of by a politician or a man of commerce. He wants to conquer *all* mankind and, of course, he has no patience. His daughter suffers likewise. She lives in terror of her father. She observes no proprieties, and lives in the honeycomb quite nude, and Mephisto sends her out on seducing errands, and she obeys him instantly, "I go, *Abba Huzoor!*"

Not long ago I had a reason to make the secret *zero-plus-zero* sign—it was given to me by my friend—and I called forth Mephisto himself. I addressed him, quite appropriately, "Your dirty, filthy, censored, mother, father, asterisking, unprintability . . . !" (the correct form, Mephisto loves it) and although I was not permitted full materialization, an indescribably fetid odor rose from an unused teapot, and it revealed that—being a friend of the girl—I would be allowed, as a special favor, to attend a *Tablet*. (This is an esoteric term for the graduating ceremony of the Devil's disciples, and it often concludes with a convocation address.) I could, alternatively, the fetid odor revealed, have the girl—such are the privileges enjoyed by those who know the secret sign—but I preferred the first offer, there being no time or place for entertaining her.

So I attended a *Tablet*.

Hereabouts, in the Western Ghats, I was waylaid by the omens to a banyan tree, and found a party of peasants sitting under it, all wearing turbans, and in the center was the largest figure of them all, about twice the size of an average peasant, and wearing a red turban—but for the size, exactly the kind worn by railway porters—and facing him was a singer.

His voice was like the cracking of drying ceramics, in a very high key, of course, and he had a single-cord instrument from which he produced a screaming sound, not unlike a combination of chronic catarrh and a dog whistle. He was improvising the phrase *A'pavitro, o! o! o!*—the bol, in all keys, up, down; high, low. As he concluded with the *o! o! o!* an unseen drummer joined him. (The phrase means more or less *Un'clean, o! o! o!* or a better translation might be *Im'purity, ee! ee! ee!*) He seemed to have enchanted the company with his song, and they applauded him solemnly with *Vah! Vah! Vah!*

It appears that I got to the meeting rather late. The proceedings were almost over when I arrived, the *Im'purity, ee! ee! ee!* was obviously the conclusion. Still, I was lucky enough to hear the big fellow speak. He said, "*Im'purity, ee! ee! ee!* Brethren, all is *One*. All is *Self*. All else is *Illusion*. Contentment is the greatest Good. I *know*. I can *judge*. That is *Truth*. All propositions are *right*. All answers *correct*. What thy right hand finds, that *do*. Self is *real*. All else is *unreal*." They applauded him with *Vah! Vah! Vah!*

Then they all got up, loosened their *dhotis*—the fiendish ritual—and there it was, for anyone to see, the little stump of a tail at the backside of each—the sort of podgy things some bulldogs sport—the mark of Mephisto's offense, and it goes without saying that only his favorite disciples may have this tail, after they have duly become *Un'clean, o!* with the needed *Im'purity, ee!*

I got rather bored with all that *Tablet*, and the speech. I recognized what the fellow said was mystic talk, and since I knew it almost by heart—it is common property—I came home.

The same evening, as I happened to be having tea in the kitchen, something reminded me of Mephisto—actually, it was a photograph of my father. I made the *zero-plus-zero* sign, sang out *A'pavitro, o! o! o!* and followed it up with *Vah! Vah! Vah!* And soon there was a materialization. Next to the kitchen table, where the breadboard is kept, stood my friend, Mephisto's daughter—who never wears any clothes, at any time of the day or night—and after taking in the entire detail of her at a glance, I put it all to her. Now, what did the Devil's disciple mean by all that mystic talk!

She spoke fast, and was out of breath. She said, "Man dear, *Abba Huzoor* is sly. He has told us to make folk happy . . ."

"Half a minute," I interrupted her, buttering a slice of bread. "Did you say happy?"

She nodded, and declined the kitchen cloth I offered her as part covering. "Man dear," she repeated, "*Abba* wants folk to be happy."

Then it flashed on me in a single instant, as it flashes on the mystics and the like. "Daddy, His Honor," I said to her, "wants folk to be happy, yes? So that they would be content, no? So that they would do nothing to attain the Enemy, eh? They would be immobilized, yes? The Sly One wants folk to be *happy*, *content*, and *immobilized*, yes? They would be paralyzed, no?"

She nodded yes.

Greatly encouraged, I went on enlightening her on her *Abba*. "His Honor has a passion, no? He is troubled by doubt, yes? He wants to conquer all mankind, but the doubt, that *one* of them might go over to the Enemy, agonizes him, no? The impossibility of complete, absolute conquest becomes more vivid day by day, eh? And another thing . . ."

I was interrupted. My friend was down on her knees, prostrate, shaking from terror. Convulsively, she was sobbing, *"Abba Huzoor! Abba Huzoor!"*

"What have I been saying!" I said, frantically moving about my arms and legs to extricate myself—right, I was caught in the honeycomb, the size of the Taj Mahal—as I realized that it was the Sly One speaking through me.

A full materialization indeed.

My father was right. It is wrong to speak to girls. No good can come of it.

Louis Guilloux

Palante

Georges Palante shot himself through the right temple on the fifth of August, 1925. This tragic break with a world in which he had known nothing but suffering seemed to demand that we remain silent. We knew Palante well enough to know the reason for his suicide. But he could not prevent two things outliving him, besides his work: the meaning of his own life and our loyal friendship.

What to some would have seemed a pressing reason to speak was, at first, an obstacle to me. Whoever knew Palante knew to what extent his friendships were "secret." To speak of such a friend, in some ways so strange, is at all times to risk wounding or betraying him.

He despised idle noise and lived in a solitude which he had succeeded, at the end, in making total. At the time of his death we had not seen each other for three years.

Besides, how can one speak of Palante without coming on the scene oneself? He played such a role in my life, my meeting him was for me such a considerable event, and I have for so long borne his mark, that when I think back to those years in which we were intimately bound to each other, I can no longer imagine myself as distinct from him.

These memories, then, take on an intimate character. They are not only my memories of Georges Palante, but also my memories of myself, of the young man I was between 1917 and 1922. And I wonder just how much they could interest people other than myself, save friends of Georges Palante or my own friends.

II

My earliest memory of Georges Palante dates back to my childhood. I was around six or eight when, one morning, it happened that my mother and I passed by the fence of the lycée where he taught philosophy. Palante was walking along that fence: his body, already heavy, weighed on his legs, which were too long and buckled under him at every step; he held his tiny head tilted lightly backward. He carried a portfolio and a cane under his arm. It was about ten o'clock in the morning. I see him very clearly. It was not until I became a lycée student myself, upon finishing the "*quatrième*," that I learned that he was "a great philosopher."

I owed this revelation to Mme X., whom I often visited in the company of my sisters. Her husband knew Palante, and owned some of his works, among which I discovered *The Individualist Sensibility*.

I soon learned that he was famous. The people I asked about him said that he was wasted on a town as small and as narrow-minded as ours. All professed a great respect for his intelligence and his "learning," and much compassion for his deformity. Nevertheless, behind the praise and the pity, I detected something being held back that I did not come to understand until later: my little town has more than one side to it.

When I entered the "*troisième*," I became a student of Palante's. He was obliged to give a course in moral philosophy to this class, and it caused him much suffering. He was defenseless against the unceasing cruelty of children who made fun of his overlong hands and feet. He suffered a thousand unnecessary harassments from what he called the *volaille*. But he never made so much as a move to get rid of this course, whose utter uselessness he was not alone in deploring.

One afternoon, about this time, I met him at Mme X.'s. But our real relationship did not begin until a year and a half later, in May or June, towards the end of the 1916–17 school year. It began one evening when he found me in the school yard reading the last volume of *Jean-Christophe*. He himself had just come across the novel, and had not yet read *The End of the Journey*, which I had in my hands. He was very impatient to read it, and I lent it to him.

My reading was then centered around Romain Rolland's *Jean-Christophe*, Jule Vallès' *Jacques Vingtras*, and Palante's own *Struggle for Individuality*. In these three works, so unlike each other, I found the necessary echo to my own urgencies and adolescent revolts. When we met each other in the yard, I had already long been in communion with Georges Palante.

I loved him for the passionate openness of his mind, for his grieving sensibility, for all that I found quivering and heroic in him. I dreamed of becoming his friend; for the time being, this dream sufficed me. He soon brought me back the borrowed volume and from that day on, we took to exchanging a few words whenever we met in the schoolyard.

He showed himself of such excessive politeness that I took it as formality. I thought he acted according to a system and I suffered to think that he numbered me among those from whom we suffered and whom we jointly despised. (At eighteen, all is excess, or all is nothing.) But when I got to know him better, I discovered that this politeness was not what I had imagined: far from being a means of self-defense, a mark of a priori hostility, or of a definite will to reduce relationships to a correct social form, his politeness came instead from a rather complex cluster of feelings, and had to be ascribed to a natural generosity, to a timidity, a delicacy and a modesty that bordered on sickness.

673

Save when enraged (and his rages aroused pity: they were a child's rages and made him suffer all the more as he knew how weak he was; his sickly imagination urging him on, he came to utter terribly wounding words and to lose control of himself, but the very excess of his insults testified, even in his rage, to his astonishing kindness), I think Palante never once willingly hurt anyone. On the contrary, he treated everyone with the greatest respect, and gave each the greatest possible credit. Often I had occasion to be surprised by his patience.

I grew bold enough to ask him for one of his books, which seemed to annoy him. He answered me evasively and led me to understand that he attached no importance to what he wrote. A few days later, when I first went to his house, and we came back to the subject of his books, I saw that he did not own a single one.

III

He lived with his wife outside town, in a squat little worker's house in La Croix-Perron. Behind the house, a garden looked out over the valley. The Heights of Brézillé were close by and he often wandered there while hunting. On Brézillé he enjoyed the solitude he was always seeking.

I thought that by seeing how he lived at home, I would be able to see into certain sides of his mind that he wished to keep secret. Between the way he kept his study, the way the kitchen was arranged, and a few words he had said to me the day before, I felt there was a hidden link which would, when I detected it, reveal to me the whole flow of his personality. This revelation might just as likely be vouchsafed me by a word or gesture as by the sight of a case of books, abandoned for months, over which I would stumble on entering his study.

What struck one, on entering that study, was the appearance of disorder. A sad, grayish light made everything look alike; the only window, with its white curtains, was never opened except on sunny days, which are so rare in Brittany. His long table, over which hung a round, green lamp, was one great litter of papers. Just by itself, the table occupied half the room; between the table and the fireplace there was a gangway so narrow that Palante always seemed to find it very difficult to reach his chair. The walls were covered by books, mostly falling apart, piled pell-mell on bare planks. Near the glass door, which gave onto the kitchen, and which he always left open for the sake of the heat from the oven, were still more books, piled into two wooden crates from the grocer.

He had told me how he had lived as a boy, in Gouëdic. A bare room, furnished with a plain wooden table, a bed, and home-made bookshelves was all he had needed: "In that room," he used to say, "I was really happy. I was something of a gambler in those days, and I'd drop all my wages in one night, playing poker. But the next day I'd go for a walk in the valley and forget everything."

This love of poverty was just one way he manifested—perhaps not fully aware of it himself—his love of freedom. But, just as he had not been completely guileless in giving his dog the name of Tartufe, so this love of poverty was not without its concealed meaning.

He saw no one. He made no visits, except those to which he was constrained by his official duties, and these obligations used to fill him with horror. Nothing was more repugnant to his frankness, his love of freedom, and honesty than these humiliating episodes of play-acting at which functionaries are such masters. He was unable to lie. This weakness caused him endless vexations. He wanted to live by his own rules, but "an original mind is less often seen as a genius than as an occasion of scandal." (Suarès: *Three Men*) "Who cares?" he used to say. And underneath it all, he suffered. This strange man had an astounding faith in men, a naïve faith: for which he was more easily wounded, and more cruelly.

IV

I soon saw him every day. A new life began for me. I went to meet him when the lycée let out (I had quit at the end of the 1916–17 school year) and accompanied him into town where he did his shopping. On our way down we used to stop in a little café near the Champ de Mars, and when the shopping was done, we would climb back up to his house; always late.

Often we would make another stop at the inn. There we had another couple of "bowls," as was our custom. Time flew. It was seven by the time we rang at his door. Mme Palante would run to open the door. We could hear her feet clip-clopping along the hall, accompanied by the yapping of the dogs, the "wee beasts" that Palante so tenderly loved. She would be shouting: "All right now! That's enough Corra!" But the barking redoubled and suddenly the "wee beasts" would throw themselves at the door.

The door would open gently and Mme Palante would appear, in wooden clogs, a blue apron around her hips, and her arms all red from being soaked in the laundry tub. She would look at us for a moment without saying anything. Only her eyes smiled. Then, finally, she would burst out, "Well, I don't believe it! Really, arriving at such an hour!"

Palante would stay on the threshold without moving, a string bag full of food hung from the tip of each arm and his pockets stuffed with bottles. He would lower his head and look out at his wife from under the brim of his hat, with an exquisite smile, as though to say, "You see, we had such fun chatting, he and I! We were so happy!" "Ah! God save us!" she would say; and in he would go, roaring with laughter.

The "wee beasts," who would not have stopped yapping since we

675

pulled the bell, and whom Mme Palante had much trouble in restraining, would jump at their master's knees, threatening to knock him over. He would shout insults at them even as he patted them, and every step caused him endless effort. Little Canne, a tiny white bitch, forever trembling, would retreat before Palante, so happy to see him that she was quite out of breath. Tartufe, who was already practically blind, barked slowly, without moving; and Corra, a magnificent hunting dog, the favorite of Palante's "wee beasts," made unbelievable leaps and bounds. Even as he protected himself against Corra's enthusiasm, Palante would cry out: "Ah, you good dog, you! Ah, what a good dog!" (He was very fond of his "wee beasts" and would have sacrificed many a man for their sake. His dislike of some man, nurtured for many years, would have been caused by no more than an unfortunate word uttered against Corra or Tartufe. For his dogs, he was quite willing to forego a trip from which he would have derived much pleasure and improved health.)

In spite of the late hour, we would not sit down directly to supper. While waiting for us, Mme Palante would have been doing her laundry. Water boiled on the stove. While hanging up her laundry in the garden, she would have prepared the food. But we had been expected to buy eggs, or milk, and we had forgotten. Palante would then trade his hat for an English cap that cut off part of his face; the cap had been brought back from Jersey by his brother. He would take a stick and off we would go again.

Other times, if we had come home early or if the weather was fine and no one had pointed out any rabid dogs in the vicinity, we would take Corra with us and take a walk up on Brézillé. Unhappily for Palante, the countryside was infested with rabid dogs, which he imagined to be roaming about in packs: great care had to be taken that Corra should not be bitten. He was very reluctant to let her off the leash, but the poor beast was full of spirit, and quite strong enough to break her leash, as happened more than once.

He had bought a little wooden whistle which he tied to a piece of black trimming like that other cord on which, behind his ear, hung his lorgnette. This line he knotted into the buttonhole of his jacket. As soon as Corra ran a little way off, he would start whistling with all his strength, stopping only to catch his breath, shout imprecations at the dog, or yell at me to run after her. I used to laugh to see him out of breath. He didn't even hear me. The more he whistled, the more I laughed. Finally he would catch sight of me and ask me why I was laughing so hard; seeing that I had Corra by her collar, the whistle would drop from his hand. "Oh, the bitch!" he'd say. "At last! We'll have to tie her up. If we were to let her run loose, we'd never have done with it."

Besides, she'd had enough of it, the vagabond! It was time to head off to a farm he knew, to buy some cheese. We would climb up a tortuous little path, blocked with brambles, along a swampy field covered with rushes and yellow flag. After a copse, we had to cross a little brook, and Palante would lean on my shoulder. I remember that this crossing was always difficult. We often had to make two or three attempts. Finally, we would reach the road. Then we climbed into the setting sun toward the farm on top of the hill, where washerwomen we could not see, but whose beetles we could hear, had spread out their white linen.

I retain a feeling from these walks on Brézillé: of fresh and clean air, of a silence that no washerwomens' beetles could disturb, of the country being made for me, being so much my true home that there was between us a kind of secret accord, a love-pact that I shall never be able to betray without unhappiness.

He loved the countryside as I did. His first stay there had enchanted him, and later, when he had been sent to Niort and Aurillac, he suffered from homesickness for Brittany and wanted to return. The lowering sky, the gray weather, the perpetual autumn that is the Breton climate, suited his Northern temperament and gave him far more satisfaction than the light-hearted brilliance of the South, to which he made only the briefest of visits and which he loved, I believe, only in books and in his own imagination.

It often happened that the sun had already set when we came back from the farm; a thin rain would be falling. We would hurry on a little, in spite of the pleasure we had walking in the dark: we thought of Mme Palante worrying about us out in the bad weather.

Dinner always lasted well into the evening. We ate in the kitchen. The table was pushed against the wall, near the window that opened out onto the garden. In summer, the evenings were often fine, but either from laziness, or from a wish not to break off our conversation, we would stay at table even when the meal was over, and drink, while we chatted, the strong coffee Mme Palante had prepared during the meal.

The particular charm of those evenings was doubtless due to our freedom with each other; but it consisted far less in what we said than in

677

what lay behind our words, in the fact that all that we said was a sign of our harmony, our friendship. "He sees it the way I do. He is my friend."

When I left him, late at night, I would sometimes set off running, to expend my joy; in a great city, this sort of fullness and the heart's impressionability are soon lost.

V

Today (these memoirs were written in 1926, and published, in part, in *La Ligne de Coeur*, in Nantes, the same year), when I think back to our conversations, and try to reconstruct them in my mind, I see that their real pleasure derived from the freedom and trust on which our friendship was based: they may have had, unknown to us, limits beyond which we would have been no more than objects of curiosity to each other, but they also had an unmoving center in which each could always rediscover the other. This point of constancy, from which we could not have strayed without ceasing to love one another, was a way of feeling and a set of views that we thought to hold in common. For the most part, we did: particularly views about life in society and its effect on our relationship. At least, these two terms, society and ourselves, seemed quite distinct; or, as he put it, antinomical.

Today, I no longer make this distinction. I think that the expression of man's relationship to society is no more than the expression of man's relationship to himself. It is in this light that I would like to view Georges Palante's philosophy, which is no more than the story of Palante's struggle with himself or, to quote the Nietzsche he admired greatly and of whom he spoke as one would of a liberator, the "account of a personal adventure."

His books, however, give no more than an incomplete account of this adventure; he who would try to form an image of Georges Palante from them would certainly err. The man was infinitely more complex, more delicately shaded, greater than his work. Certain of his pages, on irony or on friendship, admirable as they are, taught me far less than the way in which he spoke of a certain friend.

"He was," he told me, "an astonishing man, a romantic, a man full of health and verve, a book-dealer who made lots of money. Whenever he came to Saint-Brieuc, he traveled only by carriage and whenever he stopped anywhere he said, '"Coachman, you will await further orders!"'"

As he spoke, Palante's eyes shone with admiration. As he repeated those words, "Coachman, you will await further orders!" he made an exceedingly sweeping and slow gesture of his arm that seemed to lose itself in infinity. Two or three times Palante would repeat the words: "Coachman, you will await further orders!" And he would add: "There was a master! There was a king! Next to him we're just a bunch of poor buggers!"

Practical success impressed him greatly. He was in awe of the "business sense" of one of his former pupils who, of all the careers opened up to him by his degree, chose that of selling lighter-flints. "There's a man with a great sense of reality," he said. "He'll do well." He was capable of perfectly sincere admiration for a man who had no other signs of genius but that of being able to drive a car or repair a lock. "I know perfectly well," he used to say, "that the sense of the vanity of all things is forever hidden from him; but it's a weak man's sense anyway."

All conversation with Palante oscillated between these two poles: the weak and the strong, or, as he put it, "low-energy magnetos and high-energy magnetos." Ill-equipped for struggles whose stakes he in any case despised, he numbered himself among the weak and the slow who are destined to suffer all possible defeats. But defeat was what he secretly sought. In his eyes, defeat was a sort of consecration of what was greatest and best in him.

VI

Beyond the village of Hillion, near the sea, some twelve kilometers from Saint-Brieuc, he owned a little villa in which he spent most of his holidays. He had built it fifteen or twenty years before, on the side of a deep gully that runs down to the sea. The peasants call this gully the Valley of Josaphat. The house was built of local stone, small, two stories high, and roofed with red tile; it lay partly buried in the hill of Creh'Mu and dominated the beautiful valley of the Gouessant and the sea.

The trip to La Grandville was no improvised affair. It had to be thought out a week or two ahead of time, the packing done; none of the things indispensable for such a solitary place could be forgotten: they would never be found in the village of Hillion. Finally, Hardouin had to be written to, who would come to meet them with his donkey cart, in which he would pile all their parcels, the "wee beasts," and the cumbersome shower

679

contraption. Palante and his wife got in as well as they could and off they went! They were in for three or four hours of travel across the most beautiful country in the world, and then three months of walks along the shore, of hunting, reading, work, and *far niente*. It was well worth his presence, the previous day, at the annual Prize-Giving, his donning of the cap and gown, his official speech! "Besides," he said, "you'll see. I intend to make a scarecrow out of that gown, on the hill behind the house. You'll see."

If I hadn't actually ridden with them in Hardouin's donkey cart, Palante would waste no time in sending me a letter with an invitation to join them. In the same letter, he would ask me to run him a few errands, such as bringing him a book of which he was in urgent need. I would find it in the town library. (Thus it happened that on one occasion I brought him one of the volumes of *The Origins of Christianity*, and on another Taine's *English Literature*. Once he had wanted to reread *La Cousine Bette*; another time, a volume of Swift. He greatly admired Swift. We often talked about the *Tale of a Tub*, and other works: all of them subjects for endless bouts of Palante laughter.) Sometimes I was sent to buy him some medicine at the Pharmacie de l'Etoile, or, as I passed through Hillion, to bring with me a six-pound loaf of fresh bread "at the bakery you know well."

680

Many times, I would leave on my bicycle first thing in the morning, when there were still few people abroad in the streets and the road was still wet, like the sky, with the rain fallen during the night. On leaving town, I let my machine carry me full tilt and joyfully down to the bottom of Gouëdic Hill. And this joy would make me thirst even more ardently, after that I would feel, a little later, when borne similarly down Yffiniac Hill, which was both longer and more beautiful.

The brief climb up Monte-à-Regret over, I had reached the Heights of Langueux and could see the sea on my left. Sometimes I would get off my bicycle and stop there a moment, bathed in freshness. Then, sitting down on the embankment, I would try to locate myself in that silent infinity, in that gently wind-pushed gray mass through which the light, little by little, finally penetrated. More often, the view from this point would fill me with such exaltation that I would suddenly jump onto my bicycle, step on the pedals as hard and make off as fast as I could, as if I wished to merge myself with the countryside and embrace it by some other means than with my eyes. Having come down Yffiniac Hill in one great swoop, a descent whose joy consisted in being at once immobile and moving, I would turn off onto a little path on which I could no longer ride, and this path, in turn, ended up on the Hillion road, a little before the Château of Aubiers, two or three kilometers from the village. It was an open road, planted with fine oaks.

The times I came by the "little train" and got off at Yffiniac, I did the whole road, from one end to the other, on foot. This, too, was a great pleasure, quite different from that I had in looking at the sea from the steps of the train, but just as sharp.

I would not have enjoyed any of these pleasures so strongly if they had not been the presage of the much greater pleasure it was to be at La Grandville with my friend. Sometimes I met him on the road. He would come to Hillion to mail some letters or do some urgent bit of shopping: a pound of salt or a few thin rashers of bacon "for the partridges."

He would give me his news: hunting and health, "singularly better since he had come to the seaside; at least he wouldn't lay eyes on the people of Saint-Brieuc for another three months" unless there were some unforeseen occurrence, some business to take him into town. Meanwhile, he felt peaceful. "I take it easy, and—you won't believe me—I do a little work!"

In fact, he always arrived at La Grandville with great projects, but hunting would lure him away. We used to joke about it: "And your projects?" "But my dear fellow . . ." Of course, he had given them thought; he had even begun to work. Really, he hadn't forgotten about them! But he always ended up, laughing good-heartedly, saying, "It's impossible to work here . . . Hunting ruins me! But who gives a damn?"

When we went to La Croix-Perron, we stopped at the inn, just as we did in Saint-Brieuc. "Well, I must say," he would say to me, "I am glad to see you!"

He always found someone he knew at the inn. Palante was much loved at Hillion and in La Grandville. He did all sorts of favors. The peasants used to say, M. Palante is a really good man.

When we had done our shopping and were getting ready to return to La Grandville, Palante would suddenly remember that he needed a shave. Off we went to the barber's, a youth of sixteen or seventeen, a village barber who shaved in his own house, for pennies. Our duty done, we finally started home.

Those were fine mornings. We were agreed that the sun does not suit Brittany, giving it a false Sunday air, and that its true nature is revealed only in fog and rain; nevertheless, we enjoyed the sun, we admired it on the road

681

and on the leaves of the oaks. We went so far as to take a mischievous delight in finding it beautiful, for the sun was such a contrast to our love of grayness, and one of our greatest pleasures was to make fun of ourselves, of our views and preferences. Before reaching La Grandville, the road, level so far and smothered in foliage, rose and broadened. The trees grew ever scarcer, and the increasing bareness seemed made to allow the sea, which from that point one suddenly saw in all its wonderful spaciousness, to take us by surprise, "Isn't that beautiful, isn't that beautiful!" Palante would say. "Let's hurry. Perhaps there'll be time for a little walk before lunch!"

We hurried. We didn't even stop to wish a good day to the innkeeper of the Auberge des Quatres-Routes, and surprised Mme Palante in the kitchen cooking a partridge or a rabbit that Palante had shot the same morning. "Do you have time to take a stroll on the beach?" she would say, "Of course ... But before you go, Louis must get me a bucket of water from the fountain." And as I went off to the fountain, which was really a well some fifty yards from the house, Palante checked gun and binoculars on the threshold, waiting for me.

As bright and early the next morning we were to go off on the Moor of Creh'Mu to get ourselves a rabbit or two, we wanted to go down to the sea before noon and shoot some curlews, or sea-nightingales, flocks of which flew high overhead. "It's because they see the gun, the poor little beasts," Palante would say.

He went hunting with pleasure, and though not vain about his prowess, would have been angry to be taken for a bad shot. But often he forgot his gun and stretched out on the sand to dream, or to sleep. "I pass my best hours here by the sea," he used to say. "The sea reconciles all things. What are our agitations alongside such beauty? There are times when I feel myself carried away into that infinity. Sometimes I come at dawn to hide among the rocks, at the mouth of the Gouessant. I am there, lying in wait, but I forget my rifle as I watch the sun rise. It's so quiet. . . ."

VII

In the afternoon, if Palante was too tired to continue hunting, we chose some comfortable hollow in the rocks and sat down. He would bring the *Mercure* with him, or some book he had to review. (Palante was for many years the *Mercure's* regular contributor on philosophy.) "Now we'll see, my friend," he would say. "The *Mercure* is running a novel of fantasy, *M. Gretzili*, by one Maurice Beaubourg. All prodigiously vigorous, biting, and acid . . ."

We would start reading, but we had to stop all the time: "This chap is really too funny for words!" Palante would break in, adding, "Well, this is a consolation for the enormous number of books of philosophy—so they say—I have to talk about, for the most part an unforgettable intellectual mishmash!"

In much the same way, we would read the novels of Louis Dumur, laughing no less than at those of Maurice Beaubourg.

Sometimes we worked. Palante had got it into his head that he wanted to learn English. He had once been to England, had retained a wonderful memory of his trip and wanted to return there, but not before learning the language. I offered to help him. These English sessions amused us greatly. He had a child's pleasure in learning new words, but we could never work for long. Our subject brought us back to the idea of the trip, and on that score, Palante was inexhaustible.

The intoxication of a voyage was fully his only in a book or in his imagination: thinking of Italy or Spain gave him the greatest of pleasure; actually going there occasioned him nothing but torment. Before setting out, certain conditions, particularly his health and the temperature, had to be satisfactory. The moment he had left, a thousand questions arose, matters he had not thought of or considered important. These, given the state traveling put him in, suddenly loomed large: the irritating question of a passport, choosing a hotel, arguing with porters in a station, and a thousand other chimeras.

In Spain, where he had expected to make a longish stay and see Madrid and Barcelona, he got no farther than San Sebastian, where it took him three days to get a visa. Once his passport had been stamped, he got the notion that a policeman was watching him and, to avoid trouble later, preferred to return posthaste to France. A year or two later, he reached Naples; but, no sooner had he arrived than he was seized with fear. He thought people were looking at him with hostility and once again he scrambled back to France with all possible speed.

Nonetheless, he was thinking of new voyages: "As soon as I know a little English, I'll return to London."

683

But the finest trip of all, the one we were forever speaking of, was a trip beyond Europe, far from that old world without which, however, he could not survive and inside which he was so miserable. It was not so much a question of travel, as of being reborn, escaping from himself and from time. Besides, he liked to prolong these talks. While they lasted, he could believe in the voyage without committing himself. In the silent beauty of the evenings and the sunsets on the sea, we found far more than a promise: we found a real gift.

When, after supper, which lasted until very late, I went up to bed in my bare little attic with its solitary iron bed, I knew that my dreams would transform me into a far-roaming sea-captain, or a pirate like Morgan, whose adventures I had read as a child.

I also knew that when I awoke in the morning, I would enjoy the sound of the sea mingled with the croaking of frogs, and breathing deeply of the fresh air coming through my window. Palante would have left long ago and I'd find him up on Creh'Mu, hunting. A new day would lie ahead of us. I refused to think that at the end of the day I would have to leave, so far away did that departure, and so long the day ahead, still seem. It was

only when he undertook to accompany me back to Hillion, that I understood we had to separate.

We never left La Grandville before nightfall, and when we arrived in Hillion we drank a farewell. I remember one evening, as we left the little inn in Hillion, the moon shone through the trees. I was to return to Saint-Brieuc on foot. "What a beautiful night," he said to me. "What a joy to walk the open road on such a night!" He pointed at the sky with his finger, alluding to our conversation at the inn, which had come to the subject of Stirner.

"This bit of sky," he said in an odd voice, "is mine . . . mine. . . ."

And as I set off along the road toward Saint-Brieuc, he disappeared in the opposite direction.

VIII

He strayed briefly into politics, but never joined the ranks. He took part in the 1919 campaign on his own, and one of his basic ideas was that of non-re-eligibility, drawn from Robespierre's famous motion. Obviously, no party could support such a scandalous idea.

He set forth his program in a short pamphlet which appeared in 1919, called "Something New in Politics." The story of this pamphlet deserves to be told.

At first, Palante had meant it to be published in one of the major reviews. His manuscript was returned. Two fresh attempts with two other Paris publishers met a similar fate. Meanwhile, I went to Saint-Brieuc.

I found Palante in a very bad mood, but more decided than ever to publish his work.

"They want to prevent me from telling the truth . . . A league of liars is lined up against me."

I saw no other solution but that of publishing the pamphlet in Saint-Brieuc.

"No," he said, "I want to publish it in Paris."

What was I to do?

One day it occurred to me that I knew a young publisher in Paris who might take up Palante's cause and carry it off in good style.

"Why didn't I think of it earlier?" I cried out. "I have just your man! A publisher you can send your manuscript to, right away! I'll write him."

I immediately drafted a letter.

"But who is it?" asked Palante. "Are you sure he's an honest man?"

"I think so."

"He's not connected with the police?"

"I wouldn't know."

"Nor a Freemason?"

"I don't know that either."

"It all seems rather risky."

"At least send off the manuscript."

The next day, the manuscript left, and a few days later, Palante was assured that he would have a first set of proof in eight days. He came to see me.

"Wonderful!" he said. "I'm saved."

Unfortunately, after eight days, the proof still had not arrived. I told Palante, who came to see me every day after class, that there was nothing unusual about this. A few more days passed. Nothing.

"I'm worried," he said. "I find myself in difficulties."

"Wait a little."

685

We waited. Fifteen days went by and still Palante had not received his proof. He came to me one morning, even more worried than usual.

"I've written him letter after letter. He doesn't even reply!"

Even I began to worry.

"You see?" he said, "I was right to doubt your friend! He belongs to the police!"

"What's that?"

"So . . . They've confiscated my manuscript, that's what!"

I was struck dumb.

"Come on, control yourself," I said. "Write J. He'll go and see the publisher personally."

Four days later, Palante still had no proof, and J. had not answered!

"I get the picture now," Palante shouted. "It's the Jews who don't want me to open my mouth. J. is a Jew. He went to see your friend. But he was paid off."

In reality, as we knew later, J. had been in the South, and had not received our letter.

"A fine fix you've got me in!" he said.

He started making the most extraordinary threats against his enemies.

"I'll take my gun. I'll go to Paris. I'll. . . ."

We almost quarreled.

Happily, the day after this scene, Palante came to my house with the proofs.

"Look," he said. "I rather like the way they look. He does good work, the dog!"

IX

He was, he wrote me, "*no more than a dilettante, an amateur in politics, but an amateur deeply enraged with this kind of mess.*"

Actually, he acted with passion, and not with dilettantism. He claimed to indulge in public life "*to cull some interesting observations, to break the monotony of his life as a functionary.*" But passion bore him away. Not that he was seeking public office—such an office would only have caused him extreme embarrassment. The fact was, that no matter how disabused he felt or claimed to feel, he found it necessary to state certain truths.

After a lecture, he wrote me: "*I have attacked the regime, the unmention-able lie that's at the basis of our political system.*"

He spoke of democracy in scornful terms, and not at all amateurishly. But, from a letter of June 2, 1919, I draw this admission, and thus free myself of any need to penetrate more deeply into his political ideas: "*This victory of capitalism, the victory of a hypocritical and nauseating society, disgusts me. Ah! If only I were twenty-five, and could get the hell out to Java or somewhere else! Every effort in this country of liars fills me with loathing.*"

The correspondence we had begun after my departure from Saint-Brieuc is rather brief, and not very interesting to anyone but myself. He wrote few letters, always in a hurry, and for many reasons he did not reveal himself in them. His poor health, moreover, did not permit him to be a good correspondent.

In each of his letters, he complains of weariness, of migraines, of boredom. The further he goes, the more his profession weighs on him. And yet he seems to fear retirement. He now has only fleeting moments of work. Even hunting, his favorite diversion, disillusions him; he no longer shows the same eagerness. In the letters I receive, I feel him somber, isolated as he had never been.

This escapes him: "*I see no one. Sometimes this is hard. I think with sadness of our former conversations.*"

He comes to Paris: he is passing through, on his way to a cemetery on the Meuse, where a member of his family is buried. We meet in a crowd, just briefly. Where are our old walks? Our leisure, our freedom? Still, it seems to me that his wit has not weakened. He speaks to me of the books he has read. "I have begun to like reading again, that's a good sign," he says. But it does not last long. Back in Saint-Brieuc, he writes: "*Literature, in all its forms, horrifies me.*" And he underlines the word "horrifies" three times.

He would like to change his life, to flee, to flee himself. He is stifling. I speak to him of a long voyage I am about to undertake: "*Lucky man!*" he cries out, "*for whom life opens up the roads of adventure and forgetfulness, far from this old world, from this nauseating civilization.*"

At this point he has already quarreled with many of his friends. A quarrel is not long in coming between the two of us. It comes with a rapidity that I had not expected: an exchange of letters is enough. But on this, I shall remain silent.

Rare and indirect news of him still reaches me. I hear that he has not forgotten me, that he thinks of me "without rancor." But what would it serve to see each other again?

I have no business speaking of his quarrel with Jules de Gaultier. It was sensational enough for further words to be unnecessary. Still, I feel obligated to rectify the gratuitous statements of some journalists who claim that Palante committed suicide out of philosophic despair. The truth is that the two adversaries having come to challenge each other to a duel, a civil proceeding equally honorable to each prevented the duel from taking place. For a few months, all seemed forgotten. But Palante began to think that he had been dishonored. He was unable to survive this thought and killed himself.

X

A month after Palante's death, almost to the very day, I went to Hillion and La Grandville, which I had not visited for three years. I found the open road again, and the fine oaks, the Château of Aubiers, the little inn in Hillion where we used to rest on our way to La Grandville, and where, one night, he had talked of the sky and Stirner.

In the little cemetery in Hillion, where Jean Grenier, who had been present at Palante's funeral, led me, nothing marked the site of his tomb. "It's here, or there," said my friend; and there was nothing to see but grass and the wall that surrounds the cemetery. (Since, thanks to Jean Grenier's initiative, a marble plaque has been placed on his tomb.)

This abandonment, which for any other but Palante, would have seemed to me even more cruel and unjust in death than in life, I found cruel and unjust for him, but as necessary to him as the death he had chosen, thinking thereby to escape. This cruelty and this injustice I shared with him, against his will, even as his unmarked tomb, after his suicide, seemed to deprive me of any right to remember or love him. His grave appeared to me as though I were bidden to find in it the secret thought of which I have often spoken in the course of these memoirs, that secret thought as mysterious and as logical as fate.

Palante was right when he boasted about the faithful memories of peasants. The mistress of the Auberge des Quatre-Routes had not forgotten him, nor Hardouin. I found them both at the inn. Hardouin was seated. He was drinking.

"In his last days," the innkeeper said, "he came here more often. He would sit down and ask for the paper. I always put the paper aside for him. It was M.Palante's paper. If he came ten times, he asked for it ten times. He said very little, but he didn't seem changed to me, and I would never have thought that he would come to such an end."

"As for me," said Hardouin, "I suspected. Sometimes, coming back from Hillion, he would say, 'I feel dishonored, Hardouin.' I tried to keep up his spirits as well as I could, but a moment later he was again lost in his thoughts."

The innkeeper said, "He felt dishonored, did he? That's probably why he didn't want to see any gentry. One day some people came here to see him. He wasn't here. The next day, I said to him, 'Some gentlemen came from town to see you,' and he lost his temper. 'Don't talk to me about gentlemen from town,' he said. 'Don't talk to me about them!'"

Ah! He didn't utter those words without waving his hands like so, without his face showing that grimace of horror I had seen in his moments of great suffering, that was so terrible to watch. He must have uttered those words while standing at the entrance to the inn, ready to go home. Perhaps he'd even begun to walk before finishing the last of them. I see him going down the deep path leading to his house, leaning on his cane, his heavy shoulders slightly bowed, hurrying as much as he could, his soul drunk with rage and bitterness.

689

I could only fall silent, and I would have remained silent had not my friend Lambert, one of the men who best knew and best understood Palante, written me: *"Neither living nor dead. Speak of him, since you loved him."*

I have spoken of him. I wanted to show a man. But perhaps I have been completely wrong about everything.

Translated from the French by Keith Botsford

TRANSLATOR'S NOTE: *Quite apart from their intrinsic beauty and their precious recollection of a deeply felt and tragically ended friendship, these souvenirs of Georges Palante have another interest. They are, in a way, living source material for one of this century's most important and neglected French novels,*

Le Sang Noir *(issued in the United States in 1936, in an unfortunately dated translation by Samuel Putnam, under the title* "Bitter Victory"*), wherein the Palante of this same period figures as the prototype of the extraordinary Cripure* (Critique de la Raison Pure). *Since the death of Albert Camus and the retirement from literature of André Malraux, Louis Guilloux—whose classic short novel* Compagnons (Friendship) *appeared in* The Noble Savage 2—*must count as the leading French novelist of his generation. A lifetime of "absence from Paris" (the title of one of his novels) has deprived him of some renown and chic, but has preserved in him the pure narrative strain of the novel which the artifice of the capital has destroyed in even the best of writers. His work falls roughly into two genres: realistic scenes of provincial life, usually working class, in which the political cross-currents of the day play a major role; and fantasies in which a dreamlike atmosphere prevails. He has said that the latter style informs the former, and in his latest work,* Les Batailles Perdues *(1960), he attempts a fusion of the two. In the best of his work, the earlier "humble" novels grouped as* Maison du Peuple *(1930),* Le Sang Noir *(1935), and* Jeu de Patience *(1949), the two are never very far from one another. The fundamental preoccupation is with the whole man: what he dreams and aspires to, and what he is and does. This is only the third of Guilloux's longer works to be translated into English, though his books are available, almost in toto, in nearly every other European language. I hope there will be more.*

Louis Gallo

Oedipus-Schmoedipus

Reports of death were what his mother enjoyed most of all in each day's news-reports.

His mother believed there existed a God; believed in a life hereafter; believed she would meet, face to face, in her life hereafter, her God. And she'd tell Him, in the hereafter, when she met Him, her story: "saved by Grace."

> *And I shall see Him:*
> *Face to Face.*
> *And tell the story:*
> *Saved by Grace.*
>
> *Did he love his mother?*
> *He was terrified by his mother.*
> *All mothers terrified him.*
> *Mothers weren't human.*
> *Mothers were a disease.*

And his sisters, having married, having become mothers, they too became diseased. They too terrified him.

How could he get back at them? Why should it be necessary for him to get back at them? He was a grown man, old enough to be dead: thirty-seven. At his age millions had already given up the ghost and were in heaven or hell, dead. Why should he bother? Why not play dead? Wouldn't that have been the Christian and charitable way—playing dead?

He had the rooms downstairs, three rooms, very comfortable, all his; a remarkably comfortable arrangement for a man who hated work, who would never get married, who had no reason to go on living, who was terrified not only by mothers but also, perhaps even more so, by fathers, by widows and orphans, by everything that moved—by life; his mother had the rooms upstairs. Nights were lonely for his mother, who was widowed and orphaned. She, when he was thirty-seven, was seventy-two. He would hear her, at night, sometimes, in her kitchen upstairs, singing; her hymnal would be on the table. And he would hear her, saved by Grace, telling her story to God, face to face. Alone in the silence of her rooms, all her rooms dark except the kitchen, without having to look at the words in the hymnal, quietly and mournfully she'd tell her story, face to face, over and over, to God, who cared—who alone in all the universe cared: because her son, downstairs, certainly didn't care.

692

His mother had white hair.

—Why are you so mean to your mother?

He would himself, some day, perhaps, be seventy-two, and would enjoy most of all in the day's news-reports reports of death. And best of all, deaths of people he knew, people in the news, conquerors, go-getters, who had once made headlines. Yes. He would become, some day, perhaps, his mother.

—When are you getting married? Don't you ever think of getting married? Why don't you get a job in New York and live in New York? What are you going to do when your mother passes away? Do you think she'll leave the house to you? You can get a job in New York, live in New York, and still find time to write. All your friends are in New York. You're not getting any younger, you know.

They didn't understand. Nobody did. He was something new in the world. He was the world's first and finest, the only and the original, Accept-No-Substitutes, World-Beater. How could they be expected to understand? In all of recorded history nothing even approximately like him had happened before. He was not only unique, he was unimaginable. His mission in life was to make himself imaginable—and he certainly couldn't do it by getting a job in New York, living in New York, and the rest of it: a trite, very easily imagined story.

All pity was self-pity. The hideous was the norm. Art was idiocy. Self-pity, the hideous, idiocy—he could not expect to make money and achieve headlines preaching self-pity, the hideous, and idiocy. Or could he?

His mother. She angered him one day. He rarely spoke to his friends of his mother; rarely expressed, on paper, his abject terror of her; his friends, those who saw his scribblings, were left to assume that art, existentialism, psychoanalysis, the system he had contrived of levels and intensities and dimensions of consciousness and self-consciousness, his rages and outrages, directed most vociferously against Christianity and respectability and the world of cloud-cuckooland television, were all real for him, he meant every word he said, however much he preached to them his doctrine: language is madness. He had yet to make even his first convert, though his friends in New York found him entertaining enough, bemused, extraordinary enough: mad enough with words. His mother angered him, that day, fearfully. He was not yet thirty-seven; she was not yet seventy-two; it was a day in July 1958. More exactly: it was the first day of August, a Friday. He kept a diary: the day was Friday, August 1, 1958. He awoke that morning (so his diary reported it) at 5:30. The morning previous, July 31, he awoke at 2:30 (so his diary reported it) and had an "extremely difficult time getting back to sleep." "Back to sleep without too much difficulty," reads the entry under the date Friday, August 1, 1958.

Eventually, before he died, he would write, he thought, a piece honoring his mother. She had loved him. He was her baby, her angel. She had planned for him a splendid career in the service of God. She had insisted that he be treated in her large family with a special kindness and care: he would be her special gift to her Lord and Father, who dwelt in Heaven, to whom, saved by Grace, she would one day tell her story, face to face. He would prove, in this piece, that he didn't hate her, or blame her, that he could no more hate or blame her for loving him than he could hate or blame any mother for loving a worthless son. He could understand that love. James Joyce had called it the only true love a man will know in this life. Oedipus-Schmoedipus: everyone had to have a mother, one way or the other. So his own had been a fanatic Christian, a Puritan. She might have been a fanatic—who knows what? Other sons had been stuck with worse, certainly—alcoholics, kleptomaniacs, hypochondriacs, actresses, adulteresses, mothers politically inclined, scatter-brained mothers. And what was her crime, finally? She had loved him. She had showered him with kindness. Was this so unforgivable?

His notebooks contained few references to his mother. And all of them were angry, bitter, unkind. His notebooks revealed that as far in the past as 1952 his enmity had been intense. Would it serve an artful purpose to quote from his notebooks, before describing his anger (more percisely: before allowing himself to describe, in his own bitter words, in his own angry person, the first and the finest, the only and the original, accept no substitutes) that fearsome August, unforgettable day? It might. It might, too, mitigate, for the innocent, the onlooker, some of the madness to come, the art, the idiocy, first-person-singular. She was his mother. She was the only one he had, after all, or would have. One might think of that. One might think that a World-Beater, after all, everything considered, was merely the most sublime, the most sublimated, manifestation of a mother-beater—or, in its more hideous and normal state, of a wife-beater. One might think of that, reading these entries. When was he getting married? Was that a question a sane man would ask a World-Beater—the world's first, moreover, and finest? As far ago as 1952. And before that—though his notebooks remained all but silent on the subject. And, in his notebooks dated 1952, only this single entry on that dread subject:

694

> She limps into the room. Arthritis. His strange feeling that maybe she *is* suffering—*really*. "Maybe she isn't making believe."
> His bland consideration of the possibility (that her pain is real). Sad if it is—if she *isn't* making believe. But hard to believe it's real.

She was sixty-seven when the year began, 1954; he was thirty-two. His notebooks reveal him more willing now to avenge himself for the love his mother abjectly showered on him, that love he could not return. A World-Beater, indeed! A mother-beater! A wife-beater! Why didn't he get married, indeed!

From his notebooks, dated 1954:

> Harangues about the grass needing to be cut in the back yard. When it is cut (as if in defiance of her conviction that it would never be

cut), she comments that the back yard is ugly, she won't put up anymore with having it looking so ugly.

No personal gratitude felt. Indication of a ferocious will.

"I'm going to sell this house."

No opposition.

Her ferocity increases with deepening immersion in drudgery. A ferocity directed mainly against her progeny.

She watches the old-man carpenter working on the house next door. Her deep sense of comfort. If only all men would be humble like this carpenter, what a fine, wonderful world it would be. And poignance in the sight of the old man's obvious discomfort working under the hot sun. Poor man—he has to work hard to support his family. But a divine order and justice are at work here, too. It's God's will that men should work and be humble. And her heart fills with joy at this thought of all men working and being humble—like this tired old-man carpenter.

Fretful all morning worrying about when the breadman will pass. What if he passes and she fails to catch him? Fretful thinking of the kids playing in the street. Who's watching them? Are their mothers watching them to make sure they don't get run over? Fretful about the property being damaged next door—kids are throwing rocks through the paneless windows. What are the police for? Why don't they come and chase the kids away? What she should do is call the police and tell them to come and chase the kids away.

A day spent imprisoned in her house, nervous, fretting, passing from fret to fret, from irksome sensation to irksome sensation, victimized by each in turn, each specifically and separately, an unceasing torment of fretting. Yet from this pain—from out of this slough of tedium and drudgery—no sign of insight, no hope of release. Nothing will waken her from her dense delirious primordial slumber.

A crescendo of peeve and bickering, without cause, idiotic. Until, five minutes after, in the middle of her moanings, a sudden loud crashing of the bathroom door.

Suddenly explainable, the uncaused panic. She had taken a strong laxative before breakfast. Her arthritis is tormenting her again.

Attacks of terror. From reading, in her newspaper, accounts of muggings and murders. Rushes around the house locking all windows;

locks both door *and* storm door. Impossible, therefore, to get into the house even *with* a key. Must knock at the storm door; must rouse her from her sleep. She prefers this to being murdered in her sleep by a passing maniac.

Her pleasure in having told her children off. Profound comfort in knowing that her warnings have been stated and are now on the record. Told the one son he's working too hard. Told another he's too fat; all her sympathy goes out to his wife. Told a daughter she treats her child too strictly, etc. To each of her children.

"I told them! God will be my witness!"

Do the entries sufficiently reveal his terror? He was thirty-three when the year began, 1955; she was sixty-eight. Was it really possible that a grown man of thirty-three, could be terrified by an old woman of sixty-eight? But a man can be terrified by far less—by spiders and centipedes, by a crash of thunder. After all, what is terror? Terror, finally, is a fear of the unknown—not of the spider or the centipede, not of thunder, not of an old woman. A fear of. . . .

696

And yet, isn't a man to be commended for fighting this terror? Aren't the entries concerning his mother exactly that heroic struggle against breakdown into maniac panic? Men test themselves in jungles; avenge themselves on tennis courts; vengeance is indispensable to the efficient functioning of the organism. She was his mother. Her love had made him weak, unfit. What should he do? Avenge himself by becoming a Christian? Against whom would he thus be directing his vengeance? He was thirty-three years plus two months old when he wrote in his notebook, under the date 2/20/55:

Crisis when her daughter and her daughter's husband "smooch" in her kitchen while she cooks the Sunday dinner. Instant and furious explosion. The daughter's husband, hurt, quits the premises. She turns tearful, becomes contrite in her wrath, though still unrelenting in her strictures. An impossible situation.

Difficulty getting the husband back. He persists in thinking he can kiss his wife whenever and wherever he pleases.

Under the date 3/7/55:

"I don't repent having told my daughter she was wrong. No! I don't repent! I still say the same thing. In her own house, if she's married, all right, she can let her husband kiss her all over her face. In my house I won't stand for it! And I don't repent telling her. No! Her husband has to be taught what's right. There's a way to live that's God's way, and nobody can make me take up any other way to live except God's way."

Under the date 4/3/55:

Her bafflement and irritation when she sees birds in her back yard pecking at just-planted grass seeds.

"I don't know why the birds are back so early this year. No sooner do we have a little warm weather and they're here. I don't know why they're here so early, just when the grass seed is planted. One or two days of warmth and their blood feels it—and they're all back again. I don't know how they find out these things." Etc.

An incessant fretting. By which fretting she avoids expressing what she really feels—i.e., hostility toward the birds who are eating her grass seed. This enmity, as a Christian, she is forbidden to express.

697

Under the date 4/4/55:

She washes clothes the way some women eat chocolate—compulsively. She wanders around the house, on washdays, looking for things to wash. She frets over curtains and doilies and other odd items, wondering if they're dirty enough to wash; saddened if they're not. Next week, for sure, they'll be dirty enough. Everything, in time, gets dirty and has to be washed. And pretty soon the slip covers on the living-room chairs will have to be washed. Why doesn't she send her clothes to the laundry and have them washed? Why doesn't she let one of her daughters wash them? They never stop getting after her about it, telling her she's too old. She's too old, they tell her, to be washing and hanging out clothes.

No! They're *her* clothes! Every mother has to wash her *own* family's clothes! That's God's will! Dirty clothes, if they're your own family's; it isn't the same as somebody else's, not in your family. Even if it's her own daughters washing her clothes, it still isn't right. Her daughters have their *own* families' clothes to wash. That's how it *should* be. That's how God *wants* it. Every mother has to wash her *own* family's dirty clothes. That's why she's a mother. Why else is she called a mother?

Her energies released in the drudgery of washing clothes. A craving, her craving for dirty clothes to wash—i.e., her need for self-abnegation—bordering on the insane. As eating chocolate, a voluptuousness, a craving, in other women, bordering on the insane.

Under the date 4/9/55:

Her childlike response to television. When an evangelist preacher asks those in the TV audience who believe in Christ as their savior to raise their arms, she does so. A total absorption—a complete loss of self-consciousness: she feels herself physically inside the television set, inside the tent with the preacher. She comes away exalted.

Also, watching a series of still pictures—famous paintings—depicting the crucifixion, she loses herself entirely. "Look what they're doing to our Lord! They're raising him on the cross! See how he suffers!"

Impossible to tell her these are only paintings—that it's only a television screen she sees.

Under the date 4/23/55:

"Lies! All lies!" she replies to the voice over the radio announcing a special price, this week only, on storm windows.

Under the date 5/4/55:

"I knew a long time ago the day would come when I'd be abandoned by my children."

She says this to her married daughter, who has volunteered to spend a day with her during her illness. Much of her heroism, her determination to remain—or to appear—unrewarded for her sacrifices. She boasts to her friends: "my children do *nothing* for me."

Her yoke: her glory.

Under the date 11/19/55:

> To spite her he refuses to use a carpet she has placed under the chair at his desk. Prefers the cold floor to this kindness. Has reached a point so extreme that the mere thought of her in any way, no matter how small, being kind to him, paralyzes him into a sense of absolute futility.
>
> Rebukes her attempts to make conversation. Is further paralyzed by this spectacle of himself acting spiteful. His blood so full of poison he finds it impossible to read.

He was thirty-four when the year began, 1956; she was sixty-nine. Would this crucifixion never end? How much simpler to leave home, get a job, and forevermore have her out of his life. He could do his writing evenings and weekends. Perhaps he'd see the futility of his schemes and would get married. Ten years. Ten years now he was home from the army. Ten years. She had reached the end of her capacity to tolerate him in her house, useless—no! She would not tolerate it! He had to get a job! He had to get married! She had to see him married and settled before she died!

But she tolerated it. And, in October 1955, when he announced to her that he would no longer eat her food, no longer would allow her to wash his clothes or in any other way serve him, she told him to leave, she would not tolerate him in her house if the food she prepared for him was poison to him; she was his mother; he had to eat the food she prepared for him; what had she done to deserve this punishment from God, this son who persecuted and tormented her; who refused to eat the food she prepared for him!

The rooms downstairs became his on November 1, 1957. Three rooms. All his. One of the rooms a kitchen, large. He could shut her out of his life. Everything he needed was in those rooms. Shut in those rooms he was shut away from all the world. A joyful day, that ecstatic day, that first day in those rooms. Three rooms. A kitchen, a living room, a bedroom. All his.

Vengeance! They had said to him: "Move to New York!" They had wanted him—like themselves—to stifle in New York. They could not tolerate his living a worthless life, a free life, a life which allowed him to write, what he pleased, as he pleased, worthless, useless scribblings, which no publisher would accept. Vengeance!

She complained. He never came upstairs to visit her. She complained
to her married daughters: he was like a hermit down there; she never heard
him moving around; he gave her angry looks when she brought him pie and
Jell-O; and he didn't keep the rooms clean. She wouldn't have it! It was still
her house!

Vengeance! He had moved to New York. Merely by moving downstairs!

She was out of his life!

Was he mad?

Vengeance! In all of life is there a joy more ecstatic than vengeance?

He was clearly mad.

Two months after his move to New York—his move downstairs—he
began a novel, autobiographical. He called the novel *The Conqueror*. She
was out of his life! He was a conqueror!

That day, now, that unforgettable day.

That day in July 1958. More precisely: August 1, 1958.

He awoke that morning—so his yearbook reports it—at 5:30. Without
too much difficulty he fell back into sleep. "Awake again at 6:15," the report
continues, "again at 7:00. In bed, awake, until 8:30."

The conqueror! The World-Beater! The first and the finest, the only
and the original—accept no substitutes!

August 1, 1958.

In his own words.

My mother is a very stupid woman! She believes in God!

Yesterday morning she washed clothes; a fine mess it made in the
apartment downstairs, where I live, a bachelor, alone. The clothes were
washed, in point of fact, in an automatic washing machine; my mother is
not so stupid that she'd scrub her clothes by hand while there were more
efficient means available to her. It was shortly after nine; I had finished
breakfast and had put away the dishes and utensils and had made my bed;
water emptying automatically out of the washing machine in my mother's
kitchen upstairs began automatically emptying into my bathtub downstairs;
a fine mess.

I apprised her of the fact; she reacted typically, with alarm—with a
cry for help to her savior in all crises, Jesus. But she acted, too, as a woman
not so stupid might have acted; instantly halted the discharge of water from

the washing machine by cutting off the electric current which operated the motor of the machine. I returned to my apartment downstairs.

My feeling of life's tedium, its unbearable silliness, its worthlessness, is strong under the best circumstances; I wondered why it seemed no more tedious now. It was almost pleasure I felt, on the contrary, watching the water churning upward into the bathtub. There was a lot of it, dirty water; it fascinated me; I was sorry she had stopped the rest of it from filling the tub. What was I thinking? Not, certainly, that God had created this mess, the world, and good people he rewarded and bad people he punished, so fall on your knees and pray. I was thinking, perhaps, rather, that on Pacific Islands, thirteen and fourteen years ago, on Aguni Shima, Ulithi, Saipan, and Peleliu, we had never to deal with such problems. Did I long to return to those halcyon days? I doubt it. While on those islands I longed to return to the halcyon problems of washing machines and stopped-up drains. I longed, now, if for anything, for the end of the world, one bomb ending it all, and myself, alive, watching it, the little I would see of it before going up with it, my joy, my knowledge that this would indeed end it, the silliness, the unbearable stupidity, people like my mother, believing in God, believing that God would get them if they didn't watch out, so they'd better watch out.

701

My aim is not to describe in detail the mess created by the stopping-up of the drain; there was churning also in the toilet; water spilled over onto the bathroom floor; there was gurgling, though mild compared with this other, in the kitchen sink. In time, stirring myself from my fascination, I went again upstairs, returned with a plunger, applied the plunger in the bathtub, my efforts meeting with signal unsuccess. I applied the plunger in the toilet; water, receding in the toilet, churned backward up into the bathtub. My fascination became intense. I applied the plunger in the kitchen sink. The same result; churning of water in the bathtub. This might well have gone on forever—as life after death, from my mother's view, would go on forever. My fascination became somewhat dulled; forever had always this effect on me—forever meant death; death was forever.

Perhaps from a love of sheer silliness, an impulse antedating the tedium which threatened again to overpower me, I applied the plunger once more in the toilet. It was pleasure I felt—a vengeful, spiteful, ecstatic pleasure— watching the water churning backward up again into the bathtub. Plumbing systems were tedious; I had less than no interest in the intriguing possibilities of plumbing systems; I nonetheless could feel a vicious pleasure observing this breakdown in the system. In time the world, too, would break down. I felt pleasure thinking of this—the end of the world!

My mother descended from the apartment upstairs to the apartment downstairs. This was her house. She had a right to do this. Her reaction on entering the bathroom and seeing the mess in the bathtub and on the bathroom floor was fantastic. She was seized with panic. She cried to God.

I don't remember her words. I remember only the tone of her cry— terror. My mother is seventy-two years old. She believes in God. She believes she'll be going to heaven when she dies. The thought of death, however (so stupid is she), fills her with terror. My own feeling toward death is being appalled, rage; but death, for me, is the end; there'll be no heaven for me when I die; my dedication is absolutely to life, this life, this abomination, which is all I have, and will ever have. Confronted by my mother's terror, therefore, my reaction was fury.

"O, my God!" she cried. "What are we going to do now?"

But the words fail to give it—that note in her voice: terror. I've been forced to make up the words. I rarely hear what my mother says when she talks. But her terror, her cry of absolute desperation—this could not fail to reach me. My reply was ferocious:

"This *isn't* the end of the world!"

But the words, again, fail to convey it. These were in fact the words I spoke. But the frenzy, the insane murderous rage I felt—I've failed to give this. Nor will I go back, erase, and try it again; I've revealed too much already.

There was less the fear of death in my mother's voice when she spoke again. My biting words had doubtless snapped her into some sense of the reality of the situation.

"I have clothes washing in the machine. They still have to go through their rinse. What am I going to do? Today I set aside especially to wash clothes. After this I have another batch I wanted to wash. Who knows how long I'll be tied up. I can't do anything until I get these clothes washed."

She may have mentioned God once or twice. The words written down here have been made up. My problem was to get my mother and her panic back upstairs; also to control the frenzy which I knew would seize and overpower me if I should become silly enough to consider this matter of the stopped-up drain a problem. It was *not* a problem.

"Do you have lye upstairs?"

There was fear—fear of death—in her reply:

"No. I used it all last week. Is there any down here?"

There was none down here.

"You should always keep an extra can of lye around," she said. "I always try to keep an extra can around. Yesterday I knew there was something I wanted at the A&P. I told myself to remember lye. That's why it's good to write these things down. You too. Write that down. Remember that next time you go to the A&P. Keep it here under the sink. You can always use a can of lye. You'll never regret having it around."

I'm making the words up. I'm sure she mentioned God three or four times while interminably giving me her advice about always keeping a can of lye around the house. My mother's ability to hurl her energies into talk about lye, about washing machines, about writing things down, about God punishing the world for its iniquities, is boundless. My own problem was to wait her out. Eventually she'd stop. Her energies, in fact, are not boundless. I knew she'd stop. She at last got tired talking and returned to her apartment upstairs.

My aim is not to describe in detail the events of that morning; the almost three hours during which my own powers were immobilized by this problem which was not a problem. What my aim may in fact be I can't say. Needless to add, it doesn't matter.

It might almost be said that I felt serene, yes—my mother now having returned upstairs—thinking of what would happen next. Serene is not the wrong word to use to describe my feeling. Serene, yes! Here was indeed *somebody's* problem. *Somebody* had to care. But certainly *I* didn't. I was in favor of abolishing the human race, all of life, entirely; stopped-up drains could never be considered one of *my* problems. Nonetheless, there it was. Could I pretend it wasn't there? I lived in the apartment; ate and slept here. Furthermore . . .

Furthermore—I would like now to put this delicately—the bathtub. I had no immediate need to use the bathtub. I had an immediate need, however, to use something else (not the kitchen sink). I trust I've put this delicately. Clearly I had a problem which I could not pretend was somebody else's.

At any rate, I decided at last I would play the game of pretending the stopped-up drain, somebody else's problem, was *my* problem. I changed clothes. I informed my mother I was going to the A&P to buy lye. Don't buy lye, she told me, buy that other thing.

"You mean Drano," I said to her.

"No," she replied, "that isn't what it's called."

"What is it called?"

"It has a picture on it of pipes coming down. The pipes come down from the sink and curve up again."

"That's Drano. It's in a blue can."

"No, it's called something else. I don't know what it's called. Look on the shelf where the lye is and you'll find it. Look for the picture of the pipes coming down. You'll find it with the lye. When I was staying at the Correlis' in Pennsylvania that's what they used. Your sisters use it."

"You don't remember the name?"

"I can't remember it."

"Drano."

"That isn't the name."

"That's the name."

"You look where the lye is. They'll have it. Look for the picture of the pipes."

"That's Drano. The one with the picture of the pipes on it is Drano."

"Drano. Maybe that's the name. Look for the picture of the pipes."

"That's the name. It's in a blue can. Do you want anything else while I'm there?"

"Get two cans. One for upstairs and one for downstairs."

"Two cans. You have everything else you need? Lettuce? Bread?"

"Make sure you don't come back with lye. This other is better than lye. Look on the shelf where the lye is. You'll find the lye where the washing fluid is. Two cans."

"There's nothing else you need?"

"Remember! Where the washing fluid is!"

Returned from the A&P. . . .

But I move too swiftly. I've paced this piece wrong. At this breakneck speed it becomes impossible to speak convincingly about my serenity. My madness is clearly enough portrayed; it's a real enough madness; I would not, going back, rewriting, wish to eliminate this vivid effect, this image of a man wholly mad. But the madness is not, in fact, the whole, or even the better part, of the fact. I deceive by failing to show the serenity. My serenity, that morning, was enormous.

But my aim is not to extol my power to confront the world, clearly silly, hopelessly silly, silly past all possibility of finding any but the silliest reasons for its existing at all, unbearably, crushingly, hair-raisingly silly, with serenity. My aim . . . no. I can't say what my aim is. To speak of my aim, what it may or may not be, is a silliness too appalling. I have no more knowledge of my aim . . .

The piece bogs. I returned from the A&P with a bagful of groceries—two quarts of milk, a melon, bananas, two large cans of pineapple juice, a peach pie, almost $5.00 worth of good things to eat, a can of black olives, lettuce, tomatoes, plus two cans of Drano. The directions on the cans of Drano said: Empty the water from the tub before emptying the Drano into the pipes. My mother, having heard me enter my apartment, called down. Had I returned? she cried. I had, I replied. The sound of her footsteps, descending from her apartment upstairs to my apartment downstairs, instantly unnerved me. My serenity would be put to the test. The sight of her, the sound of her voice—in short, I became a madman again.

What did she say?

705

I can't remember—I refuse to make the attempt to remember—what she said.

"GO UPSTAIRS!" I said to her.

She cried to God. I knew this would happen. I was a beast. I had turned my back on God. She was unmerciful, throwing up to me the wretchedness of my state, my arrogance, my intolerance, the ferocity of my ways, my inhuman pride. But a blow would yet strike me down. A hammerblow. A sledge-hammerblow. I would awaken. I had forgotten God. God had not forgotten me. It would happen with me as it had happened with Paul.

"Are you going upstairs?" I said to her.

She went upstairs.

This doesn't give it. The appalling stupidity, my helplessness. Yes, my abject helplessness. Confronted by the stupidity of a woman who sees God striking down her own beloved son with a sledge hammer blow, as God struck down Paul, yes, abject helplessness is my response. What chance have I against this overwhelming stupidity? And not only my mother's! Where is there a place inhabited by human beings not foul and reeking with this same stupidity? There is none.

The game! Yes! The game! I was alone now. I could play the game. The game: here was a problem, the problem was a real problem, it was *my* problem. On Peleliu we had no such problems. On Peleliu we dug holes. Then covered them up. Then planted crosses on the mounds which marked where the holes had been. Life was not only possible on Peleliu, life was ecstatic. People went crazy—with the heat, with the boredom—on Peleliu. But the pitch of life—the boredom—was ecstatic, frenzied, people knew who they were on Peleliu—life was real on Peleliu. Who, in a state of civilization, could say who he was? Civilization was madness; civilization had made me into a madman; alone, playing my game with the can of Drano, playing my game that civilization was real, civilization was a *problem*, was *my* problem, I could know again (as I had known, thirteen-and-a-half years ago on Peleliu) who I was.

My feeling of serenity playing the game was extreme. Emptying the water from the bathtub, panful by panful, carrying each panful outside, dumping the filthy mess into the neighbor's back yard, soon became tedious. Became tedious, in fact, with the second panful. But my serenity was a match, that morning, for anything. I knew who I was. I was this civilized madman playing this game that civilization was real. But I knew it was a game. I knew none of it was real. I knew what was real.

This fails to give it. The intensity of the serenity I felt. My rooms hummed with it. My mother upstairs, my rooms thrilled, rejoiced in it. Serenity throbbed through my rooms like a deep-woodland murmur. The water from the pan spilled onto the floor. I splashed in it. By the rules of my game I could do this. It was my mother's house. But this was my apartment. I paid rent for it; I could dirty the floor if I pleased, as I pleased; life on Peleliu had been possible with the earth as our floor, a piece of canvas over our heads, this our only shelter through rainstorms and hurricanes. Rainstorms—these had been real. Full moons, high tides, hurricanes—these, yes, could be real, had been real, had stopped, however, in a state of civilization, seeming real. But I knew who I was. I was joyful, the water spilling on the floor. Death was real.

I go beyond my aim. The water at last emptied from the bathtub, I poured into the pipes the requisite amount of Drano. I felt an idiot pleasure hearing the sizzle, the effervescence, the frothing inside the pipes. The pleasure was real. I confess it without shame: the sound of sizzling in the pipes entranced me; I wanted smoke to come billowing forth; I wanted fireworks.

The sizzling having ceased I poured more Drano down the pipes; I wanted more sizzling. I poured Drano also into the toilet, also into the kitchen sink; again entrancement; again sizzling in the pipes. This was real. This idiot joy, this entrancement; as the entrancement had been real on Peleliu—guns, flares, flame-throwers: appalling. But all of it real, ecstatic; no need playing any of it as a game.

But how much of sizzling can a civilized man take before becoming bored with it? I became bored. Playing this game was tedious. The game wasn't real; the tedium, however, was real. But my serenity that morning was enormous, ecstatic. The instructions on the can of Drano said wait a half hour before testing the pipes; my problem now was to kill a half hour.

I enjoyed killing that half hour. My serenity was in fact a delirium, yes, an intoxication. I sat doing nothing; doing nothing I ceased feeling tedium. I even bothered to inform my mother that the Drano had been poured and that we had now only to wait a half hour. My mother replied. I of course instantly tuned her out. But I felt no bitterness toward her. My mother is an extraordinarily kind woman. She wasn't always seventy-two years old. I've often felt that if I allowed myself, for one minute, to think of my mother, to think of her as real, to think of the futility and stupidity of the love and kindness which she's given to the world, ferociously has forced onto the world, her love and kindness a madness, an unspeakable horror, all love and all kindness this same unspeakable hideous horror, tyrannical, insensate, relentless, unpitying. . . .

707

No. I can't allow my mother to be real. No. I can only want to shoot myself if once I see my mother as real. No. The nonsense she speaks when she speaks is appalling. She prays for me every night before she goes to bed. She has them praying for me in her church. No. If my mother is real then the world must come to an end. The problem is to keep her from being real.

When she's dead she'll no longer be real; I can cry for her; she'll be dead. I'll cry. O, I'll cry. I'll perhaps even say it was love I felt for her. O, the drivel I'll speak after she's dead; the drivel—appalling! O, yes, I'm capable of speaking an appalling drivel. O, the drivel, the drivel I've spoken, the drivel I'll speak, the drivel I can't stop myself from speaking. . . .

How far this is from the serenity I felt that morning. How little I care now for that serenity. What was my aim when I began this piece?

The Drano didn't work. The game ceased to be amusing. Perhaps the second can would do it. I thought of other men faced with this problem. For them it would be a problem. Because they'd *have* to care. Because their wives would *make* them care. They'd have to play hero; playing hero was real; was a game they had to think of as real; as they had to think of their wives as real; and their mothers; and their wives' mothers; all of it; all the stupidity; so little did they know who they were. . . .

Is *this* my aim?

The second can of Drano failed to clear the pipes. The game was no longer a game. Or, if it could still be imagined a game, it was a game I had stopped wanting to play. And I'm not a madman, after all, for nothing; I don't live the life I live out of sheer spite; when I stop wanting to play a game I stop playing it. I stopped playing the game of Drano. Let the Russians drop their bomb; let the world come to an end; stopped-up drains were not *my* problem; no one would tell *me* this was real; *I* knew what was real; *games* weren't real; civilization, *that* game, certainly, wasn't real; meanwhile. . . .

I would have to vacate my apartment. It came to this. I leave aside the philosophical question raised above. My brother, my mother's angel, her first-born, who did her errands for her, accompanied her to wakes and funerals, paid the electric and telephone bills for her, visited relatives with her, repaired her damaged stormwindows, in short was her Jesus Christ here on earth, a saint, a saint, moreover, mechanically inclined, a madman when it came to gadgetry, would now have to enter my apartment to ascertain the reason for the breakdown in the plumbing system. No alternative was left me, therefore, except to make myself scarce.

My serenity strangely persisted, even dealt this new blow. Where would I go? How would I kill the afternoon hours? These were not problems. I did, however, have a problem. Somewhere I would have to find an establishment in which the plumbing system was in order. I was sure I could find such an establishment. It was not a remarkable or a major problem.

Does this end it?

Why this extraordinary need to end it?

She dealt me several more paralyzing sledgehammer-blows before I at last could make my departure. Her stupidity is truly unbelievable. The stupidity of mothers is awesome. I feel, at times, that here is the force we should fall on our knees and worship, not God—this blind remorseless stupidity of the species mother. I have met no mother. . . .

Finally, there is no defense against it.

When I returned to the apartment shortly before five all was again in order. My brother had found the cause of the stoppage immediately. He was in the apartment no more than a half hour.

I would like now to return to the question raised above: "What is real?" Civilization having been defined as a game, not real. . . .

No. This is not the place to discuss the question of reality. Stupidity is real. But even stupidity isn't real—is an abstraction from reality, a concept. Concepts aren't real. Death is real. My mother thinks she's going to heaven when she dies. Yet nothing so fills her with terror as does the thought of her own death. My mother, Christian that she is, stupid as she is, knows that death is the final and the irredeemable reality.

And now the question which torments me. . . .

No. Let me end this.

Reader, you're going to die. Doesn't the thought appall you? And doesn't it make your hair stand on end when someone like my mother—?

No. No reader will take my side against my mother.

The piece is ended.

Elémire Zolla

An Angelic Visit
on Via dei Martiri

I n these first days of winter the gray of the new apartment houses on Via dei Martiri tends to silver and more than ever they seem abandoned by all life. It's not life, certainly, when the tenants meet and rapidly greet each other; or their boring, squalid conversations about this or that, which usually revolve around weary lists of facts: *how much does it cost to heat the apartment by the various methods*, that is, with naphtha or coal, wood or gas, and *how does one install this particular stove or insulation*; or, even worse, when they stir up the scraps of impressions that were stamped on their retinas by the television show of the night before; or when the men compare notes on the scores of the soccer games or variations in their pay checks and social benefits, or finally as a form of banter, they repeat, set off by a chance word, the jingles advertising certain well-known products.

They would surely be alarmed if someone ever talked to them about something else, if they were to be reminded that each of them is carrying a weight of diseased flesh—as though to break through that frozen solitude by calling on the others to witness the inflamed mucous membrane of their noses, or the catarrh rasping in their bronchial tubes, or the digestive process going on in their intestines. And when they do happen to mention this, it is only to discuss the results of the urinalysis or the X-rays, the doctor's orders: *two drops on an empty stomach, a teaspoon before going to sleep, one injection every two days*. Even those pains which, arrowing through the heart's cavity, might be able to release tears, or, at their going, might again reveal to them a sensation of joy, have now become useless, quickly shut up in another opaque habit, another blind calculation and assessment.

Or would you want to enter this house which stands across the way?—listen to what goes on there among this group of friends, resting not before a flame but before the red wires of an electric stove and who at last for a brief space of time get together to confide in one another, to communicate something that is being born and reborn, that is, something alive. The room is monstrously clean, the furniture highly polished, turned out in pieces shaped all at the same time, and no hand has ever bent them in a gesture that is not foreseen, nauseating, and mechanical, for in the shape of things rests the soul, and this is the soul of these people. On the glass-covered table a flower vase molded like a dwarf, a huge crystal ash tray, on the wall a calendar with a mountain view; and in this air their conversation totters, denuded of everything that is not the superfluous verification, by maniacs, of already given information, the useless inventory of the drab. Let us now listen to this shouting of ghosts, crazed by inane repetition: *Shall we go to Val Gardena with the tours?*—It is the voice of a man that rises up. *Val Gardena, oh, come on, to see the mail girl?*—Laughing, the lips of a woman squeak out these words. *Who is this mail girl of Val Gardena?*—At one-thirty *the radio always talks about the mail girl of Val Gardena; don't you know the mail girl of Val Gardena?*—Gosh, *one should try to listen to the radio when one's eating.*

But let's leave this room and go back into the street; for these rooms are so many graveyard cubicles, which deceptively light up, yet in which there's not a breath of the living left; and everywhere slithers a confused sound of song—though isn't this word, in which there's an echo of something ancient and enjoyed and living, inappropriate to this din which spreads through the thin walls as from so many hotbeds of suppuration?

To escape the noise we wander through the stairways of the houses, yet we hear it again at every turn, until we halt here, here at the street floor, before the most vulnerable habitation, which, however, eludes that sinister hum—in front of the janitress's alcove. The janitress, Madame Donna, is seated on a straw-backed chair. A faded blue dress with tiny white dots hangs over her forty-year-old body. The face, which peers through the window that looks out on the street, or slowly turns toward that other window on the hallway, is pudgy and wrinkled, the eyes dazed, like those of a fish, but they are blue in contrast to the black lashes, eyes that must have emitted some flash of beauty when the strands of hair that now straggle through her hairpins did not yet fall grayly, when her hands still held their delicate outlines, without those bluish splotches from the ice-cold water which, in rinsing, chaotically thrusts forward or withdraws the blood, slowly deforming the fingers. A growth of hair sprouts under her nose and on her cheeks. Madame Donna doesn't care. After all, for whom should she care? For her husband?—that man who, during the few hours he stays at home, does nothing but belch and mumble out the day's news, his pipe's stink pouring out of his mouth?

And what in the world was there to be found in this woman already old in the middle of her life, old and stupefied? She is in fact a typical product of the small towns hereabouts, accustomed for centuries to serve, so much so that she must pretend and convince herself that she does not hear right away, that she cannot come as soon as she is called, that she is slow to grasp, turning the sentence over in her mind before understanding it, saying it aloud so as to force one to repeat it, at least in this way compelling the master to engage in some sort of conversation, repeating himself over and over again, in some sort of exchange, if only an impatient one. Is there a tremble of life still hidden in her? All that we can do is resign ourselves to sitting beside her, to scrutinizing her. Just that.

In a niche burns a votive lamp beneath a picture of a red-mantled Madonna, which does not leap out beneath the flame but remains papery in the flat glare of the electric light; a rancid smell presses down on Madame Donna, who is now wrapped in a shawl. She has pulled it tightly about her, for the cold bites, the cold of the evening that leaves its shadows on the street and darkens the hallway before her alcove. Yet a thread of vapor seems to be issuing from her thin lips, and, indeed, her lips are moving, as though by themselves, forming silent words in the silence. They accompany the thoughts that are laboring through Madame Donna's head. They say: "And now go to bed, sleep, get up tomorrow morning, dress myself, prepare the food, clean the house, go back to bed. And that man who comes home and then, in the morning, goes to work with his stuff in his lunch box. Always the same trudge-trudge, trudge-trudge. And everything tastes of lukewarm water."

And yet, on that morning, as on all the others, Madame Donna has even read the newspaper, before slipping it into the subscriber's mailbox, turning quickly to the local crime news and experiencing a slight excitement due to the labor of reading, thankful for what is immortalized in this print and paper: the memorable. Because Madame Donna lives and is enthralled by one cult, one reverence; she genuinely, without unction, respects the memorable. Yes, she too has witnessed certain memorable events, or rather they have taken place before her, they have honored her. As perhaps her mountain-dwelling great-grandmothers were dismayed when admiring rocks of unexpected shapes, stones of an incredible mold, unseasonable hail-storms, stone bridges of unknown origin flung humpbacked across torrents, and also births and deaths which occurred in an unusual manner, so Madame Donna living in the apartment-house jungle catches at the incredible as a highly meaningful apparition of the world beyond the world.

Thus, going one day to the market, she had seen pass by between two *carabinieri* a pale young man with a crushed nose gushing blood that smeared his jacket. He had just been smacked by the haberdasher. And she had known in a flash by which gesture the memorable should be welcomed: placing a finger at the side of her cheek she'd murmured, "Oh, mother," and had halted for a moment, following with her blue gaze the thief and his escort. Then she had joined the cluster of people where the haberdasher was re-enacting the scene: pointing with his finger at the counter from which the thief had pulled the cloth (and the cloth was there, all in disorder with the folds just as they twisted when that memorable piece of cloth had fallen— isolated, which no one now dared to touch). The haberdasher cried, drawing back in surprise, popping out his eyes, bracing his hands on the edge of the counter to give himself support, then flinging himself into the void in which he had discovered the thief, smacking him once again with his fist. And Madame Donna had pushed in among the others, who, all in accord, encouraged the haberdasher to enact the scene another time, murmuring at each silence or pause: "What a business!"

That she had seen. And she had seen the woman dwarf of the quarter who had given birth to a normal child. And the Chinese who sold razor blades and had married a girl of the city. And one Sunday she had seen the balustrade of the terrace where the airplane had crashed, she had seen at close range the contorted rail, erect and twisted in the air, just as it had been pushed. She had seen the spot of oil on the sidewalk where two autos had collided. And she had seen the stones that had been extracted from the liver of a friend of hers, in fact she had even touched them.

Afterward there was something on which to comment, something to repeat, or, better, to sing litanies about and prolong the revelation of the unbelievable that nevertheless takes place—zealously aided by the others who echoed her. Until one fell back into what she was now lamenting: "The usual trudge-trudge. Wake up, do the shopping, make the food, clean, go back to sleep, and then go back to doing everything just like the day before and the day before that."

Truly, there must exist memorable things, so memorable that no exclamation, no placing of one's finger against one's cheek would assuage their deadly anxiety. One time she had visited the Cottolengo convent, but of course they had not shown her the more memorable monsters: the ones with human bodies and the head of a calf or the tail of an ox, hands with claws or only a single finger, twins bound together at the back or infants with the face of a dog or monkey. It wasn't by chance that she gave her alms to the Cottolengo nuns, the nuns who guarded in their cellars, tied up in chains, those creatures so intolerably memorable. How were they born? Of women (and she affirmed: "These are things I don't even understand") who'd accepted the embrace of a dog or a monkey, or—as she preferred to admit that she thought, in order not to think of that first and authentic truth— who had made great pets of such animals and had been close to them and the object of their long looks while pregnant.

The growth of her son, who now worked in the factory with his father, was not entirely memorable, although recently she had the sensation that right in her own house there was, contrary to all appearances, something memorable and unbelievable going on, from the moment she had seen yellowish, rough spots on the sheets where her son slept, and she had hoped that the women would not spoil him for her. It was a thought that often came to her, as a screen shielding that other thought: that he should not ruin himself asking of other women what she could have given him. Oh, she certainly didn't want to, but, for instance, she had known of a woman who had done it to save her son from certain troubles, or, rather, she did not know it, perhaps they'd talked of it to her, perhaps not even that, and yet that woman had done it for a good purpose; even if she, Madame Donna, *did not understand it.*

The women certainly could spoil her son for her. In fact they couldn't

715

help but spoil him, and the *diseases of the blood* would have only been proof of their wicked, usurping behavior. These diseases, she well knew, were born from the mixture, for different kinds of sperm in the womb form a *mess*— and a *mess* was also a brawl or an imbroglio—and, in fact, the bad women receive different sperms in their black wombs, where that mixture ferments, giving life to germs, to little worms (thus, as they say, "The worms are born from flour and anchovies that become stale"). Ah, *those women*, whose names she did not even dare to pronounce (as she didn't dare pronounce those of certain diseases), save when she was greatly troubled and from the conjoined impact of all her embittered forces there leaped out, inexorable and affirmative: "Bastard whore."

It had been some time now that, as if having a presentiment of some great overwhelming wave, she was careful to keep the memorable in recesses far from any alarm, falling back on the *coincidences* (diamond wedding anniversaries, a thirty-year-old woman already a grandmother, some person about to get married and then the mother dies, another person loses a wallet but finds a thousand-lire note on the street, you think of someone and then you meet him). But now, not even this: she gazed at the street dimly lit by the neon lights, and now and then she would see a tenuous, reddish gleam waver out from the sign at the end of the street, a gleam that reached all the way to her, fading on the pavement. She had already made an effort to extract the memorable from contempt, from rage; she would see a tenant out there and she would think: "She said she was sick and there she is out there, tripping by on her heels." Or: "Is she afraid her hair will crackle, that she has to wear that little green hat, that slut," turning to an invisible confidant, clucking her tongue and shaking her head. In truth, she too realized that the accusation was a feeble one, in the case of the woman who had said she was sick perhaps not (*she* had been tricky, had asked for sympathy), but in this other instance . . . and she revenged herself on that hat: that *little fancy hat*, and simply that scornful phrase was not enough, and she went on and on: "It looks like a pot . . . a flowerpot . . . a chamber pot."

When her husband and son come back from work, she puts their food on the table, because she wants to eat alone next to the kitchen sink, which is a revenge for having to cook—although this is covered up by the excuse of being closer to the stove and water—since cooking annoys her. Just as she is annoyed at making love with her husband; she'll admit it to anyone: "For me it has always been a sacrifice."

The three of them rarely speak, and for them to start a fight requires almost nothing; just let the husband say of somebody: "She still looks pretty young," for Madame Donna to snap back: "So I'm the only one who gets old, eh?" At which point he does not know enough to say that he only wished to remark that so-and-so did not get any older. No, all he knows is how to do is echo her tone, repeat the aura of her retort, hitting back with:

"If I say she looks young, I mean just that."

The son butts in: "Oh, forget it, what does it matter?"

"You just think about making some more money," the two parents, now united and furious, scream at him.

Comes All Souls' Day and Madame and Monsù Donna have decided to go to the cemetery to fix up the grave of the grandparents, demanding that the son shoulder his share of the expenses. He refuses and a fight starts which, in its own way, is memorable.

"That's what is going to happen to me when I die, not even my grave will be taken care of," Madame Donna says.

"When you're dead, you're dead," the son says.

"Did you hear that?" Madame Donna says, turning to Monsù Donna, already dressed in dark blue to go to the cemetery. "He doesn't give a damn whether his mother dies or not."

"I didn't say that," the son says with a weary air.

"Now stop talking like a boor and put on your best suit and come with us to visit the grandparents," Monsù Donna yells.

"But how can we visit them if they're dead?" the son objects.

"Boor," the father repeats, "do you want only our dead not to receive visits? Do you want the people to go around saying that we don't know what's proper to do for our dead?"

"But what people?"

"Think about making more money," they both yell.

The day spent at the cemetery is a fine day for Madame Donna, a day when all the trams are loaded with people who are doing the same thing she is, when everybody buys the same flowers she buys, when the paths of the cemetery are full of people and all of them are exactly like herself (at least that's how she thinks, and not the other way round, that she is like all the others). Coming home tired, she talks to her husband of certain memorable events: the brown comb that busted while she was pulling it through her hair; Mino, who works at the butcher's and has a new watch; but perhaps she means something quite

717

else, expecting this to be understood and, in fact, it is so understood: "If we pretend that such things are memorable and important, perhaps certain other things which we don't mention are not too much so—such as looking spell-bound at the little girl who wants to go down the stairs, scraping her wide-apart legs from step to step with an abstracted face and tightened lips, such as the protest that rises up in you at knowing that one's son goes on Sunday afternoons with his friends to certain houses."

On the way back her husband throws a look at the son, who slouches along ahead of them, and suddenly becomes gruff, saying: "Change that face of yours, you hear me," gives him a slap on the shoulder, and then, to do him a special favor, explains why they have been working without pay all that day: for one thing, the visible consensus of all the others should have already sufficed to explain matters (all the more so when in next day's newspaper it will be written: three hundred thousand people go to the cemetery), and then: "Don't you understand, is it possible you are that much of a boor? Don't you understand that if we don't do it business will die off? How about the flower sellers? And the stonecutters? And the gardeners? And all the people who take the trams? Just try and figure out how many families get work out of this."

"But where do I come in in all this? Why do I have to go?"

"Shut up. Do you think you're better than everybody else?"

Madame Donna, however, is thinking, though she keeps silent: "All this talk about nothing. What should we do instead, stay shut up in the house?" and the discussion between her husband and son seems to her typical of the way men like *to hear themselves talk big, to show off.* And perhaps she feels that even while they are excited, tied to each other by their dispute, the two of them are strangely united. Just as the father tells the truth to the son: you want only the substantial, the useful, and since the dead are by nature poor and cannot give you anything in exchange, you despise them, but then if I did not give you anything in exchange, you would ignore me, in fact it's quite clear that you would throw me into the poorhouse, so the son tells the truth to the father: your homage to the dead is mean and lifeless, and when you sent your father to the poorhouse you would have done better not even to go and see him instead of going once a month, as if to pay him something so you wouldn't feel guilty about it, and you did this only because, after all, he wasn't so poor as not to be able to offer you something in exchange—peace with yourself.

Now the son changes tone: "The parish bulletin says that it's more suitable to say Masses than to spend all your money on flowers, that it helps the souls more," and he has a false voice, to revenge himself on his father's falsity he intensifies his, becomes unctuous and greatly concerned with what's best for the dead (Madame Donna feels that something in him rings untrue, but she no longer knows, as her grandmother would have known, how to hit him suddenly with an old proverb: *Beware of the vinegar that comes from sweet wine.*)

"Oh, come off it, you sound like a parish bulletin now," the father mutters. Then, insisting on his point, "Those priests want everything for themselves! And what about the flower seller? Well, everyone has his own ideas." (Which means: nobody has any ideas on this subject, nothing remains but the ideas of everyone and no one, so let's keep quiet about it.) Then he concludes: "One does it for the memory. I too know that once you're dead, you're dead. I don't need you to come and tell me."

The son goes on, feeling everything melt within him because of this new feeling of sweetish sentimentality, captivated by his unctuous words: "We remember the dead without all this."

They all know that this is untrue, and this is how his father says it to him: "Think about making more money. And for the time being, do as I tell you to." And what he really means is: the dead cannot escape, just as we cannot get out of it; so let's give them some flowers, just as we go once a week to the movies—everything is fine if we work and they're there.

Husband and son already asleep, Madame Donna remains awake because she's the one who closes the street door at eleven o'clock, and there she is, where we first saw her, in the small alcove with her elbow resting on the table, looking outside along the street and into the hallway with a glazed eye, the eye of fish in a fishbowl, beyond which gather the last scraps of warmth in the bend of the entrance hall, while along the street the shadows are already raging under the evening whip of ice. But now, just at this moment, there passes a black shadow against the blue of the street, indistinct splotch and sign, hieroglyphic of a thousand of Madame Donna's scorn-masked fears, a thousand of her tremors disguised by derision: Miss Cri Cri.

Cri Cri is a fattish woman, with a lame leg. She has a swollen belly and the hands that come out of the sleeves of her fur coat are small and buttery to the touch, just as her feet are tiny in their gilt pumps. She swings her purse, dragging her longer leg. (And to swing her purse in the air like

719

that, to make it twirl, is in itself a scandal, the very mark of the streetwalker, and in any case the lame walk in an obscene manner, and since they seem to derive satisfaction from their way of walking, so Madame Donna reasons, they are at bottom responsible for it.) In the smooth face amid the smooth black hair stare eyes which are never opened wide but are always gripped in two folds of fat, which grow finer towards the temples and, twisting upward, disappear; without eyebrows, and often she forgets to mark out their arc with her make-up pencil. Beneath her small curved nose her lips are thick— in the apartment house they call her Butterball.

But all the things they say about her! When she was young she was pretty and tried to become famous, traveling a lot and suffering. (Immediately after the war she had in fact tried sometimes to maneuver, blowing her young breath to arouse the jaded nerves of some impresario, but afterward not even succeeding to get into his theatrical company, and after nights of love-making with young actors or painters, nights studded with tragic speeches and sighs and confessions whispered in a darkness slashed by the red tracks of two cigarette tips, she had awakened later to find her friend no longer in bed but, instead, his bill added to hers at the hotel desk.) After all these defeats she'd come back to live with her family, and now she was a painter. Her mother refused to give her the key to the street door, clinging to that last stronghold of her severity, and at night and in the morning, sometimes at dawn, the people in the house would be jolted awake by her hoarse wail from the bottom of the street. Shuffling down the stairs, her father would run to open the door, his overcoat flung over his pajamas, cursing his wife, and Madame Donna had seen him, his hands clasped over his head, beat his joined fists down on his daughter's shoulders, who was laughing and bleating and then would clutch him and say things that made his face go white.

And Madame Donna, repeating to herself, "After all I must keep my eye open, it's my duty," had gone to the door to hear Miss Cri Cri whisper: "Go ahead and hit me, hit me if you enjoy it. It doesn't matter, I've surmounted everything. You understand, I've surmounted."

She always says it in that childish voice which suddenly becomes hoarse: "I've surmounted." And that's what she said that time the man got out of the big black auto which had waited for six hours in front of the street door and, as he cried, had given her a punch and then she'd carried a black eye around for over a month, and even now she had a small furrow on her cheekbone, and she hadn't even lifted her hand to shield herself, only smiling and moaning *Mmmmm* (perhaps, just at seeing him, she felt a burning in her throat, like a flash of hot pepper). And again, at the street door, when that hunchback who, as he talked, had clenched his fists and suddenly kicked her in the belly and then had run away. What did it mean? Madame Donna asked, that word *surmount* which Cri Cri would say with a smile, sucking in her cheeks, creasing them with a small dimple and hiding completely her always moist pupils in her slits of eyes, smiling even when she was being beaten and insulted—in fact, especially then.

They said that plump Cri Cri used to sit after dinner in a bar on Via Roma, smiling at the meeting of every glance, there at the same table every evening, alongside the juke box, staying there until somebody approached her, and they were two motionless statues beneath the bar's neon light, she and the cashier, who, though they appeared two petrified beings, any man could bring to life with the alms of a joking word or a finger scraped under their soft chins. "I'm ready to do anything," Cri Cri would announce, smiling. And there was a man who once a week came and sat at her table, talking with her for a few minutes and leaving her a banknote, just to see that unchanging smile and to hear those words: "I've surmounted everything. I'm ready to do anything." He left her the money and went away, satisfied.

Once she'd stayed away from the bar for a month, after getting to know a man who had stolen an auto that contained a briefcase stuffed with money and who had taken her to a big luxury hotel in Rome until they came to arrest him. She had happily adapted herself to bringing him food in jail, food scraped together from her own, which was then reduced to two coffees a day, and to everybody she would say that she didn't love him, that in fact she thought he was loathsome. And at times she had come across young students, who fell in love with her and wanted to marry her with the same furious passion of that man in the black auto who had beaten her so badly. This was Cri Cri, for Madame Donna the object of horror and immense hidden amazement.

So much so that first hearing her and then seeing her appear, Madame Donna has again begun her hunt for the memorable, talking almost distinctly, as if there were somebody with her: Yesterday evening I saw go by (it has honored me) at a distance of not even four yards a gigantic Transylvanian from the circus, who is not a man like the others, so something less and more than a man, and I was immediately aware of it (the honor) because even the papers have published the photograph of this colossal man who touches the ceilings of the trams and, so the papers say, has to carry around with him wherever he goes a bed that will fit him.

But outside in the brown of evening passes—it is doubtlessly she—Cri Cri, limping toward the street door, attractive and abhorrent. Oh, if she, like her husband and son, only had a resource for such occasions, something that could serve to wall her in, to daze her, if she could grab the yellow sports page open as they had left it there on the table . . . Madame Donna cannot, and she is devoured by the great desire to stare at Cri Cri, to fix her glance on her, to envelop her and to hear "I've surmounted," that strange combination of words which, afterward, placates and lightens the heaviness of her heart. But she doesn't dare, she had to be content with squinting at the limping figure which appeared within the window's picture and then vanished.

Madame Donna couldn't stand it any longer; she got up from her chair, went to the window, to see Cri Cri dwindle, to make sure that she would, with that sinister rhythmic thud-thud of hers, reach the end of the street, and she had to control herself in time, for in going to the window she had the impulse of hinting that she too limped, stealing from Cri Cri a trait that might, by living it, be able to clear up Cri Cri's secret, a bit of cunning by means of which to enter perhaps Cri Cri's moist, warm, satisfied world, the world where one surmounts: for it must undoubtedly be caressing, that repeated yielding to the fall of one leg against the other, which then bends and lifts, intimately caressing, the other with itself.

Madame Donna stopped herself just in time in her imitation of that step, and to give herself a reason for finding herself on her feet began to rub the velvet lining of her work box, which was open on the table; she liked to rub the tips of her fingers over the velvet. (Oh, those other velvets, the black velvet of Cri Cri's voice, her way of squeezing her eyes shut like an animal when one strokes the silken softness of its fur, and the velvety brushing of one thigh against the other suggested by that limping of hers.) Then, as if only now had she got the idea of going there, she went to the window—indeed the incongruity of her act resembles the clues which betray a crime, and the crime to which they point is perpetrated against the buds of feeling, against the nascent movements of the soul.

She sees that Cri Cri was not the tiny point she had pictured at the end of the street (she had imagined her down there under the red sign, that red globe like a moon of the dog days), but she was coming back, and it gave her a cruel, sudden leap in her heart, almost as though Cri Cri was coming back just for her, invoked by her. She was advancing deliberately, her limping was a peremptory, more and more marked sound, *tock tock* on the pavement, as if to give the beat to a fanfare which, strangely, did not come—Cri Cri was returning. There she is, at the turn of the street door, and Madame Donna goes to the threshold murmuring to herself: "Anyway, nobody sees me," sticks out her head, and, full face receives Cri Cri's smile, that widening of the mouth, that clamping together of the eyes, not sweet, not cold, but deliberate and shining and weary.

Madame Donna tries to look at her with contempt and to say to herself: "She doesn't even know where she wants to go . . . up and down she has to go, all night long, and then no wonder she gets up at noon," but something within her gives way, as though shattered by an insinuation which has the timbre of Cri Cri's infantile, husky voice: "Nobody sees me, so why shouldn't I smile at her?"

Cri Cri continues to stare at her like a serpent and Madame Donna feels a clutching down at the bottom of her belly, like a light that blazes in her bowels; her hardened features droop into a painful, alarmed, fascinated grimace. "If you want to come in for a minute," she says, in a voice as indifferent as she can make it, as though to add: "The alcove is at the disposal of anyone who pays rent," and accompanies her words by standing up straight from the bent position she had assumed, nodding with a gesture as practical and detached as possible at the door of the toilet and in the end recomposing herself to say: "If you have to fix a stocking or something, go ahead, I mean."

Her features immobile, Cri Cri doesn't move, and Madame Donna's curt interest, her sly reserve melts and vanishes in the fear that the invitation will not be accepted, that she must fall back into the solitude which she was just about to overcome. But Cri Cri advances, her foot beats the floor sharply, peremptorily, and Madame Donna moves aside, so that there won't be any obstacle, letting Cri Cri enter.

"It's cold, sure it's cold," Madame Donna says and ends in a laugh, pushing back the curtain that separates the vestibule from the hallway. Cri Cri doesn't utter a word and sets out for Madame Donna's toilet. While Cri Cri closes the door of the latrine behind her, Madame Donna shuts the door of the alcove, muttering to herself: "So the heat doesn't go out," and sits down to wait, happy at having sized up matters correctly—Cri Cri had

723

felt her garter tear—she had indeed guessed everything and everything had passed off smoothly, without a hitch. When she would come out of there Cri Cri would talk and who knows what she would reveal, what memorable things.

In reality Madame's Donna's toilet is more than a toilet—a narrow passage where against one wall stands a dresser with rose-shaped handles of brass, in which the linens are flung in disorder together with the elementary-school diplomas and the trade-school diploma and the gas bills; on top, a slab of white marble on which are piled clothes to be thrown away or washed, socks and undershirts and shirts, and on this pile of clothes a small box, or, rather, a small drawer taken out of a night table, which is full of tweezers, curlers, toothpaste tubes, hair-clogged combs, small jars of brilliantine. On the floor, shoes are thrown in a confused heap on top and under a broken electric stove, and, among them, a toilet's metal ball, the old counterweight belonging to the water tank whose rod was broken and had been flung on the floor, which retains a film of rusty slime from the time when it had been immersed in the tank up there on the wall. A dress and a rag of a towel hang from the crooked clothesrack fastened in the wall. And under the basin a green valise and on the wall flutters a colored photograph, moved by the draft made by anyone who goes through the narrow passageway between the dresser and the wall.

Cri Cri has locked herself in there, and Madame Donna is guardedly exhilarated, even if she keeps her mind off it, thinking: "Let's hope she won't be able to read my life, seeing all that mix-up. Where am I supposed to put that stuff, anyway?" In order not to say: "I show her my most intimate things, let her accept me."

The door handle, which Madame Donna is anxiously watching, turns, here is Cri Cri again, smiling just as before, but now at last she talks: "It's cold this evening."

"Best to stay holed up in one's house," Madame Donna replies, with a little nervous laugh.

"You want to come upstairs? We'll have a chat, do you want to?" From Madame Donna's bowels right up to her heart there erupts a blaze which now reddens her cheeks. It would have been unbearable if, as she had feared, already sensing the words on Cri Cri's lips, Cri Cri had said: "Thanks, it certainly wasn't worthwhile going all the way upstairs. Good-bye."

Madame Donna would have been tricked; instead, Cri Cri had understood, she was inviting her, and she in turn was automatically mumbling: "Thanks so much. I wouldn't want to disturb you."

Cri Cri was already going up the stairs, and Madame Donna hurriedly locked her door, following her all anxious for pleasure; she knew that she didn't deserve all this, she wanted, on this unhoped-for occasion, to say only what she had to and what was necessary. And her voice is ingratiating when, at the last flight, she says: "You sure start puffing going up." Cri Cri doesn't even reply: Madame Donna realizes, biting her lips, that now all those superfluous, easy-to-say words have deserted her, those words that run off without changing anything, slipping from one's lips to elicit the reply that is already contained in them, words with which one avoids the dreadfulness of looking at each other, of undergoing the furtive force of others' looks and the unsayable words that a look demands. (And it is like going back in time, to when, as a little girl, she played the game of staring at a friend to see who would be the first to burst into laughter—which meant defeat, succumbing, surrendering to the force of staring at each other, the laughter a disarming, an appeal for mercy—it is a turning back that to her seemed to penetrate to distances even remoter than they actually were, almost a happy delusion that, with Cri Cri, she had in this way ascended the stairs toward mysterious rooms in some far-off time, joined in a tacit understanding that could tolerate only words she didn't yet know or dare to pronounce.) Cri Cri motioned to her to go in, and now her smile had started to become sly. Madame Donna went in—still silent, having understood that that was her task until the moment when those necessary, heavy words came to her lips, those words laborious to say—went in proceeded by Cri Cri, whose step resounded even more emphatically on the tiles.

They were in a huge, nearly bare room with two windows, on its whitewashed walls a dressing gown and a mandolin hanging from a wobbly nail. On the floor, paintings piled in disorder in all the corners. An easel stood upright next to a table cluttered with rolled-up sheets of drawing paper, tubes of colors, brushes, and palette knives.

Holding her hands joined on her belly, Madame Donna went to the window: from up there the houses dwindled, the people were reduced to tiny blotches; yes, truly, she had been taken out of her world, the world of *downstairs*.

"If you stand there quietly, after a while you can hear the roar of the city," Cri Cri said to her, frightening her with that strange word *roar*, breathed out with closed and resonant vowels.

"You keep plants on your terrace," Madame Donna observed. There was a balcony on which jutted up the black, spare vine of a wisteria.

"My wisteria," Cri Cri said, in a slack voice, coming up beside her and pressing her nose against the other pane of glass in the window: it was as though they were holding hands. Then she began to say, disorienting Madame Donna, who had yielded to the comfort of that contact at a distance, not looking at each other but both looking at the plant: "But do you see that wisteria well? Every morning I come to greet it, passing the palm of my hand over its trunk, pale because it's so blue, so delicate, so young. And there's a place where it's wounded, and it's tender there where the frost has wounded it, and moans out its sap. In the spring the buds will come"—she steps away from the window and brings her hands together like a cup to show how a bud looks, to imitate it—"violet they'll be," she says.

Madame Donna bites her lips; she knows that she has to drive out words from a dark cellar, catch them as they rise up inside her, in that place where Cri Cri's voice booms, echoes, and disquiets. She says: "I'm glad you used my house." No, it's no good. She feels that Cri Cri is looking at her with her merciless persistence, that she must say something that Cri Cri will accept—she unclasps her hands, places one on her breast and the other, after having fluttered in the air, goes to rest on the first. She says, and finally she has found the true words: "What does *surmount* mean?"

Oh, the world beyond the world, the memorable enclosed in a word and in that gesture of the hand with which Cri Cri would accompany the word, like pushing aside a curtain—yes, it was right there, within her grasp, maybe it has been found, very simple, the question that would have ushered her into the truly memorable, hidden (she felt it) behind the restless wrinkling of the flesh around Cri Cri's long eyes, which, from inside there, sent her a sign. It was not curiosity about Cri Cri's life (almost as though she had by now torn herself away from the search for those basely memorable things), also because it is the rule of curiosity to snatch, here and now, as it grazes by. Instead, she was asking that there be offered her that intriguing reality which itself produces the memorable, as if in church a priest might make a sign just to you, out of all people there, to come openly forward, to approach the tabernacle, up up, all the way, so that you, all by yourself, can bow your head to take the Host in your mouth with a bite; as though to accept the invitation of Christ who, from under the soft folds of his mantle, with a macabre exulting gesture of his thin hands, pulls out his halo-refulgent heart, giving it to you to swallow.

"Don't you know what *surmount* means?" Cri Cri said, stressing the questioning tone and making the three descending notes of the question wave in the air. "I have surmounted everything," she went on. It was the beginning of the litany, the start of Cri Cri's prayer, the initial supplication, and now she was going to recite it: "I accept everything. There is nothing that disgusts me or frightens me. Sometimes I go up into the hills to push my face in the earth where the mushrooms grow and the damp caterpillars crawl; I go there to breathe, I push my face into it. And yesterday I lay down right in the middle of Corso Francia, like this . . ." Cri Cri bent her leg, breaking the fall with her open hand, stretching out on the tile floor with her face up, staring at the ceiling with flashing eyes, the black gleam of her eye sockets and the wrinkles around her eyes smoothed out, no longer contracted. "It was cold and I was looking up at the moon, stretched out like this in the middle of the avenue." She drew herself up and squatted there; Madame Donna had brought her finger to her cheek. "I accept everything. Like the sea, where everything ends up. Nothing matters to me. I like everything that happens, I put it inside of me. When they beat me and when they love me. Even when they scorn me, as you were doing."

"I haven't said a thing," Madame Donna said, swallowing and going to sit on the stool.

Cri Cri bursts out laughing, a forced, cavernous laugh so that Madame Donna, all upset, says: "Was there something in what I said to laugh at?" And then, getting hold of herself: "Love is love."

And she meant, obviously, the very opposite: love is not love, it is something more (just as they once used to say about Cri Cri: "Nice things that woman does," meaning, "too nice, not nice but intolerably nice"). Did she mean to say that she absolved Cri Cri of all she had ever done or even was going to do, that she pardoned her, or, rather, that she no longer feared the example and influence of Cri Cri's actions on her? No, certainly, for now, instead, she wanted to imitate, and was trying to understand, to agree with that which Cri Cri was looking for—who knows what memorable encounter?—She was offering herself like that at the bar; asking pardon and absolution for herself, not imparting it. Or was it only, as it now seemed to her, that she wanted to say that she had understood what Cri Cri meant by *surmount*? And that was just how Cri Cri understood it and also convinced

Elémire Zolla

Madame Donna of understanding it, replying after a pause: "That's just what I wanted to say."

Now it has never happened before to Madame Donna to talk like that, with those sentences understood and not understood, feeling her whole body participate in the vibrations of the words which both hinted at things and disguised them and, being elusive, could even mean that which one must not say but only do and must afterward immediately forget.

"I am a poor woman, I can't understand all these things," Madame Donna said, but these ordinary words to which you resort not to humiliate yourself but rather to humiliate someone who humiliates you, brazenly exposing your humility word for word like a glorious wound, were said by her with her head bowed.

"What things?"

Madame Donna's finger searched in the air, finally pointing to a painting on the floor: "Did you make that? I don't understand it, I don't know what it is."

"But don't you like to look at it?" Cri Cri asked.

728   Madame Donna was seized by fear: if she were to look at that painting then really something evil might befall her—pleasure. Black gashes slashed a gray background and an orange circle emerged, slightly removed from the spot where the lines crossed that divided or broke up the background.

"You'd enjoy it if you pretended, as you look at it, that you were painting it," Cri Cri said, dragging herself toward the painting. Madame Donna hastened to obey—she looked. "If you only knew what a pleasure it is to put this black here and then scratch across it, like this." Cri Cri crooked a finger and scraped the air. In fact, at the suggestion, the scratches in the tarry tracing of the signs stood out. Madame Donna followed Cri Cri's pudgy hand as it moved before the picture, giving it life, taking out of it the gestures that had composed it. She felt she must believe in these gestures, she nodded her head in assent while Cri Cri was saying: "Like this, zaac, zaac, one scratches the lampblack. And then you step back. Come here, look how soft it is, how beautiful this pink is in the center of all this—you look at it and you relax," she said, pointing to that pinkish circle.

"A button," Madame Donna said.

"A little rosy button, all warm. A piece of candy. There in all that turmoil, that gray mess, that black which comes straight down, sad."

"I don't like candies, they make acid," Madame Donna said, fearing she might have to surrender completely, fearing that she must *get angry* at Cri Cri before that painting which she preferred when it was indifferent, not threatening. (To get angry was for her every annoying, lively feeling; to get angry was above all to experience love as a man did, so much so that *getting one's balls in an uproar* was the locution by which she defined the act of getting angry and it was, in fact, that motion of the testicles, their slow revolving after coitus, symbol, part for the whole, of man's furious pleasure which she denied herself because too dismaying, because to partake in it would mean no longer being *sacrificed*).

But Cri Cri's voice brought her back: "You're not looking. Why don't you try to look. Come on, look at it carefully. I was talking of the candies we used to eat as children. Don't you remember? How they would melt, giving you the feeling of that pink spot right in your mouth. Try to make it come into your mouth, that pink spot. And now feel how the gray all around it is clean and smooth, try and touch it with your finger."

Madame Donna obeyed. "You make me do strange things," she said, adoring Cri Cri. Then she said: "Do you also make people?"

"Of course, sometimes. Look." She reached toward the heap and took out some nudes of men and women.

"Naked," Madame Donna murmured, and by now slipping down the easy slope of the most unpremeditated words, she added in dialect: "beautiful as a brood of naked mice," evoking the expression of the mountains from which her parents had come, that coarse dialect which, however, had an almost rapt inflection.

"Do you want to pose?" Cri Cri asked, looking at her fixedly, as though to warn her of something.

"Do I have to sit still?"

"Look, I'll draw up the stove. It's hot, isn't it, near the stove? You can't stand it all dressed up, isn't that so?"

"While you paint me?"

"Look, I'll put it even closer."

"But you die if they make your portrait."

"Are you afraid to sit there naked?"

"Afraid? . . . We're both women. But I feel embarrassed, that's what."

Cri Cri jumped to her feet with a sudden movement, crookedly, twisting her entire body.

"Do you want to drink?" she asked.

Madame Donna was about to answer: "If you like," but she kept it back, assenting with her head and Cri Cri went to get a long, slender-necked bottle of sweet wine. She poured out a glass, leaving her to her thoughts.

"Do you want to sit for me? So, come on, get undressed," she said, lighting a cigarette.

By now the emotion had lasted too long, protracted for two hours with blazes flooding her head and that contracting and dilating of the flesh beneath her breastbone; Madame Donna could not endure that fought-against disintegration, all she wanted was to give in to whatever Cri Cri asked her to do, without questioning. Swallowing a gulp of wine, she said: "Just as you say."

She thought of her gray underwear, of the undershirt that was made from a sheet cut and sewn so that she could get her head through it and stick out her arms, of the man's shorts she was wearing, of the orange cotton-wool soaked in capsicum acid that she wore on the kidneys for warmth, and she thought that by chance today she didn't have newspaper on her back, which, better than any cloth, protected her from the cold. But looking around she realized that she would not offend the room, which was strewn with rags streaked with colors and crumpled-up papers; even a pair of old nylons were being used to wipe the brushes. And she thought that she too could surmount and got up from the stool while Cri Cri stretched a sheet of drawing paper on a board attached to the easel and tacked it down.

With her face smoothed out, Madame Donna gulped down the wine, lifting her elbow like a man, and then started to undress. Never had she undressed to make love with her husband—for that sacrifice she always uncovered herself only in part, not out of embarrassment but because of negligence and indifference, even if afterward, she bragged about it: "Never did I lie naked like those sluts there."

"After all," she said, pulling off her dress, "I did undress for the examination of the health insurance, when I wanted to get work papers, before I got the job downstairs, and it wasn't even as hot as it is here." (And she remembered herself that day, in line with the other women in the doctor's office, nor had it been bitter, indeed it had been she among all of them to say: "After all, we're all made the same," wishing to say, as it always happened, the opposite: "We are very much different, but let's pretend to be the same so that by chance we are not overwhelmed by the great wish to touch each other with our eyes, comparing ourselves carefully, observing each other to spy out the differences, so devastating when uncovered: the different swelling of a breast and the broad purple nipple of that woman, or the pink, proudly upright nipple of that other one, or the next's nerveless pallor." Both old and young women standing together in the white corridor, all holding in their hands that sheet of paper on which everything was marked down with a scratch of the pen—their ages and illnesses and pregnancies—under the gaze of young white-coated doctors who had checked every last scratch, listening to them, palpating them, men and not men because of that uniform which gave them the right to address them familiarly by their first names and to slap them good-naturedly, or to squeeze their arms, as if every gesture of theirs was to be accepted willingly.) "It will be like that time," Madame Donna said to herself, taking off the undershirt while the stiffening of her arm gave her the lie, since she wanted to say: "It's not at all like that time." Her clothes piled up at her feet, and her skin, exposed to the stove, turned red.

Cri Cri looked at her for a long time, then she said: "Sit where you want to. In fact, on the stool, like that. Now keep still. That's fine."

Madame Donna surprised herself thinking: "After all, I'm not ugly," as though to enter inside Cri Cri, as though she could defend herself from the examination which Cri Cri had subjected her to, telling Cri Cri that even if her breasts sagged a bit they weren't yet ruined, and if her thighs were squat the skin still held, it was solid. And from the pile of clothes a pleasant smell reached her.

731

Cri Cri was making great slashes with a charcoal pencil on the paper and Madame Donna felt gay, lightened, under that look which was encasing her in a swirl of lines, taking her from herself with that simultaneous pulling her in, thrusting her away, holding her in a cold ardor that makes her breast rise and fall in a breathing now deep and rhythmic. And, with a silent prayer, she implores that face that probes into her whole being and at the same time is abstracted from her: "Oh, Cri Cri, from today on you will tell me what I must do, I am here so that you will guide me, on my own I will not move a muscle, I for myself do not exist. Naked and defenseless and with my side scorched by the stove." The close heat makes her torpid, while Cri Cri's attentive gaze makes her stiffen beneath the torpor. But suddenly she thinks she has caught a change in Cri Cri's features, perhaps an involuntary mockery that flits over that plump face, and immediately she becomes aware of her rigid, painful torpor, her cramp, while the jealous sense of her body, which in fact Cri Cri has given her, takes offense at the weary, rapid, sibilant gesture of that hand which moves in a wide circle on the paper. A barely defined suspicion that withdraws when another sensation sweeps over her, making her stiffen again: the doorbell has rung.

Some steps in the hallway, a door bangs, another, nearer door, closes, and then again silence. "It must be my friend, my great friend," Cri Cri says, and stops with hand in midair, adding, "Should I have him come in?" with a silent laugh that closes her left eye and opens the other, letting the pupil wink.

"Well, if it's a friend of yours," Madame Donna says, full of pain and anxious to obey.

"But he's dead. He's a ghost, should I call him all the same?" Cri Cri asks, showing her teeth.

Madame Donna jumps up and plunges an anguished hand into the pile of clothes, trying to pick up her slip.

"No," mumbles Madame Donna, shaking, and Cri Cri, with an amused laugh, says: "Look at him over there, pushing out his white head."

732 Madame Donna manages to shove her head through the undershirt, looking along the line that parts from Cri Cri's pointed finger, and there in the corner where until now her glance has not rested she sees the plaster head of an old bearded man impaled against the wall.

"It's him sticking out his head, with his body outside kicking his legs."

"You're making fun of me," Madame Donna pants, completely upset by that head which she's trying to avoid looking at, which she's sure wasn't there when she came in. She scrambles into her clothes and runs to the door. There she halts and turning slowly sobs: "You shouldn't have done this to me. You shouldn't make jokes about the poor dead," and where the stove has scorched her, on the hip and the ribs, it seems to her she has a wound that seeps blood.

Cri Cri continues drawing on the paper, where now the image of Madame Donna is sprawled, clumsier than ever, monstrously obscene. That's what has come out on the paper, just like that, without her knowledge and will, and this has induced Cri Cri to detach herself from the woman subjugated by her with tenderness, turning that obedient love into a derisory anguish, anguish and love readily exchanging places. Or was it Madame Donna who wanted to undergo the anguish that is always there ready to take the place of love, was it she who wanted to believe she was in a panic because of Cri Cri's lugubrious jokes? Her own image leaps crudely to her eye and still she does not dare open the door, keeping her hand on the doorknob, hoping at least for Cri Cri to turn and tell her not to be afraid. But no, all that appears is the lame woman's back, that crooked back which flows into the broad flat hips to flaunt the swollen buttocks under the skirt, and that mass of black hair, that casque which seems to be coated with butter and gleams like a thick mat of crow's feathers encasing her head. And from behind the blackish casque the voice comes: "I'd never have been able to make up a body like yours. You'd even scare the dead."

Madame Donna thanks her for not turning around, slowly turns the doorknob, goes out into the hallway, crosses it, hearing behind her Cri Cri's now weary voice, crying after her: "Close the door." And then, "You've left your heat pad here."

Madame Donna manages to open the door and finds herself on the landing, where a cold gust of wind strikes her and brings her to her senses. Her body must fight the cold and the wound that seemed to be open on her side disappears. She starts to go down the stairs, clutching the railing tightly.

"I've been dreaming," she says, and the sound of bells reaches her, the bells of midnight that pierce the silence. The only bells one hears in the city. "It's late," she tries to think, "I must get downstairs right away," but the landings uncurl endlessly, they open out at each turn as though maliciously prolonging her descent. Madame Donna tries to get out of the spiral, hastens her step, clutched to the railing. Now she knows shame, not the vacuum shame of before, the shame that feared immodesty, but another, different, which is this feeling of being outraged, weakened, wasted. "She wanted to show me the poor dead souls," she murmurs.

She does not know or perhaps does not truly know, Miss Cri Cri up there, that after having awakened that which in Madame Donna was dormant, she could not help but let loose inside of her, at last free and powerful, those presences which Madame Donna has briefly sensed at times, when a kiss had seemed to brush her lips in the night or a hand seized the bedclothes—the spirits her ancestors had revered. Cri Cri has effectively evoked that which the chestnuts left on the table at the end of the meal on All Souls' Day had ineptly tried to call forth in an act by now totally bereft of all warmth. (In Madame Donna's house the plate of the dead and the chair of the dead were no longer left empty next to theirs, but at the end of the meal the boiled smoking chestnuts were left there: "Let them come and get them.")

Madame Donna descends the deserted stairway, pulling her shawl about her, grasping it with a contracted hand. And all around they rustle, the dead. She trembles, murmuring: "Our Lord, Our Lord," and at last the tears are released.

The alcove is just as she had left it, the light is still on. She enters, blows her nose, puts out the light, and undresses in the darkness of her bedroom, slipping under the covers beside her snoring husband. As he snores he seems to be saying strange things, atrocious things with that vibration of the jaws and nose, until in his sleep he speaks out: "It's not me."

To whom is he talking? To the head, to them, Madame Donna thinks while she forces herself to lie still beneath the covers, her eyes wide open. What can the dead want? she asks herself, and within her a voice rises: "I have wet feet. The earth is damp."

The black hours of the night drag along slowly, or is it Madame Donna's agitation that watches and hinders them? She keeps turning in bed, awaking each time the grumbling in the shadow starts—"It's not me"— which seems to her not an exculpation but also seems to mean: *It's not me here in bed*. Madame Donna lifts the edge of the blankets, pushes her feet into slippers, finds in the darkness the shawl that comforts her, and goes back to the alcove.

As soon as her eyes recover from the burst of light, she opens a drawer in the bureau, her hands run under the folded napkins and dig out a pack of her mother's and, even before that, her grandmother's, Tarot cards, thick with grease at the edges. She begins to shuffle them, seated at the table. "I might as well, since I can't sleep," automatically grazes her mind, but she does not insist on it: she no longer has any need to put all in order, to place each gesture within the frame of the reasonable, the foreseeable, in order to move the cards. To make the chaos with the Tarot cards, to mix them, is the first act of the rite, a gesture that cannot be omitted, indeed must be accompanied by the sentence: "Without trickery, yet not by chance either," because the rite cannot be performed hastily, with an eye to convenience and the strictly necessary: each moment is sacred. And especially this one, making the chaos, during which the hands lose all stiffness, the joints become flexible, nimbly the cards leap in and out of the deck, swiftly the hands move (and she must move her fingers speedily, make them winged, if not in bed, here; anxiety seems to be moving them, but anxiety is the other side of pleasure and it's by chance that one or the other comes up, and the fingers that are directed by pleasure, here too, work lightly, stopping, concentrating the rush of thoughts so as to placate it.)

After having made the chaos, one makes the extract of the chaos, one pulls out the cards from three chosen piles, one lays them out, some to form the two capitals, some to make a circle around the dominant card in the center. Here they are now, they speak. Oh, combinations, union of the figures! The malicious queens; the queen of Saba and woman who pours the water from the urns (Oh, Cri Cri, queen of bitter scorn!) they are not alone, there is a way to dodge them because all around dance the Good Lovers, the Woman Pope, the Two of Cups, the Cow, and the Earth Mother (Oh, Cri Cri, she of the whispered confidences!) Cri Cri up there makes the figures, has even turned her into a figure, stealing who knows what from her; but now here the figures become life again, attract hopes and fears, identify the monsters and ghosts that have been loosed in her by Cri Cri, the maker of images.

Just as the pleasure that restlessly moves the fingers has been eluded in the anxiety with which one extracts from chaos the essence of chaos, so the knowledge revealed by pleasure, those obscure communications which are its secret and are conveyed amidst moans and sighs and arched jerks of the arms, are here discovered indistinct and sublime. Here is the Hermit, which is Cri Cri by now far off, slyness and betrayal, but the Hermit turned upside down leads to repentance (oh, marvelous revelation, which consoles— Cri Cri can only be slyly repentant and repentantly sly!). Here is the Ace of Swords, the sign of embarrassment, but turned upside down it produces pregnancy (and Cri Cri has made her pregnant with embarrassment) and the reunion sends one on to the next card: the dog who bays at the moon, is it she or Cri Cri? Both of them, if there follows the card of the Sun with the *two* children beside a tomb, a lucky or unlucky card depending on whether it is right side up or upside down, but always lucky if there follows— as it does, miraculously—the card of the Lovers (even if it is turned upside down, to indicate: the break). Until now Madame Donna has been part of Cri Cri but now she incorporates her in herself, Cri Cri enters through her mouth, she who wanted to make her swallow the poisoned little pink button; and if something of Cri Cri still hovers around, which she Madame Donna is not and cannot be, it is the Devil, right side up happy love, upside down dishonor (thus she has escaped from the dishonor, by undergoing the first.) It is the Magician who raises the dead from the grave; illness if upside down, but it is right side up, as it has to be, and so melancholy and madness. Madness? Sleep begins to calm the fingers' agitation as on the beautiful card of Hope the angel pours water into the wine cup.

With sleepy steps Madame Donna returns to her bedroom and, finally reconciled to sleep and its dreams, stretches herself under the covers in a hospitable darkness, where the rustling of the spirits which graze her no longer threaten, where, without tremors and sudden jerks, one can abandon oneself to sleep. What the evening has been was told by the card of the Last Judgment, in which the dead come out of their graves at the angels' fanfare (right side up: quarrel; upside down: prejudice) and at the fifth round the Three of Swords has turned up: the felicitous conclusion with the Queen of Saba, the dark, passionate, and generous woman who becomes dubious if brought out upside down, and it's all a matter of chance whether a card comes up right or wrong, because no matter which way its face revolves it is always a single knot of feelings: benevolence-death, man-phantom, glory-disaster, since the Wheel of Fortune is surmounted by the crowned monkey and the Juggler continues to play and from time to time the Joker reappears.

Something has matured in this heavy sleep of Madame Donna's, a metamorphosis is taking place as her heart beats placidly, slowly, her breasts softly rising and falling in the ebb and flow of her breathing.

Let us let time rest for a few months more on the houses of Via dei Martiri before going back there, and now it is a Sunday morning, with the street strangely animated. Down there at the street's end you can see an old arthritic man supported by two women get off the tram with painful care: they are going to Madame Donna's. And, again, you can see these two girls with shiny eyes, darkly circled by the disease of love, hesitate on the threshold of the street door. They hold hands to encourage each other, with suffocated giggles quenching the anxiety that pushes them there. Then, at last, you see they make up their minds to visit Madame Donna's. It is a concourse of people to the janitress' alcove, all of them looking for Madame Donna, beseeching her for an imperious order or a reassuring shrug or a remedy in which to believe. But it is a different Madame Donna we observe on the other side of the glass panes, a Madame Donna who picks up the cards, who's grown fatter, with a necklace of flesh beneath her chin and an air that combines the haughty and the efficient.

Since that particular night she has flung into the past the miserable solace of those memorable events out of which she vainly tried to divine what kind of life she was living, so as, instead, to rediscover this meaning speaking through the ancient symbols of the cards. And by changing herself she has crushed and canceled the frightening memory of that evening with Cri Cri, of the jeered-at nakedness she had had to suffer to reenter the world where the dead lived and, through her, still live. If then someone insists on bringing Cri Cri back into her thoughts, Madame Donna falls silent, her pupils vanish, in their rotation leaving behind the veined blinking of the white cornea. And if Cri Cri goes limping by outside, everything is taken care of if she murmurs the exorcism: "Singled out by God, prey of the demon" (that demon who by now is also a little herself, after having suffered that stigma on the side during her posing, precisely at the point where, on the card of the Demon, one sees him clawing at the haunch of one of the sinners whom he is crushing underfoot). Yes, it is precisely because of the revelations received on that forgotten night, destroyed in effigy and dimly emanating from the dark gulfs that rave inside her, it is precisely because of that Madame Donna has become a witch doctor, one who knows the soul's medicines.

737

It happened like this. The morning after that night, when on awaking she had again heard the voice, or remembered it: "I have wet feet. The earth is damp"—and thinking of the shopping she had to do at the grocery, she had also remembered that the grocer's wife had always regretted her dead mother's ring which, when she was buried, she'd been obliged to leave on her finger. All disheveled she had run to the grocery, rushing up to the woman, pulling her aside by her arm and informing her in a mysterious whisper that her mother was complaining about the seeping in of water and about the ring that was tight around her finger, having appeared before her among the columns of the Tarot pack, right on the dominant card.

Then, the two women having gone to the cemetery and had the grave opened, had seen that the coffin's wood was indeed all soaked through and falling apart. With unctuous joy the gold of the ring was recovered by the grocer's wife. And from then on she had become Madame Donna's apostle, solid as a stone behind the pulpit of her counter.

Even Madame Donna's husband and son have stopped mocking her, because anyone who goes *to have a cup of coffee* at Madame Donna's leaves five hundred lire for having troubled her, and her husband says: "If it's business it's good, everything that gives people work is good." Nor could anyone ever report her to the police because, with true peasant shrewdness, she is prepared to protect herself by saying that people come to her only to have coffee, and, just like a saint, she advises the sick ones to go to Lourdes, thus getting on the good side of the parish priest, and she sends off to the doctor the others who need more than a balm for the soul.

Yes, sometimes the customers come in grinning, especially certain young ladies and girl students, but it is the same laugh with which at the movies they greet the sight of a prolonged embrace, a nervous, beseeching laugh: oh, only that it may cease, vanish, this thing that fills them with such anxiety, devours them. They well know it is not enough to say, "I might as well try it"; they come here for something much different, and they leave satisfied, even if Madame Donna is tired and wanders, improvising on a perverse brunette, on the gnawing rats which are the enemy of the mails, on impending journeys and distant wealth. In any case, someone had thought about them and for their entire life they will cherish that promise of becoming rich on the threshold of old age.

With the relatives of soldiers lost in the war or with the young girls, still adolescent and full of sighs, who do not know whether they should give themselves to their man, or with those who are already marked by a few creases on the forehead and come to her with a still slight burden in the womb and a martyred desperation in their hearts, with those Madame Donna has the perspicacity to do the cards and regard them in silence (somebody thinks of us, finally! they think) and then to hold back the reply, announcing: "I have seen—" Then closing her fists tightly and escorting them to the door, her eyes flashing, she cries: "Don't be afraid. Do it. Your heart is right."

But it is with the sick ones that she is supreme, and she feels that, for her, a great doctor makes the pure extracts from the chaos, she breathes out obscure oracles: "Weak bones that bend, and it is a disease that is of the roots, like cancer but it is not cancer. And only a dark-haired doctor will be able to call it by its name. But meanwhile you must do as I tell you, and listen carefully and remember because I will not repeat. Boil everything in your house. Everything! It will take you years to do it. Buy a large copper pot and in it you will put piece by piece all that you have in your house until it starts boiling. And as long as there remains something to be boiled you'll not be cured. Yes, even the shoes."

Or, instead: "I give you this piece of cloth. And I don't want anything in exchange, because if you sell these things they lose their power. I tell you that, after I shall have placed my hands on it, you must wear it for three months, day and night without ever taking it off—on the back." Then she places her hands on the piece of cloth and sweats and pants, for into that cloth she transfers the terrible memory through the sign of her contracted face and tense fingers, to the advantage of the person who has come *to have coffee* at Madame Donna's.

Madame Donna no longer searches for the memorable and scorns the men who read those stupid yellow sports pages—Madame Donna is in contact with her dead and she calls them to her aid if ever she's too much troubled by that *tock tock* on the stairs, the step of the demon.

Translated from the Italian by Raymond Rosenthal

Robert Coover

Blackdamp

Here I am night like an exploding black sponge no stars no *741* moon just a nervous coal mist and cold as a sonuvabitch and here I am. Up near the mine shaft there's a litter of lights the color of rotten teeth strung on haphazard wires the whole thing the image of a sad insignificant smile like Old Freeburg was keeping its chin up. Clay did not come by. Hunkering off in the trees rears up the old white tipple, lording it over the hoppers, but all of it near smudged out. It's the big Home-coming Game and they're playing it by candlelight. And my God so cold. Frost for tomorrow and me wearing pants print dress and a cotton jacket short sox and loafers no bra no scarf. I didn't think it was happening. Yet down in the belly there is still something warm. I do not mourn.

I stand out here, here far from those rotten yellow obscene bulbs and far from the women who weep in their shimmer, who weep in their likeness. Peeing their passions, those floppy heavy-souled wondering women. I am far from them, leaning here on a chicken mesh fence. And the air is sick with that goddamned coal-dust.

You are surprised that I do not mourn? Wait, wait! I will be broken. They will strap me down, those wart-hearted women, knuckle me to their gray wombs, scrape tears from my eyes, teach me the, Sister, the ways of the Lord, and I will mourn and rend my garments and gnash my teeth and suffer in the truth and fear of death. I am not so strong you see. Wait. You shall have your pleasure. But for now I stand here. In the orchestra.

A barrel of a woman with plethoric ankles and a Red Cross band on her arm is coming at me with a coffee-pot.

RED CROSS WOMAN: How about some coffee, honey? *(She can hardly talk in the greed of her role. She has a mustache and a sagging left eye and seems to think she is Mrs. Santa Claus.)* Everything okay now you ain't feelin donchu wanna come up where hits—*honey!* you looks plumb froze!

HONEY: *(I take a paper cup and hold while she pours from her field pot . . . the pot is the color of blackened coins)*: Thanks. *(I hover about the hot cup.)* You don't happen to have a couple blankets, do you?

RED CROSS: Sure, *sure*, honey, you betcha life! *(I wince.)* We got blankets sure. Red Cross heps ever way it kin, honey. You sure ain't dressed none too good. Say, you're lil Josephine Birelli, ainchu? Ainchu, child? I knows your mama, honey, knows her well. Now jist donchu go aworryin yoursef none. They'll git our boys outen there okay. You know these here days—whacha say your man's name was, honey?

HONEY: T—

RED: Now watch at coffee, child, hits hottern Billy Blue Blazes! But I hafta but donchu worry none, you hear? These days they got it all figgered scientific and hit ain't but now lookie you ain't dressed none too good, honey! Now I tell you—

HONEY: *(surprisingly calm)*: Could you just get me a couple blankets, please?

RED: Oh yeah *sure*, honey, you betcha. I know you're jist near froze t'death. Now donchu go nowhere you wait right here. *(She winks her good eye as if to bestow some sort of special benediction and moves away like an important elephant.)*

The paper cup of coffee is warm to my hands and to my ears but tasteless and hot and now my tongue is coated and hiding in my mouth. Frankly my legs are awful cold. Maybe I should ask for whiskey or something. I didn't think it was happening. All these years of thinking it was *going* to happen and then I didn't think it was happening. I *traveled through a century of broken screen doors and the resurrection was a fucking fraud!* Still I do not mourn.

Every time I thought it was going to happen, the moon as my prophet, I would get into my special night-gown, a stiff breezy fluttering crinkly pink cloister with a red ribbon. It touched in some places. I'm too skinny for pajamas I know that: they hang on my tail like boys' bluejeans only pasted thinly to my skin. It was different with the gown. I know what I can do.

The elevator in the shaft is still jammed and none of the rescue team has started down yet. They are humping around in nervous squads shouting at God for lack of another audience. More keep coming full of calisthenics all looking like they hope to make the varsity. Clay has not come.

Let me tell you about Maude. Maude is long and loose like Babe Zaharias whom she secretly loves with a male passion and she has a face tense and smooth as machined steel. She lopes about with her head hunched down over her bony chest like a young boy who likes to think he's too tall to go through doorways and she can fight like a tiger. One New Year's Eve she knocked out all of Monk's teeth and Monk is her husband and she loves him. Monk that great big lettuce-eared imperturbable heroic clown. And Maude loves him, loves him like a player loves his coach, and then a lot more too. She is dull good loyal crude rugged thoughtful hardnosed knuckle-kneed and here she comes.

743

MAUDE: Hi, kid. Fugging cage still out. Monk's brother says it was a coaldust blast. He don't know how bad but some pillars down sure. At least fifty-eight guys. Trying to pump the gases out. How you making it?

KID: Okay, I guess. A lit—

MAUDE: Swell. Keep the chin up. And stop popping paper cups or I'll pop you. You see those broads jump? Jesus, kid, you wanna lynching? What you wanna stomp on a paper cup for anyway? Look, I think I'll go over and see how those knucklenuts are coming on the cage. Back in a minute. (*She jogs away loosely, her brown leather jacket slapping softly against the rhythm of her body. Suitable sound effects.*)

KID: (*soliloquy*): Sure.

Tony is one of the fifty-eight—and yet I cannot see his face. Clay would come to the door me pink and starchy in that gown. No moon has leaped but what I have not lain alone in the breeze of a wish my anxious

flesh sliding over the landscape of the old mattress my belly worrying with
the day's flood of coffee, lain alone and screamed in my breast for what *had*
to be to be real. Clay would come to the door. He would come to the door,
boots scuffing the weathertortured wooden floor of the small open porch,
he would come and knock. I am obsessed with moons and the night would
be full of them clogging up the gaunt elm trees like super Christmas lights.
No slack piles burning but hot roses streaming over my porch where even
sweet potato vines die.

CLAY MARLOWE: (*gently, awkwardly, compassionately, in dirty soft khakis
and boots made for walking on gods*): Hello, Punk. I, there, there's
something, well, I have to tell you, I don't know exactly—
PUNK: (*astonished, eyebrows arched, right hand fingering the red ribbon at
the neck, smiling, eyes searching him for something, pink gown lazing
drowsily in a spring whisper*): Clay Marlowe! Why, what a surprise!
CLAY: It's just that—
PUNK: But won't you come in! (*The light behind me is burning shadows
into the gown.*) I guess I'm a little—
CLAY: (*entering, wiping his palms on the thighs of his khakis*): Punk, oh,
Punk, I have—
PUNK: But, but what is it, Clay? Is there, has some—?
CLAY: Yes. It, it's the mine, Punk, there's—
PUNK: Oh, Clay! What—?
CLAY: There's been an explosion, Punk. Tony has been killed.
PUNK: Tony k—? (*Paling, white hand clutching table, knees just visible under
trembling gown collapsing, lips slightly parted.*) No! No! Oh I can't,
what will I, oh *Clay!* (*Exit to bedroom.*)

Isn't that just keen? "No! No! Oh I can't—" but *here* it is, Scene:
me pooped out in a print dress reading a movie magazine on the divan
listening to our bedroom radio which is the only one we've got and is in
the living room, eating a banana and the peel is on the floor with last
Sunday's papers and two and a half pairs of shoes and a throwrug and the
house reeks of a bottle of beer that Tony broke in the sink.

BEDROOM RADIO (*in the living room*): We interrupt this program to bring
you a special bulletin . . .

I listen to the bulletin and then I wonder if I should put my nightgown on and I remember I threw it in the laundry bag. I go to the bedroom and pull it out and it smells of Tony's socks but I figure it will have to do and then I realize I need a bath. Now I am hurrying. The phone rings. I run out of the bathroom to answer it to say yes oh Judas *come* God I need you! It is Maude. Monk is on the same shift and is also trapped down there. She says she'll be by in one minute. I say okay and I get on a jacket and turn off the water and we drive out in the dark to the mine, out here to Old Freeburg. The yellow lights waggle in the black wind. A woman wails wanting God. *I* wish for witches.

RED (*galloping out of a new agitation flying an olivedrab blanket for a banner*):   Whuttid I tell ya, honey? Whuttid I tell ya? They got that cage agoin now en hit won't be no time no time tall! (*Her breath is like cabbage.*) Our boys is gonna be saved, child, praise the Lord!

HONEY: The cage is f—?

RED: Oh the good Lord be blessed amen, honey. They is but your man he's the Tonso boy ain't he, yes, I recalls. So now donchu worry, child, you hear? He's gonna be, but why ainchu up whur you kin see good, dear?

745

HONEY: The—

RED: Oh I know, hit's jist cause you're skeered, but donchu be skeered none, honey. (*She hugs me.*) You jist hole that there lil chin up and (*chucking me under the chin so I am forced to stop holding my breath*) pray to God, honey! Hit's gonna be—

HONEY: Could I please have the blanket?

RED: The blanket? I, oh yeah sure *sure*, honey! Poor child! You must be froze plumb stiff, this is weather for the dead, to be sure, ho—(*catching herself, brushing her cracked lips with a raw crooked finger, her bad eye sinking all the sadder*)—oh I'm—

HONEY: That's all right. Couldn't you find two?

RED: Whachu need two for, honey? Jist wrap that there one up good en tight—

HONEY: I wanted the other one for my friend. (*Red, bobbing her exaggerated head, carefully surveys this distant, solitary, chickenwire retreat.*) My friend is up near the shaft, but she'll—

RED: That one blanket's nuff for ya now, honey. I'll come back right soon and bring you some hot coffee. (*She binds me in the olivedrab blanket.*) There now that should oughta heachu up some. Where's your cup?

HONEY: I stepped on it.

RED   (*hesitating, staring down at the crushed cup, uncertain, confused perhaps*):   Oh. (*She looks up finally, winks her good eye.*) Well now that's too bad. I'll fetch you a new one.

More crowds are arriving and clumping up in sympathetic herds, turning their rears to the wind like guernseys in a winter pasture only it is hard to tell just where that wind is coming from. They all nod at each other like condescending deacons and blow their noses and wheeze and shake their wrapped-up heads as though to say: "Holy Smoke! How we gonna win the conference this year without Big Tank Tonso?" A miner in overalls buttoned down the front over a smooth round belly rounder even than Tony's careens by like a plucked goose snapping a lamp on his helmet, carrying a breathing apparatus, and spits thickly from a deep rake of his fat throat. Right on my shoe. I kick the chickenmesh fence with a shudder and scrape. Though it is gone I feel it all over my body. Up near the shaft a young woman is hysterical and newsmen are taking her picture. Down goes the cage. Cheers like a deep gasp. It's the toughest game of the season.

Once upon a time in the days of marginal mentalities, oh Judas so distant! there was a princess, a spindly little openhearted thing, who woke up one sunblasted morning to discover that the world was absurd. She shucked the unbending prince, married the sergeant-at-arms, and woke up that morning and cried. Who could not have told her? Lord God the heroic dissembled dash of the night before under a slice of silver, bitter and proud beating the asphalt to Carter's Junction in a borrowed car. And that wise old man, Merlin of Carter's Junction, that bent-nosed, unshaven, blue-eyed old justice, who said: "Ahh, poor children." But obeyed our mandate. Oh so distant!

TONY (*age 18*):   Well, it ain't much, Joze, but (*211 pounds of well-coached beef in a crashing shattering leap, but the bed miraculously survives*) at least there's a bed!

JOZE (*age 17 almost*).

TONY: C'mere kid! (*Yanks.*)

JOZE (*resists*).

TONY: Hey, whazza matter, Joze? We're married ain't we?

JOZE (*remembering a poem she wrote once remembering a boy named Clay remembering the tear in his eye when he read it simple for all that but remembering*).

TONY (*bouncing off the bed as the springs shriek, unbuttoning his shirt, winking, handsome, gross*):   C'mon, hot pants, the game is on.

JOZE (*sitting on a straight chair looking in her purse for a piece of paper, a pencil*).

TONY (*hooking pants and shirt on a wall nail; there is a hole in the crotch of his shorts*):   You want the bathroom first or me? (*Scratches.*)

JOZE (*writing something*).

TONY (*in the bathroom, guttersplashing into the toilet bowl*):   Jesus! This can ain't been cleaned in a month!

JOZE (*reading over what she has written*).

TONY (*emerging from the bathroom, damp spots on his shorts*):   Your turn. Whacha doin? Writin a letter? God *damn*, Joze—

JOZE (*hands paper to Tony*).

TONY (*reading laboriously*):

> "To be is as wide as
>   beside us are we."

747

What the shit is this?

JOZE (*walks to window, looks out*).

TONY: Hey, I don't get it, Joze. What's eatin you? Jesus, you wanted to git married, it was your idea, so I can't even play the last two games of the season, Jesus, Joze! What the hellza matter with you anyway? (*He spins her around.*) Now you lookie here, Joze, goddamn it, git those goddamn clothes off and git your ass into that, now you hear me, Joze?

JOZE: I don't think I—

TONY (*without undressing her, picks her up, pitches her on the bed, pushes back her skirt, rips her pants as he yanks them off over her shoes, rapes her*):   AAJ—Aj—Ahhh. Jeeeez! (*Rolls off, crawls into far side of bed.*)

JOZE (*sits up languidly on edge of bed, springs discordant, sits up and looks down at torn pants lying like a punctured pink balloon on the floor, sits there for some time; stands at last, removes all but bra, enters bed*).

TONY: The light's on.

JOZE (*looks up at the light; pause; eases out of bed, walks to bathroom, sits again; longer pause; does not look in the mirror, walks out of bathroom, looks up at light again; pause; pulls light cord and returns to bed).*

TONY: Joze? (*Pause.*) Joze? Joze, you ever done it before?

JOZE: You mean like you did tonight?

TONY: Yeah, I mean, did—

JOZE: No, I never did that before.

TONY (*age 18*): Oh. Well, I'm glad, ya hear? (*Collapses.*)

JOZE (*age 17 almost*).

I don't know what it is, it is not quite tangible, sometimes it seems to be blowing and tumbling in my head, that black something, I can't quite put my finger on what is wrong out here tonight. Cold. Still in this mouthy blanket even it is cold. Clay didn't—Oh Judas *stand that tipple high as a scream in ghostlight and let those steelshouldering hoppers rumble and crash and lay waste this slategrey earth*! I just didn't think it was happening. It was a thing for the spring not November. I never thought about poor Maude. Good Maude. And I guess I never really thought about Tony. Big Tank. Poor bastard. He's never really known what it could be like. Blackdamp now. No chance to breathe. The story of my life.

748

Clay! There he is! Fine in a plaid shirt with knee-boots strapping in the legs of his khaki pants. He is no miner, he is nothing in particular, he is a free man, and yet he is snapping on a steel helmet. He cannot see me. And now perhaps I begin to mourn.

MAUDE: Hey, kid, you still out here? Things moving fast. C'mon up now where—hey, whatsa trouble? It startin to get to you? C'mon Josie kid buck up! I gotta feelin the whole goddamn thing's gonna come out swell. Ya hear? Now come on!

KID (*working on a smile for Maude*): Hell, Maude, I'm okay. (*The blanket and I stand.*) What's up?

MAUDE (*face dry and confident, thin hair above bound by a man's red bandana; she is wearing one of Monk's hunting shirts, but no socks in her loafers*): They're down there. Second crew. They're gettin there. Inspector tested for gas. Okayed short stretches. (*We are walking toward the other women.*) Gas not too bad. *That's* a good thing. A real pisser though. First gang is already back up and says it's all loose and they can get to the worst part right quick, no sweat. Looks pretty good right now, kid.

KID: Maude, I hope—

MAUDE: Jesus! It's coldern a brass monkey's balls in Siberia! I was worried when I seen what you was wearin. (*Maude is wearing wool slacks, has a leather jacket on.*) Let's see if we can rustle up some more joe.

KID: Maude, would you like to use the blanket a bit?

MAUDE (*to a miner passing by*); Hi, Pete. How's things?

PETE: Rough, Maude. Pretty fucking rough.

MAUDE: Can I bum a couple smokes?

PETE: Yeah, sure. Take the pack, pal. Gotta get up to the cage now. I won't stop till I find Monk, Maude. You can bet on that.

MAUDE: Thanks, Pete. Go get 'em. (*To me.*) Here, kid. Light up.

Maude is strong among these people. I lean up against the ventilator housing to breathe that ragged smoke, watching the miners scuttling about in curious patterns baying their hackneyed curses. The Red Cross woman gives me a doughnut. Everybody in town is out for the show.

When I was eleven years old Clay Marlowe held a beebee gun to my head in his dad's garage and made me take off all my clothes. Outside, the plush applause of a broadleafed maple sweeping the garage roof. It was the middle of summer but naked I was shivering violently. "I'm sorry!" Clay cried suddenly, threw down the gun and ran out of the garage. It was the middle of summer. And then one night after centuries of stretching and filling and marveling he drove me home from play practice at the highschool auditorium. I didn't say a word and he didn't say a word and we went straight out to the Old Municipal Cemetery. The strangely appropriate moon that night made the tombstones stand out like happy chalk marks on a profound blackboard. The only word I said the whole time was "No," when he asked me awkwardly if I thought he needed his bee-bee gun again and then later on looking up at the sky I saw for the first time the bright star that always travels with the moon.

749

WOMAN (*rifling the sudden hush with a terror-fraught scream*): AAAAAII-IEEEHHHAAAAAH! NO JEEEEZUSS!

Black. Dull hideous devastating black. A long smoldering loaf of utter blackness that looks almost like a man. One shoe. Clothes burned off in front. Tatters peeling off hanging like wallpaper from a burned-out building.

Oh Judas. The young woman is still screaming and others are screaming but it is not her man it is not their man. It is Monk. Oh my God, Maude! The men carrying the stretcher seem to be smoldering too. The emergence from hell. Into chaos. There is no way to control it. Maude breaks for the stretcher. Some men try to restrain her but she hits hard, crashes through. Her tongue is out. She plunges on top of the body. Everything cascades to the earth, Monk thudding lumpily like a watersoaked log. Maude grabs the head in both her hands and screams at it. "MONK! MONK! SPEAK TO ME! YOU HEAR? YOU SPEAK!" The black mouth gapes. His false teeth are gone. In the fall to the ground part of the clothes have been stripped back and now a small patch of soft pink skin glows like a fresh naked mushroom in a burned forest. I am beside her. Oh Judas! I want to help. Maude is still screaming at the head. "Maude, please, *please*, Maude!" Monk's neck is broken and the body hangs long and twisted from the head. Maude is pressing her lips against the yawning black mouth, trying to blow air inside. "Please, for God's sake, *please*, Maude! *Maude!*" The roots of the body hair are not black but a soft blonde. "MAUDE!" And I vomit. All over the corpse and Maude and the people crowding trying to act. And on until that something I could not seem to feel conquers at last.

750

MAN: Hi, Joe. Howzit comin? Here, grab some mud.

JOE: Thanks, Milt. Bad, real bad. It gottem all alright.

MILT: Just come up?

JOE: Thirty minutes ago. Other shift'll be up soon. Jesus!

MILT: Rough sonuvabitch.

JOE: Yeah. Real rough.

MILT (*pause*): Your wife's brother down there I hear tell.

JOE: Beryl? Yeah. Yeah, Beryl is down there. I saw him myself. I don't wanna bring him up. Slugged by a timber. Half a head.

MILT: Jesus. I—

MAN: H'lo, Joe, Milt.

MILT: Hi, Harry. Just come up?

HARRY: Yeah. Here lemme git a shot of that stuff.

MILT: They still lookin for live ones?

HARRY: Naah. Just bringin up the bodies now. Poor fuckers.

MILT: Yeah. Jesus.

HARRY: Heard about Beryl, Joe. Sorry to hear it.

JOE: He got it fast.

HARRY: Yeah, that's right, he got it fast. That's something. Bettern blackdamp.

MILT: Yeah, that's something.

HARRY: Where the hell's all the women for this goddamn tent? The coffee's run out.

MILT: More over in that other pot, Harry.

HARRY (*louder, from other coffee pot*):   I counted over fifty. How about you, Joe?

MILT: Ssst! Tank's woman.

HARRY (*more hushed again*):   Oh.

JOE: It gottem all okay.

For a long time I have been lying here wrapped up in these vicious blankets here in front of the Red Cross emergency tent looking up at the yellow lights. It is the middle of the morning. Morning came a while back. There was nothing gratifying about it. New coffee couldn't cut through the meal in my mouth. Clothes rumpled up skin rasped raw by the rancid blankets oh Judas. When I woke up I wondered if I really knew anyone called Monk or Maude. I thought of Tony once. He wasn't black, but he was very serious, thinner maybe. He seemed older. It occurred to me that this idea I had thought about so many times was never made of any real things like dirt or bones or even real sounds. The sun after all can vanquish the moon. And Tony, poor Big Tony. He was to disappear, okay, that still seemed important somehow, but there were no bodies, it was only like trading Tony to some other team. I cannot quite remember the details of Tony's face, but I remember that I did not dislike them. It was to have been a happy thing and I suppose even Tony was to have been happy about the way things turned out. Though that seems true, it is hard to hang on to it. But mostly I have slept.

The sad yellow lights burn on each one glittering foolishly against the gray sky like a wedding ring lying in the soap scum on a lavatory. The old white tipple now stands out clearly, making the sky look even grayer, and under the chutes the hoppers now visible in the daylight stand like stolid linebackers to the gawping crowd. Up by the shaft they are carrying out the dead miners, one every ten or fifteen minutes. They keep them covered now until they get them to the tent next to the makeshift embalming shack,

751

although somehow the word seems to be getting out just ahead of the body most of the time. Fewer women near the elevator now, more townspeople. When the word is out they all pivot toward the relatives, not to miss the chance to participate in the reaction. When they brought up the husband of the young woman who was screaming all night she was so exhausted from her marathon of hysteria that she only stared. Someone led her over to the tent, the basket, as I heard one miner call it. Everyone registered a certain disappointment. I don't know where Maude is, she is not here. They will pivot on me soon.

A VOICE I KNOW: Hello, Punk. You look a little washed out.

PUNK (*looking up at Clay Marlowe, miserable in my state*).

CLAY (*mouth smiling white against his coalsmudged face*): Here, little pal, have a cigarette. (*He throws his helmet on the ground, sits down facing me, lights a cigarette, gives it to me, lights another. He cups his enormous hands around the match to protect it as he lights them and I see with a roar in my chest that I would have been safe there.*)

PUNK: It has been a long miserable night.

CLAY: Yes. Long enough.

PUNK: Nothing seems reasonable now except to go home and take a bath.

CLAY (*doubled into the scene like a condescending giant, cigarette jaunty in his staunch pale mouth, sovereign coalstained khaki knees knuckled up longly before his chest, withal incredible*): I'm sorry, Punk. (*Slight fumbling.*) Real sorry. (*Pause.*) Oh, hell! (*Pause.*) Punk, what can I say to you? (*Pause.*) Damn it, I want to be right, I want to say something to you appropriate, something impersonal, but I just can't—(*Pause.*) Punk, I miss you.

PUNK (*crying now, lightly, shivering, not cold, confused and like a child on a strange summer day*).

CLAY (*unknuckling, perhaps to rise*): I'm sorry, Punk. I'm sorry.

PUNK (*a little brokenly*): You said that once before. And then you—

ANOTHER VOICE I KNOW: Honey, *honey!* (*She is laboring with my blanket.*) Honey, donchu hear me, honey? (*It is Mrs. Santa Claus.*) Honey, I said they done found eight men alive, *alive!* All shored in! (*I am now more or less in her grip, that is, on my feet.*) *Alive*, child, and your husband, praise the good Lord, is *one of them!*

HONEY: Oh. (*I untangle myself from the olivedrab blanket and smoothe down my cotton dress. I turn toward the busy mineshaft, pause, turn back to Red. The gay saliva is pumping out of the corner of her mouth, sparkling the ends of her mustache. Her eyes are catty-corner and the left one is hopping.*) Thank you. You are quite kind.

Well, I must go. Over the slate chips under the rotting lights feeling the platinum eye of the sun disc-like in the paper sky. Sister, the ways of the Lord. I must really go. The fans are waiting for me.

John Hawkes

A Little Bit of the Old Slap and Tickle

Sparrow the Lance Corporal knew he would find his family by the sea.

Now through the underground and in a public bus with wooden seats and on foot he traveled until under the dusty tree tops he smelled the surf and brine and stood at last atop the great cliff's chalky edge. On the upward footpath the trees had fallen away and at the head of the ascent he was alone, windswept, with the sun in his eyes and a view of the whole stretch of coast before him. It was a peaceful sea, worn down by flotillas of landing boats forever beached. And away to either side of him the cliffs were crumbling, these desolate black promontories into which gun batteries had once been built. Now it was all won, all lost, all over, and he himself—a tiny figure—stood on the crest with the seawrack and the breeze of an ocean around him. He was wearing his old battledress and a red beret.

The war-worn flotillas lay a hundred feet below. Down there, spread at the cliff's bottom, was the mud that softly heaved between the line of water and the first uprisings of dry stone: and down there lay the iron fleet half-sunk in the mud. For ten miles in either direction from the stump on the cliff's high windy lip—a flat tin helmet was nailed to the stump and it was Sparrow's sign, marking the steep descent he had found for himself—

he could see once more the wreckage and this low mud of the coast, washed with foam, slick, cleaving to the sky. Terns sat with ruffled white still faces on the spars; the ends of cables sucked up rust from the low pools; the stripped hull of a destroyer rose bow first from the muck.

Here was Sparrow, come back unannounced. Leaning forward, resting his kit, grass tangling up about his boots and the wind blowing tight wads of cloud in his direction, he gazed down upon the scene and knew it was home after all. His own spot was there, the sweeper lying straight and true in the mud up to her water-line, his salt and iron house with chicken wire round one portion of the deck where the children played, the tin pipe at the stern with a breath of smoke coming up, the plank run out from her bow to a sandy place ashore. It was like living in a war memorial, and letting his eyes swing back from his own ten windy miles of devastation, fixing upon the tiny figure of a scrubby black dog that was barking at the abandoned shape of a carrier listing not fifty yards to the lea; seeing the dog at her game, and seeing a handful of slops come suddenly from one porthole, now he knew that his sweeper was inhabited and that, once aboard, he was father of this household, respectable as a lighthouse keeper's station.

The terns set up a terrible cry that afternoon as he made his way down the cliff, and the dog—Sparrow loved her bent tail, the sea lice about her eyes, loved the mangy scruff of her neck—the dog leaped, then floundered out of the mud to meet him. So with kit and cane, red beret hanging off the tip of his skull and dripping dog in arm, he climbed the plank and shouted the names of his kiddies, limped round the capstan to see that the rain-water pan was full.

"You back?" The woman stepped out of the companionway and stopped, her eyes already simmering down on Sparrow, sharp fingers unfastening the first three buttons of her khaki shirt. "Well, it *is* a good day." And then, coming no closer, speaking in the hard voice wreathed with little trails of smoke, standing with the dirty ocean and derelicts behind her: "The boys have been wanting to search the *Coventry* again. We'll let them go. And we'll put the other buggers in the brig for an hour. Funny . . . I've had it on my mind all day."

"Good girl," said Sparrow. "Good old girl."

It was the home air that he breathed, smells of mid-ocean, a steady and familiar breeze pungent on the deck with the woman, a sweeter fragrance of grass and white bones on the cliff top, an air in which he sometimes caught the burnt vapors of a far-off freighter or, closer at hand, the smells of his own small dog. Scraping paint or splicing rope, or sitting and holding a half cup of rum in the sun on the bow, or following the boys down the idleness of the beach, he smelled what the woman washed or what a hundred-foot wave discharged into that whole long coastal atmosphere. In the dawn the red sun stretched thin across the line of the eye; throughout the day there was some davit swinging and creaking; and at supper they all ate black beans together and drank their ale.

There were old ammunition boxes for Sparrow and the woman to sit on at dusk when at last the terns grew quiet. Man and wife smoked together while the night blew in across the cold slickness of the sea. A bucket of old rags at her side, her legs no more than two white streaks, the starlight making the sock or shirt turn silver, she hunched forward then and sewed, and he liked her best in the beginning of the blue night when she was thin and preoccupied and without children, digesting her meal and letting him sit with his arm across the shoulder hard as a rocker-arm. No park benches, no dancing or walking out for the woman and Sparrow. They turned to a great pile of anchor chain or to the deck when the sewing was done. In union their scars, their pieces of flat and no longer youthful flesh touched and merged. He liked her to leave the impression of damp potatoes on his belly, he liked to feel the clasp-knife in the pocket of her skirt. And love was even better when they were sick, the heart of it more true with aching arms and legs. It was a good red nose that pleased him, or the chance to kiss the water from her eyes. Love, not beauty, was what he wanted.

In the beginning of night—the time when at last the woman leaned far forward so that the shoulders disappeared from under his arm and his hand traveled down until the four glossy tips of his fingers were thrust into the crevice between her flesh and the lid of the ammunition box, feeling her more desirable than the girls he had seen in Chisling or Squadron Up—in this beginning of the night, Sparrow knew the privacy of marriage and the comfort to be taken with a woman worn to thinness, wiry and tough as the titlings on the cliff.

And the second night, after the moon had gone into the sea and after the woman had returned from helping Arthur out of a bad dream: "You're a proper fire-stick, little cock," she said. "You could spend more time at home, I should think. It's been on my mind."

He nodded, taking the offered cup of rum and the cigarette. "I could

757

do that." He put the cup to his mouth as if the burn of the rum and the fire of his own lip and loin could bring to life the great amphibious shadow around them. In the dark he looked at the bridge wings and dipping masts. "I could stay home rightly enough. No doubt of that."

The woman took the cigarette from between his lips, put it to hers and spoke while exhaling: "Why not set up for yourself?"

He shook his head. "I'm not big enough for that."

"I've thought you were. Like the old girl with the glass ball said."

He nodded. "It's the risks, that's all. You take them alone if you try it alone." And after a moment, shifting, wetting his lips for the cigarette: "Shall I send down a packet of skivvies for Arthur?"

"Oh, give us a kiss," she answered, and she was not laughing.

For the two days and nights that was all they said. Sparrow watched the woman throwing out her slops, putting the youngest to play under the cover of chicken wire, or smoking at the rail with broom in hand and eyes coming down to him. In a few old jars she put up wild berries picked from the cliff.

Once, wearing a short mended garment styled before the war, she stepped slowly into the deeper brown water off the stern, pushed her chest down into the warmth of the water while the boys clapped and Arthur, the oldest, cried: "Coo, Sparrow, why don't you teach her to swim?" Until he saw the look on his father's face and his mother's own humorless eyes and soaking wet hair turned up to him. The dog, that often lay panting in a little black hole in the mud against the carrier's enormous side, danced in after the woman and pulled abreast of her with spongy paws. While Sparrow, toes dangling in the silt and the faded old red beret tilted sharply forward on his brow, found everything in the woman that the boys were unable to see. The awkward movement of her hands and legs, the faded blue of the suit tied carefully across the narrow back but wrinkling over the stomach and stretching loose from the legs, the clot of seaweed stuck to her shoulder, the warnings she gave the dog, all this made Sparrow pause and lift himself slightly for a better view.

"Arthur," he called. "Show more respect for your mother."

At that moment he took in the swimming woman and paddling dog and sighed. For beyond those two, beyond the sweeper with its number still faintly stenciled on the bow, there lay in muddy suspension the entire field of ships, encrusted guns and vehicles. And he thought of the work it would take to set the whole thing afloat again—seeing the splash, the snort of the dog—and knew it could not be done, and smiled, clasping his knees, sucking the sun. All won, all lost, all over. But he had his.

So the leave passed. He shook Arthur's hands and the woman went with him to the end of the plank. "Send the skivvies along," she said.

Then Sparrow stood on the cliff with home flashing through his head. Then he was gone, leaving small footprints below in the mud. He chucked his cigarette as he limped back into the world from which he had come.

Nelson Algren

Dad Among the Troglodytes, or Show Me a Gypsy and I'll Show You a Nut

When I saw that little two-motored orphan waiting for me out there on the windless Spanish grass, it looked like a plane without a mother. As I had not brought my own mother along I felt sympathetic.

Once inside it I felt pure pity for the little brute. A plane without a stewardess doesn't care whether it ever gets off the ground.

The only other passenger was an American Air Force fellow in civvies who told me he makes the run to Almeria twice a week but I couldn't imagine why. My own reason was so preposterous as not to bear admission. I simply clicked the shutter of my camera once or twice to show I had film and didn't care how fast I used it, and let it go at that.

"Where's the runway?" I wanted to know, glancing out the window. "Where do they take off from?"

"Right here off the grass, Dad. There ain't no runway."

"They'll have to warm this thing up half an hour to do *that*."

"They don't warm nothing up in this country. They just take off, Dad."

"I think I'll just watch from the ground," I decided.

"Sit down, Unk," he urged me, not wanting to fly alone to Almeria. "Ozark has a very good safety record."

"OZARK? *Ozark?* Are they going to try to bring this mouse-trap into *St Louis?* For God's sake, we'll never make Cincinnati. Let me get out of this here."

"We just call it Ozark because it barely clears those big hills, Dad," pointing to the majestic heights of the Sierra Nevadas, a gesture that surprised me as the Sierra Nevadas are in another part of the country altogether.

The two-motored orphan began bumping about like a baby buffalo snouting for corn, got its wheels off the grass, ran into a storm a hundred feet off the ground though there wasn't a breath of wind inside or outside the plane, and finally got a tentative sort of grip on the air. By the time I had regained my composure I was in a damp sweat. I am never a man to be easily frightened by danger. It's imminent peril that gets me.

All the way to Almeria the pilot killed time by banking into a climb just to see what was going on up there, then shutting off the motors to slip into a plummeting glide. I'd never seen anything like it.

"Exactly what do you think he has in mind," I couldn't help wondering. "Is he trying to discover something?"

"Saving gas," Air Force Jack informed me.

Recalling an occasion when a Spanish pilot took it upon himself to discover Seville while I was in the plane, I steeled myself against the moment when this one, with some wild surmise, would discover Almeria. Ever since Columbus had his little success, the Spanish have an *idée fixe* about getting to places before anyone else. Though it will take a Spaniard the better part of a morning to fix you up with a cup of coffee, the reason is that he is bemused by the marvels of space-travel in the kitchen. That's how it *is* in Spain, Man, that's what it's actually *like.*

The people below looked like ants. As we came down and raced toward the airport I looked out and saw they really *were* ants. There was nobody around the airport at all. I don't know what made me think we were expected.

"How much gas do you figure we saved *that* trip?" I asked Air Force Jack, who handed me a pack of Air Force cigarettes for reply. This kid must be loaded.

I offered to buy him a drink, provided it was on the ground, and he accepted at the little airport bar. He really seemed a deserving sort, so I regaled him with an account of the crossing of the Remagen Bridgehead, though I happened to be playing first base for the 125th Evacuation Hospital at Camp Penally near Tenby, Wales, that day. (We lost to the nurses but

762

forced them into extra innings before they won and later they said they were proud of every single one of us.) I've told the story of the Remagen crossing so often that if I ever run into somebody who was actually there he'll begin to doubt it. As for myself I've started to believe it, and this was a good chance to really get it done, so I went into the story of the two SS officers I'd killed in the Huertgen Forest one morning, getting the first by having him chase me until he dropped dead. At this point there is a pause so the listener can ask, "What became of the other?" And then you say "he died laughing," but Air Force Jack had gone.

Gone with Goth and Byzantine; gone with Scythian and Moor; gone with the Brooklyn Robins and his PX cigarettes. He had left.

The reason I had come to Almeria was to photograph *The People from God Knows Where*, the cave-dwelling race who live in the immemorial rocks in the heights above the city. The title, inclusive of italics, was my own device, as one most likely to captivate the editor of any magazine that can afford to buy photographic plates.

Almeria is a provincial town of streets as narrow as its people, a kind of Indianapolis without smoke. Having seen Indianapolis, I didn't bother with the town. The townspeople will tell you there is nobody living up there, because the idea of Spanish people living in caves touches their pride, but I knew better, I took a cab to the end of town and told the driver not to wait as I was coming down on the other side. As that is a sheer drop of five hundred feet, he said he would be pleased to catch me, but I was suspicious and told him I'd take my own chances.

The road keeps going up into a toyless sun until there is no road, but merely loose gravel and I went slip-sliding on all fours, camera dangling, from rock to rock, wondering how Herman Wouk got *his* start. It occurred to me that the Abominable Snowman might turn out to be no more than another American trying to get pictures of people nobody had taken before. Frankly I don't even know how the Abominable Snowman got *his* start.

Nobody knows where these people came from, though there is conjecture that they might have come from caves along the Red Sea, a conjecture I made just this minute. At any rate, whoever they were, they found the rock of Greece too hard to carve. Why they didn't want to live in houses I have no idea. But in Southern Italy they found rock soft enough to dig, and in Africa, northeast of Ksar-es-Souk, they dug into the ground, where a whole town, large enough to hold ten thousand people, thrives today.

I saw two blond, stocky little blue-eyed fellows, perched on a rock and they didn't run and hide when I came up, as the Bedouins northeast of Ksar-es-Souk do. *They* run and hide in Ksar-es-Souk. I never chased one into Ksar-es-Souk myself, but if I had a Diner's card I'd go in and bring one back. It might turn out to be Martin Bormann. Well, how would *you* feel if *you* were Martin Bormann when Adolf Eichmann came along?

I was pleased the kids didn't run from me and even more pleased that they didn't start posturing when they saw the camera in hope of pay—asking "*Foto Gitane? Foto Gitane?*" even though they weren't Gypsies. They had a ten-foot bamboo pole lying between them, across their knees. It looked suspiciously like a fishing pole, but I didn't want to ask them if they'd caught anything, not being in a hurry to make a fool of myself.

Other than their bamboo pole, there is no sign of a plaything in these toyless heights. No doll, ball, or bicycle. Just the beating heat on the gravel, and the shadow of silence-colored rock. It's too hot for dogs, goats can't make it. Only men, women, and children, the hardiest brute that still roams free, can survive. If you ask me what they live on, I'll tell you that they must work as servants in the town below. That's only a guess, but it's as good as yours.

Some of the caves are natural wonders, others have been dug out and a window carved in one side, toward the morning sun, and the front whitewashed. One had palms across its doorway to remember the coming of Christ to Jerusalem. I told you they've been here a long time.

I stopped before one labyrinth that looked as if it had been old when the moon was new. A man's turtleneck sweat shirt was hanging on a line to dry beside the opening, so I looked in thinking I might find James Jones at work. Nobody was in, so I judged he was downtown taking notes. A heavy-set young woman came along carrying a bucket of water in either hand. I stepped aside to let her by, but she didn't wish me good day. I waited to give her time to set the table for lunch, then put in my head and asked her if I could come inside.

She didn't say I couldn't, so I did. Some fellow who looked like he might be boarding with her sat in a corner but I couldn't see him clearly because there wasn't enough light. But he didn't have anything to say either. Well, if the Troglodytes aren't a race of grouches at least I'd found two who were.

He took a cigarette from me, sparing the pack, and when I offered her one she didn't know what to do. He said it was all right, take one, so she did and handed it to him. If he had handed it back to me I would have figured they were both in need of analysis, but they weren't. They just wanted to know what the hell I wanted. They were sure they hadn't sent for me.

I told them I had a hard time understanding Spanish, so they both began talking so loud, both at once, with gestures, that I realized they had misunderstood me—they thought I was hard of hearing. I put my fingers in my ears and shook my head, to show there was no need of hollering.

Finally I understood that not being able to understand Spanish words to them meant I did not understand any words well. They could not conceive of a language of another country, because they did not know there was another country. "Spain" and "world" were synonymous to them. "Man" and "Spaniard" were the same thing. Unless they were taking the Fifth Amendment on me.

When I came back into the sun, the toyless boys with the bamboo pole were perched on a rock, and had their line out over a sheer drop. They really *were* fishing—for starlings. The birds ducked at the bit of bread offered them in mid-air, got hooked, and the kids hauled them in. One of them had hooked half a dozen and the other had two. How long has *this* been going on?

I asked them where I could find the Gypsies and they pointed, downhill and up again, to see the *gitanes*.

I took their pictures but didn't offer to pay them, doubting how they would take that. I guess it was a mistake, because the young woman who thought Spain was the world came to her door and told me, quietly, as I passed: "*Subir y bajar como Ud., con una camera fotográfica puede ser divertido. Pero, para nosotros, que subimos y bajamos todo el santo día, es el infierno.*" ("For you it is amusing to climb up and down with a camera, but for us, for whom there is no end of climbing up and going down, it is plain hell.")

I almost felt I was back in Chicago, where the gate is always kept wide open for me to leave by.

The cave-dwelling Gypsies were a different story. Here the road up was solid and easy, so I made it upright. At the top of the road a mob of them were waiting, for they had spotted the camera. Five-year-olds to ancestral hags in bandannas, all crowding, hollering, and posturing, "*Foto Gitane? Foto Gitane?*" I didn't see one good-looking girl in the crowd.

This race, if it is a race and not a road show, have but one cultural distinction—that of holding out the hand for you to put something in. If you do, there is, immediately, a whole host of cousins, brothers, sisters, babies, youths, grandparents, all hollering *"Foto Gitane! Foto Gitane!"*

One entrepreneur, a boy of about fourteen, was working along different lines. He was standing in the shadow of a door and, as I passed, exposed himself. "Go home, Ginsberg," I told him.

My single hope was to get out of town with the camera. There was no use of trying to take a picture. Not even Darryl Zanuck could have afforded it.

"Foto Gitane? Foto Gitane?"

Show me a Gypsy and I'll show you a nut.

Back at the airport I picked up a week-old *Herald Tribune*, Paris edition. Frank Lary of Detroit had beaten Pedro Ramos of the Senators in their second pitching duel within a week, retiring the last twelve men to face him in order.

An American wearing a pith helmet and Bermuda shorts was standing at the bar. I was going to ask him if he had checked his gun, but it's best not to start anything with an American.

Still, I couldn't help wondering what country *he* thought he was in.

Bette Howland

Aronesti

Aronesti disliked the smell of the house. It flagged a cue-card at him: NOSTALGIA. But when he sniffed—"What is it? What is this smell? What do I remember?"—his imagination dived and skidded, like a false start in a dream. That was the way that summer cabins smelled, that was all. This air of past summers trapped under the floorboards; the heat's furry embrace: SHAM. Eight years he had been coming to this town on the dunes, renting this same cabin; he had brought furniture, he had left books. But nothing changed. Whenever he returned to walk through the four small rooms, to force the fast windows and to thrust open the doors—waking up the curled wasps that would begin staggering—he sensed that he was serving a notice of eviction.

A high school biology teacher, two months' vacation, a chance to break, every year, with routine; he knew that his would be considered a "nice life," but not for the reasons he had chosen. Why anyone should want to break with routine, he could not understand; change filled him like a keg of murky water. But he adjusted to his summers—ate rare hamburgers, spat watermelon seeds, set mousetraps, mended window screens (since something chewed them). And in the night, if he heard the click of a mousetrap, he would give a start of satisfaction. But also, often, he would lower his book, and look about for its companions: he felt lonely and constricted when he was not surrounded by books, and had no choice of them. He lived like a prisoner who must exercise in his cell, to maintain his dignity.

Why, then? Ada had wanted it. Why now? His mother wanted.

"Phew," the old woman said, coming up to him with her nose buried in a pile of linen. "Damp; damp. This smell is bad for you. Take these sheets before I have to make the beds, and give them a hang up on the line."

"Miasma, miasma. Smells can't harm you."

"But the damp—the damp smell; it gets into your lungs." She held a sheet out in her fist.

"Why can't you trust me? I know about such things."

"Then go turn on light bulbs. I think we need some. I'm writing down a list for the store." She was not writing; she hated to write; it exhausted her. But it sounded busy.

So he went around the house switching on lights, crouching in dusty corners to plug in plugs. He went out to the car and brought in the sandwiches and lemonade left over from what his mother had packed for lunch. He opened the refrigerator—the little light popped on; he felt warm and happy, and then a plunging sadness; he had forgotten for a moment where he was, that he was on This Side; and on That Side was the past, everything. And on This Side, only he; and all eternity would not fill the gap between. He nudged the door, but it slammed with finality. The motor throbbed.

Aronesti's mother would answer the telephone: "Who's that?" Or the doorbell, "Who's that?" She was still in a foreign country; she would always be. There were things she did not even care to get used to, the doorlock buzzer, for instance, which she always held down with her thumb (they lived three flights up, in the city) until the caller came right to the door. She could not believe that its only function was to unlock that door way down there.

Nevertheless, she answered their telephone. Aronesti did not like telephones: it was mere forgetfulness that he had had their summer number connected again: one night when he was ranging the house with a flyswatter, developing a style of swinging (with a hook), of sliding the dead beast off the flip end—the telephone rang. His mother was in bed. It was very late. Something imperceptible as the force of gravity pressed on his bowels.

"Hello."

A hesitation. "Hello." Female.

"Hello."

"Is Jack there?" She already knew that he was not.

"Jack who?" How senseless to prolong it; he knew no Jacks.

"Jack Bramer?"

"Did you say Bramer?"

"Listen—is Jack there?"

"No. I think you must have the wrong number."

CLICK.

It was not has fault. That some piece of machinery had summoned him. Rudely. He was ready.

Maybe eternity was like that. Disembodied voices. "Who are you? Who are you? Is that you? Where are you?" Nice thought. You could look a long time. If you wanted someone. Oh God, he wanted someone.

"Ada, where are you?" His elastic heart.

She once had taped a photograph of herself on their dresser here in the bedroom. It was her only beach picture, she said, that was why. He went in, and by the yellow light, his hands on the high dresser and his bald spot tallow in the mirror, peered at her face. He often did this, for long times; there was something he was looking for that he was not seeing.

The picture had been taken when she was nineteen or twenty, and it looked like all old photographs, which seem not only to fade but to freeze. In a light now dim and wintery, six girls were sitting and posing on the sand, all smiling into the camera. Except Ada. She was holding up her hand to the camera, telling the photographer to wait a minute, probably. Her black hair was short and curly and her long eyes narrowed and confused, as if someone had just made a joke and she was waiting, with good will, to have it explained.

He tried unfocusing his eyes, to blur it, to make those faces melt in his vision. But they would not unfreeze.

To look at her caused him no pain; he saw not her face, but the photograph, and that he knew. When he had looked at the bookshelves in their apartment—at the neatly torn white paper markers that Ada had, over the time, placed among the first twenty or thirty pages of so many, the markers sticking up all over like simple headstones in the graveyard of her good intentions; that he knew; he could smile. But when in this summer house he had found an old handbag—a good one, that she had, because it was good, hardly ever used—when he opened it and saw within a crumpled

Kleenex; a comb with two teeth missing; a chewing gum wrapper—why enumerate?—when he saw what he would find in any woman's purse; when he smelled the sweet stale perfume rising out of it, and thought of her bending her head over it seriously, as women are serious with their purses; she seemed anonymous, a woman who had lived and died; and it pumped spasms through him that a defenseless creature, who had been endowed with the power to do such ordinary, inoffensive things as to acquire possessions and to keep them orderly, should have that power taken. If he had her here now; if he saw her standing in the hall, her chin on her chest, her knee slightly lifted to balance a purse and catch its contents to the light. Oh, now. Now.

Twice a day he went to the *schul* (a big, shabby house with a sign outside that said ZONED COMMERCIAL, so much frontage) where the old men from Feidelman's Resort nearby always formed a *minyan*. The old men smelled like wet, crushed cigars; their white beards were stained with yellow streaks of nicotine, and they coughed up white-yellow phlegm. Aronesti prayed loudly, the sweat erupting; no more mumbling; his pronunciation had got much

better; he knew the service so well that he did not have to think about the words, and they blended in the bloodstream that pulsed in this dry room.

He felt relaxed when he left, soothed by a trance.

Then he would walk home, past the screened-in porches where, because of the insects, the people were sitting; rearing their heads to look at him, their eyes nacreous in the darkness. He knew how he drew their eyes: big, but potbellied, the shiny spectacles set in his eyesockets, the shiny dome of the skullcap, from which the globes of sweat were swelling. And a black suit: he felt like an old rabbi in an astrakhan wandering among these—among these? What were these people? Lizards lying on the beach by day; now, like penned-in cattle, hiding from the insects that were warming up in the grass and hurtling against the resilient screens.

Twice a day; visiting hours. No one in that hospital would look you in the eye; you could wander through it like a passenger lost on a jolting subway; and see no one to ask the way of, no one who was responsible for anything—only your fellow sufferers, who would glance away from your distress and uncertainty because it might get to them. And the lights and buzzers of the corridors, going on and off like the impulses of an outsized computer-brain.

They called him up in the middle of the night. He heard the ringing; his mind parted in a smile of bewilderment, and a plume of steam spit through it. He did not have to answer; even the news of her death came from the impersonal machine.

"Mort, what's the matter, don't you go out or do anything?"

"What is it? What do you want me to do?"

"What *I* want? What matters? You can't sit around reading all your time."

"If I want to?"

"You're white like dough." She pinched his arm. "Every time you walk in the sunlight you look so pale you scare me; your face shines. I think you're going to faint from looking pale."

"People don't faint from looking pale."

"Go outside. Get out. It's hot in here. It's no good for you."

So he took his book outside, and a chair, and sat under the apple tree. On a branch he noticed a bag, an envelope of cotton candy; caterpillars, twisted like the burned-out wicks of candles, were writhing within. Two hundred maybe. He moved his chair; he could feel the caterpillars wiggling under his collar, and they might be crawling in his hair. Bits fell on his pages; bits of what? Animal? Vegetable? He did not know; he could not read. Birds yacked, dogs barked, women yelled, children cried. Nature. For the two hundredth time he rubbed his ticklish nose.

Every sound. Outside. In. These houses flimsier than the worst tenements of the city, more crowded. Shacks. Shanties. Overrun with kids. Everyone barefoot. The husbands show up on the weekends; the orphanage in the valley.

And the nights, too, could be noisy; teenagers walking up the road singing, a neighbor whistling for his dog—the sounds sudden and confused, as if they did not know what messages they carried in the darkness. Late at night, he had heard quarreling, the people next door: the man had a voice like an announcer, smooth and consistent, cake batter dripping from a spoon. Like the commentator for ERPI Classroom Films. Aronesti had to sit through a film, two showings in a row, once a month. The sound of student feet shuffling into the Assembly Hall, over the desperate buzz of voices, under the grim little lights. Then, lights out, silence; the projector palpitating, a steam of light on the vacant screen, colors jerking. So, a bazaar in China.

And then the voice, the voice that had introduced a canning factory the month before. "Why, this isn't the real thing," Aronesti would think, looking about with embarrassment at the sweet, young, light-suffused profiles; the voice was too clever, condescending; it would pretend excitement, but knew better. Awful, to be in an argument with a voice like that!

Two little boys walked in the dirt road, towels under their arms, their legs streaked with sand. One had a belly like an aborigine. They stood at the screen door pounding and calling. Must be locked. He heard bare feet running through the house. Must be bare, bouncing. The mother appeared, a pale shadow, smudge of red lipstick, behind the door. She undid the hook and held the door open for them, stretching out her arm, the white inside blue-veined, the bas-relief of a tendon.

That white arm. She looked like Ada. Ada, lying on the couch with those white arms behind her head. Ada, slowly smiling. Then her smile subsided, sinking back into her soul. "Ada," he had whispered. She turned her head. "What were you thinking, just now?" Her head lolled back; she shrugged her uplifted arms and laid her chin into her chest. It made no difference; it was not the explanation that he wanted: but the connection, the connection, the current of life that had passed through her and had passed him by.

It was the Fourth of July. Late, the sound of fireworks began in earnest, the explosions curiously soft, muffled in the absorbent darkness. Pale moths were fastened to the screen, like dull faces peeking in. His mother came wandering through, past her bedtime, making noise to show that she had no intention of disturbing him.

"How could I sleep?" she said when he looked up at her; and sat down at once beside him. "That fan is wasting its breath in here."

"Turn it off."

"That's an answer." Her hair was wet and she smelled of lipstick, which had been applied raggedly. And her breath smelled somewhat like lipstick—artificial, stale; close. Close, the smell of old people. Everything locked up in there all that time.

"You never try to be a help," she said.

Justly, too. A hot, noisy night; he knew she had not fixed herself up at this hour for nothing; so he gave in, and they went for a walk. It was pitch dark; the deep lights of the houses kept to themselves; the crickets were jittering like hot wires dropped in the grass. With warning tremors, a car approached, its beams of light thick and swarming, cutting a swath of pale leaves and black shadows. The hedges loomed around them, intricate, gleaming fretwork. The car rolled on, turned a corner. An explosion crumbled through the darkness.

The feeling the night gave you when these dense sounds diffused in it.

But the length of it. Nothing took time any more. Take? Did he want them to take his time from him? There were moments when he could hear time going, as if a movie screen had filled with luminous significance, and he could hear the projector churning. The depths of silence. The depths of the night. Fireworks; thunder. Rain.

Rain in profusion, striking the bricks, the cement, the stone steps; teeming in the gutters. Spending itself for nothing. They were safe in bed. In the freak blind light of the window he would see her, sleeping on her side, her back to him, and her hand reaching over covering her shoulder; the naked hand; the one without the ring. He would lean over her, her hair swept up and the soft shiny underside of it exposed; her particular odor rising freely in the warmth of sleep; he would whisper—not to wake her; in the abundance of the night, no need to wake her; only to nudge some response from her as she repossessed her dream.

Rain, that very afternoon that she was buried. Scant—as if that made any difference. He stood at the window, watching the dark splotches erupting on the pavement, the stone steps slickening. So she had become part of that.

From far down the beach, from the pier decorated like a bandstand with crepe-paper streamers, the fireworks were shooting out over the water, bursting needles melting into the black lake. All along the shore there were people looking up restlessly at the sky. Their faces flickered with the colors— yellow, orange, red, purple—a special sigh for purple. Like the selections from Tchaikovsky the school band was always playing, this display; no one seemed to know how to end it. Long tails of firecrackers popping off, the rockets beginning all over again. On the stage, Mr. Riga, the conductor, turning his stiff chin to the audience. As if knowing their impatience. (How could he help but?) As if dragging things out just for spite. The players, mostly girls in sticky white blouses, planting and squirming their ballet-slippered feet. The music lurching on indestructibly, the audience asking with one heart, Now? Now? Now? When? POP POP POP BOOM.

It was a few moments before the crowd started to disperse.

His mother took his arm, took full possession of it, slipping her narrow elbow through his and clasping his wrist with her other hand. She did not lean on him, but he could feel the stiffness of her bones, the heavy pacing of her steps, the strange distribution of her weight. Now her expression had lapsed interest; she knew she was out of it.

So, who was not out of it?

It was no darker, no cooler, no quieter than it had been an hour before. It was not getting any later. The summer night was opening, opening, opening; porous and fragrant. And the restless crowd scenting it; hovering, swarming; ranging the darkness—for the center of it, the heart of it. The instinct for yearning.

He knew. He felt it too. The clumsy, cumbrous feeling, some old yearning rousing itself. Some old yearning that you had never had. Just some old impatience, this vague rousing nothing but impatience. And impatience with nothing, nothing but the night.

The traffic lights were set to blinking yellow late at night, but this was a holiday weekend, and the main road fed other resort towns north and south. So there was no chance of getting across; though people were gathering: the road was full, the cars moving gelatinously. Along the curb, the pedestrians collected, blinking in the headlights' long, sticky beams, which seemed to fuse to the eyeballs before they ripped away. Like the moths hooked on the screen, their faces—moist, white, sleepy; glittering and dull.

Everyone seemed to assume, however, that something would be done; they would not be left this way. Aronesti trusted, too; he felt awed by the spectacle and yet detached, as if it were the vast activity of some other form of life. When he shut his eyes, he imagined the noises (the honking, rattling, rumbling) feeding the remote air of some night swamp where wild cattle were herding. ERPI Classroom Films again. He saw too many of them.

On the other side of the street a girl of nine or ten (skinny, large-nosed, a head of frizzy blonde hair) was trying to get across. Maybe she had been sent to get someone; she kept stepping off the curb and stepping right back. Her face, turned into the lights, had a tense, semiconscious expression, like the closeups of athletes on television; she was just calculating what car to take a chance in front of, anyone could see that. Several women in housedresses and haircurlers were discussing her ("tcching" and taking in the breath). Himself—though his tongue tensed and swelled each time that she threatened to make the dash—he could not call out. There must be some reason no one else gave a yell.

Then without even seeing, he knew she had darted out; tires screeched, screeched, screeched, sticking to the asphalt; a car-horn swooned; his mother pulled on his arm. He heard the women say that was good, that had scared her—she could have caused a real accident, the little dummy. And there she was, back on the curb; her shoulders hunched, her face popping out from them, ghastly, and her eyes like reflectors. Not only had she had a good scare—she had almost got herself run over, in front of all these people; so she looked ashamed and turned her head from the lights that were whipping over her face.

He felt a swarming emptiness, a stray grief, as if the headlights, penetrating him, had picked up some straggling animal—the startled eyes like a stopped heartbeat. Death was a dark world, and she was wandering through it.

Sometimes before sundown Aronesti walked on the beach. It was filthy by then, full of ice cream sticks, dented paper cups, cigarette butts, empty squeeze bottles. From the bath house came shrieks, volleying in that wild, unearthly way of sounds in closed, partitioned places; catacombs, prisons. Zoos. Fat-thighed girls, their stiff sprayed hairdos glimmering like beetles' wings, plunged gravely through the sand. Teenagers; for the beach was theirs, mostly; the people without responsibilities. They smoked, they petted, they rubbed sun oil into each other's backs, they cracked gum; their portable radios blared at their knees. Most of all, they looked; they looked up at everyone who passed; they looked around. Afraid of missing something, someone. (It gave him a quick, log-heaving revulsion, to think of their puppy love.)

So why did they look so glum?

After all, he was a teacher. Maybe he wore some mark of it between his brows, and it was on that they fixed and followed? No, no sign of recognition; they might have been following an optometrist's flashlight along a wall.

No, why did they look so glum?

Over the loudspeaker, a throat cleared. "ATTENTION. We are looking for a little lost girl. She is blonde, about four years old; she wears her hair in a pony tail. Her name is Kathy Lynn Begoun. She is wearing a red-and-white

775

polka dot swimsuit, and blue sunglasses. If anyone sees this little girl will you please bring her to the beach manager's office? Thank you."

Routine. At least six times a day, children turning up lost or children looked for; the clear young lifeguard voices efficient, good-humored; the sunbathers looking up from their blankets to listen only because it was impossible not to listen. So the faces lifted; some frowned with the sudden input of sound and sunlight; no one paid any attention.

But it touched him, this unison of listening, these heads going up unconsciously, these faces—against the background of glinting water—frowning with some rudimentary recognition. Ada looking up, frowning into the camera—the camera, however, not waiting; the moment never explained. Preserved merely; intense, dilated.

Close to the pier, two little boys were throwing stones. They threw as if they were casting a spell, lifting their arms up over their heads and opening their hands; and the stones sprinkled out on the water.

It was cooler on the pier but the air viscous. He stood with his hands on the railing looking at the water. It looked tepid and dirty; the foam floated on it like spit. Surely, people who jumped off bridges and things like that would not choose this kind of water. Unless you were doing it for the principle. Nihilism. Like going down the drain.

Back from the pier came a slight, pale woman, trailing her hand along the railing. Was that his next-door neighbor? Then those must be her dirty little boys throwing stones at the waves. But the neighbors' boys were older maybe. Well, when she got closer. But she pivoted around on one hand and crossed her arms on the railing. He would not be able to tell now, whether he knew this woman. She had given no sign of recognition.

Aronesti dreamed.

He sensed himself—some buttons on a coat, a weight; saw sometimes his shiny shoes against the cindered snow, now the hat on his head. And Ada too he hardly saw, but felt her—her arm through his, her black nubby coat, her small feet in high heels—bare, too bare for such a day—picking over the mushy ground. At last the train came. So they had been waiting for it. The El, blowing up the gritty dust in their faces. In spite of the blurred, smoky, yellow light inside, the car was cold. A window was open. No wonder. He got up and closed it. But they noticed another open. He got up and closed that too. There were people in the car, but nobody helped with the window closing; nobody even seemed to notice that there were windows open. More. No matter how hard he looked to be sure, there were more. And he had to get up—for the wind was bitter—though Ada was sitting patiently, turning her pale face to him and then back to the window; and he wanted to sit down with her. At last he noticed an old bum sitting right in front of them; a lean man, shirtless, in a dark colorless suit that he wore like a bathrobe, as if he had pulled it on only to answer the door. Dirty colorless hat; grizzled chin; bloodshot eyes. This man, he thought, is eyeing Ada. He sat down immediately and began looking out the window. Every time they passed a station, he tried to see the name of the stop somewhere; but they always pulled out too quickly, or he could see the sign but not make it out. Then it got darker; the yellow lights were strung in reflections in the windows. The old bum turned around and looked at them, only his eyes over the edge of the seat, dark and colorless, impossible to tell their expression as they slid to the corners, exposing the terrible bloodshot whites. Then in one sliding movement of the eyes, the head, he slumped to the window and died.

Aronesti heard the snap and recognized it instantly, even as he started; somewhere in the house, a mousetrap had gone off. He knew he had been dreaming about Ada, and did not want to think about it. He had been grateful at first for such dreams, but now they did not lend themselves to probing: the events had become incoherent, her appearance garish (rouged and powdered, covered with brown crumbling leaves), as if the dreams themselves, with time, were decomposing. So he did not want to lie in bed. He got up and turned on the light; his glasses were on the dresser, the lower half of the lenses thick and cloudy. He took up his flashlight and, sending the light along the edges of the moulding, went looking for the trap.

It was in the kitchen, right under the sink, the thumb smear of yellow cheese untouched, and a small dark mouse underneath the snap resting its head on its paws. You were supposed to be able to remove the mouse and use the trap again. What he needed was a pencil, pry the thing up; one-handed, he rolled up his pajama sleeves, and then, tucking the flashlight under his arm, picked up the trap. The slim tail hung free. With a shudder he threw the mousetrap into the garbage can. What did they cost? Eleven cents? He took the garbage can too and put it outside; there was a cantaloupe slice of a moon. Covering the flashlight with his hand, he moved quietly back to his bedroom, his fingers glowing like bloody coals.

777

He put the flashlight back on the dresser and without expecting it, looked up into his face. He stared at the face in the mirror—the strange walls, the strange threshold. He remembered the dream. He sat down on the bed, numbly pulling the sleeves down over his arms. This incident had actually happened. Some years before, on a cold snowy evening, on the way to a party; some poor down-and-out soul sitting right in front of them on the elevated had glanced back at them and died. They had been held up for at least an hour, too; what with getting the body off, the police, the passengers from that train and from several successive ones knocking and squeezing together like molecules trying to keep warm. They had gone on to the party; walked into the heat of the room, smoke, laughter, lightly perspiring faces turned toward them as they stamped the packed gray snow from their boots; and in that instant, without speaking, agreed to say nothing of the man who had died.

Now Aronesti sat on the bed, his elbows on his knees and his chin thrust forward, trying to see back into his dream, to get a look at those eyes. But they would not keep still for him; there was the looking toward him, the sliding away—and when they had slid away, he had to force them to turn back, himself to stare, all over again.

He had wondered, often, what the look was for. The simplest thing, of course—for help. But the man had made no sound, no sign; and he did not seem in pain. In fact, the glance was if anything reproachful. But let anyone turn to look at you—just look at you—over his shoulder; it would seem reproachful. And what if he knew—looked back for one last human contact, or, with some instinct, to see what was overtaking him? But there had been nothing like that in the look. It had been—just a look.

And here Aronesti knew that he was lying. He could not tell what was or was not in the man's eyes or his mind; that he could never know. But he had always known what the look had meant. Why else had they waited on the cold platform, among the gum machines and defaced posters, shivering and turning away from the wind, until the dead man had been taken into other hands? How else had they known as they walked in on the party in the overheated flat, that they could not use this man's death as an excuse for being late, as if it were an episode in the newspapers, on the radio, in the public domain. What had he seen? Frowning faces in the bony winter twilight. Faces that in the next moment would be looking on his dead body. People who would answer whatever demands his death had put on them, and then resume their temporary destinies.

When he turned, he had been looking back on his survivors.

Survivor. The word seemed like some primeval amphibian dragging itself up from a swirling sea and gasping toward the sand. Ignorant, tedious, triumphant word: containing so much of the pain and necessity of living. And he felt that there was a further significance to this word that was not beyond his comprehension; a responsibility he yearned to undertake; a connection he verged on making. He got up and pressed his hands together, tensely took off his glasses and laid them down on the dresser, on the photograph. The young, smiling faces welled up in them. He stared at the blurred, grainy faces; hers was among them; she was there. He snatched up his glasses, held them to his eyes, thumbs laid against his temples, and bent his head over the face that was still looking out, almost smiling; the eyes that were still squinting in the weakened sunlight.

Anthony Kerrigan

Don Alonso Quixano, Lineal Descendant . . .

Every morning Alonso Quixano was awakened at seven-thirty by the noise of the electric weaving machine that the neighbors—on the floor below had illegally installed in their flat. Quixano was powerless to do anything about the machine, even to complain, for he himself was a prisoner in his own house.

As soon as he had washed, he went and woke the guard, whom no noise disturbed, and the two of them had coffee. The State paid for the guard's upkeep, his meals were sent at the Corps' own expense, but the coffee was a treat furnished by Quixano. It was contraband coffee a relative sent from Majorca, and its heady aroma filled the wintry Madrid apartment with a suggestion of opulence and hope. Early in the morning, the guard and the prisoner were drawn quite close to each other by the ceremony; they felt like new men and like old comrades at the same time. Perhaps the day would bring forth unexpected developments. Quixano's father, Don Alonso Quixano, slept late in a back room, beyond the sound of the downstairs machine, and he would not emerge until noon, still dressed in his pajamas. He would have spent the night before in a café until the early hours. Quixano the younger knew he would not have spoken of the situation or even given it a thought. Honor forbade the old man's mentioning his son's plight, from complaining in any way. Moreover, he could not make any sense of it. He was a good monarchist and the circle of friends he met with was all monarchist, and it was inexplicable that his son was under house arrest—had been under house arrest now for two years—as a Red. As far as he had ever known, his son had been one of the Monarchist Youth in school, and even after that in college. He had never had a heart-to-heart talk with the boy. That type of approach did not interest him. It would have compromised his own standards of absolute authority; it was not his business to ask questions and receive explanations; he was beyond all that give-and-take. He understood about the passport, of course; the boy should not have gone behind the Iron Curtain. But he was no Red.

Quixano's mother, on the other hand, had had Reds in her family. She was in fact known for her anachronistic sympathy, so long misplaced, for that side of her family. She gritted her teeth through the years and said nothing. Life to her was suffering and resignation. Despite her Red sympathies, she went to Mass every morning. She left her son and the guard having coffee, and when she came back the maid had started the morning's work, and she herself joined in the chores.

782   Alonso Quixano had gone to Paris two springs before. He went to visit his friend Paco Jiménez, from Burgos, a friend from the university who had moved to Paris. When he got to the French capital, he found Paco had grown a smallish beard and had acquired a bright look in his eyes, a febrile expression about them as if he were perpetually in love or not eating. The sound and sight of Paris quickly made him accept Paco's peculiarities. While they strolled together in the Luxembourg Gardens, Paco talked in a low, intense voice about the love of men for each other all over the earth, of the fantastic accumulation of affection humanity could count on if all men cared for each other. One day, he suddenly proposed that Alonso keep him company on a visit to Budapest. The old city evoked imperial identifications in Alonso's mind. He thought of the Magyars and the administrative division between Buda and Pest. He went, and while he was there he saw very little of Paco from Burgos. Paco was busy with youth meetings, and, as Spanish was not one of the languages of the proceedings, Alonso never went with him to the assemblage. He wandered about the city, and was more taken by the negative impression of space and the impassivity of things than by any positive reaction; it was the very opposite of Paris, a kind of negative print slightly developed. Alonso was no sooner back in Paris than he was

summoned to the Spanish Embassy and asked for an explanation of his passport stamps. He ended up talking to a secretary who was a distant cousin, and this official, a perfectly turned-out specimen of innocuous youth, told him everything would be all right—once Quixano got back to Madrid. But he had to go back posthaste. "It is strictly forbidden to go behind the Iron Curtain. No Spaniard, unless he were a Red, ordinarily, would think of it. The matter is easily explained, but it must be explained in Madrid."

Quixano forcibly interrupted his sojourn, and as he departed for home felt that he was being deprived of an unconsummated treat.

In Madrid, everyone seemed to be suffering from a cold lethargy. The winter had been long, and an uncomfortable wind was still sweeping down from the Guadarramas. For several days he could find no one of importance at the Ministry of the Interior. Then one day, when he was conducted into the room of one of the anonymous secretaries, he was surprised to have the official pick up a piece of paper promptly, stand at attention, and read him a brief message which went as follows:

> *In compliance with regulations covering infractions of Subsection XX of the Decree on Possession of Passports by Spaniards in the Exterior, it is the decision of the Tribunal for the Suppression of Masonry and Communism of the Permanent Extraordinary Court-Martial of the First Military District that the subject Don Alonso Quixano be held under indefinite house arrest in his domicile at Ríos Rosas, 54, Madrid.*

By Order of the Court,
General Redondo, Commandant

Quixano was put into a car and taken home by his guard, who introduced himself most discreetly to the family, not venturing to offer his hand or to presume, but referring to himself always as Your Servant. The elder Quixano suffered a moment of apoplectic rage, and the son thought there might be trouble, but the older man dominated himself quickly, and put the matter— it was inexorable—out of his mind. Quixano puttered about the apartment and set himself arranging the space. He had his workroom set up just off the entrance way, his books, his desk, his papers; the guard indicated he would set up his own cot—he expected it would be sent later in the day— by the door. He would take charge of answering all calls, except those on the phone, which were unrestricted. His meals would be sent in from a nearby restaurant. On weekends, for two days and nights, he would be relieved, and the alternate guard would sleep in his bed. Nevertheless his work day amounted to a twenty-four-hour shift; Quixano marveled at the devotion and sense of duty of his guardian. He wondered if he were a volunteer for such duty, a specialist at it, and resolved to talk to him about it.

Meanwhile, Quixano took up his schoolbooks where he had left them. He found he was free to write letters and he opened a correspondence with the Secretariat of the Faculty of Philosophy and Belles-Lettres about his status. After many decisions and rulings—none of the school officials came to see him, though he was free to receive visits within earshot, theoretical earshot, of the guard—it was decided that he could go on with his school career. At this point he began to receive calls from his professors. They were all sympathetic, but very discreet in commenting on his situation. They were of varying political opinions themselves, but they all knew—they seemed to be the only official persons in the country who knew—that he was not a Red.

Juan Antonio Irribaren was the most outspoken of the lot: "In this age one is committed *nolens volens*. Only it is a question as to just what. Nowadays it is the search for *the* commitment, not *a* commitment which takes up our energy. Others commit us without knowing they have committed us, and we end by committing those we do not know. There is an interdependence similar to a modern laboratory: we are all working on different but closely related bits of ethic."

Quixano found the talk with his guard neither less nor more enlightening. The soldier was a dedicated man; he was not particularly religious, but showed a religious concept toward duty; he was willing and ready to sacrifice himself for the general good, for the *pueblo*, the people, for "everyone"; his talk was not very far different from that of Paco Jiménez in the Luxembourg.

In the first flush of morning, Quixano conspiratorially talked to the guard only about the weather. By midnight, after he had read in the classics of all time for interminable hours, he grew expansive and vented his knowledge on the guard.

"In earlier days," he would begin, "there was a more ideal moral climate, in that an elementary respect pervaded all classes. The highborn was content with his lot and responsibility, and did not, for instance, attempt to have legitimate carnal knowledge, in short, to marry, among the lower classes. The perverse was endowed with no legitimacy: a Nubian slave was not elevated to rank because he excited the sense of the exotic."

"It certainly is not right that a photographer should marry a queen," the guard would say. "It takes as much skill to point a rifle as to point a camera for a regulation portrait, and more courage to click the mechanism," he would add; "though it may be wrong to speak of the courage to do away with a man's life."

"In the old days men were quicker on the trigger, but then they also loved more madly. There might have been an advantage in that. A demented love, an all-extinguishing passion *for one person alone*, that was more than a glum prejudice in favor of everybody. For my part, I think I could love that Angela down the hall like I could love a great king."

"The King, the King . . ." began the guard.

"Don't say anything against the King," interrupted Alonso Quixano, the Red. "It can only injure your own honor."

"But we haven't had a king for so many years that we've forgotten all about it, or him. How can we know what we think of him, either good or bad?"

785

"Nevertheless, it's better to be loyal."

"Yes, it's better to be loyal," agreed the guard.

Quixano was working on a thesis—approval of which was not yet forthcoming—with the preliminary title "Miseries and Metaphysics of the Machine Age." Every morning, as the jagged noise of the textile loom below his room would wake him, he was spurred on by a dull sense of vengeance.

Down the hall, next to the door behind which Angela lived with her family, the Soriano boy was studying Russian. His father was a member of the State hierarchy. The head of the family had not missed out on a single day in power. He was seeing to it that his son should inherit the earth— the boy was already heir to his talent. The old bureaucrat played all the cards.

The elder Quixano would watch the Russian teacher going into the flat of an afternoon. He compared the Soriano boy's subtlety with his own son's obviousness. He knew the other boy would never run the risk of breaking a single rule for the Possession of Passports by Spaniards in the Exterior.

*

After two years, the guard was quite taken up with the life of the family. On saints' days, the celebration was general; the guard was included in all events. Though the family did not know his family, they knew about all the members of it. They asked after them ritually. Sometimes they sent little packages home with the guard. The guard himself often brought gifts, small delicacies, even flowers for the house. They all exchanged problems.

"Good morning, Tolo, how is your sister's son today?" Quixano's mother would ask on Monday morning.

"Better, *señora*, practically new. The doctor told her . . ."

Monday morning was a kind of fete. The guard was back. The contraband coffee tasted better. Not that there was anything wrong with the relief man either; he was equally sympathetic. Only they shared their life with Tolo more thoroughly. He had been there first. And unswerving. The relief guard had been changed several times through the years.

One day, there was a curious contretemps to all this, a disharmony which could have led to more serious consequences but for the absurdity of the situation. The young Quixano was reading aloud a monarchist editorial in the *ABC*—it was quite too little royalist for the boy, too compromising—and the guard tripped again on the subject of the King.

"That's all over, over and done with," he interrupted. "These are new times."

Quixano looked at him over the top of the newspaper in frozen silence. "What can *you* know about such a matter?" he finally asked.

"*I? I* piss on the body of the King!"

Quixano let the newspaper fall.

"Sir . . ." he began. He was going to say, "I challenge you," but he realized the guard was not *Sir*, and that he could not be challenged at all because of his low station. Quixano was powerless to have him cudgeled, even to slap his face. He stalked out of the room, and sulked in his bedroom, reappearing silently from time to time to get a book.

The guard was contrite, and by the next day Quixano had pardoned him.

"I didn't mean *your* candidate for king, but the old King . . ." he ventured.

"Let us leave the subject alone, and altogether—forever."

For his part, Alonso Quixano was concerned with the silence of the Pretender. He judged its long-drawn-out continuance ill-omened. He even toyed with the idea of warning him. After all he was a youth like himself, even younger. He might listen to a political prisoner with experience. Quixano was also disconcerted by certain socialistic overtones in the Pretender's public declarations: it was obvious he was playing the card of syndicalist support and in the end it was likely to undermine him.

One night he definitely conceived the idea of accosting the Pretender in a public place, in the theater preferably. His measured words, spoken in public, would sink deeper and have more profound reverberations than the silent gray words of an unknown correspondent locked up behind the uninspiring walls of a middle-class apartment.

For a month Quixano lived with his plan. He would elude the guard easily, playing on his trust—his own high purpose justified the maneuver—and make his appearance on the evening of All Souls', when the Pretender could be counted on to be in the audience witnessing the traditional performance of *Don Juan Tenorio*. The play, bizarre and sentimental, fixing the audience's attention on the cemeteries which would be decorated the next day, could boast a popular audience, as well as a sprinkling of the aristocracy. It was the one many-layered audience of the year, and Quixano's words would be sure of wide diffusion through the social strata, and could be assured of resonance, he was sure, even if they could count on no enthusiasm from such an agglomerate.

787

On the eve of the day set to deceive the guard and slip into the city for the midnight performance at the Teatro Español, Quixano received—by special messenger—a communication from the Ministry of the Interior. In it he was informed that henceforth he was free to leave his apartment during the hours from sunup to sunset. It was already growing dark. Quixano restrained himself from rushing out into the streets.

The first day of liberty was too sweet to let him prejudice the others. On the evening of All Souls' he came home at seven o'clock, just as dusk was settling. He was resigned to missing the Pretender at the midnight performance. As he waited for the guard to answer his knock, he beheld the Soriano boy letting himself out of his flat in the company of his Russian teacher. They were dressed for the evening. Perhaps after supper they would find places at the theater, for the traditional fete of *Don Juan Tenorio*, which this year boasted an elegant and gaudy cast, with an ex-matador as Don Juan.

Arthur Miller

Glimpse at a Jockey

I t's like this saloon, it's the best in New York, right? You can't even sit down in the can here without a hundred-dollar bill in each ear, look over there at that gray-hair loafer with the broad, getting himself loaded to put the wife out of his mind and for what? So he can make it with that Sue he paid anyway. I love them all. I bequeath myself to this world, life, the whole skam.

I'm happy here talking to you. Why is that? Who knows why you cross the bridge to some people and not to others? I'm absolutely happy right now. They underrate the whole nature of loyalty between men, it's different than with a woman, the kind of challenge. I'd win sometimes and be ashamed because the friggin' horse had me bobbling around coming over the finish line, instead of stylish. I could get down closer to the horse than any son of a bitch ordinarily, but sometimes you draw some broken-legged horse and you bump in like a trussed flounder on a no-spring truck. You ride for the other jocks, for their admiration, the style. My last race I went through the fence in Argentina, wired, screwed, and welded twenty-two bones, and after three months in the hospital the flowers stopped. A jock is like a movie star, the whole skam's night and day, the broads drooling your name printed on your friggin' forehead. Nothin'. Except two guys, mostly Virgil, that loyal son of a bitch, I'd die for the bastard.

Who understands that any more? I went to see this Doctor Hapic last year, what a sweet old starch, the greatest according to what you hear. And I lay down on the broken-down old couch and he looks around in the bins and comes up with a racing form! I figure I'm in for homosexuality because that's the hinge if men move you so much, and here's old Al diggin' me for a line on the sixth race, askin' me who's an honest bookie and all. I put in three hours with him, he cancelled one appointment after another, and when I left he charged me for half an hour! But how the hell do I know who's goin' to win? Even when I was riding I didn't know. Chrissake, the horse didn't know! Why can't they leave it alone, I mean the analyzing? Everybody I know who went come out a friggin' judge. I admit it, the whole skam is pistils and stamens, all right I surrender. But Jesus, give me room, let me die laughing if I'm goin' to die. I'm ready. If I slide off a snow bank under a cab outside there I'll cheer death. I love her, my wife, married eighteen years, and my kids, but you draw a line somewhere, someplace before there's no room left for the chalk down in the corner. The men are scared, did you see it where you been around? They keep makin' little teeny marks but they can't draw the line. Nobody knows any more where he begins or ends, it's like they pied the maps and put Chicago in Latvia. They don't allow nobody to die for loyalty any more, there's nothin' in it to steal.

What the hell do I know, ignorant, accordion-pleated mind that I have, but I know style in anything. The great thing is not winning, it's riding the friggin' horse nobody else could stay onto. That's the bastard you want to ride. Where the other jocks look and know the horse wants to kill you. That's when the flag stretches out and your corpuscles start laughing. Once I went to see my father.

I never told this to anybody, and you know how much I talk. Honest, I never told this. I made this television thing, interviewing ugly authors about their books, the line was that a jockey could actually read words, and it went over big till I threw myself in the Jag and drove to Mexico. I couldn't stand it. I'm all for stealing, but not pickpocketing, these authors weren't any goddam good authors, but every week you got to make over them like it's Man O'War did the mile in nothin' pissing all the way and a blind jock on top. Anyway, the station gets this letter from Duluth asking if I was born in Frankfort, Kentucky, and my mother's name is so and so. And if I was all them things he's probably my old man. This silly old handwriting like he wrote it on a tractor. So I throw myself into a plane and drive up to the door and he's a house painter.

I just wanted to see, you know? I wanted to lay my both eyes on him. And there he was, about seventy or a hundred. He left when I was one. I never saw him. Now I'd always dreamed of him like he was a high roller, or some kind of elegant thief, or maybe a Kentucky Rousseau or somebody stylish with broads, and left to seek his fortune. Some goddam thing interesting. But there he is, a house painter. And lives in the nigger section. I'm the last of the holdouts, I can't stand them. But there's this one next door, a real nice guy, and his wife was nice too. You could see they loved him. And I'm standing there. What did I come for? Who is he? Who am I if he's my father? But the crazy thing is I knew I belonged to him. It's like you said, I'm the son of my father. I knew it even if he was a total stranger. I just wanted to do something for him. Anything. I was ready to lay down my life for him. After all, who knows the situation? Maybe my old lady drove him out. Who knows the inside of the outside? So I ask him, what do you want?

I'll get you anything, I said, that is within my means, although I was loaded, it was after the Derby. He was small too, although not as small as me. I'm so small I'm almost un-American, but he was small too and he says, the grass in the backyard gets so high and thick I can't push the mower through it. So if I had one of them mowers with an engine on it.

So I grab the phone and they send over a truckload of all the kinds. And he was all afternoon goin' over each one and finally he picks out one with a motor bigger than this friggin' table, and I buy it for him. I had to leave to make the plane back because I promised Virgil I'd be in San Pedro to guard some broad he had to leave there a whole night, so I go into the backyard to say goodbye. And he wouldn't even turn the motor off so we could talk quietly. And I left him enjoying himself, joggling around that yard behind that friggin' mower.

Christ, how did I get so drunk! Those two broads across there have been lookin' at us. What do you say? What's the difference what they look like, they're all the same, I love 'em all.

791

Sydor Rey

Hitler's Mother

O n May 10, 1940, the day the Nazis invaded Holland, we sat at lunch time in one of the few Bohemian restaurants in New York, and spoke of the war. Our group was composed exclusively of writers. There were about a dozen besides myself and they had one characteristic in common, regardless of their attitude toward the war—to all of them Europe was remote, as if it were all happening on the moon. Yet each of these Americans knew Europe well.

Their relationship to me was characterized by the same aloofness. Though they questioned me, a newly-arrived European, with animation, and listened attentively to my remarks on the war, yet their curiosity lacked emotion. Our lively conversation reminded me of a cold desert wind, and secretly I began to seek protection from it in the tender spell of a beautiful girl who sat in silence between a liberal columnist and a young woman who wrote literary sketches.

The beautiful girl was a little over twenty, and looking at her I realized that she had nothing in common with us. She was like a bouquet of flowers placed among the talkative writers, so there was nothing surprising in her complete silence.

I asked her whether she had ever been in Europe. She answered very precisely, like a schoolgirl: "No, sir, I never was in Europe."

A young reporter who sat beside me had read her poems; they were beautiful, he said to me, but none had been published.

When we left the restaurant she asked me where I was going, and when I told her, she hesitated for a moment, then laughed. "I'll go with you." After a while she added: "Do you remember my name? Alice."

It was a beautiful spring day, one of those days when, by some miracle, the countryside makes its way to New York. We walked along the streets of the city, and I kept saying to myself, "Alice is beautiful as the day, the day her mother gave birth to her."

"But people are killed in the war, aren't they?" she asked me with a disturbing eagerness. It was as if a newborn infant had suddenly asked, "Doesn't man die?"

She said that in the restaurant they had discussed the war as if people weren't killed in it; she herself had been unable to join the conversation because she always had before her the vision of a field covered with bodies whose throats were slashed. She looked at me with solicitude and tenderness.

Alice followed me to my home, and stayed overnight.

When I woke, she was sitting on my bed, and studying me. She laughed, walked to the window, and quickly wrote something. Then she sat on my bed and read to me a short poem, in which a frozen male body was returned to life, so that she could bear her fruit on earth.

From the first hours of our friendship she interested herself in every detail of my misfortune. That I had found myself in New York alone, uprooted, isolated from my family and friends in Poland, without knowing what had happened to them—these circumstances did not arouse her sympathy so much as they excited her. Through them the world's anxiety now reached her, and in its feverish atmosphere our romance developed with wartime speed.

There was a vacant room next to mine. Without informing me, Alice went downstairs to the landlady, rented this room for a little more than the three dollars a week I paid for mine—and went home for her things. When I walked her to the subway, I met an acquaintance from Poland, with whom, at Alice's request, I spoke in Polish; she listened intently though she did not understand a word. Next to us stood a noisy group of men, and suddenly one of them began to abuse us, calling us Fascists, then Communists, and saying that we would bring misfortune on the country and drag it into the war. Alice furiously defended us, and the attacker fell silent at once, confounded by her beauty. Anger gave her delicate face a weird look. A sudden explosion of a flower. She waited for the world's business, as a flower waits for pollen from an insect.

Next day she came with two suitcases and moved into her room. After unpacking, she came to me rosy, with wide-open blue eyes, and soft golden hair, as if she had just emerged from a woods, and cried out, "There it is!"

I began to feel a profound sadness. Alice looked so unadventurous, so domestic; her face and even her bearing were ideally made for a home. I was not sorry for her, I was sorry for myself; I sensed intuitively that this affair was wastefulness—but then, I was living in dreadful turmoil. I was running away, like millions of people in Europe, and I was glad to have found a companion in misfortune and draw comfort that I would no longer have to flee alone.

But before whom was Alice fleeing? The same enemy as I?

Alice's ancestors on both sides had immigrated to the United States by the middle of the nineteenth century. On her father's side, she was of German extraction; on her mother's side, she was of Polish-Hungarian descent with an admixture of Jewish blood so small that she would easily have been cleared by the Nuremberg Laws.

795

It happened that her ancestors, both paternal and maternal, had emigrated from Europe after the 1848 revolution, in which they had participated. Although the founders of the two families had been intellectuals, their descendants in the United States were mainly workers.

Alice's father worked on the railroad from the time he was thirteen. During the First World War he served in the army, rose to the rank of sergeant, and received a number of decorations. After returning home, he worked in a factory that made fireproof safes. Then with two friends he went into business producing fireproof doors and made a considerable fortune before he lost everything in the crash of 1929. Then came the long difficult years of the depression, at the very time when he had dreamed of sending his son, Nick, to college. In his prosperous days he had told them about their ancestors' education, refinement, and ideals, about which he had seemed to know nothing previously.

But Alice's father had not only become poor, it was hard for him to find a job at all. Nevertheless, her brother—through scholarships and through jobs he and his mother and even Alice occasionally obtained—eventually managed to graduate from law school. There were thousands of jobless young

lawyers in New York, but Nick, on the recommendation of a professor—
he had always been one of the most brilliant students—secured a modest
position in the law department of a respectable New York firm.

Alice, who had always loved children, opened a seashore day camp for
children. The camp proved to be successful and even became famous: one
of the most popular magazines for young women printed a picture of Alice
along with her views about the enterprising spirit of young women and the
possibilities of their employment.

The same year she registered at a college, to study literature. She began
to write poems, and her English teacher encouraged her to continue.

Meanwhile, the land on which her summer camp had been located
was bought by a big realty firm whose president, a well-known New York
patrician, proposed to Alice that she run her camp in partnership with him.
That year her income from the camp tripled.

But about this time Alice's father broke down, like a tree that had
disintegrated within while outwardly seeming intact. For a while he dragged
himself about. He seemed to be wandering, idly and silently looking for his
way. Finally, late in the spring, he killed himself.

Alice's mother maintained that it had not been suicide, that he had
been shaving in the bathroom, and had cut his throat during a dizzy spell.
He had recently been full of hope, she said; he had repeated that he felt his
energy returning and that he would soon start something from which his
entire family would profit. Moreover, he had carried life insurance, and if
he wanted to kill himself he would have done it in such a way that his family
would have been paid the insurance. But the authorities decided that Alice's
father had committed suicide; he had swallowed an enormous dose of sleeping
medicine that his doctor had prescribed for him, then slashed his throat and
died of loss of blood. Alice's mother returned to her theory: no, he had been
shaving in the bathroom, he had a dizzy spell as a result of taking sleeping
pills, and by an unhappy accident cut his throat.

In the end Alice formed her own view of the matter; her father had
swallowed a large dose of sleeping medicine, intending to die in such a way
as not to deprive his family of the insurance money. But being an unusually
sturdy man, he had awakened and, enraged at being alive, had cut his throat
with his razor.

Alice's speculations on the subject of her father's death were only
variations of her grief. She believed that her family had been responsible for

her father's death, especially her mother. In the course of the last years, amid the protracted and difficult struggle for existence, the relations between her father and mother had grown strained, and the family became divided into two camps—the father and Alice on the one hand, the mother and Nick on the other.

When the end of the school year drew near, Alice decided to leave. Her studies had been tied up with her father's life; she felt now that she had studied only for his sake. She was delighted by the thought of her summer camp, of the children—her family had disintegrated, the camp was her new community. But the patrician, whose partner she had become, cheated her; having the addresses of her customers, he took advantage of her reputation, entrusting the camp to another young woman, reportedly his niece.

Alice now missed her father even more profoundly and decided to follow in his steps. One night she swallowed a large dose of aspirin, and the next day her mother found her in bed, apparently dying.

She was taken to a hospital, and recovering, she went to Provincetown, where she came to know the writer of literary sketches, who accompanied her whenever she swam out to sea.

We lived in furnished rooms. Our house was inhabited by lonely people, like Alice and myself, people who sought new bonds to replace the old broken ones. It was a very narrow, three-storied, brownstone house, without an elevator, one of those converted old private homes on the Hudson.

In the rooms, with their old pieces that were once beautiful, there was an air of sadness, for those who lived there possessed only their longings— some longed for the past, others for the future, and the two amounted to the same thing.

Our landlady, though in her fifties, was very beautiful; her hair was snow-white, but her face was young, without a wrinkle, and her body was small and young. Because she continually drank wine she breathed warmth as though she had just left her bed and her lover's embraces. Her name was Maria. She was Italian and though she had lived for many years in New York, she spoke English poorly and reluctantly. She said it was an animal language, or a human language meant only for animals; to give her speech a human character she was forced to throw in Italian words and even sentences, though perfectly aware that the person she addressed would not understand her.

Maria and Alice became close friends at once. They spent hours together, talking, although they did not understand each other. At times they seemed to be telling each other fairy tales in a fantastic language.

Maria leased the house and lived in the basement with her husband, Piero, an elevator operator in an apartment house. He was a handsome man—tall, broad-shouldered, with dark hair and calm gray eyes. Taciturn and concentrated, he looked at our house as a hospital where he was the nurse. Maria and he had a twenty-year-old daughter named Rosa, whose figure was beautiful but whose face was unattractive. Rosa resembled her parents in her features but her face was rough and unfinished. One had the impression that if she had grown up in the Italian sun, as both of her parents had, she would have been as beautiful as they, but having lived all her life in New York, she had somehow failed to ripen. Her parents pitied her as one does a defective child, and Rosa resented them for having denied her their only precious possession, beauty, as if they had deliberately withheld it. She lived by herself on the ground floor in a large room furnished not haphazardly like the others but in harmony with her character. All the other rooms in our house seemed like those in a funeral home where the dead body is kept for only one night.

The oldest tenant was Sylvester, a former teacher of singing, who, like Maria, was perpetually drunk. They drank together, and though there was nothing social in their drinking, yet their drunkenness had created a kind of mystical bond between them, inaccessible to the other tenants. Sylvester, who was very tall, seemed at first to be wearing some frightful mask: his swollen, pock-marked face was bluish-red, the color of dead matter. One was tempted to walk up to him and tear off his hideous mask. From under it the slits of his eyes seemed to look out imploringly.

He lived on the ground floor next to Rosa, in the most spacious room. Sylvester went to bed and got up several times daily to play the piano or to talk. Occasionally he broke into a hoarse falsetto while accompanying the jarring piano. Otherwise, he spoke beautifully, and apparently speech had replaced music for him. Most often he spoke of art, the importance of beauty in life. These were not conversations but sermons. Whenever I listened to them, it seemed to me that Sylvester had been victimized by some terrible spell—some awful charm had imprisoned a beautiful face under a grotesque bluish-red mask.

For many years Sylvester had been living, or rather drinking, on a modest monthly sum which he received from a certain "patroness." When the patroness, of whom none of us knew anything, died, she bequeathed to him funds sufficient for six months. Sylvester lived peacefully through these six months, and on the last night took poison. After his death we learned that his patroness had been his own wife, who had deserted him many years before.

The second floor was occupied by Magda and Stanley. Madga came from a village in the mountains, where her parents had a farm. From her earliest years she had dreamed of city life, and after a series of duels with vacationers, she felt strong enough to try it. With her simple formula for success she had come to New York.

She was tall and shapely, and brutal. She had ceased being a female; her sex was merely one of her weapons in the struggle for survival. Occasionally she worked in a restaurant, awaiting her great opportunity, a man who would give her a life of luxury. While waiting for this opportunity she had fallen indifferently into the most common kind of prostitution.

Stanley, who resembled a bulldog with spectacles, washed dishes in the restaurant where Magda occasionally worked and where they had met. He was a miner's son, who had worked in the mines, and then, like Magda, had come to New York. He moved to the room next to hers, hoping that near her he would run into his great opportunity, that if she got a chance he too would profit from it. Meanwhile, he attended an evening business school.

Magda and Stanley were Sylvester's most frequent visitors; apparently he considered them to be most in need of his speeches on art and beauty. He usually invited them both, but even when uninvited they came together. They in turn seemed to be his most zealous listeners; for them he represented the higher social spheres, some important hidden contacts.

Shortly after the United States declared war on Japan and Germany, Stanley enlisted in the Army, hoping to become a commissioned officer and later to become successful that way. One day he came back, a second lieutenant on a brief furlough, and stayed all that time in Sylvester's room. A few months later Magda told Sylvester and Maria that she had been made pregnant by Stanley. She could not understand what had happened to her, she had always been so careful, and curiously enough, they had lived next to each other for so long without even kissing.

She left for the country to stay with her parents, and when she gave birth, she left her child with them and returned to New York, but not to our house. Later we heard that Stanley had been killed in the Far East.

The third-floor tenants were George, a middle-aged violinist, and Joanne, a dancer. There was something very dignified about them, and I was astonished to learn that they were living in sin, all the more so because they were occasionally visited by George's two attractive daughters and by Joanne's father, who was a minister in a fashionable New England town.

George was about fifty, of medium height, broad-shouldered, balding, and wore sideburns. Joanne was about thirty, tall, slender, and dark-skinned like a Gypsy. The two dressed flawlessly but in somewhat outmoded fashions. George carried his father's gold watch with a heavy chain stretched in an old-fashioned way across his waistcoat, and Joanne wore her mother's old-fashioned silver bag.

George once had had considerable business enterprises on Long Island. When he lost his fortune, he suddenly realized that he had always wanted to be a musician. He left his wife and children and came to New York in the hope that he would first find a job in a symphony orchestra or in a quartet, and that after working hard he would become a soloist. But it had all ended up with his occasionally playing for dancers in night clubs.

Joanne had come to New York from a small-town college where her husband taught chemistry. She had come with great plans, dreaming of a new religious dance rooted in American folkways. Her plans led only to her sometimes dancing half bare in a night club with a group of other well-built "artists."

George and Joanne were twin souls and companions in misfortune. When they practiced their "true art" together at home, there was something pitiful about it. Yet the domestic productions of these two feeble, clumsy artists were moving because of the aspirations and intimacy they communicated. George and Joanne knew how ridiculous they were, and this, no doubt, accounted for their despair when one was without the other, as well as for their flawless way of dressing, their dignified manners, and their quiet pride in an extramarital union.

Maria's and Piero's house had many other tenants at the time, but only temporary ones. Maria, Piero, Rosa, Sylvester, Magda, Stanley, George, Joanne, and I formed a community, which was then joined by Alice—or was it that we became a community because of her?

Alice established contact with the tenants immediately, during her first visit to me, even before she had moved in; perhaps that was why she did move in, not merely because of me. In any case, she had found a milieu suitable to her. She in turn brought us her beauty and youth and order, and raised our sense of self-worth.

Alice replaced Maria as the only source of beauty in the sorry brownstone house, and in this sense she became our landlady. She apparently realized this, for she felt it her duty to look after all of us. I remember Sylvester singing in a falsetto, in a drunken voice, playing on his out-of-tune piano, while tears flowed from Alice's eyes. When he had finished, he walked up to her and kissed her hand; he knew that she had not been moved by his concert but by himself. Tenderly, Maria would often entrust Alice, not Rosa, with her housekeeping tasks. For Maria, Alice represented her own youth, and Maria was proud of this.

Magda, who was attractive, seemed homely and raw in the presence of Alice; and yet Alice had such a strong sense of equality that Magda, who admired her beauty, eventually began to identify with her, and thus began to feel prettier than she had before the girl arrived. The same was true of Stanley, who was obtuse and admired her intelligence; in time he too identified with her and acquired great confidence in his own intelligence. A great friendship developed among George, Joanne, and Alice. Alice read to them *801* her subtle, concise poems, and each time she managed to create an atmosphere in which George and Joanne felt that they had helped to write them, and Alice seemed to believe that they actually had.

Her presence meant more to me than to anyone else. I had moved to Maria's house soon after my arrival in New York, a few months before Hitler's invasion of Poland, and from then on I had lived there on the fourth floor, under the roof, where it was hottest during the summer. Eventually I had begun to consider the heat my only source of dejection; the New York heat paralyzed me.

Thus I was living in an attic room, deprived of my country, family, and friends, whom Hitler was destroying; deprived of my woods, fields, rivers, and mountains, songs and speech—and therefore terribly poor. I ate better than in Poland, I dressed better, but I was more impoverished. My neighbors had begun to treat me with a kind of reverence because I was a victim of Nazi persecution.

This cult had begun to give me megalomaniac ideas; I was becoming ridiculous and realized it.

Under those circumstances Alice, the beautiful, young American poet, was my salvation when she came in May, 1940, before the heat of summer, to live next to me on the top floor. Through Alice I reached America, and America me. Through her the New World became quieter, softer, and began to appear in my dreams as something very old.

At that time, I lived on an allowance I received from a refugee aid organization, and when Alice came to me she did not improve her material situation. For a long time now she had been jobless; she had been looking for suitable work, and meanwhile had acquired debts. But after moving next to me, she took the first job offered her, and began to work part time in a department store. She did this for my sake. (Her brother, having lost his job, and having been deserted by his wife, had stopped looking for work; he developed a mania for solving all world problems himself. His own problems dejected him so much that he felt them as the world's burden. The same thing might have happened to Alice had it not been for her concern for me; for she tried to get into the same kind of trouble as Nick had, as though imitating him.)

Did Alice love me? It is hard to say, for this was a stormy period. I retain nothing of our physical contact, remember none of it. Perhaps physical contact had no place in our relationship, perhaps I prefer to forget about it, because it was an abuse on my part, an abuse of her compassion for me.

For my birthday, I remember, she bought me a rather expensive pipe out of her first earnings. I was not in New York on my birthday, and returned only late the following night, to find Alice in my room, quietly sitting in the chair, reading a book near the lamp; the rest of the room was dim. When I approached her, she quietly gave me the box with the pipe in it. What a beautiful, warm color that pipe had.

On another occasion, she suddenly interrupted her vacation at the beach to join me as soon as possible: unexpectedly I found her in my room one afternoon. She sat on the bed in her dressing gown; tanned, clear as crystal, smelling of dry hay. (With reference to her I can without embarrassment use phrases like "clear as crystal," "beautiful as a rose," "marvelous as an angel." Only through her did I fully realize that those expressions are rooted in reality, and not in the ravings of romantics.) Seeing me, she burst into tears and confessed that she had betrayed me. She had written asking me to join her at the ocean; I had not gone, and there had been a young man from Hungary to whom she had spoken almost all the time about me, and he had explained to her that nothing would come of our relationship.

Once she had sat with him at the burning fireplace until late at night and talked about me; that night she had betrayed me. She finished her confession, and continued to cry quietly. Later I met that young man; he resembled me, but he was more handsome.

For some time she worked sporadically in her department store; then she was given a steady job. As a result of the war in Europe, it was easier to get jobs. She was a salesgirl and earned eighteen dollars a week. Her appearance and intelligence attracted the attention of her superior, and when he learned that she had a talent for writing, he promised to transfer her eventually to the publicity department, where she would have a better chance to make a career.

But events took a different turn.

The department store employees did not belong to a union, and an attempt to organize led to a strike. Alice had been so active from the start that after a few days she was elected a member of the strike committee.

The strike continued for weeks, and Alice worked night and day, serving as a picket, distributing leaflets, carrying banners, writing appeals and militant songs, editing the strike bulletin, attending conferences, and making speeches. She rarely slept during the strike. It was as if she no longer needed to sleep; lack of sleep did not seem to exhaust her, she was in a constant state of excitement. She behaved as if winning the strike would make her happy for life and the world happy forever.

Usually she returned home late at night, almost at daybreak, or occasionally during the day. She would go to bed, but would arise after a moment and begin to move about like a slightly drunken person whose body managed to remain steady. She was in a state of exhilaration, and like a person slightly drunk would burst into tears occasionally. At such moments we would all become sad and helpless.

Being as beautiful as she was, Alice's exalted glances and words, the heightened motions of her arms and legs and whole body were not shocking, did not arouse suspicion; instead of speaking, she declaimed, and instead of moving, she danced. She was an endless impassioned theater. After all, she was a poet, and for us her seizures were the inspirations of a priestess. I cannot recall many symptoms clearly proving that she was sick; neither can others. During one of her seizures, she kept repeating,

"Rat, be a she-wolf, for my child, my first one, sleeps in a canal."

Well, she had gone through an abortion, and the fruit of her womb had found itself in a New York sewer. Whenever she referred to Magda's pregnancy as "our pregnancy," she meant this as a joke, although she did so with great tenderness.

Her insanity—as it came to be diagnosed—seemed rather a kind of inflammatory state of love, and we were convinced that she was incapable of violence toward others or herself; while she was ill, her inherent gentleness deepened. (Her attempts at suicide reflected a desire for sleep. She first attempted it with a large dose of aspirin; later, she swam out to sea, trying to drown from exhaustion, to fall asleep in the water. However, her long swim cannot unequivocally be called attempts at suicide.) Alice adopted the madness of her brother—who for a long time after he had lost his job wandered about town with lofty manias—and she had also adopted the madness of our house. Intermittently we favored the idea of hiding her in a hospital, just as we had hidden in ourselves our own madness.

The department store strike ended in complete victory, and Alice resumed her job. A few days later she reported to the president of the firm, and made a speech in his office about his position in the world, his employees, and his duties toward them; she said that if he wanted to be a man in the full sense of the word, he must not for a moment forget that those associated with him were his equals.

It is hard to understand how she managed to make her way to this potentate—how she, an ordinary salesgirl, made her way to the head of one of the largest department stores in New York, one of the biggest business concerns in the United States. Was it because of her beauty and the rhythm of her voice, which had been unspoiled by lies?

Her speech was neither violent nor hostile, only solicitous. But it was the solicitude precisely that frightened the president, who was a giant of a man, with a face restless and quivering as if it had been attacked by wasps. The earnestness and warmth of her voice frightened him: only in a madman's heart can other people's business become so personal. The president began to scream like a startled bird, whereupon a group of store detectives rushed into the office, an ambulance was called, and Alice was taken to a hospital in a strait jacket. She was quiet, she did not resist, but the nurses asked her no questions, convinced that she had physically attacked the president—for why should an insignificant salesgirl break into his office? In the hospital she was put, fettered, into an ice-cold bath, intended to calm her.

On the same day her mother, accompanied by her minister, came to the hospital, and because of the latter's intervention, the authorities did not send Alice to an insane asylum. Next day her mother took her to a Christian Science nursing home, in which faith was the only physician.

This home was surrounded by fields and pine woods. Alice spent three months there. Throughout that period she struggled against the nurse's attempts to inject her with faith in God as one injects a serum, and Alice resisted like a child resisting vaccination. This was an ideological struggle: the nurse proposed that she seek salvation in God, and Alice stubbornly sought her salvation in man. The nurse felt that her patient would be strengthened by isolation, contemplation, flight from man to God, while the patient herself felt that she would be strengthened by living contact with the community, by her return to it. The struggle between Alice and the nurse was a bitter one. Alice was more intelligent than her nurse, and the nurse felt this; hence she defended herself against Alice by means in which she excelled, administrative ones, in the belief that those reprisals would convince Alice of the superiority of her credo, the credo of which the nurse was the representative.

By the middle of the third month Alice's mother telephoned, asking me to visit Alice with her and her preacher and to bring out our landlady Maria.

When Alice saw me she burst into tears. The two of us went for a walk—and during that walk she told me casually that she was Hitler's mother.

"What kind of nonsense is this?" I cried out. Because of her casualness I had forgotten that I was speaking to a sick person.

"You don't believe me?" she said, and burst into laughter. She did not return to this subject.

On our way back, Maria was silent, but when we got off the car, she began to tell us angrily, in her melodious Anglo-Italian mixture, that it was a crime to keep Alice locked up, that it was she who should keep us imprisoned, for then we would at least be like children with a mother.

Two weeks later Alice left the nursing home. She went to her mother's home first, but a few days later brought her suitcases to me, or rather to her room; her mother had not interfered, on her preacher's advice—he believed that Alice should live near me. Alice had written to Maria not to rent out her room, promising that after her return to New York she would pay her for that period. The landlady had not rented the room, and throughout that time I had not even once wondered why Alice's room continued to be vacant—apparently I had considered this completely natural.

We tenants arranged a wonderful reception for her, during which she recited her poems written in the nursing home, and she wept each time she danced. She was slightly drunk, and toward the end of the party she turned to me, and laughing happily, she said, "I think I told you that I am Hitler's mother."

And I did not know whether she was once again asserting that she was Hitler's mother, or if she was laughing at having told me so before.

She was in excellent shape, fresh, sun-tanned; it seemed that some inaudible melody flowed through her. We met an acquaintance who knew that she had recently returned from a home for the mentally ill, and he looked at her and listened as if she had just made a splendid trip and would tell him many beautiful and interesting things.

Shortly after returning from the nursing home Alice became an organizer for one of the large labor unions; she herself had found that job. She threw herself passionately into her work, as if this were to be her last worldly effort, after which paradise would inevitably come.

She believed that paradise had once prevailed on earth, and that man must restore it, that the mission of modern man was precisely to restore the lost paradise with the help of the modern discoveries.

She left her work in the labor union to assist in the election campaign of a progressive New York congressman; she was active in a working-class precinct, and devoted herself particularly to canvassing among women. The inhabitants of that quarter included many immigrants, and Alice felt as if she were in an exotic land. Then she found a job on a very militant Protestant periodical, where she was among people belonging to families that had lived in the United States for centuries, and whose progressive traditions reached as far back.

Throughout that period, Alice was in mental institutions several times. She committed herself for three months to a university clinic and twice for two months to private institutions. From all three institutions she returned cheerful, calmed; in each of them she had made friends with doctors and patients. And yet each time it was as though she had returned from a penal institution; she returned with the feeling that she had been punished for her failure to know how to behave in life. This feeling was somewhat that of a child coming to the conclusion that one must be careful with grownups, that their jokes do not go as far as his own, that they can suddenly become brutal.

On one other occasion, her brother took her to the psychiatric ward of a city hospital, where she stayed less than twenty-four hours, and this stay deeply upset her. It was much like the first time when she had been led away in a strait jacket from the department store. All of the patients there seemed to come from the dregs of society. Alice saw before her not mentally defective persons but the poor people of the world. The contemptuous treatment of these patients seemed merely to be an attitude of the wealthy toward the poor.

During this period she stubbornly reached for danger, as if eager for punishment—punishment for the sins she had taken upon herself, perhaps the sins of her own social group, or even society as a whole. For what is the assumption of other people's sins but an expression of the social bond, a bond so strong that sometimes we assume the burden of the very sins our fellow men have committed against us? We take them on because those who wronged us do not.

But each time we took her to an institution (her family adopted me as one of her guardians), we had the feeling that she was merely an unruly child who had to be disciplined, that it was good for her, and she must learn her lesson. Because we were the ones who took her to the hospital, and not she us, we each time felt this to be proof of our own health.

While in the psychiatric ward of the university clinic Alice began to repeat more and more often that she was Hitler's mother. She tried to draw me into a discussion of this subject, and finally succeeded in doing so. She would yield to my first argument, dismiss the whole thing with a joke, and declare that, actually, the Nazis were persecuting her, and that she was trying to put them off by such inventions. But then again she would maintain that she was Hitler's mother.

She did not expect me to believe her; but she tried to get me to regard this as her central mania. In other words, she wanted me to become seriously concerned with the subject, at least from my own point of view. She struggled for a position in the unreal world, and the notion that she was Hitler's mother was intended to define that position. All her other declarations were too fluid, and actually differed from normal statements only by their intensity, their emphasis.

"It's too late for me to be the Mother of God," she confided to me on one occasion, in tears. "I am the mother of Hitler." Occasionally she would declare in one breath that she was Hitler's mother, and I an important figure in the anti-Nazi underground. She said this with great tenderness, at the same time teasing me.

"You can't cheat me, love," she said. "You pretend you're worse than you are. How afraid he is of love, how Hitler frightened him . . ."

I could not rid myself of the painful feeling that she identified me with Hitler, that each time she referred to him as her child, she had me in mind. For what use had I made of her beautiful heart and body, of our love? Had I not behaved toward Alice, toward myself, as an enemy of life? I had not started a family with her, I had not wanted children with her; it was as if I had co-operated with Hitler in his campaign against mankind.

And what had I left as my justification? The fact that the Nazi extermi- nations had made me regard the family only as a source of fruitless suffering? That was as if I had committed suicide out of fear of death, thus depriving myself of the only possibility of salvation—struggle—and thus facilitating the enemy's task.

808   On the day of the Allied landing in France, Alice decided that she would move out. It was as if she had just regained her courage and will to live. I felt she saw that her mission had terminated. I tried to tell her that now with better days approaching, we might experience a bit of happiness together, but my opposition was so timid that it could not influence her decision.

She recovered her strength gradually; the process was almost concomi- tant with the gradual improvement of the Allied military situation, the gradual shrinking of the chances of a Hitler victory. She had liberated herself from her oppressive nightmares, and now she identified me to some extent with those nightmares. She was free now, and strong, strong because she had not forgotten her insanity; she had a distinct feeling that she had been victorious over it, she vividly remembered her struggle against it, and hence she now carried a defensive mechanism within her.

At night she often went to a USO canteen to entertain lonely soldiers, and because persons like her never pass another human indifferently, she might have slept with every soldier she met there. She did not sleep with any of them, but because of her kindness, gentleness, and warmth, she could create in each the impression that she had been ready to go to bed with him, but that it somehow had not come to pass.

Once she returned home with a soldier. He seemed to be ailing, he was very pale, his uniform hung loosely on him—he must have been the most miserable soldier in the army. I found them in my room late at night, sitting on my bed and talking.

A week later she received a letter from him recorded on a disc, and after that he showered her with letters full of love. Then, one day she received the news that he had gone through a very difficult operation, that he was in a hospital in critical condition; he begged her to come to him, and Alice went. In the hospital, his mother, his three sisters, and his nurse, and even his doctor tried to induce her to marry him, on the supposition that this was his only hope and his last chance of recovery. But Alice did not yield, she did not marry him, and he recovered nonetheless.

Well, what was I to do, now that she had decided to leave me? I had to recognize that ours had been a defensive alliance which had now ended, and I had to find her a little apartment with a fireplace. She cried when we parted but no more than someone leaving his very poor parental home for a better life.

After the war, she found a job in an organization caring for homeless war orphans of various nationalities and denominations, who were scattered all over Europe. She soon advanced so far that the organization sent her on a mission to Europe. When her friends told her that she did not know Europe or foreign languages, she replied that she was going to a land of children, a land she remembered perfectly, from her early dreams, and that all children there speak one language, which an adult can easily understand if he closes his eyes and opens his heart.

In Europe she brilliantly succeeded in her work. I ran into her in the street shortly after her return; she was about to go to Washington for her organization, or rather, for her little orphans, and we hurriedly exchanged but a few words. A few days after that meeting I dreamed that Alice and I were being married in Washington on the steps of the Capitol. The sky was dark blue, a golden moon glowed in it on one side and a silvery sun on the other. "What a beautiful night-day," the crowd assembled before the Capitol chanted. Alice was in a white gown, I was smaller than she, naked, with one half of a Hitler mustache, and a crown of thorns, and from under the thorns there dripped, instead of blood, red wine which I continually licked off.

We kept climbing the white stairs, and after each of our steps there came a sound, as if we were stepping on piano keys. I turned around and noticed that we were followed by a crowd of children in the most varied national costumes, but the children's song was in one language, which was to me unintelligible.

"What language is this?" I asked Alice.

"Listen," she said, and then I heard that the children were chanting the alphabet—a, b, c.

"Whose children are they?" I cried out anxiously.

"Nobody's," she said, smiling. "Our own."

I telephoned Alice to tell her my dream.

"You should have thought of that before," she said and laughed. "You should have warned me, then we would have had this dream together." She laughed a long time, then added: "But we surely have the same dream . . . Wasn't that the reason that we spent so many years together?"

Translated from the Polish by Norbert Guterman

Leon Rooke

The Line of Fire

The second day after the fire broke out on the Kenai Peninsula they called our company, Company D, out to fight it but by the time we made it in motor convoy up there the fire was in its fourth day, had done a lot of damage, and the people on the lake were saying that it looked like the fire-fighters brought up from Seattle were just sitting around on their cans doing nothing for the $4.50 an hour paid them. For the most part that's how it looked to us too but then we were not getting paid $4.50 an hour or even nearly that. And as we were to find out, that is the way fires are mostly fought: mostly watching and waiting and trying to guess what it is going to do next and then to be ready for that. What had happened on Kenai was that they were ready but then the wind changed on them and they couldn't have known it was going to do that, for until it did they hadn't noticed there was a wind. The wind turned and they lost control of the fire and it was then that they sent the call to post for troops. They asked for a thousand, they got two hundred, and as I have said, that two hundred was us, the doughboys of big Delta, First Battle Group, the 21st Infantry. The Post Commander couldn't very well have sent out any of the other five thousand men on post: outside of the Battle Group they were all members of one or another headquarters unit and as our CO said at the time, "Those boys don't even own boots." It is a fact that if they do, they don't use them. But there is no time now to lament the Changing Army, which our NCOs say it is. If there was I'd have begun right off with mention of Private Van Gode and not till he was established would I have mentioned the fire.

It is difficult to know which comes first. Before it was over a man was dead, and while the significance of his death has not, in retrospect, diminished, the exact manner of his going defies any category I might arbitrarily or otherwise choose for it: "He killed himself," we say—but that by itself is not enough. Nor have I, in the telling of that, given any indication of the grotesque indifference with which too many of us greeted that death. Had his name been placed on the bulletin board along with other "Coming Events" we likely would have shown no more excitement than we did in seeing there the titles of movies and their stars, or the fact that "Mass will be held at eight and ten o'clock, Sundays."

Maybe if Gode had been the one who died, it would be the death that has priority. It wasn't Gode though, it was a pint-sized Hungarian we called the Major who wasn't a major really or of any rank near to that. He, like Gode, was a private. Like Gode again, he had been a PFC but that had not lasted long. He couldn't speak English and perhaps it's true what Gode now declares: that *if* he had spoken English we'd remember him *first*. The only way we would not, Gode says, is that *if he had been able to speak English* he wouldn't be dead today. He would be dead, yes, but not buried. He'd be walking around like the rest of us. For Gode claims that had he been able to talk about what he found, and felt, he wouldn't have wanted to die. That's what it amounted to finally: he wanted to die because there was no one he could talk to. He didn't know the language. When I point out to Gode that there were other Hungarians in the company to whom he could and did talk, Gode says that is not what he meant. What he meant was that he had to talk to an American. He wanted to know what those sounds he heard, meant. For what he saw, an explanation. I would tell Gode that it looked to me that the Major knew well enough what was going on, and that I had been under the impression that this was precisely the reason he wanted to die and did.

Yes, Gode says, but all that he picked up he picked up through his sight. What little he picked up from the voices he found in the tone, not the words, for the words he didn't know. Because of that he was willing, was eager, to listen to an explanation for it, for what he had seen—but he was cut off by the language. The only answers available to him were those he supplied himself. So he's dead now. You might say that was a stupid thing to do. It was. In the beginning, I tried to tell him it was. But for all of that the old boy had pretty keen sight. He could even see around corners. That, too, is why he died.

"What do you mean?" I'd ask.

I mean that the guy knew there was nothing going to change it. "It" being what he saw. Anyway, Gode would say, what does it matter? He's dead now.

And the one point of departure in all of this is that now it obviously doesn't matter. Kuimets is dead! The "idea" of his death, although it hung about for a while ("It lay in state," Gode says), has receded till now, like the Kenai woods, it is covered over with ashes, and only when the memory is jogged by some similarity in our own conduct and desires, to that of the Major's, do we recall with any degree of astuteness the foibles and the strong points of his "suicide." The fire rages foremost in our minds—and "Why not!" Gode will demand. "We *fought* the fire. But let Kuimets go his merry way. We couldn't fight that mother. Because we knew—I knew—he was *right* to burn."

Gode. Gode is always saying something. He's like an automobile with the choke pulled all the way out and stuck to that position. Or a chicken with its head chopped off. Except that the simile is not an accurate one: Gode, having retained his head, is in control of his direction.

With the Major dead and the Kenai fire finally out, the emphasis has a habit of shifting; any final analysis slides out of proportion to the problem itself and it becomes, as Gode says, a now-you-got-it, now-you-haven't proposition. Gode, a fine one for saying things, says the Major was a martyr and from the way he says it you gather that with him at least the Major's death does take priority over the fire. The fire, to him, was simply the backdrop. Whether he mentions the Major's name, or doesn't, now when we hear him speak we naturally feel the meaning of all he says to be related somehow to the Major. "Let's fuck Santa Claus, 1962!" he says. Does he mean: "Let's fuck the Major again this year, sir?" "Let's fuck ourselves again this year, sir?"

The fire is only a backdrop for the Major's death to Gode but not so with the company for only a few even remember now which bunk was his or which platoon he was in. Another man has his bunk now and his foot

813

and wall locker and his rifle. His name on these hasn't been merely painted over; scrape off the new layer and it wouldn't be there. The new application has dissolved into the old and any proof we might have of his name ever being there rests only in the different shades of OD. And something like that, we may say, has happened to our memory of Kuimets.

The men recall that while on Kenai fighting the fire a man killed himself, and probably at the time they wrote as much home to their parents or girl friends. No doubt they got a letter back, asking: "Wha'd he do that for? Is it that bad up there? You want me to write our Congressman?" As if the Congressman wasn't a large part of the Major's trouble, in the first place.

But they remember no more. Now, they couldn't give you his name even, or tell you what he looked like.

Gode could. Gode could describe the expressions he wore at any given hour on any given day. Gode says he was a martyr, sort of, and that martyrs always have to be forgotten before they're remembered for good. "Not that the memory changes anything," he adds. I wonder sometimes where Gode picked up the wisdom even his detractors will admit he has. "The same friggin place the Major picked up his," he likes to brag when he's had a couple of beers, "the difference being that if I ever die it will be because I've laughed myself to death." Not so, the Major. Nobody ever saw the Major so much as smile. Except once when he was crossing a lake with his squad and the ice cracked beneath him and he went under. He was pulled out smiling that time. "Whadaya smiling about, Major?" they asked him. He couldn't tell them. He didn't know the language. He couldn't tell them that he was smiling because he knew that time that the joke was on himself. When I told Gode about this—for Gode wasn't in the unit then—he laughed and said the Major could understand a joke like that. The Major got cold and practically froze afterwards but even as his teeth knocked together he could see the humor in falling through ice that supported men twice his weight. "Not knowing English didn't matter that time," Gode says.

If we had had a camera on Kenai that could catch it just so, what would we see framed within the walls of the screen? If a photograph, whose faces would we see inside the white border? Gode's? The Major's? The Captain's? Behind them all there would be the fire, and I have asked myself: "Whose face shows the most severe burn?" Putting the picture flat on a table, which figure would we expect to rise and step forward? It would help to have the camera and its picture that we might see them all at once, for wasn't that the way they saw themselves?

But we didn't have a camera and the several photographs printed by the post newspaper and in the *Anchorage Times* are all of the Captain and civilians he has personally aided in evacuating, or of the civilians alone, and, of course, the fire. There are many of the fire. There is one of our captain and Captain John of Company C and their immediate commander, the Colonel, for in that last day when it looked that there was no stopping the fire and that we had just as well let it go for a lost cause the days or weeks it might take to burn itself out, we were joined on Kenai by the Colonel and the Captain and men of Charlie Company. The Colonel stands in the middle of course, and he is shaking the hand of our CO while Captain John looks on, smiling. Behind them, for photographic effect, there is the mountain behind the lake of Kenai Peninsula, and it is burning. There are no flames in that picture, but there is much smoke.

No, there are no pictures at all of the Major, nor, as one would expect, are there any of Gode. There appeared, later, in the town paper, with the headline

815

FORT RICH SOLDIER KILLS SELF

and an article beneath it, running all of thirty-six words, the headline taking up more space than the one paragraph. Although there were no pictures of the Major, if we look closely at the photograph of the Colonel and the two captains we notice on the face of our CO an expression that is at once tired, faded, screwed with fatigue, and we gather from this that whatever it is the Colonel is saying he is not listening to, is not hearing. It is odd that this would be so, but, on the other hand, it is not so odd: it is here in his face that we have preserved the only photographic reminder of the Major. We will give the Captain his due. It was the day before this that one of his men killed himself.

Kuimets was his name, he was a "hunkie" yes, but does that explain it?

II

No, of course not, but then what does?

As an event portended this one stands out in my memory, or is that only a product of reflection? Certainly this isn't: From the beginning Gode came on big, with a lusty smile, a firm handshake, and a voice that assailed anyone within hearing distance. As much as to show that he for one had nothing to fear and even less to lose—"A student of life who had no desire to hide behind his face," as he later said of the Major. (Later, I say, as an extension to this: "They say I killed him; well, then, let me erect a monument to his memory: HERE LIES IMRE KUIMETS, HUNGARIAN, WHO FUCKED HIMSELF BY NOT FUCKING OTHERS." And that, ludicrous and ill-of-taste as it was, was better and far more accurate than that one which the army saw fit to give him: HERE LIES PVT. IMRE KUIMETS—WHO DIED IN THE EXECUTION OF HIS DUTY. "Duty to what?" was Gode's protest there.)

But that was later, yes, after he had already made clear that point which was portended at the start: that he meant to take something out of us before putting anything into us; that, in his own words, "he fed on us before we fed on him."

That, in a soldier, in a private and an infantryman, was unique, and I found myself drawn to him immediately. As who would not have, except other and more professional soldiers, meeting him as I did that first day he was assigned to the unit, the day before the Kenai fire. I had got a call from Battle Group to send a vehicle around to pick up our new trainee, and as nothing much was doing in the orderly room I got the Old Man's jeep and drove over myself. And there Gode was, sitting slumped over on a duffel bag and other paraphernalia, paying no attention whatever to the S-3 lieutenant who strutted around him in stiff rigid steps like a long animated slice of finished lumber, pointing his finger at Gode the recruit and saying, "Sol-ja, goddammit, I don't know who in forty hells you think you are but I'll tell you right now that before this outfit is through with you we're gonna slap a little discipline and respect into you. Either that or you're gonna get your ass kicked from here to Kingdom Come. STAND AT ATTENTION WHEN I TALK TO YOU!"

Whether Gode would have done this with sufficient speed to please him, I don't know. At that time I interrupted the officer with my salute, and told him I had come to pick up our new man.

"Well, you got a real loser this time, Hite," the lieutenant said; I smiled, told Gode to put his stuff in the jeep, saluted again, and crossed over to the driver's side. Gode said, "Excuse me," to the officer, and began throwing his gear into the back seat. When this was done he turned to the officer and raised his hand in the approximation of a salute. The lieutenant didn't return it; he grimaced, spun about, and went inside. Gode laughed. Driving back to the company I asked him his name and where he was from. "I'm up from the guts of the Fort Benning Infantry School," he said, "where they gave us these bayonets and told us to cry out 'Kill Mother' as we plunged the blade into the bag of hay." I asked him what he had done to get the officer so riled.

"As I passed him in the hall I winked at him," Gode said. "I don't think he liked the idea I was trying to express: that although the army had us separated by class, we, as human beings, still had *that* joke in common. Ha!" He laughed, and I didn't know whether he was kidding or serious— but he had made his impression, something no one else had managed so quickly to do. And the rest of the time too, throughout the fire, with Kuimets' death and afterwards, he was to make his presence felt: as if he was behind us all, breathing down our necks, forcing us into some realization of ourselves, our lives, and a why for all this.

Then the next morning, too . . .

That morning we got the call to move up to Kenai but before we could go they had to decide what uniform we should wear and in doing this there developed among the officers an argument over entrenching tools. The Captain had given word to the First Sergeant who had sent a runner around to the platoons to tell them that they should wear the tool on their belts, when the XO, Lieutenant Webster ("Mr. Wonderful!" as Gode, an hour or so later, named him), had the bright idea that it would be best if the men carried the tools on their packs since they had more than 250 miles to ride in deuce-and-halves. Otherwise, he felt, the tools would be in the way. Probably if they wore them on their belts it would mean they could load less men to a truck because the tool would take up more space that way, and be a source of discomfort, too. That made sense: Transportation had only sent us eight trucks which made twenty-five men to a truck, plus equipment, and so the Old Man told the First Stud and when the runner

817

got back from the fifth platoon he had him go back around again and give them the word of Change #1: Carry the tool on the rucksack.

Master Sergeant Kelly, platoon sergeant of the third platoon, a lieutenant who had been riffed and who could usually be expected to do this sort of thing, when he got the word, came down and told his platoon leader that his men already had the tool on their belts and he didn't see why they had to change. His platoon leader, a second lieutenant only recently graduated from VMI, hardly more than a teenager himself and having been told repeatedly that he should not buck the old-timers, the NCOs who had more military know-how up their asses than he could hope to muster in his head in twenty years, took the matter up with an officer richer in time and grade. This led to a conference between the officers and the CO and the First Sergeant. The meeting lasted a long while and during that time the platoon sergeants came down to stand in the hall outside the First Stud's office, waiting for the word, firsthand. The mess hall was loaded up and waiting to pull out by that time, and some of the cooks were wandering up and down the hall, complaining about the KPs and trying to find out how long it would be till we pulled out. Several of the men from the fifth platoon, the weapons (mortar) platoon, the "luxury platoon," as they were called, were milling about too. Theirs is the only platoon on the first floor where the offices and mess hall are, and they had a number of college boys in their platoon who either got very angry or had a lot of fun when the officers couldn't make up their minds on a simple issue like the carrying of the entrenching tools. This morning they were excited and more or less looking forward to the trip to Kenai because it was something different and not just the old attack on a hill or squad in defense or a ski march, and so they were having fun. Mostly at the NCOs' expense.

Private Gode had been in the unit one day, but he was among those in the hall harassing the sergeants. Usually when a recruit is assigned a unit one does not see him the first month or so, for he has learned long before that to escape details he has to hide away, to make himself unnoticeable as possible. With Gode, as I have said, dating from his first moment in the unit, it was the opposite. His hair was too long, his uniform was neither clean nor pressed, his sleeves were rolled, he needed a shave, and his brass was cruddy. His boots were bloused but nothing good can be said about the manner in which this was done. He wore the OD tie which had not been issued for years, and when he spoke it was with a confidence one does not expect in a private, and his eyes looked death at you. You asked him if he was Regular Army or US and he answered "HA!" and you knew from that just where he stood on the subject.

That morning of the fire I was standing in the doorway of my office enjoying the spectacle of it all when I saw him walk up to his platoon sergeant, Sergeant Oliver, and say: "Come here a minute, sergeant. I want to talk to you."

"Huh! Whadaya want? I'm busy," Oliver said, but he followed him anyway. Gode was bringing him over to me.

"What I was thinking, sar-junt," Gode said, winking at me, "is that while the brass is in there deciding on the proper way of carrying the entrenching tool, you ought to get them to reconsider this business of the headgear."

"Whadaya mean?" Oliver asked. He had his pile cap in his hand and he looked at it as though to get the connection. "Whadaya mean, private?" Until then he had neglected to call Gode "private"; he felt he had to do this otherwise someone might not have known he was a sergeant.

"The way I figured it, sar-junt, is that we're not gonna have much use for these snow caps, fighting a fire—"

"*Pile* caps, private," Oliver said.

"The way I figured it we gonna need helmet-liners and the steel pots."

"How you figure that?" Oliver asked. You could tell he didn't trust this Gode, didn't quite know what to make of him, and he was being cautious. Also, it was the first time he'd ever heard a trooper *asking* to wear his pot.

"Tree might fall on us," Gode said. "Might even have to haul some water." The sergeant was scratching his head; it was easy enough to tell what he was thinking: By God, I haven't thought much about it till now but maybe this kid has something. Why, I remember one time in Germany . . .

Gode slapped me on the shoulder, winking again. "You know they do once in a while fight fire with water. The little fires, anyway." He laughed. I laughed with him. He had made me do the same thing the day before while I was interviewing him, laugh, and afterwards I had wondered why I laughed. Certainly at nothing he had said; more at what he appeared to be implying.

Oliver asked me where Top was and I told him he was in the Old Man's office. He asked me what the word was on headgear and I told him pile caps so far as I knew. Then he went into the First Sergeant's office where I knew he'd wait till the First Sergeant came in and then he'd say, "Top, I been thinking. Maybe we ought to wear steel pots. I mean, you know it can get dangerous out there in a fire." He was that kind of a guy, his nose always up someone's ass.

A moment later Gode came out of the mess hall, eating a sandwich, Gamble—Speedie 5 Gamble—the chief cook, right behind him, asking him who the hell he thought he was, lifting a sandwich—but Gode was ignoring him. I turned Gode around and asked Gamble how things were with him and together the three of us went back into the mess hall and had a cup of coffee. Ordinarily that was a privilege granted only the officers and noncoms but this morning in the confusion no one would notice us. Gamble sat at the table with us and I could see he was uncomfortable for there was a bunch of noncoms in their section drinking coffee and there was always the chance one of them would say something to him about fraternizing with the peons. He probably figured it was OK since I was the company clerk and he was trying to find out now the status of the other guy, Gode, without having to actually phrase the question. He was a Southerner, born and bred, and Southerners first have to hedge. I knew Gamble had read in one of the whisper-type magazines the night before of how Tempeste Storm, the stripper, was married to a Negro, and I brought this up, to impress Gode, I suppose, and to show him how enraged Gamble could become. It had made him so mad the night before that he went to the NCO Club and got drunk, although he had to borrow two bucks from me to do it. The thing that infuriated him most was the fact that the stripper was so lovely. The magazine carried a full-page color pin-up of her and he kept pointing to it and crying, "Look at that! Look at that! How can she do it?" In a small box in the corner was a picture of the man she was married to. I admit he didn't seem to hold much, but it wasn't his color that got to me, it was the fact that he had her and I didn't. I think this is what bothered Gamble too although when I told him so he told me to go screw myself. She was exciting as hell in the photograph and I had to tell myself that the picture was an early one, that now Tempeste had put on weight on her hips and that her chin was heavy. I had caught her act in Vegas before coming into the Army, and had been impressed with the thought that "big-timers" really were, in some cases, quite "small." Not that I hadn't enjoyed her act. She approaches sex the way the terrapin crosses the road. Mistress of the sublimely sensual, subtle in her motions, really a stripper of taste and culture. A woman anyone would be proud to take to bed be he Gamble or General Lemnitzer. My own feelings, I told Gamble, were that they should have given a 19-gun salute to the man who got her. Gamble was saying now, again, that she should be tarred and feathered and hung up in the sun to dry and Gode sat quietly, intently, listening to him. Gamble asked him where he was from and didn't he think so too and Gode smiled lazily and said the South. I was surprised. He didn't have the accent.

He had not given me—or I did not remember—his home address during the interview of the previous day. Most of what he had said I remembered well. I had been filling out, for Morning Report purposes, his information card. I asked him his religious preference and, winking at me, he took his ID tags from his pocket. I told him he'd better not let anyone catch them not around his neck, for that was a big thing in our unit: more than one man had been given company punishment for not wearing them. He winked again and crossed his legs. His winking at me was beginning to get on my nerves and I wrote down what it said on the tags. Religion: Christian Scientist. Not till I had written it down did he say, mockingly: "But that's a lie. The only thing I know about CS is that they don't believe in witch-doctors. Neither do I so I figured their blend of make-believe would do as well as any other."

821

I was wondering how with that attitude he had managed to keep out of the stockade when he began explaining that he was mad as hell when they drafted him so as he was being processed at Jackson when it came to the stamping of his dog tags he told them a lie just out of spite. He leaned over my desk and said: "Religion? *Nada.*"

I asked him what he meant by that. He laughed, waving the palm of his hand at me. I decided later that it was typical of Gode to select out of all the denominations open to him, one which could, under certain situations, lead to complications for him. In that respect—and others—he shares the allegiances of the Major.

He has a laugh that carries and, for no reason, I laughed with him. The First Stud's office is adjacent to mine, with a door we rarely close, and I knew from the squeak of his chair that he had turned to see what it was that I had found so interesting. He is afraid, when I am laughing, that I have pulled some joke on him. His chair, in fact, a dilapidated, uncomfortable monster, backless but for two steel prongs, had belonged to me till I swapped it for his while he was on a three-day leave. The springs are poor, rusted, and I can usually tell by their activity what his mood is on any given day.

Gode, in the meanwhile, was still laughing about the lie he'd told the people at Jackson. The sergeant, a Catholic himself, with the little yellow plastic image of Mary on his desk, snorted, mumbled a word or two, but that didn't upset Gode. The sergeant did not like smart alecks and he had a standing thing against liars. The first words he'd said upon taking over the unit was, "I don't like liars." I had been, since Basic, accustomed to hearing from NCOs that above all other forms of depraved humanity they disliked the thief most and the fact that the Top had managed to upset this tradition weighed heavily with me. He seemed to agree that one was lousy as the other, but as far as he personally was concerned, the liar took precedence. A couple of days after taking charge, an NCO, SFC Kane, reported a watch stolen off his desk and the First called a formation of the company outside the barracks, and began reaming them hard, immediately stomping from the first platoon at one end to headquarters at the other, in front and behind and through the ranks, screaming that if there was anything he couldn't

stand it was a thief, there was no slob on the face of the earth lower than a thief, except a liar. And he was going to ask the question right now: which of you bastards stole Sergeant Kane's watch? By intent or chance he was standing in front of me at the time, and he touched his nose against mine, yelling: "Hite, you sonuvabitch! Did you steal that watch?" I was stunned as hell and sweating in my boots and he had sprayed my face. "No, Sarge, I didn't steal that watch," I said. He didn't remove his nose from mine for a full thirty seconds, then he marched ten paces front and center, turned, flung his finger in my direction, and cried: "Now, there's an honest man!" A few of the men in the fifth platoon made the mistake of tittering and he bore down on them. I had to admire his timing, we all did. He only knew one method of getting across the authority of his position—the shout—but his timing on those couldn't have been better. He had all the troopers sweating, many of whom had never so much as filched a nickel from their mama's purse.

"Liars and thieves ain't human," he was saying. "If you're one you're the other too and I can't stand neither one of you. If I find out who stole that watch—and you can bet your sweet ass I will—I'm gonna turn the company loose on you. If they kill you I could care friggin less. It's just one thief and liar less. I don't believe in medics when it comes to thieves and liars. So whoever it is—give your heart to God for your ass is mine."

So saying, he paused for, I gathered, breath. It was plain that he was a man of strong beliefs. He stalked toward the company entrance, his hand on his chin: "Look at'm. He's thinking," the man beside me whispered. The sergeant was a fine actor and the man beside me was right: before he entered he turned and said: "I been thinking. Even a liar and a thief ought to get ONE break." He was speaking in a moderate tone now and I could hear passing through the ranks, the question: "Wha'd he say?" He must have heard them too. His voice boomed out: "Whoever stole Sergeant Kane's watch come by my office and give it to me and we'll forgit it ever happened. You got ten fucking minutes."

He dismissed the unit, and I went back and waited with him in his office, but when in ten minutes no one had showed, he left. "Where you going, Sarge?" I asked. "Going to git that watch, sonny," he said.

He was back in twenty minutes, Sergeant Kane behind him. It turned out that Kane had the watch in his room, around the neck of a beer bottle which had rolled, among others, under his bunk. Top put him on CQ duty that night, and the next night too, for bringing alcoholic beverages into the building.

823

But it didn't end there. Some few in the company, myself included, liked the First Stud's performance so well that the following morning Gawthrop, a short-timer, reported his hi-fi set missing.

With this in mind I could understand the sergeant's interest in Gode that day Gode sat in my office shooting the breeze like an old-timer. It confused him, possibly, that Gode was admitting to, boasting of, his lies. What's more, Gode was speaking lightly of religion. It was all right to cuss God, the sergeant thought, but to openly deny Him was too much for his Catholic nature. Hell, that made a man the same thing as a Comm-a-nist.

I was better able to excuse, or explain, Gode when we got to the education square on his card. "Twenty-one years," he said.

"Twenty-one years! You a doctor?"

"Naw," he said. "I was what they call a professional stoodunt." I wrote "21" and then looked from it to Gode. He seemed to be about sixteen years old. "That's all," I told him.

He got up, giving me a half-cocked salute, which I returned. The troopers were always doing that to me. I guess I had the military bearing of an officer. Or as I once heard Gode describe me: the bearing of the officer, the brains of the NCO, and the rank of the peon.

I had forgotten about sports and hobbies, however (because there isn't a block on the card for them), and so I called Gode back. "You got any sports or hobbies, Gode?" I asked. He thought about it a while, the only time in the interview he had hesitated.

"Sports," he said. "Yeah, you might say so."

"How about hobbies?"

"Hobbies, though . . . well, chess, I reckon."

"Chess!" I said. I didn't believe him. If he was telling the truth he was the only chess player I'd ever seen in the infantry.

"I don't know who the hell's gonna play with you," I said.

"Oh, I'll find someone, I guess." He went out then. I went back to work but looked up in a moment and there the sergeant was, staring off after Gode, pointing. He couldn't believe it either.

"Chess!" he roared. "Who the Christ was that?"

"Private Hooter Van Gode," I told him. "I sent him to the fifth. You wanted all the college boys there, didn't you?"

He didn't answer and went off shaking his head. I knew what he was thinking. Christ! A chess player in the infantry! In his company! What were they gonna send him next? What the hell was the army coming to? A chess player, for godsake, instead of a rifleman. That was as bad as having "choir girls," which is what they called the five troopers in the unit who sang in the Colonel's glee club.

As a Top he faced it every day and had it as his biggest gripe: the Changing Army. Every day Washington was sending them to Battle Group and Battle Group was sending them to him: men who all their lives had been obviously tutored to keep their heads where their asses ought to be. And vice-versa. In the old days running a company was simple, now it was *screwy*; nowadays there were too many riflemen walking around with Phi Beta Kappa pins where their sharpshooter badges used to be. There was no efficiency now, no order, no discipline. He didn't have soldiers any more, he had a bunch of old women.

I knew what he was thinking because I had heard him express it often enough. But Gode, I could have told him then, was no woman.

Gamble was finding that out, too. Gode was telling him that the way he looked at it the stripper and her Negro husband were the only brave people left. "Why you sonuvabitch!" Gamble said; he left us then, and, cursing, feeling that a fellow Southerner had betrayed him, he went back to where the other noncoms sat, drinking coffee, smoking, shooting the bull.

We left the mess hall then, as Gode said: to go out and screw a few NCOs. But, as it happened, the meeting in the Old Man's office where they were still discussing the wearing of the entrenching tool, I supposed, broke up, and the First and several of the officers came out. The noncoms snapped to attention, their backs flush against the walls, the way the officers expect them to do, leaving enough space not only for an officer to walk through but for a three-quarter truck as well. I never snap-to myself but go on about my business. This morning, however, maybe because the movement wasn't going so well or because Gode, a new man and a private, was with me, Lieutenant Webster yelled us down and stood us against the wall.

"You think you're better than these NCOs that you don't have to snap-to, Hite?" he said to me. Out of the corner of my eyes I could see the noncoms smiling. "No sir," I said. He turned to Gode. I slid into an at ease position. "And what the fuck's the matter with you, private?" he said to Gode. Low and very mean, "piercing" is, I guess, the word he would have used to describe it. Gode said nothing. He didn't move. His chest was puffed out, his shoulders back, his lips drawn tight over his teeth. I didn't know whether he was attempting to hold back a laugh or was nervous or if that was simply his way of standing at attention. His uniform was wrinkled and looked mildewed. "Didn't they teach you in basic to come to attention when you saw an officer?" Webster was talking into his face, his finger against his chest. "What's your name? How long you been in this unit, sol-ja?" He turned to the First. "Sergeant, you let privates stroll down the hall anytime they take a notion to?" The sergeant told him no sir. "Get back to your platoon—ON THE DOUBLE, PRIVATE!" Gode, measuring his steps, walked off.

Webster turned back to me: "What are you grinning about, Hite?" I told him I felt good this morning. He stared at me a while then told me that was all. I caught up with Gode and walked down the hall with him. I didn't think about it then but later realized that Webster had served to ally us. It was then that Gode gave the name Mr. Wonderful to Webster, and it was a fitting title. Webster felt that way about himself. He stood six-foot, four; he weighed two-ten; he was handsome; and unlike the majority of officers, he had graduated from college. I had often heard him speak of his fraternity days at Georgia, and how then he had been just a loose kid out to enjoy himself, the idea being, now, that this had all changed. The army had stabilized him. He never once mentioned that the wife he had married the summer after graduation, and the kid she bore him come spring of every year, might have had a hand in it.

Gode with me, I went into my room, turned on the radio, and we stretched out on the bunks. As it always happened, soon as I was comfortable, there was a knock on the door: it was one of the NCOs to tell me the First Sergeant wanted me in his office. He never needs me when I'm in the office but the moment I take a break he sends for me. I smoothed the dust-cover, waved to Gode, and went down.

Everyone was feeling good that morning. If they had not been I would have been busy the next two weeks typing courts-martial, for I found, upon entering the office, that the First Stud had exploded when Sergeant Oliver asked him what headgear the men should wear. He was in the Old Man's office now, to find out. Another conference.

This one did not last long, however, and the First came out grinning. Probably he had passed wind while in the CO's office, and he was grinning about that. He was crazy for that sort of thing, restricting himself solely to the rooms occupied by officers. He encouraged me to pull the same trick and many times we went together into their offices only to subject them to the invisible majesty of our combined efforts. It showed them just where they stood with us.

The word was that we would wear steel pots now and since the runner was out informing the platoons that the entrenching tool was to be worn on the belts, I was sent out to tell them they should wear their steel pots and helmet-liners. I didn't like climbing the steps but it gave me a kick to see the men in the platoons running around, the noncoms hazing them. This time they had all their packs out in the center aisle of their cubicles, most of the men sitting on them, waiting for the word to move out, bored in the meanwhile. They had been wakened at four, and told to be ready to roll at five, but now it was after seven and they were still waiting.

At the first platoon I couldn't find the sergeant in charge so I told one of the squad leaders about the headgear they were to take. The troopers who heard me began griping—"Why the fuck don't the fuckers make up their fucking mind?" Jake, a Speedie Four from Chicago, said, his phraseology duplicating exactly the thoughts of all those around him. This was a remotely intelligent squad leader to whom I was talking, and he asked me if the men were to wear the steel pots or pack them in their rucksacks as they had done the shovels. He said "shovel" and when he did, some recruit yelled, "*Entrenching tool*, Sar-junt!" "Fuck you, Jones," the sergeant said. "I been fucked before," Jones retorted.

It dawned on me that there had been a mix-up on the word about where they were to carry the tool, and I tried to straighten it out. I told the squad leader they were to wear the shovel on their belts but there had been no explicit word about the steel pots other than they were to take it but that I would suggest they pack it in the rucksack since they wouldn't need it for a couple of days. It would take a couple of days to reach Kenai because the convoy would not exceed 15 miles per hour. Kenai was 250 miles and we were to camp overnight at Mile 180, I had heard.

I left that platoon but looked back to see the sergeant in the hallway knocking on the platoon sergeant's door. He would be asking what to do. One's initiative—on the rare occasions any is shown—gets lost, like everything else, in the chain of command. I knew that when the troops finally did fall out there would be some in soft caps and some with the tool on their belts and some would be in field jackets and others in parkas and probably one or two in their summer uniform, the greens. There would be some in combat boots and some in K-boots and without a doubt there'd be a couple in tennis shoes. That's the way it was, the way it always was, and I knew that nothing, no word or verbal command or printed order, was going to change this. This, the infantry, the fighting shield! The queen of battle! I was reminded of how the previous year, during range firing, a guy had fallen out in the company formation with a poncho around him because, as he explained, "it was raining." "You wait till *we* tell you it's raining, private," some sergeant told him, and I noticed later the kid was in the pit pulling targets, no easy detail under any circumstances but one especially hard for the kid because they had made him keep on the poncho although the sun was shining, it was hot, and the poncho encumbered him. That night he had had to sleep in it.

Discipline! That had been their lesson, that was their theme. Yet which of them had it any more than the kid? Who has it now? Who has ever had it? The Captain, with his pegged, starched trousers, his crisp shirt and polished boots, his close-cropped GI hair—does he have it? Gode says no. Gode says the Major had arrived at it somehow, achieved it through means beyond himself, probably. But what did it earn for him except an early death?

The kid now: as he said, it was raining, so he fell out for the formation, poncho intact. What was with that kid? is a question with which Gode, for one, has been concerned. Did he see things—rain?—for what they were, and acted accordingly? And what about the sergeant who said, "It's not raining till we say it is"; was that simply his colorful way of telling a private to wait for orders before acting? Gode sees more in it than that. The fact that it *was* raining at the time doesn't even enter into it. The important thing is that here were two sets of laws, two forces of habit, colliding. That the kid's mother always told him to wear his rubbers in the rain was the basis for his troubles, no doubt, but what was the root of the Major's? How had he, a rabbit-eared, rusty, sallow-cheeked, non-English-speaking Hungarian, come forth with such expectations that, seeing their fulfillment was denied him—if that's what happened—he felt he had to knock himself off. In him was the story of the guy who fell out with his poncho because like he said it was raining, carried to its completion. In that guy, the Poncho Kid, was the story of the man who would not eat bread he bought on Thursday from the A&P, Friday, because at whichever end of the wrapper he looked he saw

828

FRESH THURSDAY

stamped; who would not wash the rings from his bathtub because he saw printed on the package of the soap he bought for washing, the words: LEAVES NO SCUM OR BATHTUB RING.

Gode's question: Who was the realist? The kid who saw it was raining and therefore wore his poncho, or the sergeant who said, "Look, kid, this ain't no motherfriggin carnival you're in. You wait till we tell you it's raining?" And if the Major could do it once: rise, shivering, from a motherfriggin lake that dumped his one-hundred-thirty-five pounds when it had held, and even as he fell, was holding, men twice his weight—if he could crawl out of that, half-frozen, but laughing, why couldn't he do it again? And keep on doing it, laughing? Like Gode, who says, "If *I* die it will be because I've laughed my motherfriggin self to death!" And what was it that cracked under the Major that final time—what, on Kenai?—that led him to walk off into the woods without a word to anyone, even those who did know his language, and never come back alive? On the lake that time the ice cracked and he went under but there was nothing that time *pushing* him under. Conceivably, he hit a weak spot; or perhaps by the time his slight weight touched on it the ice those heavier men walked on had been sufficiently weakened. But nothing *pushed* him that time. That time, too, he could climb out. Gode says that on Kenai he was in too deeply to climb out, and not only that but he was, on Kenai, *pushed* into those woods, the burned out strip which, even as he walked into it, was still smoldering. "Goddam right he was pushed," Gode says. He explained it to the Captain. Tried to. "You fucking-A he was pushed!" Gode says, slamming his fist down on a table. "He didn't walk into those woods like a man about to kill himself but like one bound and determined that one way or another he was going to get to the other side. Clear through that friggin burn to a place where there was no burn nor smoke nor even any friggin thing that might start one. Christ! Captain, he was fed up with fighting fires."

"Gode, I want to ask you one question," the Captain said. "Did you know he was going out there with the specific thought in mind of killing himself?"

"Sir, I'll tell you the bare-assed truth," Gode said. "I not only knew that mother was going out there to kill himself; I gave him the final push . . ."

"If I die it will be because I've laughed myself to death," Gode says. The night the Major killed himself he did a part of it. He walked out into that burn over almost the identical path the Major had earlier in the day taken, and from my tent I could hear him laughing. Laughing hard, as though he was the only individual alive in the whole starry-eyed universe.

III

When we finally boarded the trucks it was eight o'clock, three hours behind kick-off time. It didn't appear to matter that in Kenai millions of dollars' worth of timber and the only resort area in Alaska was being destroyed. What seemed to matter was this: the Colonel had called the Adjutant and Adjutant had ordered the band down to give us the royal send-off. But by the time the band finally showed we had already boarded the trucks and the drivers who had been warming up their motors for hours now didn't want to turn them off. That way, although the band marched in playing "Stars and Stripes," or some such jazz, about all we heard were the drums. To most of us they represented only another delay; nevertheless, there is always one, and there was then: some slob RA who said: "Boy, that colonel is one nice egg, you know? I mean, gittin the friggin band down here to play for us and all!"

Some of us who could, disembarked, and gave the band members a hard time, laughing and jeering at them. They got up this early very rarely and always felt humiliated anyway to have to play for an infantry line company, which is ironic too for the infantry is the only outfit in the whole damn army that can find it in themselves to appreciate military music. That may not be entirely true but it's a cinch the infantry makes the best audience. Next to cowboy ballads and hillbilly and rock-and-roll, for them, there's nothing to beat it. That wasn't true this morning, but you already know the reasons for that. There was a snow, too, a fluffy but rather thick snow and that early in the morning there was a sort of fog as though the Northern Lights had stayed for the day and were descended around us; it was colder than it appeared and after standing out in it a while one's ears and nose and

hands numbed. Several of the band instruments were frozen and we had fun razzing those trying to play them. Most of headquarters when they saw that we still were not pulling out, got off the truck: Handy, from commo, Ullrich, the mail clerk, and Sakren, the armorer. We tended to see things in a more humorous light since we were exempt from such greasy details as KP and Guard. We began singing "Over Hill, Over Dale," the melody the band seemed to be playing, and a bunch of guys in the platoons heard us and picked it up till their sergeants made them knock it off. They were restless, irritable now, wanting to get off.

The drivers in the deuce-and-halves were racing their motors and much of the time we couldn't hear the band at all. The sounds were discordant and we'd see a guy take the instrument from his lips and wipe the mouthpiece and his lips and bang the instrument against his leg to knock the moisture out before it froze on him. They hated us that time for sure. The snow was swirling down now, thick, and there was maybe a foot of it on the ground, very soft.

One of the guys in the band I knew and I walked over to ask him how he liked his duty these days and if he'd heard any good jazz lately and how he felt today about the benefits. He thought I was US and so I could get by with that kind of talk. An NCO, Sergeant Sprockmouth I called him, Sergeant Fernandez really, yelled at me to get the hell back to my vehicle, but seeing who I was—a clerk, nothing more, nothing less—he broke his command midway, and turned away quickly, before he thought I had recognized him. As company clerk I was in a position to louse them up a thousand ways and, knowing I would, they handled me with kid gloves. I had acted anyway as though I hadn't seen or heard him, the way I normally do when I know that by military standards I'm in the wrong but that they are being stupid to point it out. I stood around talking to the guy in the band when I noticed on the other side none other than Private Gode, talking to this PFC who held the snare drums. He evidently was trying to borrow them. When I called to him he waved me over and I said, "Excuse me," passing through the ranks to his side. Before I even got there he was yelling to me: "Tell this solja who I am, Hite," he said.

"Who you are?" I repeated, knowing he had a play in mind but uncertain of its direction.

"Sure. Tell him I'm none other than the one and only, Joe Morello."

"That's him," I said to the guy and the guy looked at both of us as if he thought we'd slipped a nut, but in a second he took the straps from his shoulders and passed the drums over to Gode. Mainly I think he was simply curious to see what Gode would do with them. The snow was coming down heavier now and nobody five feet from anyone else knew what the other was doing. The officers were shouting orders and the motors were being raced, horns were going and noncoms were running about in their usual busy, lost way, trying to silence the men in the trucks. The band finished their number (although many never knew one had begun) and the instruments were no good for another and all those standing out in the snow were white all over, shaking to keep warm. And just then Gode began playing the snares. For all I know he was Morello. He was working them like an expert, and the band members—none of us—could believe it.

Maybe because he saw he had an audience he got carried away. He ran up to the lead truck and marched down the line of trucks, tripping sometimes in the snow but always banging on the drums as though he thought himself alone in a Frisco dive. I couldn't see how his hands could take the cold. Mine were cold in my pockets. But he didn't appear to mind. At the rear of every truck he was stopping and playing a special stanza, extra loud, and all the men on the truck had their faces jammed into the doorway, a crazy happy look on them. He was smiling and we all were smiling as Gode went down the line of trucks banging out his steps in a fast, wild beat. I guess till that time all the officers and noncoms were stupefied, didn't know what to make of it, but then the drillmaster, a short, fat SFC with chevrons up to his elbow, called, "Hey, you! What you doing with them drums?" and that started it. The next thing I knew about fifty noncoms were running after Gode, many of them sliding in the snow and tumbling over on their asses, tripping up others. It looked like some of our attacks on a hill.

Gode didn't notice. He went right on drumming.

Now the troopers, forgotten by the noncoms, were pouring from the trucks, screaming, yelling, laughing, charging after that volley of NCOs, picking up snowballs on the run, and throwing them everywhere. Among all this the officers could sometimes be seen, and less often heard, trying to stop the drummer, stop the noncoms, and return the troopers to their vehicles.

The band was doubled over, laughing, and I was too, when I saw the First Sergeant bearing down on me, probably wondering if the Colonel had ordered that crazy fucker from the band to do that. "Hite!" he called, "who the hell is that?"

"That's Gode," I said, "one of our men," breaking into a new fit of laughter when I realized that Gode had eluded them all. No one knew where he was now, but the drumming was furious as ever.

"Gode? Who the hell is Gode?" the First Sergeant yelled. "There ain't no Gode in my unit."

All the while laughing, I told him Gode had reported in yesterday; and then the picture turned over inside him and he began laughing with me. "That friggin chess player!" he said. We forgot how cold it was and occasionally some member of the band would strike up a line of melody and play along with Gode until the drum major found him out and made him stop. We were still laughing when the Captain, with two officers following behind him like lap-slaves, came up and asked what the hell was going on. "This ain't no goddam sideshow," he said. That struck me as funny and I laughed. He asked me what the hell I thought I was laughing at and I told him that with this band and Gode's drums and the Kenai forest all but burned up by this time we certainly as hell came near to being a sideshow. He asked me if I was trying to get smart with him and I told him I didn't have the facilities or the rank for that. He threatened to send me to a platoon, to one of the rifle squads, if I didn't shut up and stop laughing and get back to my truck. I told him that I doubted if my truck had any gas left in it by this time, but I don't think he heard me: it doesn't pay to buck them too much and I was on my way back to the truck.

In a short while the whole thing stopped. The drums stopped, and the motors were cut, and the troopers stopped shouting, and it even stopped snowing: the Colonel had showed.

Someone shouted "ATTENTION!"—finally. I think it was, of all people, Gode—in a voice so magnificently loud, so ceremoniously lewd, so maliciously authoritative that I think it must have stunned the Colonel and his staff, no less than the rest of us.

The company snapped-to, in place. The Captain scrambled over to the Colonel where he stood some distance from his sedan, surveying all. We all listened, looking forward to hearing the Colonel chew the Old Man's ass.

"Everything is ready, sir," the Captain said. "We just waiting for the word."

"I came down to give the word, Captain," the Colonel said, "but it looks to me that if I gave the word this minute the trucks would go all the way to Kenai empty."

"Yes sir," the Captain said.

"What kind of formation do you call that, Captain?"

"Sir?"

"In what field manual did you find *that* formation?"

The Captain turned and looked over his company. The Colonel was right; it did *look* like a formation. Only their alignment left quite a bit to be desired, and their uniforms did not at the moment appear to be military sharp. Some men had left the trucks without coats and half did not have the prescribed headgear; some had their rifles with them, others did not. One man had on a hunting cap, and I could not be sure but it looked as though Private Jones had one boot on his foot, the other in his hand. They were quite motley, really. Was this what the Captain meant when he said our unit was "combat ready"?

The Captain gave word to the Top to have the troops board the trucks. The motors were running again and the platoon leaders were stirring about, disappointed that the Colonel had been so mild with the CO. There

833

are only six in the unit, but everywhere I looked I saw one: scurrying about, as they always did when the high brass was present.

In a few minutes the first truck pulled out. Waiting their interval, the others followed, lumbering along slowly, heavily, the chains on the tires grinding, clinking. Finally the driver pulled our own big headquarters truck into line with the rest of the gray, puttering, ominous convoy: we were on the way to Kenai. Behind us, bringing up the rear, was the Captain's jeep, the tall antennae of his radio waving, and his flag that read: CONVOY BEHIND.

Livesy was the Old Man's driver, had been for longer than most of us remembered, and, gazing out through the porthole, we talked of Livesy and how on normal duty days in the barracks he washed and polished and painted the Old Man's jeep, buttering up to him, bucking for that promotion to Specialist Four; but all these seventeen months now that he had been in time and grade the promotions had gone to men with much less time and grade and who goofed off ninety per cent of their working hours at the PX coffee shop. Ullrich the mail clerk shared a room with him and he liked to tell how Livesy woke him, nights, dreaming aloud of fuel pumps, oil filters, and the mud under his axles.

Near noontime we stopped for a ten-minute stretch at Mile 70, and we were saying how we hoped we did not have to bivouac overnight, and that we were making such good time we could be in Kenai by morning; but when we started up again the driver couldn't get our deuce-and-half out of low gear and the next thirty miles we drove in that condition but then because we were slowing down the speed of the convoy they stopped us and spread our personnel out two and three with the other trucks. I elected to join the fifth platoon, remembering that Gode had been tentatively assigned to that one and that I had not seen him return the man's drums.

He had not and the rest of the way, till we bivouacked that night, he performed. That kept the men feeling good and from complaining too much about the cold. The trucks have heaters, large, excellent heaters when they work, but they never do. In ours it was an icy unnatural cold and we huddled up in our parkas, pulling the hood over our faces, trying to root ourselves a space in the floor where we could from time to time stretch. We tried to sleep and a few of us did but most of the time we were much too cold to have any luck with it. We shivered and the road was bad too and the truck shimmied a great deal. "He finds um all, don't he?" one man said, meaning the ruts in the highway.

All the while Gode sat up front on the wire cage built there to protect the dead fat heater, his parka hood completely hiding his face, wearing his arctic mittens, tapping judiciously on the snares in such a way as to help us sleep rather than keep us from it. Once I must have dozed for I remember waking and looking up and thinking that there was a US Army parka beating a drum. That night we set up camp by the river, what river I don't know but probably a tributary of the big Kenai River itself although we were yet a long way from the fire, and got our plate of powdered eggs and warm raw bacon and the two pints of frozen recombined milk from the makeshift serving tent and were downing these without complaint when the Top came over from the CP tent to tell us we had four hours to catch some shut-eye. That made most of us angry because in setting up the tents we had found the stakes impossible to drive in the frozen earth and had worked for hours in the darkness in an attempt to get the tent to stand. None of us had wanted to stop anyway, including the drivers for whose benefit, it was reputed, we were stopping. But we fell asleep quickly and without too much fuss. The ride had been an exhausing one and after the first chilling moment the sleeping-bags warmed and it was much much better then than the trucks. In the trucks, closed in on all sides, a man went crazy after a while, and with all those men eventually a man's smell became not a pleasant thing. I remember the last thing I heard was Gode, who had come with me to the headquarters tent, asking the commo chief why it was that riding on a deuce-and-half always give a man a hard, and the sergeant said he didn't know, and I didn't know either but knew that it was true. Not so much that trip but in basic every morning when they used a truck to shuffle us off to one course or the other that happened down to the last man and I had wondered privately about it at the time but here as I drifted off to sleep was Gode saying: "I guess that's one of the more pleasant mysteries of human nature."

835

I smiled sleepily, thinking about it, holding myself that awful and peculiar way we do, and I remember thinking it was morning already and cussing about that when in no time at all the First Sergeant came in and kicked the boots of Ullrich and told him in a gruff voice to go unload two steel bunks from the trailer and set them up for Webster and the Old Man in their tent and to get two mattresses. I remember Ullrich cussing in long streams the XO, the Captain, and the First Sergeant, and lying inert in his sleeping-bag for the longest time, before finally he pulled himself out of the bag, cussed the cold weather, and began pecking around in the dark for his boots: the goddam Captain and the goddam XO could very well sleep in their goddam sleeping-bags the same as he and the other goddam men were doing, he said. And I remember some voice in the dark, saying: "Amen, brother, preach on," and thinking it might have been myself, my own voice, because I had been thinking the same thing, when someone stepped on my ankles and tripped himself and plunged into several sleeping now disgusted men who woke with cries of "What the Christ?" and "Who the fuck! . . ." A match was struck near my face and I rose up on my elbows and there was Gode, his teeth white, grinning, holding the match between two greasy fingers. "Ain't this the very goddam most," he said. "Ain't this the training that wins wars?" He crawled over the men and sat down by the Yukon stove and laced up his boots. "Where you going?" I asked. "To kiss the brass good night," he said.

He and Ullrich left and I never heard them come back in, although they must have, to get their gear: they sacked up the remainder of the night in a truck, the heater of which, miraculously, worked.

In the morning at four we struck and at five we were eating breakfast and asking each other why in hell they had not waited till after breakfast to strike so that we would at least have had a warmer place in which to eat. Shortly after that, everything running surprisingly smooth, we pulled out, myself and Ullrich and Gode wedging into the truck that had the good heater. The second day was the same as the first except that our excitement was gone now and we were tired of the trucks. Three more vehicles broke down and this in some cases stuffed as many as forty men into a truck designed to accommodate eighteen. Back at post the motor pool would be full of them, but it did no good to reflect on that, ours was not to reason why. Nonetheless, we rode in comparative comfort, taking advantage of the buddy system drilled into us during basic, perspiring, however, because the heater only worked when turned to HIGH and the truck had no ventilation. No one looked out the portholes as they had done the first day and it would be the return trip before any of us would know how the country had in those miles changed, how not only the tips of the mountains were covered with snow but how that snow now was over them completely, and how these mountains were higher, rougher, and the snow banking alongside the highway. Nor were we interested then in any of the numerous lakes dotting the region or the large number of caribou which stood among the trees to the side of the road like huge mounted wood carvings, watching our trucks lumber by. We took off our boots and parkas and shirts and couldn't find them when from time to time we stopped for breaks at the sparse roadside inns, the combination tavern, café, bunkhouse, and general merchandise store, the dogs barking in the rear, the snow packed down where the path leads to the outhouse—the road hotels that typify so well that region referred to as "South of the Range." Farther on, "North of the Range," not even they are seen. But we, the peons, the officers would not let inside, our number was too great! We could only stretch and breathe the frozen air, some of us out in our T-shirts, finding the cold a welcome relief after the hot truck.

Gode had his drums and the troopers crowded around him when we stopped. Once he had them fall into a column of twos, and, drumming away, he led them two hundred yards down the highway before an officer caught them with his jeep and ordered their return. I was beginning to see me at my typewriter tapping out his name on the court-martial. But no, he returned in the back seat of the jeep, the drums in his lap, and was taken inside where he had coffee with the officers and time-and-graders. Maybe they thought they could not court-martial, and hope to find guilty, a man who laughed at all he saw. At himself no less than everyone else.

We arrived in Kenai shortly after dark and set up camp where the river formed at the eastern lip of Kenai Lake. Not very far off, in the dark, we could see the flames of the fire, and overhead, the black funneling smoke. The air was charged with the sharp smell of charcoal, the drifting cinders: the fresh burn; it was a smell that opened a man's nostrils and made him take note. Word was that the civilian fighters had it under control and that it was only a matter of cleaning up now. The Captain went out in the jeep and was gone a long time. When he returned, the platoons were already sacked out, the XO and two other officers were playing pinochle, and I had entered their tent to ask for the First Stud what time the troops were to be wakened. The Captain came in angrily, greeting none of us, taking position by the Yukon stove, warming himself. He asked me if I would go get him a cup of coffee from the mess hall, and I liked the "if" and said I would be happy to. When I returned with his coffee and whatever else I had been able to stuff into my pockets, Ullrich and Gode were setting up the Captain's bunk, the Captain staring at Gode as if to decide where he'd seen him before. The officers were watching Gode also because he continually bumped into them, and they couldn't play their cards. Gode was whistling, unaware of their gaze, intent on setting up the bunk properly, but once, his back to the others, he winked at me. Before he left the tent, he asked the officers if they played chess, but when they stared at him and didn't answer, he followed me out. That night in our tent we waited up, and, as Gode said it would, the Captain's bunk collapsed on him. He cursed the officers, but they of course denied having anything to do with it.

From that night on Gode never went back to his assigned platoon, but stayed with headquarters. I am sure no one ever told him to make the switch, but neither did they tell him to return to the fifth. He took his place with the mail clerk as one of the two men in the unit who had the least to do. Back at the barracks, later, he trotted the peripheries of all our offices and gave the impression of having no end of work to complete but what that work was no one ever thought to determine. One day in garrison the First Sergeant came upon him reading a book, *Evil and the Conscience of Man*, and that day asked him: "Gode, just what the hell is your duty in this company?" Gode told him his duty was to defend the northern frontier from enemy aggression—something like that.

Near morning the civilians lost all control of the fire. Fickle winds had carried live sparks some ten miles up the lakeside and ignited small patches there which spread quickly, and by the time we made it on the trucks the new blaze was open along an estimated three-mile perimeter. They were beginning now to compare this fire with the Kenai burn of '47, a short distance north, which blighted 421,000 acres that stand now forlorn and ragged as they did two weeks after the last flames died. Kenai Lake, the Bureau of Land Management will tell you, is 100 miles long, and the many islands of black, churning smoke, descending off the mountains, settled over that lake valley as far as we could see. The civilians with bulldozers and tank trucks and our men with shovels and hoses fought against time to establish a line and before noon they started a back-fire which would work, they said, only if the wind did not shift again. The company had pulled out without breakfast and it was three in the afternoon before the mess truck found the main body of troopers. At that time C-rations were issued for the evening meal and the next day. Everyone was black with soot, and some had burns or tears in their uniforms, and they were all excited and few complaining.

In the afternoon several army helicopters flew over, circling wide with the fire, and once one came so low we made out the passenger's rank: a colonel. Not our colonel or he would have waved. Soon after that, a trio of

Piper Cubs from the airport in Kenai appeared, and we were pulled back while they dumped their loads of borate. They made three more runs before the wind and heavy smoke forced their halt.

In the excitement of the morning I had been separated from Gode and it was late in the evening that I saw him: or, rather, he saw me, for his face was black and one sleeve had been ripped from his shirt. He had lost his steel pot also. I didn't recognize him when he called my name. I asked him what he had been doing and he said he had personally taken charge of, and was alone controlling, five acres of the fire. "You know as much about firefighting as the Captain," I told him, and he smiled. It was common knowledge among the troops that the Captain had tried to take charge not only of the military operations but of the civilian professional fire-fighting element as well. And had been rebuffed. His brass and free-wheeling demeanor had not impressed the civilian chief, who perhaps realized that fighting a fire was not the same thing as conducting a war. Rumor was that this same chief had told the Old Man to take himself and his men and pull out if he didn't want to comply with what he, the chief, knew to be best. The Captain told him that there was only one civilian alive whose orders he would follow and since the Secretary of the Army was not around . . .

Gode and I were talking about this when we saw at some distance the Major sitting on a dead stump, alone. Gode asked me what I knew about him.

"Why are you interested in the Major?" I asked.

"He's stopped eating," Gode said.

"Why has he done that?"

"I don't know. He hasn't eaten all day and from all I can gather he doesn't intend to eat again. Says he isn't hungry. Gave all his C-rations away, except the cigarettes. Here, have a smoke." He passed me a Chesterfield.

"Christ!" I said. "The Captain will like that."

"He likes it all right. He's already heard about it."

"What is he doing about it?"

"Nothing. Said the guy would eat when he got hungry enough. But to let him know if he stopped working the fire."

"Is he doing that?"

"First-rate."

I told him then what I knew about the Major.

The Major's fast lasted five days and at the end of that time he went into the woods and killed himself. And here the story, like a river, follows that oxbow.

IV

We all thought the Major the least friendly of any person we had known but Gode says this is not true and he should know for in those five days he worked himself into the Major's confidence, they were together whenever possible, forming an extraordinary union which breached the language barrier. Of the thirteen Hungarians in the unit not more than two or three maintained with the troopers any relationship which could be given the name friendship and with those few it was mostly kept to that level where the men laughed at the way the hunkies had picked up the English; the way, that is, the Hungarian was willing to use those words of four-letter dimension which were the only words the troopers themselves knew and which they taught them. Once learning them the hunkies developed the habit of employing them for every occasion, however inappropriate, and the men got a big kick out of that. The others were either alone or sought out only the men in the unit and elsewhere on post of their own nationality. Until Gode, the one man most alone was the Major, for, until Gode, he sought out no one.

He felt picked on, I'm sure—and so he was. They all were, it seemed to me, and they fretted and fumed and cursed in their language or spoke to no one but went it alone and the Major five days after his fast simply went off into the brush one day and killed himself. He could have got hold of an M-1 easily enough. We had brought along two per platoon to kill the wildlife if they were suffering or the bears and caribou if they got after us but he did not want a rifle apparently for he went out and did not come back and as it turned out later he had taken his entrenching tool and used that on himself. On his wrist. Each night we had been on Kenai he had been filing down the blade to a fine cutting edge. He very nearly chopped off his hand with it. All this about the file Gode told me later: that he would sit with Kuimets for long cold hours into the night and they would talk about this and that and Gode would ask him why he wanted to kill himself and the Major would tell him and all the while they would be filing down the blade to a fine cutting edge, first one then the other, like two people discussing the weather over a cup of coffee. None of that time did the Major eat and whenever called upon he fought the fire and the company wondered where he got his amazing strength and watched him as though he had a secret they wanted to learn but none except Gode was watching him closely enough to keep him that night from stalking off through the burn and slicing his wrist. None except Gode and Gode made no attempt to stop him. The last night they were sitting together the Major ran his thumb along the blade and nodded his head to Gode and pitched the file into the woods. Gode took the blade and felt its edge with his own fingers then he passed it back to the Major and said that this was fine. Before they went to bed that night the two of them tacked a sign to a nearby tree.

HELP PREVENT FIRES

it read. This held no special significance for either of them, Gode said. The sign had fallen down and so they tacked it back up.

As Gode told the Captain, he saw the Major walk into the woods and knew he wouldn't be coming back and when asked by the Captain why he didn't stop him, his lips curling, he pronounced fiercely: "It wasn't my place to, Captain." It was none of his business. If a man wanted to kill himself and had good reason or thought he had good reason or whether he had no reason at all it wasn't his obligation to stop him.

But where does one act end and another begin? The XO and other officers of course couldn't see Gode's viewpoint. "Bring me the Code," they said. I brought them the UCMJ and they passed through it looking for an article under which to charge Gode. They could have found one easily enough but the Captain said no. "NO!" Not only did he say that but he ran them out of his tent, too. "Why you bastards," he said, "all of you, get your chickenshit brassassed ideas out of here!" It did our heart good to hear him speak that way to Mr. Wonderful and his Junior G-Men.

When the Major was reported by his platoon sergeant as being unaccounted for it was assumed that he had gone AWOL and the company talked about that but no one did anything. We at the time had AWOL personnel from our unit whom we could find on the streets of Anchorage or Palmer and talk to whenever we wished. I think there is an unwritten rule of procedure in the MP Corps which specifies that if they know where to pick up a man they will let him stay free until he has been out long enough to be charged with desertion. That way they know he'll get the brig for at least six months. But the hunkies knew this was not the case with the Major and word spread quickly enough: suicide. We were having trouble with the fire at that time and needed all the men out to fight it but the CO called the entire company in and had them conduct a search. They didn't find him and the noncoms of course said to each other how he wouldn't have the guts, a lousy hunkie, to do a thing like that, and cussed him for taking up their time. There was the mountain the base of which we were camping on and rising back of that mountain we could see another and behind us there was the fire and there was the lake too so this made a lot of ground to cover and we couldn't hope to cover all of it, looking for a man like Kuimets, a man with suicide on his mind. Finally it was two hunkies who went out and brought him back, the Major slung over the shoulder of the smaller of the two, the larger one walking along behind him with the bloody entrenching tool in his hand, as much as to testify that the shovel outweighed the Major. They brought him to the CP and in a second the medic chief was there, a young blond kid, Methodist, RA, who had intentions of studying for the ministry once he was discharged. He was already acting more like a priest than a medic. A pocketbook edition of Jim Bishop's *Go with God* protruded from his rear pocket. Mr. Wonderful was there and had the presence of mind to tell the medic to button the pocket flap of his fatigues if he meant to carry a book in it. The kid was about to cry and I honestly didn't know whether this was because of the way the Lieutenant had spoken to him or because Kuimets was dead.

It was pretty bad that night. The platoons were rotating the fire watch and those men who remained in camp did not go to sleep when night came and did not talk much either. It was as if they were afraid of what they might say. Not even Gode talked much. The First Sergeant didn't because he was angry and the Captain didn't and though the officers played pinochle they didn't say much out of respect—dutiful respect—to the CO's mood. Many seemed to be thinking though none would yet say it: that it was the army responsible; the army which drove the Major to kill himself. Those who had seen the body were or had been sick and those who had not were thinking and on top of that we were all tired. We were all very tired. We had found that fighting a fire is no easy job. The first and third platoons were in after twenty-four hours on the line, digging ravines, clearing brush and felling trees, and carrying water. Reinforcing the lines. Yes, very tired.

And they were thinking that it was the army which had driven Kuimets first to give up eating and then to kill himself in that merciless fashion and even the RAs must have been thinking this and you know, that can be very depressing and uncomfortable. I mean here we were four thousand miles from home, stuck in the army—the troopers I mean, the noncoms seemed strangely out of it, unreal, their stripes meaningless—some of us with six years to go and some with two and a number who had only months to pull but all of us in it at the moment and "it" was the army and the army was what made him kill himself, or so we were thinking then. It gave a man something to think about. In the night we heard a voice yelling once, "Fuck you, Jones!" and for that instant it struck us that we all were, including the speaker, Jones. And that we all had been sufficiently fucked. Out of the silence that grievance: "Fuck you, Jones!" and then silence again, pinpointing that grievance.

And how was Gode feeling that night? I have told how he had figured that the best way of getting through the army or any other place was to laugh his fool head off at it: that night after they brought the Major's body in and things had quieted down Gode followed the path Kuimets had taken into the burn and from that black sucking, smoldering field his laughter was flung back at me, was flung back at all of us, like knives flicking from a circus performer's sleeve, high, wild, and crazy he seemed so happy in it—till then this dribbled out, became a sound like water filling a bottle, the spaced blub-blubbing of water down a narrow neck.

843

And what did he say when I approached him but, "Only the frog croaks and gets by with it, man."

I left him there and returned to my tent. The First Sergeant was still angry (Kuimets' death had put a hitch in his Morning Report and Duty Roster, though I don't say that this alone was troubling him) and on the squawk box trying to get commo to rig up a connection with the people back at post: he had to get a copter, something, sent up to remove the corpse. He told me to get out of the tent, and I did, wandering over to the Captain's tent.

There had been times when I felt disgusted with the Captain and moments when I loathed him and a few instances when I felt a sort of respect for the guy but usually I thought of him as "army" and let it go at that. That night though I felt sorry for him, as most of us did. He was taking the Major's death hard, taking it very personally, and I don't think out of any worry of what the Colonel or any general might think or how it might reflect on his efficiency record but personally because he thought there was the possibility that in some way he had failed. He did not like the hunkie, to be sure, and as his commanding officer felt no moral obligation to play mother to the kid, but . . . because he had known the hunkie had problems and had talked to him several times about them and what they (meaning the army) could do to help him and because this, obviously, had not subtracted from but, it would seem, added to his troubles he thought, perhaps, he had failed. He liked to see any situation in terms of black and white and employed this principle in the command of his troops but there was no sense of this forthcoming in regard to Kuimets. Perhaps if he had not been a hunkie? He could after all understand the American troops. For all of their so-called "walks of life," the different backgrounds which spawned them and the sundry approaches they took to the understanding of—or not thinking about—life, their life, they arrived at an amazingly similar concept. It was all a matter of knowing where to place them on the map. But the hunkie, now, the Captain had never known where to put him. He didn't fit anywhere. And maybe the answer to this lay in his being a foreigner, a Hungarian, or maybe it exceeded the borders of any one country. On his desk in garrison there was a dispatch from headquarters instructing him to ascertain that all "aliens" complied with the law bidding them to register annually. Forms could be secured from any post-office window, the memo read, and the alien's compliance was mandatory by law; and, maybe, he was thinking, they called them aliens for a reason that went beyond their nationality. What was the second definition of a foreigner? One not belonging. Right? Well if there was any one person who did not belong it was the hunkie.

One thing leads to another. An act doesn't end with the conclusion of that act but rides into or precipitates another and this is true especially of the army where there are so many ranks who feel they must be included. We had been in garrison not long before this when the Major had been placed on KP and there he had had an argument with Gamble, the chief cook and not a bad guy at all if you know how to work him; but the Major had not known how to work him and so they argued and Gamble called him a lazy sonuvabitch, a stupid sonuvabitch, and a crazy Hungarian sonuvabitch and before the KP day was done the Major had locked Gamble in the icebox. Sound funny? Had locked him in the icebox where he very nearly froze his ass till someone heard him and then when they did the Major came to stand in front of the door and with his little knotted fists tried to fight off those cooks who managed eventually to open the door. Gamble came out blue, doubled over, expelling blue smoke, wanting to get at the hunkie but too cold to do so. He was OK the next day, didn't even have a cold but the hunkie now, he was back in the Old Man's office again. But the conferences there were always the same. They all ended with the Captain getting angry, the Major standing at attention while the Captain reamed his ass.

"That hunkie won't be able to sit down for a week," he would tell us afterwards. And that instance—because the hunkie had just plain up and quit—quit the army—which maybe it was impossible to do but which he was doing anyway: just plain outright quit: sat down and refused to work— the CO did not once mention the locking up of the cook in the icebox; did not mention that because he was blind to everything but the fact that the hunkie *had* quit, that whether it was or was not possible he had done it. Had quit, refused to work, and those noncoms could poke a fist into his face or they could even jam a pistol in his ribs but the fact of the matter was *he had quit.* It was exasperating. A man couldn't quit the army, but this one had. And if they threw him in the stockade it would still amount to that. The man had quit. That was open defiance. There were men going AWOL every day but that was nothing compared to this; that was men *running away* from the army but in this man's case it wasn't a running away from it was a standing up to. I quit, he said. And quit he did, sat down in the midst of all he hated with a go-to-hell attitude that nothing penetrated. What difference would the stockade make to a man like that! Christ, give him a war any time. Wartime you could shoot the bastard and that would be the end of it. "You're not a man, hunkie," he had told him. "You're not a man. A man would go out there and perform his duty. Would do what he had to do. A man would be willing to put in his time for his country. You're not. You're lazy. You're stupid. You're crazy. You're a crazy stupid ugly bastard you hear! You don't want to do your duty. You don't think you have a duty. You're not a man. You're a crazy stupid bastard. You make me sick. All you hunkies make me sick . . . So you quit. All right, you quit. Now get the hell out of my office." And that time, since he had quit, he had not even stood at attention. How could you talk to a sonuvabitch who wouldn't stand at attention? Going out he slammed the door. For slamming

845

the door and for not standing at attention the Captain had the First Sergeant do the first thing that came to mind. He had him restricted to his cubicle. He had guards run a two-hour shift on him through the nights, whose duty it was to see that the hunkie got no sleep. He had the tires removed from the hunkie's Ford which stood in the parking lot behind the company building. If he wasn't going to work, it was a cinch he wasn't going any place else. But did it end there? Hell, no. Two of the guards were caught sleeping and so he had to give an Article XV to each of them. Finally the hunkie had decided to return to work. Word was the platoon got fed up with pulling guard over him so one of the hunkies one day talked him into it.

So. First he had quit the army, then he had gone on a five-day fast, then he went out and killed himself. What else was there for him to do? He had run out of extremes.

But that's the army for you. One act precipitates another and one never knows where to make the distinction between the two acts but just as that act had not ended with Gamble's release from the icebox so now with the Major's death could one say that marked any real termination of events for here now the hunkies were gathering together like some ecclesiastical order, here now was a company of tired men staying up because they had to think about it and though very nearly all of them were ignorant in their thoughts and gave themselves different answers it didn't seem apt that any of it would have changed by morning and would morning usher new reverberations, new acts? Whenever had a man been able to see a thing in retrospect and say with truth: that part of me is dead, that part of me exists no more? At that moment he was thinking he knew how Gamble must have felt in the icebox. He had never thought about it before but why had the hunkie put Gamble in the icebox? There must have been some reason. Some reason, too, why he had up and quit the army. It was bad, sure, but if they, the privates and PFCs thought their job was bad they ought to try his. They didn't know it but they had the softest job in the army. No responsibility! So what was there so bad about it that a man would go out and slice off his goddam hand? Sick, that's what he was. The hunkie had a sick mind. Must have had. What other goddam infrantryman would give up chow for five days? Sick! Well, goddam, sure he was sick, but how the hell did he get that way? He'd seen the man's psychiatric evaluation; had requested one be given him back there when he up and quit the goddam army. Normal.

That's what it had said: normal. Subject of above average intelligence. Subject keenly perceptive. Subject manifests clear views of right and wrong, distorted however by different planes of reality (now what the hell did that mean?). Subject wavers between desire to rebel and desire to be manipulated. Conclusion: subject normal. Recommendation: N/A. Well, why not, with an evaluation like that; that described nearly everyone he knew, certain officers excepted. And although he had not started out thinking of the Major with this in mind he came to it now and retreated from it and came back to it again and finally said it aloud to Gode and myself because we were enlisted men like the hunkie and maybe could see it where he could not. "Maybe you can tell me," he said. He was seething with anger and we could see that at least a portion of that anger was directed at himself for not being able to see, and for asking those questions which to him touched on treason itself. He could not see. No, he could not at all see how a man in his unit could go out and hold his wrist up against a tree and smash at it with an entrenching tool, and stand there silently bleeding, silently dying. He couldn't come near seeing and understanding it and he knew he couldn't and the thought flicked at him from time to time: that maybe he was missing something, some nugget of truth, that maybe he should have been able to see it, to put himself into the hunkie's shoes and tell himself just what it was that could lead him to commit that act. "Maybe you can tell me," he said for the third time. He drove himself into it then, pacing the tent, biting his nails: he stood before us and clapped each of us on the shoulder and stared from one to the other of us, into our eyes, in a gaze the color and depth of which was as difficult to define as the color and depth of that nearby lake which the smoke of the fire had discolored, lent aspects not its own. A stare which guaranteed to us that the Captain didn't know why, couldn't know why, would never know why, but all the time wanted to, felt the need to. "Why," he said, "you could give a man a country, a home, you could bring a man out of a communist-infected land and give him all the freedoms, all that money could buy, or a man dream of wanting—a car!" he said. "Have you noticed how all the hunkies have cars, how that's the first thing they buy? before buying shoes or a suit of clothes? Have you? . . . how you give a man all the benefits of democracy in the country with the highest living standard in the world, and then that man goes out—could think of going out—and kills himself. KILLS HIMSELF!" he said, almost as if he didn't yet believe it, had not seen it with his own eyes. "Why," he asked, "a man would

847

choose death over this freedom he never had before but which they say he was willing to fight for in his own country . . . fought for, see, and then because he couldn't win it there came to this country where it was given him. GIVEN HIM, Gode! He didn't have to fight for it, it was given him." "Why?" he wanted to know. "Why?" He just couldn't see it, he said. He could not for the life of him come even near seeing it, he said.

"Given him?" Gode asked quietly. "I was under the impression he had to serve five years just to qualify for it. And if after those five years he qualified for it, I'd like to ask you, Captain—would he have had it then?"

"I don't like to hear that kind of talk, Gode," the Captain said. His face was pale; he was watching Gode closely.

"Well, maybe the Major didn't like to hear your kind of talk, Captain. You got to remember: Kuimets was a freedom fighter; not a goddam freedom mouther!"

The officers had stopped playing cards and were listening. We heard the XO say to the others that the Captain might do better than talk to privates. The Captain heard him too but said nothing. That was one thing about the Captain I had admired. He was distinguished by the class system of officer from enlisted man only inasmuch as he know he had to be to keep winning his promotions and at the same time retain the respect of his fellow officers. I had often noticed him talking to the enlisted men in the unit and often he came in and talked to me about things he had done and would like to do and about myself: things not at all connected with the military; and most of the men he knew by their first names.

He poured himself a cup of coffee from the field insert on the stove and then he approached us again. His eyes appeared to be aching for he was rubbing them. They were red, and earlier he had accepted four APC tablets from the medic and taken them to relieve a headache. I had observed prior to this how these symptoms always showed when he had been thinking hard or had had a hard day but now of course he was tired too. It was true what they said: that he had not slept in over thirty hours. He had stayed up to direct the men in their fight against the fire and to do what he could to see the civilian people did nothing foolish. He had patrolled the roads in his jeep and kept on the radio and there were occasions when he had left the jeep to join the men in their efforts to forge a clearing before the fire reached it. But then the fire had changed course again because of the wind and it had jumped the clearing and come on down, very fast, and we had to start all over again, breach a new line, and so all in all he had been awake more than thirty hours when the rumor reached him that the hunkie had gone out to kill himself; and, now, four to five hours later, the body recovered, he wanted to know how a man could do such a thing. Wanted to know why. Unlike Gode, who had been telling me not many minutes before this that it never baffled or amazed him to read in a newspaper's report of a suicide, the inevitable line: "Friends of the deceased say that only hours before he plunged to his end he seemed in the best of spirits." "It always strikes me as irrelevant and slightly humorous," Gode had said. "Why do they mention it at all? Isn't it obvious that we're bound to be strangers to one another; bound in the full sense to be islands each to ourselves; that what is real this minute is nothing the next. Isn't that obvious? A spot of water in the sun. So what the hell does it matter how the deceased appeared in the afternoon? The point is it obviously didn't matter to him. If it had he'd never have gone to the roof. *Plunged to his end!* Isn't that a striking phrase, a delightful phrase? And, you know," he had said, grinning, "I think of the vicious core that was at this man's center, hurtling down eighty stories to its end—I think of it—picture the ball at the end of a chain that's kept a road-working convict prisoner all his years—I think of it in that light and am not inclined to grieve with the victim's survivors: that grudgingly bereft mother who held him as a baby and never has quite got over seeing him that way; that aunt who brought him neckties at Christmas which he thanked her for but never wore; not even for that sweetheart of a wife who saved coupons by day and made love to him at night in the same spirit in which she washed dishes and the babies' diapers. It is as ingloriously funny as it is stupid," he had said. Unlike Gode, the Captain would be baffled. Was. "You tell me," he said.

849

I could sense Gode wanting to speak and I looked at him, waiting. There was an element of something like surprise about Gode. One never knew what he was going to say. He didn't himself, I don't think, but in the company of the Old Man now I had to admire his calmness, his ease. Already in our brief acquaintance I had noted his habit of beginning a conversation almost as one detached and then riding into that conversation with vehemence as if he found a vortex there which claimed him body and soul but from which he could centrifugally skip, laughing, at any given moment. He took a cup, one of the officers' cups no less, a tin cup, shining, from where it hung on the pin by its needle eye in the center pole of the tent, and poured himself a cup of coffee. "I'll tell you what I think, Captain," he said.

"What?" The Captain was impatient and quite probably irritated by Gode's little theatrics. He was not angry in that impatience, however. Gode's easy comportment seemed to be calming him. He was no longer biting his nails or pacing, but took a seat by the stove and began unlacing his boots.

"I'll tell you what I think. I think that maybe Kuimets killed himself because he had convinced himself finally that that which he had fought for in Hungrary and that which he'd come to this country to find was all a lie—everything: freedom, love, good—all those high-flying abstract nouns they feed you in a lifetime. To his mind, people had been depersonalized and dehumanized and at the same time blown up and stuffed and rendered foolish as a Christmas turkey. I mean, in a final way, people were not good enough for him and the end came when he realized he wasn't much better. 'I worship the ostrich!' that was his swan song, because he had worshipped everything else worthwhile and it had gradually sieved itself out till it was left that that was the only bird with sense enough to hide its foolish head for shame of all those things the world was allowing: THE SOUTH! Hell, man, leaving one Hungary he had landed smack dab in the middle of another."

"Well, I wouldn't know about that," the Captain said, "I'm from Pennsylvania." He looked quite foolish saying it and Gode only blinked his eyes. The Captain took off his boots. He would, he said, admit that all Gode said was possible all right but possible only in the mind of a crazy man. It could drive only a crazy man to suicide. He asked Gode if Kuimets was crazy (and that time he mentioned the Major by name, one of the rare instances except for Gode's use of it, in which anyone employed that name we all saw stamped on his shirts and jackets) and I answered that question myself. I said, "No sir, I didn't think he was crazy. He was sensitive," I said, and thought as the words came out that that was being crazy wasn't it, that in that sensitivity he was crazy for one learns after a while that to get by one has to lose that sensitivity or naïveté or whatever one wants to call it; either to will it lost or to have it lost by designs outside oneself—but I didn't say that. "He was sensitive—" I repeated, and they all looked at me, waiting, much as they must have looked at Gode later when he told them, "Let's help fuck Santa, 1962, '63, and '64," except that one could not, once he had said it, turn a statement back into Gode; whatever he said, whether foolish or profound or neither, had the force to penetrate—and this, I felt, is what they had done to me: had thrown up a shield that reflected my words and drove them back inside me. And rightly enough, for what did that explain: he was sensitive? Nothing! It was a statement inconclusive, one which grammatically contained an object for the verb but even so could not stand alone; a statement which should have continued, "but he was . . ." And I thought how curious it was of me to be thinking like that, much less to have said it, and how I would not have, had not Gode, a stranger to me in the last analysis, been there.

"Well, we're all wrong," Gode was saying. "Hite is, you are, Captain, and I've lied: he didn't kill himself for any of those reasons we've listed." We waited—but Gode said no more.

"Gode, I want to ask you a question," the Captain said finally. "Did you know Kuimets was going to kill himself?"

"Yes sir," Gode said.

"Why didn't you stop him?"

"It wasn't my place to, Captain. To tell you the bare-assed truth, sir, I not only knew—"

It was then that Lieutenant Webster, the XO, the self-considered Mr. Wonderful, left the card table and reared over Gode, his Gallic, beardless face colored with anger hissing between his teeth,

"You knew! You *knew!* And still you let that man go out there and kill himself!"

Gode, in profound disgust sneered back at him, his lips fumbling with what he wanted to say but knew he had best not: the officer pressing his face (all the more dirty because it was so clean) against Gode's, their eyes held to one another's much as though there was a line, driven taut, locking them that way. "You knew!" Webster again demanded, his voice rising to a broken tenor crescendo, "and yet you let him—you let him walk out there and—" till at that point Gode did something far worse than tell the XO he was acting like a fool, like a self-righteous fraud who didn't know A from X. He turned from Webster to me, hitching a thumb back over his shoulder into the officer's face, saying, "Would you look at him? Would you look at that 14-karat gold-plated American bastard!" His speech rolled in laughter, Gode hitching his thumb into Webster's face while the laughter built inside him and rained from his mouth, that thumb swinging before Webster's face much as if Gode was on a highway hitchhiking and every wave of laughter was an automobile which he thumbed. Webster was startled by Gode's outburst and I felt for a second that he was seeing himself stripped of the power of those single silver bars on each of the wings of his collar, but then he spun about and announced savagely to the Captain: "I'm going to have this man court-martialed," that straight-forward declaration of defense which I have seen so often in the army.

"Why?" the Captain asked.

"WHY?" Webster cried. "Didn't you hear him?"

"Hear what?" the Captain asked.

"Why you heard what that fucking private called me!" the Lieutenant said, but Gode, still laughing, burst out into new peals, doubled over, that arm still extended towards Webster; and then the Captain began laughing, too.

Webster didn't know what to say: his Gallic baby-fleshed face had turned red, and he was conscious of those other officers watching, some with pleasure. "Bring me the goddam Code," he said to me, and I stood there a moment waiting for the Captain to supersede that order with his own, but he did not. "BRING ME THE GODDAM CODE, HITE!" Webster screamed, impatient with me, little beads of perspiration surfacing on his face. I went to my tent and there, taking my time, rummaged in the field desk till I found the UCMJ. I returned to the Old Man's tent but just as I walked in the Captain was telling Webster—and not only Webster but those other officers as well—to get the hell out of his tent, they were a bunch of brass-assed, half-assed, chicken-livered sonsofbitches. I stood aside as they pushed the flap and trooped out one behind the other like several children playing "London Bridge Is Falling Down," stooping as they passed under the arch. We noticed a slight tremor, a chill, run through the Captain, and as if to show that this was only a matter of temperature, he turned up the gas in the Yukon stove and sat down beside the stove, warming his hands. Without looking at me he said, "Take that damn Universal Code of Military Justice and do whatever hell you want to with it," and I looked at Gode and he at me and we passed out of the Old Man's tent. Behind the mess hall there was a large hole which the detail had dug as a disposal for mess, and there we pitched the book in.

The officers were gathered in the mess tent, talking. The cook Gamble stood outside, gazing over the lake where a few easy-living flames unfolded, slid along the mountainside. The officers had probably told him to get lost for a while. Although it was dark, here and there we could see in the mountains patches untouched by fire and green as the original garden but for the most part the land sat heavily as though turned to its underside, the black ugly scars everywhere, smoke fanning out from those areas where the fire had been and passed, and where the body of the fire was going yet the flames coughed, shot about, danced, like a thousand slender jesters entertaining their queen.

Gamble came over, and in his slow Southern way began talking to Gode as if he had known him all his life. "What's going on? The lootenants come in cussing and I hear Webster say that you got ya head where ya ass ought to be! What's going on, boy?" He was chuckling and I thought Gode might also find it funny, but, no, very angrily, deliberately, he turned to Gamble and said, "You can go back and tell that bastard that maybe it is but he ought to know that I didn't put it there, and that, for all of his cocky airs, I attend the barber as regularly as he does." So saying, he stalked off, back to our tent, I thought, but, no, he went on past it, out into the woods over the trail Kuimets earlier in the day had taken. "Where you going?" I called, but he didn't look back, climbed that rise into the woods. After he was out of sight I left Gamble and followed. Not that I wanted to or gave it any thought but primarily because the darkness was a comfort and I didn't want to face the First Sergeant. I had not gone far behind him although it seemed a long time because in the dark I could not see well, when I heard him ahead of me, laughing. I couldn't see him, but his voice was clear: shaded with fatigue, with bitterness, with anything but humor—laughing! Then with something of a shock I realized that now he wasn't laughing, that that laughter had dribbled into tears, that the tears now were almost choking him. Then that passed too. Why, he's vomiting, I thought; and then I heard him plunging on, deeper into the burn, without regard for path or trail, the limbs cracking and falling when his arms struck them—and the dry rattle of the brush and fallen trees as he stumbled over them.

A moment later I too almost stepped my feet into what must have caused all this. There in front of me was the twin corpse—or what was left of them—of two caribou. The fire had burned all the fur and flesh away and their bones lay shining in the moonlight in a bed of ashes. Obviously they had been fighting, their antlers had locked, and they had been unable to free themselves, or escape it, when the fire came raging down around them. Had not the fire killed them they could only have remained there anyway till starvation got them, but as I stared at their bones, preserved in the perfect shape of their bodies, I pictured in my mind how the fire must have caught on their fur as they stood, heads locked, unable to run, and their struggle then till finally they sank to their knees and then into the burning brush where they lay without resistance to the fire that picked their bones. They lay in those ashes now, and I had this momentary thought: that had I a blanket I could drape it over their bodies and free their antlers and they would rise and trot away.

My own stomach uncertain, I turned and made my way back to camp. There was only silence now and overhead to the east, a nest of stars. At my tent I looked out over the great burn and allowed myself to indulge in these sleepy, silly thoughts: that wherever any one walked it was the great burned-out place for them; that this was true of myself no less than of Gode and the Major, and this being true, then why shouldn't a man if he had the notion walk off into the woods, throw his wrist against a tree, hack it off, and die ... And maybe, I thought, Kuimets' death was simple as this.

In my sleeping-bag a while later, the flame of the gasoline lantern flickering, dying, because none of us had had the will to pump it, I thought, as how many other soldiers were doing, of home and how home was so far away and no longer had any reality for me; of how for so many of us life was all a matter of breaking away from, and getting back to, home. And Kuimets, now? I thought. What would have his answer been to this? I thought of the two caribou out in the brush and again I saw them bucking and heaving as the fire swam round about them, but this time only one was burning and while the flames enveloped him the other kicked his legs and bulled his head and fell and rose, snorted and bellowed, kicked and pulled and fell again, drawing the other down; both rising instantly, their horns still bound, terrified and trapped; one, however, not simply trapped, but bellowing from the pain of the flames that have eaten his hide and now sizzle his flesh until with the last effort he knows he drags the other down and tramples as would a horse his smoking body; but then the other rises and out-contests that early dying one while all the time the hot licking flames touch on him, touch, stab, and drill, infuriating him; but even as the body of the first one goes still, their horns yet are locked, their noses pressed together, their eyes only inches apart ... Then the flames caught on the second and leapt over his hide as if he was made of gasoline and in no time at all he sank to his fours and then tumbled down beside the first like an empty sack. And when the fire had picked their bones it swept on down the line.

I woke not much later. Gode was beside the Yukon stove, nude but for his army shorts, standing, gazing into the circle of flames of the small burner, repeating over and over . . . "the poor shits . . . the poor shits . . . the poor . . ." The lantern had gone out and except for the light of the stove there was none. Sliding into his cold sleeping-bag he involuntarily murmured "—Christ!" and then lay still and silent; until from that dark side of the tent I again heard his voice: "Mood music, sweetheart. Give us mood music for the downtrodden soldier in his Republic."

And some time later, long after we both should have been asleep, in a tone quite different, he said: "I'll tell you one, boy. In order to get along you got to be, control, and sacrifice . . . everything and everybody . . . for *evil*, Buber says, is lack of direction . . . and that which is done in it . . . and out of it . . . he says . . . is the grasping, seizing, devouring, ignoring, torturing, compelling, seducing, humiliating, destroying . . . of what offers itself . . . and there you've got it, Buber, old clown! . . . the only exactly honest-to-god definition of life I know . . . ."

And when I fell asleep he was laughing.

855

V

In the morning the helicopter was there to transport Kuimets' body back to post but in the morning also we saw that the fire had turned a final time and that it was completely out of control now and that it would not be long before it reached the houses on the edge of the lake. The fire had originated on the shore of the lake, had been channeled up into the mountains; now it was sweeping back down. That morning while eating chow we could stand in the road and see the great white and red flames shooting from the trees. The air was thick with smoke and cinders and the raw pungent odor of the burn. Except for the five of us who remained in camp, the entire company was again ordered out. For two hours in the morning we helped the mess hall strike and load their equipment onto the two mess trucks because later in the day it was planned that we would set up camp elsewhere, but then we were sent out to help evacuate those families whose homes seemed in the most immediate danger.

The Kenai Lake people did not seem sad. They said, "Well, in a short while it will be ashes," and rested their glances momentarily on the homes and land of which they spoke; then they looked over at us and smiled, and we all went back to work then. Overhead we could see the smoke and sometimes in that smoke the white lick of a flame with its red lip and then the puff of black smoke as the flame dropped in among the trees again with the lapping roar of a wave. There was much work to be done but even so we took breaks: the Kenai people brought us beer and we sat down together and drank it and spoke of subjects other than the fire: with the flames at our backs we did not have time then to be strangers. We had to begin right off as friends. The family whom Gode and I were helping had been living on the lake seven years and when we asked them what they were going to do now they said, "We'll go back to the city," meaning of course Anchorage, the only place in Alaska which is almost but not quite Alaska the last frontier. We had the last of their furniture packed on their truck, and then they took us for a ride across the lake in their boat. As it turned out they were taking us to a small fire that had jumped up just off the lake shore, between the lake and the road, and we were hauling water from a narrow stream when the First Sergeant came by at the wheel of a jeep, alone, and saw us. He was excited and when we recognized him we ran up the hill to the road and he told us to get in the jeep, quickly, that the fire was going like hell now, was out of control and that we'd be very lucky to have a camp any longer. This excited us too and as the jeep bucked off we waved to the couple in the woods; they probably had heard what was happening for they were not looking our way but back over that direction we had just come which the fire was eating up and which we could see too, now—a wide chop of flames covering, it appeared, the very spot where we were camped. Then the couple ran for their boat. Before we even came into sight of the camp we felt the heat of the fire and heard the fierce crack and spit of the flames chewing the wood, the roar of the heavy machinery, and the yelling of the civilian crew. From the last curve in the road we saw it: the fire some fifty yards to the rear of the camp, the bulldozers being pulled out, the civilian men on foot, running. It was a full-scale retreat. The flames were too high and too hot and past the point of holding back and on top of that we didn't know where our company was and couldn't contact them on the radio, a PRIC-10 with a dead battery. The three of us and two drivers who had been goofing off and several of the civilian fighters worked to load what gear and equipment we could into the ahkios and to get these onto the trucks. We could hear the flap-flap of the flames if we did not take the time to look, and it was very hot, and in the end we pulled out with only a small portion on the trucks. The wind was very strong and our faces felt as though they should be very red, and we knew we were running and we felt very proud to be running. Gode, at the wheel of one of the big trucks, did not know how to drive it, and his truck stalled on him as the fire swept over the camp. He pulled out, the truck bucking and whining, inches ahead of the fire. The civilians were shouting at him, and he was shouting back, and laughing, and wiping the sweat away, and only rarely looking at the road. "Man, I thought that was a burned-out section!" he said. And looking back, I answered: "It is now." The tents we had left standing were going up in immediate puffs of smoke like little displays of make-believe, and the several truck-trailers, except for their tires, stood grim and forlorn, resisting the whirl of the flames. We had not managed to find and load all of the gasoline and now and then there would sound that loud ominous explosion of a five-gallon can, and the high black mushrooming of smoke.

Three miles around the lake we stopped. The flames were following us, steadily consuming the mountainside. We had never imagined a fire could move so fast, and ran along the road, watching it, dazzled by it. A stream of cars and trucks passed along the road, loaded down, the occupants serious-faced, intent on what they were doing. The road was thick with people watching. There were numerous army and civilian photographers and reporters, and the post PIO officer, chaplains, and many many high-ranking military men whose gold-braided caps, crisp uniforms, and highly polished shoes seemed more than out of place. Even from that distance the heat was intense, and none of us yet knew where our company was and, following Gode's advice, he and I had become separated from the First Sergeant. The sky was entirely obscured now by the black lurching smoke, the River Styx, Gode said. From some place Gode confiscated another PRI-10 and was from time to time speaking into it such words as: "Firebug One, this is Firebug Two, come in Firebug One," an effort for which he was recompensed when over the static and hum an angry, precisely modulated voice (our own man, Handy, for sure) cited him for using over the air not only an improper code but a highly impregnable one as well. To this Gode replied: "I read you loud and clear. This is Firebug One, signing off," and at that he ran down the aerial, slapped me on the back, and said, "Man, this fire is a *riot!*"

It was, and more. But it did not reach that section of the lake after all. Maybe the wind turned or maybe the civilian fighters or our platoons up there or a combination of them all, plus a lot of luck, turned it back. Near dusk the army whirlybirds returned, transporting more useful cargo this time than the high-ranking brass. Into the night our men stayed on in the woods combatting the blaze and that was probably just as well since most of them no longer had tents or sleeping-bags. In the morning, by copter, the men of Company C—"Charging Charlie!"—arrived. A week too late to be of much use. But the previous day, while the fire was at its peak, their CO and the Colonel had showed. That day the photographer snapped the picture we later saw in the paper, the one of which I have already spoken: of the Colonel and Captain John and our commander with the steel pot over his face and his hand limp in the palm of the Colonel who is congratulating him on a job well done (was that before the fire swept through our camp, ravaging so much equipment? I don't know). No mention had been made all that day of the Major's own small war and consequent death; and that morning, when his body was carried on the stretcher by the two medics and placed in the copter, no mention had been made. Only a handful of us had been there to see it. No mention made and very little, if any, thought given to it, but when I saw the picture in the paper later I wondered which had brought the Colonel to the scene: the new break of the fire, or the Major's embarrassing death?

858

The early part of that night Gode and I stayed around the mess hall. We had been told by the First Sergeant that around midnight we should take out and distribute coffee and cake to the troops. Near that hour Livesy woke up from wherever he was, and came, and we loaded the cake and a field mess can of coffee onto the jeep. It was cold outside but the jeep was warm and when we found the first bunch of men, the fifth platoon, we let three of the coldest of them sit inside while we filled the cups of those who wanted coffee and all of them did even those who did not like it and although we had no cream or sugar for those who drank it that way. Gode produced a warm beer from some place and I gave it to Gawthrop. He later told me it made him sick: somehow their platoon had missed out on the evening chow. They were all very cold and hungry and very grateful for the coffee and for once did not seem to begrudge us our soft headquarters job or the warm jeep. Gawthrop was angry because he was cold and the civilians under whom they were then working would not let them build a fire, but he was mostly angry at Sergeant Oliver who had gone down to the civilian camp and secured a bottle. He was in the cab of a truck now, Gawthrop said, drunk, passed out. "Do us a favor and kick hell out of him as you go by." We told him we would. We rode on, looking for other troopers and some we located and some we didn't but that is probably best too for we soon ran out of coffee. We stopped at the civilian camp and passed along the row of cats and trucks and dozers till we found Oliver asleep in the cab of one of these, and we opened both doors and turned off the heater and with a knife Gode sliced the stripes from both his sleeves and none of the time did he stir. On the way in we passed the fifth and they were disappointed that we had no more coffee but it revived them to hear of Oliver, and Gawthrop liked it when we passed him the sergeant's stripes. They asked us to see about getting them some food, and we went on back to camp. There Gamble found for us several boxes of C-rations and looted the 5-in-1 rations for fresh fruit which the men were all fond of, and gave us more coffee, and we shot off again in the jeep. The platoon had moved and it took us a long while to find them and in the process the jeep got stuck. Livesy shifted to four-wheel drive and in about twenty minutes of bucking this way and that we were free. We checked on Oliver before returning but although the doors of the cab were open as we had left them we saw him nowhere. We learned days later that he had accused the civilians of cutting off his stripes and that he had got in a fight which, to look at him, he lost, although he told it differently.

859

About three in the morning we wanted to go to the city of Kenai, fifty miles down the road, and Livesy drove us. He drives like a demon when men of his rank or under are in the jeep with him, and it seemed to take no time at all. Throughout the wild ride, our tires humming on the asphalt and crying as we rounded curves, we could look back and see the quick death lurch of flames, and at one point there was a red glare where the fire was backtracking. It was quite eerie and we were alone on the highway and we kept our thoughts to ourselves, listening and looking. Later, when we would pull out, the occasional shooting flames would still be there, and the puffs of smoke and popping, cracking wood—till finally the land lay still, burned over, burned out. And it would be many, many years till the rabbits and bear and caribou returned; and many more before the birds appeared. In that time except for the rare, lost land-rats, there would be nothing, the woods lifeless. And before any of these—before rat or caribou or rabbit or bird—there would be man.

"You know, the thing that confused me," I said, "is why he used the shovel. I mean . . . why didn't he use a bullet?"

"I would have used a bullet," Gode said.

"I would have too. Is that because we're Americans and he was Hungarian?"

"Not necessarily," Gode said, "But Christ, man, let's talk about something interesting for a change. What's Kenai like?"

"I don't know. I've never been there."

VI

At Kenai, Cook Inlet rides in, its foam curling around the cliffs of the town like a woman whose hiked skirt reveals a soiled lace-edged petticoat. Clumps of debris and ice float on the surface of the water like miniature barges, the current carrying them quickly along. Snow, too, banks over the shoreline like a thick froth at the mouth, and there is a rough wind, but the wind only whistles around corners and the slow barking of the waves points up, rather than abrogates, silence. That silence holds through the day although the town is active, its people many. They fish there too, but at four in the morning the town of Kenai is dead.

At four we arrived. Livesy put us out, told us he'd be back in the evening for us, and turned around and went back to camp. At four there was no place in Kenai which was open and, standing there at the end of what was called Chapel Road, that chapel to the front of us and below us some fifty feet the seesaw sing of the waves, we felt like two weary chroniclers stranded between epochs, what with so much of the architecture Russian in design, and beside these, the quick fly-by-night shacks peculiar to a hustling town. The streets were not paved, were without illumination, and narrow. In our walks through the town we saw two cafés put to permanent rest but at five we found one, its doors just opening. A mile down the road we learned there was another, the Aurora, in that area which until a year before had been called North Haven but which now was merely North Kenai, having been annexed. For kicks we walked that mile to the Aurora since the first café had no coffee yet because the pump had broken down which left her, the proprietress, a Mrs. Seeley, with no water for the coffee. The Aurora was empty but open and there we had as many cups of coffee

as we could hold for a dime and there we played the jukebox, selections by
Cal Yjader, Slim Whitman, Andy Williams, Charlie Parker, and Ezio Pinza.
Just beyond the Aurora the pavement ended and there was a rocky one-way
road to a remote Eskimo village, called (I believe the sign read) Nikishka
No. 2.

We returned to Kenai proper and walked again through the town
which was waking then, and at the Inlet Cafe the lady was still complaining
about the pump, but serving coffee in the meanwhile.

"City folks don't know what we go through up here," she said irritably.
"Why do you choose to stay if you don't like it?" Gode asked her, and some
time later she told us she didn't have the money to get out, but she did not
say it with conviction.

Across the street from the Inlet Cafe was the Kenai Commercial Company. Its main section was a high barn-like structure and there were two
shorter sections built on either side. It sat like a large bird with wings
outstretched. It was covered with white tin, rippled, in sheets two feet wide
and six high. While we were in the café, the daughter of the owner of Kenai
Commercial came in. Carol James was her name and she was a pretty blonde
who held her mouth so that her lips seemed square. She wore a black leotard,
slacks over it. Gode guessed that she was eighteen and said that she reminded
him of the girl in the book *Winesburg, Ohio*, who went away to college
leaving George Willard, unhappily, to his own pursuits, and who returned
to find everything changed, nothing in the town the way it had been before,
and a wall somehow thrown up between herself and George Willard. He
said I should read the book and I said I would. We heard Carol James tell the
lady that in the fall she would go away. We heard San Francisco mentioned. I
mentioned to Gode how nice it would be to be a civilian again that I could
go when and wherever I wished. He said nothing, watching the girl.

A man sitting over by the window, with a newspaper, asked: "Has
anyone heard if the road to Anchorage is clear? They say it's been snowing
for days on the pass."

"My husband started to Homer this morning," Mrs. Seeley said. "He
had to come back and take a plane." Homer, some fifty miles south of
Kenai, is reached by what in my state would be termed an "improved" road.
Meaning gravel. It meant much less here.

We had the feeling, sitting there, of . . . what? Waiting? Both young
and old seemed to be doing that, waiting. Gode said that sitting there he

felt much as he did when sitting in a café in his South. Of waiting. For something. He didn't know what. To blow up, maybe. Only here he felt some joy in waiting; there the signs: WE RESERVE THE RIGHT TO REFUSE SERVICE TO ANYONE—were a constant reminder to him that whatever joy there might have been he couldn't afford to feel.

"Did you see that sign as we entered Kenai?" he asked.

I had not noticed it.

"It read: POPULATION 65,000. And because I could see the entire town without shifting my eyes I didn't believe it. I looked back at the sign again and saw that it said population 65,000 all right, but that down in the corner they had painted: BY 1965. They hope to grow. Now if I saw that sign outside a Southern town I'd go up and cross off the three zeros. I wouldn't mind believing that 65 people could put up that WE REFUSE TO SERVE sign, but for 65,000 to do so—that's too much. You know what I mean?"

"Do 65,000 put it up?" I asked.

"They allow it," he said. "Amounts to the same thing."

I didn't look at him but gazed over at the window and what I could see of the Inlet from that window. On a small table there, the lady had placed three potted plants to catch the sun, and their green tubes were bent toward the glass, reaching for the sun.

Gode laughed.

"Look at my hands," he said.

His hands were covered with cuts, some deep, others slight. Some healing, others fresh.

"You get those in the fire?" I asked.

"Nope," he said.

"How?"

"Got them helping Kuimets file down his shovel tip."

"You helped him sharpen the damn thing!"

"Yep," he said, "nearly cut my own friggin wrist doing it."

"Why did you do it?"

He stared at me solemnly. Then he giggled. It was a dirty little-boy giggle which got on my nerves and I left the table and walked over to the window and looked down into the inlet. I had the notion then that there was something wrong with Gode, that maybe he did have a screw loose. I looked back at him and although no longer giggling his lips were set in the suggestion of a smile. He was watching me.

862

Two native boys drove up in a green Plymouth, left the car, and walked to the overlook and stood there a moment, their hands in the pockets of their seersucker jackets, gazing down into the water. Their hair was long and the wind blew it into their faces and sucked at their jackets. In one motion they wheeled about, marched to the car, and were gone. I went back to the table. A bare light bulb hung at each end of the room and I stared from one to the other. There was a socket for a third in the center but no bulb was screwed into it. It seemed rusted. The ceiling sank in the middle; the floor, on the other hand, warped, rose in the middle. Two women entered, one tall, bony, with freckles, her hair knobby also, the other short and stout—each of them the kind of woman who, if she scrubbed herself interminably would still rise from the tub looking unclean. "Don't bother with a menu bring me a tomato sandwich," the long one said, talking very fast, her voice brittle. "I'll take the same," the round one said.

"She has the kind of jaw I'd like to hit with a mallet," Gode said. The round one heard, glanced quickly away from Gode, not willing to admit to herself that he was speaking of her.

They sat at what we gathered to be the community table, the table where all the loose ends of the town sit, the large round table covered with oilcloth of striped green design, red roosters crowing, and spaced an inch or so apart, the dark stain of cigarette butts forgotten.

We heard church bells, only then realizing that the day was Sunday. From the window we could see the church, Russian in design, sitting out of the way in a corner of the village at the far loop of Chapel Road.

Mrs. Seeley sat at the table with the two ladies and watched them eat. Sometimes, her hand under her blouse, she scratched her back. Her brassiere straps, thin and slightly soiled, slid free of her shoulders, but she did not replace them. She propped her face in the palm of her hand. For no reason the door opened and, feeling a draft on his ankles, the man with the newspaper crossed to the door and closed it. He wore brogans and his black socks fell unevenly over his shoe tops because the elastic was broken.

"Did you hear?" Gode said. "They're going to give Kuimets a military funeral."

"How do you know?" I asked.

"That's what the word is," he said.

In the afternoon Livesy came for us. Nothing much had happened back at camp, he said. That morning someone had stolen forty pounds of hot dogs from the mess truck and there was some excitement generating from that. Mr. Wonderful had talked the Old Man into ordering chow held up till the dogs were returned or the thief found. After a while though the Captain had found his XO in the mess tent eating, chewed his ass, told him that he (Mr. Wonderful) was considered a member of the company and came under the same rules as the others and that he'd eat when the rest of them did. Webster had already eaten a good portion of his meal, however. Old Man had the cooks shake a leg and inside the hour the company was being fed. Indications were that the thief was in the first platoon. Only a handful from that platoon had bothered to come down for the late chow. First Sergeant had had Jones—Private Jones—on the carpet for a while, but learned nothing. "And, oh yeah!" Livesy said. "The two chaplains from post came in."

"What are they doing?" Gode asked.

"Beats shit outa me," Livesy said.

Gode asked him what truth there was in what he had been hearing.

"What's that?" Livesy asked.

"About you dreaming of oil filters and fuel pumps."

Livesy grinned.

It turned out the Catholic chaplain, a lieutenant, was holding confessional in the Old Man's tent; the Protestant chaplain, an elderly captain, was talking with the blond medic who intended studying for the ministry upon discharge but who in the meanwhile was boning up on Bishop's *Go with God* and Catherine Marshall's *Letters from Peter*. The poor Jews in the outfit were left to shift for themselves. Word was we'd be leaving for post in the morning.

No one apparently had missed us and we went into the mess tent and had coffee with Gamble and a few noncoms. The entire company was in relief now; what little there was to do, C Company was out doing it. The Catholic chaplain, a roly-poly, stubby-jolly beardless man half the length of Santa Claus who had the irksome habit of chuckling over anything he or anyone else said, was listening to confessions still, and, with a wink, Gode announced that he had to go see the father.

"You a Catholic?" I asked.

"No, man! Christian Scientist—remember?" He left.

The noncoms were talking about Jones. "Other day I asked Jones if he knew how to read a azimuth," one said. "Jones looked up to me and said, 'Sarge, I never had one in my hands.'" They all laughed. I did too. Sergeant Sprockmouth was there and he began bragging about being the only P-1 in the unit. That's proficiency pay, a recent army maneuver designed to add incentive to the enlisted man's rank and to lure more into making the army their career. On the practical side it meant, to Sergeant Sprockmouth, thirty more bucks a month. He was the only man in the unit who had taken the test and passed, and he was ribbing the others about this when we heard the roll of Gode's drums.

There was Gode in front of the CP, the confessional, banging away on the hijacked snares.

"What the hell you doing, soljar?" someone yelled. It was Mr. Wonderful. "Don't you know they having confession in that tent?"

Gode didn't let up, however; his ear bent to the skins, he tapped holy hell out of them. It struck me that in his own bizarre manner he was out to accomplish the same feat as the Major. Several men from the platoons had come down to see what was going on. We were all waiting to see what Webster would do.

Webster strutted up to him, gripped his shoulder, and spun him around but the rhythm of the snares didn't break. Then it did. It stopped entirely and Gode stared at Webster. "Yes sir?" I heard him say. Webster said something but I couldn't hear. The priest, the chaplain rather, appeared, barely stooping as he came from the tent. The expression on his fat face fluctuated between his customary chuckle and feigned seriousness. I strolled nearer to them.

"Just what the hell kind of soljar are you, Gode?" Mr. Wonderful asked.

Gode asked him what he meant by that. Perhaps if he clairfied the term.

With stronger emphasis on key words and considerable more vexation of spirit Webster repeated the question.

Gode grinned. "I don't know, sir," he said. "The same sexual congress of man and beast that produced you, I imagine, sir."

"Gode!" Webster said, "you're a smart ass and we don't have room for smart asses in this unit and I'm going to see that you get all that's coming to you."

"I'd appreciate that, sir."

Webster turned to one of the noncoms. "Sergeant," he said, "I want

865

you to see that this man is restricted to his platoon area till I tell you different."

"Yes sir," the sergeant said.

Webster apparently did not realize Gode was with his own headquarters platoon.

That night the officers went to a party at one of the civilian homes on the lake, the noncoms had theirs at a bar down the highway, and Gode continued his. He ran into Mr. Wonderful once again that night as the officer was brushing his boots before leaving for the party, and Webster, hurling the brush to the earth, asked him what the hell he was doing out of his platoon area. Gode explained, that he was in it. Webster said he'd remedy that in the morning. He called me over and told me to report it to him if Gode left the headquarters area. Since I held the opinion that head-quarters area was synonymous with company area, I didn't think it necessary to remember to tell about it, when later in the evening Gode walked down to the lake. The demarcations were not too plain anyway; aside from the Old Man's and a few others, all the tents had been destroyed by the fire, and there were lean-tos scattered all over. Gode had turned one other trick that afternoon. "After waking him with my drums," he had said, "I professed to being Catholic, and went in and told the father how I killed Kuimets."

VII

It was after he told me this that, chuckling in imitation of the chaplain, he went down to the lake. It seemed he meant to remain there and in that time I considered what he had said, wondering if possibly he had killed the Major, if so, why—but I knew all along he had not. He had not taken the shovel and sliced the man's wrist. Of that I was sure. I was not certain what else he had done.

Since no one had told me where to sleep and because I didn't want to bother with constructing a lean-to, I went down to the lake and joined him. There was a shot of moonlight over the water like a runway, and with night the smell of the burn was more noticeable. That night I talked to Gode a long time. I listened, rather. He talked.

He had gone to college, he said, quit, and gone again and quit again, followed this course till finally what to do with his time was a question taken out of his hands: he was drafted. He had been planning to drive to California with a girl about that same date, they had planned to spend the entire summer together, but BANG! the draft notice. So that made him angry. For kicks he had been growing a beard, the only man in town who sported one. He reported for induction wearing the beard. The clerk, the same clerk, was angry with him, felt he showed up with it simply to spite her, and told him to go home and shave. He couldn't go into the army looking like the wolf man. Go home! she told him.

"Is there time?" he asked.

"Yes, I'll hold the bus for you."

He laughed, however. It was the first time he'd laughed since receiving the notice and he said he said to himself right then: "Gode, old boy, if nothing else, these next two years are going to be interesting."

He stroked his beard and told her, no, he thought he'd keep it long as he could. She appealed to him. When that didn't work she almost cried. She didn't take her eyes off him as he boarded the bus that would take them to the induction station. Flat-top, beard, and motorcycle boots, and the small satchel they had suggested he bring along. She lit a cigarette and took drags off it and drank a Coke while he and the others boarded the bus and all in all he says it was probably noon before her nerves calmed down enough for her to do any work.

There were forty-seven people on the bus and forty-three of these were Negro, for Gode came from a thickly populated Negro section. They were already having a ball and had a lot more when he got on, out of his beard, and the four white boys did not join in it but sat sullenly up front in the two forward seats, two of them engrossed in comic books, the other two staring out the window or at the bus driver's neck.

Gode sat in the rear, in the very rear on the seat which went all the way across. The bus was an old Trailways coach, and he squeezed in among the four Negro boys sitting there, one of whom looked to be fourteen and obviously had never seen a beard before. Not a beard blond as his, for Gode had taken the trouble to apply peroxide, lemon juice, and sun to his hair. He had brought a Pepsi on board with him and as there were several others with carbonated drinks it didn't take very long to work up a friendly fizz battle. They shook them, aimed them, the pressure pushed at their thumbs and the juice shot into somebody's face. The acid all lost, they drank the remainder, but then someone remembered his foam-shave and there was another battle. The driver stopped the bus. He crouched at the head of the aisle and stood surveying them. He said, "YOU!" pointing to Gode, "get up here where you belong."

Gode was having too much fun to get angry. "Mister, we got a date in the capital, maybe we better get rolling, huh? Sure would hate to miss it." The others confirmed this. They'd hate to miss it too.

The driver sat back down and cranked the bus. He was a nice sort whose heart didn't seem to care where Gode sat anyway. All he was worried about was their messing up the bus. The ride was relatively quiet after that. Gode said he sat in the back and spelled out with the Negroes the signs at the front of the bus over the windshield: C-O-L . . .

COLORED PASSENGERS SEAT FROM REAR ONLY

and nobody got mad but the four white boys up front. The little guy pulled Gode's beard and Gode rubbed the guy's noggin with his knuckles. As they entered the city things really got quiet, almost if an edict to that effect had suddenly been passed. "It hit us then," Gode said, "that the sonuvabitches good as had us. We wouldn't be coming back for two goddam years." Occasionally some stud would speak up to point out a nice set of legs on the sidewalk. "Bo Peep, you gonna miss that stuff!" one of the guys on the back seat said. He might have been telling of a broken leg such was the torment in his voice. But there were no jokes.

They were assembled in a column of two outside the bus by the sergeant who met it, and led into the induction-reception station.

Many were there simply for their physical. Gode hadn't realized that and he wasn't sure they had either. At each department during the physical they wanted to know why the beard. It seemed to get under their skin. He gave a different answer each time. "I'm Santa Claus," he told one. "I'm U. Simpson Grant," he told another. "I'm Christ." "I'm beat." He passed himself in a mirror once. He didn't believe it, went back to look again. He laughed himself. He wore only his jockey shorts, the motorcycle boots, and the beard. He couldn't follow the arrows because in every hallway they were pointing both ways, one set green, the other red, and he followed a long black arrow that took him eventually into a typing pool. He didn't know whether he was supposed to be there or not. There were WACS and WAVES at the typewriters and one by one the typing halted as the girls (girls?) stared at him but then a male sergeant yelled, "SOL-JA GET THE HELL OUTA HERE." That was a mistake because as Gode told him he was not yet a sol-ja. At that moment he stood there, a civilian. He asked the sergeant how he liked that but the sergeant was already going to get an officer. "And if I was," Gode called, "I certainly as hell wouldn't claim it in public." He left soon enough though. It seemed to him that all the girls were staring at him and he wouldn't have minded if they'd been staring at his beard or his boots but they were looking at his jock. A few minutes later, on the green line again, he saw that same sergeant pointing him out to the PFC who sat at the table through which he was next to be processed. Nothing came of it, however. The PFC, it turned out, was US also, a draftee like himself.

Gode talked to the psychiatrist finally and led him a merry chase, most of the questions and answers having to do with the beard, but in the end he passed. He was made to join a group in a room where there was at one end a raised platform, flags to either side. One was the American flag but what the other was he didn't know. Brass eagles sat at the top of both the poles. Others entered, took a seat, and waited. When the room was full an officer came in, followed by two noncoms. "You will please stand," one of the noncoms said. Gode had not seen the officer, a major, until then. "Raise your right hand and repeat after me," he said. His face was stern, but blank; he looked like a man who considered his position secure. Gode had the impression that this, now, was all he did.

Gode liked the fact that they had had no opening speeches, no fanfare before the taking of the Oath of Allegiance, but to repeat it after the officer was distasteful to him. He had the queer feeling he was back in the third grade again. He stared with hard eyes at the major and did not open his mouth once. His hand was raised but that was as far as he would go. He gazed at that hand and it seemed that involuntarily the fingers were curling downward. It passed through his mind that perhaps so long as he did not take the oath he was not officially in the army. It struck him that, with the oath taken, he was sunk, done in, finished. But it was more than the army, it was the oath itself which bothered him. The idea of there being a necessity for it, and how such silly words were considered a legal bind. An hour or so before, they had given him a form, a double sheet, to sign, and while none of the others looked twice at it, he read it through: the long list of organizations held to be subversive. To this he was supposed to sign his name: had he ever been a member of, or contributed to, these organizations?

869

He, refusing to sign it, had folded the form into a neat square and placed it in his pocket. He had no argument against being a good American. But what made a good American? That was his question then. That was his question now, in taking (or not taking) the oath. All through it he didn't say a word; before it was over, his hand was by his side. The guy beside him, a big Negro, kept glancing at him. "Man," he said, "you can't fightum you gotta joinum, how come you didn't op'm yo mouf?"

Gode grinned and said: "I'll have a beer with you at Fort Jackson."

As indeed he had.

They were on the same bus to Jackson and, subsequently, in the same training company, although in different platoons. "And the funny thing," Gode said, "is that this guy never forgot how I didn't repeat the oath and every day he was reaming my ass because of it and telling me I ought to be ashamed of myself, and you know, if I had been in that guy's place I would not only have refused to take the goddam oath I would have spat on the friggin thing. And you know what else? I still write to that sonuvabitch an he's in Germany now and the Germans just love his ass but that crazy sonuvabitch can't wait to get back home. To the South. He's just like Kuimets in that respect."

"What do you mean?"

"The sonuvabitch is in a split to die. He wants to murder his friggin self."

I was getting sleepy. Neither of us had got much sleep the night before. Gode, when we were loading the company gear onto the trucks as the fire came down, had managed to include our rucksacks, and he went up to the CP to look for them. He returned in a moment. We had decided we could do worse than sleep by the lake, and we crawled into our sleeping-bags.

Gode, I learned, when he's sleepy likes to talk. There were times when I could not tell if he was talking to me or to himself. The rumor had been verified. We were to return to post in the morning. "It'll be nice to get back to civilization," I said.

"Uh-huh."

"What did you say?"

"I said uh-huh."

"What do you mean by that?" I asked. There was a cold wind off the lake and I zippered the bag so that only my nose was outside. Busy with that, Gode's first words escaped me, but, until I fell asleep, I listened to him.

... they become too real, he was saying. They tear you up. They become too complex and their complexity gets in your craw or either you're too complex, anyway, either way you want to wring your own neck or somebody wants to do it for you. They raise questions and pose situations and turn on lights and flip them off and they ... are impossible to bring to any honed, cutting edge such as we achieved with his shovel ... you couldn't chisel a man out of a piece of clay and that's what Kuimets wanted to do ... you see, truth is, Hite, I wanted that mother to die. You might say I have a Hedda Gabler complex. On the other hand I had me one pure lamb and he was my sacrifice and what did it matter since that mother wanted to be pushed just as those friggin men followed me down the road that day when I had the drums, like they thought I was the pied piper or some other Hitler.

... Now there's a thought! you know, buddy, I was just a kid and not much of one at that when Hitler ran his boxcars down the slaughter tracks and I don't say that this had made much impression on me when I stop to consider that every day there are twice that many betrayed six times over out of whatever it is inside of us that longs for it to happen to us or compels us to do it to the others. We're all postmen, man, so I mean there's the stamp, let's cancel it.

871

... We're screwed, blued, and tattooed, man, and that's from the beginning. We're sealed in walls, man, alive, like Poe's favorite slob. We are and if we try to move there goes the oxygen and if we try to knock our way loose there goes our arm or somebody else's.

Give a man a horse he can ride: you know that song? Well, Jack, there ain't no such animal. Get one you can ride and he don't go no place.

Screwed, blued, and tattooed, man, that's the theme ... the horse now he screwed himself when he dropped his claws for hooves. When did you screw yourself last, Mr. Wonderful, you great big bad man? ... You know, Hite, in basic I asked or rather I said to this officer once: 'Sir, I just recently read in a magazine a statement to the effect that military life postpones all adult responsibility and that the male menopause runs concurrent to the time of one's military service. What would you care to say to that, Sir?' Know what he said? He said just what Webster said to me today: 'Gode, you are a smart ass and there's no room for smart asses in this unit and I'm gonna see that you get what's due you.'

. . . Screwed, blued, and tattooed! Yes sir, Jack.

I mean, let's face it, man, after so many generations it gets down to this: that nobody is worth a crap . . . I mean, they may baptize them, man, but they sure as hell don't sterilize them. We're burned out, man, just like old Kenai. It's time for a new era, a new age, and I don't mean one of these friggin ages named after some goddam scientific creation by some mechanical goddam man . . . we're just no good, brother. We got that core that's rotten and a lot of good stuff may swim around it but make no mistake about it (make it and you're dead) the order of the day is "Screw Your Buddy." Next year is "Screw Santa," and the next is "Fuck a Duck" and it's anyone's guess after that . . .

872   . . . But take Kuimets now, that mother managed to transcend it somehow. I mean, that corn about how noble it is to die for your neighbor is admittedly crap but hell the way I see it Kuimets was better by one than Christ even because why'd he lay down his life—Kuimets, I mean? For nothing, man. For nobody. Because he was driven to understand that nobody was worth it. His trouble came when he couldn't decide whether he was worth it . . .

. . . I had to convince him there. I had to give him the push. And I tell you boy that doesn't make me any worse and it certainly as hell doesn't make me any better but like old Hedda it makes me. Period. The fact that I laugh about it redeems me. I tell you boy (laughing) we come into this old world from every angle and end and it's only fitting we go out the same way: screwed, blued, and tattooed . . .

. . . the Major falls in a lake when the ice beneath him breaks but he rises from the water chilled but grinning because he can understand the humor in a man falling through ice which supports—is supporting as he falls— men twice his weight and more. S'pose he climbed out with no expression at all . . . now again this final time something cracked between I mean under Kuimets that was not ice I hope since he wasn't on any friggin lake this time but from which he could not pull himself because this time he was in too deep ... too deep! That here again the joke was on him, the difference being that this time he wasn't laughing, couldn't. Hell, he was in too deep ... is it a comic thing, I wonder? I mean, to feel that you are sinking although you see your shoes right there where they are supposed to be; yet your body is descending down through those soles and heels till you have only the strings to clutch, and then finally, darkness, as you pull those shoes down over your head like a shroud.

Significant for who!

I mean, falling through a lake where heavier men have walked—are walking at the time—was simple then; nobody pushing. Question: who is pushing who? Answer: he is! VOICE OUT OF THE PAST, OF AN IRRITATED REAPER: Well if he's pushing you you're pushing him so both of you go on down and be quick and quiet about it I got trouble enough on my hands.

Yes sir!

... called out to the company formation that they may march to the firing line one lone private takes his proper place in the ranks wearing however one slightly wrinkled highly smelly OD colored poncho. Because, like he said, it was raining ...

873

... Did you hear the story of the woman who was 82 years old? I mean she could have been 47 or 24 or even three-and-a-half that doesn't matter, what matters is that that sonuvabitch walking down the other side of the street was lonely. That's right, he as the story goes, was lonely and that's all that matters, he was lonely. So he passes her on the other side of the street and tips his hat and says how do you do? She not only doesn't see him, she doesn't hear him or smell him and again that's not because she was eighty-two. Nothing wrong with her senses. Now important too is the fact that this man couldn't remember a time when he had not been lonely. He couldn't remember a time anybody eighty-two or forty-seven or twenty-four and very rarely three-and-a-half—those that age shot at him with their pistols—had heard or seen him though true enough they could smell him all right if he got dirty enough. End of story: he either raped the old bush or he walked on. What should he have done? He should have raped the hell out of her. If the old bag can't talk she at least knows sign language.

. . . Screwed, blued, and tattoed, both of um.
I mean it's those two goddam caribou all over again.

. . . A woman, jilted, goes for a swim in the Noose River and doesn't come back. A man, scorned, takes a fist and breaks a jaw.
All signs of the times, obvious as billboards but not so pretty.

. . . I wonder sometimes if the friggin bat asleep from a limb ever wakes and says to himself: Christ, but I've seen prettier bastards! What the hell you doing hanging upside down like that, anyway? What are you: a fool? I wonder. And does he answer: But, hell, man, I feel OK.
Isn't it of basic significance that, say, art is so abstract today and that they the artists will say: No, man, it's not abstract at all, that's just the way it is man—life! And you're looking, yes sir, at a mirror? Or is that only a fragment of the grand play, the royal dream, the big hoax, the "all-right-America-you-might-not-make-it-in-practice-but-BY-GOD-YOU-GOT-IT-IN-PRINCIPLE!" . . . take this artist I know, Hite; all his canvases show muddled heads and all his sculpture looks like some pig freed from a medieval torture rack. Why? I ask him. Because, he says, man, I'm trying to wiggle into a meaning. Trying to shake that old core, loose, man, I mean that vicious core. And because I'm in pain, man. Because I don't know who told me but the boat left this morning and, man, I AIN'T ON IT AND I DON'T KNOW HOW TO SWIM! Because, man, I'm standing on the pier alone. I'm standing on it AND I'M ALONE! And not only alone but bored too and restless and I'm this way when I wake up and when I go to bed and whether I'm with my best girl or my ninety-seven-year-old aunt. Because my dinner tastes like cold fish and because there's someofyesterday's in my craw and I want to throw up, Jack. Because I'm lonely and I don't care about no body. And if I work twenty hours a day getting a man's wrist out of a piece of wood or metal to look just so it ain't because I love art or man that much and you can believe that, cat. I make a living painting portraits at three dollars a throw. Dig this, man: that the way it hits me we only feel compassion for a gal when we're in love with her and there ought to be more since that's over just like a trip to the bed. It don't last, man. And why not? There ain't no grooves it knows to follow, no needles that know the way, no two stereo speakers to give you that good sound in the middle of the room. The only thing that lasts is the sentiment for it, the

wish to hold it and make it last. Man, I tell you we ought to have built-in safe-deposit boxes to hold it and a key for when we need it the way we have for our cash and jewels and the way we got a key for them when we want um. Oh, man! it's sad, but that's the only scene I can make. That's the only score I've made.

. . . well, good night, Hite, and HO! HO!

I mean it's those two caribou out in the woods again, man, and now they're just playing: stomping about, snorting, and bluffing one another with their bleats and flash of horn as much as to say: I'm mightier than you; I'm the Big Cheese! But who's to say their antlers are not to lock a final time and hold them together in their death struggle till the fire plunges down around them a final time and they sink to their knees and don't get up again.

. . . yes sir, Kuimets, they gonna give you a military funeral! Ain't that the living end?"

875

Meyer Schapiro

Three Texts by Diderot, Galiani and Lichtenberg

The three writings that are published here I translated separately at *different times without a thought of their connection. If it occurs to me now to bring them together, it is because they share a critical way of thinking in which the point is made by witty fabulation. They possess to a high degree the qualities of intelligence, affability and humor that gave a characteristic charm to the converse of intellectuals in the 18th century. Of course the problems posed in these texts are hardly resolved by them; the issues are still with us.*

877

Diderot: *Wit and Common Sense*

In Wit and Common Sense *the story of Montesquieu and Chesterfield as protagonists of French esprit and plodding English common sense is taken from Diderot's letters to Sophie Volland. It is a body of love letters unequalled in verve and spontaneity; the presence of the writer in the rhythm of his words is sometimes magical. The contrast of wit and common sense, which is dramatized in Diderot's little text, has lost some of its sharpness since that time. If we shift from esprit to reason—which is not the same as esprit, though comprised within it—we may note that reason has acquired in our own pragmatistic age a still more abstract character through the rigorous formalizations of logic, but also paradoxes and doubts. It has been observed, too, that modern logical studies owe much more to the Germans and English—traditionally monsters of unreason and common sense—than to the rationality of French esprit.*

The President de Montesquieu and Lord Chesterfield met while traveling in Italy. These two men were made for each other and were soon good friends. They were always disputing about the superiority of their own nations. The Lord conceded to the President that the French had more wit (*esprit*) than the English, but on the other hand, they had no common sense. The President agreed, but insisted that there was no comparison between wit and common sense. After several days of arguing they found themselves in Venice. The President was out a great deal, he went everywhere, he saw everything, he inquired and conversed, and in the evening recorded the observations he had made.

An hour or two after he returned, while he was occupied with his notes, an unknown person was announced. It was a rather poorly dressed Frenchman who said to Montesquieu: "Monsieur, I'm a compatriot of yours. I have been living here for twenty years; but I have always kept my friendship for the French, and I have at times been only too happy on finding an occasion to serve them, as with you today. One can do anything in this country except mix in the affairs of State. One careless word about the government will cost a man his head, and you have already uttered over a thousand. The State Inquisitors have their eyes on you, they are spying on you, you are being followed everywhere you go, they know all your plans, they suspect that you are writing. I know for certain that they are going to visit you, today perhaps or tomorrow. Take note, Monsieur, if you have in fact been writing, that a single innocent line, misinterpreted, will cost you your life. That is all I have to say. I have the honor to salute you. If you meet me in the street, I ask you, as the full reward for a service which I think has some importance, not to recognize me; and if by chance I have come too late to save you and you are arrested, please do not denounce me."

Having said this, the man disappeared and left the President de Montesquieu in the greatest consternation. His first reaction was to go quickly to his desk, to take the papers and throw them into the fire. This was hardly done when Lord Chesterfield returned. He recognized at once how terribly troubled was his friend; he asked what had happened to him. The President recounted the visit he had just had, the burning of his papers and the order he had given that a place in the stage-coach be ready for him at three in the morning. For he planned to depart without delaying a day when even a minute's delay might be fatal. Lord Chesterfield listened quietly and said: "You are right, my dear President, but let's stop for a moment and together examine your adventure with a cool head."—"You are joking", said the President, "It's impossible for my head to be cool when it hangs by a thread."—"But who is this man that so generously exposed himself to the greatest danger in order to save you? That isn't natural. He may be as French as you like, patriotic feeling doesn't impel one to these dangerous moves, and especially for the sake of an unknown person. Is that man a friend of yours?" "No."—"He was poorly dressed?"—"Yes, very poorly."—"Did he ask you for money, a small sum as the price for his advice?" "Oh! not a dime"—"That's still more extraordinary. But how does he know all the things he told you?"—"By God, I don't know . . ." "From the Inquisitors themselves? But apart from the fact that the Council here is the most secretive in the whole world, your man is hardly someone who could come near it."—"But maybe he's one of the spies they employ".—"Hardly! Would they take a foreigner as a spy, and would this spy be dressed as a beggar if he were in this vile but well-paid profession? And would this spy betray his masters for you at the risk of being strangled? Suppose they arrest you and you give him away, or suppose you escape and they suspect that he warned you! The whole story is a song and dance, my friend."—"But what's it all about then?"—"I'm thinking, but I don't get it."

After both had exhausted all possible conjectures, and the President insisted on getting away as quickly as possible, as the safest step, Lord Chesterfield, after having paced the room for a while and rubbed his brow, suddenly stopped and said: "Wait, my friend, I have an idea . . . But suppose . . . by chance . . . this man . . ." "Yes, well, this man?"—"Suppose this man . . . yes, that is possible, it is so, I'm sure of it."—"But who is this man? If you know, tell me, quick."—"Do I know him! Oh, of course I know now who he is . . . Maybe this man was sent to you by . . ." "Please, I beg you!"— "By a clever man, a certain Lord Chesterfield who wanted to prove to you by an experiment that one ounce of common sense is worth more than a hundred pounds of *esprit* (wit), for with common sense . . ."—"Oh! You wretch," cried the President, what a trick you've played on me! My manuscript! My manuscript which I burned!"

The President could never forgive the Lord this joke. He had ordered that his carriage be ready, he got in and left that same night, without saying goodby to his fellow traveller.

Diderot added: If it were me, I would have thrown myself on his neck, I would have kissed him a hundred times, and I would have told him: "Oh, my friend, you have proved to me that there are in England men of wit, and I will perhaps find the occasion some other time to prove to you that there are in France people with common sense."

Abbé Galiani: *Genius and Method*

The Abbé Galiani, while greatly appreciated in his time as an economist—he wrote a famous treatise "On Money", which was often quoted by Marx—is the least known of the three authors today. He was the secretary of the ambassador of the kingdom of Naples in Paris and a welcome figure in the intellectual salons for his wit and the liveliness of his exceptionally curious and original mind. Among his writings are astonishing essays and aperçus on language, musicality, folklore, architecture, religion, institutions and childhood. His fable of the Ass, the Cuckoo and the Nightingale—Genius and Method—is preserved in a letter from Diderot to Sophie Volland. Our trust in Diderot's mimetic skill encourages us to suppose that his text transmits the much admired gift of pantomime in the Abbé's own talk.

There was an argument between Grimm and Le Roy about the genius that creates and the method that produces order. Grimm detests method; according to him it's the pedantry of literature. Those who know only how to arrange would do as well by keeping quiet; those who can learn only from what has been arranged, would do just as well if they remained ignorant.

LE ROY: But it's method that brings out what's good.
GRIMM: And that spoils things.
LE ROY: Without it one wouldn't profit by anything.
GRIMM: Only by tiring oneself, and it wouldn't be the better for it. Why is it necessary that so many people should know something beside their own jobs?

They said many other things that I'm not reporting, and they would still be talking if the Abbé Galiani hadn't interrupted them as follows:

My friends, I remember a fable; listen to it. It will be a little long, perhaps, but it won't bore you.

One day, in the depths of a forest, there arose a debate between the nightingale and the cuckoo about singing. Each one prized his own talent. "What bird", said the cuckoo, "sings as easily, as simply, as naturally, as rhythmically, as I do?"—"What bird," said the nightingale, "has a lighter, a sweeter, a more varied, more striking, more touching song than my own?"

The cuckoo: "I say very little; but it has substance and order, and one remembers it."

The nightingale: "I love to talk; but I have always something new to say, and I'm never tiresome. I enchant the woods; the cuckoo makes them sad. He is so attached to his mother's lesson that he won't dare risk a tune that he hasn't taken from her. As for me, I recognize no master. I play with the rules. It is especially when I violate them that I'm admired. How can one compare his tiresome method and my happy flights!"

The cuckoo tried several times to interrupt the nightingale. But nightingales sing all the time and never listen; that is one of their little faults. Ours, carried along by his ideas, pursued them swiftly, without bothering about his rival's reply. However, after some debate they agreed to leave it to the judgment of a third animal. But where could one find this competent and impartial third party to judge them? It takes much trouble to find a good judge. They went looking for one everywhere.

They were crossing a meadow when they saw an ass, a very grave and solemn one. Since that species was created, none had borne such long ears. "Ah," said the cuckoo on seeing them, "we are really lucky; our argument is a matter of the ear; there is our judge; God made him precisely for us."

The ass was browsing. He hardly imagined that one day he would be a judge of music. But Providence finds amusement in many other things. Our two birds swoop down before him, compliment him on his gravity and his judgment, expound to him the subject of their debate, and very humbly implore him to hear them and decide.

But the ass, scarcely turning his big head and not losing a single bite, made a sign to them with his ears that he was hungry and that he wasn't sitting in court that day. The birds insist; the ass continues to browse. In browsing his appetite is allayed. There were some trees planted at the edge of the field. "All right," he said to them," you go there: I'll come along; you'll sing, I'll digest, I'll listen to you, and then I'll tell you my opinion." The birds flew off very swiftly and perched on a tree; the donkey followed them with the air and pace of a presiding judge in cap and gown crossing the chambers of a courthouse: he arrives, he stretches himself out on the ground and he says: "Begin, the court is listening to you." It's he who is the whole court.

The cuckoo says: "My Lord, don't miss a single word of my argument; note well the character of my song, and above all deign to observe its artifice and method." Then strutting and clapping his wings repeatedly, he sang: "Cuckoo, cuckoo, cuckookoo, cuckookoo, cuckoo, cuckookoo." After having combined this in all possible ways, he was silent.

The nightingale, without any preamble, deploys his voice, soars in the most daring modulations, sends forth the newest and most subtle songs; they are breathless cadences and notes; at times one heard the sounds descending and murmuring in the hollow of his throat like the water of a brook muffled and lost among the pebbles, at times one heard them rising, swelling little by little, filling the air and floating there as if suspended. It was in turn sweet, light, brilliant, pathetic; and whatever character is assumed it was expressive; but his song was not for everyone.

Carried away by his enthusiasm, he would still be singing; but the ass, who had yawned several times, stopped him and said: "I surmise that all you have sung is very beautiful, but I don't get it; it seems to me bizarre, mixed up, incoherent. You know more than your rival, perhaps; but he is more methodical than you are, and as for me, I'm for method."

And the Abbé, addressing M. Le Roy, and pointing to Grimm with his finger, said: "He is the nightingale and you are the cuckoo, and as for me, I'm the ass who decides in your favor."

(Diderot: from *Lettres à Sophie Volland*)

882

Lichtenberg: *A Dream*

In "A Dream", Lichtenberg (1742–1799), a professor of physics at Göttingen during the Age of Reason, could entertain the idea of science as a destructive force. He was able to conceive then the folly of a scientism seeking to apply a laboratory method to all objects of knowledge—even a chemical analysis of meaning. Lichtenberg was also a keen critic of language and physiognomics. He observed that in all languages the verb "to be" is irregular; hence metaphysics. In a delicious essay "On Tails", mocking the pretensions of the new science of physiognomonics, he offered the reader, as an exercise in the interpretation of expressive signs, a series of drawings of dogs' tails and asked: If Goethe had had a tail, which one of these would it be? This hunchbacked physicist was a great lover of the theater and especially of the English stage.

It seemed to me that I was floating far above the earth, towards a transfigured old man whose appearance filled me with something higher than mere respect. Whenever I opened my eyes towards him, I was penetrated by an irresistible feeling of reverence and trust, and I was about to prostrate myself before him, when a voice of indescribable softness addressed me. "You love to investigate nature," he said, "here is something that will interest you." As he said this, he handed me a bluish-green sphere, somewhat gray in places, which he held between his index finger and thumb. It seemed to me about an inch in diameter. "Take this mineral," he continued, "test it, and tell me what you have found. Behind you is everything that you need for such investigations, as complete as possible; I shall go off, and return when you are through."

883

Looking around, I observed a fine room with instruments of every kind, which seemed less strange to me in the dream than afterwards when I awoke. I felt as if I had been there often, and I found what I needed as readily as if I had prepared everything in advance myself. I inspected, felt, and smelled the sphere several times, I shook it and listened to it as if it were an eagle stone; I brought it to my tongue; with a clean cloth, I wiped off the dust and a kind of barely perceptible coating; I heated it and rubbed it on my sleeve for its electricity; I tested it on steel, on glass, and on magnets, and determined its specific weight, which was, if I remember right, between four and five.

From all these tests I could see that the material was worth rather little, and I remember, too, that as a child I had bought spheres of the same kind, or at least not very different, at a price of three for a penny at the Frankfurt fair. I turned now to the chemical tests and determined the components of the whole in percentages. Here again, I found nothing special. There was some clay, approximately the same amount of lime, but much more silica, and finally some iron and salt and an unknown substance, which had many characteristics of known substances but nothing peculiar to itself. I was sorry that I did not know the name of the old man, I would have liked to name the substance after him on the label in order to pay him a compliment. I must have been very exact in my investigation, for when I added up all that I had found, it came to exactly a hundred. I had no sooner made the last stroke in my calculations, than the old man stepped into the room. He took the paper and read it with a gentle, almost imperceptible, smile, and turning to me with a glance of celestial benevolence mingled with seriousness, he asked: "Do you know, O mortal, what it was that you tested?" His whole tone and manner of speaking clearly announced a supernatural being.

"No! Immortal one," I cried, prostrating myself before him, "I do not know." For I dared no longer allude to my slip of paper.

The Spirit: Know then that it was, on a reduced scale, nothing less than—the whole earth.

I: The earth? Great God eternal! And the ocean and all its inhabitants, where are they then?

The Spirit: They are in your napkin where you have wiped them off.

I: Oh! And the atmosphere and all the splendor of the continents?

He: The atmosphere? That must still be in the dish with the distilled water; and your beautiful continents? How can you ask that? It is all an imperceptible dust; some of it is still on your sleeve.

I: But I found not even the smallest trace of silver and gold that keep the world going.

He: Too bad. I see I must help you. Know that with your flame you have split off the whole of Switzerland and Savoy and the most beautiful part of Sicily, and you have ruined completely and overturned a large piece of Africa over a thousand miles square, from the Mediterranean to the table lands. And there on that glass—oh! they have just slipped off—lay the Cordilleras, and what you saw a moment ago in cutting the glass was Mount Chimborazo.

I understood and was silent. I would have given nine tenths of the rest of my life, if I could have restored the earth that my chemistry had destroyed. To ask for another one, in the face of such a being, that I could not do. The wiser and nobler the donor, the harder it is for a poor sensitive man to ask for a gift a second time, as soon as he realizes that perhaps he has not made the best use of the first. But a new request, I thought, this transfigured paternal face will surely allow me: "O great immortal being!" I cried, "What thou art I know; it is in thy power; enlarge for me a mustard seed to the thickness of the whole earth and allow me to investigate its ridges and strata until the germ develops, merely to see it transform." "What good would that do you?" was the answer. "On your planet you already have a granule, enlarged for you to the thickness of the earth. Test it. Not before your own transformation shall you come to the other side of the curtain, whether you seek it on this or another granule of creation. Take this purse, test what is in it and tell me what you have found." In departing he added half jesting: "Understand me right; test it chemically, my son; I shall be away longer this time."

How happy I was when once again I had something to investigate, for now, I thought, I will be more careful. Be careful, I said to myself, it will shine, and if it shines, it is surely the sun or a fixed star. When I opened the purse, I found, to my great surprise, a book in a rather plain dull binding. Its language and script were none of those which are known to me, and although the characters of many lines, when seen casually, appeared to be legible, they turned out, when looked at more closely, no more so than the most complicated letters. All that I could read were the words on the title page: Test this, my son, but chemically, and tell me what you have found.

I must confess that I felt perplexed in my grand laboratory. How, I asked myself, how shall I investigate the content of a book *chemically*? The content of a book is *its sense*, and chemical analysis here would be the analysis of rags and printer's ink. When I had reflected for a moment, my mind suddenly brightened, and with the light came an irrepressible blush of shame. Oh! I cried, louder and louder, I understand, I understand! Forgive me, Immortal Being, O forgive me! I grasp thy kind reproof; I thank the Eternal One that I can understand it!

I was indescribably moved, and I awoke.

Christopher Middleton, TEXT
Christoph Meckel, ILLUSTRATIONS

Pocket Elephants

I

Today we can say, with pride, that our revolution has achieved its aim. We have destroyed an economic system based on the creation of needs. We have created a new system. What is the essence of this new system? Our new system is one which fosters the need to create. To create according to one's need; to acquire according to one's need; to sleep according to one's need. All primary human questions. We have come a long way from the times when we were told what to need, and believed what we were told; when manipulators sold our needs to us; when the objects of our needs lasted, at most, for two years and then had to be replaced, so that the system could flourish for the benefit of the manipulators. We have crushed the demon surplus. We have destroyed the spectre of excess. We have the means to determine, once and for all, the nature of need. We have the means to create verifiable need-objects which last not two years but ten.

Christopher Middleton, Christoph Meckel

890   II

Now there is this question of the pocket elephants. Before our revolution, whoever would have thought of them? The pocket elephant is an elephant which fits into a pocket. There are many pocket elephants to be had, and certainly a need for them exists.

892

III   893

Now that people are acquiring coupons for pocket elephants, according to their need, those among us who have the means to create verifiable need-objects are already exploring methods for the creation of pockets to accommodate pocket elephants. That is the situation, which, granted the success of our revolution, is certain to have an assuring outcome.

Christopher Middleton, Christoph Meckel

894 IV

The creators of verifiable need-objects have succeeded in creating a pocket sufficiently ample to accommodate the pocket elephant.

896

V

The pocket elephant pocket has no material disadvantages save one: it necessitates the creation of new and more ample trousers for the accommodation of such pockets. This is an interesting situation, if one considers that both pockets in such trousers will have to be of a certain magnitude: one normal pocket and one pocket elephant pocket would assuredly introduce an imbalance into the posture of the person who needs a pocket elephant.

Christopher Middleton, Christoph Meckel

898 VI

The trousers created according to the need of the elephant pocketers are of a magnitude which exceeds the normal proportions of man, even of the men who are making our revolution. However, these men are stubbornly carrying on the fight, from inside their immense pocket elephant pocket trousers.

900

VII

The situation has not changed, for there is still a chance that smaller elephants may be created, whereby the magnitude of the trousers housing the elephants may be reduced. Our creators of verifiable need-objects are working night and day at this great revolutionary task.

902   VIII

No news from the need-object creators.

IX

The need-object creators have restored calm in their laboratories. The search for smaller elephants was a red herring drawn across our ranks by deviationists and revisionists.

906 X

> *Our cities are crowded with stalwart fighters of the revolution, who are manning their trousers with ferocious courage and skill.*

908 XII

The people are demanding a new selection of elephants. They say: What can we do with our pockets, otherwise? Our leader is already on his way to the country. Radio Bemba reports that he is nearing the frontier of Switzerland.

Umberto Saba

A Jewish Savant

I t was an October morning in 1823, in Trieste. At walking pace, a 909 heavy coach and pair were climbing the painfully steep Opcina slope: three young men followed it on foot, speaking amongst themselves and to the man who sat alone and in some discomfort amidst the baggage that cluttered up the coach. The coach of those days was to the diligence as an express is today to a local; and in the coach Samuel Vita Lolli, a teacher of religion, was moving from his native Trieste to Gorizia where, in the scholastic year of 1823–1824, he was to take over the direction of that town's Talmud Torah. Of the youths who, partly for the pleasure of the stroll and partly out of deference to the master, had offered to accompany him as far as the customs barrier, the eldest was already known among his fellow citizens and co-religionists (his whole world) for his doctrinal learning and for the occasional verse he wrote in Hebrew (composed for certain religious festivals or in honour of some potentate.) He was not attractive; he was squat and his head was enormous; but he bore a name that, in time, was to be known somewhat beyond the circles of his fellow citizens; he was none other than Samuel David Luzzatto. Born at the turn of the century, he was then twenty-three and made his living giving lessons in Hebrew and the Vulgate to young men of the best families, amongst whom he recommended himself, even more than by his reputation as a scholar, by that of a right-thinking young man of proven morality. The other two were still boys. One of them, a cousin of Luzzatto's, was called Mortara and apprenticed in trade in a stock bank in a city that was rapidly becoming a commercial center. The other, Vita Zelmann, still a school boy, amused himself during the climb by sending as many stones as he'd picked up, walking, in the toes of his boots, rolling down through the rocks with their scattered violet thorn bushes and listening to the little landslides created by their fall. Innocent as it was, the game bothered the gentleman seated in the coach. In the few minutes that remained before they reached the customs barrier, at which point they would all part, he needed the greatest possible calm, during which he could peacefully dispute with Luzzatto an issue that went back a long way between them, that was of the greatest possible interest to each, the irreducible disagreement at the very foundation of their long friendship. Samuel David Luzzatto argued that in Talmudic days there were no such things as accents and diacritical marks in Hebrew texts, from which he drew certain conclusions that contested the antiquity of the Zohar and set him against the Kabbalah in general. Samuel Vita Lolli, a man of intense and melancholic disposition who suffered from headaches, bile and desperation, was, on the contrary, a fervent Kabbalist. He believed that man could, nay should—with the assistance of his will power and of certain special formulae—raise himself to the level of pure spirit and thus forge a bond with the Sephirot, the celestial powers; they themselves in turn depended on the Almighty. His irritation derived from the fact that Luzzatto's discovery implied certain consequences against his faith. He threw himself against Luzzatto with a passionate rage, accusing the latter of being an enemy of Judaism. "It all goes back to the beginnings," he now repeated for the hundredth time, "and if today you deny the authenticity of the Zohar, I see no reason why tomorrow you shouldn't refute the Talmud and even . . . and even the Pentateuch. A fine ending, eh?"

"But listen carefully," his adversary replied, "for in my view, you don't put the question in the right way, and the question is, first and foremost, a grammatical one. Why don't you show me (though I know you can't) I'm wrong when I give you my evidence? Do you follow me? My evidence is that in Talmudic times the Bible had neither accents nor diacritical marks; and that the Zohar, therefore, which names them in a number of places, cannot be a work from the earliest times and certainly not the work of the authors of the Mishna and the Talmud. I therefore say . . ."

As usual, Samuel David Luzzatto became excited, but his opponent who, as usual, had only sentimental arguments with which to oppose him, suddenly turned against his former student Zelmann who, instead of listening carefully to this learned argument continued—the monkey!—his stupid and even dangerous game of kicking pebbles with the toe of his boot. He leaned out of the carriage as well as he could and, cupping his hands to his mouth, shouted loudly: "Zelmann always was and always will be a *hamor, hamor, hamor*," which translated means, an ass, an ass, an ass. The poor lad, not expecting the onslaught, and even as he kicked pebbles, be it said in his praise, had not lost a word of what was being said, grew all red in the face, while that pernicious discoverer of the theory of the marks and so on, looked at him with a smile and seemed just then to note his presence.

Arrived as they were at the customs barrier, the black-and-yellow pole rose to allow the coach through; and Samuel David Luzzatto, consulting his giant metal watch, said that it was time he returned to the city. He would willingly have accompanied his friend and opponent Lolli a good ways yet; but at eleven o'clock precisely he had his first lesson to give and neither could nor wished to arrive late.

At that point, the teacher of religion, having stepped down from his coach, embraced each of the three young men in turn; and for Zelmann, almost as if to be forgiven for the "hamor" of a while back and demonstrate that he had no rancor in his heart for such monkeyshines, he added a fine smack on the cheek to his embrace. Then, having climbed back into his conveyance, he again halted the horses who had set forth, to commend Luzzatto for a last time (though whispering in order not to arouse the "Reschmud" of the Slovene border guards. Antisemites, it is known, were everywhere, even—those were times of dangerous innovations!—among Jews); his dear Luzzatto "should be wary of novelty, and with all his inventiveness, take heed not to be of more damage than advantage to the ever-fraught cause of Judaism." Luzzatto himself, greatly moved and speaking in a mixture of Hebrew and Italian, reassured him concerning his intentions. He then urged his friend more than once to come back to Trieste the following Passover and there to take up his argument when they both had more time, as well as to celebrate the Seder in company. The coach finally drew away and the little farewell committee took to the road that led back to the city, paying no heed to Zelmann who claimed to be the only one to know a splendid shortcut. The air was serene, the road deserted, the sea below danced with sparks of light; the hearts of the wayfarers (three, as the angels who appeared to the patriarchs), excited by the discussion, by the farewell and the unusually long and matutinal walk were, as the countryside, radiant.

Vita Zelmann (who was to become the master Vita) no longer remembered the "hamor" of his first teacher and instead of continuing to play with his stones, had suddenly become pensive and almost sad; the apprentice trader was thinking of the thalers he might have been able to accumulate in an easy and riskless enterprise about which he had long been dreaming, had his father given him his share of his inheritance in anticipation; Samuel David Luzzatto, he who was later known to his students by the acronym of his name in Hebrew as "the great Shadall," weighed in his mind this and that anagram with which he was already considering signing his future works, which would certainly transform Judaism; with God's help, they would restore it to its original dominion of the world of religion. For the time being, according to him, everything was in the greatest possible disorder. He found the Creed altered and corrupted by the Kabbalists, Holy Scripture disfigured by copyists and commentators, grammar treated materially without a philosophical foundation, and in belles-lettres, a depraved taste in both poetry and prose. And suddenly, hearing Mortara call out Zelmann's name, it seemed to him, this time, that that name was not totally unknown to him and that he had already been favourably impressed by it. So he asked the boy whether he was that same Vita Zelmann who, at the Academy of Commerce and Navigation, had so distinguished himself as to earn an honorable mention at the end of the year, which was a feat for a Jew in a Christian school and had caused something of an ado among his co-religionists. The youngster, blushing even more deeply at the praise than he had at the "hamor" of his former teacher, replied that yes, he was the one who had been awarded the prize. But here it seemed to Luzzatto that he did not, in saying so, feel that flush of self-congratulation, that ill-concealed pride so common among the very young when they can boast of public success, even a modest scholastic success. Consequently, he thought he owed him some encouragement.

"You did very well, Zelmann, to distinguish yourself; and I, as a good Jew, owe you a debt of gratitude. We must show our enemies that we are worth as much as they, if not more. It is only a pity that no one bothered to insert a notice in the *Corriere Israelitico,* or in some other newspaper of ours. Or perhaps the notice did appear and I failed to note it?"

The student, thrown into confusion, said that no, he didn't believe so; and that in any case, an honorable mention did not seem to him sufficiently noteworthy to be mentioned in the press.

"I did not say interesting, but useful; which is far more important. How old are you, Zelmann?"

"Sixteen; seventeen soon."

"In August I will be twenty-four. Your duty is to let yourself be advised by one who has seven years more experience than yourself. Now tell me, as you would tell your father, or your friend here, why you are so little pleased by a distinction which you well deserved and which does you honor?"

The lad shrugged; he lingered in replying. "Perhaps you do not like studying commerce? Or do you feel some unease with a life in trade?"

This time the young man looked at him as he might look on God, or at the very least one of His major prophets. Who could have told him? And if no one did, how had he managed to work it out for himself?

"But it cannot be otherwise. How else explain your complete indifference, not to speak of aversion? Do you feel in yourself some quite other vocation than that for trade?"

And now Samuel David Luzzatto, who loved to speak as master to student to his young co-religionists and who readily boasted of the drudgery and privations he had suffered to adorn his mind with that little knowledge which, already then, besides making him stand out in the community also procured him soup and bread, not to speak of the battles he had fought with his turner father, who wanted him a mechanic and not a *haham*; he began recounting how, as a boy, he had, for a few months, worn the apron of an apprentice goldsmith. For just a few months; for an inner voice called him day and night to the study of the Torah. And when his father gave him a few "kreutzers" to buy his lunch, he sometimes preferred to do without and use the money to buy some useful book. "There were so many things for a good Jew to do and learn."

Mortara objected: "Good Jews have always been good businessmen. The few privileges which they enjoyed in the Middle Ages they owed to their ability as bankers. Not to mention the fact that business always allows enough time to study the Torah."

"Not for you, for example," Vita Zelmann answered sharply, "and you also have to go to work on the Sabbath. I would rather die of hunger."

"All the greater reason why you should feel satisfied with your prize," intervened Luzzatto. "It shows that a Jew can conform to all his obligations towards the state without thereby transgressing against the Law. But you too, Mortara, are right. I exchange letters with not a few Jewish men of letters who are also good businessmen. Our own great Mendelssohn, didn't he have a draper's shop, thanks to which he fed himself and his children? Didn't he have quite a few—seven or eight or even more? Things are different today, and who can say that he would have accomplished even more (if it were possible to do more) had not the ignorance of his co-religionists in the north prevented him from making a profit on his scholarship?"

"And you think you're as great as Mendelssohn?" asked Mortara, perhaps intending no irony.

"I don't believe anything," the master replied, slightly piqued. "I only believe that when one realizes one has a vocation, one should follow it, deviating not one jot."

"And I believe likewise," confessed Vita Zelmann with the same fervor with which the martyrs recited the *Sh'ema Y'Israel* while being tortured.

"One should, however," the master added intently, "examine ourselves with great care and triumph over many an ordeal before allowing ourselves to be persuaded that our vocation is genuine. Often it is nothing more than a simple disposition, like that (in another sense, of course) of an amateur musician. A disposition that can, indeed should, lead to a profession, manual or other."

Mortified, the student fell silent. Then he asked the master what profane literature he was reading at that moment.

"I am reading, or rather rereading, Father Francesco Soave's *Moral Obligations*."

"That Jesuit?" the two young men exclaimed with the same disarray with which they would if they had seen a Jew eat one of the foods proscribed by the Law.

"I don't know whether the good Father is a Jesuit. Anyway, what difference would it make? Are there not just men even among non-Jews?" replied Samuel David Luzzatto, who prided himself on his tolerance.

"Among non-Jews? Well . . . but a Jesuit!" Zelmann replied for himself and his companion.

"I repeat that I neither know nor care whether Father Soave was or was not a Jesuit. But I would prefer a Jesuit such as the author of the *Moral Obligations* to any atheistic and pantheistic Jew such as Spinoza," concluded—as he willingly did—Samuel David Luzzatto, who viewed Spinoza with that profound and unambiguous loathing that one has for people and things one does not understand. "But to return to our own affairs, Vita . . . perhaps not yet, as the evenings grow shorter and oil for the lamp is expensive; but in the spring, when the days grow longer, if some Sabbath afternoon you want to come and have a lesson from me (unpaid, to be sure) I will gladly help you with what little skill I possess and with God's help."

Thus engaged in conversation, they had reached the first houses of Trieste, the city opening up before them with its free-port bustle and the criss-crossing of new and noisy streets. They parted at the first square: Samuel David Luzzatto to give his new lesson and the two lads, who had the day off, to stroll about and, not without a lot of chaffing and mutual knocks, to chatter about what they'd heard and said on that memorable outing, more, if the truth be told, than about their other private matters.

Translated by Keith Botsford

915

AUTHORS NOTES:

Talmud Torah: *a Jewish religious school.*

Samuel David Luzzatto: *a famous orientalist and man of letters who taught Hebrew at the Rabbinical College founded in Padua by the Emperor Joseph II. In this tale, he alludes to what appears to have been his most important discovery. More than that I do not know, or have forgotten. Unfortunately I know no Hebrew and the only words I know of as his are two lines in Italian (preserved by an oral tradition) which might be, though I don't know, confessional or "nearly a morality," or—as often happens in these cases—both. They ran:*

> L'uomo ha un picciol membro
> e piu lo sfama e piu divien familico
> *[Man has but a tiny member,*
> *and the more it's satisfied, the more it starves.]*

I know he was my mother's uncle and that he had two wives; one of whom (the first) threw herself from a window, probably fleeing some nervous disorder, although a cousin of mine (she came to the same end, varying only the means) assured me she had done so out of extreme love of the virtue of frugality, an illness she caught from the learned man for whom (my cousin still speaks) the unfortunate lady (who was reportedly a remarkable cook) was rarely able to provide at lunch more than a soup known in Trieste and throughout the Veneto as a panada, *made of stale bread, oil and bay leaf. Samuel David Luzzatto was exceedingly fond of this dish and while eating it, praised its nutritional and hygienic virtues (today we would call them vitamins). Very good indeed, occasionally, and no doubt healthy; but . . . like Mendelssohn, he had a number of children. One of these (Beniamino) became a celebrated physician and diagnostician (of the sort who are summoned, sometimes over great distances, in consultation and even to the bedsides of the mighty); and I still remember the astonishment I felt in childhood when informed that on the occasion of his death, the then Minister of Education had sent a telegram to the family expressing his condolences. Another (Filosseno) came to a less happy end. Destined—as all said—to be "a second version of his father," another "light unto Judaism," he instead died young and in tragic circumstances. In Paris, whither he had been permitted to travel for his studies, he caught a venereal disease. Lacking the courage to confess the crime and its punishment to his father (or to a doctor), the disease made rapid progress and had, for the poor young man, the consequences one may imagine. I further add that my thirty years as an antiquarian bookseller (my "tale" is from 1919, but this note dates from 1952) confirms that his works still sell and are set down in my catalogue with more than one request. Especially rare and sought after is his version of the* Pentateuch, *with the original text on the facing page. Connoisseurs and amateurs say it is exceedingly well done.*

916

Reschmud: *(Saba wrote "Reschmud," but the current usage is "Risch'ut") Anti-Semitism. The word means wicked or evil.*

Seder: *the ceremonial Passover dinner, with various rituals, to commemorate the flight of the Jews from Egypt.*

Sh'ema Y'Israel *("Hear O Israel"): the Jewish prayer in which Jews affirm their monotheism.*

Kreutzer: *an Austrian coin. It was worth two cents.*

Haham: *a scholar (especially one versed in the Law). "A haham, a real haham," my good teacher of religion would say of me as he went from one class to another, referring to the miracle; when in my next-to-last year in elementary school, during the lesson on Holy Scripture, I had risen to ask him a (truly Talmudic) question, whether the rain of the Deluge had begun drop by drop or had fallen all at once. For you should know, patient reader, that I too was conceived to be, as well as a future bank employee, a potential "light unto Judaism." If, alas, I did not succeed, it was (as I have explained in the preface) because of that "goy," my madcap father. And even more (given the absent father) due to my wet-nurse (a Slovene peasant woman) who had an image of the baby Jesus (with whom she fondly identified me) at the head of her bed, and who carried me off every evening to the Church of the Rosario, which still exists in that part of the old city that has not been needlessly (and I would say bestially) knocked down. When I went to bed, she would also make me recite, not the Sh'ema Y'Israel in Hebrew, but the Our Father in Slovene. If, at the risk of repeating myself, I tell the tales of another time it is not—I swear reader—because I wish to speak of myself, but only to lament what terrible muddles were possible in Europe and in Trieste; when my little city—in spite of all, then as now, Italian in its heart—was in ascension. Until Adolf Hitler came to "restore a little order".*

917

John Auerbach

Distortions or Variations on the Theme of Broca

My name is Stefan Berdiczewski. I am 68-years-old, retired 919
now, having suffered a number of cerebral strokes, but was formerly a Jack-of-
All-Trades including what you'd call not entirely honorable and certainly
non-typical Jewish trades: long periods of sailoring in the merchant marine
or working on deep sea trawlers, serving with the Israeli Navy in wartime.
I have been married twice, widowed once, and now live with my second
wife, an American, in New England where I resent the harsh climate and
my limitations caused by the above-mentioned strokes and from encroaching
old age. Relying on old Jewish calculations of the average human life span—
three score and 10—most men of my age attempt to sum up their lives in
preparation for a trial in which their mistakes and sins would be taken
into evidence. Innocent of this sentiment I tend to settle accounts here,
before my departure for hell or heaven. Here I take advice from a writer I
adored for a good portion of my adult life, Joseph Conrad. He says a man
should stand up to his bad luck, to his mistakes, to his conscience and other
things of this sort. What else is there worth reckoning with or fighting
against?

And as to the Jewish God, I got rid of that tribal, jealous and vengeful deity right after the Holocaust (in which my whole immediate family

perished) adopting the attitude of the Warsaw ghetto rabbi: "Lord, we have been your chosen people for five thousand years, what about choosing a different people now?"

Trying to be honest with myself, I cannot even claim, in a desperate attempt at self-justification, that I wasn't warned. I was. Long ago, some four years ago, when I was released from a Princeton hospital after my second stroke, they gave me a nice little booklet issued by the US Department of Health, entitled *Aphasia, Hope Through Research*.

According to this booklet, there were certainly many physical catalysts increasing the statistical chances of my strokes: 40 years of steady smoking, a few years of excessive drinking. Perhaps stress also contributed.

There were drawings, diagrams, pictures and statistics in this booklet all centering on the fact that one million people in the US survive a cerebral stroke, and of these, 20 percent develop aphasia. There are two kinds of aphasia: one called Wernicke's aphasia impedes speech comprehension, while the other, Broca's aphasia, makes speaking difficult.

If Wernicke and Broca and modern researchers following their path were right, brain and mind seemed to be the same thing, a billion connections of a super computer, activated by electro-chemical reactions in neurons. Thus my brain damage was apparently only some kind of short circuit in these electro-chemical connections. Naturally, I am very interested in the patterns of these short circuits, try to avoid them and to trace what can be done to restore normal functioning of the brain—or mind, if you prefer. The malfunction, although it may seem a minor ailment to an outsider, is very annoying to me because it produces in the brain the strangest associations, when compared with any normal brain. I have collected many examples of these malfunctions. Take the most recent.

The people who live beneath us, our New England neighbors, become enraged when I play a Bach cantata on Sunday morning. They make no complaints about any other music, no matter how loud. It's only the Bach cantata on Sunday that they hate.

One Sunday afternoon I went downstairs and asked the man why he had pounded on his ceiling in protest against my Bach. I made my inquiry in a most polite manner, apologizing for my intrusion.

"I don't mind telling you at all," answered the man. "It is the hopeless-ness of it that makes us crazy. This music simply leads to nothing, and believe me sir, we, my wife and I, are both real music lovers, we just cannot bear music that leads to nothing." And to demonstrate their melodomanic tastes he played a disc by an Arab singer, one Staz (maestro) Abu Nidal and his band, recorded live in a Beirut night club in 1970, a piece called "Nights of Lebanon." I listened politely to the music even after it became absolutely clear to me that the endless serpentines led to nothing.

"Say, isn't it good?" He smiled. "You cannot claim I have Levantine taste. I was born in Lebanon, but my wife is from Budapest and she too thinks Abu Nidal and his band are great."

In my own flat I thought about the erroneous connection my mind had produced. I assumed that an ordinary person would have thought about the musical idiosyncrasies of his neighbors, but my short circuit threw me across the abyss of memory into the mind of a boy of 13 or 14— myself—in the fourth or fifth grade of a public school in Warsaw, Poland, and the history teacher had just ordered all the boys to bring to class tomorrow an illustrated card called *Poczet Krolow Polskich*—a list of all the Polish kings.

And what triggered this erratic connection? The simple fact that my Lebanese neighbor had a Hungarian wife. The demand of the history teacher was doubly distressing. I knew Mother would say, "You know we don't have money to spend on such things. Maybe you can borrow the card with the kings from one of your classmates?" But I knew the teacher would insist that every pupil have the damned thing, and I, the only Jew in the class, could hardly afford to turn up without it. What disturbed me even more was the fact that the list was adorned with crude drawings that presented, in a row, king after king. My distress was deepened by the truth, transparent even to the mind of a boy, that these drawings were sheer inventions, the fantasy of the two-penny artist who had compiled the list.

As I said, I knew the kings by heart. Starting with Mieszko the First, through Boleslay Chrobry, portrayed with his famous sword the Szczerbec, through Kazimierz the Great who granted the Jews asylum in Poland when they were expelled from almost every European country, and who, as the legend went, had a Jewish mistress, a certain Estherka—down to the last of the Polish kings, Stanislaw Leszczynski who was the lover of the Russian czarina, Katerina the Great. And finally, August the Strong.

Altogether, they were a very mediocre lot, even when compared with medieval and post-medieval European kings. Perhaps the standards required by the Polish nobles (the kings were elected by them in a congress called the Seym) had something to do with it. August the Saxon became a king because he could bend horseshoes in his fists and because he was able to drink the people who had elected him under the table: a gentleman of such prowess with liquor must be a good ruler. Somewhere in the middle of the list was the only outstanding king, a Hungarian prince called Stefan Batory and it was he who provided the faulty connection in my aphasia-stricken brain, presumably because my Lebanese neighbor's wife was of Hungarian origin, or maybe because my first name is Stefan.

In contrast to the other fellows in the list there was a true portrait of Batory made by a real Polish painter of the 18th century, probably Matejko, and I remembered the painting well. The king sits on a camp stool, a short sword *à la française* across his knees, while he accepts the keys of the town of Weliki Luki and the homage of the Russian nobles, the boyars; the town had just surrendered to the king's victorious troops. Batory was a short man, his feet didn't touch the ground, and I remembered that he had a very thoughtful expression: maybe he was wondering if he should accept the homage of the boyars or reject it and continue war. In the background of the picture were heavily mustached Polish knights, the king's bodyguard or dignitaries who wanted to make sure that he did nothing detrimental to Polish interests. After all he *was* a foreign prince.

The faulty short circuit in my brain continued, allowing only for a small digression that made me wonder why this Hungarian woman did not prefer some Czardas to the whining and bleating of Abu Nidal and his Lebanese band. Perhaps to keep the peace at home.

The faulty connection persists on its deranged track, only slightly veering in direction, for now I see myself 30 years later scrutinizing the list of Jewish kings that my son Adam had just shown me, asking if King Herod the Great had a beard.

I answered that I was sure he had.

"But there is no beard on the coin you have of him."

"Son, no Jewish king would dare put his image on his coin, it was forbidden. And Herod, who was an Edomite and hated by his Jewish subjects, would certainly not have done so. But I am certain he had a beard. Jews were forbidden to shave then."

So far the short circuit of my brain had crossed the memory gap of 30 years in a stride. I wondered what Broca would say about that. But Broca had been dead for more than a hundred years and the connection itself was

922

also ancient, for my son Adam was burned to death in an Israeli helicopter crash 20 years ago and I still light a Jahrzeit candle on the anniversary of his death, as I do also for my parents and sister who were burned to death in Treblinka. Being burned is a tradition in my family. But cerebral strokes followed by aphasia do not necessarily provide such a finale.

So my son dutifully brought home a printed list of Jewish kings both from Judah and Israel, for the kingdom was divided into two parts (after Solomon, I think) and I wondered how closely the list of Jewish kings resembled that of the Polish kings I remembered from my school years: the same crude idiotic drawings based on absolutely nothing, the same offensive small print, same meaningless explanations, similarly vague historical data. I thought perhaps the same person had even produced the two lists. The indisputable fact was that the initial distortion, whose source was the Hungarian woman and Stefan Batory, continued to branch out into a maze of most unexpected connection—and again I am compelled to compare it to the assumed working of an average or normal brain, which at this point would probably provide a nostalgic excursion into the tragic history of my family. Nothing of that kind happened to my mind. It stuck on the words "Herod the Great" and sent me on a rickety train of random associations.

923

Reader, I am not even sure if you are still with me: but since I have dragged you into it, I feel honor-bound to bring you safely to the end of the story.

Well, there was Herod the Great, summoned up complete (I hope with handlebar mustache and a black beard), with his passion for magnificent constructions and his rampaging paranoia. He killed half of his family and taxed his subjects to death. Wasn't it in Herod's time that a certain young Jewish man was brought to court, sentenced to death and crucified by the Romans? Of course those *were* the times. And now, as I sit writing these lines, the whole Christian world, including naturally my present neighbors in New England, is celebrating the birthday of this young Jewish man whom they declared to be God, though he himself, during his lifetime, never raised such a claim. The rest is tedious and tiresome history with its infinite variety of interpretations. But today we have a Red Cross and, affiliated with it, a Red Crescent, but the red *Magen David Adom* is denied affiliation with this international organization. I wonder why? And where was the Red Cross when the Nazis had the concentration camps going? It supplied packages to

German, British and French POWs but not to Soviet POWs, who on Goering's orders were starving and driven to cannibalism. Besides, Joe Stalin had declared he didn't have *his* people in German POW camps. In view of this fact, does the Red Cross not seem to be a distorted symbol?

Again, excuse the digression. You realize of course that it was triggered through no fault of mine by Herod, Christmas and crosses, Red and Black.

"Hope through research" says the subtitle of the booklet on aphasia they gave me as I was leaving the Princeton Hospital. I have not the slightest doubt that research will continue on this strange disease. After all, reaching into the depth of a man's skull is not a new thing. Trepanning goes back to the Stone Age. Three thousand years ago the Ancient Egyptians were also doing it. I am sure that in a not very remote future doctors, or maybe electricians, will be able to reach that blown fuse in the brain and repair the faulty connection using the latest laser technology or by inserting a completely new electronic chip—as if they were repairing a computer. And then the right connections will be reestablished, in the Broca and Wernicke areas.

But I have an inexplicable feeling this is not all.

Maybe brain is mind but perhaps there are other areas, not mapped by Broca, Wernicke and other modern researchers—as yet unknown sources of awareness—making up this strangest unit in the world, the human being.

In the beginning of this story I said that I had been a Jack-of-All-Trades. In my middle years I committed the sin of initiating myself into yet another trade, that of the storyteller (I consciously avoid the use of the word "writer"), and I published some not very successful stories. I still remember how vulnerable I was to my friends' criticisms. Many of them asked why I couldn't write a story without a dream. I would answer that my dreams are a legitimate part of my existence and that quite possibly we are all part of God's dream. They laughed at the suggestion: not so much about my *dreaming* but about *God* the dreamer. The truth is that long before the stroke, long before my aphasia I had a feeling that reality is more than the pictures in our minds. I was never associated with any formal religion and never hid my distaste for it. But the feeling, sometimes stronger, sometimes weaker, that there was something beyond the mind was always present.

And now this story's dream: a wonderful dream, but not an entirely new one. It recurred many times ... many times did I dream that I was sailing again in the Mediterranean, which I loved, and there were shores and islands and harbors and the color of the sea and the sky and we, the captain of the ship on which I served, and I, his friend, came to these immense rocks, the Pillars of Hercules as the ancient sailors called them, and the captain put his hand on my shoulder and said: "Naturally we could go beyond but we won't my friend, we have reached the limits of our sea, now we have to return the way we came, back to our own end of it." And there were not only the colors of the sea and the sky but there was also the strong smell of the waves, as deep and intoxicating as strong wine, and I felt in this dream that I was touched by the hand of God.

Which God? you are entitled to ask.

In the final sequence of the dream I was reminded that in one Jewish sacred book, the Talmud, there is a chapter emphasizing the importance of prayer. There we are told that even the Almighty himself prays. And what may be the Almighty's prayer? That His mercy may override His Judgment.

So after this wonderful dream I was lying on my bed in the darkness, eyes open, thinking: I am only an old and tired Jew and all I have is the hope to be redeemed by the Almighty's prayer.

925

The Anatomy and the Death of Dream

To tell the whole truth, when I finished "Distortions or variations on the theme of Broca" I was convinced that it was the very last piece of writing to emerge from my pen. I thought that I had 10 books to my credit and it was certainly enough for a minor writer of my stature. I had never craved fame.

Once reconciled to the thought that the deformations of my valid mind were a direct result of short circuits in the Broca and Wernicke areas of my brain, things were simpler.

I stopped accusing my wife of accelerating the tempo of my life (accusing the person nearest you is a natural impulse hardly to be resisted) since it had dawned on me that the acceleration was not prompted by her ill-will or hostility toward me, but was an objective phenomenon with an explanation possibly in some Einstein equation that I was unable to understand because of my total ignorance of the principles of higher mathematics and physics.

Mind you, what I am talking about is the acceleration of the tempo of life. These days, I watch a lot of TV and it occurs to me that the images on the screen have been passing more quickly than in the past, or was that another distortion?

This observation applied especially to commercials. There were only two possibilities: either the people who made these ads thought they should be shorter and thus more profitable (less money for less time) or the perception of the general public, the reaction of their eyes, nerves or brains was speedier than mine. That would be sad, because it would confirm the theory of the brain distortions. But we have talked of that before, no need to repeat. At this moment my concern is the velocity of the TV images, a purely techno-logical aspect of the small screen; the rapid sequence of blinks on it.

Other aspects are a completely different story.

For example, I could question the ethical or moral validity of an ad, presenting American teenagers devouring hunks of fried chicken, an ad that interrupted a documentary film about starvation in Sudan—skeleton children and dying adults covered with festering wounds and flies. I asked myself if there were any moral standards influencing TV programming (including advertising) or was profit the sole and all-embracing motive of the tube. Just before writing "Distortions" I had minor surgery involving a local anesthetic. Well, it wasn't a joyous experience, but less annoying than I had anticipated. It involved an intravenous connection, a tricky procedure because my veins are brittle, signing a document releasing the doctors from liability should something go wrong, and applying a numbing device to my throat. Then I was told to lie on my left side and try to sleep, which I did. During the following half hour the doctors would dilate my esophagus and remove scar tissue from a previous operation which interfered with swallowing food. I felt no pain. An obedient patient, I slept during the operation. But it was not a peaceful sleep. When my wife brought me home I slept a proper sleep, complete with dreams.

As usual, the beginning of the dream was a sea journey, this time on a trawler at night along the southern coast of Israel. What was not usual were the sounds and smells as main features of the dream. There were no people in it, I was standing on the trawler's deck, deeply inhaling the fra-grances of the orange groves ashore, in full bloom, which in spring the breeze carries a considerable distance over the water to the ships traveling this route. A smell, pervasive in its volume and strength, absolutely intoxicating, bitter and sweet at the same time, sexual and almost painful in its loveliness; unbearable.

There were also sounds in this dream. Unless you happen to be a sailor I doubt you are familiar with the swishing sound made by a ship's prow as it cuts through the water. I would lean against the trawler's low bulwarks and listen attentively to the murmur the water made passing along the ship's sides. I learned many secrets the sea whispered to me during the soft moonlit nights, fragrant with the citrus flower scent and now, unable to sail anymore, they returned to me in my dreams, for which I was grateful.

Reader, kindly bear in mind that I am an old man, and my several strokes and cancer operations confine me largely to an investigation of the mind (and I admit that such investigations are apt to degenerate into a very egocentric or even misanthropic quest). Thus I became fascinated by the nature of the mechanism in my brain which lets me repeat for myself the music of a Mozart piano concerto without opening my mouth or uttering a sound: where was this knowledge stored? And now, the musician in my dream which brought me to the sound of the water, heard 50 years ago. A mystery I'll never know (if I had studied neurology in my youth instead of having dealt with Adolf and the ships, perhaps I'd have answers to these questions.).

927

I have mentioned Einstein before, as a man who could perhaps explain the phenomenon of the acceleration of the world. But even here my ignorance is an obstacle. All I know about Einstein is that he had screwed up the classical Euclidean planimetry and stereometry that I had been taught in school by introducing Time as an additional dimension. Later I read somewhere that, angered by Brown's particles experiment and the principle of determinism he said, "I refuse to believe God plays dice with the world he created."

This on the cosmic scale. But based on the experience of my own long life I am inclined to believe we are very much like Brown's particles, we are accidents: we simply appear, not by our own choice, and as Saul Bellow says, we make what we can with the means "available."

We must accept this mixture as we find it—the impurity of it, the tragedy of it, the hope of it.

The impurity of it, Bellow says, and I think I can put under this heading my dreams, which pervade so much of my writing (Bellow says the soul escapes from the body during man's sleep). I am not convinced that is so, I am rather inclined to believe that the dreams are a mirror reflecting the soul's remembrance of things past. I remember, for example, vividly, an important episode in my life featuring strange occurrences and an individual named Rosti and these memories returned often in my dreams, distorted as in a fading mirror, until many years later something happened which helped me get rid of that particular dream, since it never appeared again.

I was living at my kibbutz then and was temporarily in charge of volunteers from abroad who arrive in spring and stay till late autumn with the regularity of migrating birds. They then leave for India or Nepal or Thailand where grass is both more available and cheap.

One morning a man arrived in my office, and said, "I am from Buenos Aires, Argentina." He was a swarthy man of middle height, had a shirt which looked like an explosion in a paint factory and a pair of very faded jeans. He also had a split chin, a narrow, receding forehead, bushy eyebrows and large ears. A tiny golden chain with a Magen David dangled below a prominent Adam's apple.

He reminded me so much of the man Rosti, who had played such a dominant role in my life in this memorable 1943, that I felt tempted to ask him if he was his elder brother, or maybe his father.

But the illusion ended abruptly when my eye stopped on the tiny Magen David on his neck. He was no relative of Rosti: Rosti had a little golden cross on his necklace and a St Christopher on his signet ring. I remember, after 40 years, amazing, how I pondered if I could trust a man I didn't know with my story, telling him that I had escaped from the Warsaw Ghetto to flee to Sweden, then to England to fight the Germans. Let's return for a moment to Einstein: dice or no dice, the mathematical probability of a meeting between me, Stefan Berdiczewski, recent escapee from Warsaw Ghetto, and Estevan Rosti from a suburb of Buenos Aires, were one to 400 billion. Given the circumstances and the time of meeting, multiply this number by another 200 billion. And yet we did meet and did whatever we did successfully and it was a good thing, and maybe it is the only one that counts in the final count.

The element of communication was of paramount importance at that time as I spoke no Spanish; Rosti knew a little German and little English and that's how we managed to talk at this first meeting which happened after I chased him for a couple of nights. I understood he was scared. How could he know I was not one of the Gestapo men? The whole port area of

Neufahrwasser and Weichselmünde was swarming with them. Aware I was tailing him, he had his beer in Petroleum Bar, switched over to Zut Huette and finally to the Deutsches Haus. Even after this first meeting he insisted that the Deutsches Haus was the safest meeting place.

In the vast hall 300 seamen of the German Kriegsmarine were screaming, "*Denn wir fahren, denn wir fahren gegen Engelland!*" The noise was deafening. Nobody could overhear our conversation.

I said conversation, but now I realize that talk was actually a minor part of it. There were long silences between us in the hellish noise of the place and deep looks into each others' eyes, looks which seemed to penetrate the retina and the eye nerve deep into the human soul—if and wherever such a thing exists.

And yet, between the silences and the deep looks and the random talk in half-broken German and half-broken English, Rosti had succeeded in convincing me to give up my dream of escaping to Sweden and ultimately England and to stay where I was, in Danzig. "If you hate the Nazis as much as you say, you have a much better chance to fight them here. I know people on the other side, in Gothenburg, who would be delighted to have steady information about what ships are being repaired in Danziger Werft, how many U-boats are constructed, all this sort of thing . . . you think you can supply that kind of information, don't you?"

I tried for the last time. "So you won't help me to escape to Sweden?" He moved that strange head of his in a negative motion. "And the information?" he asked after a while.

"It is apparently my destiny," I answered.

"My ship sails on Friday," he said.

"I'll bring you the stuff on Wednesday night," I said. "But we must meet on the street," he said. "We'll find a quiet little street, remember this is the real thing, dangerous." "I am not afraid," I said.

"I am," he answered. "Let me ask you one last thing, Rosti—why do you do this?"

He shrugged. "Money," he said. "Gothenburg pays me well. Don't forget I am just a poor Argentinian stoker on board an old Swedish steamer."

"And I am just a poor Jewish stoker with false papers, a stoker on a floating crane in Marine Waffenbetrieb of the Danziger Werft."

"We are a perfect couple," he laughed. We shook hands and I left. He stayed. How perfect a couple we were I saw when we met on the

Wednesday night on a blind side street ending directly on a river canal, some barges were moored there. The place was dimly lit by a single gas lantern. It was snowing heavily but was not cold. From the bar just around the corner we could hear the yelling of the drunken soldiers and seamen of the Kriegsmarine. Occasionally a siren of a submarine passing on the main canal or the hooting of a tugboat were heard. The only other noise was that of the snow crunched under Rosti's feet when he arrived for the rendezvous.

On the wall, as in all the port areas, were the war placards. One said, the *Räder müssen rollen für den Sieg* (wheels must roll for the victory) *er geht vor* (he must have the priority). On the picture, was a soldier obviously on leave, carrying his rifle and his backpack while a row of civilians patiently waited in line for their turn. Everyone was happy on this poster, the soldier smiled—well, he was on his way to see his family, escaping at least temporarily the pleasures of the frontline. And the waiting civilians were happy to let him go and be virtuous and patriotic. The other poster was very different. PSSST, it said, *Der Feind hört mit* (the Enemy listens). On the picture were two men on a dimly lit street, one of them lighting the cigarette of the other, who was handing him a thick envelope. The atmosphere was that of secrecy implying clearly that some kind of a non-kosher business was going on here. Rosti grinned, pointing to the poster when I handed him a thick envelope which he put immediately in his pants pocket.

"See?" he said, "exactly like the picture." I said, "Not exactly, where is the cigarette?"

"You were right," he said, took out a package of Old Golds and lit a cigarette for me and himself.

Of this scene I dreamed often till we met the young Jew from Buenos Aires in my kibbutz many years later. Never after that meeting. Once the recollection of the actual happening was restored, its reflection in the dream died. It was strange: the image of Rosti's face faded gradually into complete oblivion, but I was able to remember the most minute details of the affair: I know for sure it was an Old Gold cigarette and not any other brand. I remember the poster on the wall, I remember even the context of the first envelope I gave him on that night and the taste of the cheap beer we drank later in the Petroleum Bar. I recollect how anxious I was for him to take the envelope to his ship, but he was very calm and said, "don't worry, it will be on board in my cabin tonight."

This first envelope was very amateurish, I realize now. In it were detailed drawings of three sections of a submarine on the slipway, under construction, a list with dates of tanks and heavy artillery pieces unloaded by my floating 100-ton crane, a description with drawings of the damages suffered by the heavy cruiser Königsberg (in the stern by a torpedo and just below the bridge by a gun shot). I delivered such envelopes to Rosti every three weeks and on one occasion received confirmation that they were delivered to the British consulate in Gothenburg. Then the deliveries of iron ore from Sweden and German coal to Sweden in return, ceased towards the end of the war and I never saw Rosti again. I never overestimated my doings during this period: my contribution to the victory over Nazi Germany was probably less than that of a single infantry soldier on any of the many fronts. But for me the experience was one of elation; at least I had done something instead of surviving the war in the safety of the service in the German Handelsmarine and later in the Danziger Werft. Later I indulged in visualizing the information I had supplied to Rosti spread on a huge jigsaw table, mixed with countless other pieces. There must have been thousands of people like me in Nazi-occupied Europe from Norway to Greece and occupied France, and many men and women busy trying to obtain some clear picture of the enemy's plans and intentions and using this information to fight the diabolic rule of the Nazis.

Once I stopped dreaming about Rosti, and the remembrance of these past days survived my cerebral strokes and remained as pure memory labeled on the chronological calendar as years 1942–43, I was ready to lay it aside: I didn't return to it daily or nightly, but promised to write about it one day. Mind you, reader, my bag of memories is huge and I remember well almost everything in it, from the remembrance of my first sexual encounter at the age of nine. What I don't remember is where the hell I have left my reading glasses. Immediate memory is definitely weak, but maybe it is normal in a person of 67 years.

The question I asked myself when I embarked on the adventure of writing "Distortions" in the mind of Stefan Berdiczewski was, will anybody be interested in reading this piece of writing if I am doing it for my own satisfaction? A literary friend of mine offered me a critical evaluation of these pages. He said, "What you wrote is a statement, but not a story or an essay." I wholeheartedly accept this but am ready to fend off attacks by future critics pursuing the same line, trying to force me to define what the subject of writing was. I had the thing in the past. "What is it," they asked, "a novel, an essay, a short story?" "But these are only your ideas." "And what were you expecting, my nail clippings?"

And you think people will read this? Only if they want. An ancient Jewish anecdote comes to mind. A Jew is caught on a border trying to smuggle a bag of tobacco. "What do you have in this bag," asks the border guard. "Food for the birds," answers the Jew. The guard rips open the bag. "The birds will eat this?" "Only if they want. I won't force them."

I think the joke is very characteristic of the bitter Jewish sense of humor. We are a very ancient people and should be treated as senior citizens of the world, along with the Chinese and Egyptians. Paradoxically, the concept of Senior Citizen is unknown in Israel. An approximate equivalent, frequently in use is *Alte Kacker* and as to the nature of my future prospective readers,—many of whom will be *sabras* (Jews born in Israel), I define them as follows: spines, outside; bad manners, inside.

I hope you still remember that I have finished the first part of "Distortions" with a dream and Almighty's prayer.

I think that as one firmly believing in dreams and also that Time is circular and not linear (this is what Marxists believe, don't they?) that I, Alexander Berdiczewski, finish this exercise in self-disclosure with another dream, a dream of this morning which I remember in its entirety.

We were living in New York City in a flat on the 25th floor and I had a conversation with a man I had sailed with for a long time and liked. His name was Gershon and he has been dead for three years; I eulogized him at his burial. Then Gershon disappeared (have you noticed how effortlessly the dead disappear?) and I am watching a long coastline deep down below and notice some dolphins, or whales, stranded there in the surf. The window of the 25th floor was open and my dog was barking wildly. I told my wife she better close the window as the dog might jump down to the dolphins. He won't since he knows it is very far. Then I woke, wishing so much that these dolphins or whales would not be stranded and would find their way back to the open sea, to the freedom of the open sea.

Continuation of "The Anatomy"

After reading "The Anatomy", my wife (who is also my first reader) asked me, "What was it you were trying to write, a diary?"

Robert Graves once warned me a man should have his breakfast alone. We were sitting in the thin early morning sun on the terrace of Cannelun, his home in Deyá, Mallorca. He said, "In the morning a man is half asleep with his dreams and should not be disturbed. Notice that most quarrels in the family occur mainly in the morning." Well, I didn't and that was the result.

"A diary!" she said. So be it. I'd be in very good company. Stendhal, Dostoyevsky, Rimbaud, Baudelaire, Camus, Conrad, Montaigne who kept writing "for his pleasure only," and is not Don Quixote a diary of Cervantes? And what about Joyce and his Bloom diary of one complete day in Dublin? And Leonardo and his desperate cry "what makes you labor so hard?"

So much for a diary, meanwhile at least. I know people who have no talent for writing novels and the urge to write a novel drives them nuts. They remind me of the poor 19th-century composers desperately trying to produce an opera. No matter how much wonderful music you composed, you were nothing if you didn't write an opera.

Debussy finally created his Pelléas; but lovely as it is, I'd rather have three dozen of his Preludes. But it is only a matter of taste and ancient Romans advised us not to discuss tastes. I bow my white-haired head to their wisdom.

And as I embark on this journey (perhaps ultimate, perhaps penultimate, one never knows) which seems to attempt to clear up certain problems of reincarnation, I pray and invoke a blessing of an ancient writer, whom we Jews call *Kochelet*, and the rest of the world knows as the Preacher of Ecclesiastes.

In the second part of this mini trilogy, I have stated that in my opinion we are definitely accidents and so is everything that happens to us. The other day I was flying to Philadelphia, by accident, of course, and after releasing my seat belt at the altitude of some 28,000 feet, started to watch castles of cream-colored cumulus clouds far below. Contrasted with the flawless blue of the sky above them they were an eerie sight; triggered by some ancient shadow of a memory, I repeated with my inner ear the musical theme of

933

Debussy's *Nuages* and wondered what music he would compose if he could see what I saw at that moment. I decided that he wouldn't change a note of it, nor would I. Nuages were beautiful as they were, the fact that I performed the unnatural feat of flying above the clouds instead of watching them below, shouldn't change anything in the nature of things.

Watching the endless progress of these cumulus castles toward the ever-evasive distant horizon, it occurred to me that my life, as I lived it now, was only a reflection of some previous life, lived perhaps by someone else, perhaps by a relative of mine or maybe myself, but in such a remote past that what I remembered of it was only a vague shadow of remembrance. But there were parallel developments in both lives, similarities, repetitions, analogies in behavior—of the protagonists—if they were indeed two different characters, and not the same character but seen from a different angle and in a different time. Was each cumulus castle different, or were they only endless repetitions of themselves *ad infinitum*?

At any rate I thought in this present life I have spent a number of years hiding myself behind some other person, assuming this person's character, manner of speech, personal documents. For six years I was a Polish seaman, a stoker: I made a credible performance of it and thus saved my life—for what it was worth. I thought now it was only a repeat performance. I did it 500 years ago for the first time and after a moment I started remembering this first time.

Earlier, I invoked the assistance and a wish for a blessing from Kochelet, not only because he is my favorite chapter in the Bible, but also because he says there is a season and a time to every purpose under the heaven.

"A time to be born and a time to die, a time to weep and a time to laugh . . . etc." and this list contains almost every human activity. But it seems to me that it is especially fitting in setting the parameters of a seaman's life: this, a symbiosis of a sailor's existence with that of his ship in the defined and very concrete limits: time between the Sign on and Pay off. I must have participated in these ceremonies at least a hundred times, a glance at my seaman's book confirms it. My name and that of my captain are recorded there under proper rubrics. This procedure was so deeply embedded in navigational tradition that even in wartime the Germans insisted on preserving it in all details. Thus, my signature is affixed on the articles of the good ship "Marianne" opposite the signature of a certain Karl Schmidt, Master.

The occasion was hilarious as well, I was brought to the Captain's cabin under a policeman's escort and they refused to let him go until I was "signed on". Then he said with obvious relief, "Well now, he (meaning me) is all yours" and went out: I was booted down into the stokehold. That was my first sign on, as said; at least a hundred followed in the next 15 years, but I had no premonitions. I must digress: even people with a reputation for thoroughness like Germans sometimes get confused in their bureaucracy. In 1940 no Polish seaman was allowed to work on German ships. In 1941 because of the acute shortage of the labor force (all German men were mobilized) this order was annulled and they were searching for Polish seamen in prisons and labor camps. I was serving a sentence for the theft of a boat in Strafflager Stutthof when they discovered my stoker's card during a routine checkup. Stutthof was a Strafflager for Poles and Germans: it had a separate section for Untermenschen, Jews and Gypsies, it never earned the reputation of Auschwitz or Treblinka. The two sections were pretty strictly separated.

I worked on the Marianne until she was sunk and then on the Brigitte, and at the end of 1941 they changed the rules once more and transferred all the Poles to land jobs in the shipyards. Both Marianne and Brigitte were old tubs sailing to Baltic ports under German rule, Memel, Riga, Talin, Helsinki, etc. As I said before, the two sections of Stutthof were strictly separated, the Strafflager Stutthof and the K. Z. Stutthof just shared a name but I, having had a glimpse of the other installation often wondered what was it that protected me from joining the other crowd behind the double barbed wire. It was a piece of paper, saying that I was a Polish seaman, son of a Jan Wladyslav and Victoria Krukowski and that I was baptized in a church on Chlodna Steet and that this birth certificate was duly registered in the church's archives. On the basis of this fraudulent document other papers were issued which served me well till I was "signed on" on the Marianne in Danzig and even after that. Nobody cared to check what had happened to the son of the Wladyslavs in 1939. If they had checked that, they'd discover that in September of that year he was drafted into the Polish Navy and was killed on the 30th of September fighting for Westerplatte, the Polish free zone in the former Free State of Danzig. Once I started impersonating this dead man, things were relatively easy: I spoke German and Polish fluently, I knew the slang and the manner of living of my Polish colleagues, knew their games, knew how to drink and how to swear. The only danger was that I must avoid at all cost appearing naked in front of my Polish and German shipmates. The disclosure of my circumcision would be my death sentence.

Once I was very near to it.

It was a routine medical check-up of the seamen in Königsberg. We were standing in a long line and each man whose name was called had to step up on a little platform in the middle of the room and a young woman doctor examined his genitals. The moment she said all right a weary port police official affixed his stamp to the man's papers.

"Next one" she said. I stepped up. She was very young, probably just out of a medical school in some German university. I was sure she had never seen a circumcized male member in her life. I looked down at her, she looked up at me, our eyes met at the level of my hips. Then she let me live and said "All right. Next one." The bored policeman didn't bother to glance at the man whose papers he had just stamped.

And so I lived on, protected by my papers and an incredible chutzpah. I was often thinking about this episode in relation to one of my previous reincarnations in Spain around 1500. Papers would not have saved me then because I hardly knew how to read. Circumcision was not such a deadly peril as it was in Germany and Poland in 1940. Especially not in Seville where I lived after separating from my parents in 1492. Many Spaniards in the south, recently under Moorish rule, were circumcised and nobody would accuse a man of being a Jew in disguise on the evidence of his circumcision.

Why even our Saviour the Lord Jesus Christ was circumcized and the anniversary was celebrated as a holiday in some part of Italy. Besides medical examinations were definitely not in vogue, autopsies were. As a young Spanish sailor I had no difficulty in joining a ship of a conquistador, Captain Vincente Yanez Pinzon on his fourth voyage to the New World.

It was a dangerous trip. What I remembered of it were the cramped quarters, stale food, lack of water to drink and a miracle: four days before our landing water in the ocean ceased to be salty and became sweet like that of a mountain stream in Spain.

This miracle was caused by a direct all night prayer of the Captain to our Saviour Jesus Christ. After all, the captain said, He had changed water into wine in the Holy Land, so changing salt water into sweet was just a minor miracle.

Many years later I used to tell this story to my children in Salonika, Greece. They hardly believed me: the young mistrusted old men exactly as do children in 1989. Apparently this is the way of the world. But now, when my zest for living equals zero on the scale from one till infinity, I see, perhaps too late, how right was old Kochelet declaring that all is vanity and striving after the wind.

Not for nothing was he pronounced the wisest of the mortals.

Bette Howland

A Little Learning

I t was the sort of place where you expect to find a dentist's office— 939
one flight up over a grocery store; empty mail-coops, gloomy stairs—and
sure enough, you could hear the drill. The door stood open. A fan was
rattling the slats of the drawn blinds, the torn yellow covers of copies of
National Geographic. Spittoon. Coco matting. Waiting room electric chairs.
I wasn't going to the dentist but my heart sank anyway. This was the Fifties.
Dentists didn't try to be cheery. No one tried. Cheeriness came later. I never
got the hang of it. I mention this so as not to raise false hopes.

All the doors stood open. It was summer in Chicago. Streets had the
heat-DT's. They smelled of black rubber. The sun was a whetstone sharpen-
ing knives.

Across the hall a man was talking on the telephone. Actually, the voice
at the other end seemed to be doing the talking. He lounged against the
desk, one foot on the chair, chewing a little white piece of gum. Desk, chair,
file cabinet—grimmer than the dentist's, strictly War Surplus. Gun-metal,
olive drab.

"The ad?" I said. "The newspaper?"

He fished a form from his desk, pushing the chair toward me with
his shoe. I couldn't tell if he was grinning at me, or just cracking his gum.

The thing was, he looked like a Movie Star. The spotlight tan. The billboard smile. The right-angled jaw and surf of black hair. His shoulders were broad and his eyes were blue. Too blue to be true. Match-flames, Zippo lighters, spurting in the dark.

I was sixteen. I spent a lot of time smoking cigarettes in parked cars.

"Another Wahhnted," I heard him say into the phone.

TEACHERS! COLLEGE STUDENTS! HOUSEWIVES! RETIREES!

EARN GOOD MONEY

$50 WKLY GUARANTEED!

PART TIME/PUBLIC CONTACT/NO CANVASSING/NO SELLING

THE WORLD'S GREATEST ENCYCLOPEDIA

Name. *BLANK*. Address. *BLANK*. Phone #. Soc. Sec. #. Date. *BLANK BLANK BLANK*. That was it. I didn't have to lie about anything. Not even my age. Usually I had to lie about something; usually, my age.

On the wall, someone had stuck a map full of pins. The South Side of Chicago; Calumet Harbor, the Drainage Canal, the bend of Lake Michigan. All the train tracks and switchyards looked like drawings of muscles on anatomy charts. The dentist drilled; the voice bzz-bzzed in the phone. Outside, jack-hammers were splitting sidewalks. The very wires were whining on the poles.

He dropped my application onto his desk and pointed to a stack of spiral notebooks:

"Training Manual. Ten dahhlar depahhsit."

I didn't have ten dollars. I had sixty-seven cents.

"Wait a minute. Wayy-da-min-nit. Hold on, will ya?" He slapped a hand over the mouthpiece—swatting a fly. "What gives? What's your prahhblem? A Cahhlege Girl? Where's your books? A Cahhlege Girl! Whaddayaknow! So? Gimmee the lowdown. You learning anything?"

"A little," I said.

"A little." Click-Crack. Again the grin. If it was a grin. Under the tan, his cheeks were porous, gritty. What used to be called Five-O'Clock Shadow. Teen-agers notice things like that. To tell the truth, I hardly noticed much else. But even I knew a New Yorker when I heard one.

"Look, Cahhlege Girl. Take it. I can trust you, right? You won't let me down? It's a deal? Just show up. Four-thirty sharp. The YMCA Cafeteria.

940

Naturally, he said Cafeteriar.

I didn't say anything. I was trying to think of something to say. I was always trying to think of something to say. The effort must have made me look glum.

"Hey! What's the frown? Smile! You're hired! Just don't go getting me in hot wahhter, okay? A little learning!"

It was true, I was a Cahhlege Girl. The University of Chicago was still admitting high-school sophomores. According to some, including my father, it was just another Pinko-Plot; but he gave in and said I could go as long as it didn't cost any extra for carfare. The University was on the South Side, all the way east, near the Lake; we lived on the Far West Side, the city limits, the yellow brick barricades of Cicero. You took the 12th Street car and transferred to Pulaski; you took the Pulaski to Lake Street and transferred to the El; you took the El to Wabash—where it went screeching around the Loop, setting off firecrackers, scrapping pigeons—and transferred to the State Street subway. Somewhere around Cermak the train came up for air, and you transferred back to streetcars and buses. Garfield Boulevard. South Parkway. Stony Island. Cottage Grove.

I don't suppose these names mean much to you; they didn't to me, either. They were stops. Sometimes the A came first, sometimes the B; sometimes the smoke blew from the stockyards, sometimes the steel mills. Away from the lakefront, Chicago was a city without a skyline—almost, without a sky. Twenty-four hour dry cleaners, storefront churches, the barred windows of liquor stores and currency exchanges. The Tree of Heaven, more weed than tree, fanned the embankments, grew fearlessly alongside high tension wires, dread third rails. Cleaning women from the housing projects waited under viaducts, clutching transfers. Pigeon-gurgle echoed. Light fell like litter.

I was supposed to be studying; I looked out the window. Even on the subway, I looked out the window. Reflections galvanized against the dark glass made for reverie. As long as you kept getting your transfer punched, you could do it on one fare; you could do it in your sleep. Which was all right with me; I was asleep anyway.

Saturday nights I spent sitting with my boyfriend Don-Jon in automobiles of makes now long extinct: Nash, Hudson, DeSoto, the little Studebaker, bullet-shaped, that looked the same coming and going. No, he wasn't a car thief; just working after school in his father's gas station. Mr. Joncola

941

was hoping to expand the business to a parts and body shop ("Junkola's"—the local wags called it), so we had our pick of wrecks. We're talking car woes, real woes. Gears stripped, blocks cracked, rods thrown, gaskets blown. Their batteries were dead and their tires were flat. But nothing was wrong with their front seats. We never made it to the back. Front seats were more accommodating then; no stick-shifts, sporty buckets, safety belt gizmos. Don-Jon turned the radio at the cash register full blast. I wanted to listen to the ball games—these were the glory days, the Go-Go Sox—but Don-Jon was hot to get In The Mood:

Iff Sum-buddy luvs-yoo

Leather jacket, ducktail, mirrored sunglasses, a cigarette plugged behind one ear, a strap buckled to his wrist (no watch, just a strap)—his style was tough; what else could it be? He knew all the tricks; how to strike a match under his thumbnail, how to light two cigarettes at once, so he could pass mine to me, hot and seething from his lips; and he smelled—no particular order, all together—of sweat, leather, motor oil, *Lucky Strikes, Lava Soap*, and T-shirts that dried in sun and air on the line. The hairs of his chest poked through, wiry black as the hair on his head. His one and only defect: who ever heard of a *kinky* DA? His grew in bent rigid rows, like bobby pins on cards in the dime store. All the *Vitalis* in the world wouldn't make it lie down—slick and sullen, sulky with hair oil. But he kept pouring it on, the scented droplets glittering under the streetlamps.

It's no goood un-less she luvs-yoo

Box-cars clanked in the Western Avenue yards. (Or Wood Street, 40th Street, East Chicago; we were never far from Railroad Yards.) They sounded weary. In slicks and puddles rainbows were shivering; cracked windshields sparkled—spider webs spun of glass. The globes on the pumps were flying saucers, glowing moons too ripe to rise. Necking in that heat, in scrap-metal heaps, we might as well have been breathing through gas masks.

Alll the wayy

The tinny clink-chink of tires bumping the air hose; a car rolling up to the pump. Some tanned hairy arm heavy on the window. Don-Jon sauntering over, grease-rag jutting from his hip, hoping against hope all they wanted was two bucks' worth of regular. He dreaded looking under hoods. I was the only one in on his secret; he knew about as much about cars as I did. He wanted to be a Gangster when He Grew Up. It was the most Grown-Up thing we could think of.

Like I say, it was The Fifties. Even at the time, it felt like the past.

KNOCK-KNOCK. *Hello! How are you today? My name is BLANK, and I have a Special Free Gift for you, just for letting me tell you all about a unique one-time offer from THE WORLD'S GREATEST ENCYCLOPEDIA ...*

THE WORLD'S GREATEST ENCYCLOPEDIA (or, as we always said it, The Wur-rold's Greatest) was not just respectable. It was venerable. An institution. "The Cadillac of Knowledge," as it called itself. In its all-wood custom-built bookcase (a Valuable Extra Bonus with the Lo A–Z Payment Plan)—the stiff gold-splattered spines ranked side-by-side— it looked more like "The Fort Knox." A Safe or a Shrine.

That was the trouble. A Shrine-glut. Shrines weren't moving. So THE WORLD'S GREATEST was trying to get in on the Mass Market, the Credit Market—hawked, hustled, hyped, after the manner of Used Cars, Aluminum Siding, and Hot Merchandise on Street Corners. Frozen steaks from the backs of delivery vans. Diamond rings out of suitcases. Swiss watches flashed like badges on the linings of coats. We were about to fold up our tents, disconnect our telephones, and skip town on the next freight.

In other words, the job was selling. Installment selling. Door-to-door; no leads, no follow-ups, no salary, no guarantee, straight commission. That was Fifty dollars on a sale. Four-thirty sharp at the YMCA Cafeteria, and everyone seemed to be practicing multiplication tables:

943

Fifty times one ... Fifty times two ... Fifty times three ...

I couldn't afford to buy my dinner; I needed change for carfare. I squirmed into my seat, making myself scarce, gripping the edges of a damp aluminum tray. A dish of rubbery red Jello. A glass of iced tea. A Parker House roll. By and by I got up the nerve to sneak a look around:

Teachers! Housewives! Retirees!

Jello. Iced Tea. Parker House rolls.

—One! Just one a week!

—That's all it takes.

—There's your fifty right there.

—Nothing to sneeze at!

—Just a matter of time and sticking it out.

—And anyone can sell.

—One a week!

Mr. Sparky (I think I'll call him) always sat by himself at his end of the table, reading a newspaper folded and propped against a water glass—his cheek clicking and snapping, his gaze switching back-and-forth, back-and-forth, the way it did when he talked on the phone. What used to be called Nervous Energy. He was in Technicolor. He shimmered. The tan that set him off; his eyes blue-blue, too-blue, his teeth white as his gum.

The Sun-Times? The Trib? Herald-American? Daily News? Chicago papers had black headlines, flags on the mast-heads; murky photos of the latest UFO sightings on the front page. No, not one of ours; some Eastern paper, maybe. I wouldn't put it past him.

Ladies in hairnets and aprons were ladling gravy. Fluorescent lights—pink tubes, purple tubes—twitched and twittered. Basketballs thudded, billiard balls knocked. Fans performed the usual dredging operations. Light buzz-sawed the edges of the long-tattered shades. Blackout shades, left over from the wars. Aromas of disinfectant, sweaty gym mats, cold bacon grease, pressure-cooker steam, and chlorine fumes in paint-flaked turquoise pools. The walls had the lumpy tan glaze of the gravy.

Gloom. Dreggy gloom. Gloom accumulated and perpetual.

These were Training Sessions. A couple of us had to get up and go through the sales pitch from start to finish—the first KNOCK-KNOCK to the final LAST CHANCE—reading the Training Manual out loud word for word. THE WORLD'S GREATEST ENCYCLOPEDIA in the format of *Ripley's Believe It Or Not*.

24 volumes! 24,000 pages! 3,000,000 words! 5 000 illustrations! 600 full-page full-color plates! 52 maps! All the States in the Union! All the countries in the world! All the planets in the Solar System! See The Mona Lisa! The Hope Diamond (life-size)! The Declaration of Independence (an Actual Facsimile)! Teach yourself Surveying (11 pages)! Botany (3000 specimens)! Philosophy (101 entries)! Learn the Odds in Poker (2,598,960 possible hands)!

And so on.

From time to time, Mr. Sparky folded his arms and leaned back, gum stretching and cracking almost conversationally. In spite of the heat, his shirt-collar was buttoned, his necktie knotted under the bronze lump of his throat. "Cahhnfidence! Cahhnfidence! That's the ticket!" "Smile! You're on Candid Camerar!" "Let's have more action! Zip! Zing! You know the song, doncha? There's no Tomahhruh?" And once, when I had finished my turn—tilting all the way back in his chair:

Click-Snap. "No Cahhment."

Even his gum had an accent. Even his laugh. Hahh Hahh Hahh.

I guess he couldn't help it if he sounded irahhnical.

Embers of shame fan and glow in my face.

After the YMCA, we set out for The Territory. The Territory was always different, The Territory was always the same. Sub-divisions that had sprouted in the building boom since the War. Names commemorating trees chopped down and scenic attractions no longer (if ever) in view: Oak, Elm, Hickory, Willow and Maple; Brook, Grove, Bluff, Forest and Park. The new sidewalks spattered and twinkled, as if the cement had been mixed with ground glass.

Mr. Sparky called it "The Terrortory."

Fritzi Ritz was showing me the ropes.—You understand, we had nick-names. Cartoons, comics, radio serials. Dagwood. Blondie. Daisy Mae. Fibber McGee. Gildersleeve. The Shadow. ("Who knows what e-vil *lllurks* in the hearts of man? The Shadow knows.") Our Gal Sunday. ("Can an orphan girl from a little mining town in the West find happiness as the wife of England's richest and most handsome Lord?") I had a few: Cahhlege Girl. Glum Customer. Worry Wart.

KNOCK-KNOCK. *Hello! How are you today?*

Fritzi was in Show Biz, she hinted, selling encyclopedias to pay for her tap-dancing and singing lessons—and to gain Cahhnfidence. She even said it like Mr. Sparky. It sounded more Cahhnfident. She was at least six feet tall, with a tossing horsetail of hair, fingernails like lacquered red razor clams (they clacked) and a lot of makeup—the kind that glowed in the dark. She was always practicing something; posture, elocution, a sort of plunging step—"Thighs first, that's how the models do it"—swinging her briefcase up walks and down, running the gauntlet of baseball bats, catcher's mitts, overturned trikes, writhing green garden hoses.

KNOCK-KNOCK. *My name is BLANK.*

Families had finished their dinners, dishes were stacked in the sink. In the Heartland we eat early, Thank God. Through aluminum doors, picture windows, glimmered the phantom flickering screens of little rabbit-eared TVs. Bicycle bells jangled, roller skates rang and scraped, sprinklers were turned on in the grass—offering mouth-to-mouth resuscitation. CHchch CHchch CHCH chchch. Mosquitoes were recharging their teeny bug-batteries. No breeze, of course, but the sun had quit grinding its axes, the light was beginning to glower. The heat was holding its breath. The lingering whispering truce: summer dusk, summer dusk, on the prairie.

KNOCK-KNOCK. *I have a Special Free Gift for you . . .*

After a while it dawned.

"Hey" I said. "You take it back."

"*Take what back?*"

"The Special Free Gift. You take it back."

Fritzi gave me a funny look. In the twilight, her eyeballs were gloaming. Frosted, almost, like her lids and her lipstick.

"Oh. Oh, I get it. You mean I take it *back*. Well, Jeez, you better believe it. One's all we have. That's all they give us, is one. A fine howdoyado! No Special Free Gift! That's how we sell it. It's psychahhlogy."

"Yeah. But don't people mind?"

"Mind? Nope. Why should they? You can leave it if you make a sale, I guess. Maybe it's all right then. I don't know. Besides. It's just a bro-shoor. Who'd want the darn thing anyhow?"

Cahhnfidence! That was the name of the game. Cahhnfidence! You had to win it. But to win it, you had to have it. And to have it, you had to get it, and what if Cahhnfidence was not to be got? What if you couldn't beg, borrow or steal it?

Mr. Sparky sat at his end of the table, we sat at ours, a sort of herding instinct. He was The Boss, the Big Cheese, our Master of Ceremonies; a Superdooper Salesman good for two scores a night. But that wasn't all. East is East and West is West. I hope I'm not giving away state secrets.—We were Chicagoans: Hicks. Rubes. Hayseeds. Yokels. Bumpkins. Mere Country Mice. (What used to be called an Inferiority Complex.) He was a New Yorker. A City Slicker. He had Cahhnfidence. He rubbed it in. I just wish you could have heard him say Chicago. You know how, don't you? Shikawwgo. Everyone knows that. But not him. Not Mr. Sparky. Oh no. Chicahhguh. Ch-ch—as in *Chiclets* (those hard white pellets he was forever popping, his pep pills).

Chicahhguh. That said it all.

And that undulating pompadour, that gum-pumping grin! It was like being in the audience at a live stage show downtown. The Oriental, the Rialto. We packed lunches so we could stay all day and they never kicked us out. Crooners, comics; but my favorite, by far, was an accordion player whose accordion I dearly longed to be. It was ebony inlaid with mother-of-pearl buttons and it went into ecstasies. Oh to be hugged, oh to be squeezed, who wouldn't sigh, who wouldn't shiver, who wouldn't ripple and thrill to be the trill of those fingers? He wore a red silk cummerbund, black satin pants, a peasant or pirate shirt slashed to the breastbone with billowing sleeves—and kept time with his foot, with his hips, with a throb in his cheek.

His Smile! Blinding white as a Welder's torch.

His Tan! Radioactive! You needed a Geiger Counter.

Oh, he blazed brighter than any spotlight; the glow of celebrity—soaking up candlepower, basking in footlights and fame.

Thick tan crockery. Shredded paper napkins. Red jello, yellow jello, green. Light swooning in water glasses. Tremolo Vibrato Glissando.

—And if one, why not two?

—Damn right! Why not?

—What's to stop you?

—Once you click—catch on—the breaks start coming.

—One hundred smackeroos!

—Now you're talking!

—Real money!

One evening we headed East, not West, out South Shore Drive toward Calumet Harbor and the steel mills. Pillars of cloud by day and fire by night. Lake Michigan was a sort of smoking blue vat. Old factory neighborhoods; block after run-down block; brick banks, striped barber poles, hornets buzzing bruised fruit under canvas awnings. Massive ugly churches—the kind that meant business. The local movie palace was advertising, TWENTY DEGREES COOLER INSIDE and LADIES NITE FREE DISHES. The pigeons and fire escapes looked ornamental.

What happened? Did they run out of Terrortory?

It was my first time out on my own. On one side of the street, a cyclone fence, gravel lot, factory transoms, coal-hoppers. On the other, two-story houses in Insobrick siding and cars parked under mulberry trees. I may not know trees, but I know mulberries. Most of the first floors were now separate flats, below street level, because the sidewalks had been raised. The cement was weedy and cracked with up-thrusting roots.

In the cellar, the screen door was on the hook.

KNOCK-KNOCK.

"I ain't deef!"

Some skinny old guy in a baseball cap and bifocals. He wore a short-sleeved shirt with a name embroidered over the chest pocket, and he was packing a little white poodle under his arm. The dog started to bark.

"Biff! Bam! That goes for you too!" He whacked it on the snout. The tip of its nose was a wet black bumblebee.

"*Hello! How are you today?*"

"Whacha selling?" he said.

"Howja know I'm selling?"

"I ain't dumb neether!"

He began to cough, gasping and wheezing and wiping his eyes under his glasses. "That's rich, that's rich!" The bifocal lenses flashed and gleamed. I couldn't tell if he was laughing or having a fit.

"Well? You just gonna stand there swallowing flies? Come in."

"Come in?"

"Make up your mind, Girlie."

A bed. A bureau. An alarm clock. A hot plate and electric fan on the table, dog dishes under the sink. A pint-sized refrigerator—the kind with a motor on top and a pan underneath to catch the drips. It sounded like a helicopter.

"*I have a Special Free Gift for you, just for letting me tell you—*"

"Oh yeah? Thanks. That's nice." He rolled it up in his fist and whacked the dog again. "Bop! Let that be a lesson. Just so you know what's good for you."

Actually, the dog was pink; it was shaved naked as its belly, except for its head, its tail, a sort of fur ruff and its four stick-legs in poodle-booties. Like those frilly pants they put on lamb chops.

"Hafta remind her who's Boss," he said.

He sat down, tilting the fan toward his face, his face toward the fan. An abrupt abbreviated face; his jaw hung hardly lower than his lip, the chin whittled as a corncob pipe.

He stuck it out. "Okay. Shoot."

I opened the Training Manual and commenced.

24 volumes. 24,000 pages. 3,000,000 words . . .

The clock ticked; water dripped; the fan droned from side to side. The refrigerator was getting ready for takeoff. Outside horns honked, trolleys clanged, tires thump-thumped, whistles tooted. Freights? Barges? This is all landfill, you know. Sawgrass, marshland. People angle for catfish in gas-green ponds. Weeds share the depths with beer bottles, inner tubes, retired Chevrolets. Flies snapped, dragonflies hovered; the summer snored on. The sonorous, monotonous prairie summer; sounds dropping like stones down abandoned wells.

His bifocals glinted. Teardrops of mineral oil. A bald bump bulged under the elastic band of his cap.

"Say. How much does one a them things cost?"

"*For a limited time only, if you act right now . . .*"

"Just outta curiosity," he said. "Just the straight dope."

I told him.

"Woo-*wee*! You hear that?" He nudged the dog with his skinny wishbone elbow. It crowed like a rooster. And there he went again—spluttering all over the place; hacking, racking, cackling; doubling up, clutching his throat, beating the air with his hand. I thought he was done for.

"Could I get you a glass of water?"

"Oh, that's good. That's a hot one." The tears were trembling in his rimless glasses. He kept coughing; the dog kept crowing; both of them kept backing me toward the door. It was only a few steps. Cockledoodledoo and the next thing I knew, I was on the outside looking in.

The screen was on the hook.

I pushed my nose against it and squinted in.

He was squinting out. So was the dog. His cap and its snout made waves in the mesh.

"F'rget sump'n?"

"My Special Free Gift," I said.

"No you din't. Got it right here. Bingo!" He swatted a fly.

"That's what I mean. Wouldja mind? Couldja give it back?"

"Give it back? What for? You gave it to me, dincha? You said—"

"I know. That's what I'm spozed to say. And now I'm spozed to get it back."

"Who sez?"

"My Boss."

"That him?"

Don't worry. I knew it was a trick. I'm not as dumb as I look.

I turned around.

Biff! Bop! Bam! Bingo!

"The Cahhlege Girl!"

Mr. Sparky stood like one of those life-size cardboard cut-outs under the movie marquee. Next to the dishes. The T-square shoulders. The solid bronze tan. The solid white smile. He was glancing from one of us to the other, his eyes on the move, his jaw on a spring.

This was embarrassing. Nothing new: I was embarrassed a lot. Whenever I was conscious, anyhow. They seemed to go together.

"He won't give me back my Special Free Gift," I said.

"*Her* Special Free Gift? *My* Special Free Gift! She gave it to me."

"Hey, no kidding. You mean you really want it? What for?"

"None a your business. A souvenir. What's it to you. Huh, Hotshot? Huh?"

The old man's neck was getting longer, its strings were stretching, its cords quivering. The dog ditto. Two straining necks, two chinless muzzles.

"Ahh, c'mahhn. don't be that way. Give it back."

"Make me. G'wan. Big Shot! Think you're Hot Stuff! Make me!"

Mr. Sparky grabbed my arm. Not romantically, not gallantly. Not even ceremoniously. He yanked. "Let's gedoudda here."

"Sic 'em! Sic 'em!" the old man was yelling.

"I'm sorry," I said.

"Sic 'em! Sic 'em!"

"'Snothing. 'Snot your fault. Guy's goofy. Cuckoo. A loony. Consider the source."

He was gazing up and down the street. A vacant lot mobbed with white-headed dandelions. A car squatting on flat tires, hood up. It would be better off at Mr. Joncola's garage. On the top floor of a yellow brick three-flat, the fire escape door was open. Onions were frying. A couple of clay flower pots sat out on the iron rungs.

"Tell ya what. Next door we come to, we're gonna make a sale. Prahhmise. Wanna bet? Gloomy Gus?"

The onion smell got stronger as we climbed the stairs. Coming from the top floor, all right—to the left, down the hall. In the dim light you could almost conjure fumes floating through the door—onion specters at an onion seance.

Mr. Sparky was still holding onto my arm. He gave it another yank. "Knahhck."

The door opened at once. A muscle-bound young man with a baby mounted on his shoulders and a religious medal flashing on his bare chest.

The baby was in diapers, he was in pajama bottoms, and both of them were grinning from ear to ear.

Both had the same flat cheeks, glistening eyes and shocks of stiff chopped-off black hair.

"Hello. Please. Hello."

He stuck out his hand. His grip was eager. The baby's legs framing his face made his wide smile wider. With a sweep of his arm, almost a formal gesture, he stepped aside, followed us in.

A hot bright room. Very hot. The windows were shut, maybe stuck; even over the onions you could smell the varnish. Fresh sticky varnish; floors, woodwork, window-frames, trapping bubbles and flies. Thick old wallpaper buckled under a load of new paint.

In the kitchen alcove a woman was standing at the stove, her back to us, poking a fork at a frying pan. She was the size of a child; her long skirts hung unevenly about her ankles and shins; her long hair hung straight to her hips. As if she stood huddled head and shoulders in a glossy black shawl.

"Hello? Please?" The young man was offering chairs. A shiny chrome dinette set. All the furnishings were new; and not just new—still in their wrappings, price tags and all. The sofa draped in the sheet of tattered plastic it must have come in; the legs of the coffee table in corrugated cardboard and packaging tape. A large carton took up one wall: MOTOROLA MOTOROLA MOTOROLA all over it. The front was cut away to expose a blank screen. A TV console. It wasn't plugged in.

The sun against the glass had a brand-new glare.

Our host sat on the sofa, the baby crawling over his lap. Another peeped out from behind it—the same size, in diapers, the same little glittering eyes and chopped black hair. This one's ears were threaded in gold.

As soon as Mr. Sparky started to introduce himself, the young man jumped up and shook hands all over again. His name was Ramirez.

"Pleased to meet you, Mr. Ramirez. Nice place you got here. That your wife? Those your kids?"

"*Si. Muchacho. Muchacha.*" He laid his hands on their heads.

"And all this? It belongs to you? Yours?"

Mr. Sparky was glancing all about, gum-in-cheek.

"Mine?" Mr. Ramirez pointed at himself. "Mine?" He jammed a thumb against his chest. "*Si.* Yess! Mine!"

His muscles amazed me. This was before—long before—the fitness craze. Charles Atlas ads ran in the back pages of comic books, next to *Woman Driven Mad By Itch*. His chest was armor-plated—polished shields. His shoulders weren't straight across, like Mr. Sparky's. They sprang from his neck, heavy and sloping, like boughs from a tree.

"And you bought it On Time?"

Mr. Ramirez frowned. He looked regretful.

"On Time! On Time! You know? The Installment Plan?"

He nodded, relieved—almost grateful:

"Buy Now. Pay La-ter."

He didn't just say it, he enunciated. A gold tooth flashed, like his medal.

Most people I knew had things Too Good To Use. Only For Company. On Display. This was different; not a matter of safekeeping. Cartons, plastic, price tags, labels—all belonged to these objects; defined them, enhanced their value. They were of the essence. He was getting his money's worth.

The heat wasn't so bad, once you got used to it. Once your blood came to a boil, you could just sit and simmer. The door to the fire escape was open, but that didn't help any. The woman huddled, the fork scraped; sharp powdery spices made me want to sneeze. Flies were wiping their sticky fly-feet. The windows faced west; the red tongue of the sun smeared the glass. Factory transoms, chimneys, flat graveled rooftops—Chicago stretching on and on, brick by brick. Like miles and miles of boxcars loaded with ore.

24 volumes. 24,000 pages. 3,000,000 words . . .

Mr. Ramirez leaned closer, closer, a frown crushing his forehead, glancing from the Training Manual to Mr. Sparky as if he were taking some sort of test. His shoulders were hunched; his cheeks, the bridge of his nose, flattened and puffy—like a newborn's or a boxer's. Heat, onions, varnish, cartons, crawling babies, his anxious attention—all seemed offerings of hospitality. His eyes dimmed and brightened, dimmed and brightened. His language was as serious, elevated as his gestures.

Comprendo. Librero. Erudicion.

Mr. Sparky was skipping. He left out The Hope Diamond, The Mona Lisa. Poor lonely Pluto, outcast of the planets. Never Draw to an Inside Straight. Even the joke about learning all about the Atom but How To Build The Bahhmb. He was wasting no time. Straight for the jugular. The double whammy.

Education. Key To The Future.

"Your children's future, Mr. Ramirez. *Mañana*, right? That boy there—that one's the boy, isn't it? That's your *muchacho*? Well, that boy of yours could grow up to be President of the United States one of these days. *Comprendo*? President?"

"Yess-yess. I. Like. Ike."

Grinning again, biting off the syllables, evenly, deliberately baring the edges of his teeth. The little boy was pulling at his medal. He grabbed its bare foot and pretended to gobble: "*El Presidente! El Jefe!*" He planted a wet smacking kiss on its belly.

"*Sí*! President! Because this is a Free Country, Mr. Ramirez. Aww right? The Land of Ahhportunity? The American Dream?"

Mr. Ramirez looked worried again. His eyes dimmed in their niches.

"Dream?" Mr. Sparky laid his two hands under his cheek.

"Dream!" Mr. Ramirez shut his eyes and snorted. The babies giggled. He popped open an eye and winked at them sideways and snorted again.

"No no. Not sleep. Dream! Dream! What you do when you sleep!"

Mr. Sparky was leaning across the table, gum suspended, eyes blinking. It made them bluer. Earnest blue—primary—blue as elements. I thought of beaches. Not 12th Street, North Avenue, with their hotdog stands, burning pavements, broken glass, stinging things disguised as grains of sand. Real beaches. Tan, white and blue. Like the ones in *Wrigley Spearmint* posters.

953

I could smell the brass of his sweat. It trickled out of his hair, past his ears, his square-hinged jaw, like glistening sideburns. I couldn't tell if he was being corny-sincere or phonysincere, and I didn't know which was worse.

Now what? Why was he laying his hand over his heart? Was he going to recite the Pledge of Allegiance? No—only reaching for his fountain pen. Unscrewing the cap. Spreading the contract on the table.

Mr. Ramirez grasped the stub in his fingers.

I let out a squawk.

They looked up with a start. So did the babies. The one was straddling the arm of the sofa and toppled right over. An awful thwunk. It sounded like basketballs bouncing on shellacked floors at the Y.

The fork clattered. Bare feet, a swirl of skirts—the woman was swooping down, snatching him up; her shawl of black hair swaddling them both. The little boy was crying for all he was worth. She clasped him to one shoulder, gazing over the other at Mr. Ramirez—her back turned, her head lifted; profile, chin, shoulder all one rigid line. She was a statue of scorn.

And she was pregnant. Any day now. The hump was almost as big as she was. The child lay hard and low in her belly like a shot in a sling.

Mr. Ramirez sat looking up sheepishly, his eyes two buttonholes.

Her glance fell on the table. The damage was done; the weapon dripping in his hand, the ink on his fingers. Maybe she said something, maybe she didn't; a hiss, a snap—as of fat in the fire. She swiped up the contract and, all in one motion, began balling the paper in her fist and stuffing it into her mouth.

"Lady! Whadderyer doing?"

That was a dumb question. What did it look like she was doing? She was eating the contract. You heard me. Eating it.

Even the baby stopped crying and rubbed his eyes. It's not that easy to eat paper. Try it yourself, if you don't believe me. Crisp new paper. Legal-sized. A document! No one tried to stop her. Who's going to mess with a woman 4½ feet tall and 3 feet pregnant?

Her face was broader, darker than her husband's, her cheeks stony ledges. Not one to register expression.

Fist to teeth, fist to teeth.

954   She was making spitballs.

Our host rose to his feet. He handed the pen to Mr. Sparky (who still held the cap) and with a grave graceful gesture—a toreador, maybe, making a pass at a bull—indicated the door. She was standing between him and it, but not between it and us.

A good thing we didn't have to use the fire escape.

Somewhere a bell was tinkling, a wind-up toy in the distance. Otherwise, you could hear a mulberry drop. The sidewalk was black under the trees.

"Hey! What the hell! What in holy hell! Whajjer do that for?"

"Do what?" I said.

"*Do what? Do what?*" A squeaky falsetto. "Don't gimmee that. Miss Innocence. You know what! C'mahhn. What's your gimmick? You from *World Book* or something? *Encyclopediar Britannicar?*"

He was screwing the cap on the fountain pen, replacing it in the pocket-lining of his jacket. A flash of silk and labels.

"I didn't think he really wanted an Encyclopedia," I said.

"*Wahhnted? Wahhnted?*" More squeaks. "What's *wahhnted* got to do with it? Selling is you make them wahhnt. Whadder you think selling is?"

Straightening his necktie and collar, squaring his shoulders and jaw.

"Whadder they want from me? Whadder they tryna do to me? Look what they send me. Cahhlege Girls. Zahhmbies. Hard luck stories. Look where they send me. Chicahhguh. The Boondahhcks. They don't even talk English."

What did this mean? He didn't pick The Territory? He didn't pick The Team? It was the first time it occurred to me that Mr. Sparky wasn't The Boss. Not even His Own Boss. Somewhere there were Higher-Ups Calling The Shots. I bet they had real offices too; like the ones pigeons peeked into downtown from the El. Carpets. Air-conditioning. Upholstery. Not Army Surplus desks and dentist's drills.

He was pushing his face at me, nose-to-nose, so close his two eyes seemed to cross, merging into one under the roots of his brows.

It looked hurt.

It was occupied. Someone at the window. A person inside. Whatever that meant. Something told me I was not about to find out.

"Well, I didn't think *she* really wanted one," I said.

He glanced up at the fire escape. As if the woman might be standing there, long hair, skinny shanks, belly pointing like a loaded cannon. But there were only the flower pots, and the sun sinking down in a sort of magnetic haze. We didn't call it pollution.

"You can say that again."

The bell was still tinkling. We could see it now: the Good Humor Man. No face; just the white cap, white uniform, pedaling the wagon, treading dusk. The clanking sounded mechanical, melancholy, long ago and far away.

"Mr. Sparky," I said. "Why do we sell it like this?"

"Why do we sell it like this?" Thinking out loud, talking to himself. "Why do we sell it like this?" He sounded faraway, too. "We sell it like this, Sweetheart, because this is like it sells. And don't you forget it." His gum springing into action, rhythmical, resilient; his eyes blue vistas. "And I'll tell you what else. Don't take it so hard. 'Sno loss. Between you and me, I got a hunch his credit wouldn't of checked out anyhow."

S. J. Perelman

Strictly from Hunger
(A Torpid Serial)

One examines the flotsam and jetsam of James Joyce, why not the
langan of S. J. Perelman?

We are interested in how considerable writers developed their style. Usually,
and these pieces are no exception, the individuality of the writer is present early.
In Perelman's case, that means brevity, an ability to navigate through appalling
puns and a malicious use of language with a straight face.

Two years after first appearing in Judge, Perelman was at work with the
Marx Brothers. The trademarks are all there. You have but to apply their faces
to the wisecracks. As the Marx Brothers are the beginning of a recognizable style
in American humor—along with George Benchley, George Jean Nathan (a
co-editor with Perelman at Judge) and a few others—it is worth seeing where
all this verbal slapstick started.

Nor is it just in words that Perelman began: the bulging eyes, the foreshort-
ened features, the stereotyped expressions of his cartoons were soon, by other hands,
to fill the pages of the New Yorker.

Perelman was a complex man, no doubt. I did not find him, as some
later did, curmudgeonly, but rather obsessive. He polished words with the
same scrupulous care with which he invented them. A new joke was precious
freight to him. And in these pages, it's not the jokes one savors so much as his

attitude towards them, the very particular, aslant way in which he exploited them.

Yes, I was excited, and small wonder. What boy wouldn't be, boarding a huge, mysterious, puffing steam train for golden California? As Mamma adjusted my reefer and strapped on my leggings, I almost burst with impatience. Grinning red-caps, scratching their woolly polls, lifted my luggage into the compartment. Mamma began to weep silently into a small pillow-case she had brought along for the purpose.

"Oh, son, I wish you hadn't become a scenario writer!" she snuffled.

"Aw, now, Moms," I comforted her, "it's no worse then playing the piano in a call-house." She essayed a brave little smile, and reaching into her reticule, produced a flat package which she pressed into my hands. For a moment I was puzzled, then I cried out with glee.

"Jelly sandwiches! Oh, Moms!"

"Eat them all, boy o' mine," she told me, "they're good for boys with hollow little legs." Tenderly she pinned to my lapel the green tag reading "To Plushnick Productions, Hollywood, California." The whistle shrilled and in a moment I was chugging out of Grand Central's dreaming spires followed only by the cries of relatives who would now have to go to work. I had chugged only a few feet when I realized that I had left without the train, so I had to run back and wait for it to start.

As we sped along the glorious fever spots of the Hudson I decided to make a tour of inspection. To my surprise I found that I was in the only passenger car of the train; the other cars were simply dummies snipped out of cardboard and painted to simulate coaches. Even "passengers" had been cunningly drawn in colored crayons in the "windows," as well as ragged tramps clinging to the blinds below and drinking Jamaica ginger. With a rueful smile I returned to my seat and gorged myself on jelly sandwiches.

At Buffalo, the two other passengers and I discovered to our horror that the conductor had been left behind. We finally decided to divide up his duties; I punched the tickets, the old lady opposite me wore a conductor's hat and locked the washroom as we came into stations, and the young man who looked as if his feet were not mates consulted a Hamilton watch frequently. But we missed the conductor's earthy conversation and it was not until we exchanged several dirty stories that we began to forget our loss.

A flicker of interest served to shorten the trip. At Fort Snodgrass, Illinois, two young and extremely polite road-agents boarded the train and rifled us of our belongings. They explained that they were modern Robin Hoods and were stealing from the poor to give to the rich. They had intended to rape all the women and depart for Sherwood Forest, but when I told them that it was in England, their chagrin was comical in the extreme. They declined my invitation to stay and take a chance on the train's pool, declaring that the engineer had fixed the run and would fleece us, and got off at South Bend with every good wish.

The weather is always capricious in the Middle West and although it was midsummer, the worst blizzard in Chicago's history greeted us on our arrival. The streets were crowded with thousands of newsreel cameramen trying to photograph each other bucking the storm on the Lake Front. It was a novel idea for the newsreels and I wished them well. With only two hours in Chicago, I would be unable to attend the Fair, and the thought threw me into a state of composure. I noted with pleasure that a fresh coat of grime had been given to the Dearborn Street station, though I was hardly vain enough to believe that it had anything to do with my visit. There was the usual ten-minute wait while the porters withdrew my portable typewriter to a side room and flailed it with hammers, and at last I was aboard the "Sachem," crack train of the BBD & O. lines.

It was as if I had suddenly been transported into another world. "General Crook," in whom I was to make my home for the next three days, and his two neighbors, "Lake Tahoe" and "Chief Malomai," were everything that the word "Pullman" implies; they were Pullmans. Uncle Cudgo, the dusky Ethiopian in charge of "General Crook," informed me that the experiment of air-cooling the cars had been so successful that the road intended trying to heat them next winter.

"Ah suttinly looks fo'd to dem roastin' ears Ah's gwine have next winter, he, he, he!" he chuckled, rubbing soot into my hat.

The conductor told me he had been riding trains for so long that he had begun to smell like one, and sure enough, two brakemen waved their lanterns at him that night and tried to tempt him down a siding in Kansas City. We became good friends and it came as something of a blow when I

959

heard he had fallen off the train during the night. The fireman said that we had circled about for an hour trying to find him but that it had been impossible to lower a boat because we did not carry a boat.

It seemed only a scant week or ten days before we were pulling into Los Angeles. I had grown so attached to my porter that I made him give me a lock of his hair. I wonder if he still has the ten-piece I gave him? There was a gleam in his eye which could only have been insanity as he leaned over me.

"Shall Ah brush you off, sah?" he inquired.

"No, Uncle Cudgo," I said negligently, "I shall descend in the usual manner." Ah, Uncle Cudgo, faithful old retainer, where are you now? Gone to what obscure boneyard? If this should chance to meet your kindly gaze, drop me a line care of the Railroad Men's YMCA at Gloucester, Mass. They know what to do with it.

The Scenarist Perelman Reaches His Destination and Gives You a Thrilling Description of a Six-Bit Paradise

960

The violet hush of twilight was descending over Los Angeles as my hostess Violet Hush and I left the suburbs headed toward Hollywood. In the distance, the glow of huge piles of burning motion picture scripts lit up the sky. The crisp tang of frying writers and directors whetted my appetite. It was good to be alive, I thought, inhaling deep lungfuls of carbon monoxide. Suddenly our powerful Gatti-Cazazza slid to a stop in traffic.

"What is it, Jenkin?" Violet called anxiously through the speaking-tube to the chauffeur (played by Roy D'Arcy).

A *suttee* was in progress by the roadside, he said—did we wish to see it? Quickly Violet and I elbowed our way through the crowd. An enormous funeral pyre composed of thousands of feet of film and scripts, drenched with Chanel No. 5, awaited the torch of Jack Holt, who was to act as master of ceremonies. In a few terse words Violet explained this unusual custom borrowed from the Hindus. The worst disgrace that can befall a product is an unkind notice from a New York reviewer. When this happens, the producer becomes a pariah in Hollywood. He is shunned by his friends, thrown into bankruptcy, and like a Japanese electing hari-kari, he commits suttee. A great bonfire is made of the film and the luckless producer, followed by directors, actors, technicians, and producer's wives, immolate themselves. Only the scenario writers are exempt. These are tied between the tails of two spirited Caucasian ponies, who are then driven off in opposite directions. This custom is called "a conference."

Violet and I watched the scene breathlessly. Near us Harry Cohn, head of Columbia Studios, was being rubbed with huck towels preparatory to throwing himself into the flames. He was nonchalantly smoking a Rocky Ford five-center, and the man's courage drew a tear to the eye of even the most callous. Weeping relatives besought him to eschew his design, but he stood adamant. Adamant Eve, his plucky secretary, was being rubbed with huck towels preparatory to flinging herself into Cohn's embers. Assistant directors busily prepared spears, war-bonnets and bags of pemmican which the Great Chief would need on his trip to the "Happy Hunting Grounds." Wampum and beads to placate the Great Spirit (played by Will Hays [sic]) were piled high about the stoical tribesmen.

Suddenly Jack Holt (played by Edmund Lowe) raised his hand for silence. The moment had come. With bowed head, Holt made a simple invocation couched in one-syllable words so that even the executives might understand. Throwing his five-center to a group of autograph hunters, the great man poised himself for the fatal leap. But from off scene came the strident clatter of cocoanut shells, and John S. Cohen, filmdom's fearless critic, wearing the uniform of a Confederate guerrilla and the whiskers of General Jubal T. Early, galloped in on a foam-flecked pinto. It was he whose mocking review had sent Cohn into coventry. It was a dramatic moment as the two stood pitted against each other—Cohn against Cohen, the Blue against the Gray. But with true Southern gallantry Cohen was the first to extend the hand of friendship.

"Ah reckon it was an unworthy slur, Suh," he said in manly tones. "Ah-all thought you-all's pictuah was lousy but it opened at the Rialto to sensational grosses, an' Ah-all 'pologizes. Heah, have a yam." And he drew a yam from his tunic, and soon they were exchanging yams and laughing over the old days.

When Violet and I finally stole away to our waiting motor, we felt that we were somehow nearer to each other.

Hollywood! With a sharp intake of breath I snuggled luxuriously into the buffalo lap-robe Violet had provided against the treacherous night air and gazed out at the gleaming neon lights. Soon we would be in Beverly Hills, and already the quaint bumboat women were swarming alongside in their punts urging us to buy their cunning beadwork and mangoes. Occasionally I threw a handful of coppers to the Negro boys, who dove for them gleefully. The innocent squeal of the policemen as the small blackamoors pinched them were irresistible. Unable to resist them, Violet and I were soon pinching each other till our skins glowed. Violet was good to the touch, with a firm fleshy texture like a winesap or pippin, and I was about to borrow D'Arcy's bridgework when we arrived at her home—a magnificent rumbling structure built of beaverboard quarried in the mines nearby.

I had hardly entered the 118-foot living room before I was handed a sheaf of wires, telephone messages, and cables. The news of my arrival in Hollywood had thrown financial centres into an uproar. To the reporters who flocked around me I laughingly disclaimed that this was a business trip. I was simply a scenario writer to whom the idea of work was abhorrent. Telegraph instruments clicked, newsreels and microphones broadcast my message, and a balance was soon restored. I washed sparsely, curled my mustache with a heated hairpin, flicked a drop of Sheik Lure on my lapel, and rejoined my hostess.

After a copious dinner, melting-eyed beauties in lacy black underthings fought with each other to serve me kümmel. A hurried apology, and I was curled up in bed with the Autumn, 1929, issue of *The Yale Review*. Halfway through an exciting synthesis on Sir Thomas Aquinas' indebtedness to Professors Whitehead and Spengler, I suddenly detected a stowaway blonde under the bed. Turning a deaf ear to her heartrending entreaties and burning glances, I sent her packing. Then I treated my face to a feast of skin food, buried my sleepy head in the pillow and went bye-bye.

In which our Hollywood Man, with Horrible Accuracy, Describes the Local Beaneries and the Plushnick Studio

HOLLYWOOD BOULEVARD! I rolled the rich syllables over on my tongue and thirstily drank in the beauty of the scene before me. On all sides nattily attired boulevardiers clad in rich stuffs strolled nonchalantly, exchanging epigrams stolen from Oscar Wilde and inhaling cubebs. Thousands of scantily draped but none the less appetizing extra girls milled past me, their mouths a scarlet curve and their eyes clearly defined in their faces. Their voluptuous curves set the blood hammering in my pulses and as I made my way down Mammary Lane strange thoughts began to invade my brain. I realized that I had not eaten breakfast yet. With brisk step I entered the Pig and Whistle Cafe and ordered an avocado salad. The statuesque Albertina Rasch girl behind the counter covered my salad with walnuts and chocolate sauce, an organist cunningly concealed in the wall broke into "Don't Let Your Heart Go Boom-Boom, Don't Let Your Love Go Wrong." A strange giddiness overcame me and I decided to order something else.

"Well, let me see," pondered my waitress. "We have hamburgers, chickenburgers, beefburgers, baconburgers, steakburgers ... why don't you try one of our specials—a nutburger?"

"...?" I murmured faintly.

"Hamburger with chopped nuts," she offered helpfully. "Double ball of vanilla on the side."

"What would a man drink with that?" I muttered averting my eyes.

"Well, how about a Mammouth Malted Milk? It's too thick for a straw—*hey, what's the matter, mister?*" ...

When I came to, I was looking up into a circle of anxious faces and the manager was bathing my wrists in cold water. "He sorta slid off the chair barking like a dog," I heard my waitress saying excitedly. "Gawd, it was horrible." In a few moments I was again master of myself and was able to stagger out into the air. Swept along by the pleasure-mad throng, I found myself looking into a pink-and-blue shack whose neon lights told me that it was Burp Hollow, Home of the Realistic Ten Cent Hot Dog. My head began to swim again and I hurried on. Upon the glowing facade of Grauman's Egyptian Theater a message awaited me: "VOLTAIRE and Dave Hutton—No Advance in Prices!" Next door to the theater, the Goldberg Dry Cleaners, a new establishment, was having its premiere. Giant Klieg lights were smoking in the sunshine, palm leaf fans were being distributed, and autograph hunters were hungrily besieging Mr. Goldberg for his signature. A radio amplifier blared out the haunting strains of a theme song written to the air of "Pack Up Your Troubles" ...

Just let the Goldberg Service service you
And smile, smile, smile
We do your dyeing, pressing, tail'ring too
In the grandest style
What's the use of worrying?
Just keep your name on file—AND
Just let the Goldberg Service service you
And smile, smile, smile!

I smiled obediently and made a mental note to send Mr. Goldberg a box of poisoned cream puffs. A few feet beyond, a Chinese restaurant invited me with the words "BAMBOO ISLE—Strictly Kosher Turkey Sandwiches, Fifteen Cents" but I gritted my teeth. Finally, in an eatery built in the shape of an old boot I was able to procure a satisfying meal of barbecued pork fritters and orangeade for seventy-five cents. Charming platinum hair hostesses in red pajamas and peaked caps added a note of color to the scene, and a gypsy orchestra played Victor Herbert on musical saws. It was a bit of Old Vienna come to life, and the sun was a red ball in the west before I realized with a start that I had promised to report at the Plushnick Studios that morning.

Commandeering a taxicab, I arrived at the studio just in time to witness the impressive ceremony of changing the guard. In the central parade ground on a snowy white charger sat Max Plushnick resplendent in a producer's uniform, his chest glittering with first mortgage liens, injunctions and estoppels. His personal guard, composed of picked vice-presidents of the Chase National Bank, was drawn up stiffly about him in a hollow square. But the occasion was not a happy one. A writer had been caught trying to create an adult picture.

The drums rolled dismally, and the writer, his head sunk on his chest, was led out amid ghastly silence. With the aid of a small step-ladder Plushnick slid lightly from his steed. Sternly he ripped the epaulets and buttons from the traitor's tunic, broke his sword across his knee, and in a few harsh words demoted him to the mail department.

"And now," began Plushnick, "I further condemn you to eat—"

"No, no!" screamed the poor wretch, falling to his knees and embracing the general's same. "Not that, not that!" With a contemptuous gesture Plushnick spurned him.

"Stand up man," he ordered, his lip curling, "I condemn you to eat in the studio restaurant for ten days and may God have mercy on your soul." The awful words rang out on the still evening air and even Plushnick's hardened old mercenaries shuddered. The heart-rending cries of the unfortunate were drowned in the boom of the sunset gun.

In the wardrobe I was measured for the smock and Windsor tie which was to be my badge as scenario writer, and my typewriter was mounted on marshmallows to render it noiseless. Stars were twinkling in the sky as I came out again into the prison yard.

In my cell I threw myself on my bunk and had almost fallen into an uneasy slumber when a careful scratching made my eyes open. In a dark corner near the floor a little hole had appeared in the wall. As my heart began to pound madly, a hand holding a file appeared and a guarded voice whispered, "Is that you, Beansy?"

In which our Hollywood Man Finally Gets Down to Work and Is Confronted with Some Shooting Stars

The first pale streaks of a Hollywood morning crept through the Venetian blinds and tinted my tousled head the rich hue of burnished gold. In a few seconds rosy-fingered dawn and dawn-fingered Rosy, my maid-of-all-work, would come bearing my breakfast. I awoke and stretched myself like a great tawny cat. Slipping on a Japanese kimono the silkworms had woven during the night, I sauntered into the garden and crunched up the gravel path. I was hungry, and I would have gorged myself on the delicious little stones had I not remembered that breakfast was waiting.

Between sips of fragrant Oolong I tore open my mail. A card from Peets & Moultrie, Meats and Poultry, invited me to sample their line of condemned army meats, favorite of leading Hollywood hostesses. Mendel Aberration, my tailor, advertised his monthly special: four suits of Harris tweed for eleven hundred dollars, or, if I preferred, four hundred suits for eleven hundred dollars. Yawning, I finished my farina and padded into the living-room to read the papers. As I sank into an easy chair, I again congratulated myself on my good fortune in acquiring The Shambles. I had rented it under the very noses of Garbo, Gable, Crawford, Gaynor and Hepburn, and small wonder that they were livid with jealousy. It was patterned after an Italian abattoir of the sixteenth century and had been remodeled by

Christopher Wren, who had introduced chewing-gum into the left wing. Up to this time there had been no chewing-gum in the left wing. The entire house was built of lack-lustre celotex and heated by a series of smudge fires issuing from a charcoal brassiere. Consequently, there were very few mosquitoes or tenants in The Shambles.

But it was time to think of reporting to the studio. Glowing with health, I decided not to take a shower. Then came the problem of what to wear. Beeves, my man, had laid out a pair of loosely-woven monk's cloth trousers and a nutmeg-colored sweater. But my mood today was definitely creative, and I decided on a greenish garment I had purchased the day before at a students'-and-misfit-clothing store. As I pulled on Glastonbury health underwear my mind was busy with scenarios, novelettes, long short stories, short short stories, and the like. Two secretaries busily took down wise sayings, aphorisms, homespun observations, and shrewd comments on current fads and foibles as they fell from my lips.

Bowling swiftly down Sunset Boulevard toward the Plushnick studios in my motor, I dictated half a novel and an uproarious comedy drama destined to run ten months on Broadway. Mid morning found me at my desk clearing up details and making decisions. My brokers, Whitelipped & Trembling, had rung me up in panic. An ugly rumor that I would reorganize the motion-picture industry was being bruited about in the world's commodity markets. The Paris Bourse was begging me for assurances of stability and Threadneedle Street waited with drumming pulses for my next move. Film stocks ricocheted sharply, although wools and meats were sluggish, if not downright sullen. A few words murmured into the transatlantic telephone, the lift of an eyebrow here, the shrug of a shoulder there and financial equilibrium returned.

I had barely opened *Variety* and spread it over my face for a few minutes' rest when a revolver shot rang out in the hall and my secretary burst in.

"It's Baby LeRoy with a gun!" she gasped. "He's—he's out to get you!"

"We're ready for him," I said quietly, "Here, Hawkins, take this fowling piece. You, Squire Trelawney, by the stockade, and watch out for an ambush. Now, Doctor Livesey, let him in." A moment later LeRoy swaggered in, his eyes bloodshot and a smoking .44 in his hand. It was easy to see that he had been drinking.

"Well, LeRoy?" I asked curtly. His answer was a volley of fearful oaths.

"Put up that weapon, LeRoy," I said calmly, "or I promise you on my honor as Magistrate of the Crown that your worthless body will swing from Execution Dock at the next assizes!" Slowly the color drained from his bloated face, and great hulking brute that he was—over two years of age at the time—he backed away, fingering his forelock.

"No harm meant, matey," he stammered, "an old seadog wot's been battered by wind and wave, blow me down! I was with Flint in the Dry Tortugas—aye, and with Sir Henry Morgan at the taking of Panama."

"You'll do well to stay away from spirits, my man," I told him, "and as for chewing tobacco—"

"Belay there!" he screamed, his face purpling, "Blast you for an interfering swab! Why, shiver me timbers, I—" With a choked gasp, he spun about suddenly, clutching at his throat, then fell to the floor.

"Apoplexy," I said shortly. "Another scoundrel the less. But now, unless I am very much mistaken, our troubles are only beginning." And sure enough, from outside the stockade a blood-curdling yell rent the air as Shirley Temple, Bobby [sic] Coogan, Baby Peggy and their whole crew of ruffians opened fire on us with their one-pounder. Powder and ball flew thick, I can tell you, and the cries of the wounded were fearful in the extreme. We had just given up hope when I felt someone shaking me vigorously and a voice saying in my ear, "Wake up, sleepyhead, do you want to be late for school?" I sat up and rubbed my eyes with my little knuckles as I saw Mummy's laughing lineaments. What do you think? *It had all been a DREAM!*

967

The End of the Trail

The most beautiful scenario writer in the world!

My heart gave a great leap as Maurice Spaniel, potent head of the Motion Picture Academy of Arts and Sciences, held out the ornate silver cup to me. Instantly the hush which had attended Mr. Spaniel's speech of presentation gave way to echoing shouts and applause, mingled with the hisses of disappointed candidates. Cheek by jowl with the surgeons who threw themselves at my feet begging me to bequeath my brain to Johns Hopkins, envious writers already conspired to dethrone me. In a corner

W. Somerset Maugham was distributing handbills that claimed that I had swayed the judges with gifts of Hershey bars and marzipan. In another corner, Thomas Mann and Clarence Budington Kelland feverishly hatched plots to mar my face with vitriol. Ivan Bunin, in a third corner, his face distorted with envy, was hastily tearing up the Nobel prize and writing a trilogy in which I was painted as half-man and half-devil. Lineal descendants of Balzac, Dostoievsky, Zola and Kate Douglas Wiggin passionately exhorted the crowd to burn me in effigy. It needed the pen of a Hogarth to describe the scene, and sure enough, Rockwell Kent on the sidelines was rendering the occasion immortal for Simon & Schuster.

Fortunately I was too flushed with elation to heed those who would pull me from my pedestal. Blushing furiously and uttering little squeals of "No! No!" I was hoisted to the shoulders of my jubilant fellow-scenarists and carried through the throng. Slavering beauties of stage and screen caught me as I passed, attempting to snatch buttons, pieces of show-lace, my tie—anything as a souvenir. Outside, on Sunset Boulevard, a group of admirers numbering in their midst Joseph Schenck, Balaban & Katz, Samson Raphaelson, and Samson Agonistes had unhitched the horse from my barouche and seized the shafts. As I appeared, they gave vent to little cries of joy and quickly harnessing me, they piled in and we set off like the wind. Passersby, seeing the unusual spectacle, laughed good-humoredly and drew a little closer to each other for protection. "College boys," I could hear them saying tolerantly.

Several hours later, deliciously tired, I recounted the details of my triumph to Mamma, nor did I neglect to tell her how I had issued completely nude from a huge pie on the banquet table. Smiling quietly, she shook my head between her hands. It had become separated from my shoulders during the excitement of the evening. A serious look came over her face as she deftly attached it to its former vantage point.

"Don't you owe your fans a duty, Bubbles?" she urged, combing out the bits of coal-tar which had become snarled in my copper curls. "Every boy wants to know how he too can become a beautiful scenario writer. Why can't you reveal the beauty secrets which turned you from a shambles into the acknowledged leader of the cinematic beau monde?"

"You're right, Monica," I said decisively, crushing out my cigarette in the hollow of my hand, "and I'm going to do it right *now*."

First, of course, there is the problem of your skin. The ordinary scenario-writer's skin is too large for his body; consequently, bits of dermis are always getting caught on desk corners, projecting nails, and fences of ball parks. I daresay we are all familiar with that unlovely sight, a scenario-writer's desk fluttering with bits of loose skin. Begob, it looks terrible—I wouldn't wish it on a dog. So what I do after I come back from a hard day at the studio is to take a good astringent cream and rub it into the desk until about eight o'clock. This opens whatever pores you and the desk have. Then drink until I fall down in stupor and hit my head on the radiator. This brings up the people who live under me—funny little folk in red hats and pointed shoes and they help me off to bed. I have been doing this for eleven years, knock wood, and nobody the wiser, not even me.

Now what to do with your face when you awake in the morning? Here is a problem indeed, but I usually follow a very simple routine. First, the face must be combed thoroughly. A stiff wire brush will remove the strands of typewriter ribbon and spots of ink, but should be used sparingly around the ears.

At this point I am ready for my milk bath. The huge black bath-tub containing thirty gallons of steaming Grade A is my most cherished possession. Lolling back in it my mind becomes a beehive of ideas. Several efficient secretaries, who work for nothing merely to be near me, take down acid comments, pithy saws, charming vignettes, and biting sarcasms; these by products are relayed to a corps of typists to be bound and shipped to a firm of Eastern publishers, who, in turn, bind and ship them back. Meanwhile I busy myself making toy boats of letters from feminine admirers and send them sailing away on a puff of fragrant Turkish. If a letter from some pathetic little seamstress or love-starved housewife should happen to intrigue me, I have Hawkins send her a photograph of myself.

And so the day slides by and I am alone, save for the sea and the sky and the oft-remembered fragrance of your hair, you dear readers of LIFE you. At eventide the familiar lines of Percy B. Schabelitz come back to me in all their haunting poignancy "Perchance to dream and drift, and drifting down, and dreaming drift—who knows?"

Suddenly I awake with a start and realize that I have lain in my milk bath since morning, musing like the ink-stained wretch I am. Remorsefully, I adjust my tippet and rush off clippety-cloppety to my waiting tipper tapper at the studio. But laggard scribe though I be, I must halt my impetuous

969

dash to yon fusty cubicle to retail to your delighted ears one devastating suggestion made to your correspondent by a little old lady not a million miles away from the Algonquin Hotel. She it was, who, on the occasion of suggesting titles for that ponderous tome "While Perelman Burns" now in its seventy-fifth thousand, looked up from her cribbage board and was heard to utter the cryptic caption of "Mosses from an Old Nance."

Conall Ryan

Grace Notes

Minken's feet barely touched the stage as he played. He was shaped for sitting: frail legs with thick, knobby knees, water-cooler torso, short, sinewy neck, all of it straining to support a massive head. The top of his head was bald and the stage lights seemed drawn to it. Tufts of hair shot out wildly above his temples; a softer kind of hair sprouted fuzz-like inside his ears. As he played, his glasses slid down to the end of his nose, and his wiry goatee tickled the tailpiece of his violin. He squinted at his music. There were two thousand people in the audience. With four bars to go before his solo, Minken lifted his bow above the strings and pretended to keep playing, plucking the open strings with his left hand to make sure his instrument was still in tune. The strings were fine, but Minken was very drunk.

The solo started slowly, two measures of quarter and half notes climbing the E string to fourth position. Minken's vibrato was fatter than usual, the pads on his fingers numb from drink, but he didn't panic. The bass and cello sections stopped playing. Minken launched into sixteenth-note arpeggios, left hand darting up and down the resin-dusted fingerboard, right hand carving a tiny piece of wood out of the belly of his violin with the frog of his bow as he finished off a triple-stop. He glanced up from the music to satisfy himself that he hadn't caused any significant damage to his fiddle. Now the violas and the seconds dropped out. One by one the sections of the orchestra conspired to expose him: the trumpets blasted six notes and quit abruptly, as if they had run out of ammunition; the French horns squawked a muted good-bye; the bassoons and clarinets played a slow figure and sank quietly like reeds in a pond. The triplets that confronted Minken on his sheet music sprung straight up, thick as a forest that none of the other instruments were willing to enter. Before he could resynchronize his hands, only a flute remained at the edge of the woods, guiding him pleasantly to his doom. And then he was alone. Alone in seventh position, where the intervals shrink and the strings rise so high above the fingerboard it seems they can't be held down and the notes must be pressed out of air. Minken pointed his toes and tried to touch the stage, but he was sitting too far back in his chair. He struggled through the rest of his solo, unable to control the riot in his fingers or focus on his sheet music, playing from memory now. The notes went by quickly, but Minken experienced each as a separate pain.

When the conductor, Zaretsky, refused to shake his hand during the first and only curtain call, Minken was suddenly aware that he had been concertmaster for seven years, three months, and fifteen days.

A frozen wave of white hair crested over Zaretsky's forehead. Deeply tanned and deeply offended. A lifeguard in a tuxedo. That was the way he appeared to Minken. Minken's breath caught in his throat. *Don't leave me here with my hand out*, he thought, as the applause dwindled. *Take my hand. Save me.* Zaretsky locked his eyes on Minken's and shook his regal head. "I've decided to stop counting," he had announced on his seventieth birthday, to the delight of the local media. Critics said his nose was so long and so thin that he didn't need a baton to conduct. The nose twitched at Minken now in an erratic, unrecognizable tempo.

"I'm sorry," Minken said, letting his right hand drop to his side.

"You should be," Zaretsky replied. And then he was gone.

"Congratulations," Tully, the assistant concertmaster, said, turning to Minken as the other musicians began to leave the stage. Tully was seven years older than Minken and did nothing to mask his annoyance at Minken's comparative youth and privilege. "That's as well as I've heard you play."

"Don't," Minken said, his head still tracing the path of The Nose in the air.

"It won't help to imitate him," Tully said.

Minken forced his head to be still. "Was it really that bad?"

Tully, not one to become physically familiar, even with his own family, touched Minken's shoulder gently. "Are you too drunk to tell?"

"My God," Minken said to the floor.

Minken didn't get out of bed the next day until the doorbell rang at noon. It was Tully. "May I come in?"

They had sat next to each other three times a week for the better part of a decade, but Tully had never been to Minken's apartment before. His visit was the final piece of evidence Minken needed to convict himself. They went upstairs, Minken in a bathrobe, Tully in a dark suit and a bright tie, like someone who couldn't decide whether to celebrate or go into mourning. Minken reached down between the cushions of his sofa and removed a cigarette from a battered gold case with the exquisite care of a man who wasn't quite sure his fingers were up to the task. While he lit the cigarette, Tully scanned the jumble of books on Minken's shelves, the angled furniture, the dull-colored carpets, the ashtrays everywhere, some half-full of indeterminate liquids.

"Come to console me, did you?" Minken asked.

"You're not a drinker, Jerry. Why did you do it?"

"I don't know."

They sat in silence for several moments before Tully said: "Zaretsky's bringing in a Russian to challenge you."

"Who?"

"Poliakin."

Minken shrugged. It was the first time he'd heard the name. "Where's he from?"

"Most recently, Holland. No one seems to know very much about him. Originally from Moscow. Moved to Europe ten years ago. He was in a quartet in Vienna for a while before getting the Amsterdam job."

"Defector?"

"No. They just let him out."

"Just let him out, and he's not even a Jew?"

"Maybe they didn't like the way he played," Tully said encouragingly.

"It isn't fair. They should be giving you a shot at me."

"Well," Tully said, arranging his hands behind his back, "it's decent of you to say so."

"You'd lose."

"Maybe."

"Absolutely. Not to be cruel, Tully, but you just don't have the gas anymore."

"Maybe you don't have the gas anymore, either, Jerry."

"I took a chunk out of my fiddle last night," Minken said, leading Tully over to the piano, where his instrument, glued together in 1775 by the great Cremonese violin-maker, Storioni, lay in state, displaying its tiny blond wound.

Tully bent toward the violin. "Just because you had a lousy night. . . . ."

"No, no," Minken laughed bitterly. "It was an accident." He slipped his left hand under the Storioni, lifted it gently from its velvet-lined case, and tucked it under his chin. Tully looked on in wonder. Minken licked a finger and rubbed the raw spot on the belly of the fiddle. Tully had a smart wife and three reasonably presentable children, but he had never known a violin the way Minken had, and Minken knew it.

"Don't get it wet," Tully said.

"I'll break it over my knee, I feel like it."

"I broke a violin once, when I was twelve. Right on stage. Shocked the living hell out of my parents. It was almost worth it."

Minken blew smoke into the hollow body of his violin.

"That's not good for it."

"Maybe Zaretsky will reconsider."

Tully stared past Minken, clicking his eyes hurriedly at different parts of the room, as if his memory had a limited number of exposures. "As soon as they call you a prodigy, you're in trouble. You know none of my kids play?"

Minken rested his head on top of the sofa and exhaled smoke at the ceiling, cradling his violin in his lap.

"I wouldn't allow it," Tully said. "None of them showed any interest. My theory is a kid should be left alone."

Minken suddenly rose from the sofa and came straight at Tully, backing him up toward the door. The hair that remained on his head shot out in every direction. "Let me know what you find out about Poliakin."

"What you did is unforgivable, Jerry," Tully said, letting himself be backed down the stairs. "Showing up for a concert in the bag like that."

"Have you ever gotten bored, Tully?" Minken asked, gaining stature as Tully gave ground on the stairs.

Tully frowned at him. "Sure. I've been playing the same repertoire ten years longer then you have. It's an occupational hazard, Jerry, like the little lumps we have on our necks."

"Forget the lumps on our necks. Have you ever reached the point where you think nothing important is ever going to happen to you ever again?"

"Zaretsky can't wait to see you holding down the last chair in the seconds," Tully replied, fumbling with the door, wanting to leave very badly.

Minken patted down a few strands of his disobedient hair. "I don't really care what happens now."

The Russian, Poliakin, was tall and slender, with a thick tangle of hair that was not quite red and not quite brown, and a face that was punctuated by high cheekbones and a lustrous mustache. He wore a trench coat and smoked thick, brown cigarettes that produced an occasional rattle in his chest.

Leaving his violin case backstage, Poliakin made a circuit of the hall, resting for brief intervals in different seats, staring intently at the stage, measuring off the distance his sound would have to travel with a series of sharp whistles, taking the marble steps up to the balcony two at a time, testing the sight-lines. He seemed to be planning a military campaign rather than an audition.

There was a black screen on stage. It was long and U-shaped, constructed of a porous material designed to protect the identities of the musicians without wringing the essential tone out of their playing. After poking the screen several times with his fingers, Minken waited backstage with Tully, suppressing the desire to open Poliakin's case and see what kind of violin he packed. "I'm pleased Zaretsky's giving you a chance, Tully."

"I can't remember the last time I played behind a screen."

"I know about these screens," Minken said. "They don't work. They're like big sponges."

Tully turned away from Minken and played something softly.

"What's that?" Minken demanded.

"Glazunov."

"They're having us play selections from the Glazunov?"

"You could have found that out for yourself if you had got here on time."

"Well, well," Minken replied. "The Glazunov. Nothing like serving him up a nice fat pitch over the plate."

975

"What else?"

"Passages from Ysaye's Fourth Sonata, one of the Mozarts, the D Major, I think, a bit of Glinka. . . .."

"*Kamarinskaja.*"

"Yes. It's not particularly difficult."

"It's a lie detector test for Russians! Jesus. You'd think they'd be a little more subtle."

"Why don't you practice, Jerry?"

"No, I'd rather listen to you."

There are plenty of no-nonsense, tuck-it-under-the-chin-and-play purists like Tully. You can admire them in the same way that you admire the fact that no two snowflakes are alike. Their playing is precise and brilliant and very, very cold. Ice men, raised on Sevcik. Minken viewed Sevcik and his disciples with suspicion. Could a normal person have composed two books on technique exclusively dedicated to exercises in double-stopping, line after line of muscular anti-music, as dull and joyless to the practicing violinist as laying mortar? Sevcik on shifting wasn't so bad, but Minken hoped the little Bohemian was burning in hell for committing those double-stopping exercises.

Minken counted himself among the few who could tease out a phrase as if it were a living thing, producing in his finer moments a sound that could con its way directly into your heart. He was entitled to this assumption, even if he failed to admit that in addition to his technical gifts he was also lazy. Tully played through a passage of the Glazunov without making a mistake. But there was something missing. "Too bad you just don't have the gas anymore," Minken said.

The lights dimmed several times, an indication that the judges had arrived and the musicians should stop playing and stay out of view. Poliakin returned from his tour of the hall, picked up his case, and waited patiently backstage without saying a word until a young woman appeared and tacked a piece of paper on the dark red curtain. All three men bent forward at once, like students waiting for their grades. Then Tully stepped behind the black screen and began to play.

"Very clean," Poliakin said.

"Oh, yes," Minken replied. "Tully plays beautifully."

Poliakin turned his head slightly to hear better. "But it's difficult to keep your mind on him."

"Zaretsky knows it's Tully."

"I'm suprised," said Poliakin, who didn't sound it. "The way he's playing, it could be anyone."

"Poor Tully," Minken said.

Tully was finished. He waited a moment behind the screen, then walked past Poliakin and Minken and stood by himself near the stage door.

"Thank you," a voice in the audience said. "Next, please."

Poliakin opened his case and pulled out a violin so old and delicate it looked as if it might fall apart in his hands. The grain of wood rippled defiantly through the varnish. An ornately carved scroll convinced Minken that the instrument was early eighteenth-century Italian, perhaps even a Guarnerius del Gesu Fur lined the inside of the case. It could have been sable, but the identity of the animal quickly gave way in Minken's imagination to the journey it seemed to indicate Poliakin had taken: a long punishing journey through a cold country, keeping his violin warm while a rattle developed in his chest.

Any hope, however, that Poliakin would play with the same cheerless precision that marked Tully's performance disappeared with the first two notes of the Glazunov. Poliakin's left hand met the fingerboard, his bow swept across the G string to begin the piece, but the sound that reached Minken's ears seemed to come from Poliakin's throat. During the first seven measures, his bow never leaving the G string, Poliakin filled the hall with a dark, wandering tone. Here was a true artist, a man who lived his life fully and possessed the skill to translate his experiences into a performance that convinced Minken he was hearing the Glazunov for the first time. Poliakin's vibrato was soulful, but sparing. Capable of sliding up to high notes in the best Russian tradition, his shifts were imperceptible. Nothing was overdone. How had such a violinist escaped critical notice in Europe? It didn't matter. Zaretsky had found him, and now he was here to take Minken's job. Minken's heart resonated with hopelessness and elation; fear settled into his hands at the knuckles, the joints, the fingertips. His career was over. His career was just beginning. No time to think.

"Thank you," the voice in the audience said again. "Next, please."

Minken took his place behind the screen. When you competed for the first chair in an orchestra, the music asked the questions and you answered them with your instrument: How fast can you play? Try this. How accurate is your intonation? Spot on. How milky is your vibrato? Drink. How *distinctive* are you? Minken's dangling feet, shiny dome and wriggling torso gave him an edge here. He was as curious to watch as he was delightful to hear. But the screen would cancel that out.

Why even play? He had spent enough time in the service of Zaretsky. Seven years, three months, and twenty days! A duty in its way not unlike that of an ambassador, with its emphasis on ceremony and deference and ceaseless repetition. What a demeaning thing it was, Minken thought, to be concertmaster of the most overpaid lounge act in America. Let someone else try it for a while. Let someone else become boredom's bedfellow. The well-heeled season ticket-holders had to put up with changing fashions, political uncertainty, escalating prices. They liked their music to stay the same. They had no appreciation for anything but mistakes.

Not really knowing what he was about to do, Minken sank his bow into the brooding first line of the Glazunov, the throaty sound Poliakin had produced still fresh in his mind. Yes, that was the way to play Glazunov. It made all the sense in the world. Stay on the lower two strings if at all possible, control your vibrato, let the phrasing project the emotion. The Storioni didn't capture the quality Minken was trying for right away, so he adjusted by drawing his bow closer to the bridge. He played from memory, with his eyes closed, and he held nothing back. When it was done, he looked up and smiled into the black screen.

A few fingerings, a bowing here and there, had been different. Otherwise, Minken had duplicated Poliakin's performance note-for-note!

When the audition was over, the young woman returned. She studied the order in which the musicians had played, compared it to the scribbled notes on her clipboard, and turned to Tully. "You're excused," she said, without emotion.

Tully nodded at Poliakin and Minken and left.

The woman studied her notes some more.

"Well?" Minken asked.

She folded the notes under her arm. "The judges have not reached a decision. Come back tomorrow at ten sharp."

Tully was waiting for him outside. "So are you out?"

Minken shook his head. "Not yet. We continue tomorrow. How did you like my *Kamarinskaja*?"

"You won't be able to fool them for long."

"Did you see his violin?" Minken asked. "My God, what a beauty!"

The symphony's agreement with the union prevented them from firing Minken. But if Poliakin beat him in a blind vote, they could banish him from the front of the firsts to the back of the seconds. Walking home to his apartment, a much greater distance than his thin legs were in the habit of carrying him, Minken pictured the gossips in the Friday matinee crowd, stuffed on their ritual lunch of cucumber sandwiches and weak tea at the Ritz, burping behind yellowed handkerchiefs and whispering, *What happened to Minken? Has he been taken ill? Oh, good gracious, look Martha, there he is! All the way in the back! They've put him on a dunking stool!*

"He hasn't won yet!" Minken shouted at the shadow ladies as he walked, startling a bicyclist and a passing dog.

When he got home, he took out a weather-beaten copy of Paganini Caprices and sat on his balcony reading it as an ordinary person might read a thriller. The cover was frayed and most of the pages were smudged with pencil markings from the different fingerings Minken had tried over the years. His left hand took lazy runs up and down the spine of the sheet music. Horns honked in the street. Minken closed his eyes and inhaled a deep breath of smog—to others pollution, to Minken the wonderful exhaust of life and motion and city friction. His head pitched forward until his wiry goatee snuggled against his chest. Memories of concerts formed in his mind. What was strange was that the memories were completely silent. He saw himself playing, felt himself shaping the phrases on his violin as a potter might coax a vase out of a potter's wheel. He shivered as if he were absorbing all at once the collective energy of the audiences he had played to over the years. But even applause did not make any noise in Minken's mind. Finally, an ambulance turned onto Minken's street with its siren wailing. He snapped awake and sniffed the air for an emergency. When the siren passed, he took the music inside, found a knife, arranged some apples, oranges, and grapes on a glass plate, ate hurriedly, washed his hands, opened his violin case, and sat down to play. He had one night to put his technique back together.

At precisely ten in the morning, the young woman posted a fresh menu of audition pieces on the stage door. It began with a tortuous musical appetizer: the seventeenth Paganini Caprice. Poliakin negotiated the chromatic runs of thirty-second notes brilliantly. Minken played with superior intonation the

979

rapid octaves that dominate the second half of the piece. Without sacrificing any vigor, without showing any technical deficiencies, the two men gave the impression that they were just warming up. Already, they were performing at a notch above their efforts of the previous day.

Next came an excerpt from the first movement of Tchaikovsky—called "unplayable" by the great Auer, and worse things by Zaretsky, which made the selection all the more bewildering—a variation of the opening theme in which the virtuoso must use an agile left hand and a rapidly bouncing bow to create the impression that he is playing two violins at once. Again, there was nothing to choose between them. Poliakin attacked the passage with passion and humor. Minken copied his approach.

On to the *Devil's Trill*. They were scheduled to play the Kreisler cadenza: a flap of butterflies with leather wings. Minken had to go first. He was forced to make a tactical decision. Guess the way Poliakin would interpret the piece and play it that way? Or follow his own instincts? Time to take a chance. He played the cadenza softly, using only the upper half of his bow, making the judges strain to hear the notes. The piece was a secret pact. Give me dexterity, Minken thought, and I will play in this small room far, far away from everyone I know and everyone I love, and the butterfly trills will be trapped inside this dark windowless room and the rest of the world will have to strain to hear, and the screen is a maze and the sound must struggle to find its way out, and I will bend the tempo a little bit, because I have all the time in the world in this small room where I'm playing.

It was a stunning performance. Poliakin must have thought so, anyway, because he did his best to imitate it.

The young woman hummed to herself as she studied her clipboard, reviewing one piece at a time. Suddenly, she stopped humming and let out a sharp laugh.

"What? What?" Minken asked, testily.

"Nothing," she said, checking her clipboard again, looking as if she regretted her loss of composure. "It's just that I can't believe this, that's all."

"Who are the judges?" Minken asked.

She stiffened slightly. "I'm sorry," she said, "but I have to fill out this form."

"We are giving them more then they expected," Poliakin said. It wasn't clear from the expression on his face whether he was addressing the remark to the young woman, or Minken, or perhaps even to his violin.

The young woman smiled warmly at Minken, and patted Poliakin on the shoulder. "The judges haven't made a decision. Could you return tomorrow at ten?"

Two more days passed. After the first, the young woman appeared backstage holding a bouquet of flowers in each hand, shaking her head. Minken accepted his only when she reassured him that they had not been sent by Zaretsky. "I'm so happy to be a part of this," she said, accepting one of Poliakin's brown cigarettes.

It would be pleasant to report that as Minken and Poliakin reached toward perfection, each note they played surpassed all the judges had heard before. The truth is that consistency and endurance marked these middle days. Minken resented the audience of faceless judges, and feared he would lose his dexterity before the Russian. Poliakin ate cough drops and applied strange-smelling liniment to his chest. Both played with the controlled desperation of artists who knew they were leaving the best performances of their lives behind a black screen, unrecorded, to an empty concert hall.

The young woman brought them take-out containers of Chinese food the next evening after they had delivered similar renditions of the Sibelius and Beethoven concertos. "No decision," she said, brightly. Poliakin waved away the food and lit a cigarette.

Minken propped himself up near the stage door and rubbed his feet. "Want to know my theory?" he asked, quietly. "There's no one out there. Zaretsky's taken them to the Ritz for martinis. They've all gone home."

"There are six of them," the young woman said.

"Do they have ears?" Poliakin asked. "What are they waiting for?"

"I don't know," the young woman replied. She had a copy of the Paganini Caprices under her arm. "I'm working on the seventeenth," she began, fanning herself with the music. "I was wondering . . ."

"Give it to me," Poliakin said. She handed him the music and a pen. The wheeze in his chest was audible all the way over where Minken was sitting.

"They're killing us," Minken said, after he also had signed his name to the cover of the Paganini. "Tell them that."

To perform again and again without receiving any applause turned Minken inward. It was an involuntary journey. There was plenty of clapping in his memory. Thousands of pairs of hands moved, but there wasn't any noise. He was absolutely alone. He listened for the intake of his breath, the scuffing of his shoes. Even the silences that followed his performances had motion, velocity. Under less stressful circumstances, he could have been a mystic seeking enlightenment through fasting. The problem with his magical performances was that everything was going out but nothing was coming back in.

"Your violin is very tired," Poliakin said, amiably. "Have you noticed? I have the feeling that soon nothing interesting will come out of it."

This was the wrong thing to say to Minken, if his subsequent performance of the Bruch G minor was any indication. Tightening his bow an extra twist, swaying wildly from side to side, he brought an ethereal quality to the soaring passages of the Adagio, then catapulted into the Finale with the enthusiasm and innocence of a boy. He could feel himself weakening to the point of fainting, but he made the music dance. His frail legs carried him in triumph off the stage, past the wheezing, gray-faced Poliakin. "Your turn," Minken said.

"That . . ." Poliakin said.

Minken swung his water-cooler body around. "Yes?"

"That was most beautiful, Minken."

There it was, an honest response, a gesture of true sportsmanship; there for Minken to accept or reject. Minken stared at the floor and said through clenched teeth, "How would you know?"

They played on through the weekend, throwing their caution aside. Their performances were not without mistakes, but the excitement, the sense of discovery they created with each new piece, was palpable. News of the musical duel and the spellbound, deadlocked judges spread through the city. Small groups of musicians formed around the locked doors of the concert hall. Some waited to hear the name of the winner announced. But the violinists among them circled the perimeter of the building convinced that it couldn't enclose all the secrets that were being unlocked by the two remaining contestants. A phrase, a cry from the E string—*something* was bound to leak out. Inside, the once-imposing black screen that hid Minken and Poliakin from the judges seemed in danger of being ripped open by the sheer force of their musical arguments. When they were required to play the same selection, the man who played first would project an idea into the near-empty concert hall, perhaps just a few notes, but so well-formed that the idea would linger in the air long after he had stopped playing. The other would use his turn to refute the idea, probing its philosophical weaknesses because it had no technical flaws, guiding the judges to a new place. The place Minken had fixed in his mind was Odessa, the warm-water port on the Black Sea and a great exporter of world-class violinists. Poliakin was a free man, but his sound—his *technique*—still belonged to Moscow. Convinced that the judges knew which way they wanted to go, and were simply waiting to receive directions for how to get there, the sly Minken changed musical identities once again. If he could lead the judges to Odessa, they would think they were going to Russia when they were really leaving it.

It was a clever strategy, and it might have worked if Poliakin's tuning pegs hadn't slipped during the Bach *Chaconne*, sending the pitch of A and E strings on his Guarnerius del Gesu plummeting, and with them, the quality of his performance. Unjustly betrayed by his instrument, the Russian loudly exclaimed—"*Krov!*"—and stopped to retune. Minken didn't know whether Poliakin was swearing at his misfortune or simply exhorting himself to overcome it, but the consequence of his speaking was clear: the judges now knew who was playing behind the screen. He might as well have shouted "P-O-L-I-A-K-I-N!" Moments after he resumed playing, the pegs slipped again. This time, he didn't cry out. Propping the scroll against his thigh, he wedged the pegs in tightly, then completed the *Chaconne* without letting the forced pauses ruin his concentration. In fact, the *Chaconne* that emerged from this unexpected disaster was riveted together with courage, and dressed in considerable beauty. Poliakin the terrible! Poliakin the *artist*!

983

The Russian finished and came straight for Minken. "I will ask for another day."

"No need," Minken said. "No need."

Minken was left with trying to make something interesting come out of his violin one last time. The schedule called for Vieuxtemps, but Minken instead decided to play his favorite concerto, the Brahms.

He walked to the chalked spot behind the black screen and raised his violin to play. For each breath he took in, he tried to let two breaths out. He wanted to be completely empty before he began. He felt a draft at his feet. He pushed his ear against the *f*-shaped hole in his violin and listened patiently for several seconds. As he had suspected, the draft produced a soft murmur in the belly of the Storioni, not as loud as the false waves it might project into the spiral of a large seashell, but enough to calm Minken.

"You're not really tired, are you?" Minken whispered gently into the violin. "I'm not tired," he said, so quietly that he wasn't even sure that the violin could hear him. "I feel pretty good."

Without bothering to arrange his feet comfortably beneath him, he began to play a mysterious long note, its pitch precise but evolving, becoming more mature as Minken nurtured it with his bow, audibly accelerating over the black screen the way a beanstalk might be seen to grow through time-lapse photography. Minken put every good experience he could think of into that note: feeling the spray of the ocean at night from the deck of a steamship, crunching his feet into the sand, having his belly warmed by the sun. So intense was his concentration on making the first note express these feelings that he almost forgot to play the rest of the piece. But play it he did, and as the mystery of the first note unraveled, it became clear that an indescribable sadness at having lost all of these things—sun and sand and ocean and the simple joy of making music—possessed Minken. Sadness, too, at the four miserable drinks he had taken; sadness at the failed solo; sadness at having sat next to Tully for a decade. There was something brittle and dried-up inside of Minken, and the only clear way he could confess it was through his instrument. *Forgive me!* he pleaded, his bandy legs like roots that had been torn up from the stage. *Don't you realize this is all I have?* Minken was so empty, the only thing that could enter him was hope. He gathered it from every phrase in the Brahms, from every corner of the concert hall, from the young woman who had given him flowers and asked him to autograph her sheet music.

And when he was done, when he had put down his whimsical, disobedient Storioni with its tiny divot and its invisible wooden heart, Minken could hear through the black screen the sound of a judge sobbing.

Keith Botsford

The Second Life of Gioacchino Rossini

I t is the fate of artists to be adulated and then forgotten; or forgotten and then adulated, *writes Ms. Isabella Colbran, diva.* My husband, on the centenary of whose birth your newspaper so unkindly failed to ask me to write this little memoir, belonged to both these categories, plus a third— those whose fate it is to be deliberately ignored due to a cabal of determined enemies (and a second "wife") who claim he was not the man he said he was. I am writing, therefore, to rescue a great man from unmerited oblivion, to press his claims against those who say his *Barber of Seville* was written by another, and that this undying work with all its lilt and brio was written by Gioacchino Rossini who was born a hundred years before my husband and lived, I am compelled to admit, a life quite like my husband's.

Of course I have an interest in this. If my husband did not exist, nor do I. My husband's music exists to confound his critics, but it is his life I am trying to resurrect; and thus mine.

Everyone said he was Rossini. Down to the insults: that he wrote melodies barrow-boys could whistle, that he was glib and trivial, that he used the bass drum to excess. What you hear about him, if you hear anything at all, is that after a brilliant career (until his music exhausted him) he sulked in Paris and wrote nothing more, except for one mass for voices of three sexes. (That was part of the throwback in him. He honestly wrote for *castrati* even though these had, save in the Vatican, disappeared.)

This makes me reflect on change. I am a very old woman, an Italian in London, neglected (we had no children); probably despised. I think London is a poor place. I barely visited the town in his lifetime: just once when we were received at Buckingham Palace in the days of your profligate Edward, a great eater who shared some of my husband's other tastes as well. In those days, your Sunday press was less scurrilous, one did not talk about such things, or there could well have been scandals.

But I remember Edward because he did do justice to my husband. Though personally I believe his tastes ran more to Offenbach, he was the first here to say that my husband was the immortal Rossini born again. Spoken like a king: he knew when compliments were appropriate.

I am, as you know, somewhat older than my husband. If I may say so, at that time, when we met—he came down to southern Italy to make his triumphal mark and I was singing there—I was considered a striking-looking woman. An early photograph sits on my piano. I hold a lyre; my head is tilted sideways; I am in Empire dress and my hair is cropped and curly. As

we are residuals of our former selves, all that's left of me is a length of nose. My voice is gone and was never recorded.

I didn't ask to become his mistress first and his wife afterwards. The needs were all his—and imperious. Sexual and financial. I wasn't swept off my feet. I knew and understood his genius. As a singer of opera, to be allied to the greatest composer living was no disadvantage.

I had done very well in school in Madrid. I had royal patrons and they sent me abroad to study, when I was sixteen, at the turn of the century. I studied in Paris and Bordeaux; then Papa (he was a musician too) went to Sicily. Later, in Bologna, we were described as "musical virtuosos from the Court of Spain." Spanish singers were all the rage, as Mademoiselle Malibran had been a century earlier; we were throatier, stronger.

I look at the divas of today. They face none of the difficulties I did. Certainly even at the close of the last century we were *artistes*, but there was also a presumption that we were available women. In a Stendhalian sense, *à la disposition de.* That had to do with gaslight, the energy of singing, the heat, coming out of a stuffy theatre late at night, one's appetite after three hours on stage with applause ringing in one's ears, flowers at one's feet, admirers, late suppers, champagne, the prospect of luxurious mornings in hotel beds. It didn't matter much by whose side one awakened; but during, so to speak, one had to convey the same passion and fire one had shown as a woman damned or a high priestess—one's role carried over into bed, and when the chambermaid knocked in some provincial hotel, one was as surprised as one could be to find oneself real. And the gentleman, too.

That is how I came to form a liaison with Giacomo Rossi, my late husband, who was then an unknown composer from a provincial town and with a few not very successful operas to his name. He woo'd me with flowers and *involtini* and ardor.

How can I write about my husband without writing about myself? It is like one of those great arias in which a woman sings of loving and being abandoned. My story is simple. I married a man my junior. I knew I was marrying genius and I supported that genius with my own. I loved him. I then fell on hard times: my voice failed, my talent failed, I was hissed. His fame simply increased until leaving me, it failed him too.

For yes, I saw myself supplanted and thereafter I lived as one would live who had lost all, destroying myself with this terrible vice of gambling until I sold not only his manuscripts and our silver but the very shades off our lamps. Giacomo was relentless in his pursuit of fame, maniacal in his career (at times he had four or five operas in preparation at once) and he sent me back to his father because I could no longer sing his difficult roles.

Thereafter, there is an *epilogo*: I follow his life from afar. His new life, his new wife. Their friends, my friends; his fame, her fame.

It ends on a somber note. I have but one consolation: his voice, too, fails him. After me, he is as much nothing as myself.

987

He was born in Pesaro, as fate would have it, on a leap year: on February 29th, 1892. Please understand me. I have nothing against Pesaro. It is no doubt a charming small town, though it does not have many attractions: neither an opera house nor much other cultural life. What it did contain, for my husband, was the seeds of disaster, for Pesaro was also where Gioacchino Rossini was born; equally on a 29th of February; equally of parents called Giuseppe and Anna. Believe me, that is a star-crossed coincidence.

About his parents. His mother Anna was a strikingly beautiful woman: doe-eyed, pouting-lipped, a generous bust, long chestnut hair. His father Giuseppe (the same with whom I was later forced to live) was of a different type, even a different class: choleric, in later years bulbous-nosed, mutton-chopped with all the bones of his skull visible just under the skin.

What is heredity? His father and mother, like mine, performed music in backwater towns. These were musical genes. I don't think my husband's genius derived from them: rather from the closeness of their ties, the affective disposition the three of them (my husband was an only child) had for each other. Their lives were rich in operatic passion. Their trio expanded as others entered their lives. They became orchestral. Inseparable. When Anna was dying, my husband dared not return from Paris, lest the sight of him kill her.

After Giuseppe died, my husband would not return to the apartments he had bought for his father's last days: the memories were too painful.

All those experiences found their way into music of a special kind: intimate and spectacular, very feminine, sometimes hysterical. They sang to and against themselves.

There was nothing remarkable about his upbringing, his musical beginnings; no spontaneous genius, no overwhelming precocity. Inspiration came later. His youth was somewhat overcast with his father's unpopular socialism, his radical airs. Yet father and son were, as I found out to my sorrow, closely paired. Money was short, education wanting. There was a strong family tendency to approve of a certain grossness, and a disapproval of furbelows and the ways of smart society.

As an international superstar, my husband acquired the ease of moving in exalted circles. That is not to say that he was at ease in them. There was an element of the crude in his raillery: of his father in his sarcasm, or of his origins in his bitterness. I know he felt that had he been better placed (or less needy, less ambitious) he might have learned greater control over his inspiration.

As it was, his technical initiation into the profession that overlook him (no other words will do) was minimal: a piano teacher who played the scales with two fingers, sold spirits he distilled at night, and who often fell asleep, standing up, ruler (with which to rap knuckles) in hand, during lessons; a few years of counterpoint with a sour pedant who put him off all but the most spontaneous classics for life; a few lessons on stringed instruments (principally the cello and double bass, so that he could earn a few lira in the local opera pit); singing in the chorus.

True, a great loving for Mozart, so that among the coarse Bolognese he was called *il tedeschino*, but none of those melodies flowing from his pen as though he were no more than an amanuensis to angels, none of those wonderful lilting, zigzagging accompaniments and florid lines that marked the great works to come. When I met him he was barely twenty-one and had written, as I've said, only a few somber operas on classical subjects. Nothing in the slightest bit *buffo*.

I now come to the period in which we met. In many caricatures of my husband he is presented as grotesquely fat. That is surely so. Some wit called him "burdensome in bed." (It's better in Italian as *lardo al letto* which is a play on one of his better-known arias.) Even in his youth, his fat went beyond the puppy variety, but also fell short of being disfiguring. He was comely, not awkward. His chest was very broad and jutted up into the stock he wore (in honor of how things had been.)

   He was, however, a creature of appetites. One should recall that his father was an inspector (honorary) of slaughter-houses, his mother a baker's daughter, and Giacomo himself had been apprenticed in youth to a pork-butcher. It is any surprise that he should invent a form of *tournedos*? It is not a crime to have a weakness for sausages, especially the sausages of our youth on whose shiny surfaces bubbles of fat glistened and within which all was succulence.

Thus my first memories of him are connected with food: his face oleaginous, his mutton chops specked with fat, his narrow mouth with its elaborately carved lips sucking, his tongue fluttering through his teeth in search of leftover morsels. He also drank copiously. An abundant man. And I was used to that. We singers are also ample. Giacomo undoubtedly did suffer from his appetites, which he made no effort to control. When he took up with his Frenchwoman (marrying a nurse is worse than marrying a secretary) there was a period in which she (for his health's sake, of course) whipped him out of his gastronomical fantasies. It couldn't last. Olympe herself was a glutton. A rather lopsided one, with a *decolleté* and slanted, cold eyes. Daily they forged through meals. Ceremonial meals. It came to the point that they despised restaurants, places where one ate neither well nor enough.

   At that point I was starving.

   And at the end, when it was evident my husband was ill, she reimposed her frugality. From that period come those reminiscent, ruminant little pieces

989

he wrote in her albums, with titles like "Radishes," "Anchovies," "Dried Figs," and "Butter: Theme and Variations."

Some others of his appetites can be glossed over. Some profligacies, besides showing up on our bodies, pay us out in bad coin: disease, madness, and death. I don't think my husband, when he roamed those dark, narrow back streets and their gaping, lantern-lit orifices, taverns and other low-life haunts, seeking his *puttane*, considered the possible consequences. He burrowed his way into a high proportion of infectious young women. He was rash, tempestuous, and seized by ardor then as he was later by music, which is an appetite of the ear. A wonder he could still sing the next day: and cheerfully, as if relieved in the bowel.

Social factors influence such "social" diseases. Italy, when he was young, was, thanks to the mothers of the nation, a place of repression, caresses, and indulged appetites. The proportion of *canaglia* to decent people was high; ordinary brigands were rife as summer flies. One has to recall that poor Rossi's connections were largely republican, not to say proletarian. Where gentlemen could afford proper mistresses (he was to get to that stage, and beyond) the rest had to make do with whores. Schoolboys in black cloaks, like off-duty policemen, roamed certain quarters to get deflowered. Rossi overdid it.

Therefrom (why conceal it?) he contracted a life of pain. Pain is depressing; he was depressed. To be fat is one thing. To have inflamed organs which make it acutely unpleasant to perform bodily functions is another. Today's medicine might have cured him. I doubt it. My husband was extreme in all things. He was possessed by illness, by appetite, by music. He paid for the lot. For his sex, with gonococcal urethritis, with hemorrhoids, with years of inserting a steel or rubber catheter—as that's painful, you may judge how painful the stoppage was, that he resorted to such remedies. Nor did "cures" stop there. Blood-letting, too, perineal leeches: yes, alive and blood-sucking in certain orifices.

Such stifling of the body and its exits and entrances—food in, little out without pain—swelled his belly grossly, and weighed in his mind. A doctor described him as "pycnic," which comes from the Greek and means "dense" or perhaps "compacted." It is a psychological type. All the effluvia, mental and physical, are retained.

*

This is the man I married. A man who might well have floundered, financially, without me.

Your readers may have no idea what the music business was like a century ago. Today, composers are professors at universities. Few try to make a living just from inspiration.

I brought him a dowry of £100,000, a considerable sum, even if it was not all liquid, much of it being in such oddities deriving from my parents' earlier lives, such as "castles" in Sicily and the like. Plus my earnings, which were not negligible. For singers were paid better than mere composers. Why not? Singers sell operas.

Giacomo and I lived in an economic middle kingdom. Rich people had an income; shopgirls, mill-hands and bank clerks had wages. We belonged to neither group. But my husband was acute about money, and no matter how much he earned, was terrified of indigence. Earning, too, cost him: thirty-nine operas in twenty-two years! That means fifty or more librettists thieving each other's morsels; as many managers and impresarios; several hundred singers; thousands of underpaid orchestral musicians, critics, bankers, patrons, friends, the state, the intendants, music publishers, pirates, agents, creditors, Thomas Cook, parents, cousins. They weigh.

He wrote benefits into his contracts, grand subscription concerts. We collected the cachet at the stage door. When he was in this country, he made more money in a year than in a dozen years before. By dint of refusing to teach singing to gawky Victorian girls of breeding unless they paid giant sums. They did. That was sex appeal. But ordinary sexuality plays a major role in money; success is a magnet. Those wan girls helped him leave London with £50,000. They wanted to sing his arias: with him.

Acute about money, I've said. His later years in Paris were spent as much with bankers as musicians. He was lucky; his hits still paid. For me it was different: a singer without a voice is nothing. Rossi liked money. The French allow that sort of mix without feeling the artist is thereby prostituting himself. He knew the Rothschilds, was invited to their grand weddings, collected stock tips, Suez shares and more. But always like the frugal, frightened Italian he was: just give me six or seven percent, he told them.

There, I have painted him whole, as he was in his early twenties: overweight, gluttonous, ruined by venery and captivated by wealth, romantic, republican and as yet unstruck by genius.

*

Basta. We were married. I undertook that as the obligation it is. We had no children (I was in my thirties when we married); he had no children (with her) either. The fault lay either with his corpulence—they say the energies necessary to breeding go into fat—or his gonococci. Or that in truth he loved only his mother.

We had a laborious beginning. Music was all work to him. Nothing came naturally. He wrote what used to be called *opera seria*; his nature was more *buffo*. He told me of a conversation he had with Beethoven, who told him to stop writing about Moses and just let himself be funny. Beethoven was right. We singers could hear the sweat in those high-minded arias and set-pieces. As with the Red Sea in his *Moses* when the waters (made of painted paper and operated by dozens of little boys with pulleys) refused to part, so the melodies he wrote refused to come together in that seamless line that was to become his trademark.

The problem lay with the way Rossi lived in the past. He so wanted to be a good boy, he so loved his Germans. He actually did talk to Mozart and Beethoven. I have heard him do so. And also to Wagner, who would drop in on him in hotels, looking pale and arrogant. There was a side of

him so involved in opera and the imagination, so buried in absurd libretti, that he imagined himself back into the past his father probably told him about, to which he wanted, perhaps from filial piety, to conform. As he spoke to composers long dead (often they chided him), so he moved from place to place in unimaginable discomfort, going to impossible lengths to hire great, lumbering carriages rather than travel by mechanical means, loco-motive or automobilistic. In the same way, he sought the tributes formerly paid to great composers, e.g., marble busts. In his mind, when we were first married, there were brigands on the roads. Thus what was practically our wedding journey, on the eve of the Great War, ended with His Imperial Majesty, from Vienna, inviting us, in a time of disharmony, to "contribute to the harmony of nations" with his music. Unpaid, of course. But Rossi loved such pomp.

This is before he met DSB, to whom I will now refer.

One day, as we were sitting eating an ice, there came up to us a short but elegant gentleman who, before speaking to Giacomo, laid his card down on the little round table. The name to be read on this card was Dominic S. (this turned out to stand for Shikaneder) Barbaia. He had a manner about him that, even to an Italian like my husband, seemed unctuous. He was grave, frock-coated (like the waiter he had once been) and very southern: what we now think of as mafioso. He was one of those men who do not need to be able to read or write in order to do business; they carry with them an exhalation of money.

His background was preposterous. He started life as a waiter in an establishment not unlike the one we were in, graduating to *barista*. In that higher form of life, he invented, and then bottled, a soft drink that became hugely popular and made him his fortune. Not satisfied with that, he conceived the idea that, as many men were bored with the operas to which they were dragged by their wives, he would set up, along with refreshments, private gaming tables in various opera houses. Such concessions did much to keep opera houses alive, and our new friend had a genius for obtaining these concessions. The suspicion was (and remains) that he had powerful friends, for without such, as is well known, nothing in Italy is at all possible.

In that café took place the conversation which effectively changed my husband's life.

"Signor Rossi," said DSB (as he was always called), "I have listened with great pleasure to your music. You have an undoubted gift for melody and for reaching into the human heart."

"I thank you," answered my husband, bowing.

"But . . ."

"Ah, there is always a 'but'."

"It is no reflection on your merits," continued DSB, "to say that heretofore you have labored with insufficient reward. I have a few theatres (in truth, he had a near-monopoly) in the South, and nothing would please me more than to make your fortune. If, that is, you will allow yourself to be guided by me."

"Guided how?"

"A touch here, a touch there, a few little ideas. Perhaps more an attitude of mind. We are in business, we artists, are we not? To entertain the public? To send them home happy?" The question marks I write were punctuated by a pair of scallywag eyebrows, high-arched, well-defined, quasi-plucked, and a scalp wrinkled above and below. "An artist should probably live by his natural gifts, not by what other artists have done or are doing. If one is Giacomo Rossi, one should not seek to be Beethoven or Mozart. One may indeed have their musical gifts, but the use to which those gifts are put is a different matter. I know you are a great admirer of the divine Mozart, but consider for a moment: was he happier writing his *Requiem*, from which effort he expired, than writing that child's play, *The Magic Flute*? And is that happiness reflected in the music? Did people go home singing Papageno's songs? Indeed they did. You will find out, if you agree to work with me, that I am against the sacred nature of art. I believe it springs naturally from the heart. One amuses, one earns; one doesn't worry."

There was no mention of Faust and the Devil, but the temptation was plainly there. The longer Rossi listened, the more sweat broke out on his brow. Some great idea was waiting to be expressed. He who had devoted himself to the contrapunctal arts of his teachers, who had raised himself from nothing to his present prestige, saw the light. His *Barber* was born— he hummed into his sherbet.

Appetite. That is the secret. DSB's secret in manipulating my husband. More specifically, two appetites: the appetite for money, which feeds all appetites, and another for fame.

I have said Giacomo was acute about money. Creators, interpreters and impresarios feed off and on each other, and DSB chained my husband to his desk by the following means: importuning, feeding his appetites for the here and now (which must be paid for later); laying on librettists who worked at half or quarter pace, incompetent copyists ("Oh dear, we'll have to find you another one!"); taking him to meals at which he'd forgotten his wallet; producing new contracts for future works which seemed perfectly reasonable; if Giacomo was cold, sending out for extra braziers; if late, keeping a fiacre waiting down below our apartments so no time should be wasted.

I did not complain. Indeed, though I recognized a day of reckoning to come (DSB had become one of those leech-like money-lenders I knew well from a Sicilian adolescence), I could see the powerful effect of our new friend's management on my Giacomo. Like money, which exercised its voltage on him, his music became electric; he suffered a continuous power surge. While working on his *Barber* neither the librettists, hopeless hacks in DSB's employ, nor the copyists could keep up with him. He needed a new version of Act III? Two, three, four libretists would sit in an anteroom of our apartments (rented from DBS) and scribble furiously, argue, plunder their rivals' work or forgotten verses from obscure poets, drink coffee and grappa,

and eventually their sheets, scratched with crossings-out and marginal alterations, would be brought to Giacomo at his desk. Without breaking mental
stride, he would dip his pen into the inkpot and melodies—those miraculous
melodies—would pour out.

I compare his productivity in that first (and only) season in the South
with that of a man who faces death and knows he has only so much time
to record his passage through life. DSB would come by, stand respectfully
at a distance, gaze at my husband's hand flowing over the music paper, and
nod with approval. "Artists are dilatory, *cara Madama,*" he would say. "One
must give them a sense of urgency."

He knew his man. The more indebted Giacomo became, the more
urgently he wrote. Fame and fortune scampered away before him; he was on a
treadmill catching up. He would fall into bed at four or five in the morning, if
then, sleep fitfully, and be awakened shortly after by the raucousness of the
southern streets beneath our windows, the cries of hawkers, the smells of coffee,
and by his muse, which demanded instant gratification. Stupefied, he would
rise, drink four or five giant cups of coffee, and return to the task.

The result we all know—a triumph. On opening night, there were
forty-one minutes of ovations. A party of ruffianish young men carried him   *995*
on their shoulders through the streets; the theatre orchestra serenaded him
with his own tunes, the public whistled or sang full-throatedly those arias
which, but for the bitterness and jealousy of some, would have lived, unforgotten, down to our own time.

Such celebrity—for during those brief years of success (think of the rollcall,
the *Barber, Cinderella, William Tell*) Giacomo could apparently write nothing
that was not a stupendous hit—brought changes in our life. The money
owed DSB was repaid; new offers poured in from opera houses all over
Europe. Even from Buenos Aires and New York.

This was the second of the compulsions which led to his downfall:
that wooing of the public, that love of their noise. The more fat palms beat,
the more prodigious the effort he would make. Unaustere by nature, he
calculated his ovations and the effects that produced them: tremendous
roulades, piercing high notes, swaths of catchy choruses. He entered his
audience's heart as a live lobster is plunged into boiling water, exhaling
through every pore.

What did they return to him? Love, which he sought with single-minded passion. Or popularity, as critics scornfully said. Going into a bar and hearing an aria hummed; on a bandstand, an overture in the embouchures of local wind players; the sound of his music ricocheting in his ears.

And later, of course, the way he grew into his avatar and became the illustrious Rossini.

I will sketch how our early marriage was.

I am a woman. My fate is a day-by-day one. We wake up in a strange place. I do not face the mirror for some time: until after coffee and the gazettes, the reviews, the notes carried up by boys in bright buttons. Bathing and dressing take longer: one waited, often and long, for hot water. In the bath, I study my body, which shows signs of age.

By then it is noon. The Maestro is engaged. His copyists have arrived, bearing inkpots and quires of music paper. The rooms are small: art must necessarily share space with the hairdresser. Flatterers abound.

I sniff the air: is Giacomo content? We all depend on his humors, variable as the west wind.

Rehearsals take place in what passes for our salon: with a piano that has been painfully hauled up and will be hauled down two days from now when we are gone. I try a few scales and arpeggios; the Maestro coughs in the background. It's all very well: he images, he writes these people—kings of Egypt and high priests of Israel, goddesses, tormented beauties with a death wish. In humor or not, I must make them real: tonight. I hear the audience's applause; I fear its disapproval.

Waiters wheel in a giant confection. Lunch spills out from under silver salvers. We exchange our first words. By five o'clock we are in dressing room and orchestra pit. As usual, something has gone wrong. He rewrites a last scene; I fight the manager over my place on stage, to be near the bouquets when they are thrown.

When the drama is over, what have we said to each other all day? I long for the country. I hate solitude. I have admirers heaped in my dressing room. The smell of their flowers sticks to my silks. My armor (I have been an Amazon) hangs in a corner of the room, out of sight. Another life has been used up. I have survived make-believe for one more night.

How was this cabal formed against my husband? To mention names here would honor men better forgotten, but here are some samples of their malice.

"The music of a dishonest man," declared a noted painter. Said a well-known novelist: "I have considered blowing up theatres which play his music, along with the congregation of his admirers." The same man wrote (he who in his youth had produced some celebrated articles praising my husband to the skies as "the pure essence of Italian genius"): "infinite wit and little or no passion. Love in his music is no more than a form of voluptuousness. His style is never more than amusing or vivacious." Another critic echoed Berlioz's famous words about Rossini, which themselves quoted a long-forgotten musician on the great Beethoven: "I am not sure such music should be written."

Oh, they were unremitting, these people the critics, the glossolators. That was the beginning of the attack. Wagnerians, post-Wagnerians, late-romantics, modernists, postmodernists, the French, the Germans (Italians were negligible for quite a while after 1922), the academics, the critics, the rivals—they all lined up.

There are strands to the arguments which effectively obliterated my husband's music: from the repertory, from the recording catalogues, from popular memory. I'll start with vulgarity. Mozart was a vulgar man, too, though not so vulgar as in the cinema. Should God's elect be *dignified*? If Shostakovich (and André Previn) could play the piano in silent movie houses, why deny Giacomo Rossi the earthiness which even the benighted can understand? That snatches of his overtures were performed in circuses takes nothing away from his art. What is vulgarity? A man in a loud checked waistcoat? A tune the butcher whistles? Too much sentiment? In which case, why the argument of unfeelingness?

Music has retreated into the academy, that's the trouble, for that way lies silence. A century ago, Rossini fought against Glück and Spontini—mausoleum seraphs. Should opera have stayed with Monteverdi? The argument from refinement, from the taste of the few, was never my husband's.

The truth is, another musical world was growing up around him. Damage was done to the frail fabric of sound. The "modern" violated the confidence of the public. Melodies which had proceeded in inevitable fashion according to the rules of harmony suddenly grew jagged and arbitrary. New rules, new tyrannies were installed. Singers no longer *sang*, they screeched and caterwauled; tonalities were crowded into chaos; rhythms stretched and pounded. Where was that Italian purity of sound to be found? Where was that untainted lyricism?

997

The public wanted the old favorites. The critics, for a long time guardians of the old and the sacred (of what they thought they knew) and concerned first and foremost with performance, were suddenly infected with the idea of the "new."

My husband stretched his ear comfortably around a tradition which he embraced with passion. Consequently, critics found him "slight" compared to the new "profundities" of, first, a Richard Strauss (a Wagner debased), and then a whole school of composers who sidestepped the opera, that ultimate musical art.

Of course we met all these people after the war, in the twenties: a sharp-eyed, avaricious Russian who sought to *épater les bourgeois*; his rather gross patron in a black coat with velvet collar, never without one of his sexual protegés; the solemn phthisic Viennese with his gleaming pince-nez; Strauss himself, whom we both found vulgar (in the ordinary sense). Giacomo was at sea in that world. He wrote music, not theory. He had nothing to attack or defend.

998 I come now to the celebrated question of why, in 1929, aged barely thirty-seven, he should have stopped writing music altogether.

The question is misstated.

Music wrote him. When it stopped doing so, he laid down his pen. Like his beloved Mozart, he'd been so carried away by the excess of inspiration that he had to die to rid himself of his author.

Music is plucked from the air, isn't it? Great men walk in solemn woods, the woodsman goes by with his axe, whistling, and we have Humperdinck? I'll say no more. My husband's *Barber* was written in twelve days, and *Tell* in nine. He was seized; he *was* those cavatinas, that melancholy, that wit. The rest, on which he expended himself, belongs to any professional musician. An orchestra, you should know, is nothing but an addition to music; singers—those voices of the past when, unamplified, we had to carry to the top balconies—were mediums. But getting the original song and getting it right, that's listening. And something happened between pork chops and Peruvian wines. By the dessert of his life, it stopped.

I was with him. It was not a terrifying phenomenon. He did not rue music's going, quite the contrary. He heaved a sigh upon rising one morning and said, "Thank God that's over." The effect was great: impresarios at the door, musical colleagues pleading, homages, telegrams. My husband wasn't obdurate. He didn't argue, he smiled, as though his new-found peace were, like his music, a gift of the gods. What had been given had been withdrawn, though he didn't put it exactly in those words.

The matter was ardently debated in the papers of the day (some cuttings of which I enclose.) Some said he was out of sympathy with the new music and its new public; others that he was afraid to venture his "old-fashioned" music against more "modern" masters; still others that his gift had always been evanescent and imitative, that he represented a century that had passed, his obvious master Rossini, and that his silence was a natural counterpart to the rise of his unstoppable facility—that, in short, he had burned himself out.

As will be evident from my tale, there also played a part in his renunciation of that fatal merging of the two men. What Rossini had done, Rossi was bound to do. In both, the failure may have been perfectly natural; in my husband's life, it was welcomed as another "sign." Riding the Rossini star, he must fall silent. Choice or accident?

No Faustian bargain between my husband and DSB, I have said, but I do ask myself if in fact DSB did not perceive in the young Rossi an epigone, someone whom he could recreate in an older mold. He had a financial and artistic interest in my husband's success. It is at the time when Giacomo moves down south (and I myself am ready, waiting, eager to escape DSB's amorous clutches) that my husband's style undergoes a radical change: from a serious and sober-minded composer into the wittiest and most scintillating of *buffo* writers. Noble failures are succeeded by less noble but far more profitable triumphs. He starts to wear white suits and straw hats, his *foulards* grow brighter and more expansive. As a result, some artist friends turn their backs on him: as in America they would have turned on pale and earnest young writers who "sold out to Hollywood."

What is DSB's role in this? Who brought Giacomo the librettists for his *Figaro?* None other than DSB himself.

The very excess of his triumph made it impossible for us to stay in Italy. In Italy, DSB owned us. Also, the first jealousies had begun, the first whispered rumors, of plagiarism and self-plagiarism, of those subtle links that bound him to his predecessor, such as the titles of his operas, the hum of his overtures.

To Paris we went—to which Rossini, for some of the same reasons,

999

had also fled—and not very long after, the music gave up. When that happened, we had to live through the twenties somehow, and to make matters worse, his depression and the Depression coincided. If one looks at the situation honestly, what else could my husband have done? Conditions in Italy were not propitious to his music, nor was his father's reddish past, Giacomo's cutting wit, his prodigious table-talk, even his fame, which made him independent of régimes. Paris, for a man without cares, of composition or money, was the place, and like his celebrated forebear, he bought a handsome mansion beyond the *Bois*. So that it should be as like Rossini's as possible, he had its shrubs cut into topiary versions of instruments: a grand piano, a violin, a trombone, etc. Had he by then accepted his fate as a reincarnation of an earlier composer? "Accepted" is a difficult word to use. Some see a terrible determination from the start, a compulsion, a sense of dissatisfaction with the self he had, a need to displace himself sideways in time and space, into another.

True, we except a variety of old friends, of loyal people who would not hear a word against their beloved Rossi. They lasted, as friends, at least as long as I was with him—were they not loyal, as well, to me? But the *mauvaises langues*, the gossips, railed all about us; they washed right up to the gates of our villa.

In all this, nothing prevailed over silence: my silence, his silence.

Rossi was bored. Time weighed on his hands. He was unwell. I have already described the pain in which he lived, that of an awful congestion. Now it seemed that all that unwritten music further clogged both head and body. A melancholy rose to the surface within him against which I could not prevail. What joys did I have? I had sung my last part at the age of forty, in 1925; my voice gave way; the audience hissed cruelly.

The world went on around us, full of jazz. My Giacomo found a Spanish friend, a banker, and swanned off with him to Biarritz and San Sebastian. Down there, bits of reputation clung to his operas. The banker may have paid hotel trios to play old hits among the sea pines. But nothing moved Rossi, except a cynical smile, a distant admission that he was the same Giacomo Rossi they'd heard about. "My God, we thought you were dead!" they said. Then he would smile: and sometimes sit down heavily at the piano, mound-like, and play.

How did he find a banker called Aguado, who thus matched Rossini's?

Were there that many rich young men with careful, sleek moustaches who were also bankers and disposed to give him advice on investments? Or was there a great-grandson of that original Aguado who sent him up his card on some *tournée*? We all lived out our fate, that of being connected to Gioacchino's life. Including, in my husband's case, his being introduced (by that same Aguado) to Olympe. While I was giving singing lessons in Paris.

I went to Bologna, and when he took up with Olympe, he simply failed to fetch me back. I sat there in Bologna with his father and an income which Giuseppe doled out parsimoniously. It was a melancholy Christmas. We sat at a long table in his cold house: he at one end (his wife some time dead), I at the other, my two dogs, fresh from scandalizing the maids and ripping horsehair from sofas, underfoot.

I was hard on Giuseppe. The man had charity in him; it irked me. I had already lived my dreams, I had only fantasies left, but they remained real. Instead, he still had visions of a happy future for the three of us (father, son and daughter-in-law, to whom in his confusion he would sometimes add his own wife.) Giuseppe wrote endless letters to his son in Paris. I did so more rarely, as Rossi himself ceased to write to me. My servants would read me Giuseppe's letters before taking them to the post: illiterate, hearty, hopeful, vindictive, varying as his moods. According to Giuseppe, I had killed his wife with my extravagant habits. He called me "the Duchess." I was pretentious, gave myself airs. My father had been no more than a trumpeter! He complained of my hairdresser, my dogs. I fell ill.

1001

I gambled, I admit it. In desperation. Because there was nothing else to do. Because I hoped to recover my popularity. What a society to live in! The backwater of backwaters! Giuseppe doled out Giacomo's money lira by lira. I was disapproved of by juvenile blackshirts; I was not up to the smart new Italy. I lost heavily. I went to pawnbrokers. I sold scores and autographs which reached a poor price. I sold lampshades, evening dresses, bits of fox fur, jewels, orders, ribbons. What do you want? I was unhappy. I imagined Giacomo unhappy and wrote letters all over inquiring about his health, his well-being, his state of mind. None were answered. I didn't exist.

Finally I moved away, to the country. There I could act out my roles and relive my life.

While I was there, I learned much of Olympe. Report was that she had been mistress to, model for, a number of painters—Derain, Picasso. She knew writers and aristocrats, too, but was in a doubtful position, being herself born of an amorous liaison. By all accounts, a very ordinary actress, but one who managed to maintain a salon. She also had a large, shaggy dog which went to sleep on her guests' laps.

Her presence in his life caused some small stir. There were brief revivals of early operas (she wanted a slightly more *bon ton* composer for a lover.) I took unkindly to the look of her as she appeared in certain illustrated magazines: an apathetic, lopsided face, sharply sloping shoulders, a coarse, thick neck, primness in the expression—the sort of woman dreaded as a governess, pedantic in details, her hair drawn tightly back. I got reports. She bossed, she fussed. Having "arrived," she gave herself airs. Consider the scandalous will she wrote: "Rossi will decide if by my conduct I have merited reposing near him one day. . . ." No sooner installed in his bed, she plans to stay in it forever!

She is represented in one work of his, the only work of any scale he wrote after my exile, his Mass, which I have mentioned earlier. There, it was as though he were seeking to reclaim his soul from Rossini. And what did they say about this work? That it had no hope, showed little faith, and it was charitable to pass it over in silence! If it has to be put that way, let it be said that Giacomo never sought originality.

1002

It doesn't matter. Looking back on the period just before the war, on the formalities connected with obtaining a "legal" separation, the drawing up of sour contracts before provincial notaries, I was left wondering what sort of games Giacomo was playing. A few years with his inamorata had imparted even more weight to his figure and mind. His systems were shut down. He talked about his "honor" and "doing the right thing"—in fact, he was stirring up Bologna society against me, accusing me of frivolity and imaginary exactions. Money? The way he was squandering it—buying up buildings, making gifts to the *Liceo*—it seemed little would be left. What he had, *she* would waste, lumbering from Paris to Bologna with half a guard-van's worth of trunks, bulky table linen, raffia baskets—all the accoutrements of a woman who'd had no established residence but a series of love nests.

Yes, my Giacomo played that trick on me. He brought her to the town where I lived, in mid-winter of 1937, the streets full of slush, ice and black uniforms, she wearing a cloche hat, a feather like a slash down her cheek and a veil over her powdered brow. Right away she set about intriguing to meet me.

"Well," Rossi said on one of those gloomy evenings when we met at two ends of a table, his stomach rumbling, myself looking at my fifty-year-old hands which were withering, "What do you expect? I can't leave Olympe in an equivocal position. You and I have separated. In the eyes of the world, you and she are equals. I'm sure your friends will have told you it is best for you to accept the situation as it is. . . ."

Is there anything more chillingly superfluous than genius fallen on mundanity? I saw before me the artist as *bourgeois*, in cravat and frock coat, out of style and out of time. We had soared together, now we were two ugly swanlets waddling on the mudbanks of our lives, both of us bored, the actual end, death, not so near us that we could take it into account as a deliverance. I said I would not receive her. "I am a Spanish lady," I said, "your wife under God's law."

How did he prevail? He played on my weakness, which was my undiminished feeling for him. That is, my love of the man he had been. He abused this by bringing her to my apartment. I forgave him because he was out of his depth. To me he seemed a man who has lifted anchor, who drifts, who is seeking no port.

She, on the other hand, came bursting through the door (Giacomo stepping aside to let her enter first, the maid taking her sealskin coat) and grasped both my hands in hers: with such a flourish of sincerity that I was immediately repelled. "Oh my dear Isabella," she gushed, "I am so grateful to have this occasion to meet you. I do hope we can and shall be good friends." There followed a lot more of the same, and I thought to myself, she will *not* become the second Mrs. Rossi. I thought of her situation—forced to dance attendance on the aging wife of a husband deprived now not only of his genius but his health—and had a moment of weakness. I carried off the meeting to the point that *she* was pleased. Shortly thereafter, Giacomo set her up in Milan and I retired to the country, as described above.

1003

The final blow to Giacomo was the death of his father, at eighty, in the autumn of the following year. The relations between these two—the progenitor who, by name and profession, had offered his son a life that wasn't to be his, and the son who accepted the fate that befell him—were so intimate and affectionate that I emerged from my retirement one last time, in the last spring before the war, to visit with Giacomo (Olympe was in Paris). I found the man profoundly desolated. "Eighty years old," he said mournfully, "eighty years old." To another, that might have seemed no more than the pathos of a man taken away from life after so long and eventful a stay on earth; I saw it as a statement about fortune in general. He may have rued, too, the amount of time left to him: too long. The man had died who had set him on his particular path. He had died, appointedly you might say, as that other Giuseppe had died a hundred years before. Thus the condemnation that weighed on Giacomo—to outlive his own vitality and gift—seemed sealed. Giuseppe's death was proof of the covenant between himself and fate: his father (as the rest of us) was a clause therein, and gone.

He held my hand in farewell as if knowing the date of my own death.

I have now, as I reach my conclusion, to take up the complex matter of my husband's relation to the unforgettable Gioacchino Rossini. It is indeed a most curious thing to live another man's life. But it is even worse for another, myself, to be captured alive and similarly plagiarized.

I feel my great-aunt's (my namesake's) blood in me. Fair enough. I lived for many years in her house, which I eventually inherited; I also adopted her profession, married a composer, and in countless ways followed her downward spiral—the lost voice, the enforced exile, the card games, abandon-ment, and eventually unrequited love. Despite appearances, however, I never felt any inner necessity to live her life. And still, I cannot deny it happened to me. In broad outline.

I therefore have to consider who sought out, or enforced, these coinci-dences? Not I, but Giacomo Rossi.

A happy, fleshy young man, a back row in the double basses at the opera, lessons at modest cost, marriage to one of his own kind, the respect of his neighbors—such could have been his lot. Instead, he took a set of temporal and spatial coincidences and donned another man's life. Such Rossini as was in his life, in what happened about him, he simply adopted.

I say "coincidences." It was not just a matter of sensibility. Sensibility is one thing. One might acquire that at a distance, the way one imitates another's walk or dress, as young men model themselves on those they admire. Musically, that is often the case. One may have an ear attuned to another age, skills deeply attuned to the *Zeitgeist* of another composer. The early Mozart is one example, with his affinity for Haydn. In our own times, a profound nostalgia for the symphonic literature of the past ran in Rach-maninov, who was one with his teacher Rimsky.

But these composers were, as men, distinct from the musicians with whom they identified. What they loved musically did not fester in their lives. But for the eight years of his creative frenzy, through twenty-nine operas, Rossini weighed on my husband in a very particular way. Nonetheless, those who say he was merely an imitator, an adapter, are wrong. His music is full of his own sensibility—and also curiously intermingled with that of his predecessor. Take, for instance, the celebrated overture, or Figaro's aria. In Rossi's hands, these are subtly altered. In the string figuration of the overture there is a great gallop, a distinct rhythm buried beneath what is substantially the same melodic line. Sufficiently different to raise the question, where does imitation end and invention begin? My husband's arias sing in their own way. They could be called "variations," quotations within a different context. For Giacomo was not interested in "originality." He couldn't have been. His music didn't derive from his thought but from his heart. It came into his ear naturally. He was but an amanuensis to his muse.

Still, that doesn't account for the efforts he made to assimilate his own life to Rossini's. The public wasn't really aware of the mask Rossi had adopted. In part because at the end of the last century, Rossini's own music was substantially out of fashion. The public heard my husband's music and found there something it thought it had lost: as a tune whistled in childhood returns in maturity.

To be sure, the resemblance to Rossini was present physically: in his corpulence, his high brow, his dress. That could be taken as tribute. The world did not know of his physical torment, his sexual excess. It had long forgotten that other Isabella Colbran.

I can only conjecture that in youth a number of these "coincidences" made themselves manifest to him in some crucial form. They then grew on him.

For instance, one could start with his birthplace, his irascible father, the fate that would have his mother, too, be a baker's daughter. Possibly some casual remark made while he was at school, or by his father, playing his first compositions, reinforced his likeness to Rossini. Pesaro, Giuseppe-Anna, Rossi-Rossini—these uncanny homonyms of place and language may have tempted him to see how far he could take similarity.

Some such mimesis may also have taken place in me. Aware that my great-aunt had been a celebrated diva, I may have sought to emulate her, and thus to marry a composer of operas, not thinking twice that his name was Rossi.

Were all the similarities and coincidences true? I have no way of knowing. We have only Rossi's record of his teachers. Did his teacher indeed play with two fingers and ply a trade in liquor, as Rossini's certainly did? Or were these later inventions tailored to suit the myth? The fear of engines and machines likewise? Was he fated to marry Isabella Colbran's grand-niece, or did he seek me out because of my name? What about Barbaia, who was Rossini's impresario? DSB certainly existed. Not to be vulgar, I know from experience. So did his early career as a *barista* in Milan.

If these are coincidences, they are the sure-footed dispositions of a very superior god with a substantial investment in Giacomo Rossi. What part could my husband have played in reinventing a DSB a century later?

A man with the weight of history on him might, for instance: having retired to Paris, be a topiarist to his garden, seek out Aguado as his patron and friend, fall in love with the first plausible Olympe. If women become their mothers, men their fathers, it takes no great quirk of nature or sidestep in life to become someone else. Given the mimetism that prevails in life, not much is required for Giuseppe to grow to resemble that other Giuseppe, Rossini's father, for me to be drawn ineluctably down the very path that destroyed my great-aunt. We all act in someone's play, and the force of my Giacomo, as author, was considerable.

When I look back on my life, it is an imperceptible pattern which greets my eye. I offered little resistance. In truth, I was not always aware of the web. I knew only tattle about Rossini's life. My family being far away in Spain, no one pointed out what I was stepping into. Possibly I acted from the same motives as moved my great-aunt: love for the man and his talent, a degree of ambition.

In many respects I was remiss. Was it not Giacomo, for instance, who arranged for the photograph on my piano (the one with the lyre) to be taken? Did he not seek out, that afternoon in a dusty provincial city, the photographer who had just such props available? Should I not have been aware of that?

It is terrible to consider that your life may have been arranged by another—as his was in part by his own hand and, on another level, by a malicious god. As I've said, the status of a singer, even a star, was ever equivocal. I was not ignorant of such men. Still, I took Giacomo at his word.

In all this, the man Giacomo is forgotten.

People ask me what it is like to make love to an artist. I answer, it is an abstract experience. It isn't as though he hummed tunes during his love-makings (he was sanguine enough, God help us!) but that he often wasn't there—save in the physical, mechanical sense. Artists are selfish and self-concerned. We women are part of the applause in their ears. They are unaware that we women could have any part in their natures or their bodies. They imagine us; they imagine us into all sorts of people and acts and emotions that are not ours. Between that abstraction and that elementary act of making us a part of their creation, the result is seldom satisfactory.

Still, it was I who paid for his youth. Had I borne a child, my old age would have been less lonely, my life more real. And dare I say it? A child would have broken the pattern of imitating my great-aunt. It might have un-Rossini'd Giacomo Rossi.

Can a child commit suicide, I ask? No, children have no real capacity for that kind of self-hatred; or for that matter, hatred of the world. But I say that my husband's departure from music was the suicide of a child. He didn't commit suicide in the absolute sense; yet he died within. At the end, he had been abandoned. He couldn't go back to his music any more than one who leaps off a building can reverse the flight of his fall.

I was discarded as part of an old life, a part that had been used. I belonged to something he would never find again, nor desire to. With the end of his music ended the first phase of his life as Rossini. Perhaps the same fate befell Rossini. The question was, how to survive the rest of his life? He had no answer. The world—distinguished visitors, audiences at *soirées musicales*—begged him, at least in the first few years, to come back. But at the end, it must have been all emptiness: everything there was had been created long before. He was just a relict. Music, incidental, occasional, still flowed, but was a shadow of what had been.

It is my conclusion that Giacomo did not set out to reproduce Rossini's life. We can speak of the fortuitous, but not of the deliberate. There are too many asymmetries. The alterations and shifts, rhythmical and harmonic, are subtle; a divinely refined ear, but one that did its hearing in our own time, immaculately varying the sounds and structures it heard from an earlier day and an earlier hand. Giacomo's *Barbiere* and his *Cinderella* are not parodies; they are imitations. They are creations of a high order that derive from the same inspiration. Perhaps Rossini spoke to him directly. I do not know, but I think Rossini did whisper in his ear, offering the leftover fragments of another prodigal talent.

Then, one day, he was simply abandoned. Charity from a loving God, for Rossini and Rossini's music were killing him. God gave him Rossini as a second life, or gave Rossini a second life in my husband. Then He gave up trying heavenly musicians. You know the results. Now they compose by mathematics, as if music had exhausted all its themes.

This does not eliminate art! Oh no! My husband went on bended knee before those who achieved with labor what he received, lying in his bath or being sucked by leeches, between coffee and lechery, as a gift. Such people engaged in stupendous efforts; they had great powers of mind. He worshiped them for that.

He abandoned me. Not meanly, but at the same time that his music left him. That French woman nursed a hulk.

My unhappy namesake died in 1865. As is evident from this memoir, I have lived beyond my time. In that sense, I have not lived in conformity with the destiny imposed on me by my husband, who died—of who knows what mental complexity—strictly on time, on the appointed day, letting death occur as if in a fit of absent-mindedness. If you don't believe me, look at his death mask. It shows no fear, only indifference.

But I lived on.

As the allotted day approached, though still two decades off, I took certain precautions to deal with my apprehension. I loved Giacomo and his art. If I did not survive long enough, both he and his art would perish, and with them myself. Also, in 1946, as Italy was liberated (I was sixty), pride was involved. I had survived the Fascists and their vulgarity as well as the red terror in Emilia after the war, when communist partisans sought out and humiliated many who had done no more than mind their own business. I was not going to yield, now, to the importunings of the young, nor allow my life to remain entirely in *her* hands.

As I had done for several decades, I stayed immured in my house with the grandson of that same Francisco Fernandez who had been my faithful servant when I was a singer at the pinnacle of fame. He dutifully reported his mistress's passing. A simple funeral was arranged, but the coffin was filled with long-hoarded and weeviled flour. I cheated death. The world no longer inquired after me.

You may ask how it is, then, that I find myself in London.

It is due to a coincidence. In the early thirties I met a scholar who was working in Bologna on the Rossini archives, preserved there at the *Liceo*. Some functionary may have told him there was an Isabella Colbran still living in Bologna. Thinking, no doubt, that I had kept some papers of my great-aunt, letters referring to the great Rossini, he sent me a courteous note to my home.

His name was Francis Toye. It was a name that appealed to me. Also, the way he had with his words, writing, "My dear lady, there seems to be no demand for a biography of Rossini, nonetheless I am writing one. . . ."

I told him of my husband's unhappy history, of the confusion between the two men, the fatal merging of their personalities and talents, and we kept in touch throughout the war. Toye was very kind and sent me packages which in part made up for the deplorable lack of food during '43-'44. As a young officer, at the time of the Liberation, he showed up again. On that occasion he said that I should at some point come to England. To do so might jog recollections of similarities which could contribute to the memories of both Rossini and his unhappy successor.

"One never knows," he said in his diffident British way. "Your husband's story seems to offer certain intimations, psychological and other, into the mysteries of Rossini's life—his facility, the taint of being unfeeling, his abandonment of his art—so that perhaps more will emerge if you were to visit. . . ."

1009

So it was that, aged one hundred, I undertook the journey to attend a gathering of the Rossini Society, which met, I believe, in Hampstead. Feeling a certain weariness, I had not the energy to leave again. I was, if you will try to understand me, trapped in my own past. I was welcomed as the great-niece of her who had sung for the original Rossini; I was not believed when I spoke of my husband. When I showed the few scores I had preserved, I was told they were bad copies. Things had been altered, but nothing had been added. They humored me. I accepted that.

I had then, and have now, but a single purpose. That is, I have been for some years seeking to have my husband, presently accommodated in a Neuilly cemetery, transferred to the church of Santa Croce in Florence, as was done with his illustrious forebear in 1887.

I write this memoir on behalf of that fund, in the hope that any of your readers who will have been interested in Rossi's sad fate, and mine, will contribute.

Silvio d'Arzo

Two Old People

Whether it's from an excess or a lack of sensibility, I don't know, but it's a fact that great tragedies leave me indifferent. There are subtle pains, certain situations and relationships, that move me more than a city destroyed by fire.

That is the first reason why I take up the story of the two old Grimaldis.

They were born into a relatively happy time—around 1880—and for many years they were happy. They enjoyed a comfortable income, and it is said that both of them were very good looking. Then things changed.

In their fifties (after they had been living a somewhat secluded life for better than ten years) their only son died. If happiness had made them like hundreds of others, this first loss made them strikingly different. It was from that moment on that they truly became themselves. They no longer went out; they hardly ever received. In their fifties and sixties (including the last four years of war) they became increasingly aware that the ease of a time gone by was being implacably weakened, but they moved not a finger to prevent it. For ten years they merely observed, as one looks at the last curling of a piece of stationery slowly burning in the fireplace.

By then they were reduced to a single house. With a touching form of cynicism, they calculated the likely number of years that remained to them and weighed that against the sum they might receive from its sale. They decided to sell. Thus, having realized half, or even less, of what anyone else might easily have obtained, they retired to an apartment in the center of town. Or, as Signor Grimaldi said—from his past he had preserved only a minimal baggage of maxims and paradoxes—"If you like, nothing could be further from the center."

Thus began the third stage of their life, with neither of them suspecting that there would soon be a fourth stage. As a sort of ultimate coquetry, he set himself to reading Horace, while she did some light work about the house that she pretended was indispensable. In that way, the afternoons passed: and if in this world there are different kinds of happiness, I have no reason to doubt they were nearly happy.

It happened, suddenly, on a Wednesday.

The clock in the nearby square was sounding half past ten and, as usual, the woman who came every day to clean and do the shopping, took off her apron, said goodbye, and left in a hurry: before one o'clock she still had two other houses to do. But she returned immediately.

"There's a . . . gentleman asking after you," she said somewhat roughly, annoyed by the interruption. Signora Grimaldi looked around to see if everything was in order.

"I think we can manage to receive him here," she decided. "Show him in please, Maria."

Almost immediately, Maria returned. "I'm sorry, but he insists on speaking personally to you." Signor Grimaldi raised his eyes from his book.

"A young man?" he asked, turning to look at the maid.

"Yes," she answered, without grasping quite why she was asked. "Yes, definitely a young man. Barely thirty."

"Happy days, happy days," Signor Grimaldi said, shaking his head at his wife. "If you're in a hurry, don't wait for your husband to go out."

"I'd have a long wait if I did that," she answered, laughing. "It's been two years since you left the house."

Their age and condition were now such that a visit was something of an event, an adventure; and never had there been any visits from young people. But now someone, and a young man at that, was asking after her, personally. She couldn't quite understand why.

"It doesn't matter, it doesn't matter. Why apologize? Have I asked you anything?" he continued bantering in the same tone. "I was reading Horace and didn't hear a word. Don't get all upset."

Smiling, Signora Grimaldi left the room. In the neighboring drawing room she found a young man of thirty or somewhat less, whom of course she had never seen in her life, and whose name was unknown to her. He had a three- or four-day-old beard and wore an old yellow raincoat, of the kind worn some years back by cavalry officers. Neither tie nor shoes showed any pretension beyond that of responding to necessity. In short, apart from a certain aggressiveness in his manner which was not especially off-putting, he was a typical, poor literature student, destined to become a journalist, but for the time being willing to give private lessons at a most reasonable price.

After both had sat down, he began with a kind of unconstrained and impatient cumbersomeness at which he himself smiled, saying, "Well you see. It's like this, really . . . The story is a bit long, I know that. But I don't think it can be cut by much. Well, I'm twenty-six, I'll be twenty-seven in August, and I'm a law student; or rather I'm registered for a year, and that's likely to be all . . ."

"Like my son," Signora Grimaldi commented, who had decided to *1013* hear the young man out with maternal and flirtatious irony.

"I did a couple of years in Bologna. You know how it is. And another couple of years in Milan."

"Just like my son," she repeated.

"*Beh*," the young man answered smiling, a little embarrassed at this unexpected coupling, "I imagine those are the only things we have in common. So, as I was saying," he continued, pointing to his raincoat and shoes, and perhaps to another form of wretchedness even deeper and more personal than these colorless garments, "I can't believe that he's not better off than I am."

Then Signora Grimaldi changed her tone.

"I wish I could be that certain . . ."

"Oh, I'm so sorry," he said, somehow divining that her son must be dead. "I'm sorry. But even so, I think I must stand by my opinion."

And he waited with composed impatience for the wave of emotion raised in her by this allusion to die down so that he could continue his statement.

"Well," he began again after a few seconds, "If I were a little more coherent, just a little, nothing that you could think of me would matter in the least. But instead, I think I can say that you have some esteem for me. How stupid of me, isn't it?" She said nothing. "A few days ago, thinking ahead to our meeting, I had imagined a flow of fine words. True words, of course. For instance, that a man is always better than the things he says, and often better than the way he acts, or something of the sort. But being here is different. Here . . ."

He brought his armchair a little closer to hers, for with his last words she had begun to listen to him, not exactly more attentively, but with a different sort of attention.

"Here I only want to say the following. I'm twenty-seven, I've worked, I've studied, I've kept myself busy. Besides which, I spent two years in the war. I've done everything I could do, and sometimes things that I couldn't do, I assure you," he added, raising his voice as though she had objected, or her face had revealed some sort of disapproval. "I know that when one has a house like this, and armchairs like these, it's easy to look down on others."

"But I don't look down on anyone," she said quickly. "I've reached an age at which I think I manage to not even look down on myself."

"All the better. That's what I was hoping for. It will make this easier for both of us," the student interrupted. "I haven't managed to finish anything. And if I go on this way, I'll manage to finish even less."

"Even less?" she asked, astonished.

"Yes, even less. For some people, 'nothing' is already something. But right now, better we should consider the two of us. Right: I'm about to do something that could be an ignoble thing to do; yes, other people would have no hesitation in using the word 'infamy'."

Instinctively, she raised her eyes and looked at him.

"Something ignoble?" she asked.

"Yes. Something ignoble," he asserted, slowly and unhappily studying the tips of his shoes. "But take care, for I didn't lift a finger to discover it; and even if it had been the easiest thing in the world, I wouldn't have lifted a finger. I don't claim any great merit on my part, but it's the truth, so I tell you. But in fact the . . . Yes, the infamy offered itself to me, of its own accord. It sought me out. I swear. It found my name, where I lived, my room; it came to me. No more, no less. And that being the case, that changes things, I think. You have to admit that. Things like that come from God knows where; one could in fact think they come from on high . . . from on very high. Who knows?"

Naturally, she (having always thought that infamy could only come from the lowest part of our natures) could not admit that infamy should come from on high; at most she could allow that others might fall for something of the sort. The truth is that by now she was too upset to judge or reflect.

The young man continued: "Each of us has his touch of providence. And for an unbeliever like me I can't think of a better one than this. I mean to say that I don't think I have any right to look this gift horse in the mouth."

"Well then, speak up!" she said agitatedly. "What more do you expect?"

"Alright," the young man concluded, "but first I had to tell you that, to convince you that I couldn't do otherwise."

"But why on earth do you care about convincing me? About what?"

The young man extracted a letter from his pocket and put it on the little table between them.

"This, Signora, is a letter that I think should interest you greatly, and one that moreover now interests me. When, along with other furniture of yours, you sold a certain desk, I found some forty letters like this in the third drawer on the left. Didn't I tell you that fate sought me out? Right, so what I want to say is that the third party to whom these letters would be even more interesting than to us is . . . is your husband. I know perfectly well that the one person who should not read these letters is your husband, and that you will do everything in your power to see to it that he continues to believe that no such letters were ever written. I also know that this very week you have sold a house and received a fair sum for it. Another might have made more from the sale than you, but the money you received is really quite sufficient."

Signora Grimaldi was beginning to grasp the young man's meaning, and was about to reply. But he interrupted, and rushed to his conclusion.

"I think that 150,000 lire ought to resolve the matter for all three of us. For the truth is, three of us are now involved."

Once again she tried to say something; again he interrupted.

Standing up, he said: "No. Don't say a word. I know beforehand everything you might want to say to me; I've known for some days; and I

1015

think I agree with you. Yes, I agree with you. But that doesn't change a thing. Even as to the sum to be paid, there's nothing to be said: I could have asked for more, I could have asked for less. Instead, I ask for just what I need, so that I no longer need such providential interventions."

There was a moment of silence.

"Today is Wednesday," he began again. "Saturday morning at ten or eleven, or even later, if that suits you better, I'll return with all the other letters."

She stood up as well, and followed him slowly to the door. There the young man stopped briefly to study a portrait on the wall.

"There, you see," he said in a gentler voice, "my contacts with him never added up to more than a couple of years at university."

"He," she answered with melancholy irony, "was not visited by this providence." The young man left.

"Now, now," her husband said, at that moment entering the drawing room with an open book in his hand and seeing her. "You look a little gloomy now that you've got rid of him."

"Dear God," was all she felt like saying, "What an ugly tie!" And she tried to retie it.

"Now, now, that's a bad sign. Anna Karenina realized she no longer loved her husband when she saw what ugly ears he had," he continued to joke.

"But at least you can change your tie," she replied, trying to adopt the same tone.

But she did not succeed. Nor did she manage to smile.

Only later, when she had read the letter, did it dawn on her what that twenty-minute visit had really been for her. Neither more nor less than this: ruin. Everything had taken place in such a strange and unexpected manner, and the tone of the meeting had been, up to the very end, so familiar, that she'd not been able to take the disaster in. And for that matter, the events to which the letter referred were by now in so distant a past that they seemed to belong to another life, of which her present life could at most be a remembering witness.

Thirty years before, at a time when her husband took off to Livorno every month and committed discreet follies with a young woman, someone had fallen in love with her. The man in question, who had both intelligence and money, and was conscious of both, had written her beautiful letters—at a time, and in a context, in which they seemed perhaps more important than his fortune. She in turn had fallen in love with him and had promptly replied. Nothing else. Nothing else had happened. And now that man was dead, and she was but an old woman who scarcely even remembered the name of the man who had sent her that bundle of beautiful letters. The only element made remote and innocent by time was the letter itself. That represented a living sin; preserved by an ironic miracle, it was a stone from thirty years ago that fell suddenly into the lonely waters of their old age.

"Dear God," the Signora said, rising and shaking her head, "even the money's too much. Too much, far too much. And I'd have to lay my hands on it without his realizing anything . . ." She was too desperate to be distressed by a lie, but too tired to resort to one. She started to listen to the rain outside.

Just then it began to pelt down hard, and her husband wasn't able even to help her lower the blinds before the rain turned into a storm. Both of them got thoroughly wet. Then suddenly the lights went out. Down below in the street they heard shouts and laughter.

Then they sat down side by side.

After a while, he said, "I don't think it was such a brilliant idea to sell the house." Though irony was his chief form of self-defense, and he had frequent recourse to it, now, with the time of day, the darkness, the rain, it was useless.

"Oh, we won't live forever," she answered, guessing at his meaning.

"That's not what I meant," he lied.

"But I did," she said, some bitter mingling with the sweet. "That's just what I meant."

"It's all the rain's fault," he replied. "But I think we have no right to complain, not to speak of the fact that it would be in poor taste. We knew how to be young when we were young, and now we know how to be old: I don't know many people who can say as much. There's something else I want to tell you. When Riccardo died, I thought there could be no greater injustice; I thought it was against the natural order. But now I think his death was part of a certain order. I may not understand it, but I'm sure it exists . . . And much as I mourn him, I think that had he been alive he wouldn't have made our lives as united as they are. I think he too contributed to this masterpiece of ours. Seriously."

She remained silent.

1017

After a long pause, she murmured: "These are things one says in the dark."

"Of course, of course. You need a little dark to say such things. And since the power's not back on yet, I have something else to say: the shared life of two old people is a thousand times more valuable than that of two young people. A thousand times. There's no comparing."

"It could be. I don't say no. But I've never heard anyone say that."

"That's because no one listens to us," he said. "And because by now we have enough sense to know it doesn't matter one iota whether others believe us or not."

"Yes, I too think that a little darkness is sometimes necessary," she admitted hesitantly. "So now I too want to tell you something. I think it's important to you and to me, and in light of what you said earlier . . . important."

He leaned back in his armchair; she drew closer to him. At that moment the lights came back on.

"I also think it wasn't so smart to have sold the house," was all she said. For that night, there was nothing more to be said. Both of them stood up.

1018

Later, however, she waited until her husband was in bed before writing what follows:

"My dear,

What you said today when the power went out, is the truest thing I've ever heard you say to me, and I'd almost like to thank the storm for making it possible. I too wanted to tell you something, and I was about to open my mouth when the lights came back on. The result is I'm reduced to writing you a letter. It's a quarter to one, and you've been asleep for an hour.

You are about to read a letter which will pain you deeply; it will give you all the pain of which, at our age, we are capable of experiencing. And Saturday morning, sometime around nine or ten, the young man who came to see me today, and about whom you joked a bit, will bring you a whole bundle of such letters.

I could have saved you this pain by paying the young man 150,000 lire: a third of what we obtained by selling our wretched little house. Had I done so, you would have been able to continue thinking that our life truly was the kind of masterpiece you described, and that with his death our Riccardo contributed to it. But now think on it. Think on your pain and mine, think on the melancholy and coldness we'll feel to the end of our days. And all for the want of a miserable sum which our old steward could have made in a fortnight or less. How little we're worth! Any young person would be offended by so little, and I'm not sure I'd say they were wrong. But you and I, my poor Enrico, are past sixty, and we're alone in the world. Today I had to convince myself that being happy or thinking oneself happy is a luxury we can no longer afford: no more than we can our former dignity, our pride and so much else. We have three or four years left to live. Perhaps, God spare us, five. And it occurred to me that there remains only one duty for us: to be able to await, day by day, our end.

I know full well that your greatest bitterness will not be from the pain the letter will cause you, but from the realization that your happiness has been sold at such a cheap price: for much less than those presents cost you gave me in the past, not thinking that they were anything but trifles.

1019

All of this is sad, my poor Enrico. All this is so sad that I can find no word of hope or apology. It's two and you're still asleep. You're breathing a little heavily. And you don't know anything yet.

Giovanna."

Translated by Keith Botsford

TRANSLATOR'S NOTE: Born on February 6, 1920, Silvio d'Arzo— to give him the pseudonym he most frequently used—died in Reggio Emilia in 1952 after a life spent, but for a year during the war, in his native city. The son of an unknown father, he bore the name Enzo Comparoni, after his beloved mother, Rosa, who was from Cerreto Alpe in the Appenines behind Reggio and earned a living telling fortunes in the marketplace. It was she who told him some of the stories that he transposed into the lucid, hesitant prose which made his reputation.

Of the young man whose masterpiece, Casa d'Altri *(first published in truncated form in 1948, and brought out by the Marlboro Press in 1993) is considered by many, among them Moravia, Bassani, and Siciliano, one of the finest stories written in Italian in this century, exceedingly little is known. He was precocious, completing his baccalaureate or* maturitá *at sixteen, having published his first stories and poems the previous year; he studied at the University of Bologna and wrote a thesis on mountain dialects at the age of twenty; he was drafted into the army and, when Italy surrendered to the Allies in 1943, deserted back to Reggio, from which he narrowly avoided deportation. After the war, while working as a school-teacher, he painstakingly forged a literary reputation; and was about to embark on a novel, based on Lermontov's* A Hero of Our Time, *when he died of neglected lymph cancer.*

Thanks to his literary essays, recently collected under the title Contea inglesa, *we know that like many of his generation, he was devoted to English and American literature, and to Robert Louis Stevenson in particular. He had at least one major love affair, but subordinated everything to the pursuit of his own voice in literature. "There is no joy greater than writing," he would say. The testimony of his friends shows him to have had a generous disposition, to be friendly, sociable and devoted.*

Otherwise, what we have are his books. These include the early Maschere *(1935); a collection of stories,* Essi pensano ad altro *["They Think of Something Else"] first written in 1939 as* Ragazzi in città *["City Kids"] and repudiated by d'Arzo, but published posthumously in 1976; a semi-picaresque novel,* All'insegna del buon Corsiero *["At the Sign of the Good Corsair"], published in 1942;* l'Ostería *["The Inn"], some forty years later published in* Nostro lunedì *[see below];* Casa d'altri *["The House of Others"], first published in 1948 in an incomplete form, then posthumously in Vol. X of* Botteghe oscure *in 1952, and subsequently republished from 1953 on, each time in different versions derived from the surviving manuscripts—in 1953 and later; further stories, some for children, published in two different collections,* Il pinguino senza frac *["The Penguin without a Tuxedo"] and* Penny Whirton e sua madre *["Penny Whirton and her Mother"]; as well as the fragments of an uncompleted novel, collected in* Nostro lunedí *["Our Monday"], which appeared in 1986.*

The tradition of the Italian narrativa, *or extended story, is a rich and consistent one, and includes writers as diverse and compelling as Cesare Pavese and Beppe Fenoglio. It is an oral tradition in which the telling of the story, usually through the voice of a single individual, is used to reveal a whole universe. Within that brief, intense, lucid tradition, d'Arzo occupies a special position. He is of a very specific place, the town of Reggio Emilia; and of a time, the disillusionment of the war and its aftermath.* Casa d'altri, *about a woman, living a life of inescapable poverty, who consults a priest as to whether she may be allowed to shorten that life, is a singular masterpiece. However, all of d'Arzo's mature stories, written before he was thirty, reflect his unique voice: meditative, hesitant, and full of things unsaid, of long silences and chance encounters, and of that struggle between an acceptance of fate and a refusal to give in to it on which much great literature of the past, from Homer onwards, is based.*

The present story seems to have been written in its final form in 1947, and was first published in the review, Cronache, *in July of that year.*

1021

Giuseppe Tomase Di Lampedusa

Lighea, or the Siren

That late autumn of 1938 I was in a fit of misanthropy. I was living in Turin, and Girl Number One, rifling through my pockets for a bank-note while I was sleeping, found a little note from Girl Number Two which, for all its misspellings, left little doubt as to the nature of our relations.

My waking up was immediate and tempestuous. My cramped quarters on the via Peyron echoed with furious expletives in the vernacular; she wanted to scratch my eyes out, and I managed to avoid the attack only by slightly twisting the dear girl's left wrist. This perfectly justified piece of self-defense put an end to the scene; and also to our idyll. The girl got dressed in a hurry, packed powder puff, lipstick, her little hankie, and the bank-note, "cause of such travail", into her handbag, threw three "*pourcoun!*" or "pigs" in my face, and left. She'd never been as sweet as in that quarter-hour of fury. From my window I saw her walk out the door and stride off in the thin morning mist, tall, willowy, and adorned with recovered elegance.

I never saw her again, no more than I ever saw again a black cashmere pullover which had cost me a fortune and had this unfortunate quality, that in shape it was equally adaptable to man and woman. All she left behind, on the bed, was two twisted hairpins of the kind known as "invisible."

That same afternoon I had a date with Number Two in a pastry shop on the Piazza Carlo Felice. Sitting at the little round table in the western corner of the back room which had become "ours," instead of seeing that great mane of chestnut hair which belonged to the now doubly desirable girl, I saw the sly face of her little brother Tonino, a twelve-year-old who had just put away a hot chocolate with double whipped cream. As I approached him, he rose with the usual Turin urbanity. "*Monsù*," he said, "Pinotta's not coming. She told me to hand you this note. "*Cerea, Monsù*." Or, so long. Off he went, taking with him the two pastries that remained on the plate. The little ivory-colored card informed me that I was permanently dismissed, the motive being my infamy and my "southern dishonesty." Now all was clear: Number One had tracked down and stirred up Number Two, and there I was between two stools.

In half a day I'd lost two girls who usefully complemented each other, plus a pullover of which I was fond; likewise I had to pay for what that infernal Tonino had consumed. My very Sicilian sense of my own worth was humiliated; I'd been had; and I decided for a while I would turn my back on the world and its vanities.

1024 For this period of retreat, no more suitable place could have been found than the café on the via Po to which I, now lonely as a dog, repaired whenever I had a free moment; and every evening after I'd finished work at the newspaper. This was a kind of Hades populated by the bloodless shades of lieutenant colonels, magistrates, and retired professors. These idle shades played checkers or dominos in a light that was by day obscured by arcades and clouds, and by night by giant green lampshades; they never raised their voices, fearful as they were that too loud a sound might undo the feeble weave of their substance. A most fitting Limbo.

Like the creature of habit I am, I sat always at the same little corner table, one carefully designed to be as uncomfortable as possible for the client. To my left, the ghosts of two field officers played backgammon with those of two judges of the Court of Appeal; military and judicial dice tumbled silently from the leather cup. Also to my left there always sat a man of advanced age, bundled up in an old coat with a threadbare astrakhan collar. He read endless foreign magazines, smoked gnarled Tuscan cigars, and spat often; from time to time he would put down his magazines and seem to drift off among the rings of smoke into some private memory. Then he would go back to reading and spitting. He had very ugly, knobbly, reddened hands, with nails cut straight and not always clean, but on one occasion he fell on the photograph of an archaic Greek statue—one of those sculptures with eyes set far from nose and an ambiguous smile—in one of his magazines, and he surprised me by the way his pulpy fingers caressed the picture: the gesture was quite regally delicate. He noticed that I'd seen him, grunted furiously, and ordered a second espresso.

Our relations would have remained on that somewhat hostile basis had it not been for a fortunate accident. I usually brought with me from my own paper some five or six newspapers, amongst them, this time, the *Giornale di Sicilia*. Those were the years in which the Minculpop, the Ministry of Popular Culture, was at its most virulent, and all newspapers were identical to each other; that issue of the daily from Palermo was more banal than ever, and except for its typographical errors, nothing whatever distinguished it from a Milan or a Rome newspaper, so that my reading was correspondingly cursory and I left it on the table. I had barely dipped into another incarnation of Minculpop when my neighbor addressed me:

"I beg your pardon," he said, "but would it bother you if I had a glance at that Sicilian paper of yours? I am Sicilian myself, and it's been twenty years since I last saw a paper from back home." The voice was as cultivated as possible, the accent impeccable; the old man's grey eyes looked at me with utter detachment. "Please," I said. "I too am Sicilian, and if you like I can bring the paper here every night." "Thank you, but I don't think that will be necessary; mine is no more than a simple physical curiosity. If Sicily is still the way it was in my day, my guess is that, as has been the case for three thousand years, nothing good ever happens there."

He leafed through the paper, folded it up again, returned it to me and once more buried himself in his reading. When he left, it was obvious he wanted to slip away without saying goodbye; but I stood up and introduced myself; he mumbled his name through his teeth, but I didn't catch it; he did not shake my hand; but on the threshold of the café, he turned around, doffed his hat and said, "*Ciao, paesano.*" He vanished into the arcades, raising sighs of disapproval from the surrounding spectres and leaving me dumbfounded.

Having gone through the magic ritual necessary to fetch a waiter, I showed him the empty table next to mine and said, "Who was that gentleman?" "Who he is?" he replied. "That is Senator Rosario La Ciura."

Even in my restricted journalistic experience, the name had real meaning: he was one of the five or six Italians with an indisputable international reputation: that of the most illustrious hellenist of our time. Now I could make sense of those fat journals and the caress to that reproduction; likewise his prickliness, and his veiled refinement.

The following morning at the newspaper, I went through the "pending" files in the obituaries. There was La Ciura, for once decently written up. The great man, it said, had been born in Aci-Castello (Catania) into a modest middle-class family. Thanks to his fantastic devotion to the study of Greek and a number of scholarships and research publications, he had been named to the chair of Greek at the University of Pavia when he was twenty-seven; had then held the same chair at the University of Turin until his retirement; had taught at Oxford and Tübingen; and as a pre-Fascist senator—a member of the Lincean Academy, as well as the recipient of honorary degrees from Yale, Harvard, New Delhi, and Tokyo, not to mention the most illustrious European universities from Salamanca to Upsala—had traveled far and wide. The list of his works was very lengthy and many of his books, especially those on the Ionian dialect, were considered definitive; suffice it to say that he was the only foreigner to have been asked to produce the Teubner edition of Hesiod, which he had preceded with a Latin introduction of unsurpassed scientific value. Finally, to his greatest glory, he was not a member of the Italian Academy. What had always distinguished him from his colleagues, however erudite, was his vivid, even carnal, feeling for Greek antiquity, which had led to a book of essays in Italian, entitled *Men and Gods*, a work imbued not only with the highest kind of erudition, but also with real poetry. In short he was, as the author of the obituary had written, "an honor to his nation and a beacon to every culture." He was seventy-five and lived far from opulently but managed decorously on his pension and his senatorial emoluments. He was celibate.

There's no point in denying it: we Italians, elder sons or fathers of the Renaissance, consider a Great Humanist superior to any other human being. The thought that I might now be in daily contact with the most prominent representative of that delicate, necromantic, and unremunerative branch of knowledge both flattered and disturbed me; I felt exactly as a young American might feel when introduced to King Gillette: fear, respect, and a special kind of not ignoble envy.

That evening I went to my Limbo with an entirely different feeling from that of the days before. The senator was already at his table and replied to my reverential greeting with a barely perceptible mumble. But when he had finished an article he was reading, he turned my way and said in that strangely musical voice of his, "*Paesano*, judging by the way you greeted me, I see that one of these living shades has told you who I am. Forget it, and if you haven't already done so, forget as well all those aorists you learned in school. Instead, tell me your name, for last night you gave me the usual garbled introduction and, unlike you, I have no means of asking others what your name is—for here, I'm sure, no one knows who you are."

He spoke with insolent detachment; it was plain that in his eyes I ranked somewhat below a cockroach, or one of those motes of dust that float aimlessly in the rays of the sun. Yet his even tone, the precision of his speech, the familiar *tu* with which he addressed me, carried the kind of serenity implicit in a Platonic dialogue.

"My name is Paolo Corbèra, and I was born in Palermo, where I took my degree in law; currently I work here for *la Stampa*. Let me reassure you, Senator, that I got a five-plus in Greek, and there is reason to believe the 'plus' was added only that I might graduate."

He gave me a half-smile. "Thank you for telling me," he said. "It's better that way. I hate to talk to people who, like my university colleagues, think they know something when in fact they know nothing; the truth is they know but the external form of Greek, its eccentricities and deformities. The living spirit of this language—so stupidly called a 'dead' language—has not been revealed to them. In fact nothing has been revealed to them. Poor sods that they are, how could they possibly discern this spirit if they've never had occasion to hear Greek spoken?"

1027

Pride, to be sure, is better than false modesty, but I thought the Senator was exaggerating; it passed through my mind that the years might have softened his quite exceptional brain. Those poor devils, his colleagues, had just about as much opportunity to hear Greek spoken as he did: that is, none at all.

He went on: "Paolo. . . .You're lucky to bear the name of the only apostle who had some culture and a smattering of real literature. But Jerome would have been better. The other names you Christians bear are really just too vile. Slave names."

I was more and more disappointed; he seemed to me just like any other academic priest-baiter, with a dash of Fascism *à la* Nietzsche added. Surely not?

He went on talking with the same engaging modulations of his voice and the fire of a man who had perhaps long been silent. "Corbèra. . . .Am I wrong? Isn't that a famous name in Sicily? I remember that for our house in Aci-Castello my father paid a tiny annual ground-rent to the stewards of the Corbèra di Palina or Salina, I don't remember quite which. And every time he paid he would make a joke about how unlikely it was those few lira would actually get paid to the freeholders or 'fiefholders' as he called them. But are you really one of those Corbèras, or are you the son of some peasant who took his master's name?"

I admitted that I was indeed one of those Corbèras, in fact their sole descendant: all the splendors, all the sins, all those outstanding rents, all the Leopard's spots were wrapped up in my person. Paradoxically, the senator looked pleased.

"Good, good," he said. "I have a great respect for ancient families. They possess memories—for minutia it's true, but still more significant than anyone else's. They're as close as you people can get to physical immortality. Given that when it comes to survival, Corbèra, your people have found nothing better to do than spill your seed in the strangest places, I suggest you think of marrying soon."

I was getting decidedly impatient. "You people, your people." What people? All that base rabble that hadn't the good fortune to be Senator La Ciura? And what had he done about *his* physical immortality? Nothing much by the looks of his wrinkled face and that heavy body. . . .

"Corbèra di Salina," he went on, undaunted. "You won't be offended if I continue to use *tu* with you, as I would with any student in that brief moment called youth?"

I said I was not only honored by the *tu*, but happy: as indeed I was. Now that we'd disposed of such matters as our names and protocol, we talked about Sicily. For his part, he hadn't set foot there in twenty years, and the last time he'd been down (as people in Piedmont put it) there, he had stayed only five days: in Syracuse to discuss with Paolo Orsi some questions about the alternations of the semi-choruses in the performance of classical theatre. "I recall that they wanted to take me from Catania to Syracuse by car; I accepted only when I learned that at Augusta the road runs inland, far from the sea, while the train runs along the shore. Talk to me about our island; it's a fine place, though inhabited by asses. The gods lived there, and perhaps they still do so in our implacable Augusts. But don't talk to me about the four brand-new temples you have there; anyway, I'm sure you know nothing about them."

So we spoke of the eternal Sicily, of its natural prodigality, of the scent of rosemary on the hills of Nèbrodi, the flavor of Melilli honey, the waves of grain as seen on a windy May day from Etna, the solitudes around Syracuse, the gusts of citrus blown towards Palermo, people say, during certain sunsets in June. We spoke of enchanted summer evenings overlooking the bay of Castellamare when the stars are reflected in the sleeping sea and the spirit of whoever lolls under the the gummy mastic bushes gets lost in the whirling of the sky, while his body, tense and alert, fears the imminent encroachment of demons. After being away for nearly all of fifty years, the Senator had a singularly precise memory of even the most minimal facts: "The sea, the Sicilian sea is that with the deepest color, the most romantic I have ever seen; it is the one thing you will never manage to spoil apart from the cities, of course. Tell me, do they still serve *rizzi* in trattorias by the sea, those spiky sea-urchins split in half?" I reassured him they did, adding that nowadays few people ate them, for fear of typhus. "And yet they're the most beautiful thing you have down there, those blood-rich cartilegas, those simulacra of the female organ, smelling of salt and seaweed. Typhus, typhus! They're about as dangerous as any other gift of a sea which offers death as it offers immortality. When I was in Syracuse I demanded that Orsi provide some. What flavor! What beauty! They were the best thing I remember in the past fifty years!"

I was both confused and fascinated: that such a man could allow himself metaphors bordering on obscenity, could display such infantile gluttony, and for such basically ordinary fruit of the sea!

We continued talking for some time more, and when he left he insisted on paying for my espresso, not without his usual boorishness ("everyone knows that young men of good families don't have a penny in their pockets!"); we parted as friends if, that is, one doesn't take into account the fifty years between our respective ages and the thousands of light years between our cultures.

We continued to meet every evening, and though the smoke resulting from my rage against mankind was beginning to blow away, I made it my duty never to miss a meeting with the senator in our usual hell on the via Po. Not that we talked that much; he continued to read and take notes, only occasionally addressing me, but when he did talk, it was always with a harmonious blend of pride and insolence to which he added odd allusions and a vein of incomprehensible poetry. He went on spitting, and I finally noted that he did so only while reading. I think that he, too, felt a certain affection for me, but I have no illusions on that score: if affection there was, it wasn't the sort of affection that "we people," to use the senator's term, might feel for another human being but was rather like that some aged maiden aunt might experience for her pet canary, knowing how silly he was and how wanting in understanding, but whose very existence allowed her to voice complaints totally unrelated to the poor bird, complaints which, had the canary not been there, would have made her feel ill at ease. I began to note, in fact, that whenever I was late, the old man's lofty eyes were fixed on the door to the café.

It took about a month for us to pass from those highly original but purely generic remarks of his towards the kind of indiscreet talk which is the only way in which conversation between friends is distinguished from that between simple acquaintants. It was I who took the initiative. His incessant spitting bothered me (as it also bothered the guardians of Hades, who eventually put a dun-colored spittoon alongside his table), so that one evening I took my courage in my hands and asked him why he did not get his persistent catarrh looked after. I asked without thinking, and immediately repented of my boldness, expecting the plaster on the ceiling to fall on my head from senatorial ire. Instead, that pleasantly modulated voice replied calmly, "But my dear Corbèra, I have no catarrh. You who observe me with such care must have noticed that I never cough before spitting. My spit is not a symptom of illness, but of mental health: I spit out of disgust at the stupidities I read, and if you would take the trouble to examine the gadget over there (he pointed to the spittoon) you would realize that it harbors little saliva and almost no mucus. My spit is symbolic and highly cultural; and if it doesn't suit you, go back to your drawing rooms where the only reason people don't spit is that nothing really sickens them." The only thing that softened his extraordinary insolence was his faraway look; nonetheless I wanted to get up and just leave him there; but as luck would have it, I had time enough to realize that the fault lay with my own foolhardiness. So I stayed, and the impassive senator promptly counter attacked. "Now you: tell me why you frequent this Erebus with its contingent of phantoms and, as you point out, its share of catarrh, this geometrical figuration of failed lives? Turin hardly lacks those creatures you people find so desirable. A little outing to that hotel by the Castle, to Rivoli, or the bath-house at Moncalieri would soon offer you your filthy pastime." Hearing such precise information about Turin's houses of pleasure from so learned a man set me laughing. "But how do you come by such addresses, Senator?" I asked. "I know them, I know them, Corbèra. A man who frequents a senate, be it academic or political, learns about such things, and only such things. But I trust you will do me the favor of allowing yourself to be convinced that the sordid pleasures in which you people indulge play no part in the life of Rosario La Ciura." And that seemed true: his demeanor and his words were an unequivocal (a word much used in 1938) sign of a sexual reserve that had nothing to do with age.

"The truth, Senator, is that I first came to this café as a temporary asylum from the world. I had problems with two girls of the sort you have so justly stigmatized." His retort was swift and pitiless. "Cuckolded, eh, Corbèra? Or a disease?" "Neither of the two. Worse. Deserted." And I told him about the sorry events of two months ago. I made my tale witty, for the wound inflicted on my self-respect had healed; and anyone but this wretched hellenist would either have made fun of me or, more rarely, have taken pity on me. But this frightening old man did neither: instead, he was indignant. "You see what happens, Corbèra, when you couple with the sick and the squalid? I'd say the same to those sluts about you, were I to have the misfortune to meet them." "Sick, Senator? Both were utterly charming. You should have seen how they ate at the Specchi; as to squalid, nothing of the sort—they were splendid girls, and elegant to boot." A scornful trail of spit snaked from the Senator's mouth. "Sick as I said, sick; in fifty or sixty years, or perhaps long before, they'll crack up; so they're sick as of now. And squalid, too: a fine elegance theirs is, made up of costume jewels, stolen pullovers and simpering borrowed from the movies. A fine form of generosity it is to rifle in a lover's pockets for greasy banknotes instead of presenting him, as others would, with rosy pearls and branches of coral. That's what you get for mixing with doctored-up trollops. How about the disgust you must feel, you and they both, to be rolling your soon-to-be carcasses around in smelly sheets?" Stupidly, I replied: "But Senator, the sheets were spic-and-span." He got very angry: "What have sheets got to do with anything? The inevitable stink of corpse was yours. I repeat: how can you carry on revels with people of that sort, of your sort?" I was offended, I who already had my eye on one of Ventura's delicious little seamstresses, or "cousettes." "After

1031

all," I said, "a man can't be expected to bed nothing but Serene Highnesses!" "Who's talking about Serene Highnesses? They're as fit for the charnel house as any of the others, young man. But you don't seem to grasp this, and I'm wrong to bring it up. You and your girl-friends are fated to wind up in the fetid swamps of your revolting pleasures. Very few people know this." With that he raised his eyes to the ceiling and smiled; his expression was rapt. Then he gave me his hand and left.

We didn't see each other for thee days. On the fourth I got a telephone call at the newspaper. "Is that *Monsu* Corbèra? This is Bettina, *Signor*. Senator La Ciura's house-keeper. He asked me to tell you he's had a bad cold. But he's better now, and he'd like to see you after supper tonight. The address is 18 via Bertoli, second floor. Come at nine." We were cut off; there was no way to call back.

Number 18 via Bertoli was a dilapidated old building, but the Senator's apartment was vast and well-kept: I suppose thanks to the efforts of Bettina. The rows of books—modest-looking and economically bound, as a living library is—began in the entrance hall. There were thousands of them in the three rooms through which I walked. In the fourth sat the Senator, wrapped in a voluminous camel hair dressing gown, as fine and soft as any I'd ever seen. Later I found out that it wasn't camel hair, but alpaca, made from the wool of llamas and the gift of the Academic Senate of Lima. The Senator pointedly did not rise to greet me when I entered, but received me with warm cordiality; he was better, in fact in perfectly good shape, and expected to be out and about again as soon as the cold wave which had struck Turin in the past few days was over. He offered me some resinous wine, the gift of the Italian Institute in Athens, some horrible, pink *lukums* or Turkish delights, a gift of the Archaeological Mission in Ankara, and some more sensible local delicacies obtained by the provident Bettina.

He was in such good humor that he twice smiled broadly and even apologized for his diatribe in our Hades. "Corbèra, I realize I was as excessive in the way I expressed myself as I was moderate in my ideas. Forget about it." I did forget it; in fact I was full of respect for this old man who was, I suspected, despite his brilliant career, an unhappy man. He sat there devouring those abominable Turkish delights. "Sweets," he said, "should be sweet, and that's that. If they have any other taste they are like a perverse kiss." He fed tidbits to Eacus, a big boxer who had made his appearance at some point. "For one who can understand, Corbèra, this fellow here, for all his ugliness, bears a closer resemblance to the Immortals than all those hookers of yours." He refused to show me his library: "All classical stuff. Of no possible interest to one like you who morally flunked Greek." But he did take me around the room which served as his study. There were few books, though I noticed among them the plays of Tirso de Molina, Lamotte-Fouqué's *Ondine*, Giraudoux's play of the same name and, to my surprise, the works of H. G. Wells. In compensation, the walls were covered with enormous, life-sized photographs of archaic Greek statues; and not the ordinary photographs that you and I might be able to obtain, but special, superb prints, summoned up with authority and offered with devotion by museums from all around the world. They were all there, all those great creations: the Louvre's *Horseman*; the *Seated Goddess* from Taranto, now in Berlin; the *Warrior* from Delphi; the Acropolis *Maiden*; the *Piombino Apollo*; the *Lapithae Woman* and the *Phoebus* from Olympia; the world-famous *Charioteer*. . . .The room was illuminated by their ecstatic, and also ironic, smiles; exalted by the unselfconscious loftiness of their bearing. "You see, Corbèra, these yes; tarts no." On the mantelpiece were ancient amphorae and votive bowls: Odysseus tied to the mast of his ship, the Sirens who from their high cliffs shattered themselves on the rocks in expiation for having let their prey flee. "All nonsense, Corbèra, tall tales from petit-bourgeois poets; no one escapes, and had anyone fled, the Sirens would not have died for so little. Besides which, how would they have managed to die?"

1033

On a little table and in an unpretentious frame was an old, faded photograph: a young man of about twenty, nearly naked, with full windblown hair and a bold expression on a face of rare beauty. I stopped for a moment, perplexed: I thought I understood. Not at all. "And this, *paesano*, was and is (said emphatically) Rosario La Ciura."

The poor senator in his bathrobe had been a young god.

Then we talked about other matters, and before I left he showed me a letter written in French by the rector of the University of Coimbra inviting him to be a member of the committee of honor for a congress of Greek classicists to take place in Portugal in May. "I am very happy to go. I will board the *Rex* at Genoa along with the French, the Swiss, and the Germans. As Ulysses did, I shall stop my ears so as not to hear the fabulizing of cripples, and I shall have some fine days navigating: sun, blue, sea-smell."

As he was seeing me out, we passed the shelves bearing the works of

Wells and I was bold enough to express my surprise at their presence there. "You're right, Corbèra, they're awful. Among them there's a novelette that, should I re-read it, would have me spitting for a month; and you, little lap dog that you are, you'd be shocked, wouldn't you!"

After this visit, our relations became positively cordial: at least on my part. I made elaborate preparations to have some fresh sea urchins sent up from Genoa. When I learned that these would arrive on the morrow, I bought some Etna wine and country bread, and somewhat fearfully, invited the Senator to visit me in my tiny rooms. To my great relief, he happily accepted. I went to fetch him in my little Fiat Balilla and drove him all the way to the via Peyron, which is in the back of beyond. He showed himself uneasy in the car; he had no confidence whatever in my driving skills. "I know you by now, Corbèra; if we were so unfortunate as to come across one of your fancy ladies, it would be just like you to turn around and stare, and both of us would wind up with our noses smashed up against the sidewalk." In fact no such skirted abominations turned up, and we arrived intact.

1034   For the first time since I had met him, I saw the senator laugh out loud. It was when we entered my bedroom. "So this is it! This is the stage of your lubricious adventures!" He looked at my few books. "Good enough, good enough. You're perhaps less ignorant than you seem. This one," he added, picking up my Shakespeare, "understood something: 'A sea-change into something rich and strange', 'What potions have I drunk of Siren tears.'"

When the admirable Signora Carmagnola brought a tray full of sea urchins, lemons, and so on into my little drawing room, the Senator was ecstatic. "What's this? You thought of this? How do you know that's what I most want in the world?"

"You need have no fears about eating them, Senator; just this morning they were still in the Ligurian sea."

"Indeed, indeed, you people are all alike, slaves to decadence and incipient putrefaction, ears finely tuned to hear the shuffling footsteps of Death. Poor little devils! Thanks, Corbèra, you are a good *famulus*. What a pity these sea-urchins of ours are not from our southern seas, that they don't come furled in our Sicilian seaweed; these spines have pricked no godly blood. You've done all you could, that's sure, but these are polar sea urchins, the kind that snooze among the icy rocks of Nervi or Arenzano." From which you could tell that the Senator was one of those Sicilians for whom the Ligurian Riviera, positively tropical for the Milanese, was a kind of Iceland. Once split, the sea urchins yielded up their wounded, blood-soaked, oddly segmented flesh. I'd never noticed it before, but given the Senator's peculiar analogies, they really did seem to me like a cross-section of some delicate female organ. He devoured them voraciously, but without joy, withdrawn and absorbed. He wouldn't use lemon on them. "You lot and your blends of tastes! You think a sea urchin ought to taste of lemon, sugar, chocolate, who knows what? Perhaps of love in paradise, too!" When he'd finished, he took a sip of wine and shut his eyes. After a moment I saw two teardrops form under his withered eyelids. He rose and went over to the window and surreptitiously wiped away his tears. Then he turned round. "You ever been to Augusta, Corbèra?" I had in fact spent three months there during my military service; when we had a moment, we hired a boat and wandered around in the transparent waters of the bays. After my reply, he fell silent; then, irritably, he said: "How about that little inner bay up above Point Izzu, behind the hill that overlooks the salt pans? Did you milksops ever get that far?"

"Indeed. It's the most beautiful spot in Sicily, and luckily tourists don't know about it. It's a wild stretch of coast, right senator? Completely deserted, not a house around; the sea is peacock-colored; opposite, behind those ever changing waves, rises Etna. There is no other place from which Etna is so lovely: so calm, masterly, truly divine. It's one of the places in which one can see our island—which so foolishly turned its back on its true vocation, that of serving as pasture to the herds of the sun—under its divine aspect."

The Senator fell silent. Then he said: "You're a good lad, Corbèra; if you weren't so ignorant, one might have made something of you." He approached me and kissed me on the brow. "Now go and fetch that coffee mill of yours. I want to go home."

We continued to see one another as usual in the weeks that followed. We took night walks now: generally down via Po and through the martial Piazza Vittoria, to look at the turbulent river and the hill where both of these inserted a touch of fantasy into the geometrical rigor of the city. Spring was upon us, that moving season of youth in danger, of the first lilacs on the river banks, the first couples without a place to go defying damp grass. "Down there the sun already burns, the algae flourish; on moonlit nights the fish break water, and one glimpses their bodies writhing in the bright spray. Here we are, you and I, by this insipid and empty river, by these huge barracks lined up like soldiers or brothers; and what we hear are the sighs of these dying couples." But it cheered him to think of his forthcoming trip by sea to Lisbon; soon he would leave. "It will be pleasant. You should come too: it's a pity there's not a section for those who don't know Greek. You can still talk Italian to me, but to Zuckmayer or van der Voos, if you couldn't demonstrate that you knew the optative mood of all irregular verbs you'd be done for: no matter that you might be—not because you're cultivated, but by sheer animal instinct—more aware of the reality of Greek than they."

Two days before he left for Genoa, he let me know that on the morrow he wouldn't be coming to the café, but would expect me at his house at nine o'clock.

The ritual was identical to that of my previous visit: the pictures of the 3,000-year-old gods gave off youth as a stove gives off heat; the faded photograph of the godlike youth of fifty years ago seemed dismayed to see its own metamorphosis, turned white-haired and slumped in an armchair.

When we had drunk some Cypriot wine, the senator summoned Bettina and told her she could go to bed: "I myself will see Signor Corbèra out. You see, Corbèra, if I made you come here this evening, at the risk of making you miss some fornication in Rivoli, it's because I need you. I am leaving tomorrow, and at my age one doesn't know that one won't be staying afar forever: especially when one travels by sea. You know, at heart I'm really quite fond of you; I am moved by your innocence, and amused by the brazen way you display the mechanisms of your life; and then it seems to me that like a few Sicilians of the better kind you have managed a synthesis of sense and reason. So you deserve not to be left empty-handed, without my explaining to you the reason behind some of my peculiarities, for certain things I've said to you that must have seemed mad to you." I protested feebly. "Many things you said I didn't understand; but I always ascribed my incomprehension to the inadequacy of my own mind, not to any aberration in yours." "Forget it, Corbèra, it amounts to the same thing. We old people all seem crazy to the young when the contrary is often true. But to explain myself, I have to tell you of my adventure, which is unusual. It happened when I was 'that young man over there'," and he pointed to his photograph. "We must go back to 1887, which must seem like prehistory to you, but isn't to me."

He moved from his seat behind the desk, and came to sit on the sofa alongside me. "Forgive me, but I'm going to have to speak softly. One doesn't shout important matters: that 'cry of love'—or hate—exists only in melodramas or among the least civilized, which comes to the same thing. Anyway, in 1887, I was twenty-four; I looked as I look in the photograph; I already had my degree in classics and had published two papers on the Ionian dialects which had caused quite a stir in my university; and I'd been readying my candidacy for a chair at the University of Pavia for a year. Furthermore, I had never been near a woman. To tell the truth, I've never been near one before or since that year." I was sure that my face had remained as emotionless as marble, but I was wrong. "That wink of yours is thoroughly ill-mannered, Corbèra: I am telling you the truth; it is true and I am proud of it. I know that we Catanians are reputed to make our wet-nurses pregnant, and that may well be true. But in my case, not so. When, as I did in those days, one frequents gods and goddesses day and night, one has no great wish to climb up the stairs of San Berillio brothels. Besides which, in those days, I was restrained by religious scruples. Corbèra, you really should learn to control your eyelashes; they betray you time and time again. Religious scruples, I said. Yes. I also said 'in those days'. Now I have none; but in this regard, that's been of no use whatsoever.

"My little Corbuccia, you probably got your job at the newspaper thanks to a note written by some big shot; you don't know what it's like to prepare for a competition for a university chair in classics. It means two years' slog to the verge of madness. Thank God, I already knew the language fairly well, as well as I know it now; and I'm not one to talk. . . .But the rest: the variant texts, Alexandrian and Byzantine; the fragments quoted, always erroneously, by Latin authors; the numberless connections of literature to mythology, history, philosophy, science! I'll say it again: they're enough to drive you mad. So I worked like a dog, and gave lessons to boys who'd failed their exams besides, so I could have enough money to stay in town. You could say I lived off black olives and coffee. And as if that weren't enough, there was that catastrophe known as the summer of 1887, which was an inferno of the sort you get from time to time down there. At night Etna regurgitated the accumulated heat from the sun stored up during fifteen hours of daylight; if at midday you touched a balcony railing you had to run to the first aid; the lava paving stones seemed likely to revert to a liquid state; and almost daily the sirocco's sticky wings flapped in your face. I was

1037

done in. A friend saved me. He found me wandering the streets in a daze, mouthing Greek verses I no longer understood. He was startled at the way I looked. 'Listen, Rosario,' he said, 'if you go on like this you're going to go crazy and goodbye to the chair. I'm off to Switzerland (the boy had money), but I have this three-room hovel just twenty meters from the sea in Augusta, a long way out of town. Pack your bags, take your books and stay there all summer. Come by the house in an hour and I'll give you the key. You'll see, it's different there. When you get to the station, ask for the Carobene lodge, everyone knows it. But go. Go tonight.'

"I followed his advice, I left the same night, and the following morning, when I woke up, instead of the usual sewage pipes saluting me at dawn, I found myself looking out on a clear stretch of water and, in the background, Etna, wrapped in morning mist and no longer ruthless. The place was completely deserted, as you tell me it still is, and uniquely beautiful. The sum of all that little seaside lodge with its shabby rooms contained was a sofa on which I spent the night, and a table and three chairs; in the kitchen, a few earthenware pots and an old lamp. Behind the house, a fig tree and a well. Paradise. I went into town and found the peasant who looked after Carobene's patch of land and arranged that every two or three days he would bring me bread, pasta, a few vegetables, and kerosene. Oil I had: our own, which my poor mother had sent to Catania. I hired a small boat which a fisherman brought me in the afternoons, together with a lobster-pot and a few fish hooks. I had decided to stay for at least two months.

"Carobene was right: it really was different there. Augusta was not spared the violent heat, but it no longer bounced off the walls, it no longer produced an animal-like stupor, but rather a sort of submissive euphoria; and the sun, having abandoned its hangman's scowl, was content to become a source of luminous, though still brutal, energy as well as a magician who mounted moving diamonds on every slightest ripple of the sea. Studying was no longer hard labor: in the gentle rocking of the boat, in which I remained for hours at a time, a book was no longer an obstacle to be overcome but a key to ease my passage into a world whose most bewitching aspects already lay before me. I often declaimed out loud lines from the poets, and the names of forgotten gods, ignored by the many, once again flickered on the surface of a sea which at one time, just hearing them, rose in a storm or fell into a dead calm.

"My isolation was absolute, interrupted only by the peasant who

1038

brought me my supplies. He stopped by for no more than five minutes, for seeing me so exalted and dishevelled he must have thought me on the verge of a dangerous madness. And to tell the truth, the sun, the loneliness, the nights passed under the whirling of the stars, my reduced diet, the study of remote matters, wove a spell about me which predisposed me to prodigies.

"These were fulfilled at six in the morning on the fifth of August. I had woken not long before and straightaway taken to my boat; a few strokes of my oars and I was far from the pebbles of the beach and had stopped under a large rock whose shade might protect me from the rising sun, already full of a fine fury and turning the purity of the early-morning sea to gold and blue. I was reciting poems when I felt a sudden dip of the gunwale behind me and to my right, as though someone sought to climb aboard. I turned round and saw her: a smooth-skinned sixteen-year-old rising from the sea, and two small hands gripping the stern. The young creature smiled, a slight fold of her pale lips showed a set of sharp white teeth like a dog's. But this was not a smile such as you people give, forever bastardized by some accessory expression of goodwill or irony; this smile was an expression of itself—that is, of a feral joy in its own existence, a sort of divine delight. Her smile was the first of the spells so cast on me that I had a revelation of a paradise of forgotten serenity. From her straggling, sun-colored hair, sea-water dripped over super-open green eyes, features of a childlike candor.

"Our shadowy reason, however predisposed, rears up at a prodigy and, faced with one, runs to the obvious; like anyone else, I wanted to believe I had met up with a girl out bathing and, moving carefully, I moved towards her, bent over, and held out my hands to help her in. With astonishing vigor, however, she emerged waist-high from the water, put her arms about my neck, enveloped me in a perfume such as I had never smelled before, and slithered into my boat: from groin downwards, below her buttocks, her body was that of a fish, covered in minute scales of blue and mother-of-pearl and ending in a forked tail that slowly drummed on the hull. She was a Siren.

"Lying back, her head on her intertwined hands, she showed the fine down under her arms, her well-parted breasts, her perfect belly with serene impudicity; from her body rose what I mistakenly called a scent, when it was really the magic smell of the sea, of the youngest possible voluptuousness. We were in the shade, but not twenty yards away lay the shore abandoned to the sun and quivering with pleasure. My near-total nakedness failed to conceal my own feeling.

1039

"She spoke and thus I was immersed—after her smile and her smell—by the third and greatest of her enchantments, her voice. It was a trifle guttural, veiled, and resonant with untold harmonics; behind her words were the indolent laughter of summer seas, of the last foam to fall on a beach, of wind caressing moon-like waves. Siren songs, my dear Corbèra, do not exist; the music we cannot escape is that of their voice alone.

"She spoke in Greek and I labored to understand her. 'I heard you speaking a language like my own; you please me, take me. I am Lighea, daughter of Calliope. Don't believe the tales told about us; we do not kill, we only love.'

"Bent over her, I rowed, staring fixedly into her laughing eyes. We reached the shore. I took her sweet-smelling body in my arms, and we passed from glare into deep shade; in my mouth she had already instilled that voluptuousness which to our earthly kisses is as wine is to water from a tap."

The senator recounted his adventure softly, and I who in my heart had always contrasted my varied experience of women to his, which I considered mediocre, and who had stupidly thought this might diminish the distance between us, felt humiliated: even in matters of love I was consigned to the lower depths. Not even for an instant did I think he was telling me a tall tale, and even the most skeptical person, being present, would have been aware of the utter truth in the old man's words.

"Thus those three weeks began. It is not proper, nor would it be charitable towards you, to enter into details. It is enough to say that in those embraces I enjoyed the highest form of both spiritual and basic voluptuousness, quite without any social connotation, that which our lonely herders feel when coupling with their goats; and if the comparison is repugnant to you, it is because you're not up to making the transition from the animal to the superhuman, two planes that in my case are superimposed.

"Think of what Balzac dared not express in his *Passion dans le désert*. So much life sprang from her immortal limbs that any energy expended was immediately replenished, if not augmented. In those days, Corbèra, I made love more than a hundred of your Don Giovannis did in their whole lifetimes. And what love! Safe from convent and crime, from the rancor of the Commendatore or the trivilialty of Leporello, far from the pretensions of the heart, from the false sighs of romance, from the artificial deliquescences that inevitably soil your miserable kisses. Truth to tell, a Leporello did disturb us that first day, and that was the only time; towards ten I heard the heavy

shoes of my peasant on the path to the sea. I was only just in time to toss
a sheet over her curious body before he arrived at the door: her uncovered
head, neck and arms made Leporello think this was no more than some
vulgar conquest on my part, which in turn made him suddenly respectful;
he stayed even a shorter time than usual, and as he left he winked his left
eye while with the thumb and forefinger of his right hand, rolled shut, he
pretended to twiddle an imaginary moustache at the corner of his mouth;
then he climbed back up the hill.

"I spoke of our having spent twenty days together; you should not
imagine that we spent those three weeks living, as the word is, connubially,
sharing bed, food, and occupations. Lighea's absences were very frequent:
without so much as a sign to me, she would throw herself into the water
and disappear, often for hours at a time. When she returned, which was
almost always at daybreak, she either met me in my boat, or if I was still
indoors, slithered on her back along the pebbles of the shore, half in and
half out of the water, struggling with her arms and calling me to help her
up the incline. 'Sasà', she called me, because I'd told her that was my
nickname. So doing, impeded by that part of her body which made her so
agile in the water, she looked as pitiable as a wounded animal, an impression   *1041*
that was immediately cancelled by the laughter of her eyes.

"She ate only what was live: I often saw her rise from the sea, her
delicate torso shining in the sun, tearing with her teeth a still-quivering,
silvery fish; its blood dribbled in streaks down her chin, and after a few bites,
she would toss the crushed cod or John Dory over her shoulder, to bloody
the sea red and sink while she childishly cried out as she cleaned her teeth
with her tongue. Once I gave her some wine; she couldn't drink from the
glass, so I had to pour her a little in the delicately-green palm of her tiny
hand, and this she drank by lapping it up with her tongue like a dog, her
eyes meanwhile registering her surprise at this unknown taste. She said it
was good, but afterwards always refused it. From time to time she appeared
on the beach, her hands full of oysters and mussels; while I labored to open
their shells with a knife, she cracked them with a stone and sucked at the
quivering mollusk inside together with bits of shell which bothered her not
at all.

"I told you, Corbèra: she was animal, but also an Immortal, and it is
a shame that words fail to express this constant synthesis as did, with utter
simplicity, her own body. It was not only in the carnal act that she showed

such joy, and a delicacy that was the very opposite of a dreary animal rut, but her speech was of an immediacy so powerful that I have found its equal only in a few great poets. Not for nothing was she Calliope's daughter: ignorant of all cultures, unaware of wisdom, disdainful of any moral inhibition, she was nonetheless a part of the fountainhead of all culture, all wisdom and morals, and she knew well how to express this first-born superiority of hers in terms of scabrous beauty. 'I am everything because I am no more than life's current without incident; I am immortal because all deaths, from that of the cod to that of Zeus, join within me; and joined in me they once again become life, no longer individual or determined, but Pan-like and hence free.' Then she said, 'You are young and beautiful; you should follow me now into the sea and escape pain and age; you would see my home beneath the high mountains of dark and unmoving water, where all is silence and stillness and so commingled that he who possesses it never even notices it. I have loved you, and when you are weary, when you can't stand anything any more, remember that all you have to do is lean into the sea and call me; I will always be there, because I am everywhere, and your dream of sleep will come true.'

1042   "She told me of her life undersea, about bearded Tritons and blue-green caverns; but these, she said, were foolish illusions, and the truth lay far deeper, in the blind, still, shapeless, eternal water-palace, without a gleam, without a whisper.

"Once she told me she would be away for some time, until evening the next day. 'I have to go far away, where I know I'll find a gift for you.'

"She returned in fact with a fantastic branch of purple coral, incrusted with shells and barnacles. For a long time I kept it in a little chest, and every night I kissed it in those places on which I knew the Indifferent's, that is the Beneficent's, fingers had fallen. But one day Maria, my house-keeper before Bettina, stole it and gave it to her gigolo. I found it in a jeweler's shop on the Ponte Vecchio, desecrated, cleaned and polished to the point of being unrecognizable. I bought it back and one night I threw it in the Arno: it had gone through too many profane hands.

"She also told me about the not insignificant number of human lovers she'd had during her millennial adolescence: fishers and sailors, Greeks, Arabs, from Sicily or Capri, and some who'd been shipwrecked, adrift on waterlogged rafts, to whom she'd appeared in the lightning-flashes of a storm, transforming their death rattle into ecstasy. 'All accepted my invitation, all came to seek me out, some right away, some after what seemed to them a long time. Only one have I never seen again: a fine looking lad with skin white as white and bright red hair whom I joined on a distant beach where this sea of ours merges with the great Ocean; he smelled of something far stronger than that wine you gave me the other day. I think he's never been seen since: not because he's happy, but because when we met he was so drunk he didn't know what was going on; I must have seemed just an ordinary fisher-woman." '

"Those weeks of high summer passed as quickly as a single morning; when they were gone, I knew that I'd lived for centuries. That lascivious girl and wild little beast had also been the wisest of Mothers; her presence alone had uprooted beliefs, dissipated metaphysics; with her delicate, sometimes bloody fingers she had shown me the way to eternal rest, and also to an ascetic life built not on renunciation but on the impossibility of accepting lesser pleasures. I shall certainly not be the second man to disobey her summons; I will not refuse the kind of pagan Grace I was offered.

"By its very violence, that summer was brief. The first hesitant clouds appeared around the twentieth of August, a few isolated drops of rain, tepid as blood, fell. The nights were a concatenation, on the distant horizon, of slow, silent lightning-flashes, one following on another like the cogitations of a god. In the morning, a dove-colored sea bewailed its arcane restlessness like a dove, and in the evening rippled and declined, minus any noticeable breeze, into smoke-grays, steel-grays, pearl-grays, each of them gentle and more loving than its former splendor. Faraway patches of mist fingered the water: on the Greek coasts rain was perhaps already falling. Lighea's mood too altered its coloring: from resplendence to a loving grey. She was more silent, she spent hours stretched out on a rock surveying a horizon no longer still, she seldom went away. 'I want to stay with you; if I swim away my sea-friends will keep me with them. Do you hear them? They are calling me.' Sometimes I did indeed think I heard a different, lower sound among the squawks of gulls, and saw unruly flashes between rock and rock. 'They are sounding their shells, they are calling Lighea to the feast of storms.'

"That struck us at dawn on the twenty-sixth. From the rock, we saw a wind approach that stirred up the farther water, while closer by leaden swells grew vast and sluggish. Soon the squall reached us; it whistled in our ears, doubled over the dry rosemary bushes. The sea broke below us, the

1043

first wave came at us capped in white. 'Goodbye Sasà. You won't forget!' With that the breaker broke on the rock, the Siren threw herself into the iridescent surf; I didn't see her drop further; it was as though she herself broke up in the spray.

The following morning the senator left; I went to the station to see him off. As usual, he was peevish and cutting, but as the train began to move he leaned out the window and ruffled my hair.

At dawn the next day, the newspaper had a telephone call from Genoa: during the night, while the *Rex* was sailing towards Naples, Senator La Ciura had fallen from the deck, and though boats were immediately lowered, his body had not been found.

A week later his will was opened: Bettina inherited his money and his furniture; the University of Catania got his library; a recent codicil made me legatee of the Greek bowl with the Sirens and the large photograph of the Acropolis charioteer.

Both were sent to my home in Palermo. Then came the war and while I was in Marmarica with half a liter of water a day, the "liberators" destroyed my house: when I returned, the photograph had been cut into ribbons and used as torches to light the way for looters at night; the largest fragment still shows Ulysses' feet bound to the mast. The books, deposited in the basement of the university, are slowly rotting away.

Translated by Keith Botsford

TRANSLATOR'S NOTE: Lampedusa's text was first translated and published by Pantheon Books in a volume entitled Two Stories and a Memory *(1961), with an introduction by E. M. Forster. The translation was one by the two finest translators from Italian to English, Archibald Colquhoun. There are some minor variations in Lampedusa's text and this version is based on the latest corrected edition from Feltrinelli. Colquhoun's text, while highly accurate and idiomatic, did not—since the object was to capitalize on the enormous worldwide success of* The Leopard—*entirely catch the highly articulated and Latinate syntax of Lampedusa, its slow and frequently inverted rhythms. A new translation thus serves a triple purpose: it brings the English text up to date; it offers another version of what is undoubtedly one of the greatest stories ever written about a theme from classical antiquity; and it offers the text to a whole new audience.*

Karel Logher

My Father in the Mirror

Yesterday we heard that Hitler had committed suicide. Vera and I
felt no great emotion, but I felt a great satisfaction: I had outlived him, I
had circled and zigzagged and he had not been able to hit me. Leo Leder had
outsmarted Adolf Hitler. He is dead and I am eating chocolate. I had survived
the Holocaust and my own enormous stupidity. But the war was still going
on, and there was an army of fanatics still around to carry out the Führer's
testament. Like Dr. Memelmans, the shrink, who had been treating my
inexplicable ghost-ulcers, an hour at a time.

Here I was, telling him the story of my life, and when I reached the
day when Holland was liberated and Lancaster bombers dropped chocolates
on us, and stopped, there was Memelmans snoring. My sudden silence woke
him up, and his first gesture was to look at his watch. "You're thirty minutes
over time," he said, as though this were entirely my fault. Perspiration
glistened on my forehead; my diaphragm was in paroxysm. Wearily I pushed
myself up off his couch, put my finger down my throat, and vomited: the
only relief possible. I vomited on his couch, then I staggered to his desk and
vomited on his desk. Memelmans was too surprised to say a word, and it
was only after I had heaved up more brown, slimy vomit on his carpet that

he got his senses back and shouted at the top of his voice, "Get out, you crazy, foul Yid! You goddam Jew, get out!"

In spite of my misery, I smiled. He had fallen into my trap; he had laid himself bare. My divining-rod had worked and his hidden antisemitism had risen to the surface. I felt liberated and content. My revenge could not be compared to that of Miss Auschwitz; but, like her, I had used my own body to obtain it.

A day later, however, something happened which proved that my problems were far from solved.

I was shaving in the bathroom, looking in the mirror over the wash-basin, only what I saw in the mirror was not my face, but my father staring at me.

"Father," I stammered. "Is that you?"

"Yes, Leo. Let me have a good look at you." He studied my face intently, and after a while he said, "How interesting to see what I would look like if I had reached your age."

I was speechless for a moment, and then I said, "I know from the Red Cross certificate that you died at the age of fifty-six in Sobibor, together with Sophie, your fourth spouse. I even know the dates: Sophie on August 24, 1943, and you on September 29."

He nodded. "That is precisely what I want to talk to you about, to unburden my conscience. You will not understand what I am going to tell you. Nobody will. But you are not to blame for that."

"I shall do my best, father."

I had a good look at him. He looked much older than his age, which gave me an idea what I would look like if I ever reached the age of eighty. I also noticed in his eyes a glimmer of madness that had never been there before. He said, "Sophie and I were immediately separated in Sobibor. She went to the left and I was sent to the right, together with perhaps a hundred other men. We were marched to a yard where roll-call was taken. Ten hose-men,' an SS Guard called out. Another guard picked ten men at random and marched them off. The first guard then read off, 'Fifteen body-pullers, twelve body-loaders, twelve body unloaders, six body-checkers, ten body counters, twenty timber-carriers, ten body-ash-sweepers!''

"My God!" I said with awe." "Please go on."

"They made me a body-checker, and together with my five colleagues

I was taken to the other side of the camp, not far from the smoking pit and in front of a bunker with steel doors.

"A guard opened the doors. Inside, there were dead Jews standing up like matches in a box. Their final convulsions had inextricably knotted arms and legs; they were a solid block of Jewry. The stench of gas, piss, shit and vomit emerged from the bunker and mixed with the terrible smell of burned flesh that rose from the high watch-tower-high flames from the burning pit.

"'Hose-men, *antreten!*' The hose-men were driven by force to the bunker and began to hose down the bodies with water.

"'Body-pullers, *antreten!*' The body-pullers threw ropes over the crowded dead. The water made the bodies slippery, and as they pulled, the dead tumbled to the ground like herrings from a net.

"'Body-checkers, *antreten!*' The guard told me what to do. I said I could not do it. He clubbed me over the head; I cried and begged on my knees—rather be killed that do that! He kicked and clubbed me again, and before I knew what I was doing, I had my finger up the arse of a dead Jew and was searching for hidden jewels, for diamonds, for gold. I searched his navel; I went up his nose and deep into his mouth.

"Then the body-loaders piled the dead on trucks, and pushed them into a pile; the unloaders unloaded and threw the bodies into the flames, the sweepers gathered their ashes which the gardeners used as fertilizer for vegetables for the guards' canteen. The timber-carriers fed the fire with logs. There were men to collect the hair, the glasses and false teeth; others sorted confiscated clothes according to size, color and sex. The body-counters handed their totals in to the administration, which duly checked, classified and coded the information. It was perfect."

1047

"Father, if this were written down, people would say this is the work of a lunatic."

"I wish that were true, but I can tell you I found many treasures in those body-holes. I was the last link in a chain of total plunder."

"Father, how did you bring yourself to do it?"

"If you are facing death, you have no idea what you can do to others in order to stay alive. Only hyenas touch corpses. Animals have a saving instinct. I have seen and done other unimaginable things, but I don't want to speak of them." He came out from the mirror and touched my hand. "Will you forgive me" he asked.

I took his hand. "Forget this nightmare. Remember, you woke up on

September 29, 1943. Although nobody will ever understand how you did what you did, I'm absolutely sure everyone will forgive you."

He radiated a dark halo of guilt and whispered: "I am so ashamed, you see. As I was doing those things, it all felt quite natural. Anyone would have felt the same, even you, Leo."

"Father, there is a new generation of Jews that does not lie awake at night with grief at what happened."

"I never looked at it that way. You may be right."

"What is terrible is that it could happen again: all it needs is the right man in the right place at the right time."

"If it happens again, don't wait like millions of Jews did. Promise me?"

"I promise. But on condition you stop worrying about the past."

"I will."

But he didn't sound very convinced. We shook hands—at least I thought we did. But when I looked down at my own hands, they were empty.

1048　We met again in the same bathroom. This time my father stepped out from behind the mirror while I was shaving. "I want to speak to you," he said dully.

"Do you feel all right? You look tired. What's the matter?"

"I want to talk to you about something I never wanted to say to another human being." I looked at him, puzzled. "I told you about my work as a body-checker, but I did not tell you everything."

"You promised not to . . ."

He shook his head impatiently. "You may not have noticed, but I went mad in Sobibor."

So that was the new glimmer in his eyes! I said, "People who are really crazy never admit it; they always say everyone else is."

"Don't interrupt me!" he said with paternal authority. "Just listen. It started on the day when, believe it or not, I really began to like what I was doing. I had searched hundreds of bodies by then, and it dawned on me that I was still alive, and I could go on living—just as long as I kept on poking into those bodies! On that day I began to hope and pray that I would be allowed to continue doing that job: tomorrow, the day after, and until the war was over. That way I might escape death myself. I began to see each body as a stepping-stone to survival, and this will to survive took over my mind. Every minute I spent inspecting bodies for coins and gems added to my life. I became an extension of time itself. My fingers turned like the hands of a clock; I had no control over them. I became insensible to being beaten, to the stench of the bodies and their distorted features; I heard only the tick-tock of time. I searched my bodies with painstaking care. I wanted to be the perfect body-checker, a pro, someone they'd never get rid of as long as there were still bodies!

"In the barracks which I shared with the other specialists I noticed that those who were responsible for collecting the luggage of deported Jews from the railroad cars had plenty to eat. That night they were grumbling: because the day's haul was only a bunch of poor Polish Jews! But on good days, they would barter food for valuables. I had nothing to offer just then, but I saw that if I wanted to go on searching bodies, I also had to find food, or I'd die of hunger or exhaustion.

"I lay there on my bunk, but couldn't sleep. The clocks and the bells kept me awake. I got to hate those wasted hours in which I couldn't burrow into bodies. At any moment the guards might simply despatch me as useless!

"The next day I found a ruby up a man's arse. In the split second the guard wasn't looking at me, I popped it into my mouth. The taste was sickening and I began to drool. The guard looked at me with suspicion, so I swallowed the ruby. '*Aufmachen*,' he shouted, slapping my face. He searched my mouth with his finger and slapped me again because he hadn't found anything. That night, I let my diarrhoea slip through my fingers until the stone lay in my hand. I bartered it for a spoonful of peanut butter and a bar of chocolate.

1049

"The next day I found a body with a watch still on its wrist. Usually nothing shiny ever escaped the first searches: only what was secreted inside their bodies. I took the watch off the body and held it to my ear. It was ticking! It kept perfect time with the tick-tock in my head! I went wild with joy. Not only could I hear time, now I could actually see it! I was offered a Gouda for it, but I refused. I preferred to watch the hands on my watch turn. I was no longer hungry. I controlled my own survival. Or so I thought.

"It turned out I was watching and listening to the last hours of my life, because precisely four hours and thirty-seven minutes later they lined all of us body-specialists against a wall and mowed us down. They wanted no witnesses to survive and testify to the evil we had done in their name.

"A new group of body-checkers took over, and one of them spotted the watch on my wrist. He looked around carefully. When he thought no one was watching, he slipped it off my wrist. That was a big mistake. A guard saw him and shot him in the head. He tore the watch out of his hand and held it to his ear, but finally threw it away. I picked it up and put it back on my wrist. But when I looked at it, I realized it had stopped at the very moment the bullet killed me. Look, here it is."

My father showed me the watch on his wrist. The watch said seven o'clock.

"I must go," he said, turning his back to me.

"No, don't go! I have something to tell you!" I grabbed him by the arm.

"No. Look, I know what your sickness is. You can sniff out anti-semites. It's your task to warn Jews against the dangers which surround them. No Jew, dead or alive, will forgive you if you do not use that gift wholly to the benefit of all the Jews left on this earth. I am counting on you."

How did he know I had this gift? I looked at him with perplexity. He read my thought. "Don't you understand?" he said. "I gave you that gift. I wanted you to make proper use of the extra time God gave you." He took the watch from his wrist and dangled it in front of my eyes. "Look carefully," he said. "What time does it say?"

"Seven o'clock exactly."

"Right. That was the moment I died and you became my reincarnation. That was when you decided to survive. That was when you ripped off your yellow star, when you burned your ID and your summons to the transit-camp, when you faked your divorce from Vera and left your house and home. The church bells rang seven times. Remember?"

He shoved the watch on my wrist. In a strangled voice, I said, "Father, if I understand you rightly, everything that's happened to me after I left home, right up to this very moment, was in fact happening to you?"

"It was, it is and always will be. You can't deny it. I did manage to survive. True or not? In spite of the war and everything that happened to you, you're still alive, right?"

"Then look at me, Father, you'll see the state you're in!"

"That's all part of it, like it or not. I see you're writing a book. Only I can see you're wearing a cap and it says 'Writer' on it, in spite of your not knowing the difference between fact and fiction. You know why you don't know the difference? Because you've become as crazy as I became in Sobibor. It doesn't matter. You, my son Leo and my reincarnation, must go on writing. Through you I want to leave some footprint on this earth."

I looked at the watch and heard it tick. The hands had moved from seven to six minutes past. "Pardon me for saying this, Father, but from the moment you took hold of me, I have been suffering. Why did you do this to your son?"

"I deliberately wanted you to suffer for the rest of your life. To bring you nearer to God. When I left your mother, I made a mess of your childhood. So I decided that after my death I would take your life in hand again."

"You do realize, don't you, that when I die, I shall have nobody left to take up my body. I'm the only member of the family left."

"Yes, I thought about that. When the time comes, I'll let you know."

"And mother? Your other wives? What became of them?"

"They became oaks. You've seen them."

"Where?"

"You lived with them."

"I've moved twenty times in eighteen years. Many of the houses I lived in, I left without heartbreak. They have faded from my mind. I can't even remember what they were like." He let me talk; he listened. And after a while I said slowly, "There was one. There were four oaks at the foot of the garden. I spent a summer there, the leaves made them cool to sit under. And when winter came, I could see them from my window. Bare of their leaves they looked line an x-ray of a human body."

"Your mother and the others, bundled into one body."

"And why do I like dogs more than people?"

"It's another of my attempts to make you suffer."

"What about Vera?"

"She is still alive. But like all selfish people, the idea that she would live on through someone else she would find insufferable. She'll want to be herself."

"Are you willing to leave me and allow me to live my own life?"

"No, you must suffer until you return to your God."

I wanted to continue talking to him, but he'd already vanished behind the mirror.

1051

In the middle of the night I woke up and grabbed my head. A few seconds ago—I'm sure of it—someone swapped my head with another's. I was robbed of all my senses, and when I got them back, they were totally different from the ones I knew. I switched on the lamp and studied the window opposite my bed. The image reflected is familiar to me, seen from without it undoubtedly is me, but at the same time I hate what I see. "Kike, rotten Jew," my new brain said." I sniffed the air. "And how you stink! Incredible!"

I was now fully awake. I took a notebook from my bed-table and started scribbling notes, mathematical formulae; waves of hatred flowed through my brain. I knew what had happened. I have a Nazi head. My Nazi-hatred had been converted into Jew-hatred. My Einstein-like notes sketch out a plan.

In this plan, every species of creature had its own place. It was like Meccano. You can assemble whatever creature you like, and currently we were creating a locust. Like a bee, this locust has a sting; it has the same instinct as a bee, but instead of being attracted to flowers it will seek out Jews, and its sting will be fatal. A great number of Jews will be taken by surprise and their bodies will be covered with a swarm of locusts, but some will hide. But if they hide, the locusts will lack Jews to feed on, so the population will seek out the Jews and hand them over to the locusts, otherwise they themselves will perish: the locusts will consume their food.

The Jew-seeking locust with the deadly sting is the only possible answer: the whole non-Jewish population of the world will be involved; we won't have to lift a finger.

Early in the morning, I wake up. Present in my room are the fourty-four members of my family who were gassed. They wriggle their way into my small room. To gain space, they stand on my bed. In a chorus, they demand that I kill Mengele.

"Leo, from pain alone a man does not die," my father said. I replied that killing a man is no easy matter. I asked him to give me time to think. He said, "Leo, remember what I told you, You're as mad as I am."

"Father, Mengele's locusts are ready for the next holocaust."

I fell back asleep. This time, I woke up to face the TV screen. A man was addressing me. "Mister Leder," he said. "You do not know me. My name is Aldred Morgenstern. I am the one who took your place in Auschwitz when you refused to go."

"Forgive me. I didn't know that."

"I was glad to take your place," he said. "I was sick and I thought I would finally be rid of my pain."

"The pains must have been terrible if you were prepared to swop them for Auschwitz."

"They resembled yours." I looked at him, and of course it was my head sitting on his neck. "You are going to save the Jews. If not for your family, for me. You owe me that."

"I swear." For how could I refuse myself? I got out of my chair and put it back where it belonged. Then I stared for a long time at the empty spot it left on the carpet. It was a beautiful carpet, and my father's head took shape out of its arabesques.

"In view of these terrible things that will happen to Jews, don't you feel you need to get closer to God?"

"I am writing a story," I tell him.

"Tell me about it."

"In this story I have two wives, one Catholic and one Protestant. The Catholic wife wants to become a Jewess; but because I'm not a practicing Jew, I can't help her. She insists. For seven years we study: the alphabet, the rites, the laws, the Torah, the Talmud. We keep all the holy days. My Protestant wife—she was the first—also wants to convert. I think because she's jealous. She and I have a son. He takes to drugs and comes back to visit me in the shape of a stray cat.

"When my second wife and I have finished out studies, the Rabbi invites us to his Seder. I am seated between both wives, and in the end we all emigrate to Israel."

"A beautiful story. What's the title?"

"'Bit by Bit.' Everyone's story is part of a puzzle. The reader has to put all the bits together to get the story of our family."

"Tell me about my piece."

"You know the whole story. You have a tumultuous life, you go to Sobibor, you die. There is no reincarnation. Your ashes wind up as fertilizer for the garden."

"And you?" my father asked.

"I become an actor, and one day I am offered a big part in a play written by a German writer; but I refuse, because the play is a piece of antisemitic propaganda. In three acts he proves the Germans had nothing to do with the extermination of the Jews. The Jews killed themselves. But in the end I allow myself to be persuaded; the producer says he will alter the play: instead of a murdering Jew, I will play a hunted Jew.

"Every night I play the role of Salmon Davidsohn, the arch-Jew. I am so convincing that the audience thinks it is Jewish. The critics find me heartbreaking in that role.

"My first and second wife stand in the wings; they are under the spell of my performance. I have become the Jew each of them lived with but never recognized. I have become a God-fearing man, religious and devout, according to His will."

EDITOR'S NOTE: We met Logher at a reception in Holland, and in the manner of writers who have something urgent to say, he pressed a bulky manuscript on us. As such manuscripts do—one recalls G. S. Hardy dealing with the many-rupee'd-and-anna'd manuscript which he received by post from the Indian mathematician, Ramanujan—it languished for some time unread: in part because it had been translated into English by Logher himself, and he knew only as much English as the average, educated Dutchman. When, eventually, we both of us read his story, we thought it powerful and moving; and when, some several years later, we first mooted the Republic of Letters, *we said we would publish it as a book. One of us went down to Cambo-les-bains with a contract. Unfortunately, Logher's Dutch publisher, who had done absolutely nothing for the book, and whom Logher loathed, demanded an outrageous price for the rights. Logher, ever gentlemanly, said that we should not worry; this was his own, new English text, and if we would kindly fix it up, he'd be eternally grateful. Then, first his wife, and then Logher himself died. In that sense, this extract from his book is a debt of honor. In any other, it is a remarkable text that has no need of our sense of honor.—K. B.*

Saul Bellow

All Marbles Still Accounted For

The essentials, toujours the essentials and again the essentials. Beyond the age of ninety the perspectives of a lifetime wither and shrink, like all else. Reality in its lifelong configurations goes away. Frequently, I feel that my mortal car is straddling the median-line, the right-hand wheels rolling in this world, the other two in a different one. Positioned on the driver's side, I have short rushes of clairvoyance, or maybe of hallucination. Nothing—thank God—can be done about this. In these over-the-line intervals you accept what happens as you will in the grave. Is soil trickling? Is water dripping? Much you can do about that. Only the premise of the grave and its confines is extinction, whereas what I am reporting is not the void but a blessed release from disorder. That's why I say thank God. At my age, fixed points fade out and old routines fall away. You feel no obligation to obey the rules of the road, and when this happens you can only be glad, for you have long suspected that those rules are bound to bring you to a dead end.

Now let me say, upfront, that it's the rare person that can be trusted in the first person singular. You can't depend on any man to give a true account of himself. He's not likely to know what honesty—or dishonesty, for that matter—is. And I wouldn't presume to put myself forward if I didn't have a motive well beyond ego-indulgence. I come with information everybody should have and with a piece of testimony relating to questions that never stop gnawing the heart of humankind.

It was just yesterday—or was it the day before—that I was shuffling through the Customs Hall of the Miami International Airport. Tense passengers crowded around the baggage carrousels. They were mentally re-checking their false customs declarations. Would they, or would they not be caught! As for me, my declaration was blank and I had no suitcases to wait for, I was sockless in sneakers and shorts, a green visor over my eyes, and nobody tried to stop me. The inspectors seemed to understand that if they asked to look into my old flight bag (now as scaly and dry as a beached object that has gone back and forth week after week in the tides) I'd simply abandon it and keep going.

"Where have you been, grandpa?"

"Around the world. I went via Europe—France and Russia—then New Guinea. I came home via Hawaii."

"New Guinea, you don't tell me! What doing?"

"I wish I could say."

"Yeah? Well, say on."

"I was on a field trip [Idiot!]"

Chasing butterflies? Collecting birds? I might as well have answered, "I've been in outer space. Among the stars—those prickles you stare up at when you're drunk. This trip was arranged by Arthur C. Clarke. I wasn't as old as you see me when I left. Those time-warps do this to you. And now please don't bug me. I just stepped off a flying saucer which landed way out in the tall grass and I've had a long hot walk."

But I don't say anything to these inspectors (useless parties). My shanks, my skin, the veins on my head, my crustacean hands make my statement for me. They say it all. I look like thousands, hundreds of thousands of other old crocks from Miami Beach. And we ancients don't smuggle drugs. Customs officials who are trained to pounce on cocaine seldom search a senior citizen. I wasn't carrying any narcotics and my conscience was clear—on that score, anyway.

When the lady in the glass booth had examined my passport she said to me, "You've been around—all these stamps in your book—Paris, Budapest, Moscow, Cairo, Bombay, Melbourne. Where's Port Moresby?

"That's New Guinea."

"Sir, did you enjoy New Guinea?"

Enjoy? That depends ... However, I was noncommittal.

"A holiday? A business trip?"

What sort of businessman wears a T-shirt and travels without socks?

"It was partly business, partly personal."

What personal reasons could an old crock like me have?

"More like research," I informed her.

In the men's room, taking my time as nonagenarians are obliged to do, I thought, Good thing she didn't ask for my field notes. But then I could have tapped my head and said, All the information is up here.

That would have been no lie. Research, strictly speaking, was not my motive. I had left the US for mixed financial, legal (business-related) and family reasons. A man of my age would have to be crazy to go into the fever-soaked bush, risking tropical infections like dengue or the yaws. And all by his lonesome, too. I sometimes was kidded by family and friends about being an anthropologist. "Didn't you know Hilbert was a pioneer? He studied with Boas at Columbia and has an M.A in Primitivology," the jokers said. "He specialized in cannibals. And now his granddaughter is a Professor at Harvard in the same subject. She's also a real sex-pot."

1057

There's no denying that my one and only grandchild is an unusually attractive woman whose field is Comparative Religions. She is a professor, a Ph.D several times over and highly regarded in her discipline—as they call it. Meredith (Immy) will tell you herself that I influenced her, although to say that she followed in my footsteps is absurd, since I didn't know where I was going. Besides, so much progress has been made in ethnography that the square old MA they gave me some seventy years ago seems ridiculous to the specialists of today. Furthermore, my interest in the subject is now practically nil. What do I want with fetishes, totems, grass huts, cicatrized faces? True, I used to take my small granddaughter to museums to look at primitive artifacts and explain how the Indians of the Amazon made fishtraps, but that was back in the fifties.

Among what I call the essentials, Stone Age tribes do not figure.

Back to the passport lady:

In the inspector's booth, having checked my name on her computer she said, "Okay, Mr. Faucil. Welcome home."

Home! I never felt Bay Harbor Island, Fla. to be anything like home. Viewed from the side of palms, shrubs, flowers, the seas of sunlight it's a preview of the Isles of the Blest—of Heaven as the art of merchandising invites you to picture it. Where will you spend eternity? Wouldn't you like it to be a billion dollar shopping mall?

The mall at Bay Harbor Island is gorgeous—Lord and Taylor, Tiffany, Hermes and Gucci within view and hearing of the ocean. Sitting with a cup of espresso at an outdoor table, fresh gardenias all around, you look upwards into the palms and the sea-tinted heavens, but on the level of social vision what you see is the best that money can buy.

If you stray from the main arcade and wander away to the rear, as has happened to me, you smell the exhaust fumes of the ventilators. And the sewers also—as in all glamorous places at sea level, where the drainage is poor: Venice for example. Venturing further from the ocean front you observe what a powerful geometry the planners have imposed here, how the clean lines of the pavements strictly limit the riotous vegetation, the flowering shrubs. But then you turn into Collins Avenue with its bakeries, butcher-shops, boutiques, delicatessens and on Collins you meet other, less rich old men and women wearing white noseguards or thick creams against the treacherous sun. The benevolent beautifying sun into which we used to rush, stripping as we ran, turns out to be carcinogenic. Dermatologists have to cauterize the life-threatening spots of actinic keratosis on your nose or under your hair, with a freezing nitrogen spray. It hits you on the head like a hammer.

Collins Avenue looks as if all hospitals, nursing homes and mental institutions had discharged their patients at the same moment. (The charnel houses have emptied, too.) Some of these aged people are property owners, they bought condominiums at three hundred thousand and up. Others rent. Yet everybody looks homeless! It makes you despair. They don't have much to say. Just as well. Their stories would kill you if they told all. In these surroundings, great sadness and boredom lie down on your heart and nothing you can get to eat or drink, no prescription filled in a pharmacy will bring relief.

So there are plenty of reasons to leave Bay Harbor Island and few for coming back, but here I was, returning, and without an all-clear from my granddaughter Immy. She had ordered me to go because in biblical terms I would not cease from troubling (the reference is to the dead; only the grave stops them). I wasn't as wicked as all that, and I don't want to make it sound like deportation-proceedings. Immy is my heiress. The estate is large.

I had been curiously careless about investments. Millions of dollars had been wiped out. I tried to keep this from Immy but she was bound to find out eventually. I therefore made a point of telling her, and when I did she came down immediately to see what was going on. Had I become incompetent?

I didn't think so. But I couldn't stop her from taking charge.

The sort of person she is, I think I can quickly tell you. The only child of an only child, my late daughter Hilda, she grew up in a well-to-do Manhattan household. Her parents were fellow-traveling Stalinists who sent her to progressive, permissive schools. She was the sort of avant-garde kid whose psychoanalysis began in the first grade. After the Red Schoolhouse came Wellesley College, and then Oxford and the Sorbonne. The squeaky faltering little girl turned into a confident and physically "important" woman. In her prime she looked to me (forgive the strictly personal nature, the idiosyncrasy of the impression) as large and as full and glossy as a sea lion. The genes in our helix favor the women, I think, and stint the men. In all respects this woman is more distinguished, more mature, more balanced-looking than her parents, and infinitely more than her grandfather. Her physical properties go well with her professional specialty. Lecturing, she deals plainly with things like pederasty or oral sex. I don't suppose you could lecture on initiation rites or shamanism if you were squeamish. But nobody seems squeamish nowadays. (When I was young no paper would accept a Kotex ad). Old guys are inclined to exaggerate the voluptuousness of female descendants, I know. But you should see how she dresses to go out. She favors saris for evening wear. She gets herself up in oriental trousers. Kohl on the eyelids, gold-flecked face-powder, large pieces of jewelry. Substantial, busty, supple as a seal, perfumed like a temple prostitute. But she also has a briny personal odor. I probably should not be saying all this about my own daughter's daughter. But what's the point of speaking in the first person if you can't be personal? Eighty years ago, as a Brooklyn street kid, I'd have sized her up as the kind of girl who'd go all the way. But now even Immy is in her forties and her still-observant grandfather observes that she is no longer in the erotic bigtime. What do you see if you live long enough? You see the same changes over and over again.

I used to view her from the funny side. Often the viewed themselves give you the cue. They suggest that they are amusing, pathetic or stable or labile. It's like a musical signature that people carry to tell you how they should be played.

Maybe this is what comes of having two wheels over the dividing line. Being on both sides at once suggests schizophrenia.

I'm a lone cowhand;
On both sides of the Rio Grande, I'm a schizophrenic cowboy
Spurring on to beat the band.

This suggests that Immy may be justified in treating me like a custodial case. She can't altogether be blamed for blowing the whistle on me. Consider: after taxes she stands to come into twenty-five to thirty millions. That's a good bit of scratch. My estimate is that Tarquino, my investment counsellor and CPA, got into me for five millions—Immy and I differ on the figure. "I can't let him get away with it," she says. Definitely a case of fraud, and provable in court, she insists—a swindle that went on for something like ten years. The worst of the outrage was to rip off a trusting old guy.

"You made the money," she would say, "So it's not for me to criticize. You didn't even get started until you were sixty. All the more remarkable. But even your ordinary, limited, average gullible guy would have suspected after a year or two, that his investment advisor was doing him in the eye. The numbers in the quarterly reports your Mr. Tarquino prepared were one hundred percent fantasy. He was so sure of you that he became contemptuous. He made up assets that never existed. He must have chosen a digit at random and then he wrote zeros after it till his hand got tired."

"I had this idea about a professional fiduciary relationship. By definition it had to be ethical."

"Dear Grandpa, what an idea! Because he was a certified accountant?"

"Okay, I made a mess. I didn't seem able to give it my full attention."

"My Man of Business, you called him, like an imitation old-school Brit. Your confidential clark. Unreal! Totally synthetic. Assembled from defective parts. Created in his own basement. When I heard him speak I was so horrified I could only laugh."

"Portfolio managers all sound like that."

"Darling old Hilbert, you have a trained incapacity—a deformity that comes from your business. That's because the premise of what you print in your paper is that every item in it is basically impossible to believe."

Such is her opinion of *Brillig's*, the supermarket tabloid I founded thirty years ago, the source of all the dough. I still edit, publish and own it outright. Immy feels bound by a higher code to speak frankly about it.

At times she behaves as though I had lost my marbles. Her face, predominantly and massively sensual, takes on an expression of indulgence, tenderness. The kid is sorry for old Hilbert in decline. But she goes on analytically, in her usual style, and assumes that I understand her one hundred percent. She is very proud of her psychological powers, insights, character-readings and what-have-you. A common enough tendency—we all have to live with that. Moreover, she has to distance herself from the source of the legacy. In an anthropological perspective like hers there was nothing too horrid to contemplate as long as it came from some tribe on the Amazon. Sodomy, cannibalism, what-have-you. But she wanted her inheritance to have an agreeable pedigree.

It saps your confidence to be had to such an extent, it affects your judgment. That's why I asked Immy to come down to Florida. She inter-preted this invitation as a mandate to take full charge. When she saw what I had done, she put together a team of lawyers and certified accountants. These guys developed a case of criminal fraud against Tarquino and prepared a lawsuit. Then they decided that it would be best if I were out of the way. They didn't want me on the witness stand being questioned about documents I had signed. Who in his right mind would have authorized so many powers-of-attorney? Tarquino had full access to all my accounts, the pension-fund included. Millions were transferred from here to there, and he did it all legally. Therefore the lawyers would have to plead that I was incompetent. Psychiatrists would examine me and give testimony. The court might actually rule that I was utterly out of it. I wasn't about to go through such an embarrassment. Think also what harm *Brillig's* would suffer if its genius founder should be publicly certified as a case of senile dementia.

Immy ought to have been kept in the dark. See what happens when you feel too weak to go it alone. As I now see I was undermined by my shame at being swindled. I yielded to it. I let it crush me.

"I think it's best that you go abroad," Immy told me.

"But I haven't done anything. What am I, a Ponzi? A Samuel Insull?"

She didn't recognize the names of these colossal operators. There's one of the difficulties of old age. You have to explain yourself. You're never free from footnotes. To the young, your mental furniture is entirely from the flea market.

"If you leave it to me to arrange you'll have a wonderful time abroad."

"New Hampshire, maybe," I said. "I'd be willing to go to the farm. I still haven't agreed to go anywhere."

"In New Hampshire you could be served with a subpoena."

"And if I were bedridden?"

"Depositions could still be taken. You'd have court-appointed shrinkers turning up at the farm to test you. You'd better recognize that Tarquino will be desperate. This is a case that can destroy him. You aren't the only one he took. There must be twenty dupes—or marks or patsies or Johns—whatever the word is. He's got a big practice, or he wouldn't be driving that white Maseratti and sailing a super cabin-cruiser. As soon as we file, bam! All his investors will go after him . . . So my idea is that you should vanish temporarily in New Guinea."

"What an idea! The heat! The snakes and bugs! I'd die there, in the rain-forest."

"Then let's make it the highlands."

"Why does it have to be New Guinea? That's not where I want to breathe my last."

"They couldn't serve you there. I don't think they can extradite you."

It was not a good moment. Burdened with years. On the run. It would have been smarter to take a bath for a few millions. All the worst mistakes of my life have been family-related. Typical of me to turn to my granddaughter. But I did want her to crucify Tarquino. Something in me cried out for revenge, and at ninety plus I didn't have the vital resources to use a hammer on him myself or to face a major trial case. Sit in a courtroom day after day. The estate would be Immy's . . . let her do it.

I recall recognizing that this was a kind of deportation, and I saw nothing in it but disruption, inconvenience, demotion, depletion and fatigue. And if I should croak in New Guinea this fine estate would go to an heiress who had no idea what she was exposing her grandfather to. She meant no harm, I think. Mostly, I amused her. She would look at me with a big, bountiful sunshine grin. Fifty years younger than me she couldn't grasp what it was like to come up against your physical limits. Not to be able to answer the call for more when there absolutely had to be more. She was forever saying what a strong old guy I was. Her opinion was that I was very sly as well. By occupation, chief honcho of *Brillig's*, I was a kidder fundamentally.

Check-out-counter papers deal in tall stories and phony scandals. Space aliens, astronomical catastrophes, sex in Windsor Palace or in the White House. For this reason she was always prepared to laugh at my antics and couldn't connect me personally with mortality and the tragic stuff. "I don't put anything past you, outwitting is your specialty," she said. "Would you deny that you're sweet on your woman companion in New Hampshire? That you and she are dear friends? You may even have a sex life. I wouldn't give odds against it."

In a *Brillig's* caption this would have read:

GERIATRIC LOVER DISCOVERS FOUNTAIN OF YOUTH

I had run a story once about hookers who took away the Social Security checks of fellows in their seventies and eighties. They seduced them and ripped off their money. Often the old guys were unaware that they were still capable. Most had no memory of what happened every fourth week. Twelve hundred dollars worth of joy. The women knew when the checks were due and came and knocked at the door and played a bit with the old duffers and paid themselves handsomely for the trick.

1063

"You can't expect me just to take orders like any ordinary flake," I said to Immy. "I've been a C.E.O. for thirty years. I own a sixteen storey in downtown Miami . . ."

"Oh, grandfather. I think you should be discreetly absent. I won't insist on Papua New Guinea if it makes you so miserable . . ." She took my arm and looked gently, deeply into my eyes.

Does the woman in some way love me? If you view the psyche as a mine you can always assume there's a hidden vein of gold, and that if you keep digging you'll come to it. Such is the secret faith of every liberal and one way or another all of us are liberals. "There's so much good hidden in people." But Immy also has a taste for gold—her saris are gold-edged and her special-occasion face powder has sprinkles of gold in it. Is it the gold she mainly loves, or is it her grandfather for himself alone?

"You're not going to sue the banks are you?" I asked her.

"Two of the vice presidents have accounts in the Caymans and may have taken cash from Tarquino."

"Don't tell me. I can't stand that kind of information. I get agitated . . ."

What was worst about this present condition was the acceleration—
a sort of ungovernable panic triggered by speed. With speeds in the supersonic
range comes the threat of disintegration within.

"All Marbles Still Accounted For" is an excerpt from a suspended novel

Murray Bail

The Seduction of My Sister

My sister and I were often left alone together. She was younger than me, about 18 months. I hardly had the time to get to know her, although we were alone together for days on end, weekends included.

Our father worked odd hours at an Anglo-American tobacco company. And our mother, she had a job at Myers. Ladies' shoes, Manchester, toys and whitegoods were some of her departments. She worked Saturday mornings, and there was the stocktaking. She put in a lot of overtime, working herself to the bone. Some nights our mother arrived home after dark, more like a widow in black than a mother, and passed around meat pies from a paper bag, one for each of us, including our father. Otherwise, we were "left to our own devices," our mother's term; I heard her say it to a neighbor over the fence.

For a long time I hardly took any notice of her, my sister, always at my elbow, in the corner of my eye. Whatever I was doing she would be there. More than once I actually tripped over my sister. She seemed to have nothing better to do than get in the way. She said very little, hardly a word. She and I had different interests, we were interested in totally different things, yet if I was asked today what were her interests I couldn't say. Tripping over her once too often or else wanting nothing more than to be left alone, I would turn and shout at her to go, get lost, even giving her a shove; anything to get rid of her. Half an hour later she would be back, all smiles or at least smiling slightly, as if nothing had happened.

My sister was skinny, not much to look at. She had short hair in a fringe and a gap between her teeth. If anyone had asked what colour her eyes were, I could not answer, not exactly. There was a mole above her lip, to the left, almost touching her lip.

Taking an interest in something or standing near a group she had a way of holding her mouth slightly open. I can't remember a single thing she said.

The mole could have been by now transformed into a beauty spot, I've seen it on other women. Brothers though, are supposed to be blind to the attractions of their sisters.

Our father had a small face, and although he didn't himself smoke, the odour of fresh tobacco followed him about like a cloud, filling the passages of the house. I don't know about him and my mother. About their happiness, or contentment even, it was hard to say. When our father spoke it was to himself or to his shoes; he hardly looked at our mother. Sometimes she would make a strange humming sound or turn to us and say something unrelated. Arriving home after standing behind a counter all day our mother wanted nothing more than to put her feet up. After the table had been cleared our mother and father often went over various budgets, income and outgoings, gaining some sort of pleasure of satisfaction from the double-checking. If he saw us watching our father would give a wink and make a great show of scratching his head and licking the pencil.

It was a short street, the houses dark brick from the thirties. Each house had a gravel drive and a garage, although hardly anyone had a car, and a front hedge, every house had its box-hedge, except directly opposite us which was an empty block, the only one left in the street. It was surprising how long it had remained empty, swaying with grasses, lantana in the left-hand corner. Who in their right mind would want to live all day looking across at us? our father winked at us, our mother not saying a word.

It remained then, a hole in the street, a break in the hedges, in the general tidiness, an eyesore to more than one.

Nothing lasts, that is true; it goes without saying. Nevertheless, the morning we woke up and saw pyramids of sand and a cement mixer on the block it was a shock to the system, the builders more like intruders than new neighbors, trampling over habits and feelings.

Slowly, then rapidly accelerating, a house took shape out of the disorder and commotion; I would have preferred it to last forever, so much there to follow, to take in and assemble in my mind. I cannot speak for my sister.

Instead of retreating at right angles to the street like any other house, including ours, it was positioned longways, parallel to the street. It caused our father to give a brief laugh of misunderstanding. He called it "The Barn." Instead of bricks the colour of lamb chops which slowly turn brown, like ours, it had cream bricks of a speckled kind, and grey tiles on the roof instead of the painted corrugated iron as ours.

I came home one afternoon late to see my sister standing at our front gate as always, waiting for me; only I could tell by the way she was twisting one leg around the other that she was talking to someone.

The Gills had moved in, their doors and windows wide open. Gordon withdrew a hand and introduced himself. He was their only son; about my age.

The house inside was still smelling of paint. In his bedroom he had a stamp album and cigarette cards scattered on his desk, and merely shrugged at the model aeroplanes suspended from the ceiling, as if he had lost interest in them. We went from room to room, sister and I. In the lounge Gordon demonstrated the record-player which opened on silver elbows into a cocktail cabinet. Shelves and glass cabinets displayed plates and bowls and porcelain figures. From another room a clock chimed. Now and then Gordon stepped forward to explain something or take it from our hands, then returned to the window, answering a question or my sister's exclamations. Across the street directly opposite stood our house, stubborn and cramped-looking. It was all there was to see.

1067

Mr. Gill put down a lawn, bordered by roses, not ordinary roses, but dark roses, and stepping-stones of slate to the front door. Mr. Gill had a moustache, the only one in the street, and a strong set of teeth. From the moment they met he called my father "Reg", and made a habit of dropping it with informal gravity in every other sentence, sometimes flashing a smile, which pleased my father to no end. "Do you think, Reg, that this weather's going to hold?" And if he was in the middle of something, pruning or striding around to open the car door for Mrs. Gill, who remained seated looking straight ahead, he would glance up and with a single nod say, "Reg," and return to what he was doing. Even this pleased my father.

It was our mother who suggested doubts. "No-one," she was scraping the plates, "is like them, not on this street. They might as well be from another planet."

With his shirt wide open at the neck our father put his finger on it. "They're all right," he smiled, "they're extroverts."

Our mother always looked tired. I wondered why she kept on working, what on earth for, but she went on almost every day of her life, Saturdays included, at Myers. Through the store she bought a washing machine and a Hoover, demonstration models, otherwise brand new. In turn, it made a new fridge possible, the varnished ice-box ending up in the garage, along with our father's hat-stand, tennis racquet in its press, and a God-forsaken electric toaster. Chimes were added to the front door, a new letterbox smartened up the front, father's idea, displaying our number in wrought-iron beneath the silhouette of a Mexican asleep under his hat.

Taking a tour of our house late afternoon Gordon hardly said a word. A floorboard kept creaking; I noticed the light was yellowish and the walls, carpets and chairs had a scruffy plainness.

In no time we were outside by the fig tree, where I searched around to retrieve something. "That'd be a hundred years old," I pointed with my chin.

To demonstrate, my sister in her cotton dress shinnied up into the first fork. Grinning, she looked like a monkey, I could have clocked her one. I glared and hissed at her; but she took no notice, which only gave the impression she was used to such cruel treatment.

I steered Gordon into the garage, my sister scrambling down from the tree, not wanting to be left out. Our mother and father never threw anything away. Poking around I held up things I thought might be of interest, waiting for his reaction. And Gordon too began examining things, the old tools, tin boxes, the dressmaker's dummy of our mother's before she was married. He squatted down, my sister alongside. It was Gordon who came across the gramophone records, still in their brown-paper sleeves. Reading the labels one by one he carefully put them back.

I thought he was being polite.

"Tell you what," I had an idea. "You go and stand on your front lawn," I glanced up at the sky, "and I'll send a few of these over the roof at you."

"What for?" he remained squatting.

It took awhile for the penny to drop.

"See if you can catch them or something, I don't know." I had to push him. "You stay here," I told my sister.

Before Gordon could change his mind I yelled out from the back of our house, "Coming now!" And in a simple quoit-throwing motion sent up in the half-light the Great Caruso singing something in mournful Italian. It soared above our iron roof, the disc, and in a moment of dark beauty tilted, almost invisibly, and hovered like the great tenor holding a high note, before returning to earth. My sister and I both had our mouths open. I reached our gate, sister alongside, to see Gordon waiting on their patch of lawn, hands in pockets, suddenly give a hoarse cry as the black 78 brushed his shoulder and thudded into the lawn behind him.

Hardly able to run, laughing too much, I crossed the street. "What d'you reckon?" I gave him a shove. "It almost took your head off."

Picking up the record, Gordon wiped it with his sleeve.

Nobody spoke. He could have gone one way or the other, I could see. I took another look at him, my sister gaping at one of us, then the other. I ran back to my position, not saying anything.

I sent over *Land of Hope and Glory*, and before he could recover, *The Barber of Seville*, followed by the *Nutcracker Suite*. I had others in a stack at my feet when the street lights came on and Mrs. Gill began calling in her musical voice, "Gor-don".

1069

Anyone could see he was not suited for sporting activities. The sloping shoulders, the paleness: even the hang of his arms—uncoordinated. Yet the following night Gordon was in position early, pacing up and down, looking over to our side.

I waited for it to be almost dark. To my sister I called out, "Look at me. See how I do it. If you like, you can have a go later." I began throwing and threw, in quick succession, one musical disc after the other. They were hard to spot in the night sky, that of course being the idea, their closeness suddenly revealed by a faint hissing near the face or back of the head. They were lethal. Quick reflexes were necessary. And concentrating hard and working on his technique Gordon took everything I sent him. He used his feet, swaying from the hips. With each throw of mine the better he became; and so his confidence grew. It was not long before he began in a lackadaisical manner grabbing at the black shapes as they came down at him or past him, managing to pull down in mid-air one in three or four, without saying a word, even after leaping with an arm outstretched, thereby putting pressure right back on me on the other side, sister looking on. Some I tried sending in low or at unexpected angles, anything to catch him off-balance.

My sister had moved to the front gate where my efforts could not be seen, where instead she could observe Gordon facing up to the onrushing discs. For a while the pressure began to get to me; I had to talk to myself. The heads of a few of Mr. Gill's prize-winning roses were severed; another night, a disc I gave too much wrist kept on going above Gordon's shoulder and outstretched arm and smashed against the mock-louvred shutters Mr. Gill had bolted to the wall, showering Gordon with fine-grooved shards. Almost before he could recover, I sent the recital of a legendary pianist, forget his name, Jewish, who died only the other day: wide of the mark, wrong grip, it sailed though the open window of the Gill's lounge room, my sister and I waiting for the crash of all that bone china, which never came. There were moments of ordinariness, moments of poetry. Simplicity, I realised, produced elegance, not only in the throw, in Gordon's response as well. One night, Melba, collectors' item I'm told, sliced through Mr. Limb's new telephone wires next door which fell over Gordon's face and shoulders like string. Gordon froze, my sister too; hand went to her mouth. They didn't have a clue about electricity, Gordon and my sister were not mechanically minded. Realising he was not about to be electrocuted Gordon kicked the wires and some of his embarrassment aside and went back to his crouch.

Engrossed in our separate tasks we hardly spoke, every throw presenting a different set of problems. It changed Gordon, it opened him up. He would come around to my side early, rubbing his hands as if it were freezing, my sister looking on.

"One of those records the other night," he followed me into the garage, "boy, was it funny."

I was sorting through the few that were left.

"You ought to hear *Laughing Gas* one day. It had the old man rolling on the floor."

Along with *Little Brown Jug*, the Satchmo selections and *Sing, Sing, Sing*, it would have been our father's. Our mother, I was told, had a singing voice. Always with a grin hovering at the ready our father had a taste for imaginary honky-tonk playing; he made the cutlery jump on the table, sister and I watching. I began putting the remaining 78's back in the trunk.

"What are you doing?" Gordon grabbed my shoulder. He began reading the labels. "What about these?"

At that moment I wanted to pause; something felt out of place. Twice he whistled he was ready. I stared at my fingernails, waiting to think clearly. A few houses away a dog barked, and someone was trying to start a motor-bike.

It took less than a week, if that, to go through the remaining 78's, and when they were gone, we tried chipped or broken discs, until they were too difficult to throw or nothing was left of them. Even so, when I realized the entire collection had gone, a feeling spread in my stomach, of corresponding emptiness.

I dismissed Gordon's suggestion that we continue, using saucers, his idea of a joke: saw him nudge-nudging my sister. She was hanging around us, always there. A glance at her scrawniness could trigger irritation in me, I don't know why. Anything he said, she'd listen, mouth open in chat way. I would have said, look, scram, buzz off, words to that effect. I was about to, when Gordon reached for something wrapped in a newspaper under the bench, and we squatted, sister too, I could see her pants.

Lifting it out I untied the string.

"Eek!" she clutched at him.

I held up a fox with a glass eye.

"O-kay," I swung experimentally. "This'll do. What's the matter?" I stared at my sister. "I can throw it."

Before she married, our mother dressed up for special occasions, little hats, veils, dresses consisting of buttons and tiny flowers. One photo in the album has her on a shopping spree with her mother in the city, each with a cheesy smile, like sisters. Shortly after she met our father, I forget where. Near the back door I was adjusting my feet, getting the balance right. I swung a few times, began again, swung once more, again, suddenly letting go with all the smoothness I could muster, the centrifugal force of the lopsided fox hophopping me forward like a shot-putter.

Leisurely, the doglike shape began flying, its tail out-stretched. At the chimney it slowly somersaulted against the night sky, appeared to set course, and with snarling teeth nosedived straight for Gordon across the street, chatting to my sister. At her cry he tried to swerve. The fox followed, sinking its fangs into his throat, as he rolled on the lawn.

A fox is pleasant to hold, weighted at one end, a living thing. I never tired of sending it over, enjoyed the accelerating movement of release, then running up our drive to follow its twists and turns, flash of orange tail, its Stuka-dive forcing Gordon into the acrobatics of a goalkeeper, exaggerated for my sister, looking on. "Improvisation is the mother of invention!" I heard him call out. My sister swallowed anything. At the same time she had a frivolous side; I could imagine reaching our gate to find her parading in front of him, fox draped over one shoulder, hand on hip for him.

As mentioned, the houses each had a hedge, except the Gills', which had the picket fence, leaving the house naked. The Gills didn't seem to mind, on the contrary. Every other night the lights would be blazing, more like an ocean liner than a house, the rest of the street as dark as the sea. The rectangle of illuminated lawn appeared as a billiard table, the beds of roses, shutters flung open, car in the drive all added up to a welcoming, optimistic air. After the loss of the fox I sent over a rubbish-bin lid, glittering chassis of a crystal-set, tennis-racquet in its press, other objects so poor in the aerody-namics department they barely cleared the roof. They were not adding any-thing; I was beginning to lose interest.

The card table had a way of setting its legs in mid-air, to make a perfect four-point landing on the Gills' lawn; but that only happened, I think, twice.

Our father would begin picking his teeth with a match, and for the umpteenth time telling us what a time he had, the best years, working with cattle in the outback, before he married, only 10 months, but enough to deposit a slowness in his speech, a corresponding glaze in our mother's eyes, and a green trunk full of Aboriginal weapons in the garage. I had forgotten they were there. Gordon was holding the boomerangs in his hand, authentic tribal weapons, not the tourist kind.

"You might as well put them back," I said. "They're too dangerous." When I turned my sister was already skipping around to the front, Gordon at her heels.

"Listen, will you?" I crossed the street. I grabbed my sister. "You're not going to watch me, right?" I felt her squirming. "Then you'd better keep your eyes open. In case someone's coming, that's why. These things," I sounded prim, "could kill someone."

Gordon was in no doubt as to the serious turn the game had taken.

Boomerangs were altogether different to the grimacing masks and decorated shields from New Guinea displayed in the room Mr. Gill called his "study". If one caught him in the face it would have been curtains. We knew, Gordon and I, my sister, too. Gordon began going through his stretch exercises. Instead of hesitating, let alone calling a halt, I was gripping the boomerang at one end.

I gave plenty of elbow: let go.

By the time it took to reach the street the boomerang was ahead of me. Gordon on their lawn was shielding his eyes. My sister had moved from the gate to be alongside. The mulga blades came swirling out of the fading light in a fury, seeking him out. Keeping his eyes on it, swerving back and ducking at the last moment, he avoided being hit, just. He was impressive, I would have to say. From then on, the vicious insistent things kept coming at him, at the strangest angles, finding him in roundabout ways, where least expected, side-on without warning or from behind. While I had never underestimated his confidence, I think I underestimated his abilities in general. He had a certain course of life marked out, even then. He would always succeed where I would not, I could see. In the end, my life became something of a shambles. His would not.

1073

Gordon wore his father's yellow driving-gloves and was grabbing at the boomerangs as they flew past, my sister clapping encouragement whenever he managed to pull one down. Keen eyesight, reflexes played their part, fair enough, knowing which ones to leave, sure; but as I watched I began to find his way of crouching and twisting, particularly in the region of his hips, distasteful. He displayed a fleshy alertness I found off-putting, just as when he received a given object and turned it over in his hands I saw his arms were precisely the pale arms with black hairs I found unpleasant, repulsive even. I have always had trouble with such hairy arms; my sister didn't seem to mind. Every night her job was to whistle or cough if a motorcyclist appeared or a pedestrian, such as Mr. Limb next door, decided to stretch his legs, it's all she had to do; otherwise I was throwing blind. But she was more interested in warning him, Gordon, crouching there on the slippery lawn; more than once letting out a cry, which may well have saved his skin. I had to cross the street and tell her to pipe down, we didn't want the neighbors coming out. If she didn't we would have to stop, it would be the end. As I laid down the law she began to blink, I could see she was about to cry. Gordon nearby examined his elbow, saying nothing.

Gramophone music came from the Gills' open windows, men and women moved in the brightly lit rooms, now and then a man leaned back laughing his head off. This flat boomerang felt longer on one side, inscribed with dots and whorls. I threw it casually, perhaps that was it, for as I ran with it up the drive, the thing hovered like a lost helicopter blade above our chimney, before returning. Slipping on the gravel I ran back just as our father stepped out the door.

"Bloody crow!" he waved over his head. "Did you see that?"

It clattered into the fig tree, but by then our father cocked his ear to the Gills' party noise.

"Benny Goodman," he gave a bit of a jig, "at the Carnegie Hall. Hello, how's Gordon tonight?"

Gordon pulled up panting, sister alongside. As soon as our father went back in, our mother began getting stuck into him, listing things missing in him.

"Think," Gordon was shaking me. "Where did you say it landed?"

"I'll find it in the morning. Don't worry about it."

His answer startled me. "Put it off and never find it again. That'd be right."

Already up in the tree my sister dropped it at his feet. Wiping it with his handkerchief Gordon held the flat blade up to the light. Whatever he saw pleased him, for he lunged with both hands at my sister as she passed, ignoring me.

No matter how hard I tried, I never managed to make another one return. And when the trunk was empty, even of fighting boomerangs, which Gordon explained were never meant to be thrown, the problem again was finding something to send over. In this and other matters Gordon revealed a single-mindedness I never had. Gordon knew what he wanted, usually had a fair idea. What I thought hardly worth the effort he invariably thought the opposite. Already he had a single-mindedness in summing up the other person, then no longer taking them into account.

Anything I could lay my hands on I was letting go, I found all sorts of things we did not want. Nothing ever meant much to me. Even today I am casual about possessions. With people too I come and go. In this I resemble my casual father, who finally disappointed people, my mother and others.

In a single night I sent over a pair of suit-trousers striding across the sky, a row of coat-hangers, textbooks I would never open, wooden lavatory seat. I watched as every copy of *Life* presented to me by an amateur photographic uncle changed hands, the history of the post-war world turning over like a newsreel. Patterns form without anyone being fully aware, I see now. Our mother wore the same shoes for a week and a half, our father never changed his hat.

An electric light bulb lit up the sky, followed by the first fluorescent tube; another time, our pop-up toaster trailed its plaited cord. Problems of a technical kind: it took several attempts to hurl the standard-lamp over, a ceremonial spear. The electric radiator made the journey, the single red bar describing quite fantastic arabesques, catching Gordon by surprise, talking in the shadows to my sister. When occasionally she skipped over to my side, expressing interest in what I was doing, I could see she was itching to get back to him and whatever he was saying, on the other side. I set the American alarm clock for seven o'clock in mid-flight, and as it began ringing Gordon reached out and silenced it with one hand. I chucked half a dozen eggs, we kept fowls in the backyard, rotten tomato, a navel orange, another joke, Gordon collecting it on the neck. He said he confused it with the moon, but he was talking to my sister, I saw them. And for the first time my sister turned on me, "That's going to leave a bruise," as I ran up arranging a country grin, in the manner of our father.

1075

Eventually, we come up against things said by others which cannot be explained, not at the time. The night our mother talked about "taking in ironing" made us laugh our heads off, my father and I, sister too after a glance, our father laughing the loudest, almost choking, at the same time placing his weakened hand on my mother's arm, which she pulled away. "Your mother sometimes comes out with all kinds of rubbish," wiping the tears from his eyes. At the table, my sister sat demurely. It made me look twice, our mother too. The few jokes I cracked in her direction, not worth repeating, she ignored. The usual family racket we made she seemed to find irritating, which in turn irritated us, at least our mother.

From the beginning, I began to see, I was doing all the work. To Gordon, I suggested we change positions. Operating in the darkness near our back door I could do my bit with my eyes shut, whereas on his side light was absolutely essential, he pointed out. "Without proper light I've no idea what's coming my way. I'm at the receiving end, let's not forget," he actually said.

Besides, he pointed out, we have each attained a degree of efficiency in our respective roles. "Isn't that right?" he said to her, alongside.

The pale ironing board in flight reminded me of the loose skin above my mother's elbow. Difficult to send up and over it was more difficult still for Gordon receiving, a matter of maneuvering desperately to get side-on to the torpedo-shaped thing. At the same time Mr. and Mrs. Gill stepped out for a night at the theatre or somewhere. By the gate I watched Mrs. Gill, fox over one shoulder, although the night was warm, flash my sister a smile. "So this is Glenys?" I heard her say. After that, she usually stopped to say hello, Gordon looking casually bored, as Mr. Gill strode around to open her car door.

To get my sister's attention Gordon sometimes touched her with his foot. Other times, talking to me, he would drape an elbow over her shoulder. In turn, my sister remained still, no longer jumping about. He subscribed to American magazines and gave her books to read.

Bird cage, oval mirror reflecting the clouds, a perfectly good floral armchair.

The smallest things amused my sister. She had what I would say was a childish delight in small and modest things. It was one of her attractive sides. And yet when I sent over things carefully chosen for her, she reached as if they had fallen from the sky into his lap, as if it had nothing to do with me, on the other side.

I submitted silver coins when I had some to spare. "We're down to our last shekels," I called, the coins shooting across the sky as falling stars.

It was she who pointed them out to him, I could hear her cries. It would have been their appearance among the stars that caught her eye, not their value; I can't answer for him. As always, Gordon hardly said a word; I mean to me: I could hear him murmuring to her. Mostly, you never knew what he was thinking; he never gave much away. Vase of flowers, inner-spring mattress, dustpan and brush. By the time I'd reach their gate he would still be talking to her, my sister taking whatever rot he came out with. It had been the same with me. So practised had he become he would casually extend an arm and take whatever I'd sent over or simply move back a step, taking her by the waist, a protective move.

She was out of my hair, I was no longer tripping over her, a good thing; at the same time, I felt great rushes of irritation at the way she transferred her attention lock, stock and barrel to him, in that trusting way of hers, mouth slightly open. If our mother saw two people with heads together they were "as thick as thieves". And more than once she said, "No-one likes anyone whispering."

A large oil painting from our mother's side used to hang in the bedroom, a summer landscape on canvas. It aquaplaned into multiples of parched hills and fat gum trees. Gordon received it with open arms, my sister helped him lower it to the ground, and listened as he launched into a lecture, pointing out the strengths and weaknesses of the composition. After examining it and wiping it with his handkerchief he pronounced it too fragile to travel, my sister nodding in agreement.

In the way the boomerang came back over the roof it was only a matter of waiting before our father's expression returned to one of smiling slightly. Mr. Limb, a bachelor who lived next door, used to say, "I don't have a hobby or a pastime," and as he reached retirement, "Most of my life has passed, and now just when I need it I don't have a hobby or a pastime." The subject of early retirement occupied his mind so much that he suffered excruciating headaches; he took days off from the work he no longer enjoyed, on medical advice.

Even then I felt sympathy for Mr. Limb. I do not know what eventually happened to him. The umbrella jerked open and parachuted down, ironic cheers from Gordon's side, ashtrays were never used in our home, nest of tables, mother's, and our father's tan suitcase opened its mouth and dropped a sock on the telephone wires. *1077*

From my side in darkness I would hear Gordon's voice, followed by her laugh. Rolling pin tumbled over, dusted with flour. They would have trouble finding the knives and forks. I no longer bothered rushing around to see how the latest thing was received. We were going through the motions, little more. Only later do we realise something of value has slipped away. Whatever had been worth the effort in the beginning was coming to an end; a feeling I would recognise in later years.

I squatted near the garage, my sister, Gordon at her elbow, rummaging through what little was left.

Embroidered tablecloth, their idea, did not make the distance; I could have told them that. At any given time there is only a limited number of ideas of value, I wanted to say. And before long we exhaust them as well. I remained squatting, watching them. If one of them went somewhere the other one followed. I was left alone, to one side.

That night when my sister came skipping around to my side I thought she was coming around to my way of thinking, whatever that was.

Instead she had a suggestion, and as I listened I felt my father's grin beginning to run amok; but she was looking away, strangely, and speaking vaguely.

Thinking the thing she suggested was going to be the last, I got to my feet, not at all laboriously, and went inside. I came out with it rolled up.

So many things passed through my hands; nevertheless, I found it necessary to use all my skills with this one and, wondering whether it was her idea or his, dispatched after some difficulties my sister's favourite party dress. I could follow its progress slowly, walking up our gravel drive. Billowing from the waist it elbowed gently past the chimney. And in its determination, oblivious of me or anybody else, I glimpsed my sister then and in the years to come. She would always be determined, always there, her way, while I felt within a heavy casualness, settled and spreading.

Whatever Gordon was expecting it wasn't this. Directly above him the translucent dress began descending, flapping gently at the edges. Not sure whether to grab at it with both hands or perhaps deceived by its slowness, the slow hip and narrow waist movements, he was caught wrong-footed. The white cotton dress smothered him.

I waited for my sister to rush forward to help, as she had all along, but she looked on, not lifting a finger, letting Gordon disentangle himself.

From the gate-post if I glanced across the street I would see Gordon's outline, kicking gravel, my sister discussing something. I had almost forgotten what my sister looked like. The dark bulk of the house now came between her features and me, obscuring aspects of her personality even. Out of habit I hung around near our back door. From inside the kitchen I heard the soft thudding of our mother ironing, occasionally the murmur of our father.

Things at least seemed to be steady there, I remember thinking.

At the sound of her voice, my sister, I stood up. Gordon was one step behind, both hands in his pockets, pursing his lips.

My sister whispered again. Why the whisper? I wanted to ask. Facing her, I noticed a rushed, wide-open expression I had not seen before.

Still I didn't say anything. After a while my sister simply went inside, leaving us. He and I stood there. Gordon glanced at his watch. When she came out in her white party dress he stepped forward.

"How am I?" she asked in a small voice. She was speaking to me. The gap opened between her teeth as she smiled.

It allowed me to place my hands under her arms. She was much heavier than I imagined, I could feel the soft swell of her breasts. She allowed my hands to remain there; she was my sister.

I looked at her once more. "Are you all right?" I was on the point of saying. "Is this what you want?" Other questions reached my tongue, but her body had gone completely soft, and by then I had taken an interest in the whole technical question; I began gathering momentum. In an almighty heave-ho, putting my whole body into it, I let go.

Trust and optimism were always her main characteristics. Now she tilted her chin, and dog-paddled among the stars, then clasped her hands more like an angel than my sister. Putting her trust in me she was now putting her trust in him. I concentrated on the mole near her lip, a point of focus, until it too began diminishing, along with the pale hopes of her body, fringe, standing on one foot, listening: all this blotted out by the chimney.

I heard Mr. Limb's cough. He was setting out on his evening walk, for health reasons. I felt so much around me slipping, accelerating, beyond my grasp; for I was left with nothing. Running from my side towards the light, I began calling my sister's name, to where she had gone.

1079

Salvatore Scibona

Prairie

Rosalie and I are twins. We were born here in Manitoba where
our parents had settled after fleeing the war in Kentucky and President
Lincoln's Conscription Act of 1863. Our father was a Quaker and so a
pacifist and so unwilling "to kill any man for any cause, however righteous,"
as he told us. When the draft officials in Bowling Green, Kentucky, informed
him that—as he was sane, thirty-two years old, had all his fingers and sight
in both eyes—he must either enlist or pay $200 to a substitute, he persuaded
Mother that they should move north. Our mother was not a Quaker, she
was Methodist, but all three of her brothers had gone to Tennessee and
joined the Confederate army to whip the "miscegenist baboon" (as they
called Lincoln), and she had no desire to see her husband and brothers on
opposite sides of a war. They intended to return once the war ended, but
Father soon found that the prairie so cleared his mind that he could not
recall what it was in Kentucky he'd planned on missing, and Mother was
so smitten with him, she claimed, that if our father asked her "to move to
the south pole and live on penguin eggs" she thought it would be a fine
life, if he was there. So he stayed and she stayed with him, and they never
left Manitoba. I have never left it either.

We were born on June 3, 1864, the day of the Confederate victory at Cold Harbor in Virginia. Mother told us that she had thought her baby was still another month away and on that day she'd been picking strawberries two miles from the house. When the birth pangs struck, she tried to walk back home but the contractions crippled her, and she lay down in a thicket of poplars and gave birth to Rosalie. I, she had assumed, was the afterbirth. Father found us early that night. Mother had bit off our umbilical chords, cleaned us with her skirts, laid us down in the dry leaves beside her, and passed out.

I have only a few memories from early youth: the shushing sound of Rosalie's boots through unbroken snow, the snap of her leg bone after she fell out of a tree, her cold feet against my knee after I woke from a nightmare. However, when we were eight, Father began to take us with him on his biannual trips to Winnipeg to trade for the supplies we could not produce on our own, paper for example, and sugar. I remember that first trip clearly.

Rosalie and I had never seen a town, had never traveled further than five miles from home. We hardly slept the night before we left. In the morning, Father hitched Isaiah and Chester, our oxen, to the barley wagon and Mother packed us rye bread, a sack of onions, pemmican and a jar of gooseberry preserves. We headed southeast. Mother stayed home.

The prairie around our farm rolls slightly; wide patches of junipers and poplars interrupt the grasses and line the creek shores. When my sister and I were young, bison herds passed over the prairie around us so regularly that we didn't need to keep cattle or pigs, since bison meat and the pemmican we made from it were so easy to come by. But as we rode toward Winnipeg that October, Rosalie and I sitting on either side of Father at the front of the wagon, the prairie turned dead flat for as far as you could see in all directions, empty of almost anything but short, dry sedges covering the ground. We went a whole day's driving, forty miles, without seeing a tree, and there was no game at all except groundhogs and a pack of wolves we heard. The aurora those nights, with nothing on the ground and no moon even to distract your eyes from it, seemed brighter than it was at home. I had never paid much attention to it before.

Rosalie asked Father why the lights seemed to move sometimes and sometimes to be still, and why they were green and blue one night but almost red the next. He said, "I have no earthly idea, Rosie."

It took us six days to get there. As we entered Winnipeg, a noise rose up around us. It was the ugliest sound I'd ever heard. I thought it might be river rapids, but I couldn't see the river, and it sounded harsher than water rushing; there were shrill noises in it. I covered my ears as we drove past the people walking and talking hurriedly in the street. After about a minute, I realized that I was hearing the sound of many people speaking at once. This was a crowd. Rosalie was leaping in the barley, and laughing.

I also recall a blue storefront in the middle of town. Mother had taught both of us how to read the Bible, and had told us many stories—of children who had disobeyed and been switched, of men who had sinned and been cast out of their towns, and of unrepentant old people who had died and been damned forever. Until our fist trip to Winnipeg however, Rosalie and I believed that the Bible was the only story anyone had written down. Imagine our astonishment then, amid all the uncountable wonders and noises of Winnipeg, when we entered that blue building and saw hundreds of books on the walls. Rosalie and I began to trap badgers and raccoons so that we could sell their pelts twice a year in Winnipeg and buy books with the money.

We had learned to read as most children do, I suppose: by saying, in order, the sounds of the letters. After we recognized the words by sight, we continued to read them out loud, as our parents did. As far as I could tell, even reading by ourselves, all of my family spoke the words as we read them. I hadn't imagined that one could read silently until I was seventeen. And I wish I had known that before. Because for all the time I read aloud, regardless of how taken I was with the characters or the scenes of the stories, I still had to endure my own awkward, gruesome voice speaking. Mother and Rosalie had high, liquid reading voices. They often sounded as if they were singing as they read. The words came out so casually, with none of the stutters which ruined my voice, that you'd think they were talking about the weather. So usually Rosalie read our books to me. I would often take over her chores, work twice as long in the field, the barn or our kitchen and she would follow me reading Roman history or English novels or American adventure stories aloud.

While Father and I waded far out in the Assiniboine River, gathering stones with which to build the house where I still live, the house which replaced the windowless sod one that became the granary, Rosalie sat on the shore yelling out *A Tale of Two Cities* over the sound of the current. Father kept stopping her to say, "Go back a piece. I lost you." And, "Is he the scruffy one or the rich one?" By the time she finished it, we were laying the foundation. Father looked up out of the hole in the ground and said, "Go on, Rosie, start over." We heard that book three times while building the house, then Father let her move on to *David Copperfield*.

When we were sixteen, in the summer of 1880, Father began to cough, hard. His lips turned purple. One bright afternoon in late October, while Rosalie was reading *Great Expectations* to him, he died; we buried him under a patch of tamaracks on the hill. Five days later, before dusk, telling us, "Dears, nothing so confirms my faith in the Lord's grace as His sunset, I think I shall go to watching it now," Mother stepped out our front door.

An hour later, I looked on the front porch and Mother was gone. She had been taking long walks by herself along the river the last few days and not eating much, so Rosalie and I decided to have supper without her. We ate dried sturgeon, onions and buckwheat cakes. By the time we'd finished washing our dishes outside, it had gotten much colder, begun snowing, and the wind had picked up some; Mother still wasn't home.

Rosalie said, "If we don't start looking now, her tracks might get too snowed over to see." So we filled up our lanterns with bison oil and followed mother's tracks through the mud toward the river. It had rained hard all morning, so the mud was soft and her tracks were clear but our boots were sinking past our ankles and it was slow going. Just as we reached the river, the snow covered over her trail completely and we didn't know which direction to go.

I looked over the river but it was too dark to see anything further than three feet away from our lamps, except for the snow disappearing on the surface of the water. "Why don't you go upstream and I'll go down?" I said to Rosalie, then turned to her, and saw in the lamplight that she had covered her mouth with her hand and was weeping. "Or we can go together and then check back the other way."

She took her hand away from her face and said, "Yes, let's do that."

We doused the lamps so we could see further ahead of us, and walked about four miles upstream but saw only trees, mud, snow and the river, then we turned back downstream. Just before the sky began to grow light again, Rosalie said she saw something move on the other side of the river, but as we got closer to it, we saw that it was a young black bear, and then it ran off. We found Mother's body just after sunrise, washed up on the east shore of the Assiniboine, five miles downstream from the place where we had first reached the river the night before. The snow was still falling when we found her, and it continued to fall the rest of the day.

It took us about three hours to walk back home through the snow. I hitched Isaiah and Chester to the sleigh and put our canoe in the back, then we drove to the river, dropped the canoe into it, and paddled to the other shore where Mother was. Her legs and arms were twisted so I tried to straighten them out but they wouldn't bend. The canoe was too slight to hold the three of us, so I paddled Mother back over the river and left Rosalie on the far shore. Then I returned for Rosalie. By the time we had gathered Mother into the sleigh and rode back home, it was dark.

As Isaiah and Chester climbed up the slope toward the stable, Rosalie said, "I have to sleep a little, Julius. I'm tired."

Then I realized that neither or us had eaten or slept since the day before. I was tired but not hungry, and knew I wouldn't be able to sleep. So I said, "You go in and sleep then and I'll get you once I'm done digging," and I went into the barn to get a spade.

"Julius, we can't leave her out here!" she said. Mother lay in the back of the sleigh, partly covered with snow.

"She's already frozen."

"Bring her into the house," she said.

"Sister —"

"Listen to me, Julius," she said, "please bring her inside." So I did.

After I'd cleared the snow away from an open place next to Father, I found that only the top of the ground had frozen and it was still wet underneath, so the earth was soft. But the tamarack roots were hard to get through. Once I'd finished the grave, I went back home to wake Rosalie. She had wrapped Mother in a bison skin, washed Mother's face, braided her hair, and wound it in a bun at her nape.

As we carried Mother up the hill, the wind was fierce. My face was too numb to sting, but the wind had stiffened it, and I could not have moved my lips to sing "Shall We Gather at the River" with Rosalie even if I had wanted to. Once she finished singing, I closed the ground up over Mother. And we went back home and slept for a long time.

So we were alone. As the winter wore on, I grew quieter and quieter. When I poured out my whiskey at night, I began to take care to keep the bottleneck from clinking against the edge of my glass. And outside, where the wind nearly deafened one to all other sounds anyway, I tried to drove nails into stockade posts with one swing, not out of a desire to conserve my labor, but because all the sounds I made, even breathing, became hideous to me. I hardly spoke at all.

The wind that winter was harsher than any I had experienced. Blizzards followed blizzards. I went outside only rarely, to fish through the ice on the lake two miles north of our house and to keep my eyes open for bison but they had grown scarce by that time. The winter of 1880 to 1881 seems to have killed all the bison left in western Manitoba. After that time, I never saw one again. In the mornings and late afternoons I piled and repiled the snow up along the west and north walls of our house and the stable, to stifle the wind. Even so, during one especially windy and frigid week, I couldn't keep the walls buried for very long before the wind, blowing from the northwest at an angle to the walls, swept the snow away and three of our seven hens froze in the stable.

The summer before, at the bookstore in Winnipeg, Rosalie had discovered a Greek New Testament and a Greek primer, which fascinated her for some reason. She seemed to spend much of that winter studying those books at the desk in front of the window, which looked south and so was shielded from the wind. At breakfast, we had much the same conversation every day.

"That's unbecoming, Julius," Rosalie said. I was picking at my ear with the blunt end of a pencil.

"Beg pardon," I said.

She watched me eat. "Do you want more pemmican?"

"No, this's all right."

"If you want more, Brother, it won't trouble me." She had pulled up the hatch in the floor and started climbing into the cellar.

"It's enough. I'm full."

From the cellar she said, "If I were a girl you were courting and I saw that thing in your ear at my table you wouldn't get any more food from me."

"I don't want more," I said.

"It reflects poorly on one's sisters, such behavior from a boy, you know that don't you? They'll think you're a boor, which may be true, but they'll think I had no sense at all, couldn't train you to eat at table."

Later, as I was cutting the second helping of eggs she had made me, my fork squeaked on the plate and I winced. It turned my stomach, that noise. How she failed to notice the sound or just failed to be bothered by it bewildered me. She kept talking and asking my opinion of what she said but every day I had less to reply.

Maybe I got lazy. Talking had always felt like labor to me, like an obligation to respond to other people for whom speaking came easily—people, like Mother and Rosalie, who seemed to enjoy the sounds of their own voices. It satisfied me so much only to listen, not because I had nothing to tell them, but because, before I spoke, I had to steel myself against the revulsion I felt for my voice and that steeling took effort, and maybe I was sick of the effort.

Rosalie begged me to speak to her, and the more she asked the less able I felt to do it. By February I could manage little more than "I reckon not," "yes" and "thank you," and those with tremendous effort and shame. By March I was not speaking at all. Honestly, I do not understand it, even now, I can only say that I hated the sounds of my feet and the sounds of my tools striking their objects and more than all by far, I hated the sound of my voice.

Hated my voice I say, in the past tense, because I no longer remember it. One night during that winter, when Rosalie finished reading the Gospel of Mark to me, I said, "Thank you" because I was so grateful to hear her voice telling the story, grateful to her for abiding my quietness. But the next morning I could not thank her for breakfast nor say good-bye as I left the house. I have not spoken since I thanked her for reading to me that night. Probably my voice has changed much since I last used it when I was sixteen. Even if I wanted to speak now I cannot remember which muscles are used to form spoken words. I may have become a mute out of choice or complacency but by now, I believe, I am as incapable of speech as a dead man.

The thaw came early that spring and three or four acres of the field near the hill were dry enough in April that I could start plowing for seed potatoes and rye. The prairie was green everywhere and the wild strawberries seemed about to bloom already, which worried me because another frost seemed almost inevitable and if they bloomed too early they might get frozen and not bear that year. Still, the day I started plowing was warm, and there was a breeze, and no mosquitoes yet. Rosalie swept the stable and patched its roof with new shakes. When I came in for supper, she had roasted the last of our bison meat and made some rye bread. We finished supper and washed the dishes. I sat down next to the stove with Father's pipe and some willow bark to smoke while Rosalie read a history of the recent war in the United States to me. It was from the second volume of this history that we learned about the battle that had taken place on the day we were born. When she finished, she pinched out the tallow flame between her thumb and first finger and we went to bed.

After a while, she said, "Are you awake, Julius?"

I rolled over.

"So tomorrow, I'll wake up and you'll wake up and it will be just like today was won't it?" I shrugged my shoulders. There was a long silence. I was almost sleeping when she said, "Do you think it will snow again?" I thought about it. "Maybe we should get a dog in Winnipeg, hm?" she said. Her voice was getting louder.

Then she said, "Goddamn it! Will you please say something?"

I did not speak. "Damn you!" She got out of bed and paced in front of the windows. "It's as if you were a stone! As if you were sitting there on the ground and someone picked you up and threw you into the river and now you were under water, but you don't care because you're just going to sit there where you fell just as before. What difference does it make to you? Nothing. Well you're not a stone, Brother. You're not. And I'm not either. You think you can just work all day like before and pretend somebody else is talking to me. But nobody is. I am all alone."

She was screaming, "And you're thinking: To hell with my sister. Then to hell with you!"

I sat up in bed. She walked outside barefoot. I could hear her pacing on the porch and got up and sat at the desk and watched her pacing through the window. I tried to think of something to say and to find the will to say it. Then I couldn't see or hear her anymore. I took a piece of paper out of the drawer and wrote on it, "I am sorry." When I went outside to the front porch, she was sitting on its floor, leaning against the house. I gave her the paper. She looked at it, crumpled it, and threw it onto the grass.

In June, Rosalie moved us into Winnipeg. "I'm asking your opinion about this but I know you won't answer me. If you don't want to go, speak," she said, and laid her hand on the side of my neck. "I don't want to leave either, Brother, but I must have someone to talk to." Eggs snapped in the skillet and the prairie wind spilled in through the open doorway; there were no other sounds in the house. Winnipeg, I thought, would be a crowd of awful sounds. I did not wish to go there. But I did not wish my sister misery either. So I said nothing and we left home.

All we owned of value was Father's deed to our 160 acres of the prairie, our chickens, and Isaiah and Chester. We didn't want to sell the farm, though in 1881, the land boom in Manitoba was near its height and we could have gotten a fair sum for it; so we sold the chickens and our oxen who were old by then and we got only £21 altogether. We lived on that money until Rosalie was hired as the apprentice to the cook of a wealthy Quebecois named Papillon. His house was four stories, tall, built from American limestone. It had eight chimneys, fifteen-foot ceilings in all its rooms, seventy-eight windows, a chapel, a kitchen ten times the size of our home on the prairie, five French crystal chandeliers and quarters for fifteen servants in the basement. The Premier of Manitoba was said to have exclaimed one night, after a formal dinner in Papillon's house, that once Papillon died, the King of France might use his house for a second Versailles. Rosalie and I moved into a room, with one ground level window, in the basement.

I had no skills for urban life, and because I did not speak, people assumed, absurdly I have always thought, that I could not hear. In her free hours, Rosalie walked with me around the city to mills, smiths, butchers, and just about anybody, asking them if they had work for her brother who was standing beside her.

"What's he need his sister to ask for?"

"He does not speak, you see, but—"

"Then no I don't," they answered, and we moved on.

Depending on my sister's wages for my food humiliated me, but even so, my inactivity was worse. Some days, I walked through town from sun-up until dark, just to keep the sloth from stealing my mind. Twice I tried to ask for work at the railway office, even wrote down my request before I walked in. But as the secretary stood staring at me, my hand froze around the paper in my pocket until finally I ran back outside. I did not understand looking for work, as if it were hidden. On the farm, work was always there, like a great feast whose abundance outstripped the most ravenous appetite, there was always, always more to do. But in Winnipeg I starved for it. And because I was not working, I had no appetite, and I ate almost nothing of what Rosalie bought from Papillon's kitchen. Sometimes a potato in a day. I grew thin.

*

I woke in darkness one December night. The darkness was pure, more absolute than the blue light of nighttime, because there was no light at all. The perfect blackness was familiar vaguely. I felt Rosalie's back at my side and was suddenly very happy but I didn't know why. Then I realized that we were in our old house, the sod house with no windows, and all that had come after it—the riverstone house Father and I had built and laid the three windows in, Father and Mother's deaths, our move to Winnipeg and so much sadness—were all a dream, and here was Rosalie beside me, and the coals in the stove were dying out so I must go outside to get more work, and there was the door, right over there, and the prairie lay outside it. I leapt from the bed, pulled on my trousers and boots, and as I reached my hand over to the wall where my hat hung from a hook, I didn't feel the hat, but something cold, flat and smooth.

The window. It had snowed that night and the snow had piled up and blocked out the usual dim light from outside. We were in Papillon's house after all.

"Julius?" Rosalie said. I only stood there, with my hand pressed against the cold glass. She didn't say anything for a long time. It was cold and deadly quiet and all I wanted at that moment was to listen to her talking, which she knew. I didn't care what she talked about. She sat up in bed and told me about the recipe for honeyed pheasant; about the recent shooting of the President of the United States by a man who had sought office in his administration; she told me the names of clouds which she had overheard while serving lunch to Papillon's son and his tutor; and about the university student who was teaching her, on Saturday and Tuesday evenings, to read Greek. She talked for a long time, an hour maybe, and finally, just after I had taken my boots and trousers back off and got in bed and just before I'd fallen asleep, she said, "It's so dark now. It reminds me of the old house."

That spring, Papillon and his chief of staff, a short half-Blackfoot named DuPage, were inspecting leaks in the basement walls and came into our room in the afternoon. Rosalie was working in the kitchen, and I sat under the window reading. I stood as they came in.

DuPage was running his fingers down the brown cracks in the wall and saying something in French to Papillon who nodded and rubbed his eyes. Papillon did not seem to notice I was in the room until he turned around and put his glasses on.

"Who is this?" He asked DuPage in English.

"He belongs to your undercook, Monsieur."

"You pay my servants enough to have servants do you, Mr. DuPage?"

"No. He is her brother I think."

"How do you enjoy living here then, Sir?" Papillon asked me. I looked at my feet.

"Why doesn't he answer me? Do you like my house?"

"He's an idiot, Monsieur, he can't answer." I looked up quickly and glared at DuPage.

"He understands you, apparently," Papillon said to him and looked back at me. "What is your trade, young man?" He waited for me to answer. "I see that you understand me, so either you can't speak," he held out his right hand, "or you have no trade," and held out his left, "which is it?"

By now his voice had changed tone. At first he seemed annoyed to have found me there, but now he was looking at me with a wide-eyed expression I have seen people use when addressing their dogs.

"Which is it?" He said again holding out his hands, and after an uncomfortable silence he folded his hands together and said, "Perhaps it's both."

I nodded.

"His sister is the one who came in from the wild last fall, yes?" He asked DuPage.

"Yes, Monsieur."

"Probably you can hold a plow then, grow things?" He asked me.

I nodded again.

"Delightful." He told me about the twelve acres on the back of his property which he had hired a young man to cultivate with wheat, broccoli and "vegetables, you know." How this young man had recently run off, allegedly to Chicago, in the middle of his planting. I could have his job if I wanted it. By the time he finished, DuPage had left the room. I nodded to him that I would take the job, and then pulled from the desk at my right a piece of brown paper and wrote on it, "I am very grateful to you." And gave it to him. He looked down at the paper then back up at me and whispered conspiratorially, "You can write! You're not an idiot at all then!" But I did not respond to this.

Many years passed.

I often longed for our return home. But in lieu of that, living in

Papillon's house and working in his fields suited me as well as any other arrangement I could imagine. I worked alone and outside, as I wanted to. The other servants had never heard me speak and never expected me to, so my silence was never a point of contention with them. Rosalie seemed to reconcile herself to it.

Rosalie continued to study Greek with her tutor, who had graduated university and taken a teaching position at a boys' school in town. His name was Benjamin. Usually he would come to Papillon's house and they would walk back to the school together and use an empty classroom there. If Rosalie was not finished working in the kitchen when he came, he would sit at the desk in our room and he and I would converse, so to speak. Except for Rosalie, Benjamin was the only person I knew in Winnipeg who was willing to have conversations of longer than a minute with me. Those who knew that I could hear and wanted to know something from me would ask, read my response, thank me, and walk away. But Benjamin acted as if talking on paper were no different from talking in speech. We had long discussions, about the mountains in the United States where he was born, about the ocean and about books that we had both read. Sometimes we both wrote.

He said it made him think more slowly. Then Rosalie would come in and they would go.

I was allowed to leave Papillon's house on one of his horses for three weeks every summer, so that I could go back home and keep up our house and the outbuildings on the farm. All the buildings were small and so their repairs were small. I made no additions or improvements; I kept things as they were.

Throughout the year, I imagined that I could live on the farm by myself and be happy and only lacked the nerve to do it. But by the second week, I would stay up long hours to finish painting the stable and clearing the spider webs from the eaves of our house so I could get back to Winnipeg sooner. The quiet which in my youth I had been terrified to leave was, in adulthood, almost as frightening to endure.

Rosalie never came with me. She talked about the farm endlessly, to me, to Benjamin, and to the other servants, but between our leaving, in 1881, and our return here, in the spring of 1895, she never saw this place. Maybe the painting of it in her mind became too perfect to risk violating by seeing it again.

I grew to abide the sound of many people speaking together. At dinner, the housekeepers, horsekeepers, groundskeepers and ladykeepers talked up a swarm of words and often I stayed in the dining room after dinner and picked out a person's voice from the crowd and listened to it for a while.

At the end of all the day's work, after we had put down our books and our journals, we would lay down to be and Rosalie would tell me about the news or a passage from Aeschylus she'd been working on. We lived this way a long time.

Of course, Greek is a difficult language. What my sister tried to explain of its grammar seemed perfectly ridiculous. It was painful to listen to. When she read it out loud, I wrote on my pad of paper "it sounds like hoofs on slag to me." The characters, even, looked designed to be inscrutable. Even so, after twelve years of instruction, the last nine of which were free of the small tuition she had paid Benjamin, I suppose I should have suspected that my sister had that language more or less under her belt. The one time it occurred to me to wonder about this, I thought that maybe they had started in on Latin together, and put the thought away and forgot to ask her about it. I didn't suspect anything, I suppose, because it was unthinkable that my sister would ever deceive me. And she didn't deceive me, maybe she withheld some of her life from her brother—Lord, what I withheld from her—but she never lied. I'm certain that if I had asked, she would have told me the truth.

My blindness seems shocking, even reprehensible, to me now. That the darkest period of melancholy in her life—in which deep black rings grew up under her eyes; and her hitherto ceaseless talking thinned out to two or three mumbled "no thank you's" or "how do you do's" in a day; and I, in straightening our bed one morning, turned over her pillow and found it wet on the bottom—happened to coincide with Benjamin's engagement to the daughter of the boys' school's headmaster, that I who have never loved a person that way, should have been incapable of seeing that my sister did was perhaps the greatest failure of my brotherhood. For which I have been deservingly punished.

I began to fear that she would stop talking altogether. Each day her silences grew longer and my panic deepened. I found myself privately furious with her for keeping her voice from me through she knew how much I relied on it. How, I thought, could she be so treacherous, so cruel? Then for the first time I realized the extent of my own cruelty. For the first time I felt what Rosalie must have felt when she told me, "I am all alone." I had done, had continued doing for fourteen years, precisely the same thing to her. Rosalie's silence was only just.

I decided that something must be done, something drastic. I decided to speak to her. We were walking together along the edge of the field behind Papillon's house as the sun was setting red behind the trees and the wind bent the tops of rye. Then we stopped, and I turned to her, and tried to shape my mouth so that if I breathed properly, I would make the letter "r". Rosalie's mouth fell open. I tried to breathe out, but my throat seized. I tried to remember how to say the letter "r". Or to say any letter. The wind blew dust in our faces.

After five minutes, I saw that I could not do it and covered my mouth with my hand. Then she leaned over and kissed my cheek as the sun disappeared into the woods.

Two months after the engagement, Rosalie's lessons, which had stopped, began again, and although her depression seemed slowly to lift, and she began to speak and read to me at night again, she didn't talk as much or as loudly as she had before.

1094   In the fall of 1891, while his son was at university in France, Papillon paid me a visit in the field. He was seventy-three then, but continued to ride his horse through the rye on his way out to speak to his "man" as he called me to his friends. "This is my man, Mr. Julius," he would introduce me. I would tip my hat. "Don't be offended, he's a mute, that's why he doesn't greet you. Ha ha!" He would say. On that day in 1891, he was trotting up to me where I was picking a burr from the mule's foot at the edge of the field and his mouth was open—maybe he had already started talking—and then his one eye started to twitch and his tongue came out of his mouth and he fell off the horse. I heard his head strike a rock. Of all the noises I have heard and hated in my life, that one was the ugliest, a skull on a rock. It was loud enough that I could hear it over the horse's legs rustling the rye, and I knew he must be dead. He wore very short riding boots, and when he fell from the horse, one of the boots remained on his foot but the other got caught in the stirrup. So as the horse bolted away, one boot went with it and bounced against the horse's ribs, looking as if there were a ghost, with its foot in the boot, kicking the horse clumsily along. When I reached his body, I took off one of my shoes for his naked foot and brought him to the house, slung over the mule's back.

Papillon's son returned from Europe and took control of his father's household, sold off all the asbestos mines, and invested his fortune in the securities market in New York. His wealth grew enormously. On one dinner, with three hundred guests, for which Rosalie had to hire twelve extra cooks, he spent £10,000. But he held many such dinners, and by 1893 nearly all the money was gone.

After his bankruptcy in 1894, the younger Papillon managed to hold on to his house for only another year. He sold everything of value in it, the chandeliers, the wine in the cellar. Eventually he even sold the land I had tilled since his own early youth. He let all the servants go, though he let us continue to live in his house. Then finally he sold the house too, or his creditors sold it. We all had to move out.

"Why shouldn't we go back?" Rosalie said. "Why've you been tending it all this time if we weren't going back eventually?"

"We have enough money to take a flat in town." I wrote.

"If you want to go, we should go," she said.

"It's not necessary."

"Julius, you never wanted to be here. I understand that. Let me pay you back."

"It will bore you."

"It will not. If you want to go, I will be happy to go. Besides, I am tired of this place. There are things I could stand to be rid of."

"Such as what?" I wrote.

"Oh, things. Things I'd rather be far from than near to."

"I don't understand."

"Don't fret yourself about it. I miss the prairie, I do."

"Promise me you'll say if you've changed your mind." I wrote.

"I won't change my mind," she said.

"Nevertheless."

"Anyway, I promise."

We left the next week. All the property we'd amassed in the fourteen years we lived in Winnipeg fit inside two trunks that lay under our feet on the train. At Brandon, we bought two horses and a wagon and rode north. After the first day's riding, we had reached Virden and spent the night in a stopping house there. We got home just before sunset the next day. That was two springs ago.

*

The prairie is a jealous place. My family and countless others laid claim to broad portions of it, or thought we did. In fact it was the prairie that claimed us. It permits you the delusion that you own it, while all the time it behaves with such perfect indifference to your wishes and so frigidly refuses to return to you any of the attention you give it that you begin to suspect, if it has a will or feeling, they do not concern themselves with you. After three months without rain, you ask that the grasses do not catch fire; maybe it rains peacefully and the prairie goes damp again, maybe lightning strikes and your fields turn to ash all around. You hope that the blizzard will hold off until the unaccounted for heifer finds her way home; and she may or she may not. The prairie does not seem to hear you. However, if you leave the open prairie, if you move into town, as Rosalie and I did, you may find that, though it could never hear, it does speak, you may find that the prairie calls out to your thoughts, as if in longing, that though you may have no desire to return to it, you find yourself pulled back as by responsibility to leave whatever happiness you may have found elsewhere and return to the prairie, not for yourself, but out of loyalty to it. And if you return, the jealous prairie will rob your mind of nearly all the tastes and sounds and smells of your

other home. Like a wife burning the love letters her husband's mistress sent him. You may find, as I now do, watching the snowy bluff in the distance through this window, that you cannot recall the taste of an orange, the sound that a collection of tired people make as they settle in for supper, or even the smell of a room you lived in for fifteen years. Perhaps the prairie longed for you, perhaps it wanted only to dominate your imagination.

The trees were thicker now, Rosalie said, and there were more wild strawberries, and the trout in the Assiniboine seemed smaller than she remembered, but everything else looked the same. I grew barley, corn and wheat and kept the pigs and the cattle and fished a little more than I had in my youth. Rosalie did the canning and tended the vegetables and the chickens. She spent long hours watching the prairie. In the winter, from behind the window glass, and in the summer, from a chair on the porch. Even in the terrible mosquito season of June and July, she would watch calmly and smoke in Father's pipe some awful smelling plant she'd found in the woods which seemed to keep the insects away from her. She'd stare out at the bluff south of here, rapt, and looked fairly sad at these times.

Nine months ago, Rosalie and I rode into the town that had grown up about twenty miles southwest of here over the time we were away, and found that there was a letter for her at the post office. She didn't read it right then. She put it in her pocket, and tried to look calm but I saw that her hands were shaking. That night, she brought a lamp and walked to the bluff over the creek to read it. There was no moon and I could see the lamp on the bluff, even a mile away, from the window here. It was the only light anywhere. When she came back four hours later, she was still crying. I offered her a shot of the Scotch we'd bought in town, but she refused and handed me the letter.

I wrote, "This is to you. I shouldn't read it."

She pushed the letter into my chest.

The post mark said "P.M., January 24 1897 Baltimore MD"

I told her that I wanted her to go to him. What I meant was, since you are going, I will not keep you. Since a brother's love is not the same, since Benjamin postponed his other marriage repeatedly until he realized why, since he has asked you, and since you, I can see, said yes years ago, then I wish I wanted you to go to him, and though I want you to stay, I will say the opposite.

She has written four times since she left last May, imploring me, in each letter, to come live with them in Baltimore. Benjamin is now a professor at a college there and says that I am welcome and that he could find me work, but I do not feel capable of leaving the prairie again.

1097

When Father came here, he forgot Kentucky. He said that he felt incapable of telling lies on the prairie, that this place asserted itself as the only possible reality—the sun set here and no place else; this particular rush of wind along the face of the grasses in spring was the only sound of wind in spring—and so you could not make fictions of other faces or other voices because the prairie did not permit you even to imagine them. Nor to imagine the true faces of your past. In time, he said, it stole Kentucky from his brain. It robs you piecemeal—one day you cannot remember the name of a face, the next you cannot picture the face either, the next you forget what it was you were trying to remember the day before, the next you forget that you were trying to remember something. Two months ago, I remembered the names of all of Papillon's horses; today I cannot remember how many of them there were. Today I remember why Rosalie did not take her Greek books with her when she left.

But since she is no longer here, I don't know that I will remember that in a week. Soon I will not remember her voice, as I do not remember mine. This place will have taken it. Eventually, it seems, the prairie will disburden my mind of all those strange memories and I will forget that I ever had a sister and will think only of what I am seeing and hearing on the plain.

Acknowledgments

The many friends of Saul Bellow and Keith Botsford have been delighted   *1099*
to give their permission for the reprinting of their original works from the
magazines.

Every effort has been made to trace the publishers and the copyright
holders of materials reproduced in this volume. We would be grateful to
hear from anyone whom we have been unable to contact in order to rectify
any future edition.

We note below several of the works, which have been reproduced
courtesy of:

* *Message from the City*, from *Collected Earlier Poems* by Anthony Hecht
© 1990 by Anthony Hecht. Reprinted by permission of Alfred A.
Knopf, a Division of Random House, Inc.;
* *Strictly from Hunger*, reprinted by permission of PFD on behalf of
The Estate of S. J. Perelman;
* *The Portrait of Maurice Magnus*, reprinted by permission of Laurence
Pollinger Limited and the Estate of Frieda Lawrence Ravagli;
* *Count Nulin* by Alexander Pushkin. The translation by Robert C.
Stephenson originally appeared in the University of Texas Studies in

English XXXIII (1954), which is now Texas Studies in Literature and Language, University of Texas Press;

* *A Jewish Savant* by Umberto Saba. Translated from *Ricordo-Racconti* © 1964 Arnoldo Mondatori Editore;

* *Stoney Knows How: Life as a Tattoo Artist*, by Leonard St Clair and Alan B. Govenar, (University of Kentucky Press, 1981);

* *Under the Rose* by Thomas Pynchon © 1961, 1989. First appeared in *The Noble Savage 3*. Reprinted by permission of Melanie Jackson Agency, L.L.C;

* All Steinberg images by the permission of the estate of Saul Steinberg. Photographs of Saul Steinberg on page 444 by Leslie Gill; on page 450 by Stefan Moses; and on page 453 by George Platt Lynes. All photographs are from the collection of Saul and Janis Bellow;

* *Doctor of Science, Patient of Poetry*, by Stephen Spendor, is reprinted with permission of *The Observer* (London), where it appeared on July 2, 1961;

* *Friendship*, originally published in French as *Compagnons*. © Editions Bernard Grasset, 1931.

About the Authors

ALGREN, Nelson (1909–1981), a Chicago novelist, best known for *The* *Man with the Golden Arm* and *A Walk on the Wild Side*.

AMIS, Martin (born 1950), novelist, author of *Money, London Fields, Time's Arrow* and, most recently, an autobiography, *Experience*.

D'ARZO, Silvio (1920–1952), the pen name of the Italian novelist and short-story writer, Enzo Comparoni. See the translator's note to *Two Old People*.

AUERBACH, John (born 1922), writer of fiction, whose work has appeared in *Mainstream* and *Commentary*, now lives in Israel. The story we publish gives much of the turbulent remainder of his autobiography.

BAIL, Murray (born 1941), Australian novelist and short story writer. His most recent book is *Eucalyptus*. Other books include *Holden's Performance* and *Homesickness*.

BERRYMAN, John (1914–1972), poet and critic, best known for his work, *Dream Songs,* and for his brilliant essays on Shakespeare.

BLAU, Herbert (born 1926), playwright and director, co-founder of the Actor's Workshop in San Francisco.

BUTLER, Samuel (1835–1902), English novelist, satirist, author of the brilliantly autobiographical novel, published posthumously, *The Way of All Flesh* and the satirical fables, *Erewhon and Erewhon Revisited*, deriding conventional moral pretensions.

COOVER, Robert (born 1932), American writer of avant-garde fiction, plays, poetry and essays. The story here was the first of Coover's to be published. His first novel, *The Origin of the Brunists*, won the 1966 William Faulkner Award, and his most famous book was the controversial *Public Burning*. He now divides his time between London and Providence, Rhode Island.

COPELAND, Julia, violinist, lives and writes in Bloomington, Indiana.

DESANI, G.V., Indian novelist. *All About H. Hatterr*, many times reprinted, is thought by many to be one of the great comic novels of the twentieth century. Fragments of his memoirs have been appearing lately, and a few stories. He lives in Texas where, for many years, he taught Indian philosophy.

DIDEROT, Denis (1713–1784), French philosophical writer and critic.

ELLIOTT, George P. (born 1918), critic and novelist, author of *Conversions, Literature and the Modernist Deviation*.

GALIANI, Ferdinando (1728–1787) born in Naples, served as secretary to the Neapolitan ambassador to Paris and is better known as the Abbé Galiani. A friend and critic of Diderot and the Encyclopaedists, Galiani is known for his writings on economic and philosophical topics.

GOLD, Herbert (born 1924), novelist and essayist. Among his many books are *Birth of a Hero, The Man Who Was Not With It*, and *First Person Singular*. He lives in San Francisco.

GOVENAR, Alan, writer, folklorist, photographer, and filmmaker who lives in Dallas, Texas.

GRIMM, Wilhelm (1786–1825), German writer and scholar, with his brother Jakob, author of the celebrated fairy tales.

GUILLOUX, Louis (1899–1980), arguably the most significant French novelist after Proust and Gide. A Breton from a working-class family, he stayed in his hometown of Saint-Brieuc for most of his life. *Sang Noir* (published in the United States in 1936 as *"Bitter Victory"*) remains his best-known work.

HARRIS, Mark (born 1922), novelist. Harris now lives in Tempe, Arizona. Among his many books are *The Southpaw, Bang The Drum Slowly, Wake Up Stupid*, and *The Goy*.

HAWKES, John (born 1925), novelist. Among his books are *Second Skin, The Cannibal, Adventures in the Alaskan Skin Trade*, and *The Lime Twig*.

HECHT, Anthony (born 1923), poet, critic and translator. He has published numerous books and is the recipient of many distinguished prizes, including the Pulitzer Prize and, most recently, the Tanning Prize for Poetry in 1997. He is a member of the Academy of American Poets.

HERBST, Josephine (1897–1970). The Iowa-born novelist and memoirist was friendly with Hemingway and a one-time reader for H.L. Mencken and George Jean Nathan. She was a reporter in Germany and Spain in the 1930's.

HOAGLAND, Edward (born 1932), well known for his environmental essays. *Cowboys* was his first published story. He currently lives in Vermont.

HOWLAND, Bette (born 1937), author of several novels. Her books include *W-3: Life in a Psychiatric Ward, Blue in Chicago*, and her most recent, *Things to Come and Go*. Among her awards is a Guggenheim Fellowship.

HUGO, Victor (1802–1885), 19th century French poet and novelist.

HULSE, Michael (born 1955), poet and translator from the German. Hulse is the co-editor of *Stand*, and currently lives in Amsterdam, where he runs the publishing house Leviathan.

KASSNER, Rudolf (1873–1956), German critic, writer and translator, whose books include, *The Reception of Pre-Raphaelism in Fin de Siecle Vienna*.

KERRIGAN, Anthony (1918–1990), Irish poet and hispanist, was based for most of his life in Dublin, Mallorca and Barcelona.

KRIM, Seymour (1922–1998), beat writer and polemicist, author of *Views of a Nearsighted Cannoneer*.

LAHR, Oonagh, poet and academic. She currently lives in Great Britain.

LAMPEDUSA, Giuseppe Tomasi di (1896–1957), author of *il Gattopardo* ("The Leopard") and of notable insights into English and American literature.

1104 **LAWRENCE, D. H.** (1885–1930), English novelist, poet and essayist.

LOGHER, Karel, Dutch Jewish writer who died recently. *My Father in the Mirror* is translated and heavily edited from a manuscript translated by the author himself. It is his only text published in English.

MAISTRE, Joseph de (1754–1821), French diplomat and conservative polemicist, ambassador from the court of Savoy to St. Petersburg.

MECKEL, Christoph, (born in Berlin in 1935), is a German poet and illustrator. He studied graphic design and has since widely exhibited his artwork, as well as publishing numerous collections of poetry and fiction.

MIDDLETON, Christopher (born 1926), English poet and translator from the German. He teaches at the University of Texas.

MILLER, Arthur (born 1915, New York City), playwright and a contributing editor to *The Noble Savage*.

MORRIS, Wright (1910–1998), native Nebraskan, novelist. Among his best-known works are *The World in the Attic, The Works of Love, Love among the Cannibals*. Morris is widely considered among the most distinguished (and underrated) American writers.

NEMEROV, Howard (1920–1991), born in New York, poet and novelist, author of 26 books. He was Poet Laureate of the United States and winner of the Pulitzer Prize.

O'CONNOR, Philip (1916–1998), diarist and autobiographer, author of the remarkable *Memoirs of a Public Baby*. He died a year after writing the article in this collection, *Last Journal – or Philippics?*

PAVESE, Cesare (1908–1950), best known as a philosopher (*Dialogues with Leuco*) and essayist. Editor at Einaudi after the war, and great admirer of American writers. He committed suicide in a Turin hotel room at the age of 42.

PERELMAN, S. J. (1904–1979), American humorist, who started his career writing for the Marx Brothers.

1105

POLLAK, Felix (1909–1987), poet.

PUSHKIN, Alexander (1799–1837), Russian poet.

PYNCHON, Thomas (born 1937), studied literature at Cornell, worked briefly a technical writer for the Boeing Aircraft Corporation and is notably the author of *Gravity's Rainbow* (1973), *V* (1963), and *The Crying of Lot 49* (1966). His most recent book, *Vineland*, appeared in 1990.

ROSENBERG, Harold (1906–1978), influential critic and author of *The Tradition of the New*.

REY, Sydor, Polish novelist and poet, who came to the United States in 1939, and was a frequent contributor to *Commentary*.

RIBNIKAR, Jara, Serb novelist and short-story writer. *Copperhead* is her only story in English, though her autobiography is well known in Germany.

ROOKE, Leon (born 1934), writer and novelist. He lives in Manitoba.

RYAN, Conall (born 1958), American writer, violinist and software executive. He is the author of three novels, including *The House of Cards*.

SABA, Umberto (1883–1957), poet and writer, was born in Trieste and worked as a paint salesman in that busy port. Arguably, along with Montale and Ungaretti, among Italy's foremost 20th century poets. His prose is less well-known and remains almost entirely untranslated.

SCIBONA, Salvatore, a graduate of Saint John's College at the University of Santa Fe, New Mexico. He was a fellow at the Iowa Writers' Workshop, and *Prairie* was his first published work.

SCHAPIRO, Meyer (1904–1996), art historian and Professor Emeritus at Columbia University, published numerous works, most notably among them: *Art and Society*, *Paul Cezanne*, and *Words, Script and Pictures*.

SIMPSON, Louis (born 1923), poet and critic, was born in Jamaica to parents of Scottish descent. He emigrated to the United States at the age of 17, saw active duty during the Second World War, and later taught at Columbia University, among others. His poetry collections include *Honeymoon* and *Working Late*.

SŁONIMSKI, Antoni (1895–1976), poet, essayist. Known mainly for his poetry, he was also active as a writer of criticism and political and social satire. After spending the war years in England, he returned to Poland.

SPENDER, Stephen (1909–1995), poet, editor (with Melvin J. Lasky) of *Encounter*, and writer of a politically influential autobiography, *World within World*.

ST. CLAIR, Leonard "Stoney" (1912–1980), tattoo artist. He contracted rheumatoid arthritis when he was four years old. He joined a circus as a sword swallower at 15, and took up tattooing a year later.

STEPHENSON, Robert, Slavist, translator, and chess-problem author, long a teacher at the University of Texas.

TALLIS, Raymond (born 1946), philosopher, gerontologist and writer. He is a practicing physician at Manchester University.

WAKEFIELD, Dan (born 1932), novelist, critic and film writer, author of *Island in the City*, a study of New York's Puerto Rican community.

WOOD, James (born 1965), critic for the *New Republic* and *The Republic of Letters*. His collection of essays, entitled *The Broken Estate*, was recently published by Random House.

YURICK, Sol (born 1925), novelist. His books include: *The Warriors, Fertig, Richard A.*, and *The Bag.*

1107

ZOLLA, Elemire (born 1926), born in Turin and an expert on American literature; intellectual historian and critic, author (among many books) of *The Eclipse of the Intellectual* and *The Writer and the Shaman.*

Index of Authors

This is an index of Authors' contributions to all issues of *The Noble Savage*,
ANON and *The Republic of Letters*. Related selections from *Bostonia* and *The New York Times* have been included as well.

1111

1113

1115

About the Editors

SAUL BELLOW has written numerous novels, novellas and collections of stories, and he is recognized to be one of America's outstanding novelists of his generation. He has been awarded three National Book Awards, the Pulitzer Prize in 1975, and the Nobel Prize in Literature in 1976. Mr. Bellow was presented the National Book Award Foundation Medal for his distinguished contribution to American letters.

Born in Montreal, he was a long time resident of Chicago, and now lives in New England.

KEITH BOTSFORD enjoyed a notable early career as a novelist and editor, after which he was "side-tracked" into journalism, for *The Sunday Times* and *The Independent* of London, and *La Stampa* (Turin), variously in sports, food and as a US correspondent. He returned to fiction in 1989.

Born in Brussels, half Italian and half American, Mr. Botsford was educated in England. He lives in Boston, where he is a professor of journalism, history and international relations at Boston University.

In addition to their other activities, both writers continue to edit *The Republic of Letters.*

The fonts used in this book are from the Garamond and Courier families.